Directory of Financial Aids for Women 2012-2014

RSP FINANCIAL AID DIRECTORIES
OF INTEREST TO WOMEN

College Student's Guide to Merit and Other No-Need Funding
Selected as one of the "Outstanding Titles of the Year" by *Choice,* this directory describes 1,300 no-need funding opportunities for college students. 490 pages. ISBN 1588412121. $32.50, plus $7 shipping.

Directory of Financial Aids for Women
There are nearly 1,500 funding programs set aside for women described in this biennial directory, which has been called "the cream of the crop" by *School Library Journal* and the "best available reference source" by *Guide to Reference.* 514 pages. ISBN 1588412164. $45, plus $7 shipping.

Financial Aid for African Americans
Nearly 1,300 funding opportunities open to African American college students, professionals, and postdoctorates are described in this award-winning directory. 490 pages. ISBN 1588412172. $42.50, plus $7 shipping.

Financial Aid for Asian Americans
This is the source to use if you are looking for funding for Asian Americans, from college-bound high school seniors to professionals and postdoctorates; more than 900 sources of free money are described here. 350 pages. ISBN 1588412180. $40, plus $7 shipping.

Financial Aid for Hispanic Americans
The 1,100 biggest and best sources of free money available to undergraduates, graduates students, professionals, and postdoctorates of Mexican, Puerto Rican, Central American, or other Latin American heritage are described here. 446 pages. ISBN 1588412199. $42.50, plus $7 shipping.

Financial Aid for Native Americans
Detailed information is provided on nearly 1,400 funding opportunities open to American Indians, Native Alaskans, and Native Pacific Islanders for college, graduate school, or professional activities. 506 pages. ISBN 1588412202. $45, plus $7 shipping.

Financial Aid for Research and Creative Activities Abroad
Described here are more than 1,000 scholarships, fellowships, grants, etc. available to support research, professional, or creative activities abroad. 422 pages. ISBN 1588412067. $45, plus $7 shipping.

Financial Aid for Study and Training Abroad
This directory, which the reviewers call "invaluable," describes nearly 1,000 financial aid opportunities available to support study abroad. 362 pages. ISBN 1588412059. $40, plus $7 shipping.

Financial Aid for Veterans, Military Personnel, & Their Families
According to *Reference Book Review,* this directory (with its 1,100 entries) is "the most comprehensive guide available on the subject." 436 pages. ISBN 1588412091. $40, plus $7 shipping.

High School Senior's Guide to Merit and Other No-Need Funding
Here's your guide to 1,100 funding programs that *never* look at income level when making awards to college-bound high school seniors. 416 pages. ISBN 1588412105. $29.95, plus $7 shipping.

Money for Graduate Students in the Arts & Humanities
Use this directory to identify 1,000 funding opportunities available to support graduate study and research in the arts/humanities. 292 pages. ISBN 1588411974. $42.50, plus $7 shipping.

Money for Graduate Students in the Biological Sciences
This unique directory focuses solely on funding for graduate study/research in the biological sciences (800+ funding opportunities). 248 pages. ISBN 1588411982. $37.50, plus $7 shipping.

Money for Graduate Students in the Health Sciences
Described here are 1,000+ funding opportunities just for students interested in a graduate degree in dentistry, medicine, nursing, nutrition, pharmacology, etc. 304 pages. ISBN 1588411990. $42.50, plus $7 shipping.

Money for Graduate Students in the Physical & Earth Sciences
Nearly 900 funding opportunities for graduate students in the physical and earth sciences are described in detail here. 276 pages. ISBN 1588412008. $40, plus $7 shipping.

Money for Graduate Students in the Social & Behavioral Sciences
Looking for money for a graduate degree in the social/behavioral sciences? Here are 1,100 funding programs for you. 316 pages. ISBN 1588412016. $42.50, plus $7 shipping.

Directory of Financial Aids for Women 2012-2014

Gail Ann Schlachter
R. David Weber

A Listing of Scholarships, Fellowships, Grants, Awards, Internships, and Other Sources of Free Money Available Primarily or Exclusively to Women, Plus a Set of Six Indexes (Program Title, Sponsoring Organization, Residency, Tenability, Subject, and Deadline Date)

Reference Service Press
El Dorado Hills, California

Library of Congress Cataloging in Publication Data

Schlachter, Gail A.
    Directory of financial aids for women, 2012-2014
    Includes indexes.
    1. Women—United States—Scholarships, fellowships, etc.—Directories. 2. Grants-in-aid—United States—Directories. 3. Credit—United States—Directories. I. Title.
LB2338.5342 2012   378'.30'2573
ISBN 10: 1588412164
ISBN 13: 9781588412164
ISSN 0732-5215

10 9 8 7 6 5 4 3 2 1

Reference Service Press (RSP) began in 1977 with a single financial aid publication *(The Directory of Financial Aids for Women)* and now specializes in the development of financial aid resources in multiple formats, including books, large print books, print-on-demand reports, eBooks, and online sources. Long recognized as a leader in the field, RSP has been called "a true success in the world of independent directory publishers" by the *Simba Report on Directory Publishing* Both Kaplan Educational Centers and Military.com have hailed RSP as "the leading authority on scholarships."

Reference Service Press
El Dorado Hills Business Park
5000 Windplay Drive, Suite 4
El Dorado Hills, CA 95762-9319
        (916) 939-9620
        Fax: (916) 939-9626
        E-mail: info@rspfunding.com
Visit our web site: www.rspfunding.com

Manufactured in the United States of America
Price: $45, plus $7 shipping

ACADEMIC INSTITUTIONS, LIBRARIES, ORGANIZATIONS, AND OTHER QUANTITY BUYERS:
Discounts on this book are available for bulk purchases. Write or call for information on our discount programs.

Contents

Introduction

HOW THE DIRECTORY HAS GROWN IN THE PAST 35 YEARS

In 1977 and 1978, while we were furiously researching, writing, editing, and updating entries for the very first edition of the *Directory of Financial Aids for Women,* major events were occurring that would have a lasting effect on the role of women in American society:

- The first National Women's Conference was held in Houston, Texas, attended by 20,000 women who passed the landmark National Plan of Action.

- The National Coalition Against Domestic Violence was established.

- The Air Force graduated its first women pilots.

- Congress passed the Pregnancy Discrimination Act, prohibiting discrimination against pregnant women in all areas of employment.

- Congress allocated $5 million to the Department of Labor to set up centers for displaced homemakers.

- The Philadelphia Mint began stamping the Susan B. Anthony dollar.

- Dianne Feinstein became the first female mayor of San Francisco, replacing the assassinated George Moscone.

- Margaret Thatcher was chosen to become Britain's first female prime minister.

- Hanna Gray was named president of the University of Chicago, becoming the first woman to lead a major America university.

But, from our point of view, the most significant development occurred in the field of higher education. In 1978, for the first time ever, more women than men entered American colleges and universities. We knew these women would face many challenges, particularly financial ones. Numerous studies had shown that, historically, when women competed again men for college aid, they were notably unsuccessful. We believed we could help to level this funding playing field by compiling the first-ever listing of financial aid opportunities open primarily or exclusively to women. And, so, the *Directory of Financial Aids for Women* was launched. Finally, women could find out about the hundreds of funding opportunities that were available just for them!

We were right. The directory did make a difference. Orders poured in. Women wrote to us about their successes. The book was featured in numerous magazines, television shows, bibliographic guides, and reviewing sources. It became clear to us at Reference Service Press that there was an continuing need for this type of compilation. So, in 1980, we made a commitment to collect, organize, and disseminate— on an on-going basis—the most current and accurate information available on all types of funding opportunities open to women.

To accomplish this goal over the years, we have had to become sophisticated information sleuths, tracking down all possible leads, identifying even the slightest changes to existing programs, finding new sources of funding opportunities for women, and constantly expanding and updating the electronic database used to prepare each new biennial edition of the *Directory of Financial Aids for Women.* The results have been dramatic, especially when the first (1978) edition is compared, side-by-side, to this issue (2012-2014). In the past 35 years, the directory has increased fivefold in size, growing from a modest 300 programs (200 pages) to the staggering 1,489 opportunities described in the 2012-2014 edition's more than 500 pages. Access to the information has advanced significantly as well, going beyond the simple program title listing in the first edition (with basic subject, geographic, and sponsor indexes) to a user-friendly grouping of records by recipient category (undergraduates, graduate students, and professionals/postdoctorates) and six detailed and sub-divided indexes in the latest edition, making it possible to search the information by all current, variant, and former program titles; every sponsor and administering organization; each location where an applicant must live; every place where the money can be spent; hundreds of specific subject fields; and month-by-month deadline dates.

Even the physical appearance of the two editions is strikingly different. In 1978, we laboriously photocopied program information, cut and pasted the draft, and then produced the final "camera-ready" version on an IBM Selectric typewriter. If you look carefully in the first edition, you'll be able to see where we used White-Out and correction tape! In contrast, the entries in the 2012-2014 edition have been carefully selected from our database of 45,000 unique funding records, extensively reviewed electronically by editors in geographically-dispersed locations, formatted using a layout and font chosen specifically for maximum utility, and produced simultaneously in both book and electronic versions.

One thing that hasn't changed during the past 35 years, however, is our passionate commitment to making a difference. Little did we realize, when we first published the *Directory of Financial Aids for Women* in 1978, that we had taken the initial steps on what would become a life-long search for unique funding opportunities available specifically to special needs groups. And though our focus has broadened beyond women and our output has expanded beyond books, we have never lost sight of the fact that financial need is not just one of our publishing interests. It is and will be our only business. Perhaps that's why *The Simba Report on Directory Publishing* called Reference Service Press "a true success in the world of independent directory publishers" and why both Kaplan Educational Centers and Military.com have hailed the company as "the leading authority on scholarships."

WHY THIS DIRECTORY IS NEEDED

Currently, billions of dollars in financial aid are available primarily or exclusively for women. In fact, more money is available today than ever before. This funding is open to applicants at any level (high school through postdoctoral and professional) for study, research, travel, training, career development, or innovative efforts. While numerous directories have been prepared to identify and describe general financial aid programs (those open to both men and women), they have never covered more than a small portion of the programs designed primarily or exclusively for women. As a result, many advisors, librarians, scholars, researchers, and students have not been aware of the impressive array of financial aid programs established with women in mind. Now, with the 2012-2014 edition of the *Directory of Financial Aids for Women,* up-to-date and comprehensive information is available in a single source about the special resources set aside for women. No other source, in print or online, comes anywhere close to matching the extensive coverage provided by this publication.

The unique value of the *Directory* has been highly praised by the reviewers. Here are just some of the rave reviews:

- "The title is a must-purchase guide." —*American Reference Books Annual*

- "Nobody does a better job...a great resource and highly recommended." —*College Spotlight*

- "The only current source of information on financial aid specifically for women...an essential and reasonably priced purchase." —*Reference Books Bulletin*

- "The quintessential acquisition for public libraries of all sizes...feminists, homemakers, and women everywhere will welcome this book, since it is so well-done and simple to use." —*Small Press*

- "The variety of programs is amazing...an essential purchase...has become the standard source for information on scholarships, fellowships, loans, grants, awards, and internships available primarily to women." —*Library Journal*

SAMPLE ENTRY

(1) **[41]**

(2) **ANITA BORG MEMORIAL SCHOLARSHIPS**

(3) Google Inc.
Attn: Scholarships
1600 Amphitheatre Parkway
Mountain View, CA 94043-8303
(650) 253-0000
Fax: (650) 253-0001
Web: www.google.com/intl/en/anitaborg/us

(4) **Summary** To provide financial assistance to women working on a bachelor's or graduate degree in a computer-related field.

(5) **Eligibility** This program is open to women who are entering their senior year of undergraduate study or are enrolled in a graduate program in computer science, computer engineering, or a closely-related field. Applicants must be full-time students at a university in the United States and have a GPA of 3.5 or higher. They must submit essays of 400 to 600 words on 1) a significant technical project on which they have worked; 2) their leadership abilities; 3) what they would do if someone gave them the funding and resources for a 3- to 12-month project to investigate a technical topic of their choice; and 4) what they would do if someone gave them $1,000 to plan an event or project to benefit women in technical fields. Citizens, permanent residents, and international students are eligible. Selection is based on academic background and demonstrated leadership.

(6) **Financial data** The stipend is $10,000 per year.

(7) **Duration** 1 year; recipients may reapply.

(8) **Additional information** These scholarships were first offered in 2004.

(9) **Number awarded** Varies each year; recently, 25 of these scholarships were awarded.

(10) **Deadline** January of each year.

DEFINITION

(1) **Entry number:** The consecutive number assigned to the references and used to index the entry.

(2) **Program title:** Title of the scholarship, fellowship, grant, award, internship, or other source of free money described in the directory.

(3) **Sponsoring organization:** Name, address, and telephone number, toll-free number, fax number, e-mail address, and/or web site (when information was supplied) for organization sponsoring the program.

(4) **Summary:** Identifies the major program requirements; read the rest of the entry for additional detail.

(5) **Eligibility:** Qualifications required of applicants, plus information on application procedure and selection process.

(6) **Financial data:** Financial details of the program, including fixed sum, average amount, or range of funds offered, expenses for which funds may and may not be applied, and cash-related benefits supplied (e.g., room and board).

(7) **Duration:** Period for which support is provided; renewal prospects.

(8) **Additional information:** Any unusual (generally nonmonetary) benefits, features, restrictions, or limitations associated with the program.

(9) **Number awarded:** Total number of recipients each year or other specified period.

(10) **Deadline:** The month by which applications must be submitted.

Previous editions of the directory were selected as the "cream of the crop" in *School Library Journal's* "Reference Round-Up;" were included in *Recommended Reference Books for Small and Medium-sized Libraries and Media Centers;* were featured in *Glamour, Good Housekeeping, New Woman,* and *Teen* magazines; and were selected as the "Best of the Best" in education and career information print materials by members of the National Education and Information Center Advisory Committee. In the view of The Grantsmanship Center, "No organization interested in serving women should be without this directory!" Want to read more reviews? Go to: www.rspfunding.com/reviews.html.

WHAT'S UPDATED?

The preparation of each new edition of the *Directory of Financial Aids for Women* involves extensive updating and revision. To make sure that the information included here is both reliable and current, the editors at Reference Service Press 1) reviewed and updated all relevant programs covered in the previous edition of the directory, 2) collected information on all programs open primarily or exclusively to women that were added to Reference Service Press' funding database since the last edition of the directory, and then 3) searched extensively for new program leads in a variety of sources, including printed directories, news reports, journals, newsletters, house organs, annual reports, and sites on the Internet. We only include program descriptions in the *Directory* that are written directly from information supplied by the sponsoring organization in print or online (no information is ever taken from secondary sources). When that information could not be found, we sent up to four data collection letters (followed by up to three telephone or email inquiries, if necessary) to those sponsors. Despite our best efforts, however, some sponsoring organizations still failed to respond and, as a result, their programs are not included in this edition of the *Directory.*

The 2012-2014 edition of the *Directory of Financial Aids for Women* completely revises and updates the previous (15th) edition. Programs that have ceased operations have been dropped. Similarly, programs that have broadened their focus to include men have also been removed from the listing. Profiles of continuing programs have been rewritten to reflect operations in 2012-2014; more than 75 percent of the continuing programs reported substantive changes in their locations, requirements (particularly application deadline), benefits, or eligibility requirements since 2009. In addition, more than 500 new entries have been added to the program section of the *Directory.* The resulting listing describes the nearly 1,500 biggest and best sources of free money available to women, including scholarships, fellowships, grants, awards, and internships.

WHAT MAKES THIS DIRECTORY UNIQUE?

The 2012-2014 edition of the *Directory of Financial Aids for Women* identifies billions of dollars available for study, research, creative activities, past accomplishments, future projects, professional development, and work experience. The listings cover every major subject area, are sponsored by more than 900 different private and public agencies and organizations, and are open to women at any level—from high school through postdoctorate and professional. This approach is unique. No other source, in print or online, provides this type of comprehensive and current coverage of funding opportunities available primarily or exclusively to women.

Not only does the *Directory of Financial Aids for Women* provide the most comprehensive coverage of available funding (1,489 entries), but it also displays the most informative program descriptions (on the average, more than twice the detail found in any other listing). In addition to this extensive and focused coverage, the directory also offers several other unique features. First of all, hundreds of funding opportunities listed here have never been covered in any other source. So, even if you have checked elsewhere, you will want to look at the *Directory of Financial Aids for Women* for additional leads. And, here's another plus: all of the funding programs in this edition of the directory offer "free" money; not one of the programs will ever require you to pay anything back (provided, of course, that you meet the program requirements).

Further, unlike other funding directories, which generally follow a straight alphabetical arrangement, the *Directory of Financial Aids for Women* groups entries by intended recipients (undergraduates, graduate students, or professionals/postdoctorates), to make it easy for you to search for appropriate programs.

This same convenience is offered in the indexes, where program title, sponsoring organization, geographic, subject, and deadline date entries are each subdivided by recipient group.

Finally, we have tried to anticipate all the ways you might wish to search for funding. The volume is organized so you can identify programs not only by intended recipient, but also by subject focus, sponsoring organization, program title, residency requirements, where the money can be spent, and even deadline date. Plus, we've included all the information you'll need to decide if a program is right for you: purpose, eligibility requirements, financial data, duration, special features, limitations, number awarded, and application date. You even get fax numbers, toll-free numbers, e-mail addresses, and web sites (when available), along with complete contact information.

WHAT'S EXCLUDED?

While this book is intended to be the most comprehensive source of information on funding available to women, there are some programs we've specifically excluded from the directory.

- *Programs that do not accept applications from U.S. citizens or residents.* If a program is open only to foreign nationals or excludes Americans from applying, it is not covered.

- *Programs that are open equally to men and women:* Only funding opportunities set aside primarily or exclusively for women are included here.

- *Money for study or research outside the United States.* Since there are comprehensive and up-to-date directories that describe the available funding for study, research, or other activities abroad (see the list of Reference Service Press publications opposite the directory's title page), only programs that fund activities in the United States are covered here.

- *Very restrictive programs.* The emphasis here is on the biggest and best funding available. In general, programs are excluded if they are open only to a limited geographic area (less than a state) or offer limited financial support (less than $1,000). Note, however, that the majority of programs award considerably more than the $1,000 minimum requirement, paying up to full tuition or stipends that exceed $25,000 a year!

- *Programs administered by individual academic institutions solely for their own students.* The directory identifies "portable" programs—ones that can be used at any number of schools. Financial aid administered by individual schools specifically for their own students is not covered. Write directly to the schools you are considering to get information on their offerings.

- *Money that must be repaid.* Only "free money" is identified here. If a program requires repayment or charges interest, it's not listed. Now you can find out about billions of dollars in aid and know (if you meet the program requirements) that not one dollar of that will ever need to be repaid.

HOW THE DIRECTORY IS ORGANIZED

The *Directory* is divided into two sections: 1) a detailed list of financial aid programs available to women and 2) a set of six indexes to help you pinpoint appropriate funding programs.

Financial Aid Programs Open Primarily or Exclusively to Women. The first section of the *Directory* describes the nearly 1,500 biggest and best sources of free money aimed primarily or exclusively at women. These programs are sponsored by government agencies, professional organizations, corporations, sororities and fraternities, foundations, religious groups, educational associations, and military/veterans organizations. They are open to women at any level (high school through postdoctoral) for study, research, travel, training, career development, personal needs, or creative activities. All areas of the sciences, social sciences, and humanities are covered in the awards listed. The focus is on programs tenable in the United States that are open to women who are U.S. citizens or permanent residents

To help you focus your search, the entries in this section are grouped in the following three chapters:

- **Undergraduates:** Included here are more than 700 scholarships, grants, awards, internships, and other sources of free money that support women's undergraduate study, training, research, or creative activities. These programs are open to high school seniors, high school graduates, currently-enrolled college students, and students returning to college after an absence. Money is available to support these students in any type of public or private postsecondary institution, ranging from technical schools and community colleges to major universities in the United States.

- **Graduate Students:** Described here nearly 500 fellowships, grants, awards, internships, and other sources of free money that support women's post-baccalaureate study, training, research, and creative activities. These programs are open to students applying to, currently enrolled in, or returning to a master's, doctoral, professional, or specialist program in public or private graduate schools in the United States.

- **Professionals/Postdoctorates:** Included here are nearly 300 funding programs for women who are U.S. citizens or residents and 1) are in professional positions (e.g., artists, writers), whether or not they have an advanced degree; 2) are master's or professional degree recipients; 3) have earned a doctoral degree or its equivalent (e.g., Ph.D., Ed.D., M.D.); or 4) have recognized stature as established scientists, scholars, academicians, or researchers.

Within each chapter in the *Directory,* entries appear alphabetically by program title. Since some of the programs supply assistance to more than one specific group, those are listed in all relevant chapters. For example, the Ada I. Pressman Scholarship supports both undergraduate or graduate study, so the program is described in both the Undergraduates *and* Graduate Students chapters.

Each program entry has been designed to give you a concise profile that, as the sample on page 7 illustrates, includes information (when available) on organization address and telephone numbers (including toll-free and fax numbers), e-mail addresses and web site, purpose, eligibility, money awarded, duration, special features, limitations, number of awards, and application deadline.

The information reported for each of the programs in this section was gathered from research conducted through the beginning of 2012. While the listing is intended to cover as comprehensively as possible the biggest and best sources of free money available to women, some sponsoring organizations did not post information online or respond to our research inquiries and, consequently, are not included in this edition of the directory.

Indexes. To help you find the aid you need, we have constructed six indexes; these will let you access the listings by program title, sponsoring organization, residency, tenability, subject focus, and deadline date. These indexes use a word-by-word alphabetical arrangement. Note: numbers in the index refer to entry numbers, not to page numbers in the book.

Program Title Index. If you know the name of a particular funding program and want to find out where it is covered in the *Directory,* use the Program Title Index. To assist you in your search, every program is listed by all its known names, former names, and abbreviations. Since one program can be included in more than one place (e.g., a program providing assistance to both undergraduate and graduate students is described in both the first and second chapter), each entry number in the index has been coded to indicate the intended recipient group ("U" = Undergraduates; "G" = Graduate Students; "P" = Professionals/Postdoctorates). By using this coding system, you can avoid duplicate entries and turn directly to the programs that match your eligibility characteristics.

Sponsoring Organization Index. This index makes it easy to identify agencies that offer funding primarily or exclusively to women. More than 900 organizations are listed alphabetically, word by word. As in the Program Title Index, we've used a code to help you determine which organizations sponsor programs that match your educational level.

Residency Index. Some programs listed in this book are restricted to women in a particular state, region, or other geographic location. Others are open to women wherever they live. This index helps you identify programs available only to residents in your area as well as programs that have no residency requirements. Further, to assist you in your search, we've also indicated the recipient level for the funding offered to residents in each of the areas listed in the index.

Tenability Index. This index identifies the geographic locations where the funding described in the *Directory* may be used. Index entries (city, county, state, province, region) are arranged alphabetically (word by word) and subdivided by recipient group. Use this index when you are looking for money to support your activities in a particular geographic area.

Subject Index. This index allows you to identify the subject focus of each of the financial aid opportunities described in the *Directory*. More than 250 different subject terms are listed. Extensive "see" and "see also" references, as well as recipient group subdivisions, will help you in your search for appropriate funding opportunities.

Calendar Index. Since most financial aid programs have specific deadline dates, some may have closed by the time you begin to look for funding. You can use the Calendar Index to determine which programs are still open. This index is arranged by recipient group (Undergraduates, Graduate Students, and Professionals/Postdoctorates) and subdivided by month during which the deadline falls. Filing dates can and quite often do vary from year to year; consequently, this index should be used only as a guide for deadlines beyond the end of 2014.

HOW TO USE THE DIRECTORY

Here are some tips to help you get the most out the funding opportunities listed in the *Directory of Financial Aids for Women.*

To Locate Funding by Recipient Group. To bring together programs with a similar educational focus, this directory is divided into three chapters: Undergraduates, Graduate Students, and Professionals/Postdoctorates. If you want to get an overall picture of the sources of free money available to women in any of these categories, turn to the appropriate chapter and then review the entries there. Since each of these chapters functions as a self-contained entity, you can browse through any of them without having to first consulting an index.

To Locate a Particular Women's Financial Aid Program. If you know the name of a particular financial aid program, and the group eligible for that award, then go directly to the appropriate chapter in the directory (e.g., Undergraduates, Graduate Students), where you will find the program profiles arranged alphabetically by title. To save time, though, you should always check the Program Title Index first if you know the name of a specific award but are not sure in which chapter it has been listed. Plus, since we index each program by all its known names and abbreviations, you'll also be able to track down a program there when you only know the popular rather than official name.

To Locate Programs Sponsored by a Particular Organization. The Sponsoring Organization Index makes it easy to identify agencies that provide financial assistance to women or to target specific financial aid programs for women offered by a particular organization. Each entry number in the index is coded to identify recipient group (Undergraduates, Graduate Students, Professionals/Postdoctorates), so that you can easily target appropriate entries.

To Browse Quickly Through the Listings. Look at the listings in the chapter that relates to you (Undergraduates, Graduate Students, or Professionals/Postdoctorates) and read the "Summary" paragraph in each entry. In seconds, you'll know if this is an opportunity that you might want to pursue. If it is, be sure to read the rest of the information in the entry, to make sure you meet all of the program requirements before writing or going online for an application form. Please save your time and energy. Don't apply if you don't qualify!

To Locate Funding Open to Women from or Tenable in a Particular Geographic Location. The Residency Index identifies financial aid programs open to women in a particular geographic location. The Tenability Index shows where the money can be spent. In both indexes, "see" and "see also" references are used liberally, and index entries for a particular geographic area are subdivided by recipient group (Undergraduates, Graduate Students, and Professionals/Postdoctorates) to help you identify the funding that's right for you. When using these indexes, always check the listings under the term "United States," since the programs indexed there have no geographic restrictions and can be used in any area.

To Locate Financial Aid for Women in a Particular Subject Area.   Turn to the Subject Index first if you are interested in identifying financial aid programs for women in a particular subject area (more than 250 different subject fields are listed there). To make your search easier, the intended recipient groups (Undergraduates, Graduate Students, Professionals/Postdoctorates) are clearly labeled in each of the subject listings. Extensive cross-references are also provided. As part of your search, be sure to check the listings in the index under the heading "General Programs;" those programs provide funding in any subject area (although they may be restricted in other ways).

To Locate Financial Aid Programs for Women by Deadline Date.   If you are working with specific time constraints and want to weed out the financial aid programs whose filing dates you won't be able to meet, turn first to the Calendar Index and check the program references listed under the appropriate recipient group and month. Note: not all sponsoring organizations supplied deadline information; those programs are listed under the "Deadline not specified" entries in the index. To identify every relevant financial aid program, regardless of filing date, go the appropriate chapter and read through all the entries there that match your educational level.

To Locate Financial Aid Programs Open to Both Men and Women.   Only programs designed with women in mind are listed in this publication. There are thousands of other programs that are open equally to men and women. To identify these programs, talk to your local librarian, check with your campus financial aid office, look at the list of RSP print resources on the page opposite the title page in this directory, or see if your library subscribes to Reference Service Press' interactive online funding database (for more information on that resource, go online to: www.rspfunding.com/esubscriptions.html).

PLANS TO UPDATE THE DIRECTORY

This volume, covering 2012-2014, is the 16th edition of the *Directory of Financial Aids for Women.* The next biennial edition will cover the years 2014-2016 and will be released in the first half of 2014.

OTHER RELATED PUBLICATIONS

In addition to the *Directory of Financial Aids for Women,* Reference Service Press publishes dozens of other titles dealing with fundseeking, including the *High School Senior's Guide to Merit and Other No-Need Funding; Money for Christen College Students; How to Pay for Your Degree in Education; Financial Aid for the Disabled and Their Families; Financial Aid for Study and Training Abroad;* and *Financial Aid for Veterans, Military Personnel, and Their Dependents.* Since each of these titles focuses on a separate population group, there is very little duplication in the listings. For more information on all of Reference Service Press' award-winning publications, write to the company at 5000 Windplay Drive, Suite 4, El Dorado Hills, CA 95762, give us a call at (916) 939-9620, fax us at (916) 939-9626, send us an e-mail at info@rspfunding.com, or visit our expanded web site: www.rspfunding.com.

ACKNOWLEDGEMENTS

A debt of gratitude is owed all the organizations that contributed information to the 2012-2014 edition of the *Directory of Financial Aids for Women.* Their generous cooperation has helped to make this publication the most current and comprehensive survey of awards.

ABOUT THE AUTHORS

Dr. Gail Ann Schlachter has worked for more than three decades as a library administrator, a library educator, and an administrator of library-related publishing companies. Among the reference books to her credit are the biennially-issued *College Student's Guide to Merit and Other No-Need Funding* (named by *Choice* as one of the outstanding reference titles of the year) and two award-winning bibliographic guides: *Minorities and Women: A Guide to Reference Literature in the Social Sciences* (which also was chosen as an "Outstanding Reference Book of the Year" by *Choice)* and *Reference Sources in Library and Information Services* (which won the first Knowledge Industry Publications "Award for Library Literature"). She was the reference book review editor for *RQ* (now *Reference and User Services Quarterly)* for 10 years, is a past president of the American Library Association's Reference and User Services Association, is the former editor-in-chief of the *Reference and User Services Association Quarterly,* and is currently serving her fifth term on the American Library Association's governing council. In recognition of her outstanding contributions to reference service, Dr. Schlachter has been named the University of Wisconsin School of Library and Information Studies "Alumna of the Year" and has been awarded both the Isadore Gilbert Mudge Citation and the Louis Shores/Oryx Press Award.

Dr. R. David Weber taught history and economics at Los Angeles Harbor College (in Wilmington, California) for many years and continues to teach there as an emeritus professor. During his years of full-time teaching at Harbor College, and at East Los Angeles College, he directed the Honors Program and was frequently chosen "Teacher of the Year." He has written a number of critically-acclaimed reference works, including *Dissertations in Urban History* and the three-volume *Energy Information Guide.* With Dr. Schlachter, he is the author Reference Service Press's award-winning *Financial Aid for the Disabled and Their Families* and dozens of other distinguished financial aid titles, including the highly-acclaimed *Money for Graduate Students in the Social & Behavioral Sciences* and *Financial Aid for Hispanic Americans.*

Financial Aid Programs Primarily or Exclusively for Women

Undergraduates ●

Graduate Students ●

Professionals/Postdoctorates ●

Undergraduates

Listed alphabetically by program title and described in detail here are 711 scholarships, grants, awards, internships, and other sources of "free money" set aside for females who are college-bound high school seniors and continuing or returning undergraduate students. This funding is available to support study, training, research, and/or creative activities in the United States.

[1]
AARP WOMEN'S SCHOLARSHIP PROGRAM

American Association of Retired Persons
Attn: AARP Foundation
601 E Street, N.W.
Washington, DC 20049
(202) 434-3525   Toll Free: (888) OUR-AARPf
TDD: (877) 434-7598
Web: www.aarp.org/womensscholarship

Summary To provide financial assistance to mature women who are interested in returning to college.

Eligibility This program is open to women who are at least 40 years of age. Priority is given to women who 1) are raising the children of another family member; 2) are in low-paying jobs and lacking a retirement benefit and/or health insurance; or 3) have been out of the work force for more than 5 years. Applicants must be planning to enroll as an undergraduate at a community college, 4-year university, or technical school. Selection is based on personal circumstances and achievements, educational goals, financial need, and the likely impact of the scholarship on the applicants' lives, families, and communities.

Financial data Stipends range from $500 to $5,000, depending on the need of the recipient and the cost of the education or training program. Funds are paid directly to the institution to be used for payment of tuition, fees, and books.

Duration 1 year; may be renewed.

Additional information This program was established in 2007. Support is provided by Wal-Mart Foundation and individual donors to the AARP Foundation.

Number awarded Varies each year; recently, more than 200 of these scholarships, worth more than $450,000, were awarded.

Deadline March of each year.

[2]
ACHIEVEMENT SCHOLARSHIPS

Zeta Tau Alpha Foundation, Inc.
Attn: Director of Foundation Administration
3450 Founders Road
Indianapolis, IN 46268
(317) 872-0540   Fax: (317) 876-3948
E-mail: zetataualpha@zetataualpha.org
Web: www.zetataualpha.org

Summary To provide financial assistance for college or graduate school to women who are members of Zeta Tau Alpha.

Eligibility This program is open to undergraduate and graduate women who are enrolled at a 4-year college or university and student members of the school's Zeta Tau Alpha chapter. Applicants must demonstrate leadership qualities within their chapter or in campus activities while maintaining a high scholastic average. Selection is based on academic achievement (GPA of 2.75 or higher), involvement in campus and community activities, recommendations, current class status, and financial need.

Financial data The stipend is at least $1,000.

Duration 1 year; renewable.

Number awarded Varies each year; recently, the foundation awarded a total of more than $600,000 to 235 undergrad-

uate and graduate members for all of its scholarship programs.

Deadline February of each year.

[3]
ADMIRAL GRACE MURRAY HOPPER MEMORIAL SCHOLARSHIPS

Society of Women Engineers
Attn: Scholarship Selection Committee
120 South LaSalle Street, Suite 1515
Chicago, IL 60603-3572
(312) 596-5223   Toll Free: (877) SWE-INFO
Fax: (312) 644-8557
E-mail: scholarshipapplication@swe.org
Web: societyofwomenengineers.swe.org

Summary To provide financial assistance to women who will be entering college as freshmen and are interested in studying computer science or related engineering fields.

Eligibility This program is open to women who are entering college as freshmen with a GPA of 3.5 or higher. Applicants must be U.S. citizens planning to enroll full time at an ABET-accredited 4-year college or university and major in computer science or engineering. Selection is based on merit. Preference is given to students in computer-related engineering.

Financial data The stipend is $1,500.

Duration 1 year.

Additional information This program, established in 1992, is named for the "mother of computerized data automation in the naval service."

Number awarded 3 each year.

Deadline May of each year.

[4]
AGENDA FOR DELAWARE WOMEN TRAILBLAZER SCHOLARSHIPS

Delaware Higher Education Commission
Carvel State Office Building, Fifth Floor
820 North French Street
Wilmington, DE 19801-3509
(302) 577-5240   Toll Free: (800) 292-7935
Fax: (302) 577-6765   E-mail: dhec@doe.k12.de.us
Web: www.doe.k12.de.us

Summary To provide financial assistance to women who are residents of Delaware and interested in working on an undergraduate degree at a college in the state.

Eligibility This program is open to women who are Delaware residents planning to enroll in a public or private nonprofit college in the state as an undergraduate student. Applicants must have a cumulative GPA of 2.5 or higher. They must be U.S. citizens or eligible noncitizens. Selection is based on financial need (50%) and community and school activities, vision, participation, and leadership (50%).

Financial data The stipend is $2,500 per year.

Duration 1 year; recipients may reapply.

Number awarded 10 each year.

Deadline April of each year.

[5]
AGNES C. ALLEN MEMORIAL SCHOLARSHIP
Pennsylvania Masonic Youth Foundation
Attn: Educational Endowment Fund
1244 Bainbridge Road
Elizabethtown, PA 17022-9423
(717) 367-1536   Toll Free: (800) 266-8424 (within PA)
Fax: (717) 367-0616   E-mail: pmyf@pagrandlodge.org
Web: www.pmyf.org/scholar/index.html

Summary To provide financial assistance to members of Rainbow Girls in Pennsylvania who are attending college in any state.

Eligibility This program is open to active Pennsylvania Rainbow Girls in good standing. Applicants must have completed at least 1 year at an accredited college, university, or nursing school in any state.

Financial data The stipend depends on the availability of funds.

Duration 1 year; may be renewed.

Number awarded 1 each year.

Deadline Requests for applications must be submitted by January of each year. Completed applications are due by the end of February.

[6]
AGNES MISSIRIAN SCHOLARSHIP
Armenian International Women's Association
65 Main Street, Room 3A
Watertown, MA 02472
(617) 926-0171   E-mail: aiwainc@aol.com
Web: www.aiwa-net.org/scholarshipinfo.html

Summary To provide financial assistance to Armenian women who are upper-division and graduate students.

Eligibility This program is open to full-time women students of Armenian descent attending an accredited college or university. Applicants must be full-time juniors, seniors, or graduate students with a GPA of 3.2 or higher. They must submit an essay, up to 500 words, describing their planned academic program, their career goals, and the reasons why they believe they should be awarded this scholarship. Selection is based on financial need and merit.

Financial data The stipend is $2,000.

Duration 1 year.

Number awarded 1 or more each year.

Deadline April of each year.

[7]
AGNES MORRIS EDUCATION SCHOLARSHIP
Louisiana Federation of Business and Professional
  Women's Clubs, Inc.
c/o Linda Burns
1424 Evangeline Road
Glenmora, LA 71433
(318) 748-7603   E-mail: amesfchair@bpwlouisiana.org
Web: lafbpw.wildapricot.org/Default.aspx?pageId=880660

Summary To provide financial assistance to members of the Louisiana Federation of Business and Professional Women's Clubs (BPW/LA) who are interested in pursuing college or professional advancement in any state.

Eligibility This program is open to women who are 25 years of age or older and members of the BPW/LA and a BPW local organization in Louisiana. Applicants must be enrolled at or entering an accredited university, college, technical school, or program for licensing or career advancement in any state. Along with their application, they must submit transcripts from their high school and any institution of higher education they have attended, entrance examination scores, 3 letters of recommendation, and a 250-word statement on why they want this scholarship and their plans for using it. Financial need is not considered in the selection process.

Financial data The stipend is $1,000 per year.

Duration 2 years, provided the recipient completes at least 6 hours per semester and maintains a GPA of 2.5 or higher.

Additional information This program originated as the Agnes Morris Educational Loan Fund.

Number awarded 1 or more each year.

Deadline January of each year.

[8]
AHIMA FOUNDATION DIVERSITY SCHOLARSHIPS
American Health Information Management Association
Attn: AHIMA Foundation
233 North Michigan Avenue, 21st Floor
Chicago, IL 60601-5809
(312) 233-1175   Fax: (312) 233-1475
E-mail: info@ahimafoundation.org
Web: www.ahimafoundation.org

Summary To provide financial assistance to women and other members of the American Health Information Management Association (AHIMA) who are interested in working on an undergraduate degree in health information administration or technology and who will contribute to diversity in the profession.

Eligibility This program is open to AHIMA members who are enrolled at least half time in a program accredited by the Commission on Accreditation of Allied Health Education Programs. Applicants must be working on an associate degree in health information technology or a bachelor's degree in health information administration. They must have a GPA of 3.0 or higher and at least 1 full semester remaining after the date of the award. To qualify for this support, applicants must demonstrate how they will contribute to diversity in the health information management profession; diversity is defined as differences in race, ethnicity, nationality, gender, sexual orientation, socioeconomic status, age, physical capabilities, and religious beliefs. Financial need is not considered in the selection process.

Financial data Stipends are $1,000 for students working on an associate degree or $1,200 for students working on a bachelor's degree.

Duration 1 year.

Number awarded Varies each year; recently, 8 of these scholarships were awarded.

Deadline April or October of each year.

[9]
AIR FORCE OFFICERS' WIVES' CLUB OF WASHINGTON, D.C. CONTINUING EDUCATION SCHOLARSHIPS FOR NON-MILITARY AIR FORCE SPOUSES

Air Force Officers' Wives' Club of Washington, D.C.
Attn: Scholarship Committee
P.O. Box 8490
Washington, DC 20032
E-mail: scholarship@afowc.com
Web: www.afowc.com/making-difference.html

Summary To provide financial assistance for undergraduate or graduate study in any state to the non-military spouses of Air Force members in the Washington, D.C. area.

Eligibility This program is open to the non-military spouses of Air Force members residing in the Washington, D.C. metropolitan area in the following categories: active duty, retired, MIA/POW, or deceased. Spouses whose Air Force sponsor is assigned remote from the area or reassigned during the current school year are also eligible if they remained behind to continue their education. Applicants must be enrolled or planning to enroll as an undergraduate or graduate student at a college or university in any state. Along with their application, they must submit a 500-word essay on a topic that changes annually; recently, applicants were asked to write on which book is required reading for all students and why. Selection is based on academic and citizenship achievements; financial need is not considered.

Financial data A stipend is awarded (amount not specified). Funds may be used only for payment of tuition or academic fees.

Duration 1 year.

Number awarded Varies each year.

Deadline February of each year.

[10]
AIR PRODUCTS AND CHEMICALS SCHOLARSHIP FOR DIVERSITY IN ENGINEERING

Association of Independent Colleges and Universities of Pennsylvania
101 North Front Street
Harrisburg, PA 17101-1405
(717) 232-8649   Fax: (717) 233-8574
E-mail: info@aicup.org
Web: www.aicup.org

Summary To provide financial assistance to women and minority students from any state who are enrolled at member institutions of the Association of Independent Colleges and Universities of Pennsylvania (AICUP) and majoring in designated fields of engineering.

Eligibility This program is open to undergraduate students from any state enrolled full time at AICUP colleges and universities. Applicants must be women and/or members of the following minority groups: American Indians, Alaska Natives, Asians, Blacks/African Americans, Hispanics/Latinos, Native Hawaiians, or Pacific Islanders. They must be juniors majoring in chemical or mechanical engineering with a GPA of 2.7 or higher. Along with their application, they must submit an essay on their characteristics, accomplishments, primary interests, plans, goals, and uniqueness.

Financial data The stipend is $7,500 per year.

Duration 1 year; may be renewed 1 additional year if the recipient maintains appropriate academic standards.

Additional information This program, sponsored by Air Products and Chemicals, Inc., is available at the 83 private colleges and universities in Pennsylvania that comprise the AICUP.

Number awarded 1 each year.

Deadline April of each year.

[11]
AL NEUHARTH FREE SPIRIT SCHOLARSHIP AND CONFERENCE PROGRAM

Freedom Forum
Attn: Manager, Free Spirit Program
555 Pennsylvania Avenue, N.W.
Washington, DC 20001
(202) 292-6261   Fax: (202) 292-6265
E-mail: freespirit@freedomforum.org
Web: www.freedomforum.org/freespirit

Summary To provide financial assistance for college to high school journalists who demonstrate a "free spirit" (females and males are judged separately).

Eligibility This program is open to high school seniors who are active in high school journalism. Applicants must be planning to attend college to prepare for a career in journalism. They must demonstrate qualities of a "free spirit" in their academic or personal life. A "free spirit" is defined as "a risk-taker, a visionary, an innovative leader, an entrepreneur, or a courageous achiever who accomplishes great things beyond his or her normal circumstances." Along with their application, they must submit 2 essays of 500 words each: 1) explaining why they want to prepare for a career in journalism, and 2) describing their specific qualities as a free spirit and their experiences and/or struggles that make them a free spirit. Men and women are judged separately. U.S. citizenship or permanent resident status is required. Financial need is not considered in the selection process.

Financial data The stipend is $10,000 or $1,000.

Duration 1 year.

Additional information Recipients are invited to Washington in March to receive their awards and participate in a journalism conference. All travel expenses are paid. This program began in 1999.

Number awarded 102 each year: a male and a female from each state and the District of Columbia. The recipients include 100 who receive $1,000 scholarships and 2 (a male and a female) who receive $10,000 scholarships.

Deadline October of each year.

[12]
ALABAMA G.I. DEPENDENTS' SCHOLARSHIP PROGRAM

Alabama Department of Veterans Affairs
770 Washington Avenue, Suite 530
Montgomery, AL 36102-1509
(334) 242-5077   Fax: (334) 242-5102
E-mail: willie.moore@va.state.al.us
Web: www.va.state.al.us/scholarship.htm

Summary To provide educational benefits to spouses and other dependents of Alabama veterans.

Eligibility Eligible are spouses, children, stepchildren, and unremarried widow(er)s of veterans who served honorably for 90 days or more and 1) are currently rated as 20% or more service-connected disabled or were so rated at time of death; 2) were a former prisoner of war; 3) have been declared missing in action; 4) died as the result of a service-connected disability; or 5) died while on active military duty in the line of duty. The veteran must have been a permanent civilian resident of Alabama for at least 1 year prior to entering active military service; veterans who were not Alabama residents at the time of entering active military service may also qualify if they have a 100% disability and were permanent residents of Alabama for at least 5 years prior to filing the application for this program or prior to death, if deceased. Children and stepchildren must be under the age of 26, but spouses and unremarried widow(er)s may be of any age.

Financial data Eligible dependents may attend any state-supported Alabama institution of higher learning or enroll in a prescribed course of study at any Alabama state-supported trade school without payment of any tuition, book fees, or laboratory charges.

Duration This is an entitlement program for 4 years of full-time undergraduate or graduate study or part-time equivalent. Spouses and unremarried widow(er)s whose veteran spouse is rated between 20% and 90% disabled, or 100% disabled but not permanently so, may attend only 2 standard academic years.

Additional information Benefits for children, spouses, and unremarried widow(er)s are available in addition to federal government benefits. Assistance is not provided for noncredit courses, placement testing, GED preparation, continuing educational courses, pre-technical courses, or state board examinations.

Number awarded Varies each year.

Deadline Applications may be submitted at any time.

[13]
ALABAMA GOLF ASSOCIATION WOMEN'S SCHOLARSHIP FUND

Alabama Golf Association
1025 Montgomery Highway, Suite 210
Birmingham, AL 35216
(205) 979-1234   Toll Free: (800) 783-4446
Fax: (205) 979-1602
Web: www.bamagolf.com/womens-scholarship-fund

Summary To provide financial assistance to female high school seniors in Alabama who can demonstrate an interest in golf and plan to attend college in the state.

Eligibility This program is open to women graduating from high schools in Alabama who are planning to attend a college or university in the state. Applicants must be able to demonstrate an interest in the game of golf and financial need. They must have an ACT score of 22 or higher. Along with their application, they must submit a 200-word statement on why a college education is important to them, their goals, and how they hope to obtain those goals. Selection is based on academic excellence, citizenship, sportsmanship, community involvement, and financial need.

Financial data The stipend is $2,500 per year.

Duration 1 year; may be renewed up to 3 additional years if the recipient maintains a GPA of 2.4 or higher during her freshman year and 2.8 or higher during subsequent years.

Additional information This program, established in 1993, includes the Stone Hodo Scholarship and the Ann Samford Upchurch Scholarship.

Number awarded 1 each year.

Deadline March of each year.

[14]
ALASKA FREE TUITION FOR SPOUSE OR DEPENDENT OF ARMED SERVICES MEMBER

Department of Military and Veterans Affairs
Attn: Office of Veterans Affairs
P.O. Box 5800
Fort Richardson, AK 99505-5800
(907) 428-6016   Fax: (907) 428-6019
E-mail: jerry_beale@ak-prepared.com
Web: veterans.alaska.gov/state_benefits.htm

Summary To provide financial assistance for college to spouses and children of servicemembers from Alaska who died or were declared prisoners of war or missing in action.

Eligibility Eligible for this benefit are the spouses and dependent children of Alaska residents who died in the line of duty, died of injuries sustained in the line of duty, or were listed by the Department of Defense as a prisoner of war or missing in action. Applicants must be in good standing at a state-supported educational institution in Alaska.

Financial data Those eligible may attend any state-supported educational institution in Alaska without payment of tuition or fees.

Duration 1 year; may be renewed.

Additional information Information is available from the financial aid office of state-supported universities in Alaska.

Number awarded Varies each year.

Deadline Deadline not specified.

[15]
ALBERTA E. CROWE STAR OF TOMORROW AWARD

United States Bowling Congress
Attn: Youth Department
621 Six Flags Drive
Arlington, TX 76011
Toll Free: (800) 514-BOWL, ext. 3168
Fax: (817) 385-8262
E-mail: beoff@ibcyouth.com
Web: www.bowl.com/scholarships

Summary To provide financial assistance for college to outstanding women bowlers.

Eligibility This program is open to women amateur bowlers who are current members in good standing of the United States Bowling Congress (USBC) Youth organization and competitors in its sanctioned events. Applicants must be high school seniors or college students and have a GPA of 3.0 or higher. They may not have competed in a professional bowling tournament. Along with their application, they must submit a 500-word essay on how the lessons they have learned through academics, community involvement, and bowling have influenced their life and their goals for the future. Selection is based on bowling performances on local, regional, state, and national levels; academic achievement; and extracurricular involvement.

Financial data The stipend is $1,500 per year.

Duration 1 year; may be renewed for 3 additional years.
Number awarded 1 each year.
Deadline September of each year.

[16]
ALICE T. SCHAFER MATHEMATICS PRIZE
Association for Women in Mathematics
11240 Waples Mill Road, Suite 200
Fairfax, VA 22030
(703) 934-0163   Fax: (703) 359-7562
E-mail: awm@awm-math.org
Web: sites.google.com

Summary To recognize and reward undergraduate women who have demonstrated excellence in mathematics.

Eligibility Women may not apply for this award; they must be nominated by a member of the mathematical community. The nominee may be at any level in her undergraduate career. She must be a U.S. citizen or attending school in the United States. Selection is based on the quality of the student's performance in advanced mathematics courses and special programs, demonstration of real interest in mathematics, ability for independent work in mathematics, and performance in mathematical competitions at the local or national level.

Financial data The prize is $1,000.
Duration The prize is presented annually.
Additional information This prize was first presented in 1990.
Number awarded 1 each year.
Deadline Nominations must be submitted by September of each year.

[17]
ALPHA CHI OMEGA EDUCATIONAL ASSISTANCE GRANTS
Alpha Chi Omega Foundation
Attn: Educational Assistance Grants Committee
5939 Castle Creek Parkway North Drive
Indianapolis, IN 46250-4343
(317) 579-5050, ext. 262   Fax: (317) 579-5051
E-mail: foundation@alphachiomega.org
Web: www.alphachiomega.org/index.aspx?id=1031

Summary To provide financial assistance to members of Alpha Chi Omega sorority who are interested in continuing education, including study abroad.

Eligibility This program is open to members of the sorority at the undergraduate and graduate school levels. Applicants must be seeking funding for continuing education and related expenses. They may be interested in studying abroad if the credits earned will be included with credits needed to earn a degree. Along with their application, they must submit documentation of financial need, an outline of their future career goals, a description of their participation in sorority activities, transcripts, and (if studying abroad) confirmation that credits earned will be included with credits needed to earn a degree.

Financial data Grants range from $500 to $2,000.
Duration 1 year.
Additional information This program includes the Alpha Zeta Undergraduate Member Assistance Grant in Memory of Kay Roh, the Carol Edmundson Hutcheson Education Assistance Fund, the Florence Staiger Lonn Educational Grants,

the Lisa Hancock Rehrig Educational Assistance Grants, and the Mary Frances-Guilbert Mariani-Bigler Continuing Education Grant.
Number awarded Varies each year; recently, 51 of these grants, with $13,372, were awarded.
Deadline May or October of each year.

[18]
ALPHA CHI OMEGA MEMBER ASSISTANCE GRANTS
Alpha Chi Omega Foundation
Attn: Member Assistance Grants Committee
5939 Castle Creek Parkway North Drive
Indianapolis, IN 46250-4343
(317) 579-5050, ext. 262   Fax: (317) 579-5051
E-mail: foundation@alphachiomega.org
Web: www.alphachiomega.org/index.aspx?id=1032

Summary To provide funding to members of Alpha Chi Omega sorority who are facing financial difficulties because of changing life circumstances.

Eligibility This program is open to collegiate and alumnae members of Alpha Chi Omega and to persons closely related to a member of the sorority. Applicants must be facing financial difficulties because of changing life circumstances.

Financial data Grants range from $100 to $1,000.
Duration 1 year.
Additional information This program includes the Anne E. Helliwell Sisters Assistance Grants, the Mary Kuehn Powell Alumnae Assistance Grants, and the Seven Drach Sisters Fund Honoring Gladys Drach Power.
Number awarded Varies each year; recently, 6 of these grants, worth $4,493, were awarded.
Deadline Applications may be submitted at any time.

[19]
ALPHA EPSILON PHI FOUNDATION SCHOLARSHIPS
Alpha Epsilon Phi
Attn: AEPhi Foundation
11 Lake Avenue Extension, Suite 1A
Danbury, CT 06811
(203) 748-0029   Fax: (203) 748-0039
E-mail: aephifoundation@aephi.org
Web: www.aephi.org/foundation/scholarships

Summary To provide financial assistance for undergraduate or graduate education to Alpha Epsilon Phi members or alumnae.

Eligibility This program is open to active and alumnae members of the sorority who are either full-time rising juniors or seniors or graduate students who have completed at least 1 year of graduate study. Applicants must have a GPA of 3.0 or higher. Along with their application, they must submit a letter describing 1) their activities in their chapter, on campus, and in the general community; 2) what they have done to supplement their parents' contribution toward their education; and 3) their need for scholarship consideration.

Financial data Stipends range from $1,000 to $2,000 per year.
Duration 1 year; may be renewed.
Additional information This program includes the following named scholarships: the Judith Resnik Memorial Scholar-

ship (preference to those working on a degree in engineering, science, or a related field and have a GPA of 3.5 or higher), the Anne Klauber Berson Memorial Scholarship, the Edith Hirsch Miller Memorial Scholarship (preference to Jewish applicants who are members of Nu Chapter at the University of Pittsburgh or residents of Pittsburgh), the Irma Loeb Cohen Scholarship (preference to members of Rho Chapter at Ohio State University), the Ruth Rosenbaum Goldfeder Memorial Scholarship (preference to students at universities in California), the Constance Bauman Abraham Scholarship (preference to members of Eta Chapter at SUNY Albany or at universities in other northeastern states, the Ruth Bader Ginsburg Scholarship (preference to members entering their second year of law school), and the Shonnette Meyer Kahn Scholarship (preference to members of Rho Chapter at Ohio State University or Epsilon Chapter at Tulane University). Recipients must be willing to remain active in the sorority and live in the sorority house (if any) for the entire year the scholarship covers.

Number awarded Several each year.

Deadline March of each year.

[20]
ALPHA GAMMA CHAPTER RECRUITMENT GRANT

Delta Kappa Gamma Society International-Mississippi
  Alpha Gamma Chapter
c/o Donna Matthews
910 South 34th Avenue
Hattiesburg, MS 39402
(601) 268-6987   E-mail: donnamatthews527@gmail.com
Web: www.alphagammachapter.com/scholarship.htm

Summary To provide financial assistance to women enrolled at colleges in Mississippi and majoring in education, library science, or a related field.

Eligibility This program is open to women currently enrolled as juniors at colleges and universities in Mississippi. Applicants must be majoring in education, library science, or a related field. Along with their application, they must submit a brief autobiography that includes career plans and any unique financial needs. Preference is given to applicants planning to teach in Lamar, Forrest, Covington, or Perry counties in Mississippi.

Financial data The stipend is $1,000.

Duration 1 year.

Number awarded 1 each year.

Deadline December of each year.

[21]
ALPHA KAPPA ALPHA ENDOWMENT AWARDS

Alpha Kappa Alpha Sorority, Inc.
Attn: Educational Advancement Foundation
5656 South Stony Island Avenue
Chicago, IL 60637
(773) 947-0026   Toll Free: (800) 653-6528
Fax: (773) 947-0277   E-mail: akaeaf@akaeaf.net
Web: www.akaeaf.org/fellowships_endowments.htm

Summary To provide financial assistance to undergraduate and graduate students (especially African American women) who meet designated requirements.

Eligibility This program is open to undergraduate and graduate students who are enrolled full time as sophomores or higher in an accredited degree-granting institution and are planning to continue their program of education. Applicants may apply for scholarships that include specific requirements established by the donor of the endowment that supports it. Along with their application, they must submit 1) a list of honors, awards, and scholarships received; 2) a list of organizations in which they have memberships, especially minority organizations; and 3) a statement of their personal and career goals, including how this scholarship will enhance their ability to attain those goals. The sponsor is a traditionally African American women's sorority.

Financial data Award amounts are determined by the availability of funds from the particular endowment. Recently, stipends averaged more than $1,700 per year.

Duration 1 year or longer.

Additional information Each endowment establishes its own requirements. Examples of requirements include residence of the applicant, major field of study, minimum GPA, attendance at an Historically Black College or University (HBCU) or member institution of the United Negro College Fund (UNCF), or other personal feature. For further information on all endowments, contact the sponsor.

Number awarded Varies each year; recently, 30 of these scholarships, with a total value of $52,082, were awarded.

Deadline April of each year.

[22]
ALPHA KAPPA ALPHA UNDERGRADUATE SCHOLARSHIPS

Alpha Kappa Alpha Sorority, Inc.
Attn: Educational Advancement Foundation
5656 South Stony Island Avenue
Chicago, IL 60637
(773) 947-0026   Toll Free: (800) 653-6528
Fax: (773) 947-0277   E-mail: akaeaf@akaeaf.net
Web: www.akaeaf.org/undergraduate_scholarships.htm

Summary To provide financial assistance to students (especially African American women) who are working on an undergraduate degree in any field.

Eligibility This program is open to undergraduate students who are enrolled full time as sophomores or higher in an accredited degree-granting institution and are planning to continue their program of education. Applicants may apply either for a scholarship based on merit (requires a GPA of 3.0 or higher) or on financial need (requires a GPA of 2.5 or higher). Along with their application, they must submit 1) a list of honors, awards, and scholarships received; 2) a list of organizations in which they have memberships, especially minority organizations; and 3) a statement of their personal and career goals, including how this scholarship will enhance their ability to attain those goals. The sponsor is a traditionally African American women's sorority.

Financial data Stipends range from $750 to $2,500.

Duration 1 year; nonrenewable.

Number awarded Varies each year; recently, 69 of these scholarships, with a total value of $74,700 were awarded.

Deadline April of each year.

[23]
ALPHA OMICRON PI FOUNDATION NAMED SCHOLARSHIPS

Alpha Omicron Pi Foundation
Attn: Scholarship Committee
5390 Virginia Way
Brentwood, TN 37027
(615) 370-0920   Fax: (615) 370-4424
E-mail: foundation@alphaomicronpi.org
Web: www.aoiifoundation.org/scholarship.php

Summary To provide financial assistance for college or graduate school to collegiate and alumnae members of Alpha Omicron Pi who meet specified requirements.

Eligibility This program is open to collegiate members of Alpha Omicron Pi who are classified by their institutions at least as sophomores and alumnae members who wish to work on a graduate degree. Applicants must be able to qualify for specified awards by meeting extra requirements of each named award. They must be enrolled full time. Along with their application, they must submit the following 50-word statements: 1) the circumstances that have created their need for this scholarship; 2) their immediate and long-term life objectives; and 3) a letter of recommendation that they would write about themselves. Selection is based on those statements; academic achievement; Alpha Omicron Pi service, leadership, and involvement; college and community involvement; letters of recommendation; and financial need and evidence of self-help.

Financial data Stipend amounts vary; recently, the average value of each scholarship provided by this foundation was approximately $1,200.

Duration 1 year.

Additional information These named awards include the Muriel T. McKinney Scholarship for the highest-ranked undergraduate; the Helen Haller Scholarship for the highest-ranked graduate applicant; several for which membership in a particular chapter of the sorority is required or preferred; others which may be open to members in designated regions or states (the Angels of Kappa Theta Memorial Scholarship for collegiate members of southern California chapters, the Carey Griner Memorial Scholarship for collegiate members of Indiana colleges, the Jasmine Queen Scholarship for collegiate members of Maryland colleges, the Kappa Gamma Chapter Scholarship for collegiate members of Florida colleges, the Kerri Keith Memorial Scholarship for collegiate members of Georgia colleges, the Martha McKinney Wilhoite Scholarship for juniors or seniors who reside or attend college in Indiana, the Rho Omicron Chapter Scholarship for collegiate or alumna members who reside or attend college in Tennessee, and the San Diego Alumnae Chapter Honor Scholarship for alumna members who reside in California); the Caroline Craig Lazzara Scholarship for a member of a chapter that has been installed or re-colonized within the past 5 years; and a number of scholarships available to all Alpha Omicron Pi members (Karen Tucker Centennial Scholarship, Laura Gilliam McDowell Scholarship, Nancy McCain Memorial Scholarship, Nu Iota Scholarship in Memory of Julia V. Nelson and in Honor of Elaine Nelson Mackenzie, the Rho Chapter Scholarship, and the Robert and Eleanore Mac-Curdy Scholarship).

Number awarded Varies each year; recently, 23 of these scholarships were awarded (17 to undergraduates and 6 to graduate students).

Deadline February of each year.

[24]
ALPHA PHI/BETTY MULLINS JONES SCHOLARSHIP

National Panhellenic Conference
Attn: NPC Foundation
3901 West 86th Street, Suite 398
Indianapolis, IN 46268
(317) 876-7802   Fax: (317) 876-7904
E-mail: npcfoundation@npcwomen.org
Web: www.npcwomen.org/foundation/scholarships.aspx

Summary To provide financial assistance to undergraduate women who are members of Greek-letter societies.

Eligibility This program is open to Greek-affiliated women at colleges and universities in the United States. Applicants must be able to demonstrate that they have worked to further their Greek community's reputation on their campus. In the selection process, emphasis is placed on financial need and participation in university, Panhellence, chapter, and other activities.

Financial data The stipend is $1,000.

Duration 1 year.

Number awarded 1 each year.

Deadline January of each year.

[25]
ALPHA SIGMA TAU SCHOLARSHIPS

Alpha Sigma Tau National Foundation
Attn: Office Manager
P.O. Box 476
Gardendale, AL 35071
(205) 978-4512
E-mail: melinda@alphasigmataufoundation.org
Web: www.alphasigmataufoundation.org/scholarships

Summary To provide financial assistance to members of Alpha Sigma Tau sorority interested in continuing undergraduate or graduate study.

Eligibility This program is open to members of Alpha Sigma Tau who are sophomores, juniors, seniors, or graduate students. Applicants must have a GPA of 3.0 or higher. Along with their application, they must submit a 1-page essay on why they should receive this scholarship. Selection is based on academic achievement, service to Alpha Sigma Tau, academic honors, university or community service, and financial need.

Financial data Stipends range from $275 to $2,250.

Duration 1 year.

Number awarded Varies each year.

Deadline January of each year.

[26]
AMELIA KEMP MEMORIAL SCHOLARSHIP

Women of the Evangelical Lutheran Church in America
Attn: Scholarships
8765 West Higgins Road
Chicago, IL 60631-4101
(773) 380-2736   Toll Free: (800) 638-3522, ext. 2736
Fax: (773) 380-2419   E-mail: Women.elca@elca.org
Web: www.elca.org

Summary To provide financial assistance to lay women of color who are members of Evangelical Lutheran Church of America (ELCA) congregations and who wish to study on the undergraduate, graduate, professional, or vocational school level.

Eligibility This program is open to ELCA lay women of color who are at least 21 years of age and have experienced an interruption of at least 2 years in their education since high school. Applicants must have been admitted to an educational institution to prepare for a career in other than a church-certified profession. U.S. citizenship is required.

Financial data The maximum stipend is $1,000.

Duration Up to 2 years.

Number awarded 1 or more each year.

Deadline February of each year.

[27]
AMERICAN AIRLINES AND AMERICAN EAGLE ENGINEERING SCHOLARSHIP

Women in Aviation, International
Attn: Scholarships
Morningstar Airport
3647 State Route 503 South
West Alexandria, OH 45381-9354
(937) 839-4647   Fax: (937) 839-4645
E-mail: scholarships@wai.org
Web: www.wai.org/education/scholarships.cfm

Summary To provide financial assistance to members of Women in Aviation, International (WAI) who are studying engineering in college.

Eligibility This program is open to WAI members who are currently enrolled in an accredited U.S. engineering program. Applicants must be U.S. citizens or permanent residents and have a GPA of 3.0 or higher. Along with their application, they must submit an essay of 500 to 1,000 words on who or what inspired them to prepare for a career in engineering, their greatest life challenge, their greatest strength and strongest characteristic, their most memorable academic experience, and why they are the most qualified candidate for this scholarship. Selection is based on achievements, attitude toward self and others, commitment to success, dedication to career, financial need, motivation, reliability, responsibility, and teamwork.

Financial data The stipend is $5,000.

Duration 1 year.

Additional information WAI is a nonprofit professional organization dedicated to encouraging women to consider an aviation career and to providing educational outreach activities and networking resources to women active in the industry. This program is sponsored by American Airlines and its regional subsidiary, American Eagle.

Number awarded 1 each year.

Deadline November of each year.

[28]
AMERICAN AIRLINES VETERAN'S INITIATIVE SCHOLARSHIP

Women in Aviation, International
Attn: Scholarships
Morningstar Airport
3647 State Route 503 South
West Alexandria, OH 45381-9354
(937) 839-4647   Fax: (937) 839-4645
E-mail: scholarships@wai.org
Web: www.wai.org/education/scholarships.cfm

Summary To provide financial assistance to veterans who are members of Women in Aviation, International (WAI) and interested in attending college, flight school, or other institution.

Eligibility This program is open to veterans of the U.S. military who are WAI members and interested in studying aviation or aeronautics at an accredited college, flight school, or other institution of higher education. Along with their application, they must submit 2 letters of recommendation, a 500-word essay on their aviation history and goals, a resume, copies of all aviation licenses and medical certificates, and the last 3 pages of their pilot logbook (if applicable). Selection is based on achievements, attitude toward self and others, commitment to success, dedication to career, financial need, motivation, reliability, responsibility, and teamwork.

Financial data The stipend is $5,000. Funds are paid directly to the college, flight school, or other institution.

Duration 1 year.

Additional information WAI is a nonprofit professional organization dedicated to encouraging women to consider an aviation career and to providing educational outreach activities and networking resources to women active in the industry. This program was established in 2011 by American Airlines.

Number awarded 1 each year.

Deadline November of each year.

[29]
AMERICAN ASSOCIATION OF JAPANESE UNIVERSITY WOMEN SCHOLARSHIP PROGRAM

American Association of Japanese University Women
c/o Scholarship Committee
3543 West Boulevard
Los Angeles, CA 90016
E-mail: scholarship@aajuw.org
Web: www.aajuw.org/Scholarship.htm

Summary To provide financial assistance to female students currently enrolled in upper-division or graduate classes in California.

Eligibility This program is open to women enrolled at accredited colleges or universities in California as juniors, seniors, or graduate students. Applicants must be involved in U.S.-Japan relations, cultural exchanges, and leadership development in the areas of their designated field of study. Along with their application, they must submit a current resume, an official transcript of the past 2 years of college work, 2 letters of recommendation, and an essay (up to 2 pages in English or 1,200 characters in Japanese) on what they hope to accomplish in their field of study and how that will contribute to better U.S.-Japan relations.

Financial data   The stipend is $2,000.

Duration   1 year.

Additional information   The association was founded in 1970 to promote the education of women as well as to contribute to U.S.-Japan relations, cultural exchanges, and leadership development.

Number awarded   2 or 3 each year. Since this program was established, it has awarded nearly $100,000 worth of scholarships to more than 90 women.

Deadline   October of each year.

[30]
AMERICAN BAPTIST WOMEN'S MINISTRIES OF COLORADO STUDENT GRANTS

American Baptist Churches of the Rocky Mountains
Attn: American Baptist Women's Ministries
9085 East Mineral Circle, Suite 170
Centennial, CO 80112
(303) 988-3900   E-mail: web@abcrm.org
Web: www.abcrm.org

Summary   To provide financial assistance to women who are members of churches affiliated with the American Baptist Churches (ABC) USA in Colorado, New Mexico, and Utah and interested in attending an ABC college or seminary in any state.

Eligibility   This program is open to women older than 26 years of age who are active members of churches cooperating with ABC in Colorado, New Mexico, or Utah. Applicants must be enrolled or planning to enroll at an ABC college, university, or seminary in any state. Along with their application, they must submit a personal letter describing their Christian experience; their participation in the life of their church, school, and community; and their goals for the future. Selection is based on academic performance, Christian participation in church and school, and financial need.

Financial data   A stipend is awarded (amount not specified). Funds are sent directly to the recipient's school.

Duration   1 year; recipients may reapply.

Number awarded   1 or more each year.

Deadline   March of each year.

[31]
AMERICAN BAPTIST WOMEN'S MINISTRIES OF MASSACHUSETTS SCHOLARSHIP PROGRAM

American Baptist Women's Ministries of Massachusetts
c/o Penny Mulloy, Scholarship Committee Chair
27 Ox Road
Billerica, MA 01821-4439
(978) 667-7496   E-mail: pennymulloy@gmail.com
Web: www.abwmofma.org

Summary   To provide financial assistance to American Baptist women in Massachusetts interested in church-related vocations.

Eligibility   This program is open to women who intend to offer Christian service in their chosen vocation, have been active members of an American Baptist Church in Massachusetts for at least 1 year prior to submitting an application, and are able to supply satisfactory references. They must be nom-

inated by their pastor. Applicants should include a written statement of faith and a separate letter of life purpose that clearly indicates how they intend to serve in the Christian community after their education is completed. Selection is based on dedication, need, and scholastic ability.

Financial data   A stipend is awarded (amount not specified).

Duration   1 year; may be renewed.

Additional information   Of the scholarships awarded, 2 are designated as the Lenore S. Bigelow Scholarships, for graduate study at Andover Newton Theological School in Newton Centre, Massachusetts and/or Colgate-Rochester Divinity School in Rochester, New York. An interview with the committee or designated members is required of first-time applicants.

Number awarded   Varies each year.

Deadline   April of each year.

[32]
AMERICAN BAPTIST WOMEN'S MINISTRIES OF NEW YORK STATE SCHOLARSHIPS

American Baptist Women's Ministries of New York State
Attn: Scholarship Committee
5865 East Seneca Turnpike
Jamesville, NY 13078
(315) 469-4236   Fax: (315) 492-2369
E-mail: isingram@rochester.rr.com
Web: www.abwm-nys.org/M_M/scholarship.html

Summary   To provide financial assistance to women who are members of American Baptist Churches in New York and interested in attending college in any state.

Eligibility   This program is open to women who are residents of New York and active members of an American Baptist Church. Applicants must be enrolled or planning to enroll full time at a college or university in any state. While in college, they must maintain Christian fellowship, preferably with the American Baptist Church (although any Protestant church or campus ministry is acceptable). Along with their application, they must submit a 1-page essay on an event that occurred in their life during the past year and how it has impacted their faith. Women may be of any age; graduate students are considered on an individual basis. Financial need is considered in the selection process.

Financial data   A stipend is awarded (amount not specified).

Duration   1 year.

Number awarded   Varies each year.

Deadline   February of each year.

[33]
AMERICAN BAPTIST WOMEN'S MINISTRIES OF WISCONSIN CONTINUING EDUCATION FOR ADULT WOMEN SCHOLARSHIP

American Baptist Women's Ministries of Wisconsin
c/o Lois A. Horsman, Scholarship Committee Chair
P.O. Box 68
Wyocena, WI 53969
(608) 429-2485
Web: www.abcofwi.org/abwinfo.htm

Summary To provide financial assistance to adult female members of American Baptist Churches in Wisconsin who are interested in attending college in any state.

Eligibility This program is open to adult women who are residents of Wisconsin and attending or planning to attend college in any state. Applicants must have been an active member of an American Baptist Church in Wisconsin for the preceding 3 years. The college does not need to be affiliated with the American Baptist Churches USA.

Financial data A stipend is awarded (amount not specified).

Duration 2 or 4 years.

Number awarded 1 or more each year.

Deadline Deadline not specified.

[34]
AMERICAN GI FORUM WOMEN'S RE-ENTRY SCHOLARSHIPS

American GI Forum of the United States
2870 North Speer Boulevard, Suite 103
Denver, CO 80211
(303) 458-1700   Toll Free: (866) 244-3628
Fax: (303) 458-1634   E-mail: agifnat@gmail.com
Web: www.agifusa.org/women

Summary To provide financial assistance to mature women who are members of the American GI Forum and interested in returning to college.

Eligibility This program is open to women who have been members of a women's chapter of the American GI Forum for at least 2 years. Applicants must be at least 25 years of age and enrolled or planning to enroll at a college or university as a full- or part-time student. Along with their application, they must submit transcripts, 3 letters of recommendation, proof of income, and a biographical essay.

Financial data A stipend is awarded (amount not specified).

Duration 1 year; recipients may reapply.

Additional information The American GI Forum is the largest federally-charter Hispanic veterans organization in the United States.

Number awarded 1 or more each year.

Deadline Deadline not specified.

[35]
AMERICAN LEGION AUXILIARY EMERGENCY FUND

American Legion Auxiliary
8945 North Meridian Street
Indianapolis, IN 46260
(317) 569-4500   Fax: (317) 569-4502
E-mail: alahq@legion-aux.org
Web: www.legion-aux.org

Summary To provide funding to members of the American Legion Auxiliary who are facing temporary emergency needs or need educational training.

Eligibility This program is open to members of the American Legion Auxiliary who have maintained their membership for the immediate past 2 consecutive years and have paid their dues for the current year. Applicants must need emergency assistance for the following purposes: 1) food, shelter, and utilities during a time of financial crisis; 2) food and shel-

ter because of weather-related emergencies and natural disasters; or 3) educational training because of the death of a spouse, divorce, separation, or the need to become the main source of support for their family. They must have exhausted all other sources of financial assistance, including funds and/or services available through the local Post and/or Unit, appropriate community welfare agencies, or state and federal financial aid for education. Grants are not available to settle already existing or accumulated debts, handle catastrophic illness, resettle disaster victims, or other similar problems.

Financial data The maximum grant is $2,400. Payments may be made directly to the member or to the mortgage company or utility. Educational grants may be paid directly to the educational institution.

Duration Grants are expended over no more than 3 months.

Additional information This program was established in 1969. In 1981, it was expanded to include the Displaced Homemaker Fund (although that title is no longer used).

Number awarded Varies each year.

Deadline Applications may be submitted at any time.

[36]
AMERICAN METEOROLOGICAL SOCIETY UNDERGRADUATE NAMED SCHOLARSHIPS

American Meteorological Society
Attn: Fellowship/Scholarship Program
45 Beacon Street
Boston, MA 02108-3693
(617) 227-2426, ext. 246   Fax: (617) 742-8718
E-mail: scholar@ametsoc.org
Web: www.ametsoc.org

Summary To provide financial assistance to undergraduates (particularly women, minorities, and individuals with disabilities) who are majoring in meteorology or an aspect of atmospheric sciences.

Eligibility This program is open to full-time students entering their final year of undergraduate study and majoring in meteorology or an aspect of the atmospheric or related oceanic and hydrologic sciences. Applicants must intend to make atmospheric or related sciences their career. They must be U.S. citizens or permanent residents enrolled at a U.S. institution and have a cumulative GPA of 3.25 or higher. Along with their application, they must submit 200-word essays on 1) their most important attributes and achievements that qualify them for this scholarship, and 2) their career goals in the atmospheric or related sciences. Financial need is considered in the selection process. The sponsor specifically encourages applications from women, minorities, and students with disabilities who are traditionally underrepresented in the atmospheric and related oceanic sciences.

Financial data Stipend amounts vary each year.

Duration 1 year.

Additional information All scholarships awarded through this program are named after individuals who have assisted the sponsor in various ways.

Number awarded Varies each year; recently, 20 of these scholarships were awarded.

Deadline February of each year.

[37]
AMERICAN SOCIETY OF WOMEN ACCOUNTANTS UNDERGRADUATE SCHOLARSHIPS

American Society of Women Accountants
Attn: Educational Foundation
1760 Old Meadow Road, Suite 500
McLean, VA 22102
(703) 506-3265   Toll Free: (800) 326-2163
Fax: (703) 506-3266   E-mail: foundation@aswa.org
Web: www.aswa.org/PageDisplay.asp?p1=1386

Summary To provide financial assistance to undergraduate women interested in preparing for a career in accounting or finance.

Eligibility This program is open to women who are entering their third, fourth, or fifth year of undergraduate study at a college, university, or professional school of accounting. Applicants must have completed at least 60 semester hours with a declared major in accounting or finance and a GPA of 3.0 or higher. Selection is based on leadership, character, communication skills, scholastic average, and financial need. Membership in the American Society of Women Accountants (ASWA) is not required. Applications must be submitted to a local ASWA chapter.

Financial data A stipend is awarded (amount not specified).

Duration 1 year; recipients may reapply.

Number awarded Varies each year.

Deadline Local chapters must submit their candidates to the national office by February of each year.

[38]
AMVETS NATIONAL LADIES AUXILIARY SCHOLARSHIPS

AMVETS National Ladies Auxiliary
Attn: Scholarship Officer
4647 Forbes Boulevard
Lanham, MD 20706-4380
(301) 459-6255   Fax: (301) 459-5403
E-mail: auxhdqs@amvets.org
Web: amvetsaux.org/about_us.htm

Summary To provide financial assistance to members and certain dependents of members of AMVETS Auxiliary who are already enrolled in college.

Eligibility Applicants must belong to AMVETS Auxiliary or be the child or grandchild of a member. They must be in at least the second year of undergraduate study at an accredited college or university. Applications must include 3 letters of recommendation and an essay (from 200 to 500 words) about their past accomplishments, career and educational goals, and objectives for the future. Selection is based on the letters of reference (15%), academic record (15%), the essay (25%), and financial need (45%).

Financial data Scholarships are $1,000 or $750 each.

Duration 1 year.

Number awarded Up to 7 each year: 2 at $1,000 and 5 at $750.

Deadline June of each year.

[39]
ANCHOR GRANTS

Delta Gamma Foundation
Attn: Assistant Executive Director
3250 Riverside Drive
P.O. Box 21397
Columbus, OH 43221-0397
(614) 481-8169, ext. 324   Toll Free: (800) 644-5414
Fax: (614) 481-0133   E-mail: kathleen@deltagamma.org
Web: www.deltagamma.org

Summary To provide assistance to members of Delta Gamma who are facing a financial emergency.

Eligibility This program is open to collegiate and alumnae members of Delta Gamma who find themselves in financial distress, emergency, or crisis because of aging, medical, or other severe personal or family problems. Applicants must submit a financial statement and a description of their reasons for need.

Financial data The amount of the assistance depends on the need of the recipient.

Number awarded Varies each year.

Deadline Applications may be submitted at any time.

[40]
ANDY STONE SCHOLARSHIPS

US Youth Soccer-Region III
c/o Denise Davis
12320 Jacksonville Cato Road
North Little Rock, AR 72120
(501) 834-1300   Fax: (501) 835-1300
E-mail: r3usysa@swbell.net
Web: regioniii.usyouthsoccer.org/awards/index.asp

Summary To provide financial assistance for college to female and male high school seniors (judged separately) in selected southern states who have been active in soccer.

Eligibility This program is open to seniors graduating from high schools in states that are part of Region III of US Youth Soccer (Alabama, Arkansas, Florida, Georgia, Louisiana, Mississippi, North Carolina, Oklahoma, South Carolina, Tennessee, and Texas). Applicants must have been an active member of Region III as a player, coach, and/or referee. Selection is based on years and depth of involvement in US Youth Soccer and soccer in general, academic achievement, financial need, citizenship, and extracurricular activities. Boys and girls and considered separately.

Financial data The stipend is $1,500. The first $1,000 is issued at the beginning of the school year and the second $500 is issued upon receipt of proof of an overall "C" average for the first grading period.

Duration 1 year.

Additional information This program was established in 1999 and limited to applicants from Mississippi. In subsequent years, it has rotated among the states that comprise Region III in alphabetical order. Applicants must be from North Carolina in 2012, Oklahoma in 2013, South Carolina in 2014, etc.

Number awarded 2 each year: 1 to a boy and 1 to a girl.

Deadline April of each year.

[41]
ANITA BORG MEMORIAL SCHOLARSHIPS

Google Inc.
Attn: Scholarships
1600 Amphitheatre Parkway
Mountain View, CA 94043-8303
(650) 253-0000   Fax: (650) 253-0001
E-mail: anitaborgscholarship@google.com
Web: www.google.com/intl/en/anitaborg/us

Summary   To provide financial assistance to women working on a bachelor's or graduate degree in a computer-related field.

Eligibility   This program is open to women who are entering their senior year of undergraduate study or are enrolled in a graduate program in computer science, computer engineering, or a closely-related field. Applicants must be full-time students at a university in the United States and have a GPA of 3.5 or higher. They must submit essays of 400 to 600 words on 1) a significant technical project on which they have worked; 2) their leadership abilities; 3) what they would do if someone gave them the funding and resources for a 3- to 12-month project to investigate a technical topic of their choice; and 4) what they would do if someone gave them $1,000 to plan an event or project to benefit women in technical fields. Citizens, permanent residents, and international students are eligible. Selection is based on academic background and demonstrated leadership.

Financial data   The stipend is $10,000 per year.

Duration   1 year; recipients may reapply.

Additional information   These scholarships were first offered in 2004.

Number awarded   Varies each year; recently, 25 of these scholarships were awarded.

Deadline   January of each year.

[42]
ANN ARBOR AWC SCHOLARSHIP FOR WOMEN IN COMPUTING

Association for Women in Computing-Ann Arbor Chapter
Attn: Scholarship
P.O. Box 1864
Ann Arbor, MI 48106-1864
E-mail: students@awc-aa.org
Web: www.awc-aa.org/scholarship.aspx

Summary   To provide financial assistance to women undergraduates from any state working on a degree in a computer- or technology-related field at institutions in Michigan.

Eligibility   This program is open to undergraduate women from any state enrolled at institutions of higher education in Michigan. Applicants may be 1) enrolled full or part time with at least 2 semesters of course work remaining and preparing for a career in a field related to computers or technology; or 2) seeking certification to change their career or enhance their current career in a field related to computers or technology. Along with their application, they must submit answers of 300 to 600 words on 3 essay questions that change annually; recently, students were asked to write on 1) their most fulfilling computer-related project or experience; 2) what intrigued them most about their chosen course of study; and 3) how they would encourage other women to join the field. Based on those essays, awards are presented to applicants who dem-

onstrate motivation, passion, thoughtfulness, creativity, skillful communication, and participation in the computing community. Financial need is not considered.

Financial data   A stipend is awarded (amount not specified).

Duration   1 year.

Additional information   This program was established in 2003.

Number awarded   1 or more each year.

Deadline   March of each year.

[43]
ANN CLARK NURSING SCHOLARSHIP

American Association of University Women-Honolulu Branch
Attn: Scholarship Committee
1802 Ke'eaumoku Street
Honolulu, HI 96822
(808) 537-4702   Fax: (808) 537-4702
E-mail: Edu@aauw-honolulu.org
Web: aauw.xodev01.com

Summary   To provide financial assistance to women in Hawaii who are interested in working on an advanced degree in nursing at a school in the state.

Eligibility   This program is open to female residents of Hawaii who are currently enrolled in an R.N. to B.S.N., M.S.N., or nursing doctoral program in the state. Applicants must submit a 500-word biographical statement that includes information on their family, work, school, community service, and future goals. Financial need is not considered in the selection process.

Financial data   A stipend is awarded (amount not specified).

Duration   1 year.

Number awarded   1 or more each year.

Deadline   May of each year.

[44]
ANN IRWIN LEADERSHIP SCHOLARSHIP

Women's Transportation Seminar-Heart of Texas Chapter
c/o Lindsay Liggett, Scholarship Chair
Jacobs Engineering Group Inc.
2705 Bee Cave Road, Suite 300
Austin, TX 78746-5688
(512) 314-3100   Fax: (512) 314-3135
E-mail: lindsay.liggett@jacobs.com
Web: www.wtsinternational.org/Chapters.aspx?ID=8336

Summary   To provide financial assistance to women undergraduates from any state who have demonstrated an interest in leadership and are preparing for a career in transportation at selected colleges and universities in Texas, Arkansas, or New Mexico.

Eligibility   This program is open to women from any state enrolled in an undergraduate degree program at a designated college or university in Texas, Arkansas, or New Mexico. Applicants must be majoring in a field related to transportation (e.g., engineering, finance, planning, logistics) and have a GPA of 3.0 or higher. They must be preparing for a career in a transportation-related field, especially in a leadership role. Along with their application, they must submit a 500-word statement about their career goals after graduation, why they think they should receive this scholarship, the importance of leadership in a transportation career, and their leadership achievements. Selection is based on transportation involvement and goals, job skills, academic record, and leadership potential; financial need is not considered. Minority women are especially encouraged to apply.

Financial data The stipend is $1,000.

Duration 1 year.

Additional information The winner is also nominated for scholarships offered by the national organization of the Women's Transportation Seminar. For a list of the eligible schools in Arkansas, New Mexico, and Texas, contact the sponsor.

Number awarded 1 each year.

Deadline April of each year.

[45]
ANNA GEAR JUNIOR SCHOLARSHIP

American Legion Auxiliary
Department of Virginia
Attn: Education Chair
1708 Commonwealth Avenue
Richmond, VA 23230
(804) 355-6410   Fax: (804) 353-5246

Summary To provide financial assistance to junior members of the American Legion Auxiliary in Virginia who plan to attend college in any state.

Eligibility This program is open to seniors graduating from high schools in Virginia and planning to attend college in any state. Applicants must have held junior membership in the American Legion Auxiliary for the 3 previous years. They must have completed at least 30 hours of volunteer service within their community and submit a 500-word article on "The Value of Volunteering in the Community."

Financial data The stipend is $1,000.

Duration 1 year.

Number awarded 1 each year.

Deadline March of each year.

[46]
ANNA LIND SCHOLARSHIP

International Order of the Rainbow for Girls-Grand
  Assembly of California
California Rainbow for Girls Foundation
c/o J. Dennis Conwell, Scholarship Committee Chair
424 Colfax Drive
San Jose, CA 95123-3403
(408) 629-7663   E-mail: dencon21@sbcglobal.net
Web: gocarainbow.org/scholarships.htm

Summary To provide financial assistance to members of the International Order of the Rainbow for Girls in California who plan to attend college in any state.

Eligibility This program is open to Rainbow Girls in California who are graduating high school seniors and planning to attend college in any state. Applicants must submit a brief essay on their career goals, how they plan to accomplish those, personal philosophy, and any unusual family or financial circumstances.

Financial data The stipend is $1,000.

Duration 1 year; nonrenewable.

Number awarded 1 each year.

Deadline February of each year.

[47]
ANNE MAUREEN WHITNEY BARROW MEMORIAL SCHOLARSHIP

Society of Women Engineers
Attn: Scholarship Selection Committee
120 South LaSalle Street, Suite 1515
Chicago, IL 60603-3572
(312) 596-5223   Toll Free: (877) SWE-INFO
Fax: (312) 644-8557
E-mail: scholarshipapplication@swe.org
Web: societyofwomenengineers.swe.org

Summary To provide financial assistance to women interested in studying engineering or engineering technology in college.

Eligibility This program is open to women who are enrolled or planning to enroll full time at an ABET-accredited 4-year college or university. Applicants must be planning to major in engineering or computer science. Entering freshmen must have a GPA of 3.5 or higher; current undergraduates must have a GPA of 3.0 or higher. Selection is based on merit.

Financial data The stipend is $7,000 per year.

Duration 1 year; may be renewed for 4 additional years.

Additional information This program was established in 1992.

Number awarded 1 every 5 years.

Deadline May of the years in which it is offered.

[48]
ANNE SOWLES CALHOUN MEMORIAL SCHOLARSHIP

Print and Graphics Scholarship Foundation
Attn: Scholarship Competition
200 Deer Run Road
Sewickley, PA 15143-2600
(412) 259-1740   Toll Free: (800) 910-GATF
Fax: (412) 741-2311   E-mail: pgsf@printing.org
Web: www.printing.org/pgsf

Summary To provide financial assistance for college to women who want to prepare for a career in the printing or publishing industry.

Eligibility This program is open to women who are high school seniors or full-time college students. Applicants must be interested in preparing for a career in graphic communications or printing. This is a merit-based program; financial need is not considered.

Financial data The stipend ranges from $1,000 to $5,000, depending upon the funds available each year.

Duration 1 year; may be renewed for up to 3 additional years, provided the recipient maintains a GPA of 3.0 or higher.

Additional information This program was established in 2006.

Number awarded 1 or more each year.

Deadline February of each year for high school seniors; March of each year for students already in college.

[49]
AOWCGWA SCHOLARSHIP PROGRAM

Army Officers' Wives' Club of the Greater Washington
   Area
c/o Fort Myer Thrift Shop
Attn: Mary Pawlow, Scholarship Committee Chair
P.O. Box 1124
Fort Myer, VA 22211
(703) 764-9656 E-mail: aowcgwascholarship@gmail.com
Web: www.aowcgwa.org/scholarshippage.html

Summary   To provide financial assistance for college to the spouses and children of U.S. Army personnel and veterans in the Washington, D.C. metropolitan area.

Eligibility   This program is open to 1) high school seniors who are children of Army personnel, 2) college students under 22 years of age who are children of Army personnel; and 3) spouses of Army personnel. High school seniors and spouses must reside with their sponsor in the Washington metropolitan area; the sponsor of college students must reside in that area. Sponsors may be active-duty, retired, or deceased, and officer or enlisted. Applicants must submit an essay of 200 to 300 words on a topic that changes annually but relates to their experience as the member of an Army family; a list of extracurricular activities, honors, church activities, community service, and employment; an official transcript that includes (for high school seniors) their SAT or ACT scores; and a letter of recommendation. Students who plan to attend a service academy or receive another full scholarship are not eligible. Selection is based on scholastic merit and community involvement; financial need is not considered.

Financial data   The maximum stipend is $2,000.

Duration   1 year.

Additional information   The Washington metropolitan area is defined to include the Virginia cities of Alexandria, Fairfax, Falls Church, Manassas, and Manassas Park; the Virginia counties of Arlington, Fairfax, Fauquier, Loudoun, Prince William, and Stafford; the Maryland counties of Calvert, Charles, Frederick, Montgomery, and Prince George's; and the District of Columbia. This program is supported in part by the First Command Educational Foundation.

Number awarded   1 or more each year.

Deadline   March of each year.

[50]
APPRAISAL INSTITUTE MINORITIES AND WOMEN EDUCATIONAL SCHOLARSHIP PROGRAM

Appraisal Institute
Attn: Appraisal Institute Education Trust
200 West Madison Street, Suite 1500
Chicago, IL 60606
(312) 335-4133   Fax: (312) 335-4134
E-mail: educationtrust@appraisalinstitute.org
Web: www.appraisalinstitute.org

Summary   To provide financial assistance to women and minority undergraduate students majoring in real estate or allied fields.

Eligibility   This program is open to members of groups underrepresented in the real estate appraisal profession. Those groups include women, American Indians, Alaska Natives, Asians and Pacific Islanders, Blacks or African Americans, and Hispanics. Applicants must be full- or part-time students enrolled in real estate courses within a degree-granting college, university, or junior college. They must have a GPA of 2.5 or higher and be able to demonstrate financial need. U.S. citizenship is required.

Financial data   The stipend is $1,000. Funds are paid directly to the recipient's institution to be used for tuition and fees.

Duration   1 year.

Number awarded   At least 1 each year.

Deadline   April of each year.

[51]
AREVA NP SCHOLARSHIP

Society of Women Engineers-Eastern Washington
   Section
Attn: Sandy Brower, Scholarship Committee Chair
P.O. Box 364
Richland, WA 99352
(509) 375-3112   E-mail: embrower@aol.com
Web: www.eastwashingtonswe.org

Summary   To provide financial assistance to female residents of the northwestern United States who are working on an undergraduate or graduate degree in nuclear engineering at a school in any state.

Eligibility   This program is open to female residents of Alaska, Idaho, Montana, Oregon, and Washington who have completed at least 1 year of study at an ABET-accredited school in any state. Applicants must be planning to work on an undergraduate or graduate degree in nuclear engineering in the following year. Along with their application, they must submit an essay of 100 to 300 words on their short-term and long-term career goals, their plan to reach those goals, how they decided on their course of study, their interest in a career in nuclear energy, and anything else about themselves or their situation that could affect the evaluation of their application. Financial need and academic success are considered in the selection process, but greater weight is given to the applicant's affiliation with AREVA NP (e.g., internship, summer job, family member employed by the company), intention to enter the nuclear energy industry, motivation, leadership potential, and ability to follow projects through to completion. All other factors being equal, preference is given to residents of eastern Washington.

Financial data   The stipend is $1,000.

Duration   1 year.

Additional information   This program is sponsored by AREVA NP Inc.

Number awarded   1 each year.

Deadline   February of each year.

[52]
ARFORA UNDERGRADUATE SCHOLARSHIP FOR WOMEN

Association of Romanian Orthodox Ladies Auxiliaries of
   North America
Attn: Scholarship Committee
222 Orchard Park Drive
New Castle, PA 16105
(724) 652-4313   E-mail: adelap@verizon.net
Web: www.arfora.org/scholarships.htm

Summary To provide financial assistance to women who are members of a parish of the Romanian Orthodox Episcopate of America and currently enrolled in college.

Eligibility This program is open to women who have been voting communicant members of a parish of the Romanian Orthodox Episcopate of America for at least 1 year or are daughters of a communicant member. Applicants must have completed at least 1 year of undergraduate study at a college or university. Along with their application, they must submit a 300-word statement describing their personal goals; high school, university, church, and community involvement; honors and awards; and why they should be considered for this award. Selection is based on academic achievement, character, worthiness, and participation in religious life.

Financial data The stipend is $1,000.

Duration 1 year; nonrenewable.

Additional information This scholarship was first awarded in 1994. The Association of Romanian Orthodox Ladies Auxiliaries (ARFORA) was established in 1938 as a women's organization within the Romanian Orthodox Episcopate of America.

Number awarded 1 or more each year.

Deadline May of each year.

[53]
ARIZONA BPW FOUNDATION ANNUAL SCHOLARSHIPS

Arizona Business and Professional Women's Foundation
Attn: Administrator
P.O. Box 32596
Phoenix, AZ 85064
Web: www.arizonabpwfoundation.com/scholarships.html

Summary To provide financial assistance to women in Arizona who are attending or interested in attending a community college in the state.

Eligibility This program is open to women, at least 25 years of age, who are attending a community college or trade school in Arizona. Applicants must fall into 1 of the following categories: women who have been out of the workforce and wish to upgrade their skills; women with no previous experience in the workforce who are seeking a marketable skill; and women who are currently employed who are interested in career advancement or change. Along with their application, they must submit 2 letters of recommendation, a statement of financial need (latest income tax return must be provided), a career goal statement, and their most recent transcript (when available). Selection is based on financial need, field of study, and possibility of success.

Financial data The stipend is $1,000 per year.

Duration 1 year; renewable for up to 3 consecutive semesters if the recipient maintains a GPA of 2.0 or higher.

Additional information In addition to the general scholarship, there are 3 named endowments: Dr. Dorine Chancellor (established in 1990 and open to students at any community college in Arizona, although 1 is set aside specifically for a student at Eastern Arizona College), Lynda Crowell (established in 1999 and open to students at community colleges in Maricopa County), and Muriel Lothrop-Ely (established in 2006 and open to students at any community college in Arizona).

Number awarded Several each year.

Deadline February of each year.

[54]
ARKANSAS MILITARY DEPENDENTS' SCHOLARSHIP PROGRAM

Arkansas Department of Higher Education
Attn: Financial Aid Division
114 East Capitol Avenue
Little Rock, AR 72201-3818
(501) 371-2050   Toll Free: (800) 54-STUDY
Fax: (501) 371-2001   E-mail: finaid@adhe.edu
Web: www.adhe.edu

Summary To provide financial assistance for educational purposes to spouses and other dependents of certain categories of Arkansas veterans.

Eligibility This program is open to the natural children, adopted children, stepchildren, and spouses of Arkansas residents who have been declared to be a prisoner of war, killed in action, missing in action, killed on ordnance delivery, or 100% totally and permanently disabled during, or as a result of, active military service. Applicants and their parent or spouse must be residents of Arkansas. They must be working on, or planning to work on, a bachelor's degree or certificate of completion at a public college, university, or technical school in Arkansas.

Financial data The program pays for tuition, general registration fees, special course fees, activity fees, room and board (if provided in campus facilities), and other charges associated with earning a degree or certificate.

Duration 1 year; undergraduates may obtain renewal as long as they make satisfactory progress toward a baccalaureate degree; graduate students may obtain renewal as long as they maintain a minimum GPA of 2.0 and make satisfactory progress toward a degree.

Additional information This program was established in 1973 as the Arkansas Missing in Action/Killed in Action Dependents Scholarship Program to provide assistance to the dependents of veterans killed in action, missing in action, or declared a prisoner of war. In 2005, it was amended to include dependents of disabled veterans and given its current name. Applications must be submitted to the financial aid director at an Arkansas state-supported institution of higher education or state-supported technical/vocational school.

Number awarded Varies each year; recently, 4 of these scholarships were awarded.

Deadline July of each year for fall term, November of each year for spring or winter term, April of each year for first summer session, or June of each year for second summer session.

[55]
ARLENE DAVIS SCHOLARSHIP

Delta Zeta Sorority
Attn: Foundation Coordinator
202 East Church Street
Oxford, OH 45056
(513) 523-7597   Fax: (513) 523-1921
E-mail: DZFoundation@dzshq.com
Web: www.deltazeta.org

Summary   To provide financial assistance for undergraduate study of aviation to members of Delta Zeta Sorority.

Eligibility   This program is open to members of the sorority who have a GPA of 3.0 or higher. Applicants should be entering their sophomore or junior year and working on a degree closely related to aviation. They must submit an official transcript, a statement of their career goals, information on their service to the sorority, documentation of campus activities and/or community involvement, a list of academic honors, and an explanation of their financial need.

Financial data   The stipend ranges from $500 to $2,500, depending on the availability of funds.

Duration   1 year; nonrenewable.

Number awarded   1 each year.

Deadline   February of each year.

[56]
ARLINE ANDREWS LOVEJOY SCHOLARSHIP

Maine Federation of Business and Professional Women's Clubs
Attn: BPW/Maine Futurama Foundation
c/o Susan Tardie, Co-President
25 Hall Street
Fort Kent, ME 04743
E-mail: susan.tardie@maine.edu
Web: www.bpwmefoundation.org/files/index.php?id=10

Summary   To provide financial assistance to female high school seniors and recent graduates in Maine who plan to attend college in any state.

Eligibility   This program is open to women who are seniors graduating from high schools in Maine or recent graduates of those schools. Applicants must be planning to attend an accredited college or university in any state. They must have a realistic goal for their education. Along with their application, they must submit a statement describing their educational and personal goals, including their financial need.

Financial data   The stipend is $1,200. Funds are paid directly to the recipient's school.

Duration   1 year.

Number awarded   1 or more each year.

Deadline   April of each year.

[57]
ARMY EMERGENCY RELIEF STATESIDE
SPOUSE EDUCATION ASSISTANCE PROGRAM

Army Emergency Relief
200 Stovall Street
Alexandria, VA 22332-0600
(703) 428-0000   Toll Free: (866) 878-6378
Fax: (703) 325-7183   E-mail: aer@aerhq.org
Web: www.aerhq.org

Summary   To provide financial assistance for college to the dependent spouses of Army personnel living in the United States.

Eligibility   This program is open to spouses of Army soldiers on active duty, widow(er)s of soldiers who died while on active duty, spouses of retired soldiers, and widow(er)s of soldiers who died while in a retired status. Applicants must be residing in the United States. They must be enrolled or accepted for enrollment as a full-time student at an approved postsecondary or vocational institution. Study for a second undergraduate or graduate degree is not supported. Financial need is considered in the selection process.

Financial data   The maximum stipend is $2,800 per academic year.

Duration   1 year; may be renewed up to 3 additional years.

Additional information   Army Emergency Relief is a private nonprofit organization dedicated to "helping the Army take care of its own." Its primary mission is to provide financial assistance to Army people and their dependents in time of valid emergency need; its educational program was established as a secondary mission to meet a need of Army people for their dependents to pursue vocational training, preparation for acceptance by service academies, or an undergraduate college education.

Number awarded   Varies each year; recently, 546 spouses received $1,517,400 in support.

Deadline   February of each year.

[58]
ASSOCIATION FOR WOMEN GEOSCIENTISTS
MINORITY SCHOLARSHIP

Association for Women Geoscientists
Attn: AWG Foundation
12000 North Washington Street, Suite 285
Thornton, CO 80241
(303) 412-6219   Fax: (303) 253-9220
E-mail: minorityscholarship@awg.org
Web: www.awg.org/EAS/scholarships.html

Summary   To provide financial assistance to underrepresented minority women who are interested in working on an undergraduate degree in the geosciences.

Eligibility   This program is open to women who are African American, Hispanic, or Native American (including Eskimo, Hawaiian, Samoan, or American Indian). Applicants must be full-time students working on, or planning to work on, an undergraduate degree in the geosciences (including geology, geophysics, geochemistry, hydrology, meteorology, physical oceanography, planetary geology, or earth science education). They must submit a 500-word essay on their academic and career goals, 2 letters of recommendation, high school and/or college transcripts, and SAT or ACT scores. Financial need is not considered in the selection process.

Financial data   A total of $6,000 is available for this program each year.

Duration   1 year; may be renewed.

Additional information   This program, first offered in 2004, is supported by ExxonMobil Foundation.

Number awarded   1 or more each year.

Deadline   June of each year.

[59]
ASSOCIATION FOR WOMEN IN ARCHITECTURE
SCHOLARSHIPS

Association for Women in Architecture
Attn: Scholarship Chair
22815 Frampton Avenue
Torrance, CA 90501-5034
(310) 534-8466   Fax: (310) 257-6885
E-mail: scholarship@awa-la.org
Web: www.awa-la.org/scholarships.php

Summary To provide financial assistance to women under-graduates in California who are interested in preparing for a career in architecture.

Eligibility This program is open to women who have completed at least 18 college units of study in any of the following fields: architecture; civil, structural, mechanical, or electrical engineering as related to architecture; landscape architecture; urban and land planning; interior design; architectural rendering and illustration; or environmental design. Applicants must be residents of California or attending school in the state. Students in their final year of study are also eligible and may use the funds for special projects (such as a trip abroad). Selection is based on grades, a personal statement, recommendations, and the quality and organization of materials submitted; financial need is not considered.

Financial data The stipend is $1,000.

Duration 1 year.

Number awarded 5 each year.

Deadline April of each year.

[60]
ASSOCIATION FOR WOMEN IN SCIENCE INTERNSHIPS

Association for Women in Science
Attn: Internship Coordinator
1442 Duke Street
Alexandria, VA 22314
(703) 372-4380   Toll Free: (800) 886-AWIS
Fax: (703) 778-7807   E-mail: awis@awis.org
Web: www.awis.org/careers/internship.html

Summary To provide an opportunity for underrepresented minority female undergraduates to gain summer work experience at the offices of the Association for Women in Science (AWIS) in the Washington, D.C. area.

Eligibility This program is open to women who are working on an undergraduate degree in a field of science, technology, engineering, or mathematics (STEM) and interested in a summer internship at AWIS. Applicants must be members of a group currently underrepresented in STEM fields (African Americans, Latinas/Hispanics, Native Americans, and Pacific Islanders). Along with their application, they must submit a resume, cover letter, writing sample, and letter of recommendation.

Financial data The stipend is $3,500.

Duration 10 weeks during the summer.

Additional information Interns may be assigned to publish the Washington Wire, contribute to the AWIS Magazine, develop content for the AWIS web site, advocate at Capitol Hill briefings, conduct research grants, perform special projects affiliated with AWIS committees, and interact with board members and top STEM professionals.

Number awarded Varies each year.

Deadline March of each year.

[61]
ASSOCIATION FOR WOMEN IN SPORTS MEDIA SCHOLARSHIP/INTERNSHIP PROGRAM

Association for Women in Sports Media
Attn: President
3899 North Front Street
Harrisburg, PA 17110
(717) 703-3086   E-mail: internships@awsmonline.org
Web: awsmonline.org/intern-scholarship

Summary To provide financial assistance and work experience to women undergraduate and graduate students who are interested in preparing for a career in sports writing.

Eligibility This program is open to women who are enrolled in college or graduate school full time and preparing for a career in sports writing, sports copy editing, sports broadcasting, or sports public relations. Applicants must submit a 750-word essay describing their most memorable experience in sports or sports media, a 1-page resume highlighting their journalism experience, a letter of recommendation, up to 5 samples of their work, and a $20 application fee. They must apply for and accept an internship with a sports media organization.

Financial data The highest-ranked applicant receives a $1,000 scholarship and a paid trip to the sponsor's convention (including hotel stay, reimbursement for travel, and free convention registration). Other winners receive a $500 scholarship. Half of the funds are paid at the beginning of the internship and half after its completion.

Duration 1 year; nonrenewable.

Additional information This program, which began in 1990, includes the Jackie and Gene Autry Memorial Scholarship, the Jim Brennan Scholarship, and the Betty Brennan Scholarship.

Number awarded At least 12 each year.

Deadline October of each year.

[62]
ASSOCIATION FOR WOMEN JOURNALISTS SCHOLARSHIPS

Association for Women Journalists
Attn: AWJ Grant
P.O. Box 2199
Fort Worth, TX 76113
(817) 685-3876
E-mail: jessamybrown@star-telegram.com
Web: www.awjdfw.org/scholarships_awards.html

Summary To provide financial assistance to upper-division women from any state studying journalism at a college or university in Texas.

Eligibility This program is open to women who are full-time juniors or seniors at colleges and universities in Texas. Applicants must be majoring in print, broadcast, or photojournalism and have a GPA of 2.5 or higher in their major. They must submit 3 samples of their print or broadcast work or photographs, a letter of recommendation from an instructor or adviser, a statement of professional goals and how the scholarship will help, and a statement of financial need (if that is to be considered).

Financial data The stipend is $1,000. Funds are paid directly to the college or university to be applied to tuition.

Duration 1 year.

Number awarded   Up to 4 each year.

Deadline   March of each year.

[63]
ASSOCIATION OF THE UNITED STATES NAVY EDUCATION ASSISTANCE PROGRAM

Association of the United States Navy
Attn: Education Assistance Program
1619 King Street
Alexandria, VA 22314-2793
(703) 548-5800   Toll Free: (877) NAVY-411
Fax: (866) 683-3647   E-mail: cfo@ausn.org
Web: www.ausn.org/?tabid=79

Summary   To provide financial assistance for college to widows and other relatives of members of the Association of the United States Navy (formerly the Naval Reserve Association).

Eligibility   This program is open to 1) dependent children, under 24 years of age, of association members; and 2) widows or widowers of deceased members. Applicants must be enrolled or planning to enroll full time at a college, university, or technical school. They must be U.S. citizens. Preference is given to applicants who have demonstrated an interest in the "hard sciences" (e.g., mathematics, medicine, engineering). Selection is based on academic and leadership ability, potential, character, personal qualities, and financial need.

Financial data   The amounts of the stipends vary but recently averaged more than $4,000 per year.

Duration   1 year; may be renewed 1 additional year.

Additional information   The Association of the United States Navy was formed in 2009 as a successor to the Naval Reserve Association.

Number awarded   Varies each year.

Deadline   April of each year.

[64]
AWARDS FOR ADVANCED PLACEMENT

Siemens Foundation
170 Wood Avenue South
Iselin, NJ 08830
Toll Free: (877) 822-5233   Fax: (732) 603-5890
E-mail: foundation.us@siemens.com
Web: www.siemens-foundation.org

Summary   To recognize and reward female and male high school students (judged separately) who have exceptional scores on the Advanced Placement (AP) examinations in mathematics and the sciences.

Eligibility   All students in U.S. high schools are eligible to be considered for these awards (including home-schooled students and those in U.S. territories). Each fall, the College Board identifies the male and female seniors in each state who have earned the highest number of scores of 5 on 8 AP exams: biology, calculus BC, chemistry, computer science A, environmental science, physics C mechanics, physics C electricity and magnetism, and statistics. Males and females are considered separately. Students with the highest scores nationally receive separate awards. The program also provides awards to teachers who demonstrate excellence in teaching AP mathematics and science.

Financial data   State scholarships are $2,000; in addition, national winners receive $5,000 scholarships. State awards

for teachers high schools are $1,000; the National AP Teacher of the Year receives $5,000.

Duration   The awards are presented annually.

Additional information   Information from the College Board is available at (800) 626-9795, ext. 5849.

Number awarded   100 state scholarships (1 female and 1 male from each state) and 2 national scholarships (1 female and 1 male) are awarded each year. In addition, 50 teachers (1 from each state) receive awards and 1 of those is designated the National AP Teacher of the Year.

Deadline   There is no application or nomination process for these awards. The College Board identifies the students and teachers for the Siemens Foundation.

[65]
AWIC-DC MATRIX SCHOLARSHIP

Association for Women in Communications-Washington
   DC Chapter
Attn: Ady Dewey, Student Affairs Committee
USA Weekend
7950 Jones Branch Drive
McLean, VA 22108-0001
Toll Free: (800) 487-2956   Fax: (703) 854-2122
E-mail: ady@ideasandvision.com
Web: www.awcdc.net/scholar_app.shtml

Summary   To provide financial assistance to women from any state who are working on undergraduate degrees in a communications-related field at specified universities in the Washington, D.C. area.

Eligibility   This program is open to female sophomores and juniors from any state who are attending a specified Washington, D.C. area university or college and studying advertising, communications, graphic arts, journalism, marketing, public relations, or a related field. Both full- and part-time students are eligible. Applicants must have an overall GPA of 3.0 or higher and work experience in communications or a related field. They must be active in extracurricular activities, including family obligations, volunteer work, clubs, and organizations, and their involvement must show versatility and commitment. Along with their application, they must submit a 500-word essay on how their present communications-related activities will contribute to the achievement of their career goals. Selection is based on that essay, at least 2 letters of recommendation, academic achievement, and communications activities; financial need is not considered.

Financial data   The stipend is $1,000.

Duration   1 year.

Additional information   The eligible universities are American University, Catholic University of America, Corcoran College of Art + Design, Gallaudet University, George Mason University, Georgetown University, George Washington University, Howard University, Marymount University, Southeastern University, Trinity College, University of the District Columbia, and University of Maryland at College Park. This program is sponsored by Professional Solutions, LLC and hosted by the Washington, DC Chapter of the Association for Women in Communications (AWC) in affiliation with the AWC Matrix Foundation.

Number awarded   1 each year.

Deadline   April of each year.

[66]
B. JUNE WEST RECRUITMENT GRANT

Delta Kappa Gamma Society International-Theta State
  Organization
c/o Megan Savage, Committee on Professional Affairs
  Chair
1101 West Third Street
Roswell, NM 88201-3031
E-mail: meganandjames@cableone.net
Web: deltakappagamma.org/NM

Summary To provide financial assistance to women in New Mexico who are interested in preparing for a career as a teacher.

Eligibility This program is open to women residents of New Mexico who are 1) graduating high school seniors planning to go into education; 2) college students majoring in education; or 3) teachers needing educational assistance. Applicants must submit a list of activities in which they are involved, 3 letters of recommendation, a list of achievements and awards, and a statement of their educational goal and how this grant would be of assistance to them. Financial need is not considered in the selection process.

Financial data A stipend is awarded (amount not specified).

Duration 1 year.

Number awarded 1 or more each year.

Deadline February of each year.

[67]
BAKER HUGHES SCHOLARSHIPS

Society of Women Engineers
Attn: Scholarship Selection Committee
120 South LaSalle Street, Suite 1515
Chicago, IL 60603-3572
(312) 596-5223   Toll Free: (877) SWE-INFO
Fax: (312) 644-8557
E-mail: scholarshipapplication@swe.org
Web: societyofwomenengineers.swe.org

Summary To provide financial assistance to women working on an undergraduate or graduate degree in designated engineering specialties.

Eligibility This program is open to women who are sophomores, juniors, seniors, or graduate students at 4-year ABET-accredited colleges and universities. Applicants must be working on a degree in computer science or chemical, electrical, mechanical, or petroleum engineering and have a GPA of 3.0 or higher. Preference is given to members of groups underrepresented in engineering or computer science. Selection is based on merit.

Financial data The stipend is $5,000 per year.

Duration 1 year; may be renewed up to 2 additional years.

Additional information This program is sponsored by Baker Hughes Incorporated.

Number awarded 3 each year.

Deadline February of each year.

[68]
BANNER ENGINEERING MINNESOTA SWE SCHOLARSHIP

Society of Women Engineers-Minnesota Section
Attn: Scholarship Committee
P.O. Box 582813
Minneapolis, MN 55458-2813
E-mail: scholarships@swe-mn.org
Web: swe-mn.org/scholarships.html

Summary To provide financial assistance to women from any state working on an undergraduate or graduate degree in electrical or mechanical engineering at colleges and universities in Minnesota, North Dakota, and South Dakota.

Eligibility This program is open to female undergraduate and graduate students at ABET-accredited engineering programs in Minnesota, North Dakota, or South Dakota. Applicants must be working full time on a degree in electrical or mechanical engineering. Along with their application, they must submit a short paragraph describing how they plan to utilize their engineering skills after they graduate. Selection is based on potential to succeed as an engineer (20 points), communication skills (10 points), extracurricular or community involvement and leadership skills (10 points), demonstrated successful work experience (10 points), and academic success (5 points).

Financial data The stipend is $2,000.

Duration 1 year.

Additional information This program is sponsored by Banner Engineering Corporation.

Number awarded 1 each year.

Deadline March of each year.

[69]
BARBARA ALICE MOWER MEMORIAL SCHOLARSHIP

Barbara Alice Mower Memorial Scholarship Committee
c/o Nancy A. Mower
1536 Kamole Street
Honolulu, HI 96821-1424
(808) 373-2901   E-mail: nmower@hawaii.edu

Summary To provide financial assistance to female residents of Hawaii who are interested in women's studies and are attending studying on the undergraduate or graduate level in the United States or abroad.

Eligibility This program is open to female residents of Hawaii who are at least juniors in college, are interested in and committed to women's studies, and have worked or studied in the field. Selection is based on interest in studying about and commitment to helping women, previous work and/or study in that area, previous academic performance, character, personality, and future plans to help women (particularly women in Hawaii). If there are several applicants who meet all these criteria, then financial need may be taken into consideration.

Financial data The stipend ranges from $1,000 to $3,500.

Duration 1 year; may be renewed.

Additional information Recipients may use the scholarship at universities in Hawaii, on the mainland, or in foreign countries. They must focus on women's studies or topics that relate to women in school.

Number awarded   1 or more each year.

Deadline   April of each year.

[70]
BARBARA MCBRIDE SCHOLARSHIP

Society of Exploration Geophysicists
Attn: SEG Foundation
8801 South Yale, Suite 500
P.O. Box 702740
Tulsa, OK 74170-2740
(918) 497-5500   Fax: (918) 497-5557
E-mail: scholarships@seg.org
Web: www.seg.org/web/foundation/programs/scholarship

Summary   To provide financial assistance to women who are interested in studying applied geophysics or a related field on the undergraduate or graduate school level.

Eligibility   This program is open to women who are 1) high school students planning to enter college in the fall, or 2) undergraduate or graduate students whose grades are above average. Applicants must intend to work on a degree directed toward a career in applied geophysics or a closely-related field (e.g., geosciences, physics, geology, or earth and environmental sciences). Along with their application, they must submit a 150-word essay on how they plan to use geophysics in their future. Financial need is not considered in the selection process.

Financial data   Stipends provided by this sponsor average $2,500 per year.

Duration   1 academic year; may be renewable, based on scholastic standing, availability of funds, and continuance of a course of study leading to a career in applied geophysics.

Number awarded   1 each year.

Deadline   February of each year.

[71]
BARNUM FESTIVAL FOUNDATION/JENNY LIND COMPETITION FOR SOPRANOS

Barnum Festival Foundation
Attn: Director
1070 Main Street
Bridgeport, CT 06604
(203) 367-8495   Toll Free: (866) 867-8495
Fax: (203) 367-0212   E-mail: barnumfestival@aol.com
Web: www.barnumfestival.com

Summary   To recognize and reward (with scholarships and a concert trip to Sweden) outstanding young female singers who have not yet reached professional status.

Eligibility   This program is open to sopranos between 20 and 30 years of age who have not yet attained professional status. They must be U.S. citizens. Past finalists may reapply, but former first-place winners and mezzo-sopranos are not eligible. Applicants must submit a CD or audio cassette tape with 2 contrasting arias and 1 art song. Based on the CD or tape, 12 semifinalists are selected for an audition at the Barnum Festival in Bridgeport, Connecticut every April. From that audition, 6 finalists are chosen. Selection of the winner is based on technique, musicianship, diction, interpretation, and stage presence.

Financial data   The winner of the competition is presented with a $2,000 scholarship award to further her musical education at a recognized voice training school, academy, or col-

lege or with a recognized voice teacher or coach. She is featured in a concert in June with the Swedish Jenny Lind at a locale in Connecticut and is sent to Sweden with her Swedish counterpart to perform in concerts for 2 weeks in July and August. The runner-up receives a $500 scholarship.

Duration   The competition is held annually.

Additional information   The winner of this competition serves as the American Jenny Lind, a 21st-century counterpart of the Swedish Nightingale brought to the United States for a successful concert tour in 1850 by P.T. Barnum. There is a $35 application fee.

Number awarded   2 each year: 1 winner and 1 runner-up.

Deadline   March of each year.

[72]
BASIC MIDWIFERY STUDENT SCHOLARSHIPS

American College of Nurse-Midwives
Attn: ACNM Foundation, Inc.
8403 Colesville Road, Suite 1550
Silver Spring, MD 20910-6374
(240) 485-1850   Fax: (240) 485-1818
Web: www.midwife.org/foundation_award.cfm

Summary   To provide financial assistance for midwifery education to student members of the American College of Nurse-Midwives (ACNM).

Eligibility   This program is open to ACNM members who are currently enrolled in an accredited basic midwife education program and have successfully completed 1 academic or clinical semester/quarter or clinical module. Applicants must submit a 150-word essay on their midwifery career plans and a 100-word essay on their intended future participation in the local, regional, and/or national activities of the ACNM. Selection is based on leadership potential, financial need, academic history, and potential for future professional contribution to the organization.

Financial data   The stipend is $3,000.

Duration   1 year.

Additional information   This program includes the following named scholarships: the A.C.N.M. Foundation Memorial Scholarship, the TUMS Calcium for Life Scholarship (presented by GlaxoSmithKline), the Edith B. Wonnell CNM Scholarship, and the Margaret Edmundson Scholarship.

Number awarded   Varies each year; recently, 4 of these scholarships were awarded.

Deadline   March of each year.

[73]
BEALL SCHOLARSHIP

Presbyterian Church (USA)
Attn: Office of Financial Aid for Studies
100 Witherspoon Street, Room M-052
Louisville, KY 40202-1396
(502) 569-5224   Toll Free: (888) 728-7228, ext. 5224
Fax: (502) 569-8766   E-mail: finaid@pcusa.org
Web: www.pcusa.org/financialaid/programs/beall.htm

Summary   To provide financial assistance to female Presbyterian residents of designated southeastern states who are interested in studying the arts at a school in any state.

Eligibility   This program is open to women who are members of the Presbyterian Church (USA) between 16 and 36 years of age. Applicants must be residents of Alabama, Florida, Georgia, Kentucky, Louisiana, Mississippi, North Carolina, South Carolina, Tennessee, or Virginia. They must be enrolled or planning to enroll full time at a college or university in any state to major in the arts. Selection is based on academic standing (GPA of 2.5 or higher) and financial need.

Financial data Stipends range up to $5,000 per year, depending upon the financial need of the recipient.

Duration 1 year; may be renewed up to 3 additional years.

Number awarded 1 or more each year.

Deadline June of each year.

[74]
BECHTEL FOUNDATION SCHOLARSHIP

Society of Women Engineers
Attn: Scholarship Selection Committee
120 South LaSalle Street, Suite 1515
Chicago, IL 60603-3572
(312) 596-5223   Toll Free: (877) SWE-INFO
Fax: (312) 644-8557
E-mail: scholarshipapplication@swe.org
Web: societyofwomenengineers.swe.org

Summary To provide financial assistance to undergraduate women who are members of the Society of Women Engineers and majoring in engineering.

Eligibility This program is open to women who are entering their sophomore, junior, or senior year at an ABET-accredited college or university. Applicants must be studying computer science or architectural, civil, electrical, environmental, or mechanical engineering or equivalent fields of engineering technology. They must have a GPA of 3.0 or higher. Only members of the society are considered for this award. Selection is based on merit.

Financial data The stipend is $1,400.

Duration 1 year.

Additional information This program, established in 2000, is sponsored by Bechtel Group Foundation.

Number awarded 2 each year.

Deadline February of each year.

[75]
BERNICE F. ELLIOTT MEMORIAL SCHOLARSHIP

Baptist Convention of New Mexico
Attn: Missions Mobilization Team
5325 Wyoming Boulevard, N.E.
P.O. Box 94485
Albuquerque, NM 87199-4485
(505) 924-2315   Toll Free: (800) 898-8544
Fax: (505) 924-2320   E-mail: cpairett@bcnm.com
Web: www.bcnm.com

Summary To provide financial assistance to women who are Southern Baptists from New Mexico and interested in attending a college or seminary in any state.

Eligibility This program is open to women college and seminary students who are members of churches affiliated with the Baptist Convention of New Mexico. Preference is given to applicants who are committed to full-time Christian service, have a background in the Woman's Missionary Union, and can demonstrate financial need.

Financial data A stipend is awarded (amount not specified).

Duration 1 year; may be renewed.

Number awarded 1 or more each year.

Deadline March of each year.

[76]
BERNICE MURRAY SCHOLARSHIP

Vermont Student Assistance Corporation
Attn: Scholarship Programs
10 East Allen Street
P.O. Box 2000
Winooski, VT 05404-2601
(802) 654-3798   Toll Free: (888) 253-4819
Fax: (802) 654-3765   TDD: (800) 281-3341 (within VT)
E-mail: info@vsac.org
Web: services.vsac.org/wps/wcm/connect/vsac/VSAC

Summary To provide financial assistance for child care to single parents in Vermont who wish to improve their education or skills.

Eligibility Applicants must be Vermont residents, single parents with primary custody of at least 1 child 12 years of age or younger, able to demonstrate financial need, and enrolled in a full- or part-time degree program at an approved postsecondary school. Along with their application, they must submit 1) a 100-word essay on any significant barriers that limit their access to education; 2) a 250-word essay on their short- and long-term academic, educational, career, vocational, and/or employment goals; and 3) a 100-word essay on how the program in which they will be enrolled will enhance their career or vocation. Selection is based on their essays, a letter of recommendation, financial need, and a personal interview.

Financial data The maximum stipend is $2,000; funds must be used to pay for child care services while the recipient attends an approved postsecondary institution.

Duration 1 year; recipients may reapply.

Additional information This program is sponsored by U.S. Senator James Jeffords and the Federal Executives' Association.

Number awarded 1 or 2 each year.

Deadline March of each year.

[77]
BERTHA LAMME MEMORIAL SCHOLARSHIP

Society of Women Engineers
Attn: Scholarship Selection Committee
120 South LaSalle Street, Suite 1515
Chicago, IL 60603-3572
(312) 596-5223   Toll Free: (877) SWE-INFO
Fax: (312) 644-8557
E-mail: scholarshipapplication@swe.org
Web: societyofwomenengineers.swe.org

Summary To provide financial assistance to women who will be entering college as freshmen and are interested in studying electrical engineering.

Eligibility This program is open to women who are entering college as freshmen with a GPA of 3.5 or higher. Applicants must be U.S. citizens planning to enroll full time at an ABET-accredited 4-year college or university and major in electrical engineering. Selection is based on merit.

Financial data The stipend is $1,200.

Duration 1 year.

Number awarded 1 each year.

Deadline May of each year.

[78]
BERTHA PITTS CAMPBELL SCHOLARSHIP PROGRAM

Delta Sigma Theta Sorority, Inc.
Attn: Scholarship and Standards Committee Chair
1707 New Hampshire Avenue, N.W.
Washington, DC 20009
(202) 986-2400   Fax: (202) 986-2513
E-mail: dstemail@deltasigmatheta.org
Web: www.deltasigmatheta.org

Summary To provide financial assistance to members of Delta Sigma Theta who are working on an undergraduate degree in education.

Eligibility This program is open to current undergraduate students who are working on a degree in education. Applicants must be active, dues-paying members of Delta Sigma Theta. Selection is based on meritorious achievement.

Financial data The stipends range from $1,000 to $2,000. The funds may be used to cover tuition, fees, and living expenses.

Duration 1 year; may be renewed for 1 additional year.

Additional information This sponsor is a traditionally-African American social sorority. The application fee is $20.

Deadline April of each year.

[79]
BESSIE BARROW MEMORIAL FOUNDATION SCHOLARSHIPS

Baptist Convention of Maryland/Delaware
Attn: United Baptist Women of Maryland, Inc.
10255 Old Columbia Road
Columbia, MD 21046
(410) 290-5290   Toll Free: (800) 466-5290
E-mail: gparker@bcmd.org
Web: bcmd.org/wmu

Summary To provide financial assistance to women who are members of Baptist churches associated with an affiliate of United Baptist Women of Maryland and interested in working on an undergraduate degree at a college in any state.

Eligibility This program is open to women who are enrolled or planning to enroll full time at an accredited college or university in any state to work on an undergraduate degree in any field. Applicants must be a member in good standing of a Baptist church associated with an affiliate of United Baptist Women of Maryland. They must have a grade average of "C" or higher and be able to demonstrate financial need. Along with their application, they must submit brief statements on their Christian experience, school activities, church and community activities, and career goals.

Financial data A stipend is awarded (amount not specified).

Duration 1 year.

Number awarded Varies each year.

Deadline June of each year.

[80]
BEST FRIENDS COLLEGE SCHOLARSHIP FUND

Best Friends Foundation
5335 Wisconsin Avenue, N.W., Suite 440
Washington, DC 20015
(202) 478-9677   Fax: (202) 478-9678
E-mail: ebennett@bestfriendsfoundation.org
Web: www.bestfriendsfoundation.org/BFDGLeadership.html

Summary To provide financial assistance for college to high school senior girls who have been members of the Best Friends organization in selected cities.

Eligibility This program is open to girls who are high school seniors at schools that participate in the Best Friends program. Applicants must have participated in Best Friends for at least 6 years before high school graduation. Selection is based on enthusiasm and overall commitment to Best Friends and its messages, demonstrated leadership, academic aptitude and performance, and courage in overcoming personal adversity.

Financial data A stipend is awarded (amount not specified).

Duration 1 year.

Additional information This program, which began in 1996, currently operates in Charlotte, North Carolina, Newark, New Jersey, and Washington, D.C.

Number awarded Varies each year; since the program was established, it has awarded more than $500,000 in scholarships.

Deadline Deadline not specified.

[81]
BETSY B. AND GAROLD A. LEACH SCHOLARSHIP FOR MUSEUM STUDIES

Delta Zeta Sorority
Attn: Foundation Coordinator
202 East Church Street
Oxford, OH 45056
(513) 523-7597   Fax: (513) 523-1921
E-mail: DZFoundation@dzshq.com
Web: www.deltazeta.org

Summary To provide financial assistance to members of Delta Zeta Sorority working on an undergraduate or graduate degree to prepare for a career in museum work.

Eligibility This program is open to upper-division and graduate members of the sorority who have a GPA of 3.0 or higher. Applicants must be working on a degree in a field that will prepare them for a career in museum work, including library science, archaeology, geology, or art history. Along with their application, they must submit an official transcript, a statement of their career goals, information on their service to the sorority, documentation of campus activities and/or community involvement, a list of academic honors, and an explanation of their financial need.

Financial data The stipend ranges from $500 to $2,500 for undergraduates or from $1,000 to $15,000 for graduate students, depending on the availability of funds.

Duration 1 year; nonrenewable.

Number awarded 1 each year.

Deadline February of each year.

[82]
BETTY HANSEN NATIONAL SCHOLARSHIPS

Danish Sisterhood of America
Attn: Donna Hansen, Scholarship Chair
1605 South 58th Street
Lincoln, NE 68506
(402) 488-5820   E-mail: djhansen@windstream.net
Web: www.danishsisterhood.org/DanishHTML/rschol.asp

Summary   To provide financial assistance for educational purposes in the United States or Denmark to members or relatives of members of the Danish Sisterhood of America.

Eligibility   This program is open to members or the family of members of the sisterhood who are interested in attending an accredited 4-year college or university as a full-time undergraduate or graduate student. Members must have belonged to the sisterhood for at least 1 year. They must have a GPA of 2.5 or higher. Selection is based on academics (including ACT or SAT scores), academic awards or honors, other special recognition and awards, employment record, special talents or hobbies, and participation in Danish Sisterhood and other civic activities. Upon written request, the scholarship may be used for study in Denmark.

Financial data   The stipend is $1,000.

Duration   1 year; nonrenewable.

Number awarded   Up to 8 each year.

Deadline   February of each year.

[83]
BETTY MCKERN SCHOLARSHIP

Association for Iron & Steel Technology-Midwest Chapter
c/o Love Kalra, Scholarship Chair
ArcelorMittal
Number 3 Steel Producing, Door 453
3001 Dickey Road
East Chicago, IN 46312
(219) 391-2259   E-mail: love.kalra@arcelormittal.com
Web: www.aist.org/chapters/midwest_scholarship.htm

Summary   To provide financial assistance to women who are members or dependents of members of the Midwest Chapter of the Association for Iron & Steel Technology (AIST) and plan to study engineering at a college in any state to prepare for a career in the iron and steel industry.

Eligibility   This program is open to women who are members or dependents of members of the AIST Midwest Chapter and are graduating high school seniors or currently enrolled full time in the first, second, or third year at an accredited college or university in any state. Applicants must be studying or planning to study engineering and have an interest in preparing for a career in the iron and steel industry. Along with their application, they must submit a letter of recommendation, a current transcript (including SAT/ACT scores), and a 1- to 2-page essay describing their objectives for college and career. Selection is based on merit.

Financial data   The stipend is $3,000.

Duration   1 year.

Additional information   The AIST was formed in 2004 by the merger of the Iron and Steel Society (ISS) and the Association of Iron and Steel Engineers (AISE). The Midwest Chapter replaced the former AISE Chicago Section in northern Illinois and northwestern Indiana and also includes the states of Wisconsin, Minnesota, Iowa, Nebraska, South Dakota, and North Dakota.

Number awarded   1 each year.

Deadline   March of each year.

[84]
BETTY RENDEL SCHOLARSHIPS

National Federation of Republican Women
Attn: Scholarships and Internships
124 North Alfred Street
Alexandria, VA 22314-3011
(703) 548-9688   Fax: (703) 548-9836
E-mail: mail@nfrw.org
Web: www.nfrw.org/programs/scholarships.htm

Summary   To provide financial assistance to undergraduate Republican women who are majoring in political science, government, or economics.

Eligibility   This program is open to women who have completed at least 2 years of college. Applicants must be majoring in political science, government, or economics. Along with their application, they must submit 3 letters of recommendation, an official transcript, a 1-page essay on why they should be considered for the scholarship, and a 1-page essay on career goals. Applications must be submitted to the Republican federation president in the applicant's state. Each president chooses 1 application from her state to submit for scholarship consideration. Financial need is not a factor in the selection process. U.S. citizenship is required.

Financial data   The stipend is $1,000.

Duration   1 year; nonrenewable.

Additional information   This program was established in 1995.

Number awarded   3 each year.

Deadline   Applications must be submitted to the state federation president by May of each year.

[85]
BETTY TURNER GEORGIA GIRLS STATE SCHOLARSHIP

American Legion Auxiliary
Department of Georgia
3035 Mt. Zion Road
Stockbridge, GA 30281-4101
(678) 289-8446   Fax: (678) 289-9496
E-mail: amlegaux@bellsouth.net
Web: www.georgiagirlsstate.org/scholarships.htm

Summary   To provide financial assistance to participants in Georgia Girls State who plan to attend college in any state.

Eligibility   This program is open to girls who have successfully completed the current session of Georgia Girls State. Applicants must be planning to attend a college or university in any state. Selection is based on financial need (40%), academic achievement (30%), character (10%), Americanism (10%), and leadership (10%).

Financial data   A stipend is awarded (amount not specified). Funds must be used within 18 months of the date of the award; they are sent directly to the recipient's college or university.

Duration   1 year.

Number awarded 2 each year.

Deadline Deadline not specified.

[86]
BIENNIAL STUDENT AUDITION AWARDS

National Federation of Music Clubs
1646 Smith Valley Road
Greenwood, IN 46142
(317) 882-4003   Fax: (317) 882-4019
E-mail: info@nfmc-music.org
Web: www.nfmc-music.org

Summary To recognize and reward outstanding student musicians (including a separate competition for women singers) who are members of the National Federation of Music Clubs (NFMC).

Eligibility This competition is open to instrumentalists and vocalists between 19 and 26 years of age. Student membership in the federation and U.S. citizenship are required. Competition categories include: women's voice, men's voice, piano, organ, harp, classical guitar, violin, viola, cello, double bass, orchestral woodwinds, orchestral brass, and percussion. Awards are presented at the national level after auditions at the state and district levels.

Financial data The winner in each category is awarded $1,200.

Duration The competition is held biennially, in odd-numbered years.

Additional information Students who enter this competition are also automatically considered for a number of supplemental awards. The entry fee is $30 for each category.

Deadline January of odd-numbered years.

[87]
BILLINGS CHAPTER ASWA TWO-YEAR COLLEGE SCHOLARSHIP

American Society of Women Accountants-Billings
   Chapter
Attn: Meghan Ekholt, Scholarship Chair
P.O. Box 20593
Billings, MT 59104-0593
E-mail: mrekholt@gmail.com
Web: www.billingsaswa.org/Scholarships.html

Summary To provide financial assistance to women working on an associate degree in accounting at a 2-year or community college in Montana.

Eligibility This program is open to women working on an associate degree in accounting or finance at a 2-year or community college in Montana. Applicants must have completed at least 15 semester hours and have a GPA of 3.0 or higher. Along with their application, they must submit an essay of 150 to 250 words on their career goals and objectives, the impact they want to have on the accounting world, their community involvement, and leadership activities. Selection is based on leadership, character, scholastic average, communication skills, and financial need.

Financial data The stipend is $1,000.

Duration 1 year.

Additional information The application of the recipient is forwarded to the American Society of Women Accountants (ASWA) Educational Foundation for consideration for a national scholarship.

Number awarded 1 each year.

Deadline March of each year.

[88]
BILLINGS CHAPTER ASWA UNDERGRADUATE SCHOLARSHIPS

American Society of Women Accountants-Billings
   Chapter
Attn: Meghan Ekholt, Scholarship Chair
P.O. Box 20593
Billings, MT 59104-0593
E-mail: mrekholt@gmail.com
Web: www.billingsaswa.org/Scholarships.html

Summary To provide financial assistance to women working on an bachelor's degree in accounting at a college or university in Montana.

Eligibility This program is open to women working on a bachelor's degree in accounting or finance at a college or university in Montana. Applicants must have completed at least 60 semester hours and have a GPA of 3.0 or higher. Along with their application, they must submit an essay of 150 to 250 words on their career goals and objectives, the impact they want to have on the accounting world, their community involvement, and leadership examples. Selection is based on leadership, character, scholastic average, communication skills, and financial need.

Financial data The stipend is $1,500.

Duration 1 year.

Additional information The application of 1 of the recipients is forwarded to the American Society of Women Accountants (ASWA) Educational Foundation for consideration for a national scholarship.

Number awarded 2 each year.

Deadline March of each year.

[89]
BIRMINGHAM SECTION SWE SCHOLARSHIP

Society of Women Engineers-Birmingham Section
c/o Theresa Carter, Scholarship Chair
P.O. Box 361311
Birmingham, AL 35236
(205) 397-3800, ext. 128
E-mail: Theresa.carter@neel-schaffer.com
Web: www.swebham.org/scholars.htm

Summary To provide financial assistance to female high school seniors planning to study engineering at a college or university in Alabama.

Eligibility This program is open to women graduating from high schools in any state and planning to enter a college or university in Alabama that has an ABET-accredited engineering program. Applicants must submit an essay about their career goals and why they need this scholarship. Selection is based on that essay (10 points); SAT or ACT test scores (10 points); GPA, honors received, and early college courses completed (10 points); high school science and mathematics courses completed by date of graduation (10 points); leadership and extracurricular activities (10 points); community and civic activities and employment (10 points); communication skills (10 points); and financial need (5 points). U.S. citizenship or permanent resident status is required.

Financial data A stipend is awarded (amount not specified).

Duration 1 year.

Number awarded 1 or more each year.

Deadline June of each year.

[90]
BISA SCHOLARSHIP ASSISTANCE PROGRAM

Black Women in Sisterhood for Action, Inc.
Attn: Chair of Scholarship Committee
P.O. Box 1592
Washington, DC 20013
(202) 543-6013   Fax: (202) 543-5719
E-mail: info@bisa-hq.org
Web: www.bisa-hq.org/newscholarships.htm

Summary To provide financial assistance for college to disadvantaged Black women.

Eligibility This program is open to Black women graduating from inner-city high schools and planning to attend a college or university, especially a designated Historically Black College or University (HBCU). Applicants must submit a transcript, SAT or ACT scores, documentation of financial need, and a 1-page self-portrait highlighting where they expect to be in their career development in 10 years. Selection is based on academic achievement, leadership potential, financial need, honors, and potential for academic growth and leadership development.

Financial data The stipend is $1,000 per year. Support is also provided for books and transportation.

Duration 4 years.

Additional information Black Women in Sisterhood for Action (BISA) was established in 1980. In 1995, it established partnership relationships with HBCUs where students receive mentoring, counseling for themselves and their parents, networking among distinguished Black women, and monthly contacts by a BISA member.

Number awarded Recently, the program was supporting 18 continuing students.

Deadline April of each year.

[91]
B.J. HARROD SCHOLARSHIPS

Society of Women Engineers
Attn: Scholarship Selection Committee
120 South LaSalle Street, Suite 1515
Chicago, IL 60603-3572
(312) 596-5223   Toll Free: (877) SWE-INFO
Fax: (312) 644-8557
E-mail: scholarshipapplication@swe.org
Web: societyofwomenengineers.swe.org

Summary To provide financial assistance to women who will be entering college as freshmen and are interested in studying computer science or engineering.

Eligibility This program is open to women who are entering college as freshmen with a GPA of 3.5 or higher. Applicants must be planning to enroll full time at an ABET-accredited 4-year college or university and major in computer science or engineering. Selection is based on merit.

Financial data The stipend is $1,500.

Duration 1 year.

Additional information This program was established in 1999.

Number awarded 2 each year.

Deadline May of each year.

[92]
B.K. KRENZER MEMORIAL REENTRY SCHOLARSHIP

Society of Women Engineers
Attn: Scholarship Selection Committee
120 South LaSalle Street, Suite 1515
Chicago, IL 60603-3572
(312) 596-5223   Toll Free: (877) SWE-INFO
Fax: (312) 644-8557
E-mail: scholarshipapplication@swe.org
Web: societyofwomenengineers.swe.org

Summary To provide financial assistance to women (particularly women engineers) who are interested in returning to college or graduate school to continue their study of engineering or computer science.

Eligibility This program is open to women who are planning to enroll at an ABET-accredited 4-year college or university. Applicants must have been out of the engineering workforce and school for at least 2 years and must be planning to return as an undergraduate or graduate student to work on a degree in computer science or engineering. They must have a GPA of 3.0 or higher. Selection is based on merit. Preference is given to engineers who already have a degree and are planning to reenter the engineering workforce after a period of temporary retirement.

Financial data The stipend is $2,000.

Duration 1 year.

Additional information This program was established in 1996.

Number awarded 1 each year.

Deadline February of each year.

[93]
BOBBI MCCALLUM MEMORIAL SCHOLARSHIP

Seattle Foundation
Attn: Scholarship Administrator
1200 Fifth Avenue, Suite 1300
Seattle, WA 98101-3151
(206) 622-2294   Fax: (206) 622-7673
E-mail: scholarships@seattlefoundation.org
Web: www.seattlefoundation.org

Summary To provide financial assistance to women college students in Washington who are interested in preparing for a career in journalism.

Eligibility This program is open to female residents of Washington who are entering their junior or senior year and studying print journalism at a 4-year public college or university in the state. Applicants must submit 5 samples of news writing (published or unpublished); brief essays on topics related to their interest in journalism; 2 letters of recommendation; and documentation of financial need. Selection is based on need, talent, and motivation to prepare for a career in print journalism.

Financial data The stipend is $3,000 per year.

Duration 1 year; may be renewed.

Additional information This scholarship was established in 1970 by the late Dr. Walter Scott Brown in memory of Bobbi McCallum, a prizewinning reporter and columnist for the *Seattle Post-Intelligencer* who died in 1969 at age 25 while a patient of Dr. Brown. The scholarship was administered by the newspaper until it suspended publication in 2010 and the program was transferred to the Seattle Foundation.

Number awarded 2 each year.

Deadline May of each year.

[94]
BOBBY SOX HIGH SCHOOL SENIOR SCHOLARSHIP PROGRAM

Bobby Sox Softball
Attn: Scholarship
P.O. Box 5880
Buena Park, CA 90622-5880
(714) 522-1234   Fax: (714) 522-6548
Web: www.bobbysoxsoftball.org/scholar.html

Summary To provide financial assistance for college to high school seniors who have participated in Bobby Sox Softball.

Eligibility This program is open to girls graduating from high school with a GPA of 2.0 or higher. Applicants must have participated in Bobby Sox Softball for at least 5 seasons. They must submit an essay on "The Value of Participation in Bobby Sox Softball." Selection is based on the essay (60 points), academic excellence (20 points), and letters of recommendation from Bobby Sox officials, community leaders, and school representatives (20 points).

Financial data Stipends range from $100 to $2,500.

Duration 1 year.

Number awarded Approximately 45 each year.

Deadline April of each year.

[95]
BOSTON AFFILIATE AWSCPA SCHOLARSHIP

American Woman's Society of Certified Public
  Accountants-Boston Affiliate
c/o Andrea Costantino
Oxford Bioscience Partners
222 Berkeley Street, Suite 1650
Boston, MA 02116
(617) 357-7474   E-mail: acostantino@oxbio.com
Web: www.awscpa.org/affiliate_scholarships/boston.html

Summary To provide financial assistance to women from any state who are working on an undergraduate or graduate degree in accounting at a college or university in New England.

Eligibility This program is open to women from any state who are attending a college in New England and majoring in accounting. Applicants must have completed at least 12 semester hours of accounting or tax courses and have a cumulative GPA of 3.0 or higher. They must be planning to graduate between May of next year and May of the following year or, for the 15-month graduate program, before September of the current year. Along with their application, they must submit a brief essay on why they feel they would be a good choice for this award. Selection is based on that essay, academic achievement, work experience, extracurricular activities, scholastic honors, career plans, and financial need.

Financial data The stipend is $1,000.

Duration 1 year.

Number awarded 2 each year.

Deadline September of each year.

[96]
BOSTON SCIENTIFIC MINNESOTA SWE SCHOLARSHIP

Society of Women Engineers-Minnesota Section
Attn: Scholarship Committee
P.O. Box 582813
Minneapolis, MN 55458-2813
E-mail: scholarships@swe-mn.org
Web: swe-mn.org/scholarships.html

Summary To provide financial assistance to women from any state working on an undergraduate or graduate degree in biomedical or mechanical engineering at colleges and universities in Minnesota, North Dakota, and South Dakota.

Eligibility This program is open to female undergraduate and graduate students at ABET-accredited engineering programs in Minnesota, North Dakota, or South Dakota. Applicants must be working full time on a degree in biomedical or mechanical engineering. Along with their application, they must submit a short paragraph describing how they plan to utilize their engineering skills after they graduate. Selection is based on potential to succeed as an engineer (20 points), communication skills (10 points), extracurricular or community involvement and leadership skills (10 points), demonstrated successful work experience (10 points), and academic success (5 points).

Financial data The stipend is $1,500.

Duration 1 year.

Additional information This program is sponsored by Boston Scientific.

Number awarded 1 each year.

Deadline March of each year.

[97]
BOSTON SCIENTIFIC SCHOLARSHIPS

Society of Women Engineers
Attn: Scholarship Selection Committee
120 South LaSalle Street, Suite 1515
Chicago, IL 60603-3572
(312) 596-5223   Toll Free: (877) SWE-INFO
Fax: (312) 644-8557
E-mail: scholarshipapplication@swe.org
Web: societyofwomenengineers.swe.org

Summary To provide financial assistance to upper-division women majoring in computer science or designated engineering specialties at designated universities.

Eligibility This program is open to women who are entering their senior year at a designated ABET-accredited college or university. Applicants must be majoring in computer science or chemical, computer, electrical, industrial, manufacturing, materials, or mechanical engineering and have a GPA of 3.5 or higher. Selection is based on merit.

Financial data The stipend is $5,000.

Duration 1 year.

Additional information This program, established in 2004, is supported by Boston Scientific. For a list of the designated colleges and universities, contact the sponsor.

Number awarded 2 each year.

Deadline February of each year.

[98]
BPW FOUNDATION OF MARYLAND SCHOLARSHIP

Business and Professional Women of Maryland
Attn: BPW Foundation of Maryland
c/o Joyce Draper, Chief Financial Officer
615 Fairview Avenue
Frederick, MD 21701
Web: www.bpwmaryland.org

Summary To provide financial assistance for college to mature women in Maryland.

Eligibility This program is open to women who are at least 25 years of age and who are interested in pursuing undergraduate studies to upgrade their skills for career advancement, to train for a new career field, or to reenter the job market. Applicants must be residents of Maryland or, if a resident of another state, a member of Business and Professional Women of Maryland. They must have been accepted into an accredited program or course of study at a Maryland academic institution and be able to demonstrate critical financial need. U.S. citizenship is required.

Financial data The stipend is $1,000.

Duration 1 year.

Number awarded 1 or more each year.

Deadline July of each year.

[99]
BRILL FAMILY SCHOLARSHIP

Society of Women Engineers
Attn: Scholarship Selection Committee
120 South LaSalle Street, Suite 1515
Chicago, IL 60603-3572
(312) 596-5223   Toll Free: (877) SWE-INFO
Fax: (312) 644-8557
E-mail: scholarshipapplication@swe.org
Web: societyofwomenengineers.swe.org

Summary To provide financial assistance to undergraduate women majoring in designated engineering specialties.

Eligibility This program is open to women who are entering their sophomore, junior, or senior year at an ABET-accredited 4-year college or university. Applicants must be majoring in computer science or aeronautical or biomedical engineering and have a GPA of 3.0 or higher. Selection is based on merit.

Financial data The stipend is $1,000.

Duration 1 year.

Number awarded 1 each year.

Deadline February of each year.

[100]
BROOKHAVEN NATIONAL LABORATORY SCIENCE AND ENGINEERING PROGRAMS FOR WOMEN AND MINORITIES

Brookhaven National Laboratory
Attn: Diversity Office, Human Resources Division
Building 400B
P.O. Box 5000
Upton, New York 11973-5000
(631) 344-2703   Fax: (631) 344-5305
E-mail: palmore@bnl.gov
Web: www.bnl.gov/diversity/programs.asp

Summary To provide on-the-job training in scientific areas at Brookhaven National Laboratory (BNL) during the summer to women and underrepresented minority students.

Eligibility This program at BNL is open to women and underrepresented minority (African American/Black, Hispanic, Native American, or Pacific Islander) students who have completed their freshman, sophomore, or junior year of college. Applicants must be U.S. citizens or permanent residents, at least 18 years of age, and majoring in applied mathematics, biology, chemistry, computer science, engineering, high and low energy particle accelerators, nuclear medicine, physics, or scientific writing. Since no transportation or housing allowance is provided, preference is given to students who reside in the BNL area.

Financial data Participants receive a competitive stipend.

Duration 10 to 12 weeks during the summer.

Additional information Students work with members of the scientific, technical, and professional staff of BNL in an educational training program developed to give research experience.

Deadline April of each year.

[101]
BUSINESS AND PROFESSIONAL WOMEN OF IOWA FOUNDATION EDUCATIONAL SCHOLARSHIP

Business and Professional Women of Iowa Foundation
c/o Maxine Losen
2149 108th Street
Hazelton, IA 50641
(319) 636-2491   E-mail: mwlosen@iowatelecom.net

Summary To provide financial assistance for college to female and other nontraditional students who reside in Iowa.

Eligibility Applicants must be Iowa residents (although they may be currently attending school in another state) who have completed at least 1 year of education beyond high school. They must be nontraditional students who 1) have been out of the workforce and need additional education to go back to work or 2) completed high school 5 or more years ago and now want to restart their college education. Along with their application, they must submit 3 letters of reference. Financial need is considered in the selection process. U.S. citizenship is required.

Financial data The stipend is $1,000. Funds are sent directly to the recipient's school.

Duration 1 year.

Additional information Recipients may attend school in any state.

Number awarded 1 or more each year.

Deadline March of each year.

[102]
CADY MCDONNELL MEMORIAL SCHOLARSHIP

American Congress on Surveying and Mapping
Attn: Scholarships
6 Montgomery Village Avenue, Suite 403
Gaithersburg, MD 20879
(240) 632-9716, ext. 109   Fax: (240) 632-1321
E-mail: ilse.genovese@acsm.net
Web: www.acsm.net

Summary To provide financial assistance for undergraduate study in surveying to female members of the American Congress on Surveying and Mapping (ACSM) from designated western states.

Eligibility This program is open to women who are ACSM members and enrolled full or part time at a 2- or 4-year college or university in any state. Applicants must be residents of Alaska, Arizona, California, Colorado, Hawaii, Idaho, Montana, Nevada, New Mexico, Oregon, Utah, Washington, or Wyoming. They must be majoring in surveying or a closely-related program (e.g., mapping, surveying engineering, geographic information systems, geodetic science). Along with their application, they must submit a statement describing their educational program, future plans for study or research, and why the award is merited. Selection is based on that statement (30%), academic record (30%), letters of recommendation (20%), and professional activities (20%); if 2 or more applicants are judged equal based on those criteria, financial need might be considered.

Financial data The stipend is $1,000.

Duration 1 year.

Number awarded 1 each year.

Deadline December of each year.

[103]
CALIFORNIA FEE WAIVER PROGRAM FOR DEPENDENTS OF TOTALLY DISABLED VETERANS

California Department of Veterans Affairs
Attn: Division of Veterans Services
1227 O Street, Room 105
Sacramento, CA 95814
(916) 503-8397   Toll Free: (800) 952-LOAN (within CA)
Fax: (916) 653-2563   TDD: (800) 324-5966
E-mail: ruckergl@cdva.ca.gov
Web: www.cdva.ca.gov/VetService/Waivers.aspx

Summary To provide financial assistance for college to spouses or children of disabled and other California veterans.

Eligibility Eligible for this program are spouses (including registered domestic partners), children, and unremarried widow(er)s of veterans who are currently totally service-connected disabled (or are being compensated for a service-connected disability at a rate of 100%) or who died of a service-connected cause or disability. The veteran parent must have served during a qualifying war period and must have been discharged or released from military service under honorable conditions. The child cannot be over 27 years of age (extended to 30 if the student was in the military); there are no age limitations for spouses or surviving spouses. This pro-

gram does not have an income limit. Dependents in college are not eligible if they are qualified to receive educational benefits from the U.S. Department of Veterans Affairs. Applicants must be attending or planning to attend a community college, branch of the California State University system, or campus of the University of California.

Financial data Full-time college students receive a waiver of tuition and registration fees at any publicly-supported community or state college or university in California.

Duration Children of eligible veterans may receive post-secondary benefits until the needed training is completed or until the dependent reaches 27 years of age (extended to 30 if the dependent serves in the armed forces). Widow(er)s and spouses are limited to a maximum of 48 months' full-time training or the equivalent in part-time training.

Number awarded Varies each year.

Deadline Deadline not specified.

[104]
CALIFORNIA JOB'S DAUGHTERS FOUNDATION SCHOLARSHIPS

California Job's Daughters Foundation
303 West Lincoln, Suite 210
Anaheim, CA 92805-2928
(714) 491-4994   Fax: (714) 991-6798
E-mail: cajdfoundation@hotmail.com
Web: www.cajdfoundation.org

Summary To provide financial assistance to members of the International Order of Job's Daughters in California who plan to attend college in any state.

Eligibility This program is open to members of Job's Daughters in good standing, active or majority, in California. Applicants may indicate their choice of an academic or vocational scholarship. Selection is based on scholastic standing, Job's Daughters activities, the applicant's self-help plan, recommendations from the Executive Beth Guardian Council, faculty recommendations, achievements outside of Job's Daughters, and financial need.

Financial data Stipends are $2,000, $1,500 or $1,000.

Duration 1 year; some of the scholarships may be renewed up to 3 additional years, but most are nonrenewable.

Number awarded Varies each year; recently, 13 of these scholarships were awarded: 2 at $2,000, 3 at $1,500 and 8 at $1,000 (of which 1 was renewable).

Deadline March of each year.

[105]
CALIFORNIA LEGION AUXILIARY PAST DEPARTMENT PRESIDENT'S JUNIOR SCHOLARSHIP

American Legion Auxiliary
Department of California
Veterans War Memorial Building
401 Van Ness Avenue, Room 113
San Francisco, CA 94102-4586
(415) 861-5092   Fax: (415) 861-8365
E-mail: calegionaux@calegionaux.org
Web: www.calegionaux.org/scholarships.htm

Summary To provide financial assistance for college to the daughters and other female descendants of California veterans who are active in the American Legion Junior Auxiliary.

Eligibility This program is open to the daughters, granddaughters, and great- granddaughters of veterans who served during wartime. Applicants must be in their senior year at an accredited high school, must have been members of the Junior Auxiliary for at least 3 consecutive years, and must be residents of California (if eligibility for Junior Auxiliary membership is by a current member of the American Legion or Auxiliary in California, the applicant may reside elsewhere). They must be planning to attend college in California. Selection is based on scholastic merit (20%); active participation in Junior Auxiliary (15%); record of service or volunteerism within the applicant's community, school, and/or unit (35%); a brief description of the applicant's desire to pursue a higher education (15%); and 3 letters of reference (15%).

Financial data The stipend depends on the availability of funds but ranges from $300 to $1,000.

Duration 1 year.

Number awarded 1 each year.

Deadline April of each year.

[106]
CALIFORNIA P.E.O. SELECTED SCHOLARSHIPS

P.E.O. Foundation-California State Chapter
c/o Carol Born, Scholarship Committee Chair
718 Via La Paloma
Riverside, CA 92507-6403
(951) 686-2728
Web: www.peocalifornia.org/ssc.html

Summary To provide financial assistance to female residents of California attending college or graduate school in any state.

Eligibility This program is open to female residents of California who have completed 4 years of high school (or the equivalent); are enrolled at or accepted by an accredited college, university, vocational school, or graduate school in any state; and have an excellent academic record. Selection is based on financial need, character, academic ability, and school and community activities. Some awards include additional requirements.

Financial data Stipends recently ranged from $400 to $2,500.

Duration 1 year; may be renewed for up to 3 additional years.

Additional information This program includes the following named scholarships: the Barbara Furse Mackey Scholarship (for women whose education has been interrupted); the Beverly Dye Anderson Scholarship (for the fields of teaching or health care); the Marjorie M. McDonald P.E.O. Scholarship (for women who are continuing their education after a long hiatus from school); the Ora Keck Scholarship (for women who are preparing for a career in music or the fine arts); the Phyllis J. Van Deventer Scholarship (for women who are preparing for a career in music performance or music education); the Jean Gower Scholarship (for women preparing for a career in education); the Helen D. Thompson Memorial Scholarship (for women studying music or fine arts); the Stella May Nau Scholarship (for women who are interested in reentering the job market); the Linda Jones Memorial Fine Arts Scholarship (for women studying fine arts); the Polly Thompson Memorial Music Scholarship (for women studying music); the Ruby W. Henry Scholarship; the Jean W. Gratiot Scholarship; the Pearl Prime Scholarship; the Helen Beards-

ley Scholarship; the Chapter GA Scholarship; and the Nearly New Scholarship.

Number awarded Varies each year; recently, 43 of these scholarships were awarded.

Deadline January of each year.

[107]
CAPTAIN SALLY TOMPKINS NURSING AND APPLIED HEALTH SCIENCES SCHOLARSHIP

United Daughters of the Confederacy-Virginia Division
c/o Janice Busic, Education Committee Chair
P.O. Box 356
Honaker, VA 24260
E-mail: 2vp@vaudc.org
Web: vaudc.org/gift.html

Summary To provide financial assistance for college to women from Virginia who are Confederate descendants and working on a degree in nursing.

Eligibility This program is open to women residents of Virginia interested in working on a degree in nursing. Applicants must be 1) lineal descendants of Confederates, or 2) collateral descendants and also members of the Children of the Confederacy or the United Daughters of the Confederacy. They must submit proof of the Confederate military record of at least 1 ancestor, with the company and regiment in which he served. They must also submit a personal letter pledging to make the best possible use of the scholarship; describing their health, social, family, religious, and fraternal connections within the community; and reflecting on what a Southern heritage means to them (using the term "War Between the States" in lieu of "Civil War"). They must have a GPA of 3.0 or higher and be able to demonstrate financial need.

Financial data The amount of the stipend depends on the availability of funds. Payment is made directly to the college or university the recipient attends.

Duration 1 year; may be renewed up to 3 additional years if the recipient maintains a GPA of 3.0 or higher.

Number awarded This scholarship is offered whenever a prior recipient graduates or is no longer eligible.

Deadline April of the years in which a scholarship is available.

[108]
CAREER DEVELOPMENT GRANTS

American Association of University Women
Attn: AAUW Educational Foundation
301 ACT Drive, Department 60
P.O. Box 4030
Iowa City, IA 52243-4030
(319) 337-1716, ext. 60   Fax: (319) 337-1204
E-mail: aauw@act.org
Web: www.aauw.org

Summary To provide financial assistance to women who are seeking career advancement, career change, or reentry into the workforce.

Eligibility This program is open to women who are U.S. citizens or permanent residents, have earned a bachelor's degree, received their most recent degree more than 4 years ago, and are making career changes, seeking to advance in current careers, or reentering the work force. Applicants must be interested in working toward a master's degree, second bachelor's or associate degree, professional degree (e.g., M.D., J.D.), certification program, or technical school certificate. They must be planning to undertake course work at an accredited 2- or 4-year college or university (or a technical school that is licensed, accredited, or approved by the U.S. Department of Education). Special consideration is given to women of color and women pursuing credentials in nontraditional fields. Support is not provided for prerequisite course work or for Ph.D. course work or dissertations. Selection is based on demonstrated commitment to education and equity for women and girls, reason for seeking higher education or technical training, degree to which study plan is consistent with career objectives, potential for success in chosen field, documentation of opportunities in chosen field, feasibility of study plans and proposed time schedule, validity of proposed budget and budget narrative (including sufficient outside support), and quality of written proposal.

Financial data Grants range from $2,000 to $12,000. Funds may be used for tuition, fees, books, supplies, local transportation, dependent child care, or purchase of a computer required for the study program.

Duration 1 year, beginning in July; nonrenewable.

Additional information The filing fee is $35.

Number awarded Varies each year; recently, 47 of these grants, with a value of $500,000, were awarded.

Deadline December of each year.

[109]
CARLOZZI FAMILY SCHOLARSHIP

New York Women in Communications, Inc.
Attn: NYWICI Foundation
355 Lexington Avenue, 15th Floor
New York, NY 10017-6603
(212) 297-2133   Fax: (212) 370-9047
E-mail: nywicipr@nywici.org
Web: www.nywici.org/foundation/scholarships

Summary To provide financial assistance to female residents of designated eastern states who are working on an undergraduate degree in communications at a college in any state.

Eligibility This program is open to women who are residents of New York, New Jersey, Connecticut, or Pennsylvania and currently enrolled as undergraduates at a college or university in any state. Also eligible are women who reside outside the 4 states but are currently enrolled at a college or university within 1 of the 5 boroughs of New York City. All applicants must be working on a degree in a communications-related field (e.g., advertising, broadcasting, communications, English, film, journalism, marketing, new media, public relations) and be an accomplished writer. They must have a GPA of 3.2 or higher. Along with their application, they must submit a 2-page resume that includes school and extracurricular activities, significant achievements, academic honors and awards, and community service work; a personal essay of 300 to 500 words on their choice of an assigned topic that changes annually; 2 letters of recommendation; and an official transcript. Selection is based on academic record, need, demonstrated leadership, participation in school and community activities, honors, work experience, goals and aspirations, and unusual personal and/or family circumstances. U.S. citizenship is required.

Financial data The stipend ranges up to $10,000.

Duration 1 year.

Number awarded 1 each year.

Deadline January of each year.

[110]
CAROL GREEN WILSON SCHOLARSHIP

Kappa Alpha Theta Foundation
Attn: Scholarships
8740 Founders Road
Indianapolis, IN 46268-1337
(317) 876-1870   Toll Free: (800) KAO-1870
Fax: (317) 876-1925
E-mail: FDNmail@kappaalphatheta.org
Web: www.kappaalphathetafoundation.org

Summary To provide financial assistance to members of Kappa Alpha Theta who are working on an undergraduate degree in creative writing, English, or journalism.

Eligibility This program is open to members of Kappa Alpha Theta who are full-time undergraduates at a college or university in Canada or the United States. Applicants must be working on a degree in creative writing, English, or journalism. Along with their application, they must submit an official transcript, personal essays on assigned topics related to their involvement in Kappa Alpha Theta, and 2 letters of reference. Financial need is not considered in the selection process.

Financial data The stipend is $1,875.

Duration 1 year.

Number awarded 1 each year.

Deadline January of each year.

[111]
CAROLYN B. ELMAN NATIONAL UNDERGRADUATE SCHOLARSHIP

American Business Women's Association
Attn: Stephen Bufton Memorial Educational Fund
11050 Roe Avenue, Suite 200
Overland Park, KS 66211
Toll Free: (800) 228-0007
Web: www.sbmef.org/Opportunities.cfm

Summary To provide financial assistance to female undergraduate students who are working on a degree in a specified field (the field changes each year).

Eligibility This program is open to women who have completed at least 60 credit hours of work on an undergraduate degree. Applicants are not required to be members of the American Business Women's Association. Along with their application, they must submit a 250-word biographical sketch that includes information about their background, activities, honors, work experience, and long-term educational and professional goals. Financial need is not considered in the selection process. Annually, the trustees designate an academic discipline for which the scholarship will be presented that year; recently, that was foreign language. U.S. citizenship is required.

Financial data The stipend is $10,000 (paid over a 2-year period). Funds are paid directly to the recipient's institution to be used only for tuition, books, and fees.

Duration 2 years.

Additional information This scholarship was first awarded in 2011 as part of ABWA's Stephen Bufton Memorial Education Fund. The ABWA does not provide the names and addresses of local chapters; it recommends that applicants check with their local Chamber of Commerce, library, or university to see if any chapter has registered a contact's name and number.

Number awarded 1 each odd-numbered year.

Deadline May of each odd-numbered year.

[112]
CATERPILLAR SWE SCHOLARSHIPS

Society of Women Engineers
Attn: Scholarship Selection Committee
120 South LaSalle Street, Suite 1515
Chicago, IL 60603-3572
(312) 596-5223   Toll Free: (877) SWE-INFO
Fax: (312) 644-8557
E-mail: scholarshipapplication@swe.org
Web: societyofwomenengineers.swe.org

Summary To provide financial assistance to women who are working on an undergraduate or graduate degree in selected fields of engineering or computer science.

Eligibility This program is open to women who are sophomores, juniors, seniors, or graduate students at ABET-accredited 4-year colleges and universities. Applicants must be working on a degree in computer science or agricultural, chemical, electrical, industrial, manufacturing, materials, or mechanical engineering. They must be U.S. citizens or authorized to work in the United States and have a GPA of 3.0 or higher. Selection is based on merit.

Financial data The stipend is $2,400.

Duration 1 year.

Additional information This program is sponsored by Caterpillar, Inc.

Number awarded 3 each year.

Deadline February of each year.

[113]
CATHERYN SMITH MEMORIAL SCHOLARSHIP

Delta Sigma Theta Detroit Foundation, Inc.
24760 West Seven Mile Road
P.O. Box 441921
Detroit, MI 48244-1921
(313) 537-7137   E-mail: President@dstdfi.org
Web: www.dstdfi.org/scholarship-application.html

Summary To provide financial assistance to members of Delta Sigma Theta (a traditionally African American social sorority) who are majoring in education at a college in Michigan.

Eligibility This program is open to members of the sorority who are currently enrolled at an accredited 4-year college or university in Michigan. Applicants must be majoring in education and have a GPA of 3.0 or higher. Along with their application, they must submit 1) an essay up to 150 words on why they chose education as a major and how they plan to impact positively the field of education after graduating; 2) an essay up to 75 words describing their community service activities and involvement; and 3) an essay up to 75 words providing any other information that might be relevant to their application. Financial need is not considered in the selection process.

Financial data The stipend is $2,500.

Duration 1 year.

Number awarded 2 each year.

Deadline October of each year.

[114]
CENTRAL INDIANA SECTION SWE SCHOLARSHIPS

Society of Women Engineers-Central Indiana Section
Attn: Scholarship Coordinator
P.O. Box 44450
Indianapolis, IN 46244
E-mail: swe-ci_scholarship@swe.org
Web: www.swe-ci.com

Summary To provide financial assistance to women who live or attend college in Indiana and are studying computer science or engineering.

Eligibility This program is open to women who are residents of Indiana or attending a college or university in the state. Applicants must be sophomores, juniors, or seniors and working full time on a bachelor's degree in an ABET/CSAB-accredited program in engineering or computer sciences. They must have a GPA of 3.0 or higher. Along with their application, they must submit a 500-word essay on the ways in which they are fulfilling the mission of the Society of Women Engineers (SWE): to stimulate women to achieve full potential in careers as engineers and leaders, expand the image of the engineering profession as a positive force in improving the quality of life, and demonstrate the value of diversity. Financial need may be considered in the selection process.

Financial data Stipends are $1,000, $750, or $500.

Duration 1 year.

Additional information This program was established in 2007. The 2 smaller scholarships are sponsored by Rolls-Royce Corporation.

Number awarded 3 each year: 1 each at $1,000, $750, and $500.

Deadline April of each year.

[115]
CENTRAL NEW MEXICO RE-ENTRY SCHOLARSHIP

Society of Women Engineers
Attn: Scholarship Selection Committee
120 South LaSalle Street, Suite 1515
Chicago, IL 60603-3572
(312) 596-5223   Toll Free: (877) SWE-INFO
Fax: (312) 644-8557
E-mail: scholarshipapplication@swe.org
Web: societyofwomenengineers.swe.org

Summary To provide financial assistance to members of the Society of Women Engineers (SWE) from any state who are reentering college or graduate school in New Mexico to work on a degree in engineering or computer science.

Eligibility This program is open to members of the society who are sophomores, juniors, seniors, or graduate students at an ABET-accredited college, university, or 4-year engineering technology program in New Mexico. Applicants must be returning to college or graduate school after an absence of several years to work on a degree in computer science or engineering. They must have a GPA of 3.0 or higher. Selection is based on merit. U.S. citizenship is required.

Financial data   The stipend is $1,250 per year.

Duration   1 year; may be renewed up to 5 additional years.

Additional information   This program was established in 2005 by the Central New Mexico section of SWE.

Number awarded   1 each year.

Deadline   February of each year.

[116]
CHANGING THE WORLD SCHOLARSHIP

Women in Aviation, International
Attn: Scholarships
Morningstar Airport
3647 State Route 503 South
West Alexandria, OH 45381-9354
(937) 839-4647   Fax: (937) 839-4645
E-mail: scholarships@wai.org
Web: www.wai.org/education/scholarships.cfm

Summary   To provide financial assistance to members of Women in Aviation, International (WAI) who have a record of outstanding community service and are interested in attending flight school or other educational institution.

Eligibility   This program is open to WAI members who are interested in flight training advancement or educational advancement at a flight school or other institution of higher education. Applicants must be able to demonstrate a record of "continuous work for any organization or group of individuals that make contributions to their community to make the world a better place." Along with their application, they must submit 2 letters of recommendation; a 500-word essay on their aviation history and goals; another 500-word essay describing their community involvement, why they feel community involvement is important, their plans or aspirations for a better future, and how they plan to use the scholarship; a resume; copies of all aviation licenses and medical certificates; and the last 3 pages of their pilot logbook (if applicable). Selection is based on achievements, attitude toward self and others, commitment to success, dedication to career, financial need, motivation, reliability, responsibility, and teamwork.

Financial data   The stipend is $1,000. Funds are paid directly to the flight school or educational institution.

Duration   1 year.

Additional information   WAI is a nonprofit professional organization dedicated to encouraging women to consider an aviation career and to providing educational outreach activities and networking resources to women active in the industry. This program was established in 2011.

Number awarded   1 each year.

Deadline   November of each year.

[117]
CHARLES C. BLANTON AFBA FAMILY SURVIVOR COLLEGE SCHOLARSHIP

Armed Forces Benefit Association
AFBA Building
909 North Washington Street
Alexandria, VA 22314-1556
(703) 549-4455   Toll Free: (800) 776-2322
E-mail: info@afba.com
Web: www.afba.com

Summary   To provide financial assistance for college to surviving spouses and children of members of the Armed Forces Benefit Association (AFBA) who were killed on duty.

Eligibility   This program is open to surviving spouses and children of deceased members of AFBA. Membership in AFBA is open to active-duty, National Guard, or Reserve members of the armed forces; those who are retired or separated from service; and emergency service providers (law enforcement officers, fire fighters, and emergency medical service providers). The AFBA member's death must have been in a combat zone, as a result of combat action, as a result of acts of foreign or domestic terrorism, or at an event to which an emergency service provider is dispatched in a situation where there is the potential for loss of life. Applicants must be attending or planning to attend an undergraduate college or university.

Financial data   The stipend is $10,000 per year.

Duration   1 year; may be renewed for up to 3 additional years.

Number awarded   1 or more each year.

Deadline   Deadline not specified.

[118]
CHARLINE CHILSON SCHOLARSHIPS

Delta Zeta Sorority
Attn: Foundation Coordinator
202 East Church Street
Oxford, OH 45056
(513) 523-7597   Fax: (513) 523-1921
E-mail: DZFoundation@dzshq.com
Web: www.deltazeta.org

Summary   To provide financial assistance to members of Delta Zeta Sorority working on an undergraduate or graduate degree in science.

Eligibility   This program is open to upper-division and graduate members of the sorority who have a high GPA in their major. Applicants must be working on a degree in science. Along with their application, they must submit an official transcript, a statement of their career goals, information on their service to the sorority, documentation of campus activities and/or community involvement, a list of academic honors, and an explanation of their financial need.

Financial data   The stipend ranges from $500 to $2,500 for undergraduates or from $1,000 to $15,000 for graduate students, depending on the availability of funds.

Duration   1 year; nonrenewable.

Number awarded   Varies each year; recently, 12 of these scholarships were awarded: 6 to undergraduates and 6 to graduate students.

Deadline   February of each year.

[119]
CHERYL A. RUGGIERO SCHOLARSHIP

Rhode Island Society of Certified Public Accountants
45 Royal Little Drive
Providence, RI 02904
(401) 331-5720   Fax: (401) 454-5780
E-mail: info@riscpa.org
Web: student.riscpa.org/index.html

Summary To provide financial assistance to female undergraduate and graduate students from any state who are working on a degree in accounting at a school in Rhode Island.

Eligibility This program is open to female students at Rhode Island colleges and universities who have expressed an interest in public accounting during their undergraduate and/or graduate years. Applicants must be U.S. citizens who have a GPA of 3.0 or higher. They are not required to be residents of Rhode Island. Selection is based on demonstrated potential to become a valued member of the public accounting profession. Finalists are interviewed.

Financial data The stipend is $1,250.

Duration 1 year.

Additional information This program was established in 2005.

Number awarded 1 each year.

Deadline January of each year.

[120]
CHERYL DANT HENNESY SCHOLARSHIP

National FFA Organization
Attn: Scholarship Office
6060 FFA Drive
P.O. Box 68960
Indianapolis, IN 46268-0960
(317) 802-4419   Fax: (317) 802-5419
E-mail: scholarships@ffa.org
Web: www.ffa.org

Summary To provide financial assistance to female FFA members from Kentucky, Georgia, or Tennessee who plan to attend college in any state.

Eligibility This program is open to female members who are seniors graduating from high schools in Kentucky, Georgia, or Tennessee. Applicants must be interested in working on a 2- or 4-year degree in any area of study at a college or university in any state. They must demonstrate financial need and personal motivation. Selection is based on academic achievement (10 points for GPA, 10 points for SAT or ACT score, 10 points for class rank), leadership in FFA activities (30 points), leadership in community activities (10 points), and participation in the Supervised Agricultural Experience (SAE) program (30 points). U.S. citizenship is required.

Financial data The stipend is $1,250 per year.

Duration 1 year; may be renewed up to 3 additional years if the recipient maintains a GPA of 2.0 or higher.

Number awarded Approximately 3 each year.

Deadline February of each year.

[121]
CHERYL KRAFF-COOPER, M.D. GIRAFFE FUND EMERGENCY GRANTS FOR UNDERGRADUATES

Alpha Epsilon Phi
Attn: AEPhi Foundation
11 Lake Avenue Extension, Suite 1A
Danbury, CT 06811
(203) 748-0029   Fax: (203) 748-0039
E-mail: aephifoundation@aephi.org
Web: www.aephi.org/foundation/scholarships

Summary To provide assistance to undergraduate members of Alpha Epsilon Phi who are facing severe financial emergencies.

Eligibility This program is open to undergraduate members of the sorority who can demonstrate that they will be forced to withdraw from school if they do not receive emergency assistance. Applicants must submit statements on their career and professional objectives, academic or professional honors, other honors received, scholarships and loans received, Alpha Epsilon Phi activities, college and community activities, work experience, and why they are in need of emergency assistance.

Financial data Stipends are $1,000; funds may be used only for tuition, fees, and books.

Duration These are 1-time grants.

Number awarded Several each year.

Deadline Applications may be submitted at any time.

[122]
CHEVRON SWE SCHOLARSHIPS

Society of Women Engineers
Attn: Scholarship Selection Committee
120 South LaSalle Street, Suite 1515
Chicago, IL 60603-3572
(312) 596-5223   Toll Free: (877) SWE-INFO
Fax: (312) 644-8557
E-mail: scholarshipapplication@swe.org
Web: societyofwomenengineers.swe.org

Summary To provide financial assistance to members of the Society of Women Engineers (SWE) who are attending specified colleges and universities and majoring in designated engineering specialties.

Eligibility This program is open to members of the society who are sophomores at specified ABET-accredited 4-year colleges or universities. Applicants must be majoring in computer science or chemical, computer, electrical, environmental, mechanical, or petroleum engineering and have a GPA of 3.0 or higher. Preference is given to members of groups underrepresented in computer science and engineering. Selection is based on merit. U.S. citizenship is required.

Financial data The stipend is $2,000. The award includes a travel grant for the recipient to attend the SWE national conference.

Duration 1 year.

Additional information This program, established in 1991, is sponsored by Chevron Corporation. For a list of the specified schools, contact SWE.

Number awarded 5 each year.

Deadline February of each year.

[123]
CHUNGHI HONG PARK SCHOLARSHIPS

Korean-American Scientists and Engineers Association
Attn: Scholarship Committee
1952 Gallows Drive, Suite 300
Vienna, VA 22182
(703) 748-1221   Fax: (703) 748-1331
E-mail: sejong@ksea.org
Web: scholarship.ksea.org/InfoUndergraduate.aspx

Summary To provide financial assistance to women who are undergraduate student members of the Korean-American Scientists and Engineers Association (KSEA).

Eligibility This program is open to women who are Korean American undergraduate students, are KSEA members, have completed at least 40 credits as a college student, and are majoring in science, engineering, or a related field. Along with their application, they must submit an essay on a topic that changes annually but relates to science or engineering; recently, students were asked to discuss the pros and cons of development vs. the environment. Selection is based on the essay (20%), KSEA activities and community service (30%), recommendation letters (20%), and academic performance (30%).

Financial data The stipend is $1,000.

Duration 1 year.

Number awarded 2 each year.

Deadline February of each year.

[124]
CHURCHILL FAMILY SCHOLARSHIP FUND

Maine Community Foundation
Attn: Program Director
245 Main Street
Ellsworth, ME 04605
(207) 667-9735   Toll Free: (877) 700-6800
Fax: (207) 667-0447   E-mail: info@mainecf.org
Web: www.mainecf.org/statewidescholars.aspx

Summary To provide financial assistance to female high school seniors in Maine who are interested in studying music at a college in any state.

Eligibility This program is open to women graduating from high schools in Maine. Applicants must be planning to attend a college in any state to work on a degree in vocal music education or performance.

Financial data A stipend is awarded (amount not specified).

Duration 1 year.

Additional information Support for this program is provided by the Musica de Filia Girlchoir, 550 Forest Avenue, Portland, ME 04101, (207) 767-4815, E-mail: musicadefilia@gmail.com.

Number awarded 1 or more each year.

Deadline April of each year.

[125]
CITRUS DISTRICT 2 DAUGHTERS OF PENELOPE SCHOLARSHIPS

Daughters of Penelope-District 2
c/o Nicole P. Sackedis
9003 Spring Garden Way
Tampa, FL 33626
(813) 749-6000   E-mail: chickref@hotmail.com
Web: www.ahepad2.org

Summary To provide financial assistance to women from Florida who are members of organizations affiliated with the American Hellenic Educational Progressive Association (AHEPA) and interested in attending college or graduate school in any state.

Eligibility This program is open to women who are residents of AHEPA Citrus District 2 (Florida) and high school seniors, undergraduates, or graduate students. Applicants must have been a member of the Maids of Athena for at least 2 years or have an immediate family member who has belonged to the Daughters of Penelope or Order of AHEPA for at least 2 years. They must have an unweighted high

school or college GPA of 3.0 or higher. Along with their application, they must submit a personal essay of 300 to 600 words on how the AHEPA family has influenced their goals, personal effort, and/or educational experiences. Selection is based on merit and financial need. Only single women are eligible.

Financial data A stipend is awarded (amount not specified).

Duration 1 year; may be renewed.

Additional information This program includes the Past District Governors/Julie P. Microutsicos Scholarship, awarded to the runner-up.

Number awarded 2 each year.

Deadline April of each year.

[126]
COCHRAN/GREENE SCHOLARSHIP

National Naval Officers Association-Washington, D.C. Chapter
Attn: Scholarship Program
2701 Park Center Drive, A1108
Alexandria, VA 22302
(703) 566-3840   Fax: (703) 566-3813
E-mail: Stephen.Williams@Navy.mil
Web: dcnnoa.memberlodge.com

Summary To provide financial assistance to female minority high school seniors from the Washington, D.C. area who are interested in attending college in any state.

Eligibility This program is open to female minority seniors graduating from high schools in the Washington, D.C. metropolitan area who plan to enroll full time at an accredited 2- or 4-year college or university in any state. Applicants must have a GPA of 2.5 or higher. Selection is based on academic achievement, community involvement, and financial need.

Financial data The stipend is $1,500.

Duration 1 year; nonrenewable.

Additional information Recipients are not required to join or affiliate with the military in any way.

Number awarded 1 each year.

Deadline March of each year.

[127]
COLLEEN CONLEY MEMORIAL SCHOLARSHIP

New Mexico Engineering Foundation
Attn: Scholarship Chair
P.O. Box 3828
Albuquerque, NM 87190-3828
(505) 615-1800   E-mail: info@nmef.net
Web: www.nmef.net/?section=scholarship

Summary To provide financial assistance to female high school seniors in New Mexico who plan to study engineering at a college or university in any state.

Eligibility This program is open to female seniors graduating from high schools in New Mexico who are planning to enroll at a college or university in any state and major in engineering, engineering technology, or a related field (including scientific disciplines). Applicants must have a GPA of 3.0 or higher. Along with their application, they must submit a 300-word letter discussing their interest in science or engineering and their future plans. Financial need is not considered in the selection process. Preference is given to applicants who are the first member of their family to attend college.

Financial data   The stipend is $1,000.

Duration   1 year; may be renewed up to 3 additional years, provided the recipient remains enrolled at least half time and maintains a GPA of 2.5 or higher.

Additional information   This program is sponsored by the Central New Mexico Section of the Society of Women Engineers.

Number awarded   1 each year.

Deadline   February of each year.

[128]
COLLEGE SCHOLARSHIPS FOUNDATION WOMEN'S SCHOLARSHIP

College Scholarships Foundation
5506 Red Robin Road
Raleigh, NC 27613
(919) 630-4895   Toll Free: (888) 501-9050
E-mail: info@collegescholarships.org
Web: www.collegescholarships.org

Summary   To provide financial assistance to women working on an undergraduate or graduate degree.

Eligibility   This program is open to women who are working full time on an undergraduate or graduate degree. Applicants must have a GPA of 3.0 or higher. Along with their application, they must submit a 300-word essay on how their education plans have affected their plans of starting a family, what trends they foresee occurring for women in the workforce, and where they see themselves in 10 years. U.S. citizenship is required.

Financial data   The stipend is $1,000.

Duration   1 year.

Additional information   This scholarship was first awarded in 2006. The sponsor was formerly known as the Daniel Kovach Scholarship Foundation.

Number awarded   1 each year.

Deadline   December of each year.

[129]
COLONEL HAROLD M. BEARDSLEE MEMORIAL SCHOLARSHIP AWARDS

Army Engineer Association
Attn: Fort Leonard Wood Operations
P.O. Box 634
Fort Leonard Wood, MO 65473
(573) 329-6678   Fax: (573) 329-3203
E-mail: flw@armyengineer.com
Web: www.armyengineer.com/AEA_scholarships.html

Summary   To provide financial assistance for college to spouses and children of members of the Army Engineer Association (AEA).

Eligibility   This program is open to spouses and children of AEA members in the following 4 categories: 1) graduating high school seniors who are children of active-duty or civilian members (including active-duty retired); 2) graduating high school seniors who are children of Reserve or National Guard members (including Reserve or National Guard retired); 3) children and spouses of members in the second, third, or fourth year of a baccalaureate degree program; and 4) the next best qualified applicant, regardless of category, not

receiving any of those awards. Applicants must be enrolled or planning to enroll full time at an accredited college or university. Along with their application, they must submit an essay on their reasons for seeking this award. Selection is based on the essay, scholastic aptitude, and letters of recommendation.

Financial data   The stipend is $1,000.

Duration   1 year; nonrenewable.

Number awarded   5 each year, including at least 1 in each category.

Deadline   April of each year.

[130]
COLORADO LEGION AUXILIARY DEPARTMENT PRESIDENT'S SCHOLARSHIP FOR JUNIOR AUXILIARY MEMBERS

American Legion Auxiliary
Department of Colorado
7465 East First Avenue, Suite D
Denver, CO 80230
(303) 367-5388   Fax: (303) 367-5388
E-mail: ala@impactmail.net
Web: www.freewebs.com/ala-colorado

Summary   To provide financial assistance to junior members of the American Legion Auxiliary in Colorado who plan to attend college in the state.

Eligibility   This program is open to seniors at high schools in Colorado who have been junior members of the auxiliary for the past 3 years. Applicants must be Colorado residents planning to attend college in the state. Along with their application, they must submit a 1,000-word essay on the topic, "My Obligations as an American." Selection is based on character (20%), Americanism (20%), leadership (20%), scholarship (20%), and financial need (20%).

Financial data   The stipend is $1,000.

Duration   1 year; nonrenewable.

Number awarded   1 each year.

Deadline   March of each year.

[131]
COLORADO LEGION AUXILIARY PAST PRESIDENT'S PARLEY NURSE'S SCHOLARSHIP

American Legion Auxiliary
Department of Colorado
7465 East First Avenue, Suite D
Denver, CO 80230
(303) 367-5388   Fax: (303) 367-5388
E-mail: ala@impactmail.net
Web: www.freewebs.com/ala-colorado

Summary   To provide financial assistance to wartime veterans and their spouses or descendants in Colorado who are interested in attending school in the state to prepare for a career in nursing.

Eligibility   This program is open to 1) daughters, sons, spouses, granddaughters, and great-granddaughters of veterans, and 2) veterans who served in the armed forces during eligibility dates for membership in the American Legion. Applicants must be Colorado residents who have been accepted by an accredited school of nursing in the state. Along with their application, they must submit a 500-word essay on the topic, "Americanism." Selection is based on scholastic ability (25%), financial need (25%), references (13%), a 500-word essay on Americanism (25%), and dedication to chosen field (12%).

Financial data Stipends range from $500 to $1,000.

Duration 1 year; nonrenewable.

Number awarded Varies each year, depending on the availability of funds.

Deadline April of each year.

[132]
COLORADO WOMEN'S EDUCATION FOUNDATION SCHOLARSHIPS

Colorado Federation of Business and Professional
  Women
Attn: Colorado Women's Education Foundation
P.O. Box 1189
Boulder, CO 80306-1189
(303) 443-2573   Fax: (720) 564-0397
E-mail: office@cwef.org
Web: www.cbpwef.org

Summary To provide financial assistance for college to mature women residing in Colorado.

Eligibility This program is open to women 25 years of age and older who are enrolled at an accredited Colorado college, university, or vocational school. Applicants must be U.S. citizens who have resided in Colorado for at least 12 months. They must have a GPA of 3.0 or higher. Along with their application, they must submit a copy of their most recent high school or college transcript, proof of Colorado residency and U.S. citizenship, a statement of their educational and career goals, 2 letters of recommendation, and documentation of financial need.

Financial data Stipends range from $250 to $1,000. Funds are to be used for tuition, fees, or books.

Duration 1 semester; recipients may reapply.

Number awarded Varies each year; recently, 22 of these scholarships were awarded.

Deadline May of each year for fall semester; October of each year for spring semester.

[133]
COLUMBUS CHAPTER WOMEN'S TRANSPORTATION SEMINAR SCHOLARSHIPS

Women's Transportation Seminar-Columbus Chapter
c/o Tracey Nixon, Scholarship Committee Chair
Parsons Brinckerhoff
2545 Farmers Drive, Suite 350
Columbus, OH 43235
(614) 791-5181   E-mail: ixon@pbworld.com
Web: www.wtsinternational.org/Chapters.aspx?ID=14102

Summary To provide financial assistance to women from Ohio who are working on an undergraduate or graduate degree in a transportation-related field.

Eligibility This program is open to women who are residents of Ohio or currently enrolled as an undergraduate or graduate student at a college or university in the state. Applicants must be preparing for a career in a transportation-related field and be working on a degree in transportation engineering, planning, aviation, finance, public policy, logistics, or a related field. They must have a GPA of 3.0 or higher. Along with their application, they must submit a personal

statement about their career goals after graduation and why they think they should receive this scholarship. Minority candidates are encouraged to apply. Selection is based on transportation goals, academic record, and transportation-related activities or job skills.

Financial data Stipends are $1,000 for undergraduates or $1,200 for graduate students.

Duration 1 year.

Number awarded 3 each year: 2 for undergraduates and 1 for a graduate student.

Deadline November of each year.

[134]
COMMUNITY SERVICE SCHOLARSHIPS

Miss America Pageant
Attn: Scholarship Department
222 New Road, Suite 700
Linwood, NJ 08221
(609) 653-8700, ext. 127   Fax: (609) 653-8740
E-mail: info@missamerica.org
Web: www.missamerica.org

Summary To recognize and reward, with college scholarships, women who participate in the Miss America Pageant at the state level and demonstrate outstanding community service.

Eligibility This competition is open to women who compete at the state level of the Miss America Pageant. Applicants must demonstrate that they have fulfilled a legitimate need in their community through the creation, development, and/or participation in a community service project. Selection is based on excellence of community service.

Financial data The stipend is $1,000.

Duration 1 year.

Additional information This program, established in 1998, is administered by Scholarship Management Services, a division of Scholarship America, One Scholarship Way, P.O. Box 297, St. Peter, MN 56082, (507) 931-1682, (800) 537-4180, Fax: (507) 931-9168, E-mail: smsinfo@csfa.org.

Number awarded Up to 52 each year: 1 for each of the states, the District of Columbia, and the Virgin Islands.

Deadline Varies, depending upon the date of local pageants leading to the state finals.

[135]
CONGRESSIONAL BLACK CAUCUS FOUNDATION ENVIRONMENTAL STUDIES SCHOLARSHIPS

Congressional Black Caucus Foundation, Inc.
Attn: Director, Educational Programs
1720 Massachusetts Avenue, N.W.
Washington, DC 20036
(202) 263-2800   Toll Free: (800) 784-2577
Fax: (202) 775-0773   E-mail: info@cbcfinc.org
Web: www.cbcfinc.org/scholarships.html

Summary To provide financial assistance to female and minority upper-division students who are working on a degree in environmental science.

Eligibility This program is open to minorities and women who are currently enrolled as full-time juniors at a 4-year college or university. Applicants must be working on a degree in environmental science and have a GPA of 2.5 or higher. They must be able to demonstrate understanding and acceptance of ServiceMaster's core values. Along with their application, they must submit a personal statement of 500 to 1,000 words on 1) their future goals, major field of study, and how that field of study will help them to achieve their future career goals; 2) involvement in school activities, community and public service, hobbies, and sports; 3) how receiving this award will affect their current and future plans; and 4) other experiences, skills, or qualifications. They must also be able to demonstrate financial need, leadership ability, and participation in community service activities. Preference is given to students who plan to complete a 4-year degree and work in an underserved community. U.S. citizenship or permanent resident status is required.

Financial data The stipend is $10,000. Funds are paid directly to the student's institution.

Duration 1 year.

Additional information This program is sponsored by ServiceMaster.

Number awarded 2 each year.

Deadline March of each year.

[136]
CONNECTICUT ELKS ASSOCIATION GIRL SCOUT GOLD AWARD SCHOLARSHIP

Girl Scouts of Connecticut
Attn: Program Department
340 Washington Street
Hartford, CT 06106
(860) 522-0163
Fax: (860) 548-0325
Toll Free: (800) 922-2770
E-mail: program@gsoft.org
Web: www.gsoft.org

Summary To provide financial assistance to Girl Scouts in Connecticut who plan to attend college in any state.

Eligibility This program is open to high school seniors who are registered Girl Scouts in Connecticut and planning to attend college in any state. Applicants must have earned the Gold Award. Selection is based on leadership accomplishments (30 points), community and religious service activities (30 points), classroom and extracurricular activities (15 points), scholastic achievements or awards (10 points), individual interests and hobbies (5 points), and overall review by the selection committee (10 points).

Financial data The stipend is $1,000.

Duration 1 year.

Additional information This program is sponsored by the Connecticut Elks Association.

Number awarded 1 each year.

Deadline April of each year.

[137]
CORINNE JEANNINE SCHILLINGS FOUNDATION ACADEMIC SCHOLARSHIPS

Corinne Jeannine Schillings Foundation
10645 Nebraska Street
Frankfort, IL 60423-0507
(815) 534-5598
E-mail: dschillings1@comcast.net
Web: www.cjsfoundation.org/html/academic_study.html

Summary To provide financial assistance to Girl Scouts who plan to study a foreign language in college.

Eligibility This program is open to members of the Girl Scouts who have earned the Silver or Gold Award. Applicants must be enrolled or planning to enroll full time at a 4-year college or university and major or minor in a foreign language. They must have a GPA of 3.0 or higher. Along with their application, they must submit a 5-page essay about themselves, including the impact of Girl Scouting on their life, why they have chosen to major or minor in a foreign language, how they plan to utilize their language skills, and why they feel they should receive this scholarship. Financial need is not considered in the selection process.

Financial data The stipend is $1,500 per year.

Duration 1 year; may be renewed up to 3 additional years, provided the recipient maintains a GPA of 3.0 or higher, both overall and in foreign language classes.

Additional information This program began in 2005.

Number awarded Varies each year; recently, this program awarded 13 new and renewal scholarships.

Deadline May of each year.

[138]
CPO SCHOLARSHIP FUND

Senior Enlisted Academy Alumni Association
Attn: CPO Scholarship Fund
1269 Elliot Avenue
Newport, RI 02841-1525
E-mail: cposfboard@cposf.org
Web: www.cposf.org

Summary To provide financial assistance for college to the spouses and children of Navy Chief Petty Officers (CPOs).

Eligibility This program is open to the spouses and children (natural born, adopted, or step) of active, Reserve, retired, and deceased Navy CPOs. Applicants must be high school seniors or students currently enrolled at a college, university, or vocational/technical school with the goal of obtaining an associate or bachelor's degree or certificate. Along with their application, they must submit an autobiographical essay of 200 to 500 words that discusses their significant experiences, community involvement, and qualities of character and leadership important in achieving their goals. Selection is based on the essay, honors and awards received during high school, extracurricular activities, community activities, and employment experience; financial need is not considered. Members of the armed services are not eligible.

Financial data The stipend is $2,000.

Duration 1 year.

Additional information The applicant judged most outstanding receives the Tom Crow Memorial Scholarship.

Number awarded Varies each year; recently, 56 of these scholarships were awarded.

Deadline March of each year.

[139]
CUMMINS SCHOLARSHIPS

Society of Women Engineers
Attn: Scholarship Selection Committee
120 South LaSalle Street, Suite 1515
Chicago, IL 60603-3572
(312) 596-5223   Toll Free: (877) SWE-INFO
Fax: (312) 644-8557
E-mail: scholarshipapplication@swe.org
Web: societyofwomenengineers.swe.org

Summary To provide financial assistance to women working on an undergraduate or graduate degree in designated engineering specialties.

Eligibility This program is open to women who are sophomores, juniors, seniors, or graduate students at 4-year ABET-accredited colleges and universities. Applicants must be working on a degree in computer science or automotive, chemical, computer, electrical, industrial, manufacturing, materials, or mechanical engineering and have a GPA of 3.5 or higher. Preference is given to members of groups underrepresented in engineering or computer science. Selection is based on merit. U.S. citizenship is required.

Financial data The stipend is $1,000.

Duration 1 year.

Additional information This program is sponsored by Cummins, Inc.

Number awarded 2 each year.

Deadline February of each year.

[140]
D. ANITA SMALL SCIENCE AND BUSINESS SCHOLARSHIP

Business and Professional Women of Maryland
Attn: BPW Foundation of Maryland
c/o Joyce Draper, Chief Financial Officer
615 Fairview Avenue
Frederick, MD 21701
Web: www.bpwmaryland.org

Summary To provide financial assistance to women in Maryland who are interested in working on an undergraduate or graduate degree in a science or business-related field.

Eligibility This program is open to women who are at least 21 years of age and have been accepted to a bachelor's or advanced degree program at an accredited Maryland academic institution. Applicants must be preparing for a career in 1 of the following or a related field: accounting, aeronautics, business administration, computer sciences, engineering, finance, information technology, mathematics, medical sciences (including nursing, laboratory technology, therapy, etc.), oceanography, or physical sciences. They must have a GPA of 3.0 or higher and be able to demonstrate financial need.

Financial data The stipend is $1,000 per year.

Duration 1 year.

Number awarded 1 or more each year.

Deadline July of each year.

[141]
DAGMAR JEPPESON GRANT

Delta Kappa Gamma Society International-Alpha Rho State Organization
c/o Alyce Sandusky, State Scholarship Chair
7619 Highway 66
Klamath Falls, OR 97601-9538
(541) 884-0524   E-mail: terryandalyce@charter.net
Web: www.deltakappagamma.org

Summary To provide financial assistance to women from Oregon who are enrolled as upper-division students at a college in any state and preparing for a career in elementary education.

Eligibility This program is open to female residents of Oregon who are at least juniors at a college in any state and interested in preparing for a career in elementary education. Applicants may not be members of Delta Kappa Gamma (an honorary society of women educators), but they must be sponsored by a local chapter of the society. Along with their application, they must submit a summary of their education from high school through the present, high school and college activities and achievements, community service, employment history, career goals, and financial need.

Financial data A stipend is awarded (amount not specified).

Duration 1 year.

Additional information Recipients may not accept a scholarship from the Alpha Rho state organization and from Delta Kappa Gamma International in the same year.

Number awarded 1 or more each year.

Deadline February of each year.

[142]
DANIEL LADNER SCHOLARSHIPS

New York Women in Communications, Inc.
Attn: NYWICI Foundation
355 Lexington Avenue, 15th Floor
New York, NY 10017-6603
(212) 297-2133   Fax: (212) 370-9047
E-mail: nywicipr@nywici.org
Web: www.nywici.org/foundation/scholarships

Summary To provide financial assistance to female upper-division and graduate students who reside in designated eastern states and are interested in preparing for a career in financial or political communications at a college or graduate school in any state.

Eligibility This program is open to female residents of New York, New Jersey, Connecticut, or Pennsylvania who are attending a college or university in any state. Also eligible are women who reside outside the 4 states but are currently enrolled at a college or university within 1 of the 5 boroughs of New York City. Applicants must be college juniors, seniors, or graduate students who are preparing for a career in either 1) financial communications (e.g., marketing, advertising, investor relations, public relations, corporate communications, media/journalism); or 2) political communications (e.g., political journalism; advertising; analysis; consulting; public, government, or international affairs; diplomacy; speechwriting; advocacy). They must have a GPA of 3.2 or higher. Graduate students must be members of New York Women in Communications, Inc. (NYWICI). Along with their application, they must submit a 2-page resume that includes school and extra-curricular activities, significant achievements, academic honors and awards, and community service work; a personal essay of 300 to 500 words on their choice of an assigned topic that changes annually; 2 letters of recommendation; and an official transcript. Selection is based on academic record, need, demonstrated leadership, participation in school and community activities, honors, work experience, goals and aspirations, and unusual personal and/or family circumstances. U.S. citizenship is required.

Financial data The stipend ranges up to $10,000.

Duration 1 year.

Number awarded 2 each year.

Deadline January of each year.

[143]
DASSAULT FALCON JET CORPORATION SCHOLARSHIP

Women in Aviation, International
Attn: Scholarships
Morningstar Airport
3647 State Route 503 South
West Alexandria, OH 45381-9354
(937) 839-4647   Fax: (937) 839-4645
E-mail: scholarships@wai.org
Web: www.wai.org/education/scholarships.cfm

Summary To provide financial assistance to women who are working on an undergraduate or graduate degree in a field related to aviation.

Eligibility This program is open to women who are working on an undergraduate or graduate degree in an aviation-related field. Applicants must be U.S. citizens, be fluent in English, and have a GPA of 3.0 or higher. Along with their application, they must submit 2 letters of recommendation; a 1-page essay on their current educational status, what they hope to achieve by working on a degree in aviation, and their aspirations in the field; a resume; copies of all aviation licenses and medical certificates; and the last 3 pages of their pilot logbook (if applicable). Selection is based on achievements, attitude toward self and others, commitment to success, dedication to career, financial need, motivation, reliability, responsibility, and teamwork.

Financial data The stipend is $1,000.

Duration 1 year.

Additional information WAI is a nonprofit professional organization dedicated to encouraging women to consider an aviation career and to providing educational outreach activities and networking resources to women active in the industry. This program is sponsored by Dassault Falcon Jet Corporation.

Number awarded 1 each year.

Deadline November of each year.

[144]
DAUGHTERS OF PENELOPE UNDERGRADUATE SCHOLARSHIPS

Daughters of Penelope
Attn: Daughters of Penelope Foundation, Inc.
1909 Q Street, N.W., Suite 500
Washington, DC 20009-1007
(202) 234-9741   Fax: (202) 483-6983
E-mail: dophq@ahepa.org
Web: www.dopfoundationinc.com/?page_id=382

Summary To provide financial assistance for college to women of Greek descent.

Eligibility This program is open to women who have been members of the Daughters of Penelope or the Maids of Athena for at least 2 years, or whose parents or grandparents have been members of the Daughters of Penelope or the Order of AHEPA for at least 2 years. Applicants must be 1) high school seniors or recent high school graduates applying to a college, university, or accredited technical school, or 2) current undergraduates at the college level. They must have taken the SAT or ACT (or Canadian, Greek, or Cypriot equivalent) and must write an essay (in English) about their educational and vocational goals. Selection is based on academic merit only.

Financial data Stipends are $1,500 or $1,000.

Duration 1 year; nonrenewable.

Additional information This program includes the following endowed awards: the Daughters of Penelope Past Grand Presidents' Memorial Scholarship, the Alexandra Apostolides Sonenfeld Scholarship, the Helen J. Beldecos Scholarship, the Hopewell Agave Chapter 224 Scholarship, the Kottis Family Scholarship, the Mary M. Verges Scholarship, the Joanne V. Hologgitas Ph.D. Scholarship, the Eos #1 Mother Lodge Chapter Scholarship, the Barbara Edith Quincey Thorndyke Memorial Scholarship, and the Paula J. Alexander Memorial Scholarship.

Number awarded Varies each year; recently, 17 of these scholarships were awarded: 3 at $1,500 and 14 at $1,000.

Deadline April of each year.

[145]
DAUGHTERS OF THE CINCINNATI SCHOLARSHIP PROGRAM

Daughters of the Cincinnati
Attn: Scholarship Administrator
20 West 44th Street, Suite 508
New York, NY 10036
(212) 991-9945 E-mail: scholarships@daughters1894.org
Web: www.daughters1894.org

Summary To provide financial assistance for college to high school seniors who are the daughters of active-duty, deceased, or retired military officers.

Eligibility This program is open to high school seniors who are the daughters of career commissioned officers of the regular Army, Navy, Air Force, Coast Guard, or Marine Corps on active duty, deceased, or retired. Applicants must be planning to enroll at a college or university in any state. Along with their application, they must submit an official school transcript, SAT or ACT scores, a letter of recommendation, and documentation of financial need.

Financial data Scholarship amounts have recently averaged $4,000 per year. Funds are paid directly to the college of the student's choice.

Duration 1 year; may be renewed up to 3 additional years, provided the recipient remains in good academic standing.

Additional information This program was originally established in 1906.

Number awarded Approximately 12 each year.

Deadline March of each year.

[146]
DAVIS & DAVIS SCHOLARSHIP

National Naval Officers Association-Washington, D.C.
  Chapter
Attn: Scholarship Program
2701 Park Center Drive, A1108
Alexandria, VA 22302
(703) 566-3840   Fax: (703) 566-3813
E-mail: Stephen.Williams@Navy.mil
Web: dcnnoa.memberlodge.com

Summary To provide financial assistance to female African American high school seniors from the Washington, D.C. area who are interested in attending college in any state.

Eligibility This program is open to female African American seniors graduating from high schools in the Washington, D.C. metropolitan area who plan to enroll full time at an accredited 2- or 4-year college or university in any state. Applicants must have a GPA of 2.5 or higher and be U.S. citizens or permanent residents. Selection is based on academic achievement, community involvement, and financial need.

Financial data The stipend is $1,000.

Duration 1 year; nonrenewable.

Additional information Recipients are not required to join or affiliate with the military in any way.

Number awarded 1 each year.

Deadline March of each year.

[147]
DEALER DEVELOPMENT SCHOLARSHIP PROGRAM

General Motors Corporation
Women's Retail Network
Attn: GM Scholarship Administration Center
700 West Fifth Avenue
Mail Code 2001
Naperville, IL 60563
Toll Free: (888) 377-5233
E-mail: wrnscholarshipinfo@gmsac.com
Web: www.gmsac.com

Summary To provide financial assistance to women attending college or graduate school to prepare for a retail automotive career.

Eligibility This program is open to women who are enrolled full time in undergraduate, graduate, and nontraditional continuing education institutions that offer degrees in the automotive retail field. Applicants must be interested in preparing for a career in automotive retail and/or service management. They must be citizens of the United States or have the ability to accept permanent employment in the United States without the need for visa sponsorship now or in

the future. Current and former enrollees in the General Motors National Candidate Program are not eligible, but applications are accepted from female employees and female employee dependents working at GM dealerships. Selection is based on academic performance, community service and volunteerism, work experience, and a personal statement. Financial need is not considered.

Financial data The stipend is $5,000 per year.

Duration 1 year; recipients may reapply.

Additional information This program was established in 2011.

Number awarded Several each year.

Deadline April of each year.

[148]
DEAN WEESE SCHOLARSHIP

University Interscholastic League
Attn: Texas Interscholastic League Foundation
1701 Manor Road
P.O. Box 8028
Austin, TX 78713-8028
(512) 232-4937   Fax: (512) 232-7311
E-mail: bbaxendale@mail.utexas.edu
Web: www.uil.utexas.edu/tilf/scholarships.html

Summary To provide financial assistance to high school seniors who participate in programs of the Texas Interscholastic League Foundation (TILF), have competed in girls' high school varsity basketball, and plan to attend college in the state.

Eligibility This program is open to seniors graduating from high schools in Texas who have competed in a University Interscholastic League (UIL) academic state meet and have participated in girls' high school varsity basketball. Applicants must be planning to attend a college or university in the state and major in any field. Along with their application, they must submit high school transcripts that include SAT and/or ACT scores and documentation of financial need.

Financial data The stipend is $1,000.

Duration 1 year; nonrenewable.

Additional information This program is sponsored by Whataburger Inc. and Southwest Shootout Inc.

Number awarded 1 each year.

Deadline May of each year.

[149]
DEFENSE INTELLIGENCE AGENCY UNDERGRADUATE TRAINING ASSISTANCE PROGRAM

Defense Intelligence Agency
Attn: Human Resources, HCH-4
200 MacDill Boulevard, Building 6000
Bolling AFB, DC 20340-5100
(202) 231-8228   Fax: (202) 231-4889
TDD: (202) 231-5002   E-mail: staffing@dia.mil
Web: www.dia.mil/employment/student/index.htm

Summary To provide funding and work experience to high school seniors and lower-division students (particularly women, minorities, and individuals with disabilities) who are interested in majoring in specified fields and working for the U.S. Defense Intelligence Agency (DIA).

Eligibility This program is open to graduating high school seniors and college freshmen and sophomores interested in working full time on a baccalaureate degree in 1 of the following fields in college: biology, chemistry, computer science, engineering, foreign area studies, intelligence analysis, international relations, microbiology, pharmacology, physics, political science, or toxicology. High school seniors must have a GPA of 2.75 or higher and either 1) an SAT combined critical reading and mathematics score of 1000 or higher plus 500 or higher on the writing portion or 2) an ACT score of 21 or higher. College freshmen and sophomores must have a GPA of 3.0 or higher. All applicants must be able to demonstrate financial need (household income ceiling of $70,000 for a family of 4 or $80,000 for a family of 5 or more) and leadership abilities through extracurricular activities, civic involvement, volunteer work, or part-time employment. Students and all members of their immediate family must be U.S. citizens. Minorities, women, and persons with disabilities are strongly encouraged to apply.

Financial data Students accepted into this program receive tuition (up to $18,000 per year) at an accredited college or university selected by the student and endorsed by the sponsor; reimbursement for books and needed supplies; an annual salary to cover college room and board expenses and for summer employment; and a position at the sponsoring agency after graduation. Recipients must work for DIA after college graduation for at least 1 and a half times the length of study. For participants who leave DIA earlier than scheduled, the agency arranges for payments to reimburse DIA for the total cost of education (including the employee's pay and allowances).

Duration 4 years, provided the recipient maintains a GPA of 2.75 during the freshman year and 3.0 or higher in subsequent semesters.

Additional information Recipients are provided a challenging summer internship and guaranteed a job at the agency in their field of study upon graduation.

Number awarded Only a few are awarded each year.

Deadline November of each year.

[150]
DEGENRING SCHOLARSHIP FUND

American Baptist Women's Ministries of New Jersey
36-10 Garden View Terrace
East Windsor, NJ 08520
Web: www.abwminnj.org/custom.html

Summary To provide financial assistance to Baptist women in New Jersey who are interested in attending college in any state to prepare for a career in Christian service.

Eligibility This program is open to Baptist women in New Jersey who are at least sophomores at postsecondary institutions in any state and preparing for a career involving Christian work. Applicants must be members of an American Baptist Church in New Jersey. Selection is based on financial need and career goals.

Financial data The amount awarded varies, depending upon the need of the recipient and her career goals in Christian work.

Duration 1 year.

Number awarded 1 or more each year.

Deadline February of each year.

[151]
DELAYED EDUCATION SCHOLARSHIP FOR WOMEN

American Nuclear Society
Attn: Scholarship Coordinator
555 North Kensington Avenue
La Grange Park, IL 60526-5592
(708) 352-6611   Toll Free: (800) 323-3044
Fax: (708) 352-0499   E-mail: outreach@ans.org
Web: www.ans.org/honors/scholarships

Summary To provide financial assistance to mature women whose formal studies in nuclear science or nuclear engineering have been delayed or interrupted.

Eligibility Applicants must be mature women who have experienced at least a 1-year delay or interruption of their undergraduate studies and are returning to school to work on an undergraduate or graduate degree in nuclear science or nuclear engineering. They must be members of the American Nuclear Society (ANS), but they may be citizens of any country. Along with their application, they must submit an essay on their academic and professional goals, experiences that have affected those goals, and other relevant information. Selection is based on that essay, academic achievement, letters of recommendation, and financial need.

Financial data The stipend is $5,000. Funds may be used by the student to cover any educational expense, including tuition, books, room, and board.

Duration 1 year; nonrenewable.

Number awarded 1 each year.

Deadline January of each year.

[152]
DELL COMPUTER CORPORATION SCHOLARSHIPS

Society of Women Engineers
Attn: Scholarship Selection Committee
120 South LaSalle Street, Suite 1515
Chicago, IL 60603-3572
(312) 596-5223   Toll Free: (877) SWE-INFO
Fax: (312) 644-8557
E-mail: scholarshipapplication@swe.org
Web: societyofwomenengineers.swe.org

Summary To provide financial assistance to upper-division women majoring in computer science or designated engineering specialties.

Eligibility This program is open to women who are entering their junior or senior year at an ABET-accredited college or university. Applicants must be majoring in computer science or electrical, computer, or mechanical engineering and have a GPA of 3.0 or higher. Financial need is considered in the selection process.

Financial data The stipend is $2,250.

Duration 1 year.

Additional information This program, established in 1999, is sponsored by Dell Inc.

Number awarded 2 each year.

Deadline February of each year.

[153]
DELLA VAN DEUREN MEMORIAL SCHOLARSHIPS

American Legion Auxiliary
Department of Wisconsin
Attn: Education Chair
2930 American Legion Drive
P.O. Box 140
Portage, WI 53901-0140
(608) 745-0124   Toll Free: (866) 664-3863
Fax: (608) 745-1947   E-mail: alawi@amlegionauxwi.org
Web: www.amlegionauxwi.org/Scholarships.htm

Summary   To provide financial assistance to Wisconsin residents who are members or children of members of the American Legion Auxiliary and interested in attending college in any state.

Eligibility   This program is open to members and children of members of the American Legion Auxiliary. Applicants must be high school seniors or graduates with a GPA of 3.5 or higher and be able to demonstrate financial need. They must be Wisconsin residents, although they are not required to attend school in the state. Along with their application, they must submit a 300-word essay on "Education—An Investment in the Future."

Financial data   The stipend is $1,000.

Duration   1 year; nonrenewable.

Number awarded   2 each year.

Deadline   March of each year.

[154]
DELTA AIR LINES AIRCRAFT MAINTENANCE TECHNOLOGY SCHOLARSHIPS

Women in Aviation, International
Attn: Scholarships
Morningstar Airport
3647 State Route 503 South
West Alexandria, OH 45381-9354
(937) 839-4647   Fax: (937) 839-4645
E-mail: scholarships@wai.org
Web: www.wai.org/education/scholarships.cfm

Summary   To provide financial assistance to members of Women in Aviation, International (WAI) who are interested in a career in aviation maintenance.

Eligibility   This program is open to WAI members who are full-time students with at least 2 semesters of study remaining. Applicants must be preparing for an aviation maintenance technician license (A&P) or a degree in aviation maintenance technology. They must have a cumulative GPA of 3.0 or higher and be U.S. citizens or eligible non-citizens. Along with their application, they must submit an essay of 500 to 1,000 words on who or what inspired them to prepare for a career in aviation maintenance technology, their greatest life challenge, their greatest strength and strongest characteristic, their most memorable academic experience, and why they are the most qualified candidate for this scholarship. Selection is based on achievements, attitude toward self and others, commitment to success, dedication to career, financial need, motivation, reliability, responsibility, and teamwork.

Financial data   The stipend is $5,000.

Duration   1 year.

Additional information   WAI is a nonprofit professional organization dedicated to encouraging women to consider an aviation career and to providing educational outreach activities and networking resources to women active in the industry. This program is sponsored by Delta Air Lines. In addition to the scholarship, recipients are reimbursed for up to $2,000 in travel and lodging expenses to attend the WAI annual conference.

Number awarded   1 each year.

Deadline   November of each year.

[155]
DELTA AIR LINES AVIATION MAINTENANCE MANAGEMENT/AVIATION BUSINESS MANAGEMENT SCHOLARSHIPS

Women in Aviation, International
Attn: Scholarships
Morningstar Airport
3647 State Route 503 South
West Alexandria, OH 45381-9354
(937) 839-4647   Fax: (937) 839-4645
E-mail: scholarships@wai.org
Web: www.wai.org/education/scholarships.cfm

Summary   To provide financial assistance to members of Women in Aviation, International (WAI) who are interested in a career in aviation management.

Eligibility   This program is open to WAI members who are full-time students with at least 2 semesters of study remaining. Applicants must be working on an associate or baccalaureate degree in aviation maintenance management or aviation business management and have a cumulative GPA of 3.0 or higher. They must be U.S. citizens or eligible non-citizens. Along with their application, they must submit an essay of 500 to 1,000 words on who or what inspired them to prepare for a career in aviation maintenance management or aviation business management, their greatest life challenge, their greatest strength and strongest characteristic, their most memorable academic experience, and why they are the most qualified candidate for this scholarship. Selection is based on achievements, attitude toward self and others, commitment to success, dedication to career, financial need, motivation, reliability, responsibility, and teamwork.

Financial data   The stipend is $5,000.

Duration   1 year.

Additional information   WAI is a nonprofit professional organization dedicated to encouraging women to consider an aviation career and to providing educational outreach activities and networking resources to women active in the industry. This program is sponsored by Delta Air Lines. In addition to the scholarship, recipients are reimbursed for up to $2,000 in travel and lodging expenses to attend the WAI annual conference.

Number awarded   1 each year.

Deadline   November of each year.

[156]
DELTA AIR LINES ENGINE MAINTENANCE INTERNSHIP

Women in Aviation, International
Attn: Scholarships
Morningstar Airport
3647 State Route 503 South
West Alexandria, OH 45381-9354
(937) 839-4647   Fax: (937) 839-4645
E-mail: scholarships@wai.org
Web: www.wai.org/education/scholarships.cfm

Summary To provide summer work experience with Delta Air Lines to upper-division female engineering students.

Eligibility This program is open to students entering their junior or senior year of full-time study with a major in aeronautical, aerospace, industrial, or mechanical engineering. Applicants must be interested in working during the summer at Delta Air Lines on projects in support of engine maintenance production. They must be U.S. citizens and have a GPA of 3.0 or higher. Along with their application, they must submit a 500-word essay on their aviation history and goals, 2 letters of recommendation, a resume, copies of all aviation licenses and medical certificates, and the last 3 pages of their pilot logbook, if applicable. Selection is based on achievements, attitude toward self and others, commitment to success, dedication to career, financial need, motivation, reliability, responsibility, and teamwork.

Financial data The stipend is $2,253 per month for juniors or $2,427 per month for seniors. The intern also receives round-trip airfare, hotel accommodations, and payment of the registration fee to attend the annual conference of Women in Aviation, International.

Duration 13 weeks during the summer.

Additional information WAI is a nonprofit professional organization dedicated to encouraging women to consider an aviation career and to providing educational outreach activities and networking resources to women active in the industry. This program is sponsored by Delta Air Lines.

Number awarded 1 each year.

Deadline November of each year.

[157]
DELTA AIR LINES ENGINEERING SCHOLARSHIP

Women in Aviation, International
Attn: Scholarships
Morningstar Airport
3647 State Route 503 South
West Alexandria, OH 45381-9354
(937) 839-4647   Fax: (937) 839-4645
E-mail: scholarships@wai.org
Web: www.wai.org/education/scholarships.cfm

Summary To provide financial assistance to members of Women in Aviation, International (WAI) who are studying engineering in college.

Eligibility This program is open to WAI members who are full-time juniors or seniors with at least 2 semesters of study remaining. Applicants must be working on a baccalaureate degree in aerospace, aeronautical, electrical, or mechanical engineering with a cumulative GPA of 3.0 or higher. They must be U.S. citizens or eligible non-citizens. Along with their application, they must submit an essay of 500 to 1,000 words on who or what inspired them to prepare for a career in engineering, their greatest life challenge, their greatest strength and strongest characteristic, their most memorable academic experience, and why they are the most qualified candidate for this scholarship. Selection is based on achievements, attitude toward self and others, commitment to success, dedication to career, financial need, motivation, reliability, responsibility, and teamwork.

Financial data The stipend is $5,000.

Duration 1 year.

Additional information WAI is a nonprofit professional organization dedicated to encouraging women to consider an aviation career and to providing educational outreach activities and networking resources to women active in the industry. This program is sponsored by Delta Air Lines. In addition to the scholarship, recipients are reimbursed for up to $2,000 in travel and lodging expenses to attend the WAI annual conference.

Number awarded 1 each year.

Deadline November of each year.

[158]
DELTA DELTA DELTA UNRESTRICTED UNDERGRADUATE SCHOLARSHIPS

Delta Delta Delta
Attn: Tri Delta Foundation
2331 Brookhollow Plaza Drive
P.O. Box 5987
Arlington, TX 76005-5987
(817) 633-8001   Fax: (817) 652-0212
E-mail: foundation@trideltaeo.org
Web: www.tridelta.org/Document/Foundation/Scholarships

Summary To provide financial assistance for undergraduate study to women students who are members of Delta Delta Delta.

Eligibility This program is open to undergraduate women, majoring in any field, who are current members of the sorority. Applicants must be entering their junior or senior year and planning to remain enrolled full time. Selection is based on academic achievement, past and present involvement in the sorority, community and campus involvement, and financial need.

Financial data The stipends range from $500 to $1,500. Funds are sent directly to the financial aid office of the recipient's college or university.

Duration 1 year.

Additional information This program, originally established in 1942, includes the following named scholarships: the Zoe Gore Perrin Scholarship, the Luella Atkins Key Scholarship, the Sarah Shinn Marshall Scholarship, and the Martin Sisters Scholarship.

Number awarded Varies each year; recently, a total of 36 undergraduate scholarships were awarded.

Deadline February of each year.

[159]
DELTA GAMMA SCHOLARSHIPS

Delta Gamma Foundation
Attn: Director of Scholarships, Fellowships and Loans
3250 Riverside Drive
P.O. Box 21397
Columbus, OH 43221-0397
(614) 481-8169   Toll Free: (800) 644-5414
Fax: (614) 481-0133
E-mail: FNScholarFellow@deltagamma.org
Web: www.deltagamma.org

Summary To provide financial assistance for college to members of Delta Gamma sorority who have made a significant contribution to both their chapter and their campus.

Eligibility This program is open to initiated members of a collegiate chapter of Delta Gamma in the United States or Canada who have completed 3 semesters or 4 quarters of their college course and have maintained a GPA of 3.0 or higher. Applicants must submit a 1- to 2-page essay in which they introduce themselves, including their career goals, their reasons for applying for this scholarship, and the impact Delta Gamma has had on their life. Selection is based on scholastic excellence and participation in chapter, campus, and community leadership activities.

Financial data The stipend is $1,000. Funds are sent directly to the university or college to be used for tuition, books, laboratory fees, room, and board. They may not be used for sorority dues, house fees, or other chapter expenses.

Duration 1 year.

Additional information This program includes several special endowment scholarships that give preference to members of specified chapters. Recipients are expected to remain active participating members of their collegiate chapter throughout the following academic year.

Number awarded Varies each year; recently, 196 of these scholarships were awarded.

Deadline January of each year.

[160]
DELTA PHI EPSILON SCHOLARSHIPS

Delta Phi Epsilon Educational Foundation
Attn: Executive Director
251 South Carnac Street
Philadelphia, PA 19107
(215) 732-5901   Fax: (215) 732-5906
E-mail: info@dphie.org
Web: www.dphie.org

Summary To provide financial assistance for college or graduate school to Delta Phi Epsilon Sorority members, alumnae, and relatives.

Eligibility This program is open to undergraduate Delta Phi Epsilon sorority sisters (not pledges) and alumnae who are returning to college or graduate school. Sons and daughters of Delta Phi Epsilon members or alumnae are also eligible for some of the programs. Selection is based on service and involvement, academics, and financial need.

Financial data The stipend is $1,000.

Duration 1 year or longer, depending upon the scholarship awarded.

Number awarded Varies each year; recently, 8 of these scholarships were awarded.

Deadline March of each year.

[161]
DELTA SIGMA THETA SORORITY GENERAL SCHOLARSHIPS

Delta Sigma Theta Sorority, Inc.
Attn: Scholarship and Standards Committee Chair
1707 New Hampshire Avenue, N.W.
Washington, DC 20009
(202) 986-2400   Fax: (202) 986-2513
E-mail: dstemail@deltasigmatheta.org
Web: www.deltasigmatheta.org

Summary To provide financial assistance to members of Delta Sigma Theta who are working on an undergraduate or graduate degree in any field.

Eligibility This program is open to active, dues-paying members of Delta Sigma Theta who are currently enrolled in college or graduate school. Applicants must submit an essay on their major goals and educational objectives, including realistic steps they foresee as necessary for the fulfillment of their plans. Financial need is considered in the selection process.

Financial data The stipends range from $1,000 to $2,000. The funds may be used to cover tuition, fees, and living expenses.

Duration 1 year; may be renewed for 1 additional year.

Additional information This sponsor is a traditionally-African American social sorority. The application fee is $20.

Deadline April of each year.

[162]
DELTA ZETA GENERAL UNDERGRADUATE SCHOLARSHIPS

Delta Zeta Sorority
Attn: Foundation Coordinator
202 East Church Street
Oxford, OH 45056
(513) 523-7597   Fax: (513) 523-1921
E-mail: DZFoundation@dzshq.com
Web: www.deltazeta.org

Summary To provide financial assistance for continued undergraduate study to members of Delta Zeta Sorority.

Eligibility This program is open to members of the sorority who are entering their junior or senior year and have a GPA of 3.0 or higher. Applicants must submit an official transcript, a statement of their career goals, information on their service to the sorority, documentation of campus activities and/or community involvement, a list of academic honors, and an explanation of their financial need.

Financial data The stipend ranges from $500 to $2,500, depending on the availability of funds.

Duration 1 year; nonrenewable.

Number awarded Varies each year; recently, 6 of these scholarships were awarded.

Deadline February of each year.

[163]
DENSLOW SCHOLARSHIP

Alpha Chi Omega Foundation
Attn: Foundation Programs Coordinator
5939 Castle Creek Parkway North Drive
Indianapolis, IN 46250-4343
(317) 579-5050, ext. 262   Fax: (317) 579-5051
E-mail: foundation@alphachiomega.org
Web: www.alphachiomega.org/index.aspx?id=1030

Summary To provide financial assistance for college to undergraduate members of Alpha Chi Omega.

Eligibility This program is open to women full-time college students who are members of Alpha Chi Omega. Applicants may be at any undergraduate level. Selection is based on academic achievement, chapter involvement, campus and community service, and financial need.

Financial data A stipend is awarded (amount not specified).

Duration 1 year.

Number awarded 1 each year.

Deadline March of each year.

[164]
DEPARTMENT OF STATE STUDENT INTERN PROGRAM

Department of State
Attn: HR/REE
2401 E Street, N.W., Suite 518 H
Washington, DC 20522-0108
(202) 261-8888   Toll Free: (800) JOB-OVERSEAS
Fax: (301) 562-8968   E-mail: Careers@state.gov
Web: www.careers.state.gov/students/programs

Summary To provide a work/study opportunity to undergraduate and graduate students (especially women and minority students) who are interested in foreign service.

Eligibility This program is open to full- and part-time continuing college and university juniors, seniors, and graduate students. Applications are encouraged from students with a broad range of majors, such as business or public administration, social work, economics, information management, journalism, and the biological, engineering, and physical sciences, as well as those majors more traditionally identified with international affairs. U.S. citizenship is required. The State Department particularly encourages eligible women and minority students with an interest in foreign affairs to apply.

Financial data Most internships are unpaid. A few paid internships are granted to applicants who can demonstrate financial need. If they qualify for a paid internship, they are placed at the GS-4 step 5 level (currently with an annual rate of $27,786). Interns placed abroad may also receive housing, medical insurance, a travel allowance, and a dependents' allowance.

Duration Paid internships are available only for 10 weeks during the summer. Unpaid internships are available for 1 semester or quarter during the academic year, or for 10 weeks during the summer.

Additional information About half of all internships are in Washington, D.C., or occasionally in other large cities in the United States. The remaining internships are at embassies and consulates abroad. Depending upon the needs of the department, interns are assigned junior-level professional duties, which may include research, preparing reports, drafting replies to correspondence, working in computer science, analyzing international issues, financial management, intelligence, security, or assisting in cases related to domestic and international law. Interns must agree to return to their schooling immediately upon completion of their internship.

Number awarded Approximately 800 internships are offered each year, but only about 5% of those are paid positions.

Deadline February of each year for fall internships; June of each year for spring internships; October of each year for a summer internships.

[165]
DETROIT SECTION SCHOLARSHIPS

Society of Women Engineers-Detroit Section
Attn: Scholarship Chair
P.O. Box 2978
Southfield, MI 48037-2978
(248) 288-9487   E-mail: Mary.clor@swe.org
Web: www.swe.org/SWE/RegionH/Detroit/student.html

Summary To provide financial assistance to female high school seniors in Michigan who are interested in studying engineering at a school in any state.

Eligibility This program is open to female seniors at high schools in Michigan who are planning to enroll the following fall at a university or college in any state that has an ABET-accredited engineering program. Along with their application, they must submit a 1-page essay on why they want to be an engineer. Selection is based on that essay (40%); awards and honors received in high school (20%); leadership, activities (community, church, school, etc.), and employment (30%); and academic performance (10%).

Financial data The stipend is $1,000.

Duration 1 year.

Number awarded Varies each year; recently, 2 of these scholarships were awarded.

Deadline February of each year.

[166]
DEXTER/USBC HIGH SCHOOL ALL-AMERICAN TEAM

United States Bowling Congress
Attn: USBC High School
621 Six Flags Drive
Arlington, TX 76011
Toll Free: (800) 514-BOWL, ext. 3168
Fax: (817) 385-8260
E-mail: usbchighschool@bowl.com
Web: www.bowl.com/scholarships

Summary To recognize and reward, with college scholarships, high school students who are affiliated with the United States Bowling Congress (USBC) and are selected for its All-American Team (females and males are judged separately).

Eligibility This program is open to high school students who participate on a high school bowling team that has USBC membership or is registered in the Coaches Registration Program. Candidates must be nominated by their high school coach or athletic director. They must have a GPA of 3.0 or higher. Nominees must submit a 500-word essay on the life lesson they have learned through high school bowling. Selection is based on the essay, bowling accomplishments in the current school year, academic achievement, recommendations, extracurricular and community involvement, and a resume.

Financial data Awards, in the form of college scholarships, are $1,000.

Duration Awards are presented annually.

Additional information Nominees must submit a fee of $20 along with their application.

Number awarded 10 each year: 5 boys and 5 girls.

Deadline Nominations must be submitted by March of each year.

[167]
DIAMOND JUBILEE FOUNDATION SCHOLARSHIPS

Alpha Omicron Pi Foundation
Attn: Scholarship Committee
5390 Virginia Way
Brentwood, TN 37027
(615) 370-0920   Fax: (615) 370-4424
E-mail: foundation@alphaomicronpi.org
Web: www.aoiifoundation.org/scholarship.php

Summary To provide financial assistance for college or graduate school to collegiate and alumnae members of Alpha Omicron Pi.

Eligibility This program is open to collegiate members of Alpha Omicron Pi who are classified by their institutions at least as sophomores and alumnae members who wish to work on a graduate degree. Applicants must be enrolled full time. Along with their application, they must submit the following 50-word statements: 1) the circumstances that have created their need for this scholarship; 2) their immediate and long-term life objectives; and 3) a letter of recommendation that they would write about themselves. Selection is based on those statements; academic achievement; Alpha Omicron Pi service, leadership, and involvement; college and community involvement; letters of recommendation; and financial need and evidence of self-help.

Financial data Stipend amounts vary; recently, the average value of each scholarship provided by this foundation was approximately $1,200.

Duration 1 year.

Additional information This program was established in 1962.

Number awarded Varies each year; recently, 35 of these scholarships were awarded (25 to undergraduates and 10 to graduate students).

Deadline February of each year.

[168]
DINAH SHORE SCHOLARSHIP

Ladies Professional Golf Association
Attn: LPGA Foundation
100 International Golf Drive
Daytona Beach, FL 32124-1082
(386) 274-6200   Fax: (386) 274-1099
E-mail: foundation.scholarships@lpga.com
Web: www.lpgafoundation.org

Summary To provide financial assistance for college to female graduating high school seniors who played golf in high school.

Eligibility This program is open to female high school seniors who have a GPA of 3.2 or higher. Applicants must have played in at least 50% of their high school golf team's scheduled events or have played golf "regularly" for the past 2 years. They must be planning to enroll full time at a college or university in the United States, but they must not be planning to play collegiate golf. Along with their application, they must submit a letter that describes how golf has been an integral part of their lives and includes their personal, academic, and professional goals; chosen discipline of study; and how this scholarship will be of assistance. Financial need is not considered in the selection process.

Financial data The stipend is $5,000.

Duration 1 year.

Additional information This program, established in 1994, is supported by Kraft Foods, Inc.

Number awarded 1 each year.

Deadline May of each year.

[169]
DISPLACED HOMEMAKER SCHOLARSHIPS

Association on American Indian Affairs, Inc.
Attn: Director of Scholarship Programs
966 Hungerford Drive, Suite 12-B
Rockville, MD 20850
(240) 314-7155   Fax: (240) 314-7159
E-mail: lw.aaia@verizon.net
Web: www.indian-affairs.org

Summary To provide financial assistance to Native American displaced homemakers who are trying to complete their college education.

Eligibility This program is open to full-time college students who are Native Americans and have special needs because of family responsibilities. Examples of displaced homemakers include students who are attending college for the first time at the age of 40 because they have put off higher education to raise their children, students who are entering or returning to college after their children enter elementary school, and men or women who have been divorced and had to leave college to care for children and are now returning. Applicants must submit documentation of financial need, a Certificate of Indian Blood showing at least one-quarter Indian blood, proof of tribal enrollment, an essay on their educational goals and family responsibilities, 2 letters of recommendation, and their most recent transcript.

Financial data The stipend is $1,500. Awards are intended to assist recipients with child care, transportation, and some basic living expenses as well as educational costs.

Duration 1 year; recipients may reapply.

Number awarded Varies each year; recently, 6 of these scholarships were awarded.

Deadline June of each year.

[170]
DISTINGUISHED YOUNG WOMEN SCHOLARSHIPS

Distinguished Young Women
Attn: Foundation Administrator
751 Government Street
Mobile, AL 36602
(251) 438-3621   Fax: (251) 431-0063
E-mail: foundation@distinguishedyw.org
Web: www.distinguishedyw.org/about/scholarships

Summary To recognize and reward, with college scholarships, female high school seniors who participate in the Distinguished Young Women competition.

Eligibility This competition is open to girls who are seniors in high school, are U.S. citizens, have never been married, and have never been pregnant. Contestants first enter local competitions, from which winners advance to the state level. The winner in each state is invited to the national competition, held in Mobile, Alabama in June of each year. Prior to the contestants' arrival for the national competition, the judges evaluate their high school academic records and test scores for the scholastics score (20% of the overall score). At the competition, girls are given scores on the basis of their personality, ability to relate to others, maturity, and ability to express themselves in an interview (25% of overall score); their performing arts talent presented during a 90-second audition on stage in front of an audience (25% of overall score); their fitness as demonstrated during a choreographed group aerobic routine (15% of overall score); and their self-expression, grace, poise, demeanor, carriage, posture, and speaking ability (15% of overall score). The girls with the highest scores in each of the 5 categories receive awards. Overall scores are used for selection of 10 finalists, from whom the "Distinguished Young Woman of America" and 2 runners-up are selected. In addition, "satellite awards" are presented to girls who excel in special activities.

Financial data The "Distinguished Young Woman of America" receives a $40,000 scholarship; other scholarships are $25,000 for the first runner-up, $15,000 for the second runner-up, $3,000 for each of the 7 other finalists, $1,000 for each of the category winners, and "satellite awards" ranging from $500 to $1,500 for other activities.

Duration The competition is held annually.

Additional information This program began in 1958 as America's Junior Miss. It acquired its current name in 2010.

Number awarded More than $140,000 in scholarships are awarded at the national finals each year.

Deadline Each local competition sets its own deadline.

[171]
DIVERSITY IN PSYCHOLOGY AND LAW RESEARCH AWARD

American Psychological Association
Attn: Division 41 (American Psychology-Law Society)
c/o Jennifer Hunt, Minority Affairs Committee Chair
Buffalo State University of New York, Psychology
  Department
Classroom Building C308
1300 Elmwood Avenue
Buffalo, NY 14222
(716) 878-3421   E-mail: huntjs@buffalostate.edu
Web: www.ap-ls.org

Summary To provide funding to women and other student members of the American Psychology-Law Society (AP-LS) who are interested in conducting a research project related to diversity.

Eligibility This program is open to undergraduate and graduate student members of AP-LS who are interested in conducting research on issues related to psychology, law, multiculturalism, and/or diversity (e.g., research pertaining to psycholegal issues on race, gender, culture, sexual orientation). Students from underrepresented groups are strongly encouraged to apply; underrepresented groups include, but are not limited to: racial and ethnic minorities; first-generation college students; lesbian, gay, bisexual, and transgender students; and physically disabled students. Applicants must submit a project description that includes a statement of the research problem, the project's likely impact on the field of psychology and law broadly, methodology, budget, and an overview of relevant literature. Selection is based on the impact of the project on diversity and multiculturalism and the expected completion within the allocated time.

Financial data The grant is $1,000.

Duration The project must be completed within 1 year.

Number awarded 3 each year.

Deadline November of each year.

[172]
DOLORES E. FISHER AWARD

Mel Fisher Maritime Heritage Society and Museum
Attn: Curator, Department of Education
200 Greene Street
Key West, FL 33040
(305) 294-2633   Fax: (305) 294-5671
E-mail: office@melfisher.org
Web: www.melfisher.org/deoaward.htm

Summary To recognize and reward, with funding for college or graduate school, women who submit outstanding essays on the oceans.

Eligibility This competition is open to women in 2 age groups: 16 to 21 and 22 to 30. Candidates must submit a 1,000-word essay on how they hope to make a difference in the world through their passion for the oceans, their career goals, where they currently stand along that career path, and how this award will help them achieve those goals. They must also include 3 letters of recommendation and a brief statement on the personality characteristics they value most in themselves and why. If they are currently enrolled in school, they must identify their program, but school enrollment is not required. Finalists in each age group compete for the award.

Financial data The award is $1,000.

Duration The award is presented annually.

Number awarded 1 each year.

Deadline March of each year.

[173]
DOMINIQUE LISA PANDOLFO SCHOLARSHIP

Community Foundation of New Jersey
Attn: Donor Services
35 Knox Hill Road
P.O. Box 338
Morristown, NJ 07963-0338
(973) 267-5533, ext. 221   Toll Free: (800) 659-5533
Fax: (973) 267-2903   E-mail: mrivera@cfnj.org
Web: www.cfnj.org/funds/scholarship/index.php

Summary To provide financial assistance to female residents of New Jersey who demonstrate outstanding scholarship, character, personality, and leadership qualities.

Eligibility This program is open to women graduating from high schools in New Jersey who have already been accepted at a postsecondary educational institution in any state. Applicants may not necessarily be the top student in their class, but they must have shown outstanding potential, merit, and/or improvement. Selection is based primarily on financial need, but academic performance, extracurricular activities, and work experience are also considered.

Financial data The stipend is $1,250 per year. Funds are made payable jointly to the recipient and her educational institution.

Duration 4 years, provided the recipient maintains a GPA of 2.8 or higher.

Additional information This program was established after September 11, 2001 to honor a student who was killed in the attack on the World Trade Center.

Number awarded 1 each year.

Deadline March of each year.

[174]
DONNA REIFSCHNEIDER SCHOLARSHIP

Delta Zeta Sorority
Attn: Foundation Coordinator
202 East Church Street
Oxford, OH 45056
(513) 523-7597   Fax: (513) 523-1921
E-mail: DZFoundation@dzshq.com
Web: www.deltazeta.org

Summary To provide financial assistance for continued undergraduate or graduate study in music or music education to members of Delta Zeta Sorority.

Eligibility This program is open to upper-division and graduate members of the sorority who have a GPA of 3.0 or higher. Applicants must be working on a degree in music or music education. Along with their application, they must submit an official transcript, a statement of their career goals, information on their service to the sorority, documentation of campus activities and/or community involvement, a list of academic honors, and an explanation of their financial need. Preference is given to members of the Iota Upsilon chapter at California State University at Fullerton or Iota Iota chapter at Middle Tennessee State University.

Financial data The stipend ranges from $500 to $2,500 for undergraduates or from $1,000 to $15,000 for graduate students, depending on the availability of funds.

Duration 1 year; nonrenewable.

Number awarded 1 each year.

Deadline February of each year.

[175]
DOROTHEA DEITZ MEMORIAL SCHOLARSHIPS

New York State Association for Health, Physical
   Education, Recreation and Dance
77 North Ann Street
Little Falls, NY 13365
(315) 823-1015   Fax: (315) 823-1012
E-mail: ccorsi@nysahperd.org
Web: www.nysahperd.org/deitz_scholarship.htm

Summary To provide financial assistance to women in New York who plan to major in physical education in college.

Eligibility This program is open to women graduating from high schools in New York who plan to attend a 4-year college or university, preferably in New York. Applicants must be planning to major in physical education. Along with their application, they must submit an essay about themselves, including their interests, significant occurrences in their lives, and their reasons for attending college. Selection is based on academic achievement, character, physical education competence, participation in athletics, qualities of leadership, and financial need.

Financial data Stipends are $7,500, $6,500, or $5,000.

Duration 1 year (the freshman year in college). Loans are available to students after their freshman year.

Number awarded 3 each year.

Deadline February of each year.

[176]
DOROTHY ANDREWS KABIS MEMORIAL INTERNSHIPS

National Federation of Republican Women
Attn: Scholarships and Internships
124 North Alfred Street
Alexandria, VA 22314-3011
(703) 548-9688   Fax: (703) 548-9836
E-mail: mail@nfrw.org
Web: www.nfrw.org/programs/scholarships.htm

Summary To provide summer work experience to undergraduate women interested in working at the headquarters of the National Federation of Republican Women.

Eligibility This program is open to women who are at least juniors in college but have not graduated. Applicants may be majoring in any field, but they should have a general knowledge of government and a keen interest in politics, including campaign experience and clerical office skills. Along with their application, they must submit 3 letters of recommendation, an official transcript, a 1-page essay on their interest in the internship, and a 1-page description of a particular political, extracurricular, or community activity in which they have been involved, including an account of their personal contribution to the activity. Applications must be submitted to the federation president in the applicant's state. Each president chooses 1 application from her state to submit for scholarship consideration. U.S. citizenship is required.

Financial data Interns receive housing in the Washington, D.C. metropolitan area, round-trip airfare, and a small stipend.

Duration 6 weeks during the summer.

Number awarded 3 each year.

Deadline February of each year.

[177]
DOROTHY C. WISNER SCHOLARSHIP

P.E.O. Foundation-California State Chapter
c/o Carol Born, Scholarship Committee Chair
718 Via La Paloma
Riverside, CA 92507-6403
(951) 686-2728
Web: www.peocalifornia.org/dcw.html

Summary To provide financial assistance to women from California who are interested in working on an undergraduate degree in the medical field at a school in any state.

Eligibility This program is open to female residents of California who have completed at least their first year of undergraduate work in the broad field of medicine. Graduate students are not eligible. Applicants may be studying in any state. They must submit a personal narrative that describes their background, interests, scholastic achievements, extracurricular activities, service, talents, and goals. Selection is based on character, integrity, academic excellence, and financial need.

Financial data The stipend ranges from $500 to $1,000 per year.

Duration 1 year; recipients may reapply.

Additional information This fund was established in 1990.

Number awarded 1 each year.

Deadline January of each year.

[178]
DOROTHY CAMPBELL MEMORIAL SCHOLARSHIP

Oregon Student Assistance Commission
Attn: Grants and Scholarships Division
1500 Valley River Drive, Suite 100
Eugene, OR 97401-2146
(541) 687-7395   Toll Free: (800) 452-8807, ext. 7395
Fax: (541) 687-7414   TDD: (800) 735-2900
E-mail: awardinfo@osac.state.or.us
Web: www.osac.state.or.us/osac_programs.html

Summary To provide financial assistance to women in Oregon who are interested in golf and planning to attend college in the state.

Eligibility This program is open to residents of Oregon who are U.S. citizens or permanent residents. Applicants must be female high school seniors or graduates with a cumulative GPA of 2.75 or higher and a strong continuing interest in golf. They must be enrolled or planning to enroll full-time at an Oregon 4-year college. Along with their application, they must submit a 1-page essay on the contribution that golf has made to their development. Financial need is considered in the selection process.

Financial data The stipend is at least $1,500.

Duration 1 year; may be renewed up to 3 additional years.

Additional information This program is administered by the Oregon Student Assistance Commission (OSAC) with funds provided by the Oregon Community Foundation, 1221 S.W. Yamhill, Suite 100, Portland, OR 97205, (503) 227-6846, Fax: (503) 274-7771.

Number awarded Varies each year; recently, 2 of these scholarships were awarded.

Deadline February of each year.

[179]
DOROTHY COOKE WHINERY MUSIC BUSINESS/ TECHNOLOGY SCHOLARSHIP

Sigma Alpha Iota Philanthropies, Inc.
One Tunnel Road
Asheville, NC 28805
(828) 251-0606   Fax: (828) 251-0644
E-mail: nh@sai-national.org
Web: www.sigmaalphaiota.org

Summary To provide financial assistance to members of Sigma Alpha Iota (an organization of women musicians) working on a degree in music, business, or technology.

Eligibility This program is open to members of the organization entering their junior or senior year of college. Applicants must be working on a degree in the field of music business or music technology, including music marketing, music business administration, entertainment industry, commercial music, recording and production, music management, or other related fields. They must have a GPA of 3.0 or higher. Along with their application, they must submit a statement of purpose that includes their career goals.

Financial data The stipend is $2,000.

Duration 1 year.

Additional information This program was established in 2003.

Number awarded 1 each year.

Deadline March of each year.

[180]
DOROTHY E. SCHOELZEL MEMORIAL SCHOLARSHIP

General Federation of Women's Clubs of Connecticut
c/o JoAnn Calnen, President
74 Spruceland Road
Enfield, CT 06082-2359
E-mail: gfwcct@yahoo.com
Web: www.gfwcct.org

Summary To provide financial assistance to women in Connecticut who are working on an undergraduate or graduate degree in education.

Eligibility This program is open to female residents of Connecticut who have completed at least 3 years of college. Applicants must have a GPA of 3.0 or higher and be working on a bachelor's or master's degree in education. Selection is based on academic ability, future promise, and financial need.

Financial data The stipend is $2,000.

Duration 1 year.

Number awarded 1 each year.

Deadline February of each year.

[181]
DOROTHY L. WELLER PEO SCHOLARSHIP

P.E.O. Foundation-California State Chapter
c/o Carol Born, Scholarship Committee Chair
718 Via La Paloma
Riverside, CA 92507-6403
(951) 686-2728
Web: www.peocalifornia.org/dlw.html

Summary To provide financial assistance for law school or paralegal studies to women in California.

Eligibility This program is open to female residents of California who have been admitted to an accredited law school or a licensed paralegal school. Applicants must have completed 4 years of high school and be able to demonstrate excellence in academic ability, character, integrity, and school activities. Financial need is also considered in the selection process.

Financial data Recently, the stipend was $2,500.

Duration 1 year.

Number awarded Varies each year; recently, 4 of these scholarships were awarded.

Deadline January of each year.

[182]
DOROTHY LEMKE HOWARTH SCHOLARSHIPS

Society of Women Engineers
Attn: Scholarship Selection Committee
120 South LaSalle Street, Suite 1515
Chicago, IL 60603-3572
(312) 596-5223   Toll Free: (877) SWE-INFO
Fax: (312) 644-8557
E-mail: scholarshipapplication@swe.org
Web: societyofwomenengineers.swe.org

Summary To provide financial assistance to lower-division women majoring in computer science or engineering.

Eligibility This program is open to women who are entering their sophomore year at a 4-year ABET-accredited college or university. Applicants must be U.S. citizens who are majoring in computer science or engineering and have a GPA of 3.0 or higher. Selection is based on merit.

Financial data The stipend is $2,500.

Duration 1 year.

Additional information This program was established in 1991.

Number awarded 6 each year.

Deadline February of each year.

[183]
DOROTHY M. AND EARL S. HOFFMAN SCHOLARSHIPS

Society of Women Engineers
Attn: Scholarship Selection Committee
120 South LaSalle Street, Suite 1515
Chicago, IL 60603-3572
(312) 596-5223   Toll Free: (877) SWE-INFO
Fax: (312) 644-8557
E-mail: scholarshipapplication@swe.org
Web: societyofwomenengineers.swe.org

Summary To provide financial assistance to women who will be entering college as freshmen and are interested in studying engineering or computer science.

Eligibility This program is open to women who are entering college as freshmen with a GPA of 3.5 or higher. Applicants must be planning to enroll full time at an ABET-accredited 4-year college or university and major in computer science or engineering. Selection is based on merit. Preference is given to students at Bucknell University and Rensselaer Polytechnic Institute.

Financial data The stipend is $3,000 per year.

Duration 1 year; may be renewed for up to 3 additional years.

Additional information This program was established in 1999.

Number awarded Varies each year; recently, 7 of these scholarships were awarded.

Deadline May of each year.

[184]
DOROTHY P. MORRIS SCHOLARSHIP

Society of Women Engineers
Attn: Scholarship Selection Committee
120 South LaSalle Street, Suite 1515
Chicago, IL 60603-3572
(312) 596-5223   Toll Free: (877) SWE-INFO
Fax: (312) 644-8557
E-mail: scholarshipapplication@swe.org
Web: societyofwomenengineers.swe.org

Summary To provide financial assistance to undergraduate women majoring in computer science or engineering.

Eligibility This program is open to women who are entering their sophomore, junior, or senior year at a 4-year ABET-accredited college or university. Applicants must be U.S. citizens majoring in computer science or engineering and have a GPA of 3.0 or higher. Selection is based on merit.

Financial data The stipend is $1,500.

Duration 1 year.

Number awarded 1 each year.

Deadline February of each year.

[185]
DR. BEA OKWU GIRL SCOUT GOLD AWARD SCHOLARSHIP

Girl Scouts of Connecticut
Attn: Program Department
340 Washington Street
Hartford, CT 06106
(860) 522-0163   Toll Free: (800) 922-2770
Fax: (860) 548-0325   E-mail: program@gsoft.org
Web: www.gsoft.org

Summary To provide financial assistance to Girl Scouts in Connecticut who plan to attend college in any state.

Eligibility This program is open to high school seniors who are registered Girl Scouts in Connecticut and planning to attend college in any state. Applicants must have earned the Gold Award. Along with their application, they must submit essays on 1) what they have gained from Girl Scouting, and 2) their Gold Award project. Selection is based on the essays, community service, and commitment to Girl Scouting.

Financial data The stipend is $1,000.

Duration 1 year.

Number awarded 1 each year.

Deadline March of each year.

[186]
DR. BLANCA MOORE-VELEZ WOMAN OF SUBSTANCE SCHOLARSHIP

National Association of Negro Business and Professional
Women's Clubs
Attn: Scholarship Committee
1806 New Hampshire Avenue, N.W.
Washington, DC 20009-3206
(202) 483-4206　　　　　　　　Fax: (202) 462-7253
E-mail: education@nanbpwc.org
Web: www.nanbpwc.org/ScholarshipApplications.asp

Summary To provide financial assistance to mature African American women from North Carolina who are interested in working on an undergraduate degree at a college in any state.

Eligibility This program is open to African American women over 35 years of age who are residents of North Carolina. Applicants must be working on an undergraduate degree at an accredited college or university in any state. They must have a GPA of 3.0 or higher. Along with their application, they must submit a 500-word essay on "Challenges to the Mature Student and How I Overcame Them." Financial need is not considered in the selection process.

Financial data A stipend is awarded (amount not specified).

Duration 1 year.

Number awarded 1 each year.

Deadline February of each year.

[187]
DR. CAROLANN S. NAJARIAN SCHOLARSHIPS

Armenian International Women's Association
65 Main Street, Room 3A
Watertown, MA 02472
(617) 926-0171　　　　　　　E-mail: aiwainc@aol.com
Web: www.aiwa-net.org/scholarshipinfo.html

Summary To provide financial assistance to Armenian women who are upper-division and graduate students.

Eligibility This program is open to full-time women students of Armenian descent attending an accredited college or university. Applicants must be full-time juniors, seniors, or graduate students with a GPA of 3.2 or higher. They must submit an essay, up to 500 words, describing their planned academic program, their career goals, and the reasons why they believe they should be awarded this scholarship. Selection is based on financial need and merit.

Financial data The stipend is $1,000.

Duration 1 year.

Number awarded 5 each year.

Deadline April of each year.

[188]
DR. JULIANNE MALVEAUX SCHOLARSHIP

National Association of Negro Business and Professional
Women's Clubs
Attn: Scholarship Committee
1806 New Hampshire Avenue, N.W.
Washington, DC 20009-3206
(202) 483-4206　　　　　　　Fax: (202) 462-7253
E-mail: education@nanbpwc.org
Web: www.nanbpwc.org/ScholarshipApplications.asp

Summary To provide financial assistance to African American women studying journalism, economics, or a related field in college.

Eligibility This program is open to African American women enrolled at an accredited college or university as a sophomore or junior. Applicants must have a GPA of 3.0 or higher and be majoring in journalism, economics, or a related field. Along with their application, they must submit an essay, up to 1,000 words in length, on their career plans and their relevance to the theme of the program: "Black Women's Hands Can Rock the World." U.S. citizenship is required.

Financial data The stipend is $1,000.

Duration 1 year.

Number awarded 1 or more each year.

Deadline February of each year.

[189]
DUPONT SCHOLARSHIPS

Society of Women Engineers
Attn: Scholarship Selection Committee
120 South LaSalle Street, Suite 1515
Chicago, IL 60603-3572
(312) 596-5223　　　　　　　Toll Free: (877) SWE-INFO
Fax: (312) 644-8557
E-mail: scholarshipapplication@swe.org
Web: societyofwomenengineers.swe.org

Summary To provide financial assistance to women interested in studying chemical or mechanical engineering at a college or university in the East or Midwest.

Eligibility This program is open to women entering their sophomore, junior, or senior year as a full-time student at an ABET-accredited 4-year college or university in an eastern or midwestern state. Applicants must have a GPA of 3.0 or higher and be planning to major in chemical or mechanical engineering. Selection is based on merit.

Financial data The stipend is $1,000.

Duration 1 year.

Additional information This program, established in 2000, is sponsored by E.I. duPont de Nemours and Company.

Number awarded 2 each year.

Deadline February of each year.

[190]
DWIGHT F. DAVIS MEMORIAL SCHOLARSHIPS

United States Tennis Association
Attn: USTA Serves
70 West Red Oak Lane
White Plains, NY 10604
(914) 696-7223　　　　　　　E-mail: foundation@usta.com
Web: www.usta.com

Summary To provide financial assistance for college to high school seniors who have participated in an organized community tennis program (females and males are judged separately).

Eligibility This program is open to high school seniors who have excelled academically, demonstrated achievements in leadership, and participated extensively in an organized community tennis program. Applicants must be planning to enroll as a full-time undergraduate student at a 4-year college or university. They must have a GPA of 3.0 or higher and be able to demonstrate financial need. Along with their application, they must submit an essay of 1 to 2 pages about how their participation in a tennis and education program has influenced their life, including examples of special mentors, volunteer service, and future goals. Women and men are judged separately in the selection process.

Financial data The stipend is $1,875 per year. Funds are paid directly to the recipient's college or university.

Duration 4 years.

Number awarded 2 each year: 1 to a woman and 1 to a man.

Deadline February of each year.

[191]
E. WAYNE COOLEY SCHOLARSHIP AWARD

Iowa Girls High School Athletic Union
Attn: Scholarships
2900 Grand Avenue
P.O. Box 10348
Des Moines, IA 50306-0348
(515) 288-9741   Fax: (515) 284-1969
E-mail: jasoneslinger@ighsau.org
Web: www.ighsau.org/aspx/cooley_award.aspx

Summary To provide financial assistance to female high school seniors in Iowa who have participated in athletics and plan to attend college in the state.

Eligibility This program is open to women graduating from high schools in Iowa who have a GPA of 3.75 or higher and an ACT score of 23 or higher. Applicants must have earned a varsity letter in at least 2 different sports and have participated in at least 2 sports each year of high school. They must be planning to attend a college or university in Iowa. Each high school in the state may nominate 1 student. Selection is based on academic achievements, athletic accomplishments, non-sports extracurricular activities, and community involvement.

Financial data The winner's stipend is $3,750 per year. Finalists receive a $1,000 scholarship.

Duration 4 years for the winner, provided she maintains at least a 2.5 GPA while enrolled in college. The scholarships for finalists are for 1 year.

Additional information This program was established in 1993.

Number awarded 6 each year: 1 winner and 5 finalists.

Deadline December of each year.

[192]
ECL CAREER IN TEACHING SCHOLARSHIPS

American Baptist Churches of the Rocky Mountains
Attn: American Baptist Women's Ministries
9085 East Mineral Circle, Suite 170
Centennial, CO 80112
(303) 988-3900   E-mail: web@abcrm.org
Web: www.abcrm.org

Summary To provide financial assistance to women who are members of churches affiliated with the American Baptist Churches (ABC) USA in Colorado, New Mexico, and Utah and interested in attending college in Colorado to prepare for a career as a teacher.

Eligibility This program is open to women under 26 years of age who are active members of churches cooperating with ABC in Colorado, New Mexico, or Utah. Applicants must be enrolled or planning to enroll full time at a 4-year college or university in Colorado. They must be preparing for a career in teaching. Along with their application, they must submit a personal letter describing their Christian experience; their participation in the life of their church, school, and community; and their goals for the future. Selection is based on academic performance, Christian participation in church and school, and financial need.

Financial data The stipend is $1,000 per year.

Duration 1 year; recipients may reapply.

Number awarded 1 or more each year.

Deadline March of each year.

[193]
EDITH GREEN GRANT

Delta Kappa Gamma Society International-Alpha Rho
   State Organization
c/o Alyce Sandusky, State Scholarship Chair
7619 Highway 66
Klamath Falls, OR 97601-9538
(541) 884-0524   E-mail: terryandalyce@charter.net
Web: www.deltakappagamma.org

Summary To provide financial assistance to women from Oregon who are enrolled as upper-division students at a college in any state and preparing for a career in secondary education.

Eligibility This program is open to female residents of Oregon who are at least juniors at a college in any state and interested in preparing for a career in secondary education. Applicants may not be members of Delta Kappa Gamma (an honorary society of women educators), but they must be sponsored by a local chapter of the society. Along with their application, they must submit a summary of their education from high school through the present, high school and college activities and achievements, community service, employment history, career goals, and financial need.

Financial data A stipend is awarded (amount not specified).

Duration 1 year.

Additional information Recipients may not accept a scholarship from the Alpha Rho state organization and from Delta Kappa Gamma International in the same year.

Number awarded 1 or more each year.

Deadline February of each year.

[194]
EDITH HEAD SCHOLARSHIP

Delta Zeta Sorority
Attn: Foundation Coordinator
202 East Church Street
Oxford, OH 45056
(513) 523-7597   Fax: (513) 523-1921
E-mail: DZFoundation@dzshq.com
Web: www.deltazeta.org

Summary To provide financial assistance for continued undergraduate or graduate study in fashion design to members of Delta Zeta Sorority.

Eligibility This program is open to upper-division and graduate members of the sorority who have a GPA of 3.0 or higher. Applicants must be working on a degree in a field related to the design, production, or merchandising of textile and apparel products and/or costume design. Along with their application, they must submit an official transcript, a statement of their career goals, information on their service to the sorority, documentation of campus activities and/or community involvement, a list of academic honors, and an explanation of their financial need.

Financial data The stipend ranges from $500 to $2,500 for undergraduates or from $1,000 to $15,000 for graduate students, depending on the availability of funds.

Duration 1 year; nonrenewable.

Number awarded 1 each year.

Deadline February of each year.

[195]
EDUCATIONAL FOUNDATION FOR WOMEN IN ACCOUNTING IMA UNDERGRADUATE SCHOLARSHIP

Educational Foundation for Women in Accounting
Attn: Foundation Administrator
136 South Keowee Street
Dayton, OH 45402
(937) 424-3391   Fax: (937) 222-5749
E-mail: info@efwa.org
Web: www.efwa.org/scholarships_ima.php

Summary To provide financial support to women who are working on an undergraduate accounting degree.

Eligibility This program is open to women who are enrolled at any stage in an accounting degree program at an accredited college or university. Applicants may be completing a fifth-year requirement through general studies. Selection is based on aptitude for accounting and business, commitment to the goal of working on a degree in accounting (including evidence of continued commitment after receiving this award), clear evidence that the candidate has established goals and a plan for achieving those goals (both personal and professional), financial need, and a demonstration of how the scholarship will impact her life. U.S. citizenship is required.

Financial data The stipend is $1,000.

Duration 1 year.

Additional information This program is funded by the Institute of Management Accountants (IMA).

Number awarded 1 each year.

Deadline April of each year.

[196]
EDWIN G. AND LAURETTA M. MICHAEL SCHOLARSHIP

Christian Church (Disciples of Christ)
Attn: Disciples Home Missions
130 East Washington Street
P.O. Box 1986
Indianapolis, IN 46206-1986
(317) 713-2652   Toll Free: (888) DHM-2631
Fax: (317) 635-4426   E-mail: mail@dhm.disciples.org
Web: www.discipleshomemissions.org

Summary To provide financial support to ministers' wives whose basic education was interrupted to enable their husbands to complete their theological education.

Eligibility This program is open to ministers' wives who are working on an undergraduate degree and whose husbands have completed their basic theological education, are employed full time in ministry, and hold standing in the ministry of the Christian Church (Disciples of Christ) in the United States or Canada. Primary consideration is given to ministers' wives who will be in institutions of higher education accredited by 1 of the major regionally accrediting bodies for secondary schools and colleges. Evidence of financial need is required.

Financial data The stipend is $1,000.

Duration 1 year.

Number awarded A limited number are awarded each year.

Deadline March of each year.

[197]
EFWA SEATTLE CHAPTER ASWA SCHOLARSHIP

Educational Foundation for Women in Accounting
Attn: Foundation Administrator
136 South Keowee Street
Dayton, OH 45402
(937) 424-3391   Fax: (937) 222-5749
E-mail: info@efwa.org
Web: www.efwa.org/scholarships_seattle.php

Summary To provide financial support to women who are enrolled in an undergraduate or graduate accounting degree program at a school in Washington.

Eligibility This program is open to women from any state who are working on a bachelor's or master's degree in accounting at an accredited school in Washington. Selection is based on aptitude for accounting and business, commitment to the goal of working on a degree in accounting (including evidence of continued commitment after receiving this award), clear evidence that the candidate has established goals and a plan for achieving those goals (both personal and professional), and financial need. U.S. citizenship is required.

Financial data The stipend is $2,000 per year.

Duration 1 year; may be renewed 1 additional year if the recipient completes at least 12 hours each semester.

Additional information This program was established in 2007 with funds provided by the Seattle Chapter of the American Society of Women Accountants (ASWA).

Number awarded 1 each year.

Deadline April of each year.

[198]
ELEANORE KLINE MEMORIAL SCHOLARSHIP

Michigan Association of Certified Public Accountants
Attn: Michigan Accountancy Foundation
5480 Corporate Drive, Suite 200
Troy, MI 48098-2642
(248) 267-3723   Toll Free: (888) 877-4CPE (within MI)
Fax: (248) 267-3737   E-mail: maf@michcpa.org
Web: www.michcpa.org/Content/22461.aspx

Summary To provide financial assistance to single mothers at Michigan colleges and universities who are working on a degree in accounting.

Eligibility This program is open to single mothers enrolled full time at accredited Michigan colleges and universities with a declared concentration in accounting. Applicants must be seniors planning to enter the fifth or graduate year of their school's program. They must intend to or have successfully passed the Michigan C.P.A. examination and intend to practice public accounting in the state. Along with their application, they must submit a 500-word statement about their educational and career aspirations, including internships and/or other employment, volunteer and community activities, professional affiliations, and full-time employment. Documentation of financial need may also be included. U.S. citizenship or eligibility for permanent employment in the United States is required.

Financial data   The stipend is $4,000 per year; funds are disbursed directly to the recipient's college or university.

Duration   1 year.

Number awarded   1 each year.

Deadline   January of each year.

[199]
ELECTRONICS FOR IMAGING SCHOLARSHIPS

Society of Women Engineers
Attn: Scholarship Selection Committee
120 South LaSalle Street, Suite 1515
Chicago, IL 60603-3572
(312) 596-5223   Toll Free: (877) SWE-INFO
Fax: (312) 644-8557
E-mail: scholarshipapplication@swe.org
Web: societyofwomenengineers.swe.org

Summary   To provide financial assistance to women working on an undergraduate or graduate degree in engineering or computer science.

Eligibility   This program is open to women who will be sophomores, juniors, seniors, or graduate students at ABET-accredited colleges and universities. Applicants must be working on a degree in computer science or engineering and have a GPA of 3.0 or higher. Selection is based on merit. Preference is given to students at designated colleges and universities; for a list, contact the sponsor.

Financial data   The stipend is $4,000.

Duration   1 year.

Additional information   This program, established in 2001, is sponsored by Electronics for Imaging, Inc.

Number awarded   4 each year.

Deadline   February of each year.

[200]
ELIZABETH AHLEMEYER QUICK/GAMMA PHI BETA SCHOLARSHIP

National Panhellenic Conference
Attn: NPC Foundation
3901 West 86th Street, Suite 398
Indianapolis, IN 46268
(317) 876-7802   Fax: (317) 876-7904
E-mail: npcfoundation@npcwomen.org
Web: www.npcwomen.org/foundation/scholarships.aspx

Summary   To provide financial assistance to undergraduate women who are members of Greek-letter societies.

Eligibility   This program is open to women enrolled full time as juniors or seniors at colleges and universities in the United States. Applicants must have a GPA of 3.0 or higher and be able to demonstrate financial need. They must be nominated by their college Panhellenic and have demonstrated outstanding service to that organization. Selection is based on campus, chapter, and community service; financial need; academic standing; and nomination by the applicant's college Panhellenic.

Financial data   The stipend is $2,000.

Duration   1 year.

Number awarded   1 each year.

Deadline   January of each year.

[201]
ELIZABETH BANTA MUELLER SCHOLARSHIPS

Kappa Delta Sorority
Attn: Foundation Manager
3205 Players Lane
Memphis, TN 38125
(901) 748-1897   Toll Free: (800) 536-1897
Fax: (901) 748-0949 E-mail: kappadelta@kappadelta.org
Web: www.kappadelta.org/scholarships

Summary   To provide financial assistance to members of Kappa Delta Sorority who are majoring in speech and communications.

Eligibility   This program is open to undergraduate members of Kappa Delta Sorority. Applicants must submit a personal statement giving their reasons for applying for this scholarship, an official undergraduate transcript, and 2 letters of recommendation. Special consideration is given to members majoring in speech and communications. Selection is based on academic excellence; service to the chapter, alumnae association, or national Kappa Delta; service to the campus and community; personal objectives and goals; potential; recommendations; and financial need.

Financial data   The stipend is $2,000 per year. Funds may be used only for tuition, fees, and books, not for room and board.

Duration   1 year; may be renewed.

Number awarded   3 each year: 2 to speech and communication majors and 1 to a member with any major.

Deadline   January of each year.

[202]
ELIZABETH LOWELL PUTNAM PRIZE

Mathematical Association of America
1529 18th Street, N.W.
Washington, DC 20036-1358
(202) 387-5200   Toll Free: (800) 741-9415
Fax: (202) 265-2384   E-mail: maahq@maa.org
Web: www.maa.org/awards/putnam.html

Summary   To recognize and reward outstanding women participants in a mathematics competition.

Eligibility   This program is open to women at colleges and universities in Canada and the United States. Entrants participate in an examination containing mathematics problems designed to test originality as well as technical competence. The woman with the highest score receives this prize.

Financial data   The prize is $1,000.

Duration   The competition is held annually.

Additional information   This program was established in 1992.

Number awarded   1 each year.

Deadline   Deadline not specified.

[203]
ELIZABETH MCLEAN MEMORIAL SCHOLARSHIP

Society of Women Engineers
Attn: Scholarship Selection Committee
120 South LaSalle Street, Suite 1515
Chicago, IL 60603-3572
(312) 596-5223   Toll Free: (877) SWE-INFO
Fax: (312) 644-8557
E-mail: scholarshipapplication@swe.org
Web: societyofwomenengineers.swe.org

Summary To provide financial assistance to undergraduate women majoring in civil engineering.

Eligibility This program is open to women who are entering their sophomore, junior, or senior year at an ABET-accredited 4-year college or university. Applicants must be majoring in civil engineering and have a GPA of 3.0 or higher. Selection is based on merit.

Financial data The stipend is $1,500.

Duration 1 year.

Number awarded 1 each year.

Deadline February of each year.

[204]
ELKS NATIONAL FOUNDATION "MOST VALUABLE STUDENT" SCHOLARSHIP AWARD

Elks National Foundation
Attn: Scholarship Department
2750 North Lakeview Avenue
Chicago, IL 60614-2256
(773) 755-4732   Fax: (773) 755-4729
E-mail: scholarship@elks.org
Web: www.elks.org/enf/scholars/mvs.cfm

Summary To provide financial assistance to outstanding high school seniors who can demonstrate financial need and are interested in attending college (females and males are judged separately).

Eligibility This program is open to graduating high school students (or the equivalent) who are U.S. citizens residing within the jurisdiction of the B.P.O. Elks of the U.S.A. Applicants must be planning to work on a 4-year degree on a full-time basis at a college or university within the United States. Along with their application, they must submit 1) a 500-word essay on their choice of 3 assigned topics, and 2) exhibits, up to 20 pages, on their achievements in scholarship, leadership, athletics, performing arts, community service, or other activities. Selection is based on that essay and exhibits, transcripts, SAT and/or ACT scores, a report from their school counselor, letters of recommendation, and financial need. Female and male students compete separately.

Financial data First place is $15,000 per year; second place is $10,000 per year; third place is $5,000 per year; fourth place is $4,000 per year; fifth place is $3,000 per year; sixth place is $2,500 per year, seventh place is $2,000 per year, and runners-up receive $1,000 per year. Nearly $2.3 million is distributed through this program each year.

Duration 4 years.

Additional information In addition to this program, established in 1931, many Elks State Associations and/or Lodges also offer scholarships. Applications must be submitted to an Elks Lodge in your community.

Number awarded 500 each year: 2 first awards (1 male and 1 female), 2 second awards (1 male and 1 female), 2 third awards (1 male and 1 female), 2 fourth awards (1 male and 1 female), 2 fifth awards (1 male and 1 female), 4 sixth awards (2 males and 2 females), 4 seventh awards (2 males and 2 females), and 482 runners-up (241 males and 241 females).

Deadline January of each year.

[205]
ELLEN BOWERS HOFSTEAD SCHOLARSHIPS

Kappa Alpha Theta Foundation
Attn: Scholarships
8740 Founders Road
Indianapolis, IN 46268-1337
(317) 876-1870   Toll Free: (800) KAO-1870
Fax: (317) 876-1925
E-mail: FDNmail@kappaalphatheta.org
Web: www.kappaalphathetafoundation.org

Summary To provide financial assistance to undergraduate members of Kappa Alpha Theta who demonstrate "Panhellenic spirit."

Eligibility This program is open to members of Kappa Alpha Theta who are full-time sophomores or juniors at a college or university in Canada or the United States. Applicants must be able to demonstrate the true meaning of "Panhellenic spirit" in some capacity. Along with their application, they must submit an official transcript, personal essays on assigned topics related to their involvement in Kappa Alpha Theta, and 2 letters of reference. Financial need is not considered in the selection process.

Financial data The stipend varies, but recently ranged from $1,475 to $5,000.

Duration 1 year.

Number awarded Varies each year; recently, 3 of these scholarships were awarded.

Deadline January of each year.

[206]
ELOISE CAMPBELL MEMORIAL SCHOLARSHIPS

United Daughters of the Confederacy
Attn: Education Director
328 North Boulevard
Richmond, VA 23220-4057
(804) 355-1636   Fax: (804) 353-1396
E-mail: hqudc@rcn.com
Web: www.hqudc.org/scholarships/scholarships.html

Summary To provide financial assistance for college to women, particularly in selected areas of Arkansas or Texas, who are lineal descendants of Confederate veterans.

Eligibility Eligible to apply for these scholarships are lineal descendants of worthy Confederates or collateral descendants who are members of the Children of the Confederacy or the United Daughters of the Confederacy. Applicants must be female and have at least a 3.0 GPA in high school. Preference is given to candidates from Bowie County, Texas and Miller County, Arkansas. Applications must be accompanied by a family financial report and certified proof of the Confederate military record of 1 ancestor, with the company and regiment in which he served.

Financial data The amount of the scholarship depends on the availability of funds.

Duration 1 year; may be renewed for up to 3 additional years.

Additional information Members of the same family may not hold scholarships simultaneously, and only 1 application per family will be accepted within any 1 year. Requests for applications must be accompanied by a self-addressed stamped envelope.

Number awarded 1 each year.

Deadline April of each year.

[207]
ELSIE G. RIDDICK SCHOLARSHIP

North Carolina Federation of Business and Professional
  Women's Club, Inc.
Attn: BPW/NC Foundation
P.O. Box 276
Carrboro, NC 27510
Web: www.bpw-nc.org/Default.aspx?pageId=837230

Summary To provide financial assistance to women attending North Carolina colleges, community colleges, or graduate schools.

Eligibility This program is open to women who are currently enrolled in a community college, 4-year college, or graduate school in North Carolina. Applicants must be endorsed by a local BPW unit. Along with their application, they must submit a 1-page statement that summarizes their career goals, previous honors, or community activities and justifies their need for this scholarship. U.S. citizenship is required.

Financial data The stipend is $1,000. Funds are paid directly to the recipient's school.

Duration 1 year; recipients may reapply.

Additional information This program was established in 1925 as a loan fund. Since 1972 it has been administered as a scholarship program.

Number awarded 1 each year.

Deadline April of each year.

[208]
EMILY SCHOENBAUM RESEARCH AND COMMUNITY DEVELOPMENT GRANTS

Tulane University
Newcomb College Center for Research on Women
Attn: Executive Director
200 Caroline Richardson Hall
New Orleans, LA 70118
(504) 865-5238   Fax: (504) 862-8948
E-mail: nccrow@tulane.edu
Web: tulane.edu/nccrow/programs/schoenbaum-grant.cfm

Summary To provide funding to scholars and students in Louisiana interested in conducting research or other projects related to women and girls.

Eligibility This program is open to students, faculty, and staff of primary and secondary schools, colleges, and universities in Louisiana, as well as community scholars and activists. Applicants must be interested in conducting a project with potential to bring about change in women's lives or effect public policy so as to improve the well-being of women and girls, particularly those in the New Orleans area.

Financial data The grant is $1,500.

Duration 1 year.

Additional information This program was established in 1999.

Number awarded 1 each year.

Deadline March of each year.

[209]
EMMA HARPER TURNER FUND

Pi Beta Phi
Attn: Pi Beta Phi Foundation
1154 Town and Country Commons Drive
Town and Country, MO 63017
(636) 256-1357   Fax: (636) 256-8124
E-mail: fndn@pibetaphi.org
Web: www.pibetaphifoundation.org/emma-harper-turner

Summary To provide assistance to members or alumnae of Pi Beta Phi Sorority who are in extreme financial need.

Eligibility Any member of Pi Beta Phi needing financial assistance is eligible to be considered for this funding. Each potential recipient must be sponsored by 3 Pi Beta Phi alumnae who are aware of the candidate's need and are personally acquainted with her. Applicants must submit a confidential financial information form to validate their need. The program includes 3 types of grants: collegian (for college students who have experienced a life change that jeopardizes their ability to stay in school), alumna (for college graduates who are experiencing financial difficulties), and immediate needs (for alumnae who are victims of a natural disaster).

Financial data Small monthly gifts are awarded.

Duration Awards are provided for 1 year; the recipient's application is then reviewed to determine if the "gifts of love" should continue.

Additional information This fund was established in 1946.

Number awarded Varies each year.

Deadline Applications may be submitted at any time.

[210]
EPA GREATER RESEARCH OPPORTUNITIES (GRO) FELLOWSHIPS FOR UNDERGRADUATE ENVIRONMENTAL STUDY

Environmental Protection Agency
Attn: National Center for Environmental Research
Ariel Rios Building
1200 Pennsylvania Avenue, N.W.
Washington, DC 20460
(202) 347-8049   Toll Free: (800) 490-9194
E-mail: boddie.georgette@epa.gov
Web: epa.gov/ncer/rfa

Summary To provide financial assistance and summer internships to undergraduates (particularly women, minorities, and students with disabilities) who are enrolled at colleges and universities that receive limited federal funding and who are interested in majoring in fields related to the environment.

Eligibility This program is open to U.S. citizens or permanent residents who are enrolled full time at a college or university in this country that receives less than $35 million in federal research and development expenditures. Students attending eligible institutions with significant minority enrollment (defined as Minority-Serving Institutions) are particularly encouraged to apply. Applicants must have at least 2 years remaining for completion of a bachelor's degree in an environmentally-related field, such as physics, biology, health, the social sciences, or engineering. They must be available to work as interns at an EPA facility during the summer between their junior and senior years. A goal of the program is to meet the need for scientists from diverse cultural backgrounds, so the sponsor strongly encourages women, minorities, and persons with disabilities to apply. A minimum average of "B" overall is required.

Financial data The fellowship provides up to $19,700 per year, including up to $10,000 for tuition and academic fees, a stipend of $7,200 ($200 per month for 9 months), and an expense allowance of up to $2,500 for items and activities for the direct benefit of the student's education, such as books, supplies, and travel to professional conferences and workshops. The summer internship grant is $9,500, including a stipend of $7,000 for living expenses, an allowance of $1,000 for travel to and from the site, and an allowance of $1,500 for travel while at the site.

Duration The final 2 years of baccalaureate study, including 12 weeks during the summer between those years.

Additional information This program began in 1982. It was formerly known as Culturally Diverse Academic Institutions Undergraduate Student Fellowships program and subsequently as Minority Academic Institutions Undergraduate Student Fellowships.

Number awarded Approximately 40 each year.

Deadline December of each year.

[211]
ERMA METZ BROWN SCHOLARSHIP

Kappa Delta Sorority
Attn: Foundation Manager
3205 Players Lane
Memphis, TN 38125
(901) 748-1897 Toll Free: (800) 536-1897
Fax: (901) 748-0949 E-mail: kappadelta@kappadelta.org
Web: www.kappadelta.org/scholarships

Summary To provide financial assistance to members of Kappa Delta Sorority who are majoring in elementary education.

Eligibility This program is open to undergraduate members of Kappa Delta Sorority. Applicants must submit a personal statement giving their reasons for applying for this scholarship, an official undergraduate transcript, and 2 letters of recommendation. They must be majoring in elementary education. Selection is based on academic excellence; service to the chapter, alumnae association, or national Kappa Delta; service to the campus and community; personal objectives and goals; potential; recommendations; and financial need.

Financial data The stipend is $2,000 per year. Funds may be used only for tuition, fees, and books, not for room and board.

Duration 1 year; may be renewed.

Additional information This program was established in 2005.

Number awarded 2 each year.

Deadline January of each year.

[212]
ESPERANZA SCHOLARSHIP

New York Women in Communications, Inc.
Attn: NYWICI Foundation
355 Lexington Avenue, 15th Floor
New York, NY 10017-6603
(212) 297-2133 Fax: (212) 370-9047
E-mail: nywicipr@nywici.org
Web: www.nywici.org/foundation/scholarships

Summary To provide financial assistance to Hispanic women who are residents of designated eastern states and interested in preparing for a career in communications at a college or graduate school in any state.

Eligibility This program is open to Hispanic women who are seniors graduating from high schools in New York, New Jersey, Connecticut, or Pennsylvania or undergraduate or graduate students who are permanent residents of those states; they must be attending or planning to attend a college or university in any state. Graduate students must be members of New York Women in Communications, Inc. (NYWICI). Also eligible are Hispanic women who reside outside the 4 states but are currently enrolled at a college or university within 1 of the 5 boroughs of New York City. All applicants must be working on a degree in a communications-related field (e.g., advertising, broadcasting, communications, English, film, journalism, marketing, new media, public relations) and have a GPA of 3.2 or higher. Along with their application, they must submit a 2-page resume that includes school and extracurricular activities, significant achievements, academic honors and awards, and community service work; a personal essay of 300 to 500 words on their choice of an assigned topic that changes annually; 2 letters of recommendation; and an official transcript. Selection is based on academic record, need, demonstrated leadership, participation in school and community activities, honors, work experience, goals and aspirations, and unusual personal and/or family circumstances. U.S. citizenship is required.

Financial data The stipend ranges up to $10,000.

Duration 1 year.

Additional information This program is funded by Macy's and Bloomingdale's.

Number awarded 1 each year.

Deadline January of each year.

[213]
ETHEL LEE HOOVER ELLIS SCHOLARSHIP

National Association of Negro Business and Professional Women's Clubs
Attn: Scholarship Committee
1806 New Hampshire Avenue, N.W.
Washington, DC 20009-3206
(202) 483-4206 Fax: (202) 462-7253
E-mail: education@nanbpwc.org
Web: www.nanbpwc.org/ScholarshipApplications.asp

Summary To provide financial assistance to African American women from designated southern states studying business at a college in any state.

Eligibility This program is open to African Americans women who are residents of Alabama, Florida, Georgia, Mississippi, North Carolina, South Carolina, Tennessee, or West Virginia. Applicants must be enrolled at an accredited college or university in any state as a sophomore or junior. They must have a GPA of 3.0 or higher and be majoring in business. Along with their application, they must submit an essay, up to 750 words in length, on the topic, "Business and Community United: How the Two Can Work Together for Success." U.S. citizenship is required.

Financial data A stipend is awarded (amount not specified).

Duration 1 year.

Number awarded 1 or more each year.

Deadline February of each year.

[214]
ETHEL O. GARDNER PEO SCHOLARSHIP

P.E.O. Foundation-California State Chapter
c/o Carol Born, Scholarship Committee Chair
718 Via La Paloma
Riverside, CA 92507-6403
(951) 686-2728
Web: www.peocalifornia.org/eog.html

Summary To provide financial assistance to women from California who are upper-division or graduate students at a school in any state.

Eligibility This program is open to female residents of California who have completed at least 2 years at a college or university in any state. Applicants must be enrolled as full-time undergraduate or graduate students. Selection is based on financial need, character, and a record of academic and extracurricular activities achievement.

Financial data Stipends range from $500 to $1,500.

Duration 1 year.

Number awarded Varies each year; recently, 69 of these scholarships were awarded.

Deadline January of each year.

[215]
EUGENIA VELLNER FISCHER AWARD FOR THE PERFORMING ARTS

Miss America Pageant
Attn: Scholarship Department
222 New Road, Suite 700
Linwood, NJ 08221
(609) 653-8700, ext. 127   Fax: (609) 653-8740
E-mail: info@missamerica.org
Web: www.missamerica.org/scholarships/eugenia.aspx

Summary To provide financial assistance to women who are working on an undergraduate or graduate degree in the performing arts and who, in the past, competed at some level in the Miss America competition.

Eligibility This program is open to women who are working on an undergraduate, master's, or higher degree in the performing arts and who competed at the local, state, or national level in a Miss America competition within the past 10 years. Applicants may be studying dance, instrumental, monologue, or vocal. They must submit an essay, up to 500 words, on the factors that influenced their decision to enter the field of performing arts, what they consider to be their major strengths in the field, and how they plan to use their degree in the field. Selection is based on GPA, class rank, extracurricular activities, financial need, and level of participation within the system.

Financial data The stipend is $1,000.

Duration 1 year; renewable.

Additional information This scholarship was established in 1999.

Number awarded 2 each year.

Deadline June of each year.

[216]
EUNICE RIGGINS MEMORIAL SCHOLARSHIP

Alpha Delta Kappa-North Carolina Chapter
c/o Rebecca R. Meyst, President
351 North Peace Haven Road
Winston-Salem, NC 27104-2536

Summary To provide financial assistance to female high school seniors in North Carolina who plan to attend college in the state.

Eligibility This program is open to women graduating from high schools in North Carolina and planning to enroll at a 4-year college or university in the state. Applicants must rank in the top 10% of their class and have scores of at least 1344 on the SAT or 20 on the ACT. Along with their application, they must submit a letter on their plans, career goals, and reasons for wanting this scholarship. Selection is based on character and participation in extracurricular activities; financial need is not considered.

Financial data The stipend is $2,000.

Duration 1 year; nonrenewable.

Number awarded 1 each year.

Deadline January of each year.

[217]
EVE KRAFT EDUCATION AND COLLEGE SCHOLARSHIPS

United States Tennis Association
Attn: USTA Serves
70 West Red Oak Lane
White Plains, NY 10604
(914) 696-7223   E-mail: foundation@usta.com
Web: www.usta.com/About-USTA/USTA-Serves

Summary To provide financial assistance for college to high school seniors who have participated in an organized community tennis program (females and males are judged separately).

Eligibility This program is open to high school seniors who have excelled academically, demonstrated achievements in leadership, and participated extensively in an organized community tennis program. Applicants must be planning to enroll as a full-time undergraduate student at a 4-year college or university. They must be able to demonstrate financial need. Along with their application, they must submit an essay of 1 to 2 pages about how their participation in a tennis and education program has influenced their life, including examples of special mentors, volunteer service, and future goals. Males and females are considered separately.

Financial data The stipend is $2,500. Funds are paid directly to the recipient's college or university.

Duration 1 year; nonrenewable.

Number awarded 2 each year: 1 male and 1 female.

Deadline February of each year.

[218]
EXELON SCHOLARSHIPS

Society of Women Engineers
Attn: Scholarship Selection Committee
120 South LaSalle Street, Suite 1515
Chicago, IL 60603-3572
(312) 596-5223   Toll Free: (877) SWE-INFO
Fax: (312) 644-8557
E-mail: scholarshipapplication@swe.org
Web: societyofwomenengineers.swe.org

Summary To provide financial assistance to women who will be entering college as freshmen and are interested in studying electrical or mechanical engineering or computer science.

Eligibility This program is open to women who are entering college as freshmen with a GPA of 3.5 or higher. Applicants must be planning to enroll full time at an ABET-accredited 4-year college or university and major in computer science, electrical engineering, or mechanical engineering. Selection is based on merit.

Financial data The stipend is $1,000.

Duration 1 year.

Additional information This program is sponsored by Exelon Corporation, parent of ComEd and PECO, the electric utilities for northern Illinois and southeastern Pennsylvania, respectively.

Number awarded 5 each year.

Deadline May of each year.

[219]
EXEMPTION FOR DEPENDENTS OF TEXAS VETERANS

Texas Higher Education Coordinating Board
Attn: Grants and Special Programs
1200 East Anderson Lane
P.O. Box 12788
Austin, TX 78711-2788
(512) 427-6340   Toll Free: (800) 242-3062
Fax: (512) 427-6420   E-mail: grantinfo@thecb.state.tx.us
Web: www.collegeforalltexans.com

Summary To exempt spouses and children of disabled or deceased U.S. veterans from payment of tuition at public universities in Texas.

Eligibility This program is open to residents of Texas whose parent or spouse was a resident of the state at the time of entry into the U.S. armed forces, the Texas National Guard, or the Texas Air National Guard. The veteran parent or spouse must have died as a result of service-related injuries or illness, be missing in action, or have become totally disabled as a result of service-related injury or illness. Applicants must have no remaining federal education benefits. They must be attending or planning to attend a public college or university in the state. Children of veterans must be 25 years of age or younger.

Financial data Eligible students are exempt from payment of tuition, dues, fees, and charges at state-supported colleges and universities in Texas.

Duration 1 year; may be renewed.

Additional information This program was established under provisions of the Hazlewood Act; it is also referred to as Hazlewood Exemption for Dependents of Texas Veterans.

Number awarded Varies each year; recently, 9 of these awards were granted.

Deadline Deadline not specified.

[220]
EXEMPTION FROM TUITION FEES FOR DEPENDENTS OF KENTUCKY VETERANS

Kentucky Department of Veterans Affairs
Attn: Division of Field Operations
321 West Main Street, Room 390
Louisville, KY 40202
(502) 595-4447   Toll Free: (800) 928-4012 (within KY)
Fax: (502) 595-4448   E-mail: Pamela.Cypert@ky.gov
Web: www.veterans.ky.gov/benefits/tuitionwaiver.htm

Summary To provide financial assistance for undergraduate or graduate studies to the unremarried widow(er)s or children of deceased Kentucky veterans.

Eligibility This program is open to the children, stepchildren, adopted children, and unremarried widow(er)s of veterans who were residents of Kentucky when they entered military service or joined the Kentucky National Guard. The qualifying veteran must have been killed in action during a wartime period or died as a result of a service-connected disability incurred during a wartime period. Applicants must be attending or planning to attend a state-supported college or university in Kentucky to work on an undergraduate or graduate degree.

Financial data Eligible dependents and survivors are exempt from tuition and matriculation fees at any state-supported institution of higher education in Kentucky.

Duration There are no age or time limits on the waiver.

Number awarded Varies each year.

Deadline Deadline not specified.

[221]
EXERCISE FOR LIFE SCHOLARSHIPS

Boomer Esiason Foundation
c/o Jerry Cahill
483 Tenth Avenue, Suite 300
New York, NY 10018
(646) 292-7930   Fax: (646) 292-7945
E-mail: jcahillbef@aol.com
Web: www.cfscholarships.com/ExerciseForLife/index.htm

Summary To provide financial assistance for college to female and male high school seniors (judged separately) who have been involved in athletics and who have cystic fibrosis (CF).

Eligibility This program is open to CF patients who are college-bound high school seniors. Applicants must have been involved in athletics. They should be jogging on a regular basis and training for a 1.5 mile run. Along with their application, they must submit a letter from their doctor confirming the diagnosis of CF and a list of daily medications, information on financial need, a detailed breakdown of tuition costs from their academic institution, transcripts, and a 2-page essay on 1) their post-graduation goals and 2) the importance of compliance with CF therapies and what they practice on a daily basis to stay healthy. Selection is based on academic ability, athletic ability, character, leadership potential, service to the community, financial need, and daily compliance to CF therapy. Male and female students compete separately.

Financial data The stipend is $10,000. Funds are paid directly to the academic institution to assist in covering the cost of tuition and fees.

Duration 1 year; nonrenewable.

Number awarded 2 each year: 1 to a male and 1 to a female.

Deadline June of each year.

[222]
EXPLOSIVE ORDNANCE DISPOSAL (EOD) MEMORIAL SCHOLARSHIPS

Explosive Ordnance Disposal Memorial
Attn: Executive Director
7040 CR 772
Webster, FL 33597
(813) 389-0351   E-mail: scholarship@eodmemorial.org
Web: www.eodmemorial.org/scholarship.html

Summary To provide financial assistance for college to spouses and other family members of technicians or military officers who have worked in explosive ordnance disposal.

Eligibility This program is open to children, stepchildren, spouses, grandchildren, and other recognized dependents of graduates of Naval School Explosive Ordnance Disposal (NAVSCOLEOD) who served or are serving in the Army, Navy, Air Force, or Marine Corps. Active-duty personnel and NAVSCOLEOD graduates are not eligible. Selection is based on GPA, community involvement and volunteerism, extracurricular activities, awards, paid employment, an essay, future goals, letters of recommendation, and overall impression.

Financial data A stipend is awarded (amount not specified). Funds are paid directly to the academic institution for the student's tuition, books, fees, and on-campus housing.

Duration 1 year; may be renewed up to 3 additional years.

Number awarded Varies each year.

Deadline March of each year.

[223]
EXXONMOBIL BERNARD HARRIS MATH AND SCIENCE SCHOLARSHIPS

Council of the Great City Schools
1301 Pennsylvania Avenue, N.W., Suite 702
Washington, DC 20004
(202) 393-2427   Fax: (202) 393-2400
Web: www.cgcs.org/about/award_programs.aspx

Summary To provide financial assistance to high school seniors who are African American or Hispanic and interested in studying science, technology, engineering, or mathematics (STEM) in college (females and males are judged separately).

Eligibility This program is open to African American and Hispanic seniors graduating from high schools in a district that is a member of the Council of the Great City Schools, a coalition of 65 of the nation's largest urban public school systems. Applicants must be planning to enroll full time at a 4-year college or university and major in a STEM field of study. They must have a GPA of 3.0 or higher. Along with their application, they must submit 1-page essays on 1) how mathematics and science education has impacted their lives so far; and 2) why they have chosen to prepare for a career in a STEM field. Selection is based on those essays; academic achievement; extracurricular activities, community service, or other

experiences that demonstrate commitment to a career in a STEM field; and 3 letters of recommendation. Financial need is not considered. Males and females are judged separately.

Financial data The stipend is $5,000.

Duration 1 year; nonrenewable.

Additional information This program, which began in 2010, is sponsored by the ExxonMobil Corporation and The Harris Foundation.

Number awarded 4 each year: an African American male and female and an Hispanic male and female.

Deadline May of each year.

[224]
FANNIE WILDER EDUCATIONAL FUND SCHOLARSHIP

Center for Scholarship Administration, Inc.
Attn: Wells Fargo Accounts
4320 Wade Hampton Boulevard, Suite G
Taylors, SC 29687
Toll Free: (866) 608-0001
E-mail: allisonlee@bellsouth.net
Web: www.csascholars.org/wilder/index.php

Summary To provide financial assistance to women from Georgia who plan to attend college in any state.

Eligibility This program is open to female residents of Georgia who have a cumulative GPA of 2.5 or higher. Applicants must be attending or planning to attend an accredited 4-year college or university in any state. Selection is based on academic ability, educational goals, participation in extracurricular activities, career ambitions, and financial need.

Financial data A stipend is awarded (amount not specified).

Duration 1 year; may be renewed up to 3 additional years or until completion of a bachelor's degree (whichever comes first).

Number awarded 1 or more each year.

Deadline April of each year.

[225]
FEDERAL CITY ALUMNAE CHAPTER ACADEMIC EXCELLENCE SCHOLARSHIPS

Delta Sigma Theta Sorority, Inc.-Federal City Alumnae Chapter
Attn: Educational Development Committee
P.O. Box 1605
Washington, DC 20013
(202) 545-1913   E-mail: thefcacdst@yahoo.com
Web: thefcacdst.org

Summary To provide financial assistance to high school seniors (especially female African Americans) in Washington, D.C. who plan to attend a 4-year college or university in any state.

Eligibility This program is open to seniors graduating from high schools in the District of Columbia and planning to enroll full time at an accredited 4-year college or university in any state. Applicants must have a GPA of 3.3 or higher. Along with their application, they must submit a 500-word essay on either how they plan to use their education to make the world a better place or why they should be selected to receive this scholarship.

Financial data The stipend is $5,000.

Duration 1 year.

Additional information The sponsor is the local alumnae chapter of a traditionally African American social sorority.

Number awarded 2 each year.

Deadline February of each year.

[226]
FEDERATION OF HOUSTON PROFESSIONAL WOMEN EDUCATIONAL FOUNDATION SCHOLARSHIPS

Federation of Houston Professional Women
Attn: Educational Foundation
P.O. Box 27621
Humble, TX 77227-7621
E-mail: scholarshipapps@fhpw.org
Web: www.fhpw.org/scholarship_application.html

Summary To provide financial assistance for college or graduate school to women from Texas.

Eligibility This program is open to women who are residents of Texas and have completed at least 30 semesters hours of work on an associate, bachelor's, or graduate degree at an accredited college or university in the state. Applicants must be U.S. citizens or permanent residents and have a GPA of 3.0 or higher. They must submit a 200-word statement on their reasons for applying for this scholarship, a 200-word statement on their short- and long-term goals, their most recent transcript, 2 letters of recommendation, and a 100-word biographical sketch. Financial need is considered in the selection process.

Financial data Stipends are $2,000 for students at 4-year colleges and universities or $1,000 for students at community colleges. Funds are issued payable jointly to the student and the educational institution.

Duration 1 year.

Number awarded 2 each year.

Deadline May of each year.

[227]
FINANCIAL WOMEN INTERNATIONAL OF HAWAII SCHOLARSHIP

Hawai'i Community Foundation
Attn: Scholarship Department
827 Fort Street Mall
Honolulu, HI 96813
(808) 537-6333   Toll Free: (888) 731-3863
Fax: (808) 521-6286
E-mail: scholarships@hcf-hawaii.org
Web: www.hawaiicommunityfoundation.org/scholarships

Summary To provide financial assistance to women in Hawaii who are studying business on the upper-division or graduate school level at a school in any state.

Eligibility This program is open to female residents of Hawaii who are working on a degree in business or a business-related field as a junior, senior, or graduate student at a school in any state. Applicants must be able to demonstrate academic achievement (GPA of 3.5 or higher), good moral character, and financial need. Along with their application, they must submit a short statement indicating their reasons for attending college, their planned course of study, their career goals, and what community service means to them.

Financial data The amounts of the awards depend on the availability of funds and the need of the recipient. Recently, the average value of each of the scholarships awarded by the foundation was more than $2,000.

Duration 1 year.

Additional information This program was established in 1998.

Number awarded 1 or more each year.

Deadline February of each year.

[228]
FIRST LIEUTENANT MICHAEL L. LEWIS, JR. MEMORIAL FUND SCHOLARSHIP

American Legion Auxiliary
Department of New York
112 State Street, Suite 1310
Albany, NY 12207
(518) 463-1162   Toll Free: (800) 421-6348
Fax: (518) 449-5406   E-mail: alanyterry@nycap.rr.com
Web: www.deptny.org/Scholarships.htm

Summary To provide financial assistance to members of the American Legion Auxiliary in New York who plan to attend college in any state.

Eligibility This program is open to 1) junior members of the New York Department of the American Legion Auxiliary who are high school seniors or graduates younger than 20 years of age; and 2) senior members who are continuing their education to further their studies or update their job skills. Applicants must be attending or planning to attend college in any state. Along with their application, they must submit a 200-word essay on "Why a college education is important to me," or "Why I want to continue my post high school education in a business or trade school." Selection is based on character (25%), Americanism (25%), leadership (25%), and scholarship (25%).

Financial data A stipend is awarded (amount not specified).

Duration 1 year.

Number awarded 2 each year: 1 to a junior member and 1 to a senior member. If no senior members apply, both scholarships are awarded to junior members.

Deadline March of each year.

[229]
FLO IRWIN/AIRCRAFT SPRUCE MEMORIAL SCHOLARSHIP

Women in Aviation, International
Attn: Scholarships
Morningstar Airport
3647 State Route 503 South
West Alexandria, OH 45381-9354
(937) 839-4647   Fax: (937) 839-4645
E-mail: scholarships@wai.org
Web: www.wai.org/education/scholarships.cfm

Summary To provide financial assistance to members of Women in Aviation, International (WAI) who are interested in attending college to earn a degree in aviation management and start their own business.

Eligibility This program is open to WAI members who are entering their junior or senior year of college. Applicants must be interested in earning a degree in aviation management and starting their own aviation business after graduating. Along with their application, they must submit 2 letters of recommendation, a 500-word essay on their aviation history and goals, a resume, copies of all aviation licenses and medical certificates, and the last 3 pages of their pilot logbook (if applicable). Selection is based on achievements, attitude toward self and others, commitment to success, dedication to career, financial need, motivation, reliability, responsibility, and teamwork.

Financial data　The stipend is $1,000.

Duration　1 year.

Additional information　WAI is a nonprofit professional organization dedicated to encouraging women to consider an aviation career and to providing educational outreach activities and networking resources to women active in the industry. This program was established in 2008.

Number awarded　1 each year.

Deadline　November of each year.

[230]
FLORENCE ALLEN SCHOLARSHIPS

The Allen Endowment
c/o Holly S. Goodyear
3500 Granger Road
Medina, OH 44256-8602
(330) 725-3333　　　E-mail: allenendowmen@gmail.com

Summary　To provide financial assistance to women from Ohio who are interested in attending college in any state.

Eligibility　This program is open to women from Ohio who are either traditional students (graduating high school seniors or recent GED recipients) or nontraditional students (at least 30 years of age). Traditional students must be enrolled or planning to enroll full time at a 4-year college or university in Ohio; nontraditional students must also attend a 4-year college or university in Ohio, but they are not required to enroll full time. All applicants must submit a 500-word essay describing their short-term goals and how the proposed training will help them to accomplish those goals and make a difference in their professional career. Selection is based on that essay; academic, employment, and/or volunteer record; and financial need. Special consideration is given to members of the Ohio Federation of Business and Professional Women (BPW/Ohio) and/or applicants endorsed by a BPW/Ohio local organization. U.S. citizenship is required.

Financial data　A stipend is awarded (amount not specified).

Duration　1 year.

Additional information　This program was originally established in 1924, but became a tax-exempt endowment fund in 1988; since that time, it has awarded more than $71,000 in scholarships.

Number awarded　1 or more each year.

Deadline　February of each year.

[231]
FLORIDA ALPHA DELTA KAPPA PAST STATE PRESIDENTS' SCHOLARSHIP AWARD

Alpha Delta Kappa-Florida Chapter
c/o Deborah King
1198 Three Meadows Drive
Rockledge, FL 32955
Web: www.flalphadeltakappa.org

Summary　To provide financial assistance to female residents of Florida attending college in the state, especially those majoring in education.

Eligibility　This program is open to women attending 1) a 4-year university in Florida and working on an undergraduate degree, or 2) a community college in Florida and planning to transfer to a 4-year university in the state to work on an undergraduate degree. Applicants must have maintained an unweighted GPA of 3.3 or higher in high school and 3.0 or higher in college. Preference is given to students majoring in education. In the selection process, some consideration is given to financial need.

Financial data　The stipend is $1,000.

Duration　1 year.

Number awarded　1 each year.

Deadline　December of each year.

[232]
FLORIDA BOARD OF ACCOUNTANCY MINORITY SCHOLARSHIPS

Florida Board of Accountancy
240 N.W. 76th Drive, Suite A
Gainesville, FL 32607-6656
(850) 487-1395　　　　　　　　Fax: (352) 333-2508
Web: www.myflorida.com/dbpr/cpa

Summary　To provide financial assistance to female and minority residents of Florida who are entering the fifth year of an accounting program.

Eligibility　This program is open to Florida residents who have completed at least 120 credit hours at a college or university in the state and have a GPA of 2.5 or higher. Applicants must be planning to remain in school for the fifth year required to sit for the C.P.A. examination. They must be members of a minority group, defined to include African Americans, Hispanic Americans, Asian Americans, Native Americans, and women. Selection is based on scholastic ability and performance and financial need.

Financial data　The stipend is $3,000 per semester.

Duration　1 semester; may be renewed 1 additional semester.

Number awarded　Varies each year; a total of $100,000 is available for this program annually.

Deadline　May of each year.

[233]
FLORIDA LEGION AUXILIARY MEMORIAL SCHOLARSHIP

American Legion Auxiliary
Department of Florida
1912A Lee Road
P.O. Box 547917
Orlando, FL 32854-7917
(407) 293-7411   Fax: (407) 299-6522
E-mail: contact@alafl.org
Web: alafl.org

Summary To provide financial assistance to members and female dependents of members of the Florida American Legion Auxiliary who are interested in attending college in the state.

Eligibility Applicants must be members of the Florida Auxiliary or daughters or granddaughters of members who have at least 3 years of continuous membership. They must be sponsored by their local units, be Florida residents, and be enrolled or planning to enroll full time at a college, university, community college, or vocational/technical school in the state. Selection is based on academic record and financial need.

Financial data The stipends are up to $2,000 for a 4-year university or up to $1,000 for a community college or vocational/technical school. All funds are paid directly to the institution.

Duration 1 year; may be renewed if the recipient needs further financial assistance and has maintained at least a 2.5 GPA.

Number awarded Varies each year, depending on the availability of funds.

Deadline January of each year.

[234]
FORD MOTOR COMPANY SWE FRESHMAN SCHOLARSHIP

Society of Women Engineers
Attn: Scholarship Selection Committee
120 South LaSalle Street, Suite 1515
Chicago, IL 60603-3572
(312) 596-5223   Toll Free: (877) SWE-INFO
Fax: (312) 644-8557
E-mail: scholarshipapplication@swe.org
Web: societyofwomenengineers.swe.org

Summary To provide financial assistance to women entering college and planning to major in designated engineering specialties.

Eligibility This program is open to women who are entering freshmen at a 4-year ABET-accredited college or university. Applicants must be planning to major in automotive, electrical, industrial, or mechanical engineering and have a GPA of 3.5 or higher. Selection is based on merit.

Financial data The stipend is $4,500. The award includes a travel grant for the recipient to attend the national conference of the Society of Women Engineers.

Duration 1 year.

Additional information This program is sponsored by the Ford Motor Company.

Number awarded 1 each year.

Deadline May of each year.

[235]
FORD MOTOR COMPANY SWE UNDERGRADUATE SCHOLARSHIPS

Society of Women Engineers
Attn: Scholarship Selection Committee
120 South LaSalle Street, Suite 1515
Chicago, IL 60603-3572
(312) 596-5223   Toll Free: (877) SWE-INFO
Fax: (312) 644-8557
E-mail: scholarshipapplication@swe.org
Web: societyofwomenengineers.swe.org

Summary To provide financial assistance to undergraduate women majoring in designated engineering specialties.

Eligibility This program is open to women who are entering their junior year at a 4-year ABET-accredited college or university. Applicants must be majoring in automotive, electrical, industrial, or mechanical engineering and have a GPA of 3.5 or higher. Selection is based on merit and leadership potential.

Financial data The stipend is $1,000.

Duration 1 year.

Additional information This program, established in 2002, is sponsored by the Ford Motor Company.

Number awarded 3 each year.

Deadline February of each year.

[236]
FORD OPPORTUNITY PROGRAM SCHOLARSHIP

Oregon Student Assistance Commission
Attn: Ford Family Foundation Scholarship Office
440 East Broadway, Suite 200
Eugene, OR 97401
(541) 485-6211   Toll Free: (877) 864-2872
TDD: (800) 735-2900   E-mail: fordscholarships@tfff.org
Web: www.osac.state.or.us/ford.html

Summary To provide financial assistance to residents of Oregon and Siskiyou County, California who are single parents working on a college degree at a school in Oregon or California.

Eligibility This program is open to residents of Oregon and Siskiyou County, California who are U.S. citizens or permanent residents. Applicants must be single heads of household with custody of a dependent child or children. They must have a cumulative high school or college GPA of 3.0 or higher or a comparable GED score, and they must be planning to earn a bachelor's degree. Students from Oregon must attend a college or university in the state; students from Siskiyou County, California must attend a college or university in California. Selection is based on leadership ability through participation in school and community activities, concern for others and contribution of time and energy to volunteer projects and/or service organizations, motivation and desire to contribute to personal success through paid work experience, ability to succeed in college, and ability to communicate personal strengths and goals clearly.

Financial data This program provides up to 90% of a recipient's unmet financial need, to a maximum of $25,000 per year.

Duration 1 year; may be renewed for up to 3 additional years.

Additional information This program, funded by the Ford Family Foundation, began in 1996.

Number awarded 55 each year: 50 from Oregon and 5 from Siskiyou County.

Deadline February of each year.

[237]
FRAN SARGENT SCHOLARSHIP

Ninety-Nines, Inc.-Florida Goldcoast Chapter
c/o Kimberley Lowe
100 Edgewater Drive, Unit 342
Coral Gables, FL 33133-6980
(305) 984-0561   E-mail: flynlowe@comcast.net
Web: www.flgoldcoast99s.org/scholarships.html

Summary To provide financial assistance to female pilots in Florida who are interested in an aviation training program at a college or flight school in the state.

Eligibility This program is open to women who are either 1) residents of Florida and have a private pilot's certificate; or 2) private pilots currently enrolled in an aviation training program in the state. Applicants must be interested in acquiring an additional rating or certificate, attending a college program, or engaging in another aviation endeavor. Along with their application, they must submit a statement describing their education, aviation training and experience, aviation organizations, and employment history; another statement covering their educational purpose and/or aviation goals, their goals, why they chose aviation, and the pilot certificate or rating, college degree, or other goal they plan to attain using this scholarship; and 2 letters of reference. Selection is based on financial need, desire to prepare for a career in aviation, ability to represent women in aviation, likelihood of success in reaching goals, and neatness and completeness of application package.

Financial data The stipend is $2,000.

Duration 1 year.

Number awarded 1 or more each year.

Deadline September of each year.

[238]
FRANCIS M. KEVILLE MEMORIAL SCHOLARSHIP

Construction Management Association of America
Attn: CMAA Foundation
7926 Jones Branch Drive, Suite 800
McLean, VA 22101-3303
(703) 356-2622   Fax: (703) 356-6388
E-mail: foundation@cmaanet.org
Web: www.cmaafoundation.org

Summary To provide financial assistance to female and minority undergraduate and graduate students working on a degree in construction management.

Eligibility This program is open to women and members of minority groups who are enrolled as full-time undergraduate or graduate students. Applicants must have completed at least 1 year of study and have at least 1 full year remaining for a bachelor's or master's degree in construction management or a related field. Along with their application, they must submit essays on why they are interested in a career in construction management and why they should be awarded this scholarship. Selection is based on that essay (20%), aca-

demic performance (40%), recommendation of the faculty adviser (15%), and extracurricular activities (25%).

Financial data The stipend is $3,000. Funds are disbursed directly to the student's university.

Duration 1 year.

Number awarded 1 each year.

Deadline June of each year.

[239]
FRESH START SCHOLARSHIP

Wilmington Women in Business
Attn: Fresh Start Scholarship Foundation, Inc.
P.O. Box 7784
Wilmington, DE 19803
(302) 656-4411   E-mail: fsscholar@comcast.net
Web: www.wwb.org?page_id=11

Summary To provide financial assistance to women from any state who have experienced an interruption in their education and are interested in attending college in Delaware.

Eligibility This program is open to women from any state who are at least 20 years of age, have a high school diploma or GED, and have been admitted to an accredited Delaware college in a 2- or 4-year undergraduate degree program. Applicants must have had at least a 2-year break in education either after completing high school or during college studies. They must have at least a "C" average if currently enrolled in college and be recommended by a social service agency (or a college representative if a social service agency is not available). U.S. citizenship or permanent resident status is required. Financial need is considered in the selection process.

Financial data The stipend varies annually, depending on the availability of funds. Awards are paid to the college at the beginning of each semester.

Duration 1 year.

Additional information This program was established in 1996.

Number awarded Varies each year. Since the program was established, it has awarded more than $425,000 to 120 women.

Deadline May of each year.

[240]
FRIENDSHIP FUND SCHOLARSHIPS

Pi Beta Phi
Attn: Pi Beta Phi Foundation
1154 Town and Country Commons Drive
Town and Country, MO 63017
(636) 256-1357   Fax: (636) 256-8124
E-mail: fndn@pibetaphi.org
Web: www.pibetaphifoundation.org/scholarship-program

Summary To provide financial assistance to members of Pi Beta Phi who are working on an undergraduate degree.

Eligibility This program is open to women who are officially enrolled at a college or university where there is a Pi Beta Phi chapter. They must be active members in good standing in the sorority and have a GPA of 3.0 or higher (70% or higher for Canadian members). Selection is based on financial need, academic record, and service to the sorority, campus, and community.

Financial data The stipend is $1,000.

Duration 1 year.
Number awarded Varies each year; recently 14 of these scholarships were awarded.
Deadline February of each year.

[241]
FUTURAMA FOUNDATION CAREER ADVANCEMENT SCHOLARSHIP

Maine Federation of Business and Professional Women's
  Clubs
Attn: BPW/Maine Futurama Foundation
c/o Susan Tardie, Co-President
25 Hall Street
Fort Kent, ME 04743
E-mail: susan.tardie@maine.edu
Web: www.bpwmefoundation.org/files/index.php?id=10

Summary To provide financial assistance to women in Maine who are over 30 years of age and continuing a program of higher education or retraining.
Eligibility This program is open to women who are older than 30 years of age and residents of Maine. Applicants must be continuing in, or returning to, an accredited program of higher education or job-related training, either full or part time. They must have a definite plan to use the desired training in a practical and immediate way to improve chances for advancement, train for a new career field, or enter or reenter the job market. Along with their application, they must submit a statement describing their educational, personal, and career goals, including financial need, expectations of training, and future plans for using this educational program. Preference is given to members of Maine Federation of Business and Professional Women's Clubs.
Financial data The stipend is $1,200. Funds are paid directly to the school.
Duration 1 year.
Number awarded 1 or more each year.
Deadline April of each year.

[242]
GAIL BURNS-SMITH "DARE TO DREAM" FUND

Connecticut Sexual Assault Crisis Services, Inc.
Attn: Special Projects Coordinator
96 Pitkin Street
East Hartford, CT
(860) 282-9881   Fax: (860) 291-9335
E-mail: ayana@connsacs.org
Web: www.connsacs.org

Summary To provide financial assistance to students from Connecticut interested in preparing for a career in the field of women's issues or sexual violence prevention.
Eligibility This program is open to students who are residents of Connecticut or currently enrolled at a college or university in the state. Applicants must have paid or volunteer work experience in the field of women's issues or sexual violence prevention and advocacy. They must be committed to continuing work in those fields. Along with their application, they must submit essays on 1) their experience working in the field of sexual violence prevention and/or advocating on behalf of sexual assault victims; and 2) their plans for future work in that field and how they feel they can make a difference.

Financial data The stipend is $1,000.
Duration 1 year.
Additional information This program, established in 2004, is offered through the Hartford Foundation for Public Giving, 10 Columbus Boulevard, Eighth Floor, Hartford, CT 06106, (860) 548-1888, Fax: (860) 524-8346, E-mail: scholarships@hfpg.org.
Number awarded 1 each year.
Deadline February of each year.

[243]
GAIL PATRICK CHARITABLE TRUST SCHOLARSHIP

Delta Zeta Sorority
Attn: Foundation Coordinator
202 East Church Street
Oxford, OH 45056
(513) 523-7597   Fax: (513) 523-1921
E-mail: DZFoundation@dzshq.com
Web: www.deltazeta.org

Summary To provide financial assistance for continued undergraduate study to members of Delta Zeta Sorority.
Eligibility This program is open to members of the sorority who are entering their junior or senior year. Applicants must submit an official transcript, a statement of their career goals, information on their service to the sorority, documentation of campus activities and/or community involvement, a list of academic honors, and an explanation of their financial need.
Financial data The stipend is $2,500.
Duration 1 year; nonrenewable.
Number awarded 1 each year.
Deadline February of each year.

[244]
GAT WINGS TO THE FUTURE MANAGEMENT SCHOLARSHIP

Women in Aviation, International
Attn: Scholarships
Morningstar Airport
3647 State Route 503 South
West Alexandria, OH 45381-9354
(937) 839-4647   Fax: (937) 839-4645
E-mail: scholarships@wai.org
Web: www.wai.org/education/scholarships.cfm

Summary To provide financial assistance to members of Women in Aviation, International (WAI) who are interested in attending college to prepare for a career in aviation management.
Eligibility This program is open to WAI members who are enrolled in an aviation management or aviation business program at an accredited college or university. Applicants must be full-time students with a GPA of 3.0 or higher and interested in preparing for an aviation management career. Along with their application, they must submit 2 letters of recommendation, a 500-word essay on their aviation history and goals, a resume, copies of all aviation licenses and medical certificates, and the last 3 pages of their pilot logbook (if applicable). Selection is based on achievements, attitude toward self and others, commitment to success, dedication to career, financial need, motivation, reliability, responsibility, and teamwork.

Financial data   The stipend is $2,500. Funds may be used only for tuition, not flight fees.

Duration   1 year.

Additional information   WAI is a nonprofit professional organization dedicated to encouraging women to consider an aviation career and to providing educational outreach activities and networking resources to women active in the industry. This program is sponsored by GAT Airline Ground Support. In addition to the scholarship, recipients are reimbursed for travel and lodging expenses to attend the WAI annual conference.

Number awarded   1 each year.

Deadline   November of each year.

[245]
GENERAL DYNAMICS AIS SCHOLARSHIP

Society of Women Engineers-Minnesota Section
Attn: Scholarship Committee
P.O. Box 582813
Minneapolis, MN 55458-2813
E-mail: scholarships@swe-mn.org
Web: swe-mn.org/scholarships.html

Summary   To provide financial assistance to women from any state working on an undergraduate or graduate degree in electrical or computer engineering at colleges and universities in Minnesota, North Dakota, or South Dakota.

Eligibility   This program is open to female undergraduate and graduate students at ABET-accredited engineering programs in Minnesota, North Dakota, or South Dakota. Applicants must be working full time on a degree in electrical or computer engineering. Along with their application, they must submit a short paragraph describing how they plan to utilize their engineering skills after they graduate. Selection is based on potential to succeed as an engineer (20 points), communication skills (10 points), extracurricular or community involvement and leadership skills (10 points), demonstrated successful work experience (10 points), and academic success (5 points). U.S. citizenship is required.

Financial data   The stipend is $1,000.

Duration   1 year.

Additional information   This program is sponsored by General Dynamics-Advanced Information Systems.

Number awarded   1 each year.

Deadline   March of each year.

[246]
GENERAL ELECTRIC WOMEN'S NETWORK SCHOLARSHIPS

Society of Women Engineers
Attn: Scholarship Selection Committee
120 South LaSalle Street, Suite 1515
Chicago, IL 60603-3572
(312) 596-5223   Toll Free: (877) SWE-INFO
Fax: (312) 644-8557
E-mail: scholarshipapplication@swe.org
Web: societyofwomenengineers.swe.org

Summary   To provide financial assistance to undergraduate members of the Society of Women Engineers (SWE) majoring in computer science or specified fields engineering.

Eligibility   This program is open to members of the society who are entering their sophomore, junior, or senior year at a

4-year ABET-accredited college or university. Applicants must be majoring in computer science or aeronautical, civil, electrical, industrial, or mechanical engineering and have a GPA of 3.0 or higher. Selection is based on why they want to be an engineer or computer scientist, how they believe they will make a difference as an engineer or computer scientist, and what influenced them to study engineering or computer science. Selection is based on merit. Preference is given to students attending selected schools; for a list, contact the sponsor. U.S. citizenship is required.

Financial data   The stipend is $3,000.

Duration   1 year.

Additional information   This program, established in 2002, is sponsored by the General Electric Women's Network of the General Electric Company.

Number awarded   15 each year.

Deadline   February of each year.

[247]
GENERAL HENRY H. ARNOLD EDUCATION GRANT PROGRAM

Air Force Aid Society
Attn: Education Assistance Department
241 18th Street South, Suite 202
Arlington, VA 22202-3409
(703) 607-3072, ext. 51   Toll Free: (800) 429-9475
Fax: (703) 607-3022
Web: www.afas.org/Education/ArnoldEdGrant.cfm

Summary   To provide financial assistance for college to spouses, widows, and children of active-duty, retired, disabled, or deceased Air Force personnel.

Eligibility   This program is open to 1) dependent children of Air Force personnel who are active duty, Reservists on extended active duty, retired due to length of active-duty service or disability, or deceased while on active duty or in retired status; 2) spouses of active-duty Air Force members and Reservists on extended active duty; and 3) surviving spouses of Air Force members who died while on active duty or in retired status. Applicants must be enrolled or planning to enroll as full-time undergraduate students in an accredited college, university, or vocational/trade school. Spouses must be attending school within the 48 contiguous states. Selection is based on family income and education costs.

Financial data   The stipend is $2,000.

Duration   1 year; may be renewed if the recipient maintains a GPA of 2.0 or higher.

Additional information   Since this program was established in the 1988-89 academic year, it has awarded more than 88,000 grants.

Number awarded   Varies each year.

Deadline   March of each year.

[248]
GENERAL MOTORS FOUNDATION UNDERGRADUATE SCHOLARSHIPS

Society of Women Engineers
Attn: Scholarship Selection Committee
120 South LaSalle Street, Suite 1515
Chicago, IL 60603-3572
(312) 596-5223   Toll Free: (877) SWE-INFO
Fax: (312) 644-8557
E-mail: scholarshipapplication@swe.org
Web: societyofwomenengineers.swe.org

Summary To provide financial assistance to women majoring in designated engineering specialties at designated colleges and universities.

Eligibility This program is open to women who are entering their sophomore or junior year at a designated ABET-accredited college or university. Applicants must be majoring in automotive, electrical, industrial, manufacturing, or mechanical engineering and have a GPA of 3.5 or higher. Selection is based on merit. U.S. citizenship is required.

Financial data The stipend is $3,000.

Duration 1 year.

Additional information This program, established in 1991, is sponsored by the General Motors Foundation. Recipients must attend a designated college or university. For a list, contact the sponsor.

Number awarded 3 each year.

Deadline February of each year.

[249]
GEORGIA LEGION AUXILIARY PAST PRESIDENT PARLEY NURSING SCHOLARSHIP

American Legion Auxiliary
Department of Georgia
3035 Mt. Zion Road
Stockbridge, GA 30281-4101
(678) 289-8446   E-mail: amlegaux@bellsouth.net
Web: www.galegion.org/auxiliary.htm

Summary To provide financial assistance to daughters of veterans in Georgia who are interested in attending college in any state to prepare for a career in nursing.

Eligibility This program is open to George residents who are 1) interested in nursing education and 2) the daughters of veterans. Applicants must be sponsored by a local unit of the American Legion Auxiliary. Selection is based on a statement explaining why they want to become a nurse and why they need a scholarship, a transcript of all high school or college grades, and 4 letters of recommendation (1 from a high school principal or superintendent, 1 from the sponsoring American Legion Auxiliary local unit, and 2 from other responsible people).

Financial data The amount of the award depends on the availability of funds.

Number awarded Varies, depending upon funds available.

Deadline May of each year.

[250]
GIFT FOR LIFE SCHOLARSHIPS

United States Bowling Congress
Attn: Youth Department
621 Six Flags Drive
Arlington, TX 76011
Toll Free: (800) 514-BOWL, ext. 3168
Fax: (817) 385-8262
E-mail: beoff@ibcyouth.com
Web: www.bowl.com/scholarships

Summary To provide financial assistance for college to members of the United State Bowling Congress (USBC) who demonstrate financial hardship (females and males are judged separately).

Eligibility This program is open to USBC members who are high school students (grades 9-12) with a GPA of 2.5 or higher. Applicants must be able to demonstrate a financial hardship, defined as residing in a household where the number of children, the income level of their parents, and possible extenuating circumstances make obtaining a college education financially unlikely. They must submit either 1) an essay, up to 500 words, explaining how their financial situation could hinder or stop them from achieving their educational goals; or 2) if their parents submit a statement of family financial need, an essay of up to 500 words on a topic of their choice. Other factors considered in the selection process include academic achievements, community service, scholastic honors, and extracurricular activities. Applications from males and females are evaluated separately. In honor of the heroes of September 11, 2001, 2 scholarships are reserved for an eligible son or daughter of fire/police/emergency rescue personnel.

Financial data The stipend is $1,000.

Duration Scholarships are presented annually. Students may apply each year they are eligible and may win 1 scholarship each year before their high school graduation.

Number awarded 12 each year: 6 specifically for females and 6 for males. That total includes 2 awards reserved for children (1 daughter and 1 son) of fire/police/emergency rescue department employees.

Deadline March of each year.

[251]
GIRL SCOUT ACHIEVEMENT AWARD

American Legion Auxiliary
8945 North Meridian Street
Indianapolis, IN 46260
(317) 569-4500   Fax: (317) 569-4502
E-mail: alahq@legion-aux.org
Web: www.legion-aux.org

Summary To provide financial assistance for college to members of the Girl Scouts.

Eligibility This program is open to Girl Scouts who have received the Gold Award; are high school juniors or seniors; are active members of a religious institution (and have received the appropriate religious emblem at the Cadette or Senior Scout level); have demonstrated practical citizenship in their religious institution, school, Girl Scouting, and community; and submit at least 4 letters of recommendation, with 1 letter required from a representative of each of the following: church, school, community, and Scout troop. Candidates must submit a 500-word essay describing their Gold Award project and explaining why they chose the project they did and how it made an impact on them and their community. They must be nominated at the local level; those selected at the state level compete at the national level.

Financial data   The stipend is $1,000.

Duration   1 year; the award must be utilized within 1 year of high school graduation.

Number awarded   1 each year.

Deadline   Applications must be submitted to a local American Legion Auxiliary Unit by March of each year.

[252]
GIRLS GOING PLACES ENTREPRENEURSHIP AWARDS

Guardian Life Insurance Company of America
Attn: Girls Going Places
7 Hanover Square, H26-J
New York, NY 10004-2616
(212) 598-7881   Toll Free: (888) 600-4667
Fax: (212) 919-2586
E-mail: guardianwomenschannel@glic.com
Web: www.girlsgoingplaces.com/home

Summary   To recognize and reward outstanding girls between 12 and 18 years of age who demonstrate "budding entrepreneurship."

Eligibility   Eligible to be nominated are girls between the ages of 12 and 18 who are U.S. citizens or legal residents and enrolled in middle school, high school, or a home school program; students enrolled at a college or university are ineligible. Nominators must submit a 750-word recommendation letter in which they explain how their nominee makes a difference in her school, her community, or people's lives; how she has demonstrated budding entrepreneurship or financial acumen; and how she has taken the first steps toward financial independence. Nominees must submit 250-word personal statements on such topics as entrepreneurship, business leadership, financial independence, or making a difference in the community through entrepreneurship. Selection is based on the nominee's demonstration of budding entrepreneurship; significance of nominee's steps toward financial independence; nominee's ability to make a difference in her school and community; and nominee's initiative to start a new business or service.

Financial data   First prize is $10,000, second $5,000, and third $3,000; 12 other finalists receive $1,000. Winners may use the funds to further their entrepreneurial pursuits or save for college.

Duration   The competition is held annually.

Additional information   This competition was established in 1999.

Number awarded   15 each year.

Deadline   February of each year.

[253]
GLADYS ANDERSON EMERSON SCHOLARSHIP

Iota Sigma Pi
c/o Kathryn A. Thomasson, National Director for Student Awards
University of North Dakota, Department of Chemistry
Abbott Hall Room 236
151 Cornell Street, Stop 9024
Grand Forks, ND 58202-9024
(701) 777-3199   Fax: (701) 777-2331
E-mail: kthomasson@chem.und.edu
Web: www.iotasigmapi.info

Summary   To provide financial assistance to women undergraduates who have achieved excellence in the study of chemistry or biochemistry.

Eligibility   The nominee must be a female chemistry or biochemistry student who has attained at least junior standing but has at least 1 semester of work to complete. Both the nominator and the nominee must be members of Iota Sigma Pi, although students who are not members but wish to apply for the scholarship may be made members by National Council action. Selection is based on transcripts; a list of all academic honors and professional memberships; a short essay by the nominee describing herself, her goals in chemistry, any hobbies or talents, and her financial need; and letters of recommendation.

Financial data   The stipend is $2,000.

Duration   1 year.

Additional information   This scholarship was first awarded in 1987.

Number awarded   1 or 2 each year.

Deadline   February of each year.

[254]
GLADYS C. ANDERSON MEMORIAL SCHOLARSHIP

American Foundation for the Blind
Attn: Scholarship Committee
11 Penn Plaza, Suite 300
New York, NY 10001
(212) 502-7661   Toll Free: (800) AFB-LINE
Fax: (212) 502-7771   TDD: (212) 502-7662
E-mail: afbinfo@afb.net
Web: www.afb.org/Section.asp?Documentid=2962

Summary   To provide financial assistance to legally blind women who are studying classical or religious music on the undergraduate or graduate school level.

Eligibility   This program is open to women who are legally blind, U.S. citizens, and enrolled in an undergraduate or graduate degree program in classical or religious music. Along with their application, they must submit a 200-word essay that includes their past and recent achievements and accomplishments; their intended field of study and why they have chosen it; and the role their visual impairment has played in shaping their life. They must also submit a sample performance tape or CD of up to 30 minutes. Financial need is considered in the selection process.

Financial data   The stipend is $1,000.

Duration   1 academic year.

Number awarded   1 each year.

Deadline   April of each year.

[255]
GLADYS L. MERSEREAU GRANTS-IN-AID

Delta Kappa Gamma Society International-Pi State
 Organization
c/o Joan Slagle
1524 Amsterdam Road
Balston Spa, NY 12020-3318
(518) 885-7215   E-mail: jns172@yahoo.com
Web: www.deltakappagamma.org/NY/ASaGiA.html

Summary To provide financial assistance to women in New York whose education was interrupted and who now need help to become teachers.

Eligibility This program is open to women in New York who are interested in completing teacher certification requirements but whose education has been interrupted. Along with their application, they must submit a statement on their educational philosophy, documentation of their financial need, and 3 letters of recommendation (including at least 1 from a member of the sponsoring organization). Members of that organization are not eligible.

Financial data The amounts of the grants depend on the availability of funds.

Duration 1 year.

Additional information This program was established in 1975.

Number awarded Varies each year; recently, 5 of these grants were awarded.

Deadline January of each year.

[256]
GLAMOUR'S TOP TEN COLLEGE WOMEN COMPETITION

Glamour Magazine
4 Times Square, 16th Floor
New York, NY 10036-6593
Toll Free: (800) 244-GLAM   Fax: (212) 286-6922
E-mail: TTCW@glamour.com
Web: www.glamour.com/about/top-10-college-women

Summary To recognize and reward outstanding college women.

Eligibility This competition is open to women enrolled full time in their junior year at accredited colleges and universities in the United States and Canada. Applications must be approved and signed by the appropriate members of the school's faculty and administration (i.e., faculty adviser, the director of public relations, the director of student activities, or the dean of students). There is no limit on the number of applicants from any 1 school. Applicants must submit an essay (up to 500 words) describing their most meaningful achievements and how those relate to their field of study and future goals. Selection is based on leadership experience (34%), personal involvement in campus and community affairs (33%), and academic excellence (33%).

Financial data The grand prize is $20,000 and other prizes are $3,000. Each winner also receives a trip to New York City and recognition in the October issue of *Glamour* magazine.

Duration The competition is held annually.

Additional information The first competition was held in 1990.

Number awarded 10 each year: 1 grand prize and 9 other prizes.

Deadline July of each year for the early deadline; September of each year for the late deadline.

[257]
GLOBAL CHANGE SUMMER UNDERGRADUATE RESEARCH EXPERIENCE (SURE)

Oak Ridge Institute for Science and Education
Attn: Global Change Education Program
120 Badger Avenue, M.S. 36
P.O. Box 117
Oak Ridge, TN 37831-0117
(865) 576-7009   Fax: (865) 241-9445
E-mail: gcep@orau.gov
Web: www.atmos.anl.gov/GCEP/SURE/index.html

Summary To provide undergraduate students (especially women and minorities) with an opportunity to conduct research during the summer on global change.

Eligibility This program is open to undergraduates in their sophomore and junior years, although outstanding freshman and seniors are also considered. Applicants must be proposing to conduct research in a program area within the Department of Energy's Office of Biological and Environmental Research (DOE-BER): the atmospheric science program, the environmental meteorology program, the atmospheric radiation measurement program, the terrestrial carbon processes effort, the program for ecosystem research, and studies carried out under the direction of the National Institute for Global Environmental Change. They must have a GPA of 3.0 or higher overall and in their major. Minority and female students are particularly encouraged to apply. U.S. citizenship is required.

Financial data Participants receive a weekly stipend of $475 and support for travel and housing.

Duration 10 weeks during the summer. Successful participants are expected to reapply for a second year of research with their mentors.

Additional information This program, funded by DOE-BER, began in summer 1999. The first week is spent in an orientation and focus session at a participating university. For the remaining 9 weeks, students conduct mentored research at 1 of the national laboratories or universities conducting BER-supported global change research.

Number awarded Approximately 20 each year.

Deadline December of each year.

[258]
GOLDMAN SACHS 10,000 WOMEN BUSINESS LEADERSHIP AWARD

Hispanic Scholarship Fund
Attn: Selection Committee
55 Second Street, Suite 1500
San Francisco, CA 94105
(415) 808-2376   Toll Free: (877) HSF-INFO
Fax: (415) 808-2302   E-mail: scholar1@hsf.net
Web: www.hsf.net/GoldmanSachs.aspx

Summary To provide financial assistance to Hispanic American women who are attending specified universities to prepare for a career in business.

Eligibility This program is open to Hispanic American women entering their junior year at their choice of 26 specified universities. Applicants must be enrolled full time and have a GPA of 3.0 or higher. They must be able to demonstrate an interest in business leadership or a business career and be majoring in a business-related field (e.g., accounting, advertising, business administration, communications, finance, information technology, management, marketing, public relations, telecommunications). Along with their application, they must submit a personal statement, resume, and letter of recommendation that attest to their leadership, entrepreneurial and business activities, and how participation in the Goldman Sachs 10,000 Women scholarship and mentoring program would advance those interests. An interview may be included as part of the selection process. U.S. citizenship or permanent resident status is required.

Financial data The stipend is $5,000 per year.

Duration 2 years (the junior and senior years of college).

Additional information This program is sponsored by Goldman Sachs as part of its 10,000 Women Business Leadership program. Recipients are supported by a Goldman Sachs mentor and a student adviser from the Hispanic Scholarship Fund. The specified universities are Baruch College (CUNY), California State University at San Bernardino, California State University at Fresno, California State University at Fullerton, Fordham University, Georgia Institute of Technology, Georgia State University, Gordon College, Kennesaw State University, New York University, Pace University, Rutgers University, San Diego State University, St. John's University (New York), Texas Tech University, University of Arizona, University of California at Los Angeles, University of Colorado at Denver, University of Florida, University of Georgia, University of Houston-Downtown, University of Miami, University of Southern California, University of Tampa, University of Texas at Austin, or University of Texas at San Antonio.

Number awarded 1 or more each year.

Deadline January of each year.

[259]
GOLDMAN SACHS SCHOLARSHIPS

Society of Women Engineers
Attn: Scholarship Selection Committee
120 South LaSalle Street, Suite 1515
Chicago, IL 60603-3572
(312) 596-5223   Toll Free: (877) SWE-INFO
Fax: (312) 644-8557
E-mail: scholarshipapplication@swe.org
Web: societyofwomenengineers.swe.org

Summary To provide financial assistance to upper-division women who are members of the Society of Women Engineers (SWE) and majoring in designated engineering specialties.

Eligibility This program is open to members of the society who are entering their junior or senior year at an ABET-accredited 4-year college or university. Applicants must be studying computer science or electrical or computer engineering and have a GPA of 3.2 or higher. They must be SWE members. Selection is based on merit.

Financial data The stipend is $2,000. The award includes a travel grant for the recipient to attend the SWE national conference.

Duration 1 year.

Additional information This program is sponsored by Goldman Sachs.

Number awarded 4 each year.

Deadline February of each year.

[260]
GOOGLE ANITA BORG SCHOLARSHIPS FOR FIRST YEARS

Google Inc.
Attn: Scholarships
1600 Amphitheatre Parkway
Mountain View, CA 94043-8303
(650) 253-0000   Fax: (650) 253-0001
E-mail: anitaborgscholarship@google.com
Web: www.google.com/intl/en/anitaborg/us/first-years.html

Summary To provide financial assistance to female high school seniors planning to attend college and major in a computer-related field.

Eligibility This program is open to women who are graduating from high schools in the United States and planning to enroll full time at a college or university. Applicants must be planning to attend a college that has a computer science department and take at least 1 computer science course during their first year. They must major in computer science, computer engineering, software engineering, or a related field. Along with their application, they must submit 3 essays of 200 words each and 3 short answer questions. International students are eligible if they intend to enroll at a university in the United States. Selection is based on academic background, passion for computer science, community service, and leadership.

Financial data The stipend is $10,000.

Duration 1 year.

Number awarded Varies each year; recently, 7 of these scholarships were awarded.

Deadline January of each year.

[261]
GRADY-RAYAM PRIZE IN SACRED MUSIC

"Negro Spiritual" Scholarship Foundation
P.O. Box 547728
Orlando, FL 32854-7728
(407) 841-NSSF
Web: www.negrospiritual.org/competition

Summary To recognize and reward African American high school students in selected eastern states who excel at singing "Negro spirituals" (females and males are judged separately).

Eligibility This competition is open to high school juniors and seniors of Afro-ethnic heritage in 5 districts: 1) Florida; 2) Southeast (Georgia, North Carolina, and South Carolina); 3) Mid-south (Alabama, Arkansas, Louisiana, Mississippi, and Tennessee); 4) New England (Connecticut, Maine, Massachusetts, New Hampshire, Rhode Island, and Vermont); and 5) Capital (Delaware, Maryland, Virginia, Washington, D.C., and West Virginia). Participants must perform 2 "Negro spiritual" songs, 1 assigned and 1 selected. Selection is based on technique (tone quality, intonation, and vocal production), musicianship and artistry (inflection, diction, authenticity, rhythmic energy, and memorization), and stage presence (demeanor, posture, and sincerity of delivery). U.S. citizenship or permanent resident status is required.

Financial data Winners earn tuition assistance grants for college of $3,000 and cash prizes of $300. In Florida, the second-place winners receive tuition assistance grants of $2,000 and cash prizes of $200. Other finalists receive cash prizes of $100.

Duration The competition is held annually at a site in each of the 5 regions.

Additional information This program began in Florida in 1997, in the Mid-south district in 2006, in the New England and Capital districts in 2008, and in the Southeast district in 2010. The entry fee is $20.

Number awarded 10 tuition assistance grants and cash prizes (1 to a male and 1 to a female in each of the 5 districts) and 2 second-place tuition grants and cash prizes (1 to a male and 1 to a female in Florida) are awarded each year. The number of other cash prizes awarded to finalists varies each year.

Deadline December of each year for Florida; January of each year for the Southeast and Mid-south districts; February of each year for the New England and Capital districts.

[262]
GRAND GUARDIAN COUNCIL OF CALIFORNIA SCHOLARSHIPS

International Order of Job's Daughters-Grand Guardian
  Council of California
c/o Patricia Mosier, Grand Secretary
303 West Lincoln, Suite 210
Anaheim, CA 92805-2928
(714) 535-4575   Fax: (714) 991-6798
E-mail: GrSecCAiojd@aol.com
Web: www.caiojd.org

Summary To provide financial assistance to members of the International Order of Job's Daughters in California who plan to attend college in any state.

Eligibility This program is open to members of Job's Daughters in good standing, active or majority, in California. Applicants must submit 1) a transcript of 7 completed semesters if they are still in high school or of all completed course work if they are already in college; 2) a letter of recommendation signed by all members of their Executive Bethel Guardian Council; 3) a letter of recommendation from their high school principal, dean, counselor, or instructor, or, if in college, their college counselor; and 4) a letter describing their educational plans and goals. Transcripts account for 75% of the selection criteria.

Financial data Stipends range from $200 to $1,800.

Duration 1 year; nonrenewable.

Additional information The applicant with the highest score receives the Elise Bonneville Daskam Memorial Scholarship. The applicant with the second highest score receives the Harold Aggesen Grand Bethel Memorial Scholarship.

Number awarded Varies each year; recently, 38 of these scholarships were awarded: 1 at $1,800, 1 at $1,500, 3 at $1,250, 1 at $1,200, 1 at $1,000, 11 at $900, 1 at $800, 14 at $500, 1 at $300, and 4 at $200.

Deadline March of each year.

[263]
GRAND GUARDIAN COUNCIL OF PENNSYLVANIA SCHOLARSHIPS

Pennsylvania Masonic Youth Foundation
Attn: Educational Endowment Fund
1244 Bainbridge Road
Elizabethtown, PA 17022-9423
(717) 367-1536   Toll Free: (800) 266-8424 (within PA)
Fax: (717) 367-0616   E-mail: pmyf@pagrandlodge.org
Web: www.pmyf.org/scholar/index.html

Summary To provide financial assistance for college to members of Job's Daughters in Pennsylvania.

Eligibility This program is open to Pennsylvania Job's Daughters and unmarried majority members who are younger than 30 years of age and are in good standing in their Bethels. Applicants must be high school seniors, high school graduates, or current college students enrolled or planning to enroll in a higher education program as a full-time student. Along with their application, they must submit 100-word essays on 1) the reason they are apply for a scholarship and the manner in which they will use it; 2) how they feel their participation in Job's Daughters has prepared them for life's challenges; and 3) the appeal of participating in Job's Daughters and how the organization can be better marketed. the Selection is based on Bethel and other Job's Daughters activities.

Financial data The stipend depends on the availability of funds.

Duration 1 year.

Number awarded 1 or more each year.

Deadline January of each year.

[264]
GRANDMA MOSES SCHOLARSHIP

Western Art Association
Attn: Foundation
13730 Loumont Street
Whittier, CA 90601

Summary To provide financial assistance for art school to female high school seniors whose art demonstrates a "congruence with the art of Grandma Moses."

Eligibility This program is open to female graduating high school seniors. Applicants must be planning to study art in a college, university, or specialized school of art. Preference is given to applicants from the western United States. Candidates must submit samples of their artwork; selection is based on the extent to which their work "manifests a congruence with the work of the famed folk artist, Grandma Moses." Financial need is not considered.

Financial data The stipend is $3,000 per year.

Duration 1 year; may be renewed up to 3 additional years.

Additional information Requests for applications should be accompanied by a self-addressed stamped envelope, the student's e-mail address, and the source where they found the scholarship information.

Number awarded 1 each year.

Deadline March of each year.

[265]
GREATER DALLAS-FORT WORTH WTS CHAPTER UNDERGRADUATE SCHOLARSHIP

Women's Transportation Seminar-Greater Dallas/Fort Worth Chapter
c/o Amanda Wilson, Scholarship Chair
North Central Texas COG
616 Six Flags Drive
P.O. Box 5888
Arlington, TX 76005-5888
(817) 695-9284   Fax: (817) 640-3028
E-mail: awilson@nctcog.org
Web: www.wtsinternational.org/Chapters.aspx?ID=6888

Summary To provide financial assistance to women from any state working on an undergraduate degree in a field related to transportation at specified colleges and universities in Oklahoma or Texas.

Eligibility This program is open to women from any state who are enrolled at a college or university in Oklahoma or Texas that has been selected to participate. Applicants must be working on an undergraduate degree in a transportation-related field, such as transportation engineering, planning, finance, or logistics and have a GPA of 3.0 or higher. They must be preparing for a career in a transportation-related field. Along with their application, they must submit a 500-word statement about their career goals after graduation and why they think they should receive this scholarship. Selection is based on transportation involvement and goals, job skills, and academic record. Minority women are especially encouraged to apply.

Financial data The stipend is $1,000.

Duration 1 year; nonrenewable.

Additional information The winner is also nominated for scholarships offered by the national organization of the Women's Transportation Seminar (WTS). For a list of the eligible Oklahoma and Texas schools, contact the sponsor.

Number awarded 1 each year.

Deadline November of each year.

[266]
GREATLAND SWE SECTION SCHOLARSHIPS

Society of Women Engineers-Greatland Section
c/o Rebecca Carroll, Scholarship Chair
Adams Morgenthaler and Company, Inc.
701 East Tudor Road, Suite 250
Anchorage, AK 99503
(907) 257-9100   Fax: (907) 257-9191
E-mail: rcarr@amc-engineers.com
Web: www.swealaska.org/scholarships.html

Summary To provide financial assistance to female high school seniors in Alaska who plan to major in engineering at a college in any state.

Eligibility This program is open to women graduating from high schools in Alaska and planning to enroll in an ABET-accredited engineering program at a 4-year college or university in any state. Applicants must submit a 2-page essay discussing their interest in engineering, their major area of study or specialization, the job they wish to pursue after receiving their college degree, their long-term goals, and how they hope to achieve those. Selection is based on that essay, academic performance, activities and work experience, recom-

mendations, honors and awards, application presentation, and financial need.

Financial data The stipend is $1,500 or $1,000.

Duration 1 year.

Number awarded 2 each year: 1 at $1,500 and 1 at $1,000.

Deadline February of each year.

[267]
GROTTO/JOB'S DAUGHTERS SCHOLARSHIP

International Order of Job's Daughters
c/o Anna Rhoads, Educational Scholarships Committee Chair
35 Ridgewood Drive
Troy, MO 63379
(636) 462-6834   E-mail: alrhoad@centurytel.net
Web: www.iojd.org/Scholarships/index.htm

Summary To provide financial assistance to members of Job's Daughters who are working on an undergraduate or graduate degree in a dental field.

Eligibility This program is open to high school seniors and graduates; students in early graduation programs; junior college, technical, and vocational students; and college and graduate students. Applicants must be Job's Daughters in good standing in their Bethels; unmarried majority members under 30 years of age are also eligible. They must be working on a degree in a dental field, preferably with some training in the field of disabilities. Selection is based on scholastic standing, Job's Daughters activities, the applicant's self-help plan, recommendation by the Executive Bethel Guardian Council, faculty recommendations, achievements outside Job's Daughters, and financial need.

Financial data The stipend is $1,500.

Duration 1 year.

Number awarded 1 or more each year.

Deadline April of each year.

[268]
GWOT ASSISTANCE FUND

Navy-Marine Corps Relief Society
Attn: Education Division
875 North Randolph Street, Suite 225
Arlington, VA 22203-1757
(703) 696-4960   Fax: (703) 696-0144
E-mail: education@nmcrs.org
Web: www.nmcrs.org/goldstar.html

Summary To provide financial assistance for college to the spouses of Navy and Marine Corps military personnel who became disabled or died during the Global War on Terrorism (GWOT).

Eligibility This program is open to the spouses of disabled or deceased sailors and Marines who were injured or died while on active duty under hostile fire in a theater of combat operations during the GWOT. Applicants must be enrolled or planning to enroll full or part time at a college, university, or vocational/technical school. They must have a GPA of 2.0 or higher and be able to demonstrate financial need.

Financial data Stipends range from $500 to $2,500 per year. Funds are disbursed directly to the financial institution.

Duration 1 year; may be renewed up to 3 additional years.

Number awarded Varies each year.

Deadline February of each year.

[269]
HADASSAH-BRANDEIS INSTITUTE UNDERGRADUATE INTERNSHIPS

Brandeis University
Hadassah-Brandeis Institute
Attn: Program Manager
515 South Street
Mailstop 079
Waltham, MA 02454-9110
(781) 736-2064 Fax: (781) 736-2078
E-mail: hbi@brandeis.edu
Web: www.brandeis.edu/hbi/internship/details.html

Summary To provide summer work experience to undergraduate students in the field of Jewish women's studies at the Hadassah-Brandeis Institute of Brandeis University.

Eligibility This program is open to undergraduate students attending universities in the United States and abroad. Applicants must have a demonstrated interest in women's studies, Jewish women's studies, or issues relating to Jewish women around the world. They must be interested in working at the institute with Brandeis staff and scholars on new and established research projects. Current projects include spirited women, radical feminism and Jewish women, contemporary Jewish identity narratives, outreach for women's films, women artists re-vision religion, and teen involvement in Jewish life; applicants must select 2 of those projects and write a brief explanation on why they would like to assist on it. They must also submit a 250-word statement describing a personal project focusing on Jewish women and/or gender issues that they wish to pursue during the internship; the proposed project may be a piece of original scholarly research, a work in the visual or performing arts, a multimedia project, a piece of creative writing, or other work approved by the internship program. Along with their application, they must submit a 500-word essay explaining from where their interest in Jewish women's and gender studies originates, which particular issues relating to Jewish women's studies and gender particularly intrigue them, what they will bring to the internship that will contribute to the experience of the other participants, and what they hope to take away from the program. Selection is based on intellectual promise, independence, originality, initiative, capacity for growth, enthusiasm, unique skills, and strengths and weaknesses.

Financial data Interns receive subsidized housing on the Brandeis campus and a stipend of $1,000 at the completion of the program.

Duration 8 weeks during the summer.

Additional information The Hadassah-Brandeis Institute was formerly the Hadassah International Research Institute on Jewish Women at Brandeis University. <NA>6 each year.

Deadline March of each year.

[270]
HANNAH KEENAN SCHOLARSHIPS

Alpha Chi Omega Foundation
Attn: Foundation Programs Coordinator
5939 Castle Creek Parkway North Drive
Indianapolis, IN 46250-4343
(317) 579-5050, ext. 262 Fax: (317) 579-5051
E-mail: foundation@alphachiomega.org
Web: www.alphachiomega.org/index.aspx?id=1030

Summary To provide financial assistance for college to undergraduate members of Alpha Chi Omega.

Eligibility This program is open to women attending college full time who are members of Alpha Chi Omega. Applicants must have junior or senior standing. Selection is based on academic achievement, chapter involvement, campus and community service, and financial need.

Financial data A stipend is awarded (amount not specified).

Duration 1 year.

Number awarded Up to 5 each year.

Deadline March of each year.

[271]
HASMIK MGRDICHIAN SCHOLARSHIP

Armenian International Women's Association-Los
Angeles Affiliate
c/o Lily Ring Balian
2311 Roscomare Road, Number 10
Los Angeles, CA 90077
E-mail: hyelil@aol.com
Web: www.aiwala.org/index.php/projects

Summary To provide financial assistance to Armenian women from California who are interested in attending college in any state.

Eligibility This program is open to female residents of California who are of Armenian descent. Applicants must be enrolled or planning to enroll full time at an accredited college or university in any state. They must have a GPA of 3.5 or higher and be able to demonstrate financial need. Along with their application, they must submit a 500-word statement describing their planned academic program, their career goals, and the reasons why they believe they should be awarded this scholarship.

Financial data The stipend is $2,500.

Duration 1 year.

Number awarded 2 each year.

Deadline April of each year.

[272]
HAZEL BEARD LEASE SCHOLARSHIP

Kappa Alpha Theta Foundation
Attn: Scholarships
8740 Founders Road
Indianapolis, IN 46268-1337
(317) 876-1870 Toll Free: (800) KAO-1870
Fax: (317) 876-1925
E-mail: FDNmail@kappaalphatheta.org
Web: www.kappaalphathetafoundation.org

Summary To provide financial assistance to members of Kappa Alpha Theta who are working on an undergraduate or graduate degree in speech therapy or speech communication.

Eligibility This program is open to members of Kappa Alpha Theta who are full-time sophomores, juniors, seniors, or graduate students at a college or university in Canada or the United States. Applicants must be working on a degree in speech therapy or speech communication. Along with their application, they must submit an official transcript, personal essays on assigned topics related to their involvement in Kappa Alpha Theta, and 2 letters of reference. Financial need is not considered in the selection process.

Financial data The stipend is $1,175.

Duration 1 year.

Number awarded 1 each year.

Deadline January of each year.

[273]
HAZEL STONE MEMORIAL SCHOLARSHIP

Jews for Jesus
60 Haight Street
San Francisco, CA 94102
(415) 864-2600   Fax: (415) 552-8325
E-mail: ruthrosen@jewsforjesus.org
Web: www.jewsforjesus.org

Summary To provide financial assistance to "Jewish women proclaiming Jesus" who are interested in going to a Bible college.

Eligibility This program is open to Jewish women who have committed their life to Jesus, are committed to going to Bible college or seminary, are going to be committed to an evangelistic ministry after graduation, and are having difficulty meeting the cost of their education.

Financial data The amount awarded varies, depending upon the needs of the recipient.

Duration 1 year.

Number awarded 1 or more each year.

Deadline Deadline not specified.

[274]
HBCU SCHOLARSHIPS

Delta Sigma Theta Sorority, Inc.-Federal City Alumnae Chapter
Attn: Educational Development Committee
P.O. Box 1605
Washington, DC 20013
(202) 545-1913   E-mail: thefcacdst@yahoo.com
Web: thefcacdst.org

Summary To provide financial assistance to high school seniors in Washington, D.C. (especially female African Americans) who plan to attend a 4-year Historically Black College or University (HBCU) in any state.

Eligibility This program is open to seniors graduating from high schools in the District of Columbia and planning to enroll full time at an accredited 4-year HBCU in any state. Applicants must have a GPA of 3.3 or higher. Along with their application, they must submit a 500-word essay on either how they plan to use their education to make the world a better place or why they should be selected to receive this scholarship.

Financial data The stipend is $2,000.

Duration 1 year.

Additional information The sponsor is the local alumnae chapter of a traditionally African American social sorority.

Number awarded 2 each year.

Deadline February of each year.

[275]
HDR ENGINEERING SCHOLARSHIP FOR DIVERSITY IN ENGINEERING

Association of Independent Colleges and Universities of Pennsylvania
101 North Front Street
Harrisburg, PA 17101-1405
(717) 232-8649   Fax: (717) 233-8574
E-mail: info@aicup.org
Web: www.aicup.org

Summary To provide financial assistance to women and minority students from any state who are enrolled at member institutions of the Association of Independent Colleges and Universities of Pennsylvania (AICUP) and majoring in designated fields of engineering.

Eligibility This program is open to undergraduate students from any state enrolled full time at AICUP colleges and universities. Applicants must be women and/or members of the following minority groups: American Indians, Alaska Natives, Asians, Blacks/African Americans, Hispanics/Latinos, Native Hawaiians, or Pacific Islanders. They must be juniors majoring in civil, geotechnical, or structural engineering with a GPA of 3.0 or higher. Along with their application, they must submit a 2-page essay on their characteristics, accomplishments, primary interests, plans, and goals.

Financial data The stipend is $5,000 per year.

Duration 1 year; may be renewed 1 additional year if the recipient maintains appropriate academic standards.

Additional information This program, sponsored by HDR Engineering, Inc., is available at the 83 private colleges and universities in Pennsylvania that comprise the AICUP.

Number awarded 1 each year.

Deadline April of each year.

[276]
HEARST SCHOLARSHIP OF NEW YORK WOMEN IN COMMUNICATIONS, INC.

New York Women in Communications, Inc.
Attn: NYWICI Foundation
355 Lexington Avenue, 15th Floor
New York, NY 10017-6603
(212) 297-2133   Fax: (212) 370-9047
E-mail: nywicipr@nywici.org
Web: www.nywici.org/foundation/scholarships

Summary To provide financial assistance to female residents of designated eastern states who are enrolled as undergraduates at a college in any state and preparing for a career in magazine publishing or digital media.

Eligibility This program is open to women who are residents of New York, New Jersey, Connecticut, or Pennsylvania and currently enrolled as sophomores, juniors, or seniors at a college or university in any state. Also eligible are women who reside outside the 4 states but are currently enrolled at a college or university within 1 of the 5 boroughs of New York City. Applicants must be able to demonstrate a commitment to a career in magazines (editorial or advertising sales) or digital media. They must have a GPA of 3.2 or higher. Along with their application, they must submit a 2-page resume that includes school and extracurricular activities, significant achievements, academic honors and awards, and community service work; a personal essay of 300 to 500 words on their choice of an assigned topic that changes annually; 2 letters of recommendation; and an official transcript. Selection is based on academic record, need, demonstrated leadership, participation in school and community activities, honors, work experience, goals and aspirations, and unusual personal and/ or family circumstances. U.S. citizenship is required.

Financial data The stipend ranges up to $10,000.

Duration 1 year.

Additional information This program is sponsored by the Hearst Corporation, which may invite the recipient to apply for a summer internship at its New York City headquarters.

Number awarded 1 each year.

Deadline January of each year.

[277]
HEART OF TEXAS SHARON D. BANKS MEMORIAL SCHOLARSHIP

Women's Transportation Seminar-Heart of Texas Chapter
c/o Lindsay Liggett, Scholarship Chair
Jacobs Engineering Group Inc.
2705 Bee Cave Road, Suite 300
Austin, TX 78746-5688
(512) 314-3100   Fax: (512) 314-3135
E-mail: lindsay.liggett@jacobs.com
Web: www.wtsinternational.org/Chapters.aspx?ID=8336

Summary To provide financial assistance to women undergraduates from any state preparing for a career in transportation at designated colleges and universities in Arkansas, New Mexico, or Texas.

Eligibility This program is open to women from any state enrolled in an undergraduate degree program at designated colleges and universities in Arkansas, New Mexico, and Texas. Applicants must be majoring in a field related to transportation (e.g., engineering, finance, planning, logistics) and preparing for a career in the field. They must have a GPA of 3.0 or higher. Along with their application, they must submit a 500-word statement about their career goals after graduation and why they think they should receive this scholarship. Selection is based on transportation involvement and goals, job skills, and academic record. Minority women are especially encouraged to apply.

Financial data The stipend is $1,000.

Duration 1 year.

Additional information The winner is also nominated for scholarships offered by the national organization of the Women's Transportation Seminar. For a list of the eligible schools in Arkansas, New Mexico, and Texas, contact the sponsor.

Number awarded 1 each year.

Deadline April of each year.

[278]
HEATHER WESTPHAL MEMORIAL SCHOLARSHIP AWARD

International Association of Fire Chiefs
Attn: IAFC Foundation
4025 Fair Ridge Drive
Fairfax, VA 22033-2868
(703) 273-0911   Fax: (703) 273-9363
E-mail: foundation@iafc.org
Web: www.iafcf.org./Scholarship.htm

Summary To provide financial assistance to female fire fighters who wish to further their academic education.

Eligibility This program is open to women who are active members of state, county, provincial, municipal, community, industrial, or federal fire departments in the United States or Canada and have demonstrated proficiency as members for at least 2 years of paid or 3 years of volunteer service. Dependents of members are not eligible. Applicants must be planning to attend a recognized institution of higher education. Along with their application, they must submit a 250-word essay that includes a brief description of the course work, how the course work will benefit their fire service career and department and improve the fire service, and their financial need. Preference is given to members of the International Association of Fire Chiefs (IAFC).

Financial data A stipend is awarded (amount not specified).

Additional information This program was established in 2009.

Number awarded 1 each year.

Deadline May of each year.

[279]
HELEN MUNTEAN EDUCATION SCHOLARSHIP FOR WOMEN

Association of Romanian Orthodox Ladies Auxiliaries of
    North America
Attn: Scholarship Committee
222 Orchard Park Drive
New Castle, PA 16105
(724) 652-4313   E-mail: adelap@verizon.net
Web: www.arfora.org/scholarships.htm

Summary To provide financial assistance to women who are members of a parish of the Romanian Orthodox Episcopate of America and interested in working on a degree in education in college.

Eligibility This program is open to women who have been voting communicant members of a parish of the Romanian Orthodox Episcopate of America for at least 1 year or are daughters of a communicant member. Applicants must have completed at least 1 year of work on a baccalaureate degree in education at a college or university. Along with their application, they must submit a 300-word statement describing their personal goals; high school, university, church, and community involvement; honors and awards; and why they should be considered for this award. Selection is based on academic achievement, character, worthiness, and participation in religious life.

Financial data The stipend is $1,000.

Duration 1 year; nonrenewable.

Additional information The Association of Romanian Orthodox Ladies Auxiliaries (ARFORA) was established in 1938 as a women's organization within the Romanian Orthodox Episcopate of America.

Number awarded 1 or more each year.

Deadline May of each year.

[280]
HELEN TRUEHEART COX ART SCHOLARSHIP

National League of American Pen Women
1300 17th Street, N.W.
Washington, DC 20036-1973
(202) 785-1997   Fax: (202) 452-8868
E-mail: nlapw1@verizon.net
Web: www.americanpenwomen.org

Summary To provide financial assistance to Native American women interested in studying art in college.

Eligibility This program is open to women between 17 and 24 years of age who are members of a Native American tribe. Applicants must be interested in attending a college or university and majoring in art. They must submit 3 prints (4 by 6 inches) in any media (e.g., oil, water color, original works on paper, mixed media, acrylic) or 3 prints (4 by 6 inches) of art work, sculpture, or photographic works. U.S. citizenship is required. Financial need is considered in the selection process.

Financial data A stipend is awarded (amount not specified).

Duration 1 year.

Number awarded 1 each even-numbered year.

Deadline January of even-numbered years.

[281]
HELOISE WERTHAN KUHN SCHOLARSHIP

Community Foundation of Middle Tennessee
Attn: Scholarship Committee
3833 Cleghorn Avenue, Suite 400
Nashville, TN 37215-2519
(615) 321-4939   Toll Free: (888) 540-5200
Fax: (615) 327-2746   E-mail: mail@cfmt.org
Web: www.cfmt.org/scholarships

Summary To provide financial assistance to residents of Tennessee who are pregnant or parenting teens and interested in attending college in any state.

Eligibility This program is open to residents of middle Tennessee who are pregnant or parenting teens. Applicants must be attending or planning to attend an accredited college, university, junior college, technical school, or job training program in any state to increase their job skills and become more employable. Along with their application, they must submit an essay describing their educational plans and how those plans will help them reach their career goals. Financial need is considered in the selection process.

Financial data Stipends range from $500 to $2,500 per year. Funds are paid to the recipient's school and must be used for tuition, fees, books, supplies, room, board, or miscellaneous expenses.

Duration 1 year; recipients may reapply.

Additional information This program was established in 2000.

Number awarded 1 or more each year.

Deadline March of each year.

[282]
HERMINE DALKOWITZ TOBOLOWSKY SCHOLARSHIP

Texas Business Women
Attn: Texas Business and Professional Women's Foundation
P.O. Box 70
Round Rock, TX 78680-0070
(806) 922-7090   Toll Free: (877) 225-4TBW
E-mail: info@texasbusinesswomen.org
Web: www.texasbpwfoundation.org/scholarships.php

Summary To provide financial assistance to women from any state who are attending college in Texas to prepare for a career in selected professions.

Eligibility This program is open to women from any state who are interested in preparing for a career in law, public service, government, political science, or women's history. Applicants must have completed at least 2 semesters of study at an accredited college or university in Texas, have a GPA of 3.0 or higher, and be U.S. citizens. Selection is based on academic achievement and financial need.

Financial data A stipend is awarded (amount not specified).

Duration 1 year.

Additional information This program was established in 1995 when Texas Business Women was named Texas Federation of Business and Professional Women's Clubs.

Number awarded 1 or more each year.

Deadline December of each year.

[283]
HERMIONE GRANT CALHOUN SCHOLARSHIP

National Federation of the Blind
Attn: Scholarship Committee
1800 Johnson Street
Baltimore, MD 21230
(410) 659-9314, ext. 2415   Fax: (410) 685-5653
E-mail: scholarships@nfb.org
Web: www.nfb.org/nfb/scholarship_program.asp

Summary To provide financial assistance to female blind students interested in working on an undergraduate or graduate degree.

Eligibility This program is open to legally blind women who are working on or planning to work full time on an undergraduate or graduate degree. Along with their application, they must submit transcripts, standardized test scores, proof of legal blindness, 2 letters of recommendation, and a letter of endorsement from their National Federation of the Blind state president or designee. Selection is based on academic excellence, service to the community, and financial need.

Financial data The stipend is $3,000.

Duration 1 year; recipients may resubmit applications up to 2 additional years.

Additional information Scholarships are awarded at the federation convention in July. Recipients attend the convention at federation expense; that funding is in addition to the scholarship grant.

Number awarded 1 each year.

Deadline March of each year.

[284]
HONEYWELL INTERNATIONAL SCHOLARSHIPS

Society of Women Engineers
Attn: Scholarship Selection Committee
120 South LaSalle Street, Suite 1515
Chicago, IL 60603-3572
(312) 596-5223   Toll Free: (877) SWE-INFO
Fax: (312) 644-8557
E-mail: scholarshipapplication@swe.org
Web: societyofwomenengineers.swe.org

Summary To provide financial assistance to women interested in studying specified fields of engineering in college.

Eligibility This program is open to women who are graduating high school seniors or rising college sophomores, juniors, or seniors. Applicants must be enrolled or planning to enroll full time at an ABET-accredited 4-year college or university and major in computer science or aerospace, chemical, computer, electrical, industrial, manufacturing, materials, or mechanical engineering. Preference is given to members of groups underrepresented in computer science and engineering. U.S. citizenship is required. Financial need is considered in the selection process.

Financial data The stipend is $5,000.

Duration 1 year.

Additional information This program is sponsored by Honeywell International Inc.

Number awarded 3 each year.

Deadline February of each year for current college students; May of each year for high school seniors.

[285]
HORIZONS FOUNDATION SCHOLARSHIP PROGRAM

Women in Defense
c/o National Defense Industrial Association
2111 Wilson Boulevard, Suite 400
Arlington, VA 22201-3061
(703) 247-2552   Fax: (703) 522-1885
E-mail: wid@ndia.org
Web: wid.ndia.org/horizons/Pages/default.aspx

Summary To provide financial assistance to women (including those already working in national security fields) who are upper-division or graduate students working on a degree related to the national security interests of the United States.

Eligibility This program is open to women who are already working in national security fields as well as women planning such careers. Applicants must 1) be currently enrolled at an accredited college or university, either full time or part time, as graduate students or upper-division undergraduates; 2) demonstrate financial need; 3) be U.S. citizens; 4) have a GPA of 3.25 or higher; and 5) demonstrate interest in preparing for a career related to national security. The preferred fields of study include business (as it relates to national security or defense), computer science, economics, engineering, government relations, international relations, law (as it relates to national security or defense), mathematics, military history, political science, physics, and security studies; others are

considered if the applicant can demonstrate relevance to a career in national security or defense. Selection is based on academic achievement, participation in defense and national security activities, field of study, work experience, statements of objectives, recommendations, and financial need.

Financial data The stipend ranges up to $12,000.

Duration 1 year; renewable.

Additional information This program was established in 1988.

Number awarded Varies each year; recently, 3 of these scholarships were awarded: 1 at $12,000, 1 at $10,000, and 1 at $3,000. Since the program was established, 104 women have received more than $119,000 in support.

Deadline June of each year.

[286]
HORIZONS-MICHIGAN SCHOLARSHIP

Women in Defense-Michigan Chapter
Attn: Scholarship Director
P.O. Box 4744
Troy, MI 48099
E-mail: scholarships@wid-mi.org
Web: www.wid-mi.org/scholarships.aspx

Summary To provide financial assistance to women in Michigan who are upper-division or graduate students working on a degree related to national defense.

Eligibility This program is open to women who are residents of Michigan and enrolled either full or part time at a college or university in the state. Applicants must be juniors, seniors, or graduate students and have a GPA of 3.25 or higher. They must be interested in preparing for a career related to national security or defense. Relevant fields of study include security studies, military history, government relations, engineering, computer science, physics, mathematics, business (as related to national security or defense), law (as related to national security or defense), international relations, political science, or economics; other fields may be considered if the applicant can demonstrate relevance to a career in national security or defense. Along with their application, they must submit brief statements on their interest in a career in national security or defense, the principal accomplishments in their life that relate to their professional goals, and the objectives of their educational program. Selection is based on those statements, academic achievement, participation in defense and national security activities, field of study, work experience, recommendations, and financial need. U.S. citizenship is required.

Financial data Stipends have averaged at least $3,000.

Duration 1 year.

Additional information This program was established in 2009.

Number awarded Varies each year; recently, 6 of these scholarships were awarded.

Deadline September of each year.

[287]
HOUSTON CHAPTER SHARON D. BANKS MEMORIAL SCHOLARSHIP

Women's Transportation Seminar-Houston Chapter
c/o Tracy Rudder, Scholarship Chair
Parsons Brinckerhoff, Inc.
16285 Park Ten Place, Suite 400
Houston, TX 77084
(281) 589-5900 Fax: (281) 759-5164
E-mail: rudder@pbworld.com
Web: www.wtsinternational.org/Chapters.aspx?ID=10172

Summary To provide financial assistance to women undergraduates from any state preparing for a career in transportation at designated colleges and universities in Louisiana and Texas.

Eligibility This program is open to women from any state enrolled in an undergraduate degree program at designated colleges and universities in Louisiana and Texas. Applicants must be majoring in a field related to transportation (e.g., engineering, finance, planning, logistics) and preparing for a career in the field. They must have a GPA of 3.0 or higher. Along with their application, they must submit a 500-word statement about their career goals after graduation and why they think they should receive this scholarship. Selection is based on transportation involvement and goals, job skills, and academic record. Minority women are especially encouraged to apply.

Financial data The stipend is $1,000.

Duration 1 year.

Additional information The winner is also nominated for scholarships offered by the national organization of the Women's Transportation Seminar. For a list of the eligible schools in Louisiana and Texas, contact the sponsor.

Number awarded 1 each year.

Deadline November of each year.

[288]
HOUSTON/NANCY HOLLIMAN SCHOLARSHIP

Delta Zeta Sorority
Attn: Foundation Coordinator
202 East Church Street
Oxford, OH 45056
(513) 523-7597 Fax: (513) 523-1921
E-mail: DZFoundation@dzshq.com
Web: www.deltazeta.org

Summary To provide financial assistance for continued undergraduate study to members of Delta Zeta Sorority who are majoring in a field related to hearing and speech.

Eligibility This program is open to members of the sorority who are entering their junior or senior year and have a GPA of 3.0 or higher. Applicants must be working on a degree in hearing and speech, audiology, or a related field. Along with their application, they must submit an official transcript, a statement of their career goals, information on their service to the sorority, documentation of campus activities and/or community involvement, a list of academic honors, and an explanation of their financial need.

Financial data The stipend ranges from $500 to $2,500, depending on the availability of funds.

Duration 1 year; nonrenewable.

Number awarded 1 each year.

Deadline February of each year.

[289]
H.S. AND ANGELINE LEWIS SCHOLARSHIPS

American Legion Auxiliary
Department of Wisconsin
Attn: Education Chair
2930 American Legion Drive
P.O. Box 140
Portage, WI 53901-0140
(608) 745-0124 Toll Free: (866) 664-3863
Fax: (608) 745-1947 E-mail: alawi@amlegionauxwi.org
Web: www.amlegionauxwi.org/Scholarships.htm

Summary To provide financial assistance to Wisconsin residents who are related to veterans or are members of the American Legion Auxiliary and interested in working on an undergraduate or graduate degree at a school in any state.

Eligibility This program is open to the children, wives, and widows of veterans who are high school seniors or graduates and have a GPA of 3.5 or higher. Grandchildren and great-grandchildren of members of the American Legion Auxiliary are also eligible. Applicants must be residents of Wisconsin and interested in working on an undergraduate or graduate degree at a school in any state. Along with their application, they must submit a 300-word essay on "Education-An Investment in the Future." Financial need is considered in the selection process.

Financial data The stipend is $1,000.

Duration 1 year; nonrenewable.

Number awarded 6 each year: 1 to a graduate student and 5 to undergraduates.

Deadline March of each year.

[290]
HUENEFELD/DENTON SCHOLARSHIP

Delta Zeta Sorority
Attn: Foundation Coordinator
202 East Church Street
Oxford, OH 45056
(513) 523-7597 Fax: (513) 523-1921
E-mail: DZFoundation@dzshq.com
Web: www.deltazeta.org

Summary To provide financial assistance for continued undergraduate study to members of Delta Zeta Sorority who are majoring in child development or library science.

Eligibility This program is open to members of the sorority who are entering their junior or senior year. Applicants must be working on a degree in child development (including kindergarten through primary education) or library science. Along with their application, they must submit an official transcript, a statement of their career goals, information on their service to the sorority, documentation of campus activities and/or community involvement, a list of academic honors, and an explanation of their financial need.

Financial data The stipend ranges from $500 to $2,500, depending on the availability of funds.

Duration 1 year; nonrenewable.

Number awarded 1 each year.

Deadline February of each year.

[291]
IBM CORPORATION SWE SCHOLARSHIPS

Society of Women Engineers
Attn: Scholarship Selection Committee
120 South LaSalle Street, Suite 1515
Chicago, IL 60603-3572
(312) 596-5223   Toll Free: (877) SWE-INFO
Fax: (312) 644-8557
E-mail: scholarshipapplication@swe.org
Web: societyofwomenengineers.swe.org

Summary   To provide financial assistance to undergraduate women majoring in designated engineering specialties.

Eligibility   This program is open to women who are entering their sophomore or junior year at a 4-year ABET-accredited college or university. Applicants must be majoring in computer science or electrical or computer engineering and have a GPA of 3.4 or higher. Preference is given to members of groups underrepresented in engineering or computer science. Selection is based on merit. U.S. citizenship is required.

Financial data   The stipend is $1,000.

Duration   1 year.

Additional information   This program is sponsored by the IBM Corporation.

Number awarded   4 each year.

Deadline   February of each year.

[292]
IDA M. POPE MEMORIAL SCHOLARSHIPS

Hawai'i Community Foundation
Attn: Scholarship Department
827 Fort Street Mall
Honolulu, HI 96813
(808) 537-6333   Toll Free: (888) 731-3863
Fax: (808) 521-6286
E-mail: scholarships@hcf-hawaii.org
Web: www.hawaiicommunityfoundation.org/scholarships

Summary   To provide financial assistance to Native Hawaiian women who are interested in working on an undergraduate or graduate degree in designated fields at a school in any state.

Eligibility   This program is open to female residents of Hawaii who are Native Hawaiian, defined as a descendant of the aboriginal inhabitants of the Hawaiian islands prior to 1778. Applicants must be enrolled at a school in any state in an accredited associate, bachelor's, or graduate degree program and working on a degree in health, science, or education (including counseling and social work). They must be able to demonstrate academic achievement (GPA of 3.5 or higher), good moral character, and financial need. Along with their application, they must submit a short statement indicating their reasons for attending college, their planned course of study, their career goals, and what community service means to them.

Financial data   The amounts of the awards depend on the availability of funds and the need of the recipient. Recently, the average value of each of the scholarships awarded by the foundation was more than $2,000.

Duration   1 year; may be renewed.

Number awarded   Varies each year; recently, 61 of these scholarships were awarded.

Deadline   February of each year.

[293]
ILLINOIS MIA/POW SCHOLARSHIP

Illinois Department of Veterans' Affairs
833 South Spring Street
P.O. Box 19432
Springfield, IL 62794-9432
(217) 782-6641   Toll Free: (800) 437-9824 (within IL)
Fax: (217) 524-0344   TDD: (217) 524-4645
E-mail: webmail@dva.state.il.us
Web: www.veterans.illinois.gov/benefits/education.htm

Summary   To provide financial assistance for 1) the undergraduate education of spouses or children of Illinois disabled or deceased veterans or those listed as prisoners of war or missing in action, and 2) the rehabilitation or education of disabled spouses or children of those veterans.

Eligibility   This program is open to the spouses, natural children, legally adopted children, or stepchildren of a veteran or servicemember who 1) has been declared by the U.S. Department of Defense or the U.S. Department of Veterans Affairs to be permanently disabled from service-connected causes with 100% disability, deceased as the result of a service-connected disability, a prisoner of war, or missing in action, and 2) at the time of entering service was an Illinois resident or was an Illinois resident within 6 months of entering such service. Special support is available for dependents who are disabled.

Financial data   An eligible dependent is entitled to full payment of tuition and certain fees at any Illinois state-supported college, university, or community college. In lieu of that benefit, an eligible dependent who has a physical, mental, or developmental disability is entitled to receive a grant to be used to cover the cost of treating the disability at 1 or more appropriate therapeutic, rehabilitative, or educational facilities. For all recipients, the total benefit cannot exceed the cost equivalent of 4 calendar years of full-time enrollment, including summer terms, at the University of Illinois.

Duration   This scholarship may be used for a period equivalent to 4 calendar years, including summer terms. Dependents have 12 years from the initial term of study to complete the equivalent of 4 calendar years. Disabled dependents who elect to use the grant for rehabilitative purposes may do so as long as the total benefit does not exceed the cost equivalent of 4 calendar years of full-time enrollment at the University of Illinois.

Additional information   An eligible child must begin using the scholarship prior to his or her 26th birthday. An eligible spouse must begin using the scholarship prior to 10 years from the effective date of eligibility (e.g., prior to August 12, 1989 or 10 years from date of disability or death).

Number awarded   Varies each year.

Deadline   Deadline not specified.

[294]
ILLINOIS SCHOLARSHIPS FOR JUNIOR MEMBERS

American Legion Auxiliary
Department of Illinois
2720 East Lincoln Street
P.O. Box 1426
Bloomington, IL 61702-1426
(309) 663-9366   Fax: (309) 663-5827
E-mail: Karen.boughan@ilala.org
Web: www.ilala.org/scholar.html

Summary To provide financial assistance to high school seniors or graduates in Illinois who are junior members of the American Legion Auxiliary and planning to attend college in any state.

Eligibility This program is open to junior members of the Illinois American Legion Auxiliary who are daughters, granddaughters, great-granddaughters, or sisters of veterans who served during eligibility dates for membership in the American Legion. Applicants must be high school seniors or graduates who have not yet attended an institution of higher learning and are planning to attend college in any state. Along with their application, they must submit a 1,000-word essay on "The Veteran in My Life." Selection is based on that essay (25%) character and leadership (25%), scholarship (25%), and financial need (25%).

Financial data The stipend is $1,000.

Duration 1 year.

Number awarded Varies each year.

Deadline March of each year.

[295]
IMMIGRANT WOMEN PROGRAM INTERNSHIPS AT LEGAL MOMENTUM

Legal Momentum
Attn: Immigrant Women Program
1101 14th Street, N.W., Suite 300
Washington, DC 20005
(202) 326-0040   Fax: (202) 589-0511
E-mail: dcinternships@legalmomentum.org
Web: www.legalmomentum.org`

Summary To provide work experience to students and recent graduates who are interested in working on the Legal Momentus's immigrant women program in Washington, D.C.

Eligibility The internship is open to undergraduates, graduate students, and recent graduates interested in an immigrant women internship at Legal Momentum. Applicants must be interested in working on a range of tasks, including researching and analyzing legislation; drafting letters, fact sheets, and articles; attending briefings and coalition meetings; answering requests for technical assistance; assisting with administrative tasks as needed; and coordinating the work of coalitions dealing with violence against women, welfare reform, child care, and immigrant women's rights. They should have a strong interest in women's legal rights. A love of feminist issues, politics, and hard work is useful and a working knowledge of the American political process is recommended. Women and men of all ethnic, cultural, economic, and sexual orientations who support feminist concerns are eligible. Bilingual individuals are especially encouraged to apply.

Financial data These are paid internships (stipend not specified).

Duration Interns are asked to work from 15 to 35 hours per week for 10 to 12 weeks. Positions are available in the fall, spring, or summer.

Additional information Legal Momentum was formerly known as the NOW Legal Defense and Education Fund.

Number awarded Varies each year.

Deadline Applications may be submitted at any time.

[296]
INDEPENDENT WOMEN'S FORUM COLLEGE ESSAY CONTEST

Independent Women's Forum
Attn: Essay Competition
4400 Jenifer Street, Suite 240
Washington, DC 20015
(202) 419-1820   E-mail: info@iwf.org
Web: iwf.org/campus/essay

Summary To recognize and reward women who submit outstanding essays on topics related to free markets.

Eligibility This competition is open to female undergraduate students enrolled full time at 4-year colleges and universities. Applicants are invited to submit essays, up to 750 words in length, on a topic that changes annually but relates to issues of free markets.

Financial data Prizes are $5,000 for first, $2,000 for second, $1,000 for third, and $250 for honorable mention.

Duration The competition is held annually.

Additional information The sponsor is a nonprofit organization dedicated to building support for free markets, limited government, and individual responsibility.

Number awarded 13 each year: 1 first, 1 second, 1 third, and 10 honorable mentions.

Deadline December of each year.

[297]
INDIANA AMERICAN LEGION GOLD AWARD GIRL SCOUT OF THE YEAR SCHOLARSHIP ACHIEVEMENT AWARD

American Legion
Department of Indiana
777 North Meridian Street
Indianapolis, IN 46204
(317) 630-1200   Fax: (317) 630-1277
Web: www.indlegion.org

Summary To recognize and reward, with scholarships to attend college in any state, members of the Girl Scouts in Indiana who have received the Gold Award.

Eligibility This program is open to high school seniors in Indiana who plan to attend college in any state. Applicants must be registered Girl Scouts who have received the Gold Award; are active members of their religious institution and have received the appropriate religious emblem at the Ambassador or Senior Scout level; have demonstrated good and practical citizenship in their Girl Scouting, school, religious institution, and community; and submit letters of recommendation from a leader in each of the following groups: Scouting, school, religious institution, and community.

Financial data The awards are a $1,000 scholarship for the state winner and $200 scholarships for each district winner.

Duration The awards are presented annually.

Additional information Winners must utilize their awards within 1 year of graduating from high school as full-time students at an accredited institution of higher education in the United States.

Number awarded 12 each year: 1 state winner and 11 district winners.

Deadline April of each year.

[298]
INDIANA BPW GIRL SCOUT SCHOLARSHIP

Indiana Women's Education Foundation, Inc.
P.O. Box 33
Knightstown, IN 46148-0033
(765) 345-9812   Fax: (765) 345-9812
E-mail: bpwin@msn.com
Web: indianawomensfoundation.org/scholarships.htm

Summary To provide financial assistance to Girl Scout members in Indiana who are interested in attending college, preferably in the state.

Eligibility This program is open to Girl Scouts who have completed the Business and Professional Women (BPW) patch and have been residents of Indiana for at least 1 year. Applicants must be between their senior year of high school and their senior year of college in any state; preference is given to students at schools in Indiana. Along with their application, they must submit a statement (up to 200 words) on their career goals and how their education relates to those goals. Financial need is not considered in the selection process.

Financial data A stipend is awarded (amount not specified). Funds are paid directly to the recipient's school.

Duration 1 year; recipients may reapply.

Additional information This program was established in 2008. The Indiana Women's Education Foundation was formerly named the Indiana Business and Professional Women's Foundation.

Number awarded 1 each year.

Deadline February of each year.

[299]
INDIANA WOMEN IN PUBLIC FINANCE SCHOLARSHIP

Indiana Women in Public Finance
c/o Katie Aeschliman, Scholarship Committee
Harris Bank
3901 West 86th Street
Indianapolis, IN 46268
(317) 228-5193   E-mail: indianawpf@gmail.com

Summary To provide financial assistance to women from Indiana who are working on a degree in a field related to public finance at a college in the state.

Eligibility This program is open to women who are residents of Indiana and currently enrolled as juniors at a college or university in the state. Applicants must be majoring in finance, public finance, law, government accounting, public policy, public management, or a closely-related field. Along with their application, they must submit 500-word essays on

1) any extracurricular activities in which they have participated, and 2) their post-collegiate work plans.

Financial data The stipend is $1,000.

Duration 1 year.

Additional information Indiana Women in Public Finance was organized in 2009.

Number awarded 1 each year.

Deadline March of each year.

[300]
INDIANA WOMEN IN TRANSITION SCHOLARSHIP

Indiana Women's Education Foundation, Inc.
P.O. Box 33
Knightstown, IN 46148-0033
(765) 345-9812   Fax: (765) 345-9812
E-mail: bpwin@msn.com
Web: indianawomensfoundation.org/scholarships.htm

Summary To provide financial assistance for college to mature women in Indiana.

Eligibility This program is open to women who are 30 years of age or older and have been an Indiana resident for at least 1 year. Applicants must be reentering the workforce, be changing careers, or be a displaced worker. They must have applied to a postsecondary institution for at least part-time attendance. Along with their application, they must submit 1) a statement (up to 200 words) on their career goals and how their education relates to those goals, and 2) documentation of financial need.

Financial data The stipend is $1,000. Funds are paid directly to the recipient's school.

Duration 1 year; recipients may reapply.

Additional information This scholarship was first awarded in 1995, when the Indiana Women's Education Foundation was formerly named the Indiana Business and Professional Women's Foundation.

Number awarded 2 each year.

Deadline February of each year.

[301]
INDIANA WORKING WOMAN SCHOLARSHIP

Indiana Women's Education Foundation, Inc.
P.O. Box 33
Knightstown, IN 46148-0033
(765) 345-9812   Fax: (765) 345-9812
E-mail: bpwin@msn.com
Web: indianawomensfoundation.org/scholarships.htm

Summary To provide financial assistance for college to women in Indiana who are also working at least part time.

Eligibility This program is open to women who are 25 years of age or older and have been an Indiana resident for at least 1 year. Applicants must be employed at least 20 hours per week and must have applied to or be attending a postsecondary institution on at least a part-time basis. Along with their application, they must submit 1) a statement (up to 200 words) on their career goals and how their education relates to those goals, and 2) documentation of financial need.

Financial data The stipend is $1,000. Funds are paid directly to the recipient's school.

Duration 1 year; recipients may reapply.

Additional information This scholarship was first awarded in 1995, when the Indiana Women's Education Foundation was formerly named the Indiana Business and Professional Women's Foundation.

Number awarded 2 each year.

Deadline February of each year.

[302]
INSTITUTIONAL EQUITY WOMEN'S COLLEGE FELLOWSHIP PROGRAM

Morgan Stanley
Attn: Diversity Recruiting
1585 Broadway
New York, NY 10036
(212) 762-0211   Fax: (212) 507-4972
E-mail: iedwomenscollegefellowship@morganstanley.
  com
Web: www.morganstanley.com

Summary To provide financial assistance and work experience to college sophomore women who are interested in a career in the institutional equities business.

Eligibility This program is open to women who are currently enrolled as sophomores at a 4-year college or university with a GPA of 3.3 or higher. Applicants may be majoring in any field, but they must desire to work within the institutional equities business. Selection is based on academic achievement, extracurricular activities, leadership qualities, and an on-site interview.

Financial data The program provides a stipend of $12,500 during the spring semester of their junior year, a paid internship at Morgan Stanley's Institutional Equity Division during the summer between their junior and senior years, and another stipend of $12,500 for the fall semester of the senior year.

Duration 1 year; may be renewed for a second year, providing the student maintains a GPA of 3.3 or higher and completes the summer internship following the junior year.

Number awarded 1 or more each year.

Deadline April of each year.

[303]
INTERMOUNTAIN SECTION AWWA DIVERSITY SCHOLARSHIP

American Water Works Association-Intermountain
  Section
3430 East Danish Road
Sandy, UT 94093
(801) 712-1619   Fax: (801) 487-6699
E-mail: nicoleb@ims-awwa.org
Web: www.ims-awwa.org

Summary To provide financial assistance to female and minority undergraduate and graduate students working on a degree in the field of water quality, supply, and treatment at a university in Idaho or Utah.

Eligibility This program is open to women and students who identify as Hispanic or Latino, Black or African American, Native Hawaiian or other Pacific Islander, Asian, or American Indian or Alaska Native. Applicants must be entering or enrolled in an undergraduate or graduate program at a college or university in Idaho or Utah that relates to water quality, supply, or treatment. Along with their application, they must

submit a 2-page essay on their academic interests and career goals and how those relate to water quality, supply, or treatment. Selection is based on that essay, letters of recommendation, and potential to contribute to the field of water quality, supply, and treatment in the Intermountain West.

Financial data The stipend is $1,000. The winner also receives a 1-year student membership in the Intermountain Section of the American Water Works Association (AWWA) and a 1-year subscription to *Journal AWWA*.

Duration 1 year; nonrenewable.

Number awarded 1 each year.

Deadline October of each year.

[304]
INTERNATIONAL COMMUNICATIONS INDUSTRIES FOUNDATION AV SCHOLARSHIPS

InfoComm International
International Communications Industries Foundation
11242 Waples Mill Road, Suite 200
Fairfax, VA 22030
(703) 273-7200   Toll Free: (800) 659-7469
Fax: (703) 278-8082   E-mail: srieger@infocomm.org
Web: www.infocomm.org

Summary To provide financial assistance to high school seniors and college students (especially women and minorities) who are interested in preparing for a career in the audiovisual (AV) industry.

Eligibility This program is open to high school seniors, undergraduates, and graduate students already enrolled in college. Applicants must have a GPA of 2.75 or higher and be majoring or planning to major in audiovisual subjects or related fields, including audio, video, electronics, telecommunications, technical aspects of the theater, data networking, software development, or information technology. Students in other programs, such as journalism, may be eligible if they can demonstrate a relationship to career goals in the AV industry. Along with their application, they must submit 1) an essay of 150 to 200 words on the career path they plan to pursue in the audiovisual industry in the next 5 years, and 2) an essay of 250 to 300 words on the experience or person influencing them the most in selecting the audiovisual industry as their career of choice. Minority and women candidates are especially encouraged to apply. Selection is based on the essays, presentation of the application, GPA, AV-related experience, work experience, and letters of recommendation.

Financial data The stipend is $1,200 per year. Funds are sent directly to the school.

Duration 1 year; recipients may reapply.

Additional information InfoComm International, formerly the International Communications Industries Association, established the International Communications Industries Foundation (ICIF) to manage its charitable and educational activities.

Number awarded Varies each year; recently, 29 of these scholarships were awarded.

Deadline May of each year.

[305]
INTERPUBLIC GROUP SCHOLARSHIP AND INTERNSHIP

New York Women in Communications, Inc.
Attn: NYWICI Foundation
355 Lexington Avenue, 15th Floor
New York, NY 10017-6603
(212) 297-2133   Fax: (212) 370-9047
E-mail: nywicipr@nywici.org
Web: www.nywici.org/foundation/scholarships

Summary   To provide financial assistance and work experience to women from ethnically diverse groups who are residents of designated eastern states and enrolled as juniors at a college in any state to prepare for a career in advertising or public relations.

Eligibility   This program is open to female residents of New York, New Jersey, Connecticut, or Pennsylvania who are from ethnically diverse groups and currently enrolled as juniors at a college or university in any state. Also eligible are women who reside outside the 4 states but are currently enrolled at a college or university within 1 of the 5 boroughs of New York City. Applicants must be preparing for a career in advertising or public relations and have a GPA of 3.2 or higher. They must be available for a summer internship with Interpublic Group (IPG) in New York City. Along with their application, they must submit a 2-page resume that includes school and extracurricular activities, significant achievements, academic honors and awards, and community service work; a personal essay of 300 to 500 words on their choice of an assigned topic that changes annually; 2 letters of recommendation; and an official transcript. Selection is based on academic record, need, demonstrated leadership, participation in school and community activities, honors, work experience, goals and aspirations, and unusual personal and/or family circumstances. U.S. citizenship is required.

Financial data   The scholarship stipend ranges up to $10,000; the internship is salaried (amount not specified).

Duration   1 year.

Additional information   This program is sponsored by IPG, a holding company for a large number of firms in the advertising industry.

Number awarded   1 each year.

Deadline   January of each year.

[306]
IOTA SIGMA PI MEMBERS-AT-LARGE REENTRY AWARD

Iota Sigma Pi
c/o Karen Knaus, MAL National Coordinator
University of Colorado at Denver, Department of Chemistry
1201 Fifth Street
Campus Box 194
Denver, CO 80204
(303) 352-3628   E-mail: karen.knaus@ucdenver.edu
Web: www.iotasigmapi.info

Summary   To provide financial assistance to women who are reentering college to work on an undergraduate or graduate degree in chemistry.

Eligibility   This program is open to women who have returned to academic studies after an absence of 3 or more years and have completed at least 1 academic year of college chemistry since returning. Students must be working on an undergraduate or graduate degree in chemistry or a related field at a 4-year college or university. They must be nominated by a member of Iota Sigma Pi or by a member of the faculty at their institution. Nominees must submit a short essay describing their goals, pertinent experiences that influenced their choice of major, any interests or talents that will assist them in succeeding in their professional career, and how the scholarship will benefit them in meeting their goals. Financial need is not considered in the selection process.

Financial data   The winner receives a stipend of $1,500, a certificate, and a 1-year waiver of Iota Sigma Pi dues.

Duration   1 year.

Additional information   This award was first presented in 1991.

Number awarded   1 each year.

Deadline   March of each year.

[307]
IRENE AND LEETA WAGY MEMORIAL SCHOLARSHIP

Daughters of the American Revolution-Missouri State Society
Attn: State Scholarship Chair
821 Main Street
Boonville, MO 65233-1657
(660) 882-5320   E-mail: hyhope@sbcglobal.net
Web: www.mssdar.org

Summary   To provide financial assistance to female high school seniors in Missouri who plan to study education at a college or university in the state.

Eligibility   This program is open to female seniors graduating from high schools in Missouri in the top 10% of their class. Applicants must be planning to attend an accredited college or university in Missouri to major in education. They must be sponsored by a chapter of the Daughters of the American Revolution in Missouri and able to demonstrate financial need. U.S. citizenship is required.

Financial data   A stipend is awarded (amount not specified).

Duration   1 year.

Number awarded   1 or more each year.

Deadline   January of each year.

[308]
ISABELLA CARVALHO HEALTH SCHOLARSHIP

North Carolina Society of Hispanic Professionals
8450 Chapel Hill Road, Suite 209
Cary, NC 27513
(919) 467-8424   Fax: (919) 469-1785
E-mail: mailbox@thencshp.org
Web: www.thencshp.org

Summary   To provide financial assistance to Hispanic high school seniors (preference given to women) in North Carolina who plan to major in a health-related field at colleges in any state.

Eligibility   This program is open to seniors graduating from high schools in North Carolina who are of Hispanic/Latino background (both parents are at least half Hispanic or 1 parent is fully Hispanic). Applicants must be planning to enroll at a community college or 4-year college or university in any state to prepare for a career in a field related to health care, including (but not limited to) medicine, nursing, public health, pharmacy, dentistry, sports medicine, or allied health. Preference is given to female applicants.

Financial data Stipends range from $500 to $2,500 per year. Funds are paid directly to the college or university.

Duration 1 year; may be renewed up to 1 additional year, but preference is given to new applicants.

Number awarded 1 or more year.

Deadline January of each year.

[309]
ISABELLA M. GILLEN MEMORIAL SCHOLARSHIP

Aviation Boatswain's Mates Association
7 Geneva Road
P.O. Box 1106
Lakehurst, NJ 08733
E-mail: Scholarship@abma-usn.org
Web: www.abma-usn.org

Summary To provide financial assistance for college to the spouses and children of paid-up members of the Aviation Boatswains Mates Association (ABMA).

Eligibility Applicants must be dependents whose sponsor has been an active, dues-paying member of the ABMA for at least 2 years. They must prepare a statement describing their vocational or professional goals and relating how their past, present, and future activities make the accomplishment of those goals probable. Other submissions include transcripts, SAT or ACT scores, letters of recommendation, and honors received in scholarship, leadership, athletics, dramatics, community service, or other activities. Selection is based on financial need, character, leadership, and academic achievement.

Financial data The stipend is $3,500 per year.

Duration 1 year; may be renewed.

Additional information This program was established in 1976. Membership in ABMA is open to all U.S. Navy personnel (active, retired, discharged, or separated) who hold or held the rating of aviation boatswains mate.

Number awarded 1 each year.

Deadline May of each year.

[310]
ITT SCHOLARSHIPS

Society of Women Engineers
Attn: Scholarship Selection Committee
120 South LaSalle Street, Suite 1515
Chicago, IL 60603-3572
(312) 596-5223   Toll Free: (877) SWE-INFO
Fax: (312) 644-8557
E-mail: scholarshipapplication@swe.org
Web: societyofwomenengineers.swe.org

Summary To provide financial assistance to women working on an undergraduate or graduate degree in specified fields of engineering or computer science.

Eligibility This program is open to women who will be juniors, seniors, or graduate students at ABET-accredited colleges and universities. Applicants must be working on a degree in computer science or aeronautical, chemical, civil,

electrical, environmental, industrial, manufacturing, or mechanical engineering and have a GPA of 3.5 or higher. Preference is given to applicants attending specified schools. Selection is based on merit.

Financial data The stipend is $2,500.

Duration 1 year.

Additional information For a list of the specified schools, contact SWE.

Number awarded 2 each year.

Deadline February of each year.

[311]
ITW SCHOLARSHIPS

Society of Women Engineers
Attn: Scholarship Selection Committee
120 South LaSalle Street, Suite 1515
Chicago, IL 60603-3572
(312) 596-5223   Toll Free: (877) SWE-INFO
Fax: (312) 644-8557
E-mail: scholarshipapplication@swe.org
Web: societyofwomenengineers.swe.org

Summary To provide financial assistance to undergraduate women majoring in designated engineering specialties.

Eligibility This program is open to women who are entering their junior year at a 4-year ABET-accredited college or university. Applicants must be majoring in computer science, electrical or mechanical engineering, or polymer science. They must have a GPA of 3.0 or higher. Preference is given to members of groups underrepresented in engineering or computer science. Selection is based on merit. U.S. citizenship is required.

Financial data The stipend is $2,500.

Duration 1 year.

Additional information This program is sponsored by Illinois Tool Works, Inc.

Number awarded 2 each year.

Deadline February of each year.

[312]
IVY M. PARKER MEMORIAL SCHOLARSHIP

Society of Women Engineers
Attn: Scholarship Selection Committee
120 South LaSalle Street, Suite 1515
Chicago, IL 60603-3572
(312) 596-5223   Toll Free: (877) SWE-INFO
Fax: (312) 644-8557
E-mail: scholarshipapplication@swe.org
Web: societyofwomenengineers.swe.org

Summary To provide financial assistance to upper-division women majoring in computer science or engineering.

Eligibility This program is open to women who are entering their junior or senior year at an ABET-accredited college or university. Applicants must be majoring in computer science or engineering and have a GPA of 3.0 or higher. Financial need is considered in the selection process.

Financial data The stipend is $1,500.

Duration 1 year.

Additional information This program was established in 1986.

Number awarded 1 each year.

Deadline February of each year.

[313]
JACQUELYN R. SMITH/SHARON D. BANKS MEMORIAL UNDERGRADUATE SCHOLARSHIP

Women's Transportation Seminar-Boston Chapter
c/o Sasha Wood
Tetra Tech Rizzo
One Grant Street
Framingham, MA 01701
(508) 902-2000   E-mail: sasha.wood@tetratech.com
Web: www.wtsinternational.org/Chapters.aspx/ID=6758

Summary To provide financial assistance to women working on a transportation-related undergraduate degree at a college or university in Massachusetts.

Eligibility This program is open to women enrolled at colleges and universities in Massachusetts who are working on an undergraduate degree in a transportation-related field, including transportation engineering, planning, finance, or logistics. Applicants must have a GPA of 3.0 or higher and plans to prepare for a career in a transportation-related field. Along with their application, they must submit a 500-word personal statement about their career goals after graduation and why they think they should receive this scholarship. Selection is based on the applicant's specific transportation involvement and goals, job skills, and academic record. Minority women are especially encouraged to apply.

Financial data The stipend is $4,000.

Duration 1 year.

Additional information This program was established in 2007.

Number awarded 1 or more each year.

Deadline November of each year.

[314]
JAIME HORN MEMORIAL SOFTBALL SCHOLARSHIP

Babe Ruth League, Inc.
1770 Brunswick Pike
P.O. Box 5000
Trenton, NJ 08638
(609) 695-1434   Fax: (609) 695-2505
E-mail: scholarships@baberuthleague.org
Web: www.baberuthleague.org

Summary To provide financial assistance for college to high school senior girls who played Babe Ruth League softball.

Eligibility This program is open to graduating high school senior girls who played Babe Ruth League softball previously. Applicants must be planning to attend college. Along with their application, they must submit brief statements on why they played softball, what they enjoyed most as a participant, the benefits they gained by playing Babe Ruth softball, and how they feel having played Babe Ruth softball will help them to be successful in college and in life after graduation. Financial need is considered in the selection process.

Financial data The stipend is $1,000.

Duration 1 year.

Number awarded 1 each year.

Deadline August of each year.

[315]
JAMES J. WYCHOR SCHOLARSHIPS

Minnesota Broadcasters Association
Attn: Scholarship Program
3033 Excelsior Boulevard, Suite 440
Minneapolis, MN 55416
(612) 926-8123   Toll Free: (800) 245-5838
Fax: (612) 926-9761
E-mail: llasere@minnesotabroadcasters.com
Web: www.minnesotabroadcasters.com

Summary To provide financial assistance to women, minority, and other Minnesota residents interested in studying broadcasting at a college in any state.

Eligibility This program is open to residents of Minnesota who are accepted or enrolled at an accredited postsecondary institution in any state offering a broadcast-related curriculum. Applicants must have a high school or college GPA of 3.0 or higher and must submit a 500-word essay on why they wish to prepare for a career in broadcasting or electronic media. Employment in the broadcasting industry is not required, but students who are employed must include a letter from their general manager describing the duties they have performed as a radio or television station employee and evaluating their potential for success in the industry. Financial need is not considered in the selection process. Some of the scholarships are awarded only to minority and women candidates.

Financial data The stipend is $1,500.

Duration 1 year; recipients who are college seniors may reapply for an additional 1-year renewal as a graduate student.

Number awarded 10 each year, distributed as follows: 3 within the 7-county metro area, 5 allocated geographically throughout the state (northeast, northwest, central, southeast, southwest), and 2 reserved specifically for women and minority applicants.

Deadline June of each year.

[316]
JAN GWATNEY SCHOLARSHIP

United Daughters of the Confederacy
Attn: Education Director
328 North Boulevard
Richmond, VA 23220-4057
(804) 355-1636   Fax: (804) 353-1396
E-mail: hqudc@rcn.com
Web: www.hqudc.org/scholarships/scholarships.html

Summary To provide financial assistance to female lineal descendants of Confederate Veterans, especially those from designated southern states.

Eligibility Eligible to apply for these scholarships are female lineal descendants of worthy Confederates or collateral descendants who are current or former members of the Children of the Confederacy or current members of the United Daughters of the Confederacy. Applicants must submit a family financial report and certified proof of the Confederate record of 1 ancestor, with the company and regiment in which he served. They must have at least a 3.0 GPA in high school. Preference is given to residents of Georgia, Louisiana, or Texas.

Financial data The amount of this scholarship depends on the availability of funds.

Duration 1 year; may be renewed.

Additional information Members of the same family may not hold scholarships simultaneously, and only 1 application per family will be accepted within any 1 year. All requests for applications must be accompanied by a self-addressed stamped envelope.

Number awarded 1 each year.

Deadline April of each year.

[317]
JANE LORING JONES SCHOLARSHIPS

American Baptist Churches of the Rocky Mountains
Attn: American Baptist Women's Ministries
9085 East Mineral Circle, Suite 170
Centennial, CO 80112
(303) 988-3900   E-mail: web@abcrm.org
Web: www.abcrm.org

Summary To provide financial assistance to women who are members of churches affiliated with the American Baptist Churches (ABC) USA in Colorado, New Mexico, and Utah and interested in attending an ABC college in any state.

Eligibility This program is open to women under 26 years of age who are active members of churches cooperating with ABC in Colorado, New Mexico, or Utah. Applicants must be enrolled or planning to enroll full time at an ABC college or university in any state. They are not required to enter Christian service as a vocation, but they must have a real desire to prepare themselves for Christian leadership in the home, church, and community. Along with their application, they must submit a personal letter describing their Christian experience; their participation in the life of their church, school, and community; and their goals for the future. Selection is based on academic performance, Christian participation in church and school, and financial need. Preference is given to women entering their first or second year at an ABC school.

Financial data The stipend is $2,000 per year.

Duration 1 year; recipients may reapply.

Number awarded 1 or more each year.

Deadline March of each year.

[318]
JANE M. KLAUSMAN WOMEN IN BUSINESS SCHOLARSHIPS

Zonta International
Attn: Foundation
1211 West 22nd Street, Suite 900
Oak Brook, IL 60523-3384
(630) 928-1400   Fax: (630) 928-1559
E-mail: programs@zonta.org
Web: www.zonta.org

Summary To provide financial assistance to women working on an undergraduate or master's degree in business at a school in any country.

Eligibility This program is open to women who are working on a business-related degree at a college or university anywhere in the world at the level of the second year of an undergraduate program through the final year of a master's degree program. Applicants first compete at the club level, and then advance to district and international levels. Along with their

application, they must submit a 500-word essay that describes their academic and professional goals, the relevance of their program to the business field, and how this scholarship will assist them in reaching their goals. Selection is based on that essay, academic record, demonstrated intent to complete a program in business, achievement in business-related subjects, and 2 letters of recommendation.

Financial data District winners receive a $1,000 scholarship; the international winners receive a $5,000 scholarship.

Duration 1 year.

Additional information This program was established in 1998.

Number awarded The number of district winners varies each year; recently, 12 international winners (including 6 from the United States) were selected. Since this program was established, it has awarded nearly 200 of these scholarships to women from 34 countries.

Deadline Clubs set their own deadlines but must submit their winners to the district governor by May of each year.

[319]
JANE RING AND SUE RING-JARVI GIRLS'/ WOMEN'S HOCKEY SCHOLARSHIP

Saint Paul Foundation
Attn: Program Assistant
55 Fifth Street East, Suite 600
St. Paul, MN 55101-1797
(651) 325-4202   Toll Free: (800) 875-6167
Fax: (651) 224-8123
E-mail: jmu@saintpaulfoundation.org
Web: www.saintpaulfoundation.org/scholarships

Summary To provide financial assistance to female high school seniors in Minnesota who have played hockey in high school and plan to attend college in any state.

Eligibility This program is open to female hockey players graduating from high schools in Minnesota. Applicants must have a GPA of 3.0 or higher and be planning to attend an accredited 4-year college or university in any state. Along with their application, they must submit a 2-page personal statement describing how hockey has affected their life, the contributions they have made to hockey in high school, and what role they expect hockey to play in their future. Selection is based on athletic and academic achievement, character, leadership ability, ambition to succeed, and evidence of present and future useful citizenship.

Financial data The stipend is $2,000.

Duration 1 year; nonrenewable.

Additional information This program was established in 1996.

Number awarded Varies each year.

Deadline April of each year.

[320]
JANE WALKER SCHOLARSHIP

United Methodist Church-Alabama-West Florida
Conference
Attn: Commission on the Status and Role of Women
100 Interstate Park Drive, Suite 120
Montgomery, AL 36109
(334) 356-8014   Toll Free: (888) 873-3127
Fax: (334) 356-8029   E-mail: awfcrc@awfumc.org
Web: www.awfumc.org

Summary To provide financial assistance to female residents of the Alabama-West Florida Conference of the United Methodist Church (UMC) who are undergraduate or seminary students preparing for a church-related career.

Eligibility This program is open to women who are residents of the Alabama-West Florida Conference of the UMW and who affirm, represent, and advocate women's leadership in the church. Applicants must be accepted or enrolled at an approved UMC seminary or working on an undergraduate degree in Christian education at an approved UMC institution in any state. They must be a candidate for ministry or preparing for a UMC church-related career. Along with their application, they must submit a 500-word essay on why they are preparing for full-time Christian ministry and how they can promote the cause of women through this ministry. Financial need is considered in the selection process.

Financial data The stipend is $1,000.
Duration 1 year.
Number awarded 1 each year.
Deadline May of each year.

[321]
JANET CLARK MEMORIAL SCHOLARSHIP

Women in Aviation, International
Attn: Scholarships
Morningstar Airport
3647 State Route 503 South
West Alexandria, OH 45381-9354
(937) 839-4647   Fax: (937) 839-4645
E-mail: scholarships@wai.org
Web: www.wai.org/education/scholarships.cfm

Summary To provide financial assistance to members of Women in Aviation, International (WAI), especially those from Washington, who are studying aviation in college.

Eligibility This program is open to WAI members who are enrolled in school to prepare for a career in aviation (including, but not limited to, pilot, mechanic, avionics technician, engineer, meteorologist, dispatcher, flight attendant, air traffic controller, or airport manager). If they plan a career as a pilot, they must have a private pilot's license. Along with their application, they must submit 2 letters of recommendation, a 500-word essay on their aviation history and goals, a resume, copies of all aviation licenses and medical certificates, and the last 3 pages of their pilot logbook (if applicable). Selection is based on achievements, attitude toward self and others, commitment to success, dedication to career, financial need, motivation, reliability, responsibility, and teamwork. If they are enrolled in a program that issues grades, the selection process also includes GPA. Preference is given to residents of Washington and to applicants who have already made steps toward their chosen aviation career. An interview may be conducted at the WAI conference or at a location in Washington.

Financial data The stipend is $1,500. Funds are paid directly to an accredited program to be used for tuition, books, specific training, or housing.
Duration Funds must be used within 1 year of receipt.
Additional information WAI is a nonprofit professional organization dedicated to encouraging women to consider an aviation career and to providing educational outreach activities and networking resources to women active in the industry. This program is sponsored by the Washington State Chapter of WAI.
Number awarded 1 each year.
Deadline November of each year.

[322]
JANET CULLEN TANAKA SCHOLARSHIP

Association for Women Geoscientists
Attn: AWG Foundation
12000 North Washington Street, Suite 285
Thornton, CO 80241
(303) 412-6219   Fax: (303) 253-9220
E-mail: office@awg.org
Web: www.awg.org/EAS/scholarships.html

Summary To provide financial assistance to women from any state who are working on an undergraduate degree in geoscience at a college or university in Oregon or Washington.

Eligibility This program is open to undergraduate women from any state who are working on a bachelor's degree and committed to preparing for a career or graduate work in the geosciences, including geology, environmental or engineering geology, geochemistry, geophysics, hydrogeology, or hydrology. Applicants must be currently enrolled in a 2- or 4-year college or university in Oregon or Washington and have a GPA of 3.2 or higher. Along with their application, they must submit a 1-page essay summarizing their commitment to a career in the geosciences. Selection is based on potential for professional success, academic achievements, and financial need.

Financial data The stipend is $1,000. A second-place award of $500 may also be awarded, depending on the availability of funding.
Duration 1 year.
Additional information This program is sponsored by the Pacific Northwest Chapter of the Association for Women Geoscientists.
Number awarded 1 or 2 each year.
Deadline November of each year.

[323]
JAZZ PERFORMANCE AWARDS

Sigma Alpha Iota Philanthropies, Inc.
One Tunnel Road
Asheville, NC 28805
(828) 251-0606   Fax: (828) 251-0644
E-mail: nh@sai-national.org
Web: www.sigmaalphaiota.org

Summary To provide financial assistance to members of Sigma Alpha Iota (an organization of women musicians) who are interested in working on an undergraduate or graduate degree in jazz performance.

Eligibility This program is open to members of the organization who are enrolled in an undergraduate or graduate degree program in jazz performance or studies. Applicants must be younger than 32 years of age. Along with their application, they must submit a CD recording of a performance "set" of 30 to 45 minutes.

Financial data Stipends are $2,000 for the winner or $1,500 for the runner-up.

Duration 1 year.

Additional information These awards were first presented in 2006.

Number awarded 2 every 3 years.

Deadline March of the year of the awards (2012, 2015, etc.).

[324]
JAZZ STUDIES SCHOLARSHIP

Sigma Alpha Iota Philanthropies, Inc.
One Tunnel Road
Asheville, NC 28805
(828) 251-0606   Fax: (828) 251-0644
E-mail: nh@sai-national.org
Web: www.sigmaalphaiota.org

Summary To provide financial assistance to members of Sigma Alpha Iota (an organization of women musicians) who are interested in working on an undergraduate degree in jazz studies.

Eligibility This program is open to members of the organization who are working on an undergraduate music degree with an emphasis in jazz studies. Applicants must submit a 500-word essay on their career plans and professional goals in jazz studies and why they feel they are deserving of this scholarship. Financial need is not considered in the selection process.

Financial data The stipend is $1,500.

Duration 1 year.

Number awarded 1 each year.

Deadline March of each year.

[325]
JCDA NATIONAL SCHOLARSHIP

Catholic Daughters of the Americas
Attn: Scholarship Chair
10 West 71st Street
New York, NY 10023
(212) 877-3041   Fax: (212) 724-5923
E-mail: CDofANatl@aol.com
Web: www.catholicdaughters.org

Summary To provide financial assistance for college to members of the Junior Catholic Daughters of the Americas (JCDA).

Eligibility This program is open to students entering college who have been JCDA members for at least 2 years. Applicants must submit a 500-word essay on their Catholic values that were enhanced during their years as a JCDA member and that they will use in college. Financial need is not considered in the selection process.

Financial data The stipend is $1,000.

Duration 1 year.

Number awarded 1 each year.

Deadline April of each year.

[326]
JEAN FITZGERALD SCHOLARSHIP

Hawai'i Community Foundation
Attn: Scholarship Department
827 Fort Street Mall
Honolulu, HI 96813
(808) 537-6333   Toll Free: (888) 731-3863
Fax: (808) 521-6286
E-mail: scholarships@hcf-hawaii.org
Web: www.hawaiicommunityfoundation.org/scholarships

Summary To provide financial assistance to women tennis players in Hawaii who are entering freshmen at a college in any state.

Eligibility This program is open to female Hawaiian residents who are active tennis players entering their freshman year at a college or university in any state as full-time students. Preference may be given to members of the Hawai'i Pacific Section of the United States Tennis Association (USTA). Applicants must be able to demonstrate academic achievement (GPA of 2.7 or higher), good moral character, and financial need. Along with their application, they must submit a short statement indicating their reasons for attending college, their planned course of study, their career goals, and what community service means to them.

Financial data The amounts of the awards depend on the availability of funds and the need of the recipient. Recently, the average value of each of the scholarships awarded by the foundation was more than $2,000.

Duration 1 year.

Number awarded Varies each year; recently, 2 of these scholarships were awarded.

Deadline February of each year.

[327]
JEAN TUCKER STRADLEY SCHOLARSHIP

Kappa Delta Sorority
Attn: Foundation Manager
3205 Players Lane
Memphis, TN 38125
(901) 748-1897   Toll Free: (800) 536-1897
Fax: (901) 748-0949 E-mail: kappadelta@kappadelta.org
Web: www.kappadelta.org/scholarships

Summary To provide financial assistance to members of Kappa Delta Sorority who are majoring in elementary education.

Eligibility This program is open to undergraduate members of Kappa Delta Sorority. Applicants must submit a personal statement giving their reasons for applying for this scholarship, an official undergraduate transcript, and 2 letters of recommendation. They must be majoring in elementary education. Selection is based on academic excellence; service to the chapter, alumnae association, or national Kappa Delta; service to the campus and community; personal objectives and goals; potential; recommendations; and financial need.

Financial data The stipend is $2,000 per year. Funds may be used only for tuition, fees, and books, not for room and board.

Duration 1 year; may be renewed.
Number awarded 1 each year.
Deadline January of each year.

[328]
JEANNE L. HAMMOND MEMORIAL SCHOLARSHIP

Maine Federation of Business and Professional Women's
Clubs
Attn: BPW/Maine Futurama Foundation
c/o Susan Tardie, Co-President
25 Hall Street
Fort Kent, ME 04743
E-mail: susan.tardie@maine.edu
Web: www.bpwmefoundation.org/files/index.php?id=10

Summary To provide financial assistance to female high school seniors and recent graduates in Maine who plan to attend college in any state.

Eligibility This program is open to women who are seniors graduating from high schools in Maine or recent graduates of those schools. Applicants must be planning to enroll at least half time for their first year of postsecondary study at an accredited college or university in any state. They must have a realistic goal for their education. Along with their application, they must submit a statement describing their educational and personal goals, including their financial need. First priority is given to women who can demonstrate a record of school and/or community involvement. Second priority is given to applicants who are interested in working on a journalism degree, members of the Maine Federation of Business and Professional Women's Clubs (BPW/Maine) and their dependents, and members of the American Association of University Women (AAUW) and their dependents.

Financial data The stipend is $1,200. Funds are paid directly to the recipient's school.

Duration 1 year.
Number awarded 1 or more each year.
Deadline April of each year.

[329]
JEANNETTE RANKIN AWARD

Jeannette Rankin Foundation, Inc.
1 Huntington Road, Suite 701
Athens, GA 30606
(706) 208-1211   Fax: (706) 548-0202
E-mail: info@rankinfoundation.org
Web: www.rankinfoundation.org

Summary To provide financial assistance for college to women who are 35 years of age or older.

Eligibility This program is open to women who are 35 years of age or older and working on a technical or vocational certificate, associate degree, or first bachelor's degree. Applicants must meet standards of a low-income household, currently defined as net income less than $13,958 for a family of 1, rising to $53,491 for a family of 6. Along with their application, they must submit a 2-page essay that includes a description of their academic and career goals, what they have done that makes them proud, and how their education will benefit themselves, their family, and their community. Selection is based on the applicants' goals, plan for reaching those goals,

challenges they have faced, and their financial situation. U.S. citizenship is required.

Financial data The stipend is $2,000.
Duration 1 year; nonrenewable.
Additional information This program began in 1978. Awards are not given to students enrolled in graduate courses or working on a second undergraduate degree.
Number awarded Varies each year; recently, 80 of these scholarships were awarded.
Deadline February of each year.

[330]
JESSICA POWELL LOFTIS SCHOLARSHIP FOR ACTEENS

Woman's Missionary Union
Attn: WMU Foundation
100 Missionary Ridge
Birmingham, AL 35242
(205) 408-5525   Toll Free: (877) 482-4483
Fax: (205) 408-5508   E-mail: wmufoundation@wmu.org
Web: www.wmufoundation.com

Summary To provide financial assistance for college or other activities to female high school seniors who have been active in the Southern Baptist Convention's Acteens (Academic/Events/Training).

Eligibility This program is open to female high school seniors who are members of a Baptist church and active in Acteens. Applicants must 1) be planning to attend college and have completed *Quest for Vision* in the MissionsQuest program or StudiAct; 2) have been an Acteen for at least 1 year and be planning to attend an Acteens event; or 3) be an Acteens leader who is pursuing academic or leadership training to lead an Acteens group. Along with their application, they must submit an essay listing their major accomplishments and missions activities.

Financial data A stipend is awarded (amount not specified).
Duration 1 year.
Additional information This program was established in 1995 by Woman's Missionary Union, an Auxiliary to Southern Baptist Convention.
Number awarded 1 or more each year.
Deadline February of each year.

[331]
JESSIE D. NELSON MEDICAL SCHOLARSHIP

International Order of the Rainbow for Girls-Grand
Assembly of California
California Rainbow for Girls Foundation
c/o J. Dennis Conwell, Scholarship Committee Chair
424 Colfax Drive
San Jose, CA 95123-3403
(408) 629-7663   E-mail: dencon21@sbcglobal.net
Web: gocarainbow.org/scholarships.htm

Summary To provide financial assistance to members of the International Order of the Rainbow for Girls in California who are studying a health or medical field at a school in any state.

Eligibility This program is open to Rainbow Girls in California who are enrolled as sophomores or higher at a college in any state. Applicants must be working on a degree in a field of health or medicine. Along with their application, they must submit a brief essay on their career goals, how they plan to accomplish those, personal philosophy, and any unusual family or financial circumstances.

Financial data   The stipend is $2,500.

Duration   1 year.

Number awarded   1 each year.

Deadline   February of each year.

[332]
JESSIE FANYO PAYNE SCHOLARSHIP

Alpha Chi Omega Foundation
Attn: Foundation Programs Coordinator
5939 Castle Creek Parkway North Drive
Indianapolis, IN 46250-4343
(317) 579-5050, ext. 262   Fax: (317) 579-5051
E-mail: foundation@alphachiomega.org
Web: www.alphachiomega.org/index.aspx?id=1030

Summary   To provide financial assistance to undergraduate or alumnae members of Alpha Chi Omega who are interested in working on a degree in communications.

Eligibility   This program is open to junior, senior, and graduate members of Alpha Chi Omega who are full-time students in the field of communications with an emphasis on journalism and public relations. Selection is based on academic achievement, chapter involvement, campus and community involvement, and financial need.

Financial data   A stipend is awarded (amount not specified).

Duration   1 year.

Number awarded   1 each year.

Deadline   March of each year.

[333]
JILL S. TIETJEN P.E. SCHOLARSHIP

Society of Women Engineers
Attn: Scholarship Selection Committee
120 South LaSalle Street, Suite 1515
Chicago, IL 60603-3572
(312) 596-5223   Toll Free: (877) SWE-INFO
Fax: (312) 644-8557
E-mail: scholarshipapplication@swe.org
Web: societyofwomenengineers.swe.org

Summary   To provide financial assistance to women working on an undergraduate or graduate degree in engineering or computer science.

Eligibility   This program is open to women who will be sophomores, juniors, seniors, or graduate students at ABET-accredited colleges and universities. Applicants must be U.S. citizens majoring in computer science or engineering and have a GPA of 3.0 or higher. Selection is based on merit.

Financial data   The stipend is $1,500.

Duration   1 year.

Number awarded   1 each year.

Deadline   February of each year.

[334]
JOHN AND MURIEL LANDIS SCHOLARSHIPS

American Nuclear Society
Attn: Scholarship Coordinator
555 North Kensington Avenue
La Grange Park, IL 60526-5592
(708) 352-6611   Toll Free: (800) 323-3044
Fax: (708) 352-0499   E-mail: outreach@ans.org
Web: www.ans.org/honors/scholarships

Summary   To provide financial assistance to undergraduate or graduate students (especially women and minorities) who are interested in preparing for a career in nuclear-related fields.

Eligibility   This program is open to undergraduate and graduate students at colleges or universities located in the United States who are preparing for, or planning to prepare for, a career in nuclear science, nuclear engineering, or a nuclear-related field. Qualified high school seniors are also eligible. Applicants must have greater than average financial need and have experienced circumstances that render them disadvantaged. They must be sponsored by an organization (e.g., plant branch, local section, student section) within the American Nuclear Society (ANS). Along with their application, they must submit an essay on their academic and professional goals, experiences that have affected those goals, etc. Selection is based on that essay, academic achievement, letters of recommendation, and financial need. Women and members of minority groups are especially urged to apply. U.S. citizenship is not required.

Financial data   The stipend is $5,000, to be used to cover tuition, books, fees, room, and board.

Duration   1 year; nonrenewable.

Number awarded   Up to 8 each year.

Deadline   January of each year.

[335]
JOHN EDGAR THOMSON FOUNDATION AID

John Edgar Thomson Foundation
Attn: Director
201 South 18th Street, Suite 318
Philadelphia, PA 19103
(215) 545-6083   Toll Free: (800) 888-1278
Fax: (215) 545-5102   E-mail: sjethomson@aol.com

Summary   To provide financial assistance for education or maintenance to daughters of railroad employees who died while employed by a railroad in the United States.

Eligibility   This program is open to women whose parent died in the active employ of a railroad in the United States, although the cause of death need not be work related. Applicants must live in the home of the surviving parent or guardian (unless attending college full time and living on campus), be in good health, and receive satisfactory academic grades. Eligibility of the daughter is also dependent upon the parent's remaining unmarried. Consideration is given to other factors as well, including the financial status of the family.

Financial data   Payments are made on a monthly basis to assist with the education or maintenance of eligible daughters. The payment is available from infancy to age 18 or, under certain circumstances, to age 22 (for pursuit of higher education). This supplement to family income is to be used in its entirety for the benefit of the recipient. The grant may be terminated at any time if the financial need ceases or the daughter or surviving parent is either unable or fails to meet the eligibility requirements.

Duration Monthly payments may be made up to 22 years.

Additional information This foundation was established in 1882. Grantees are encouraged to participate in religious services of their faith.

Number awarded Varies; generally, 100 or more each year.

Deadline Deadline not specified.

[336]
JOHN L. AND ELEANORE I. MCKINLEY SCHOLARSHIP

Delta Zeta Sorority
Attn: Foundation Coordinator
202 East Church Street
Oxford, OH 45056
(513) 523-7597   Fax: (513) 523-1921
E-mail: DZFoundation@dzshq.com
Web: www.deltazeta.org

Summary To provide financial assistance for continued undergraduate study to members of Delta Zeta Sorority.

Eligibility This program is open to members of the sorority who are entering their junior or senior year and have a GPA of 3.0 or higher. Applicants must submit an official transcript, a statement of their career goals, information on their service to the sorority, documentation of campus activities and/or community involvement, a list of academic honors, and an explanation of their financial need.

Financial data The stipend ranges from $500 to $2,500, depending on the availability of funds.

Duration 1 year; nonrenewable.

Number awarded 1 each year.

Deadline February of each year.

[337]
JOSEPHINE AND BENJAMIN WEBBER TRUST SCHOLARSHIPS

Arizona Association of Family and Consumer Sciences
Attn: Webber Educational Grant Committee
Kathryn L. Hatch
4843 North Via Sonrisa
Tucson, AZ 85718-5724
(502) 577-6109   E-mail: klhatch@u.arizona.edu
Web: ag.arizona.edu/webbertrusts

Summary To provide financial assistance to Hispanic women from mining towns in Arizona who are interested in working on an undergraduate or graduate degree in a field related to family and consumer sciences at a school in the state.

Eligibility This program is open to Hispanic women who reside in the following Arizona mining towns: Ajo, Arizona City, Bisbee, Clifton, Douglas, Duncan, Globe, Green Valley, Hayden, Kingman, Kearny, Mammoth, Morenci, Prescott, Safford, Sahuarita, San Manuel, Seligman, Superior, or Winkelman. If too few female Hispanic residents of those towns apply, the program may be open to 1) non-Hispanic women who live in those towns, and/or 2) Hispanic women who currently live elsewhere in Arizona and whose parents or grandparents had lived or continue to live in those communities.

Applicants must be enrolled or planning to enroll at a college or university in Arizona to work on an undergraduate or graduate degree. Eligible fields of study include those in the following categories: foods, nutrition, and/or dietetics; restaurant and food service management; culinary arts; family studies; interior design; family and consumer science education; dietetic education; early childhood education; or apparel and clothing. Along with their application, they must submit a 4-page essay that includes information on 1) why they have chosen to work on a degree in family and consumer sciences; 2) what they think will be the major obstacles to the successful completion of their first year as a Webber scholar; and 3) what they think their personal and professional life will be like following completion of their postsecondary education. Financial need is also considered in the selection process.

Financial data Funding at public colleges and universities provides for payment of tuition and fees, books, educational supplies, housing, food, and transportation to and from campus. At private institutions, stipend amounts are equivalent to those at public schools.

Duration 1 year; may be renewed for a total of 8 semesters and 2 summers of undergraduate study or 4 semesters and 2 summers of graduate study.

Additional information This program was established in 1980.

Number awarded Varies each year; recently, 5 of these scholarships were awarded.

Deadline March of each year.

[338]
JOYCE ANNE VITELLI MEMORIAL SCHOLARSHIP

Kappa Alpha Theta Foundation
Attn: Scholarships
8740 Founders Road
Indianapolis, IN 46268-1337
(317) 876-1870   Toll Free: (800) KAO-1870
Fax: (317) 876-1925
E-mail: FDNmail@kappaalphatheta.org
Web: www.kappaalphathetafoundation.org

Summary To provide financial assistance to undergraduate members of Kappa Alpha Theta, especially those majoring in music or fine arts.

Eligibility This program is open to members of Kappa Alpha Theta who are full-time undergraduates at a college or university in Canada or the United States. Preference is given to applicants majoring in music or fine arts. Along with their application, they must submit an official transcript, personal essays on assigned topics related to their involvement in Kappa Alpha Theta, and 2 letters of reference. Financial need is not considered in the selection process.

Financial data The stipend is $10,150.

Duration 1 year.

Number awarded 1 each year.

Deadline January of each year.

[339]
JUANITA KIDD STOUT SCHOLARSHIP PROGRAM

Delta Sigma Theta Sorority, Inc.
Attn: Scholarship and Standards Committee Chair
1707 New Hampshire Avenue, N.W.
Washington, DC 20009
(202) 986-2400　　　　　Fax: (202) 986-2513
E-mail: dstemail@deltasigmatheta.org
Web: www.deltasigmatheta.org

Summary To provide financial assistance to members of Delta Sigma Theta who are working on an undergraduate degree in criminal justice.

Eligibility This program is open to current undergraduate students who are working on a degree in criminal justice. Applicants must be active, dues-paying members of Delta Sigma Theta. Selection is based on meritorious achievement.

Financial data The stipends range from $1,000 to $2,000. The funds may be used to cover tuition, fees, and living expenses.

Duration 1 year; may be renewed for 1 additional year.

Additional information This sponsor is a traditionally-African American social sorority. The application fee is $20.

Deadline April of each year.

[340]
JUDGE HAZEL PALMER GENERAL SCHOLARSHIP

Missouri Business and Professional Women's Foundation, Inc.
P.O. Box 28243
Kansas City, MO 64188
(816) 333-6959　　　　　Fax: (816) 333-6959
E-mail: jo.mofedbpw@gmail.com
Web: www.mofedbpw.org/files/index.php?id=14

Summary To provide financial assistance to members of the Missouri Federation of Business and Professional Women (BPW Missouri) who are interested in working on a college degree leading to public service.

Eligibility This program is open to BPW Missouri members who have been accepted into an accredited program or course of study in any state to work on a degree leading to public service. Along with their application, they must submit brief statements on the following: achievements and/or specific recognitions in their field of endeavor; professional and/or civic affiliations; present and long-range career goals; how they plan to participate in and contribute to their community upon completion of their program of study; why they feel they would make a good recipient; and any special circumstances that may have influenced their ability to continue or complete their education. They must also demonstrate financial need and U.S. citizenship.

Financial data A stipend is awarded (amount not specified).

Duration 1 year.

Number awarded 1 each year.

Deadline December of each year.

[341]
JUDGE WILLIAM F. COOPER SCHOLARSHIP

Center for Scholarship Administration, Inc.
Attn: Wells Fargo Accounts
4320 Wade Hampton Boulevard, Suite G
Taylors, SC 29687
Toll Free: (866) 608-0001
E-mail: sallyking@bellsouth.net
Web: www.csascholars.org/copr/index.php

Summary To provide financial assistance to female high school seniors in Georgia who plan to attend college in any state.

Eligibility This program is open to female seniors graduating from high schools in Georgia. Preference is given to residents of Chatham County. Applicants must be planning to enroll at an accredited 2- or 4-year college, university, or technical college in any state to study any field except law, theology, or medicine. They must be able to demonstrate financial need. Along with their application, they must submit a 1-page essay on their strengths and their most important achievements in their school and community, including hobbies, interests, sports, volunteer work, employment, future plans, and career goals. Selection is based on academic achievement, community service, and financial need.

Financial data A stipend is awarded (amount not specified).

Duration 1 year; may be renewed up to 3 additional years or until completion of a bachelor's degree, whichever is earlier, provided the recipient maintains a GPA of 2.0 or higher.

Number awarded 1 or more each year.

Deadline February of each year.

[342]
JUDITH MCMANUS PRICE SCHOLARSHIPS

American Planning Association
Attn: Leadership Affairs Associate
205 North Michigan Avenue, Suite 1200
Chicago, IL 60601
(312) 431-9100　　　　　Fax: (312) 786-6700
E-mail: fellowship@planning.org
Web: www.planning.org/scholarships/apa

Summary To provide financial assistance to women and underrepresented minority students enrolled in undergraduate or graduate degree programs at recognized planning schools.

Eligibility This program is open to undergraduate and graduate students in urban and regional planning who are women or members of the following minority groups: African American, Hispanic American, or Native American. Applicants must be citizens of the United States and able to document financial need. They must intend to work as practicing planners in the public sector. Along with their application, they must submit a 2-page personal and background statement describing how their education will be applied to career goals and why they chose planning as a career path. Selection is based (in order of importance), on: 1) commitment to planning as reflected in their personal statement and on their resume; 2) academic achievement and/or improvement during the past 2 years; 3) letters of recommendation; 4) financial need; and 5) professional presentation.

Financial data Stipends range from $2,000 to $4,000 per year. The money may be applied to tuition and living expenses only. Payment is made to the recipient's university and divided by terms in the school year.
Duration 1 year; recipients may reapply.
Additional information This program was established in 2002.
Number awarded Varies each year; recently, 3 of these scholarships were awarded.
Deadline April of each year.

[343]
JUDITH RESNIK MEMORIAL SCHOLARSHIP
Society of Women Engineers
Attn: Scholarship Selection Committee
120 South LaSalle Street, Suite 1515
Chicago, IL 60603-3572
(312) 596-5223   Toll Free: (877) SWE-INFO
Fax: (312) 644-8557
E-mail: scholarshipapplication@swe.org
Web: societyofwomenengineers.swe.org

Summary To provide financial assistance to undergraduate members of the Society of Women Engineers (SWE) who are majoring in designated engineering specialties.
Eligibility This program is open to society members who are entering their sophomore, junior, or senior year at an ABET-accredited 4-year college or university. Applicants must be studying aerospace, aeronautical, or astronautical engineering and have a GPA of 3.0 or higher. Selection is based on merit.
Financial data The stipend is $3,000.
Duration 1 year.
Additional information This award was established in 1988 to honor society member Judith Resnik, who was killed aboard the Challenger space shuttle.
Number awarded 1 each year.
Deadline February of each year.

[344]
JUDY CORMAN MEMORIAL SCHOLARSHIP AND INTERNSHIP
New York Women in Communications, Inc.
Attn: NYWICI Foundation
355 Lexington Avenue, 15th Floor
New York, NY 10017-6603
(212) 297-2133   Fax: (212) 370-9047
E-mail: nywicipr@nywici.org
Web: www.nywici.org/foundation/scholarships

Summary To provide financial assistance and work experience to female residents of designated eastern states who are interested in preparing for a career in public relations at a college or graduate school in any state.
Eligibility This program is open to women who are seniors graduating from high schools in New York, New Jersey, Connecticut, or Pennsylvania or undergraduate or graduate students who are permanent residents of those states; they must be attending or planning to attend a college or university in any state. Graduate students must be members of New York Women in Communications, Inc. (NYWICI). Also eligible are women who reside outside the 4 states but are currently enrolled at a college or university within 1 of the 5 boroughs of

New York City. Applicants must be preparing for a career in public relations and be interested in a summer internship with Scholastic. They must have a GPA of 3.2 or higher. Along with their application, they must submit a 2-page resume that includes school and extracurricular activities, significant achievements, academic honors and awards, and community service work; a personal essay of 300 to 500 words on their choice of an assigned topic that changes annually; 2 letters of recommendation; and an official transcript. Selection is based on academic record, need, demonstrated leadership, participation in school and community activities, honors, work experience, goals and aspirations, and unusual personal and/or family circumstances. U.S. citizenship is required.
Financial data The scholarship stipend ranges up to $10,000; the internship is salaried (amount not specified).
Duration 1 year.
Additional information This program is sponsored by Scholastic, Inc.
Number awarded 1 each year.
Deadline January of each year.

[345]
JUNIOR GIRLS SCHOLARSHIPS
Ladies Auxiliary to the Veterans of Foreign Wars
c/o National Headquarters
406 West 34th Street
Kansas City, MO 64111
(816) 561-8655   Fax: (816) 931-4753
E-mail: info@ladiesauxvfw.org
Web: www.ladiesauxvfw.org/html/scholarships.html

Summary To provide financial assistance for college to outstanding members of a Junior Girls Unit of the Ladies Auxiliary to the Veterans of Foreign Wars.
Eligibility Applicants must have been active members of a unit for 1 year, have held an office in the unit, and be between 13 and 16 years of age. Previous winners are not eligible, although former applicants who did not receive scholarships may reapply. Selection is based on participation in the Junior Girls Unit (40 points), school activities (30 points), and scholastic grades (30 points).
Financial data The winner receives a $7,500 scholarship. Funds are paid directly to the college of the recipient's choice. In addition, $100 is awarded to each Junior Girl who is selected as the department winner and entered in the national competition.
Duration 1 year.
Number awarded 1 each year.
Deadline March of each year.

[346]
JUNIOR VOLUNTEER SCHOLARSHIP AWARD
American Legion Auxiliary
8945 North Meridian Street
Indianapolis, IN 46260
(317) 569-4500   Fax: (317) 569-4502
E-mail: VA&R@legion-aux.org
Web: www.legion-aux.org

Summary To provide financial assistance for college to junior members of the American Legion Auxiliary who have provided outstanding volunteer service.

Eligibility This program is open to college-bound high school seniors who are junior members of the American Legion Auxiliary. Applicants must submit documentation of the total number of volunteer hours they have served in a Veterans Administration facility and/or in combination with Field or Home Service hours. The president or education chair of their unit should submit a 500-word introduction of the candidate. Selection is based on the total number of hours served.

Financial data The stipend is $1,000.

Duration 1 year.

Additional information Applications are available from the president of the candidate's own unit or from the secretary or education chair of the department.

Number awarded 5 each year: 1 in each division of the American Legion Auxiliary.

Deadline Applications must be submitted to the unit president by March of each year.

[347]
KA'IULANI HOME FOR GIRLS TRUST SCHOLARSHIP

Hawai'i Community Foundation
Attn: Scholarship Department
827 Fort Street Mall
Honolulu, HI 96813
(808) 537-6333   Toll Free: (888) 731-3863
Fax: (808) 521-6286
E-mail: scholarships@hcf-hawaii.org
Web: www.hawaiicommunityfoundation.org/scholarships

Summary To provide financial assistance to women of Native Hawaiian ancestry who are attending college in any state.

Eligibility This program is open to women of Native Hawaiian ancestry who are entering their freshman or sophomore year at a college or university in any state. Applicants must demonstrate academic achievement (GPA of 3.0 or higher), good moral character, and financial need. Along with their application, they must submit a short statement indicating their reasons for attending college, their planned course of study, their career goals, and what community service means to them.

Financial data The amounts of the awards depend on the availability of funds and the need of the recipient. Recently, the average value of each of the scholarships awarded by the foundation was more than $2,000.

Duration 1 year; may be renewed.

Additional information This fund was established in 1963 when the Ka'iulani Home for Girls, formerly used to provide boarding home facilities for young women of Native Hawaiian ancestry, was demolished and the property sold.

Number awarded Varies each year.

Deadline February of each year.

[348]
KANSAS LEGION AUXILIARY L.P.N. SCHOLARSHIPS

American Legion Auxiliary
Department of Kansas
1314 S.W. Topeka Boulevard
Topeka, KS 66612-1886
(785) 232-1396   Fax: (785) 232-1008
E-mail: alakansas@sbcglobal.net
Web: www.kslegionaux.org/edcaschol.html

Summary To provide financial assistance to veterans' spouses, widows, or children from Kansas who are attending a college or university in any state to prepare for a career as a Licensed Practical Nurse (L.P.N.).

Eligibility This program is open to the children, spouses, and unremarried widows of veterans who are entering college for the first time. Applicants must be residents of Kansas attending a school in any state that offers certification as an L.P.N. Financial need is considered in the selection process.

Financial data A stipend is awarded (amount not specified).

Duration 1 year.

Number awarded 1 or more each year.

Deadline March of each year.

[349]
KAPPA ALPHA THETA FOUNDERS' MEMORIAL SCHOLARSHIPS

Kappa Alpha Theta Foundation
Attn: Scholarships
8740 Founders Road
Indianapolis, IN 46268-1337
(317) 876-1870   Toll Free: (800) KAO-1870
Fax: (317) 876-1925
E-mail: FDNmail@kappaalphatheta.org
Web: www.kappaalphathetafoundation.org

Summary To provide financial assistance for undergraduate study in the United States or abroad to members of Kappa Alpha Theta.

Eligibility This program is open to members of Kappa Alpha Theta who are enrolled full time as juniors at a college or university in Canada or the United States. Along with their application, they must submit an official transcript, personal essays on assigned topics related to their involvement in Kappa Alpha Theta, and 2 letters of reference. Financial need is not considered in the selection process.

Financial data The stipend is $12,000.

Duration 1 year.

Additional information Recipients may study abroad, provided they do so as part of a program leading to a degree from an institution in the United States or Canada. This program consists of the following named scholarships: the Bettie Locke Hamilton Memorial Scholarship, the Alice Allen Brant Memorial Scholarship, the Bettie Tipton Lindsey Memorial Scholarship, and the Hannah Fitch Shaw Memorial Scholarship.

Number awarded 4 each year.

Deadline December of each year.

[350]
KAPPA ALPHA THETA UNDERGRADUATE SCHOLARSHIPS

Kappa Alpha Theta Foundation
Attn: Scholarships
8740 Founders Road
Indianapolis, IN 46268-1337
(317) 876-1870   Toll Free: (800) KAO-1870
Fax: (317) 876-1925
E-mail: FDNmail@kappaalphatheta.org
Web: www.kappaalphathetafoundation.org

Summary To provide financial assistance for college in the United States or abroad to members of Kappa Alpha Theta.

Eligibility This program is open to members of Kappa Alpha Theta who are enrolled full time at a college or university in Canada or the United States. Along with their application, they must submit an official transcript, personal essays on assigned topics related to their involvement in Kappa Alpha Theta, and 2 letters of reference. Financial need is not considered in the selection process.

Financial data Stipends range from $1,000 to $7,100. Recently, the average was $2,700.

Duration 1 year. Recipients may reapply, but they may receive a maximum lifetime amount of $20,000 from the foundation.

Additional information Recipients may study abroad, provided they do so as part of a program leading to a degree from an institution in the United States or Canada.

Number awarded Varies each year; recently, the organization awarded more than 200 undergraduate and graduate scholarships, with a total value of more than $500,000.

Deadline January of each year.

[351]
KAPPA DELTA SORORITY UNDERGRADUATE SCHOLARSHIPS

Kappa Delta Sorority
Attn: Foundation Manager
3205 Players Lane
Memphis, TN 38125
(901) 748-1897   Toll Free: (800) 536-1897
Fax: (901) 748-0949 E-mail: kappadelta@kappadelta.org
Web: www.kappadelta.org/scholarships

Summary To provide financial assistance to members of Kappa Delta Sorority who are interested in continuing their undergraduate education.

Eligibility This program is open to undergraduate members of Kappa Delta Sorority. Applicants must submit a personal statement giving their reasons for applying for this scholarship, an official undergraduate transcript, and 2 letters of recommendation. Most scholarships are available to all undergraduate members, but some restrict the field of study and others are limited to members at specified chapters. Selection is based on academic excellence; service to the chapter, alumnae association, or national Kappa Delta; service to the campus and community; personal objectives and goals; potential; recommendations; and financial need.

Financial data Stipends range from $500 to $4,000 per year. Funds may be used only for tuition, fees, and books, not for room and board.

Duration 1 year; may be renewed.

Additional information This program includes the following named scholarships that have no additional restrictions: the Kappa Delta Founders' Scholarships, the Grayce Chase Scholarship, the Grace Follmer Scholarship, the Helen Follmer Lutz Scholarship, the M. Amanda Gordon Scholarships, the Marilyn Mock Scholarship, the Dorothy Ramage Scholarship, the Margaret Budd Haemer Scholarship, the Muriel Johnstone Scholarships, and the Ernestine L. Newman Scholarship.

Number awarded Varies each year; recently, the sorority awarded a total of 41 scholarships: 4 at $4,000, 27 at $2,000, 8 at $1,000, and 2 at $500.

Deadline January of each year.

[352]
KAPPA KAPPA GAMMA UNDERGRADUATE SCHOLARSHIPS

Kappa Kappa Gamma Fraternity
Attn: Foundation Administrator
530 East Town Street
P.O. Box 38
Columbus, OH 43216-0038
(614) 228-6515   Toll Free: (866) KKG-1870
Fax: (614) 228-7809   E-mail: kkghq@kappa.org
Web: www.kappakappagamma.org

Summary To provide financial assistance for college to members of Kappa Kappa Gamma.

Eligibility This program is open to members of Kappa Kappa Gamma who are enrolled full time and have a GPA of 3.0 or higher for each academic term. Applicants must be initiated members; associate members are not eligible. Along with their application, they must submit a personal essay or letter describing their educational and career goals and financial need. Selection is based on merit, academic achievement, participation in sorority activities, and financial need.

Financial data A stipend is awarded (amount not specified).

Duration 1 year.

Number awarded Varies each year; recently, the foundation awarded a total of 152 undergraduate and graduate scholarships with a value of $466,812.

Deadline January of each year.

[353]
KAREN HAUSCHILD FRIDAY SCHOLARSHIP

American Meteorological Society
Attn: Fellowship/Scholarship Program
45 Beacon Street
Boston, MA 02108-3693
(617) 227-2426, ext. 246   Fax: (617) 742-8718
E-mail: scholar@ametsoc.org
Web: www.ametsoc.org

Summary To provide financial assistance to female undergraduates majoring in meteorology or an aspect of atmospheric sciences.

Eligibility This program is open to full-time female students entering their final year of undergraduate study and majoring in meteorology or an aspect of the atmospheric or related oceanic and hydrologic sciences. Applicants must intend to make atmospheric or related sciences their career. They must be U.S. citizens or permanent residents enrolled at a

U.S. institution and have a cumulative GPA of 3.25 or higher. Along with their application, they must submit 200-word essays on 1) their most important achievements that qualify them for this scholarship, and 2) their career goals in the atmospheric or related oceanic or hydrologic fields. Financial need is considered in the selection process.

Financial data   The stipend is $2,500.

Duration   1 year.

Number awarded   1 each year.

Deadline   February of each year.

[354]
KATE GLEASON SCHOLARSHIP

ASME International
Attn: Centers Administrator
Three Park Avenue, 22nd Floor
New York, NY 10016-5990
(212) 591-8131   Toll Free: (800) THE-ASME
Fax: (212) 591-7143   E-mail: LefeverB@asme.org
Web: www.asme.org

Summary   To provide financial assistance to female undergraduate and graduate students from any country who are working on a degree in mechanical engineering.

Eligibility   This program is open to women who are enrolled in an ABET-accredited or equivalent mechanical engineering, mechanical engineering technology, or related undergraduate or graduate program. Applicants must submit a nomination from their department head, a recommendation from a faculty member, and an official transcript. Only 1 nomination may be submitted per department. There are no citizenship requirements, but study must be conducted in the United States. Selection is based on academic ability and potential contribution to the mechanical engineering profession.

Financial data   The stipend is $3,000.

Duration   1 year.

Number awarded   1 each year.

Deadline   February of each year.

[355]
KATHERN F. GRUBER SCHOLARSHIPS

Blinded Veterans Association
477 H Street, N.W.
Washington, DC 20001-2694
(202) 371-8880   Toll Free: (800) 669-7079
Fax: (202) 371-8258   E-mail: bva@bva.org
Web: www.bva.org/services.html

Summary   To provide financial assistance for undergraduate or graduate study to spouses and children of blinded veterans.

Eligibility   This program is open to dependent children and spouses of blinded veterans of the U.S. armed forces. The veteran need not be a member of the Blinded Veterans Association. The veteran's blindness may be either service connected or nonservice connected, but it must meet the following definition: central visual acuity of 20/200 or less in the better eye with corrective glasses, or central visual acuity of more than 20/200 if there is a field defect in which the peripheral field has contracted to such an extent that the widest diameter of visual field subtends an angular distance no greater than 20 degrees in the better eye. Applicants must

have been accepted or be currently enrolled as a full-time student in an undergraduate or graduate program at an accredited institution of higher learning. Along with their application, they must submit a 300-word essay on their career goals and aspirations. Financial need is not considered in the selection process.

Financial data   The stipend is $2,000; funds are intended to be used to cover the student's expenses, including tuition, other academic fees, books, dormitory fees, and cafeteria fees. Funds are paid directly to the recipient's school.

Duration   1 year; recipients may reapply.

Additional information   Scholarships may be used for only 1 degree (vocational, bachelor's, or graduate) or non-graduate certificate (e.g., nursing, secretarial).

Number awarded   6 each year.

Deadline   April of each year.

[356]
KATHY LOUDAT MUSIC SCHOLARSHIP

New Mexico Baptist Foundation
5325 Wyoming Boulevard, N.E.
P.O. Box 16560
Albuquerque, NM 87191-6560
(505) 332-3777   Toll Free: (877) 841-3777
Fax: (505) 332-2777   E-mail: foundation@nmbf.com
Web: www.bcnm.com

Summary   To provide financial assistance to female members of Southern Baptist churches in New Mexico who are attending college in any state to prepare for a career in church music.

Eligibility   This program is open to full-time female college, university, and seminary students who are preparing for a career in church music. Applicants must have a GPA of 3.0 or higher and be able to demonstrate financial need. They must be members of Southern Baptist churches in New Mexico or former members in good standing with the Southern Baptist Convention.

Financial data   A stipend is awarded (amount not specified).

Duration   1 year.

Number awarded   1 or more each year.

Deadline   April of each year.

[357]
KATIE ROSE MARTIN SCHOLARSHIP

Community Foundation of Middle Tennessee
Attn: Scholarship Committee
3833 Cleghorn Avenue, Suite 400
Nashville, TN 37215-2519
(615) 321-4939   Toll Free: (888) 540-5200
Fax: (615) 327-2746   E-mail: mail@cfmt.org
Web: www.cfmt.org/scholarships

Summary   To provide financial assistance to female residents of any state attending a school of cosmetology in Tennessee.

Eligibility   This program is open to women who are high school graduates or second career adults. Applicants must be attending an accredited cosmetology school in Tennessee. Along with their application, they must submit an essay describing their educational plans and how those plans will help them reach their career goals. Financial need is considered in the selection process.

Financial data Stipends range from $500 to $2,500 per year. Funds are paid to the recipient's school and must be used for tuition, fees, books, supplies, room, board, or miscellaneous expenses.

Duration 1 year.

Additional information This program was established in 2010.

Number awarded 1 or more each year.

Deadline March of each year.

[358]
KAY MADRY SULLIVAN FELLOWSHIP

Alpha Kappa Alpha Sorority, Inc.
Attn: Educational Advancement Foundation
5656 South Stony Island Avenue
Chicago, IL 60637
(773) 947-0026   Toll Free: (800) 653-6528
Fax: (773) 947-0277   E-mail: akaeaf@akaeaf.net
Web: www.akaeaf.org/fellowships_endowments.htm

Summary To provide financial assistance to residents of designated states (especially African American women) who have been involved in foster care and are interested in attending college in any state.

Eligibility This program is open to undergraduate students who are enrolled full time as sophomores or higher in an accredited degree-granting institution in any state. Applicants must have been involved in the foster care system and be residents of Florida; if no residents of Florida apply, the scholarship may be awarded to a resident of Georgia or South Carolina. Along with their application, they must submit 1) a list of honors, awards, and scholarships received; 2) a list of organizations in which they have memberships, especially minority organizations; and 3) a statement of their personal and career goals, including how this scholarship will enhance their ability to attain those goals. The sponsor is a traditionally African American women's sorority.

Financial data A stipend is awarded (amount not specified).

Duration 1 year.

Number awarded 1 or more each even-numbered year.

Deadline April of each even-numbered year.

[359]
KELLI STATHEROS RE-ENTRY SCHOLARSHIP

Daughters of Penelope-District 11
Attn: AHEPA Buckeye Scholarship Foundation
25590 West County Line Road
Sunman, IN 47041
(513) 310-5299
Web: www.ahepabuckeye.org

Summary To provide financial assistance to women who wish to reenter the workforce and are members of the Daughters of Penelope in its District 11 (Kentucky, Ohio, and parts of Pennsylvania and West Virginia).

Eligibility This program is open to residents of Kentucky, Ohio, and parts of Pennsylvania and West Virginia who have been members of the Daughters of Penelope for the past 2 years and the current year. Applicants must be women entering an accredited college, vocational school, or university in

any state to obtain training necessary to prepare for a career in the field of her choice. Financial need is considered in the selection process.

Financial data A stipend is awarded (amount not specified).

Duration 1 year.

Additional information This program was established in 1987.

Number awarded 1 or more each year.

Deadline April of each year.

[360]
KELLOGG'S SCHOLARSHIPS

Society of Women Engineers
Attn: Scholarship Selection Committee
120 South LaSalle Street, Suite 1515
Chicago, IL 60603-3572
(312) 596-5223   Toll Free: (877) SWE-INFO
Fax: (312) 644-8557
E-mail: scholarshipapplication@swe.org
Web: societyofwomenengineers.swe.org

Summary To provide financial assistance to undergraduate members of the Society of Women Engineers (SWE) who are majoring in designated engineering specialties.

Eligibility This program is open to society members who are entering their sophomore or junior year at an ABET-accredited 4-year college or university. Applicants must be majoring in computer science or chemical or mechanical engineering and have a GPA of 3.2 or higher. Selection is based on merit. Preference is given to students attending designated universities.

Financial data The stipend is $3,000 or $1,000.

Duration 1 year.

Additional information For a list of the designated universities, contact SWE.

Number awarded 3 each year: 1 at $3,000 and 2 at $1,000.

Deadline February of each year.

[361]
KENNEDY CENTER INTERNSHIP

Sigma Alpha Iota Philanthropies, Inc.
One Tunnel Road
Asheville, NC 28805
(828) 251-0606   Fax: (828) 251-0644
E-mail: nh@sai-national.org
Web: www.sigmaalphaiota.org

Summary To provide summer internships at the Kennedy Center to members of Sigma Alpha Iota (an organization of women musicians).

Eligibility This program is open to student members of the organization who are interested in a summer internship at the Institute for Arts Management at the John F. Kennedy Center for the Performing Arts in Washington, D.C. Applicants must be juniors, seniors, graduate students, or graduates out of school for less than 2 years.

Financial data The stipend is $800 per month.

Duration 3 months during the summer.

Additional information Assignments are full time, with possible college credit available.

Number awarded 1 or more each year.

Deadline January of each year.

[362]
KENTUCKY COLONELS BETTER LIFE SCHOLARSHIPS

Kentucky Community and Technical College System
Attn: Financial Aid
300 North Main Street
Versailles, KY 40383
(859) 256-3100   Toll Free: (877) 528-2748 (within KY)
Web: www.kctcs.edu

Summary To provide financial assistance to single parents attending or planning to attend 1 of the schools within the Kentucky Community and Technical College System (KCTCS).

Eligibility This program is open to Kentucky residents who are single working parents with at least 1 child under 12 years of age. Applicants must be attending or planning to attend a KCTCS institution and able to demonstrate unmet financial need. Selection is based on demonstrated enthusiasm for learning and potential for academic success.

Financial data The stipend is $2,500 per year.

Duration 1 year; may be renewed 1 additional year if the recipient maintains full-time enrollment and satisfactory academic progress.

Additional information This program was established in 2004.

Number awarded 16 each year: 1 in each of the KCTCS districts.

Deadline Deadline not specified.

[363]
KENTUCKY VETERANS TUITION WAIVER PROGRAM

Kentucky Department of Veterans Affairs
Attn: Division of Field Operations
321 West Main Street, Room 390
Louisville, KY 40202
(502) 595-4447   Toll Free: (800) 928-4012 (within KY)
Fax: (502) 595-4448   E-mail: Pamela.Cypert@ky.gov
Web: www.veterans.ky.gov/benefits/tuitionwaiver.htm

Summary To provide financial assistance for college to the spouses, widows, or children of disabled or deceased Kentucky veterans.

Eligibility This program is open to the children, stepchildren, spouses, and unremarried widow(er)s of veterans who are residents of Kentucky (or were residents at the time of their death). The qualifying veteran must meet 1 of the following conditions: 1) died on active duty (regardless of wartime service); 2) died as a result of a service-connected disability (regardless of wartime service); 3) has a 100% service-connected disability; 4) is totally disabled (non-service connected) with wartime service; or 5) is deceased and served during wartime. The military service may have been as a member of the U.S. armed forces, the Kentucky National Guard, or a Reserve component; service in the Guard or Reserves must have been on state active duty, active duty for training, inactive duty training, or active duty with the U.S. armed forces. Children of veterans must be under 23 years of age; no age limit applies to spouses or unremarried

widow(er)s. All applicants must be attending or planning to attend a 2-year, 4-year, or vocational technical school operated and funded by the Kentucky Department of Education.

Financial data Eligible dependents and survivors are exempt from tuition and matriculation fees at any state-supported institution of higher education in Kentucky.

Duration Tuition is waived until the recipient completes 45 months of training, receives a college degree, or (in the case of children of veterans) reaches 26 years of age, whichever comes first. Spouses and unremarried widow(er)s are not subject to the age limitation.

Number awarded Varies each year.

Deadline Deadline not specified.

[364]
KERRI KEITH MEMORIAL SCHOLARSHIP

Alpha Omicron Pi Foundation
Attn: Scholarship Committee
5390 Virginia Way
Brentwood, TN 37027
(615) 370-0920   Fax: (615) 370-4424
E-mail: foundation@alphaomicronpi.org
Web: www.aoiifoundation.org/scholarship.php

Summary To provide financial assistance for college to members of Alpha Omicron Pi from Georgia, especially those majoring in actuarial science or a related field.

Eligibility This program is open to full-time juniors and seniors who are members of Alpha Omicron Pi and wish to continue their undergraduate education. Applicants must be Gamma Sigma chapter members who exhibit high involvement in the fraternity and have a GPA of 3.0 or higher. Special attention is given to applicants working on a degree in actuarial science or a related field. If no Gamma Sigma chapter member applies, sisters from other Georgia chapters may be considered. Applicants must submit the following 50-word statements: 1) the circumstances that have created their need for this scholarship; 2) their immediate and long-term life objectives; and 3) a letter of recommendation that they would write about themselves. Selection is based on those statements; academic achievement; Alpha Omicron Pi service, leadership, and involvement; college and community involvement; letters of recommendation; and financial need and evidence of self-help.

Financial data Stipend amounts vary; recently, the average value of each scholarship provided by this foundation was approximately $1,200.

Duration 1 year.

Number awarded 1 each year.

Deadline February of each year.

[365]
KRAUSE CORPORATION WOMEN IN AGRICULTURE SCHOLARSHIPS

Kansas FFA Association
Attn: Executive Secretary
Kansas State University
110 Umberger Hall
Manhattan, KS 66506
(785) 532-6424   E-mail: mrkane@ksu.edu
Web: www.hpj.com

Summary To provide financial assistance to female high school seniors in Kansas who are FFA members and planning to major in agriculture at a college in the state.

Eligibility This program is open to female seniors graduating from high schools in Kansas who have been members of the Kansas FFA Association for 4 years. Applicants must be planning to major in agriculture at a college or university in the state. They must have a GPA of 2.8 or higher. Along with their application, they must submit a brief statement on why the committee should choose them as a scholarship recipient. Selection is based on academic achievement (10 points each for GPA, ACT or SAT score, and class rank), leadership in FFA activities (30 points), leadership in community activities (10 points), and participation in the FFA Supervised Agricultural Experience program (30 points). Financial need is not considered. Special consideration may be given to applicants from general areas where Krause Corporation dealers are located.

Financial data The stipend is $1,000.

Duration 1 year; nonrenewable.

Additional information This program is sponsored by Krause Corporation.

Number awarded 2 each year.

Deadline March of each year.

[366]
LA FRA SCHOLARSHIP

Ladies Auxiliary of the Fleet Reserve Association
Attn: Administrator
P.O. Box 490678
Everett, MA 02149-0012
(617) 548-1191   E-mail: msakathy@live.com
Web: www.la-fra.org/scholarship.html

Summary To provide financial assistance for college to the daughters and granddaughters of naval personnel.

Eligibility Eligible to apply for these scholarships are the daughters and granddaughters of Navy, Marine, Coast Guard, active Fleet Reserve, Fleet Marine Corps Reserve, and Coast Guard Reserve personnel on active duty, retired with pay, or deceased while on active duty or retired with pay. Applicants must submit an essay on their life experiences, career objectives, and what motivated them to select those objectives. Selection is based on academic record, financial need, extracurricular activities, leadership skills, and participation in community activities. U.S. citizenship is required.

Financial data The stipend is $2,500.

Duration 1 year; may be renewed.

Number awarded 1 each year.

Deadline April of each year.

[367]
LAMBDA THETA NU SORORITY LATINA SCHOLARSHIP PROGRAM

Lambda Theta Nu Sorority, Inc.
Attn: Director of Community Service
1220 Rosecrans, Suite 543
San Diego, CA 92106
E-mail: community@lambdathetanu.org
Web: www.lambdathetanu.org

Summary To provide financial assistance for college to female high school seniors with a connection to the Latino community.

Eligibility This program is open to female graduating high school seniors who are either of Latino heritage or able to demonstrate dedication to community service and empowerment of the Latino community. Applicants must be planning to attend an accredited community college, university, or vocational/technical school. Along with their application, they must submit a personal statement that covers their family background, academic achievements, educational and career goals, commitment to the Latino community, and financial need.

Financial data A stipend is awarded (amount not specified).

Duration 1 year.

Number awarded Approximately 35 each year (1 selected by each chapter of the sorority).

Deadline April of each year.

[368]
LAO AMERICAN WOMEN ASSOCIATION OF WASHINGTON D.C. METROPOLITAN AREA VOCATIONAL TRAINING/GED SCHOLARSHIP FUND

Lao American Women Association
Attn: Scholarship Fund
1628 16th Street, N.W.
Washington, DC 20009
E-mail: info@lawadc.org
Web: www.lawadc.org

Summary To provide financial assistance to women of Lao ancestry in the Washington, D.C. area who need additional training to find a job.

Eligibility This program is open to women in Maryland, Virginia, and the District of Columbia who are of Lao parentage. Applicants must be in need of additional training to find a job, to obtain work at a higher level, or to complete a GED certificate. They must provide information on their personal situation, proposed training program, work experience, family and community activities, and financial situation. They must also submit a 150-word personal statement on their motivation for enrolling in a program of vocational training or GED completion.

Financial data The stipend is $1,000.

Duration 1 year.

Number awarded 1 or more each year.

Deadline April of each year.

[369]
LEGISLATIVE POLICY INTERNSHIPS AT LEGAL MOMENTUM

Legal Momentum
Attn: Legal Department
1101 14th Street, N.W., Suite 300
Washington, DC 20005
(202) 326-0040   Fax: (202) 589-0511
E-mail: dcinternships@legalmomentum.org
Web: www.legalmomentum.org

Summary To provide work experience to students and recent graduates (particularly women) who are interested in working on legislative policy issues at Legal Momentum in Washington, D.C.

Eligibility　The internship is open to undergraduates, graduate students, and recent graduates interested in working on legislative policy issues at Legal Momentum. Issues covered include poverty and welfare reform, immigrant women (including immigration law reform and cultural diversity issues), violence against women, and child care. Applicants must be interested in working on a range of tasks, including researching and analyzing legislation; drafting letters, fact sheets, and articles; attending briefings and coalition meetings; answering requests for technical assistance; assisting with administrative tasks as needed; and coordinating the work of coalitions dealing with issues of concern to the office. They should have a strong interest in women's legal rights. A love of feminist issues, politics, and hard work is useful and a working knowledge of the American political process is recommended. Women and men of all ethnic, cultural, economic, and sexual orientations who support feminist concerns are eligible. Bilingual individuals are especially encouraged to apply.

Financial data　These are paid internships (stipend not specified).

Duration　Interns are encouraged to work from 15 to 35 hours per week for 10 to 12 weeks. Positions are available in the fall, spring, or summer.

Additional information　Legal Momentum was formerly known as the NOW Legal Defense and Education Fund.

Number awarded　Varies each year.

Deadline　Applications may be submitted at any time.

[370]
LESLIE S. PARKER MEMORIAL SCHOLARSHIP

Order of the Eastern Star-Grand Chapter of Oregon
c/o Candice Hampton, Scholarship Committee Chair
P.O. Box 66
Lyons, OR 97358
Web: www.oregonoes.org/scholarships/index.html

Summary　To provide financial assistance to women who are residents of Oregon and attending college or graduate school in the state.

Eligibility　This program is open to female residents of Oregon who have completed at least 2 years of undergraduate or graduate study at an accredited non-sectarian college or university in the state. Applicants must be able to demonstrate financial need.

Financial data　Stipends are approximately $1,000. Funds are sent directly to the recipient's college or university to be used for books, tuition, room and board, clothing, or medical aid.

Duration　1 year.

Number awarded　1 or more each year.

Deadline　April of each year.

[371]
LETA ANDREWS SCHOLARSHIP

University Interscholastic League
Attn: Texas Interscholastic League Foundation
1701 Manor Road
P.O. Box 8028
Austin, TX 78713-8028
(512) 232-4937　　　　　　　　　Fax: (512) 232-7311
E-mail: bbaxendale@mail.utexas.edu
Web: www.uil.utexas.edu/tilf/scholarships.html

Summary　To provide financial assistance to high school seniors who have competed in girls' high school varsity basketball, participate in programs of the Texas Interscholastic League Foundation (TILF), and plan to attend college in the state.

Eligibility　This program is open to seniors graduating from high schools in Texas who have competed in a University Interscholastic League (UIL) academic state meet and have participated in girls' high school varsity basketball. Applicants must be planning to attend a college or university in the state and major in any field. Along with their application, they must submit high school transcripts that include SAT and/or ACT scores and documentation of financial need.

Financial data　The stipend is $1,000.

Duration　1 year; nonrenewable.

Additional information　This program is sponsored by Whataburger Inc. and Southwest Shootout Inc.

Number awarded　1 each year.

Deadline　May of each year.

[372]
LIBRARY OF CONGRESS JUNIOR FELLOWS PROGRAM

Library of Congress
Library Services
Attn: Junior Fellows Program Coordinator
101 Independence Avenue, S.E., Room LM-642
Washington, DC 20540-4600
(202) 707-0901　　　　　　　　　Fax: (202) 707-6269
E-mail: jrfell@loc.gov
Web: www.loc.gov/hr/jrfellows/index.html

Summary　To provide summer work experience at the Library of Congress (LC) to upper-division students, graduate students, and recent graduates, particularly women, minorities, and persons with disabilities.

Eligibility　This program is open to U.S. citizens with subject expertise in the following areas: American history, including veterans and military history; American popular culture; area studies (African, Asian, European, Hispanic, Middle Eastern); bibliographic description and access; film, television, and radio; folklife; geography and maps; history of photography; history of popular and applied graphic arts, architecture, and design; manuscript collections processing; music; preservation and conservation; rare books and manuscripts; science, technology, and business; serials and government publications and newspapers; or sound recordings. Applicants must 1) be juniors or seniors at an accredited college or university, 2) be graduate students, or 3) have completed their degree in the past year. Applications from women, minorities, and persons with disabilities are particularly encouraged. Selection is based on academic achievement, letters of recommendation, and an interview.

Financial data Fellows are paid a taxable stipend of $300 per week.

Duration 3 months, beginning in either May or June. Fellows work a 40-hour week.

Additional information Fellows work with primary source materials and assist selected divisions at LC in the organization and documentation of archival collections, production of finding aids and bibliographic records, preparation of materials for preservation and service, completion of bibliographical research, and digitization of LC's historical collections.

Number awarded Varies each year; recently, 6 of these internships were awarded.

Deadline March of each year.

[373]
LILLIAN MOLLER GILBRETH MEMORIAL SCHOLARSHIP

Society of Women Engineers
Attn: Scholarship Selection Committee
120 South LaSalle Street, Suite 1515
Chicago, IL 60603-3572
(312) 596-5223　　　　Toll Free: (877) SWE-INFO
Fax: (312) 644-8557
E-mail: scholarshipapplication@swe.org
Web: societyofwomenengineers.swe.org

Summary To provide financial assistance to upper-division women majoring in computer science or engineering.

Eligibility This program is open to women who are entering their junior or senior year at an ABET-accredited 4-year college or university. Applicants must be majoring in computer science or engineering and have a GPA of 3.0 or higher. Selection is based on merit.

Financial data The stipend is $10,000 per year.

Duration 1 year; may be renewed 1 additional year.

Additional information This program was established in 1958.

Number awarded 1 each year.

Deadline February of each year.

[374]
LILLIAN WALL SCHOLARSHIP

Zonta Club of Bangor
c/o Barbara A. Cardone
P.O. Box 1904
Bangor, ME 04402-1904
Web: www.zontaclubofbangor.org/?area=scholarship

Summary To provide financial assistance to women attending or planning to attend college in Maine and major in special education or a related field.

Eligibility This program is open to women who are attending or planning to attend an accredited 2- or 4-year college in Maine. Applicants must major in special education or a related field. Along with their application, they must submit brief essays on 1) their goals in seeking higher education and their plans for the future, and 2) any school and community activities that have been of particular importance to them and why they found them worthwhile. Financial need may be considered in the selection process.

Financial data The stipend is $1,000.

Duration 1 year.

Number awarded 1 each year.

Deadline March of each year.

[375]
LILLIE LOIS FORD SCHOLARSHIPS

American Legion
Department of Missouri
P.O. Box 179
Jefferson City, MO 65102-0179
(573) 893-2353　　　　Toll Free: (800) 846-9023
Fax: (573) 893-2980　　E-mail: info@missourilegion.org
Web: www.missourilegion.org

Summary To provide financial assistance for college to descendants of Missouri veterans who have participated in specified American Legion programs (females and males are judged separately).

Eligibility This program is open to the unmarried children, grandchildren, and great-grandchildren under 21 years of age of honorably-discharged Missouri veterans who served at least 90 days on active duty. Applicants must be enrolled or planning to enroll at an accredited college or university in any state as a full-time student. Boys must have attended a complete session of Missouri Boys State or Cadet Patrol Academy. Girls must have attended a complete session of Missouri Girls State or Cadet Patrol Academy. Financial need is considered in the selection process.

Financial data The stipend is $1,000.

Duration 1 year (the first year of college).

Number awarded 2 each year: 1 for a boy and 1 for a girl.

Deadline April of each year.

[376]
LINDA LAEL MILLER SCHOLARSHIPS FOR WOMEN

Linda Lael Miller Scholarships
c/o Nancy Berland Public Relations, Inc.
2816 N.W. 57th Street, Suite 101
Oklahoma City, OK 73112
Toll Free: (800) 308-3169
E-mail: NBPR@nancyberland.com
Web: www.lindalaelmiller.com

Summary To provide financial assistance for college to mature women.

Eligibility This program is open to women who are 25 years of age or older and legal residents of the United States or Canada. Applicants must be enrolled or planning to enroll at a college, university, or other postsecondary institution. Along with their application, they must submit a 500-word essay on why they are applying for this scholarship, how achieving their educational goals will enhance their and their family's future, the specific purpose for which they would use the funds, and the dollar amount they are requesting. Selection is based on the essay's readability, demonstration of commitment to education and/or career, and the possible impact of the scholarship on the life of the recipient, her family, and/or her community.

Financial data Stipend amounts vary; recently, they averaged $1,500. Funds are disbursed to the registrar of the recipient's college for payment of tuition, and/or the college bookstore for purchase of books and other supplies, and/or the accredited child care facility that the recipient's children will attend.

Duration   1 year.

Number awarded   Varies each year; recently, 10 of these scholarships were awarded.

Deadline   August of each year.

[377]
LOCKHEED MARTIN FRESHMAN SCHOLARSHIPS

Society of Women Engineers
Attn: Scholarship Selection Committee
120 South LaSalle Street, Suite 1515
Chicago, IL 60603-3572
(312) 596-5223   Toll Free: (877) SWE-INFO
Fax: (312) 644-8557
E-mail: scholarshipapplication@swe.org
Web: societyofwomenengineers.swe.org

Summary   To provide financial assistance to women entering their freshman year at a college or university to major in computer science or engineering.

Eligibility   This program is open to women who are entering their freshman year at an ABET-accredited 4-year college or university. Applicants must be planning to major in computer science or engineering and have a GPA of 3.5 or higher. Selection is based on merit.

Financial data   The stipend is $3,000. The award includes a travel grant for the recipient to attend the national conference of the Society of Women Engineers.

Duration   1 year.

Additional information   This program, established in 1996, is supported by Lockheed Martin Corporation.

Number awarded   2 each year.

Deadline   May of each year.

[378]
LOUISE MORITZ MOLITORIS LEADERSHIP AWARD

Women's Transportation Seminar
Attn: WTS Foundation
1701 K Street, N.W., Suite 800
Washington, DC 20006
(202) 955-5085   Fax: (202) 955-5088
E-mail: wts@wtsinternational.org
Web: www.wtsinternational.org

Summary   To provide financial assistance to undergraduate women interested in a career in transportation.

Eligibility   This program is open to women who are working on an undergraduate degree in transportation or a transportation-related field (e.g., transportation engineering, planning, finance, or logistics). Applicants must have a GPA of 3.0 or higher. Along with their application, they must submit a 500-word statement about their career goals after graduation and why they think they should receive the scholarship award; their statement should specifically address the issue of leadership. Applications must be submitted first to a local chapter; the chapters forward selected applications for consideration on the national level. Minority women are especially encouraged to apply. Selection is based on transportation involve-

ment and goals, job skills, academic record, and leadership potential; financial need is not considered.

Financial data   The stipend is $3,000.

Duration   1 year.

Additional information   Local chapters may also award additional funding to winners for their area.

Number awarded   1 each year.

Deadline   Applications must be submitted by November to a local WTS chapter.

[379]
LOUISIANA EDUCATIONAL BENEFITS FOR CHILDREN, SPOUSES, AND SURVIVING SPOUSES OF VETERANS

Louisiana Department of Veterans Affairs
Attn: Education Program
1885 Wooddale Boulevard, Room 1013
P.O. Box 94095, Capitol Station
Baton Rouge, LA 70804-9095
(225) 922-0500, ext. 206   Toll Free: (877) GEAUXVA
Fax: (225) 922-0511   E-mail: Bill.Dixon@vetaffairs.la.gov
Web: vetaffairs.la.gov/education

Summary   To provide financial assistance to spouses, surviving spouses, and children of certain disabled or deceased Louisiana veterans who plan to attend college in the state.

Eligibility   This program is open to children (between 16 and 25 years of age), spouses, or surviving spouses of veterans who served during specified periods of wartime and 1) were killed in action or died in active service; 2) died of a service-connected disability; 3) are missing in action (MIA) or a prisoner of war (POW); 4) sustained a disability rated as 90% or more by the U.S. Department of Veterans Affairs; or 5) have been determined to be unemployable as a result of a service-connected disability. Deceased, MIA, and POW veterans must have resided in Louisiana for at least 12 months prior to entry into service. Living disabled veterans must have resided in Louisiana for at least 24 months prior to the child's or spouse's admission into the program.

Financial data   Eligible persons accepted as full-time students at Louisiana state-supported colleges, universities, trade schools, or vocational/technical schools are admitted free and are exempt from payment of tuition, laboratory, athletic, medical, and other special fees. Free registration does not cover books, supplies, room and board, or fees assessed by the student body on themselves (such as yearbooks and weekly papers).

Duration   Support is provided for a maximum of 4 school years, to be completed in not more than 5 years from date of original entry.

Additional information   Attendance must be on a full-time basis. Surviving spouses must remain unremarried and must take advantage of the benefit within 10 years after eligibility is established.

Number awarded   Varies each year.

Deadline   Applications must be received no later than 3 months prior to the beginning of a semester.

[380]
LUCILE B. KAUFMAN WOMEN'S SCHOLARSHIPS

Society of Manufacturing Engineers
Attn: SME Education Foundation
One SME Drive
P.O. Box 930
Dearborn, MI 48121-0930
(313) 425-3300   Toll Free: (800) 733-4763, ext. 3300
Fax: (313) 425-3411   E-mail: foundation@sme.org
Web: www.smeef.org

Summary To provide financial assistance to undergraduate women enrolled in a degree program in manufacturing engineering or manufacturing engineering technology.

Eligibility This program is open to women enrolled full time at a degree-granting institution in North America and preparing for a career in manufacturing engineering. Applicants must have completed at least 30 units in a manufacturing engineering or manufacturing engineering technology curriculum and have a GPA of 3.0 or higher. Along with their application, they must submit a 300-word essay that covers their career and educational objectives, how this scholarship will help them attain those objectives, and why they want to enter this field. Financial need is not considered in the selection process.

Financial data Stipend amounts vary; recently, the value of all scholarships provided by this foundation averaged approximately $2,728.

Duration 1 year; may be renewed.

Number awarded 1 or 2 each year.

Deadline January of each year.

[381]
LUCILE MILLER WRIGHT SCHOLARS PROGRAM

Girls Incorporated
Attn: Scholarships and Awards
120 Wall Street, Third Floor
New York, NY 10005-3902
(212) 509-2000   Toll Free: (800) 374-4475
Fax: (212) 509-8708
E-mail: communications@girlsinc.org
Web: www.girlsinc.org/about/national-scholars.html

Summary To provide financial assistance for college to Girls Incorporated members.

Eligibility This program is open to members of Girls Incorporated affiliates who are currently in high school (in grades 11 or 12) and have been members of the association for at least 2 years. They must have a GPA of 2.8 or higher. Selection is based on extracurricular activities, goals and objectives, soundness of ideas, motivation, communication skills, and presentation. Financial need is not considered. Academic record is of secondary importance.

Financial data The scholarships are either $15,000 or $2,500. Funds are held in escrow and paid directly to the recipient's college, professional school, or technical institute.

Duration Up to 5 years.

Additional information This program was established in 1992. Funds may not be used for education at a vocational or technical school.

Number awarded Varies each year; recently, 26 of these scholarships were awarded: 10 at $15,000 and 16 at $2,500.

Since this program was established, it has awarded $2.58 million in scholarships to 413 high school women.

Deadline Deadline not specified.

[382]
LUCY KASPARIAN AHARONIAN SCHOLARSHIPS

Armenian International Women's Association
65 Main Street, Room 3A
Watertown, MA 02472
(617) 926-0171   E-mail: aiwainc@aol.com
Web: www.aiwa-net.org/scholarshipinfo.html

Summary To provide financial assistance to Armenian women who are upper-division or graduate students working on a degree in specified fields.

Eligibility This program is open to full-time women students of Armenian descent attending an accredited college or university. Applicants must be full-time juniors, seniors, or graduate students with a GPA of 3.2 or higher. They must be working on a degree in architecture, computer science, engineering, mathematics, science, or technology. Selection is based on financial need and merit.

Financial data Stipends range from $2,000 to $10,000.

Duration 1 year.

Additional information This program, established in 2008, is offered in conjunction with the Boston Section of the Society of Women Engineers.

Number awarded 2 each year.

Deadline April of each year.

[383]
LYDIA I. PICKUP MEMORIAL SCHOLARSHIP

Society of Women Engineers
Attn: Scholarship Selection Committee
120 South LaSalle Street, Suite 1515
Chicago, IL 60603-3572
(312) 596-5223   Toll Free: (877) SWE-INFO
Fax: (312) 644-8557
E-mail: scholarshipapplication@swe.org
Web: societyofwomenengineers.swe.org

Summary To provide financial assistance to women working on an undergraduate or graduate degree in engineering or computer science.

Eligibility This program is open to women who will be sophomores, juniors, seniors, or graduate students at ABET-accredited colleges and universities. Applicants must be majoring in computer science or engineering and have a GPA of 3.0 or higher. Preference is given to graduate students. Selection is based on merit.

Financial data The stipend is $3,000.

Duration 1 year.

Additional information This program was established in 2001.

Number awarded 1 each year.

Deadline February of each year.

[384]
LYDIA PICKUP MEMORIAL SCHOLARSHIP

Society of Women Engineers-Pacific Northwest Section
Attn: Scholarship Committee
P.O. Box 1601
Bellevue, WA 98009
E-mail: pnw@swe.org
Web: www.swe-pnw.org/scholarship.html

Summary To provide financial assistance to women from any state studying engineering at a university in Montana or western Washington.

Eligibility This program is open to women from any state who have, at the time of application, completed at least 50% of the requirements toward college graduation in an engineering field. Applicants must be attending an ABET-accredited engineering school in Montana or western Washington. They must be U.S. citizens and members of the Society of Women Engineers (SWE) student section at their school or, if no student section exists, of the national SWE organization. Along with their application, they must submit 1) a 300-word essay on their educational and career goals; and 2) a 500-word essay describing why they have chosen their particular field of engineering; the person, event, or job experience influencing their decision to work on an engineering degree; and the most and least favorite courses they have taken and which course they are most looking forward to and why. Selection is based on the essays, academic achievement, extracurricular and community service activities, and financial need.

Financial data Stipends range from $1,000 to $2,000.

Duration 1 year.

Number awarded 1 each year.

Deadline April of each year.

[385]
M. JOSEPHINE O'NEIL ARTS AWARD

Delta Kappa Gamma Society International-Lambda State
  Organization
c/o Linda McDonnell
3201 Newell Drive
Granite City, IL 62040-5160
(618) 452-3201   E-mail: llmcdonnell@excite.com
Web: www.deltakappagamma.org

Summary To provide financial assistance to female residents of Illinois who are studying an arts-related field at a college in any state.

Eligibility This program is open to female residents of Illinois who are in or approaching junior standing at an accredited college or university or in the sophomore year at an accredited community college. Applicants must be majoring in 1 or more areas of the arts, including music, visual arts, dance, theater, or the literary arts. Along with their application, they must submit 1) evidence of the quality and extent of accomplishment in the arts, such as programs of performances, catalogs, articles from the media, published reviews of their work, listings of awards and prizes, or other recognition; 2) samples of their work on 35mm slides, CD, videotapes, or audio tapes; 3) college transcripts; 4) letters of recommendation; and 5) a personal essay on their family, personal interests, awards, achievements, goals (short- and long-term), and philosophy. Selection is based on the essay, letters of recommendation, academic background, and evidence from all sources of potential for contribution to society.

Financial data The stipend ranges up to $6,000.

Duration 1 year.

Additional information The sponsor is an honorary society of women educators.

Number awarded 1 each year.

Deadline January of each year.

[386]
MABEL HEIL SCHOLARSHIP

United Methodist Church-Wisconsin Conference
Attn: Board of Higher Education and Campus Ministry
750 Windsor Street
P.O. Box 620
Sun Prairie, WI 53590-0620
(608) 837-7328   Toll Free: (888) 240-7328
Fax: (608) 837-8547
Web: www.wisconsinumc.org

Summary To provide financial assistance to United Methodist women from Wisconsin who are interested in attending college or graduate school in any state.

Eligibility This program is open to women who are members of congregations affiliated with the Wisconsin Conference of the United Methodist Church and attending or planning to attend college or graduate school in any state. Applicants must submit an essay on why they consider themselves a worthy student and a letter of recommendation from their pastor or the president of the local United Methodist Women. Preference is given to women who are responsible for others and are returning to the employment field.

Financial data A stipend is awarded (amount not specified).

Duration 1 semester; recipients may reapply.

Number awarded 1 or more each year.

Deadline April of each year for the first semester; September of each year for the second semester.

[387]
MAHINDRA USA WOMEN IN AG SCHOLARSHIPS

National FFA Organization
Attn: Scholarship Office
6060 FFA Drive
P.O. Box 68960
Indianapolis, IN 46268-0960
(317) 802-4419   Fax: (317) 802-5419
E-mail: scholarships@ffa.org
Web: www.ffa.org

Summary To provide financial assistance to female FFA members interested in studying fields related to agriculture in college.

Eligibility This program is open to female members from 38 designated states who are graduating high school seniors or currently-enrolled college students. Applicants must be working on or planning to work on a 2- or 4-year degree in agriculture (excluding food service, packaging, biosciences or technology, marine biology, natural resource management, parks and recreation studies, public service, or dietetics). They must have a GPA of 3.0 or higher. Selection is based on academic achievement (10 points for GPA, 10 points for SAT or ACT score, 10 points for class rank), leadership in FFA activities (30 points), leadership in community activities (10 points), and participation in the Supervised Agricultural Experience (SAE) program (30 points). Financial need is also considered. U.S. citizenship is required.

Financial data The stipend is $2,500. Funds are paid directly to the recipient.

Duration 1 year; nonrenewable.

Additional information This program is sponsored by Mahindra USA, Inc. For a list of the designated 38 states, contact FFA.

Number awarded 4 each year.

Deadline February of each year.

[388]
MAINE BPW CONTINUING EDUCATION SCHOLARSHIP

Maine Federation of Business and Professional Women's
Clubs
Attn: BPW/Maine Futurama Foundation
c/o Susan Tardie, Co-President
25 Hall Street
Fort Kent, ME 04743
E-mail: susan.tardie@maine.edu
Web: www.bpwmefoundation.org/files/index.php?id=10

Summary To provide financial assistance to women in Maine who are attending college in any state.

Eligibility This program is open to women who are residents of Maine. Applicants must have completed at least 1 year of college or an accredited training program in any state requiring attendance for more than a year. They must have a definite plan to complete the educational program, regardless of whether it leads to an associate or bachelor's degree or other certificate. Along with their application, they must submit a statement describing their educational, personal, and career goals, including their financial need. Preference is given to members of Maine Federation of Business and Professional Women's Clubs.

Financial data The stipend is $1,200.

Duration 1 year.

Number awarded 1 or more each year.

Deadline April of each year.

[389]
MAINE VETERANS DEPENDENTS EDUCATIONAL BENEFITS

Bureau of Veterans' Services
117 State House Station
Augusta, ME 04333-0117
(207) 626-4464   Toll Free: (800) 345-0116 (within ME)
Fax: (207) 626-4471   E-mail: mainebvs@maine.gov
Web: www.maine.gov/dvem/bvs/educational_benefits.htm

Summary To provide financial assistance for undergraduate or graduate education to spouses and children of disabled and other Maine veterans.

Eligibility Applicants for these benefits must be children (high school seniors or graduates under 22 years of age), non-divorced spouses, or unremarried widow(er)s of veterans who meet 1 or more of the following requirements: 1) living and determined to have a total permanent disability resulting from a service-connected cause; 2) killed in action; 3) died from a service-connected disability; 4) died while totally and permanently disabled due to a service-connected disability but whose death was not related to the service-con-

nected disability; or 5) a member of the armed forces on active duty who has been listed for more than 90 days as missing in action, captured, forcibly detained, or interned in the line of duty by a foreign government or power. The veteran parent must have been a resident of Maine at the time of entry into service or a resident of Maine for 5 years preceding application for these benefits. Children may be working on an associate or bachelor's degree. Spouses, widows, and widowers may work on an associate, bachelor's, or master's degree.

Financial data Recipients are entitled to free tuition at institutions of higher education supported by the state of Maine.

Duration Children may receive up to 8 semesters of support; they have 6 years from the date of first entrance to complete those 8 semesters. Continuation in the program is based on their earning a GPA of 2.0 or higher each semester. Spouses are entitled to receive up to 120 credit hours of educational benefits and have 10 years from the date of first entrance to complete their program.

Additional information College preparatory schooling and correspondence courses are not supported under this program.

Number awarded Varies each year.

Deadline Deadline not specified.

[390]
MAKING A DIFFERENCE LEADER SCHOLARSHIP

Royal Neighbors of America
Attn: Fraternal Services
230 16th Street
Rock Island, IL 61201-8645
(309) 788-4561   Toll Free: (800) 627-4762
E-mail: contact@royalneighbors.org
Web: www.royalneighbors.org

Summary To provide financial assistance to female members of the Royal Neighbors of America (RNA) who are high school seniors planning to attend college.

Eligibility This program is open to female high school seniors who are beneficial members of RNA and rank in the top quarter of their senior class. Applicants must have an outstanding record of volunteerism. They must be planning to enroll full time at an accredited college, university, or junior college to work eventually on a bachelor's degree.

Financial data The stipend is $5,000 per year.

Duration 1 year; may be renewed up to 3 additional years.

Number awarded 1 each year.

Deadline Requests for applications must be submitted by December of each year.

[391]
MANAHAN-BOHAN AWARD

Philanthrofund Foundation
Attn: Scholarship Committee
1409 Willow Street, Suite 210
Minneapolis, MN 55403-3251
(612) 870-1806   Toll Free: (800) 435-1402
Fax: (612) 871-6587   E-mail: info@PfundOnline.org
Web: www.pfundonline.org/scholarships.html

Summary   To provide financial assistance to lesbian students from rural Minnesota.
Eligibility   This program is open to residents of Madelia, Minnesota; if no resident of Madelia applies, the award is available to residents of any rural area in Minnesota. Applicants must be self-identified as lesbian. They may be attending or planning to attend trade school, technical college, college, or university in any state (as an undergraduate or graduate student). Selection is based on the applicant's 1) affirmation of lesbian identity or commitment to lesbian communities; 2) evidence of experience and skills in service and leadership; and 3) evidence of service and leadership in lesbian communities, including serving as a role model, mentor, and/or adviser.
Financial data   The stipend is $1,000. Funds must be used for tuition, books, fees, or dissertation expenses.
Duration   1 year.
Number awarded   1 each year.
Deadline   January of each year.

[392]
MARA CRAWFORD PERSONAL DEVELOPMENT SCHOLARSHIP

Kansas Federation of Business & Professional Women's
  Clubs, Inc.
Attn: Kansas BPW Educational Foundation, Inc.
c/o Kathy Niehoff, Executive Secretary
605 East 15th
Ottawa, KS 66067
(785) 242-9319   Fax: (785) 242-1047
E-mail: kathyniehoff@sbcglobal.net
Web: kansasbpw.memberlodge.org

Summary   To provide financial assistance to women in Kansas who are already in the workforce but are interested in pursuing additional education.
Eligibility   This program is open to women residents of Kansas who graduated from high school more than 5 years previously and are already in the workforce. Applicants may be seeking a degree in any field of study and may be attending a 2-year, 4-year, vocational, or technological program. They must submit a 3-page personal biography in which they express their career goals, the direction they want to take in the future, their proposed field of study, their reason for selecting that field, the institutions they plan to attend and why, their circumstances for reentering school (if a factor), and what makes them uniquely qualified for this scholarship. Preference is given to applicants who demonstrate they have serious family responsibilities and obligations. Applications must be submitted through a local unit of the sponsor.
Financial data   A stipend is awarded (amount not specified).
Duration   1 year.
Number awarded   1 or more each year.
Deadline   December of each year.

[393]
MARIAN MCKEE SMITH–ROSALIE MCKINNEY JACKSON SCHOLARSHIPS

Alpha Chi Omega Foundation
Attn: Foundation Programs Coordinator
5939 Castle Creek Parkway North Drive
Indianapolis, IN 46250-4343
(317) 579-5050, ext. 262   Fax: (317) 579-5051
E-mail: foundation@alphachiomega.org
Web: www.alphachiomega.org/index.aspx?id=1030

Summary   To provide financial assistance for college to Alpha Chi Omega members.
Eligibility   This program is open to full-time junior or senior college women who are members of the sorority. Selection is based on academic achievement, chapter and campus activity, and leadership.
Financial data   A stipend is awarded (amount not specified).
Duration   1 year.
Number awarded   1 or more each year.
Deadline   March of each year.

[394]
MARIAN NORBY SCHOLARSHIP

Society for Technical Communication
9401 Lee Highway, Suite 300
Fairfax, VA 22031
(703) 522-4114   Fax: (703) 522-2075
E-mail: stc@stc.org
Web: www.stc.org/edu/scholarships.asp

Summary   To provide financial assistance to female employees of the federal government who are interested in training or academic study related to technical communications.
Eligibility   This program is open to women who working full or part time for the federal government as a secretary or administrative assistant. Applicants must be interested in enrolling in a training or academic class related to technical communication, including technical writing, editing, graphical design, interface design, or web design. Along with their application, they must submit a 1- to 3-page description of their career goals and significant achievements to date. Financial need is not considered in the selection process.
Financial data   The stipend is $2,500.
Duration   1 academic year.
Number awarded   1 each year.
Deadline   May of each year.

[395]
MARILYNN SMITH SCHOLARSHIP

Ladies Professional Golf Association
Attn: LPGA Foundation
100 International Golf Drive
Daytona Beach, FL 32124-1082
(386) 274-6200   Fax: (386) 274-1099
E-mail: foundation.scholarships@lpga.com
Web: www.lpgafoundation.org

Summary   To provide financial assistance to female graduating high school seniors who played golf in high school and plan to continue playing in college.

Eligibility This program is open to female high school seniors who have a GPA of 3.2 or higher. Applicants must have played in at least 50% of their high school golf team's scheduled events or have played golf "regularly" for the past 2 years. They must be planning to enroll full time at a college or university in the United States and play competitive golf. Along with their application, they must submit a letter that describes how golf has been an integral part of their lives and includes their personal, academic, and professional goals; their chosen discipline of study; and how this scholarship will be of assistance. Financial need is not considered in the selection process.

Financial data The stipend is $10,000.

Duration 1 year.

Additional information This program was established in 1999.

Number awarded 10 each year.

Deadline May of each year.

[396]
MARINE CORPS COUNTERINTELLIGENCE ASSOCIATION SCHOLARSHIPS

Marine Corps Counterintelligence Association
c/o Samuel L. Moyer, Scholarship Committee Chair
315 Palmdale Drive
Oldsmar, FL 34677
E-mail: oldjarhd@aol.com
Web: www.mccia.org

Summary To provide financial assistance for college to spouses and children of members of the Marine Corps Counterintelligence Association (MCCIA).

Eligibility This program is open to children, grandchildren, and spouses of 1) current MCCIA members; 2) deceased Marines who were MCCIA members at the time of death; and 3) counterintelligence Marines who lost their lives in the line of duty (whether they were a member of MCCIA or not). Spouses of deceased Marines must also be MCCIA Auxiliary members. Applicants must be enrolled or planning to enroll as a full-time undergraduate student at an accredited college or university and have a GPA of 3.0 or higher. Along with their application, they must submit a 1-page essay on a topic of their choice, letters of recommendation, SAT or ACT scores, transcripts, copies of awards and other honors, and evidence of acceptance at a college or university. Financial need is not considered.

Financial data Stipends range from $250 to $1,000. Funds must be used to help pay for tuition, books, fees, and materials; they may not be used for personal or living expenses.

Duration 1 year; may be renewed up to 4 additional years (need not be consecutive).

Number awarded Varies each year; recently, 7 of these scholarships, at $1,000 each, were awarded.

Deadline June of each year.

[397]
MARION DAY MULLINS SCHOLARSHIP

Kappa Delta Sorority
Attn: Foundation Manager
3205 Players Lane
Memphis, TN 38125
(901) 748-1897   Toll Free: (800) 536-1897
Fax: (901) 748-0949 E-mail: kappadelta@kappadelta.org
Web: www.kappadelta.org/scholarships

Summary To provide financial assistance to members of Kappa Delta Sorority who are majoring in business.

Eligibility This program is open to undergraduate members of Kappa Delta Sorority. Applicants must submit a personal statement giving their reasons for applying for this scholarship, an official undergraduate transcript, and 2 letters of recommendation. They must be majoring in business, including accounting, economics, finance, and marketing. Selection is based on academic excellence; service to the chapter, alumnae association, or national Kappa Delta; service to the campus and community; personal objectives and goals; potential; recommendations; and financial need.

Financial data The stipend is $1,000 per year. Funds may be used only for tuition, fees, and books, not for room and board.

Duration 1 year; may be renewed.

Number awarded 1 each year.

Deadline January of each year.

[398]
MARTHA C. JOHNSON TUITION SCHOLARSHIPS

Kentucky Community and Technical College System
Attn: Financial Aid
300 North Main Street
Versailles, KY 40383
(859) 256-3100   Toll Free: (877) 528-2748 (within KY)
Web: www.kctcs.edu

Summary To provide financial assistance to sophomores (preferably women) attending a school within the Kentucky Community and Technical College System (KCTCS).

Eligibility This program is open to KCTCS students entering their sophomore year with a GPA of 3.0 or higher. Applicants must have completed at least 30 hours of a pre-baccalaureate program for transfer to a 4-year college or university. They must be able to demonstrate financial need and outside community service and involvement. Along with their application, they must submit a 1-page essay on their career choice, personal values, and community service. Preference is given to women.

Financial data Stipends vary at each participating college but are intended to provide full payment of tuition and required fees.

Duration 1 year.

Number awarded Varies each year.

Deadline Deadline not specified.

[399]
MARTHA DROUYOR BELKNAP DECAMP SCHOLARSHIP

Alpha Sigma Tau National Foundation
Attn: Office Manager
P.O. Box 476
Gardendale, AL 35071
(205) 978-4512
E-mail: melinda@alphasigmataufoundation.org
Web: www.alphasigmataufoundation.org/scholarships

Summary To provide financial assistance to undergraduate members of Alpha Sigma Tau who have been involved in philanthropic service.

Eligibility This program is open to members of Alpha Sigma Tau who are entering their sophomore, junior, or senior year. Applicants be able to demonstrate a desire to "contribute to the progress of mankind." They must have a GPA of 3.0 or higher and a record of leadership ability to involve others in philanthropic endeavors. Along with their application, they must submit academic transcripts and 4 letters of recommendation.

Financial data The stipend is $1,275.

Duration 1 year.

Number awarded 1 each year.

Deadline January of each year.

[400]
MARTHA GUERRA-ARTEAGA SCHOLARSHIP

National Organization of Professional Hispanic Natural Resources Conservation Service Employees
c/o Amanda N. Hasemeier, Scholarship and Endowment Committee
1612 Bridge Street
New Cumberland, PA 17070-1122
(717) 237-2236   E-mail: scholarships@nophnrcse.org
Web: www.nophnrcse.org/index.php/scholarships

Summary To provide financial assistance to Hispanic women interested in working on a bachelor's degree in a field related to public affairs or natural resources conservation.

Eligibility This program is open to Hispanic women who are graduating high school seniors or current full-time college students with at least 1 year remaining before graduation. Applicants must be interested in working on a bachelor's degree in public affairs, communications, or natural resources conservation. They must have a GPA of 2.75 or higher. Along with their application, they must submit a personal statement (in English) of 350 to 500 words on their background, name of school they attend or plan to attend, personal and career goals, extracurricular activities, and interest in preparing for a career related to natural resources conservation. Financial need is not considered in the selection process. U.S. citizenship is required.

Financial data The stipend is $1,000.

Duration 1 year.

Additional information The National Organization of Professional Hispanic Natural Resources Conservation Service Employees (NOPRNRCSE) is comprised of Hispanic employees of the Natural Resources Conservation Service of the U.S. Department of Agriculture (USDA-NRCS).

Number awarded 1 each year.

Deadline February of each year.

[401]
MARTHA STICKLAND SCHOLARSHIP

Epsilon Sigma Alpha International
Attn: ESA Foundation
363 West Drake Road
Fort Collins, CO 80526
(970) 223-2824   Fax: (970) 223-4456
E-mail: esainfo@epsilonsigmaalpha.org
Web: www.epsilonsigmaalpha.org

Summary To provide financial assistance to women from Florida who are interested in attending college in any state.

Eligibility This program is open to female residents of Florida who are 1) graduating high school seniors with a GPA of 3.0 or higher or with minimum scores of 22 on the ACT or 1030 on the combined critical reading and mathematics SAT; 2) enrolled in college with a GPA of 3.0 or higher; 3) enrolled at a technical school or returning to school after an absence for retraining of job skills or obtaining a degree; or 4) engaged in online study through an accredited college, university, or vocational school. Applicants may be attending or planning to attend school in any state to work on a degree in any field. Selection is based on character (10%), leadership (20%), service (10%), financial need (30%), and scholastic ability (30%).

Financial data The stipend is $1,000.

Duration 1 year; may be renewed.

Additional information Epsilon Sigma Alpha (ESA) is a women's service organization. This scholarship was first awarded in 1999. Completed applications must be submitted to the ESA state counselor who then verifies the information before forwarding them to the scholarship director. A $5 processing fee is required.

Number awarded 1 each year.

Deadline January of each year.

[402]
MARY BARRETT MARSHALL SCHOLARSHIP

American Legion Auxiliary
Department of Kentucky
c/o Lois Smith, Student Loan Fund Committee
812 Madison Street
Rockport, IN 47635-1241
(812) 649-2163
Web: www.kyamlegionaux.org

Summary To provide financial assistance to female dependents of veterans in Kentucky who plan to attend college in the state.

Eligibility This program is open to the daughters, wives, sisters, widows, granddaughters, or great-granddaughters of veterans eligible for membership in the American Legion who are high school seniors or graduates and 5-year residents of Kentucky. Applicants must be planning to attend a college or university in Kentucky.

Financial data The stipend is $1,000. The funds may be used for tuition, registration fees, laboratory fees, and books, but not for room and board.

Duration 1 year.

Number awarded 1 each year.

Deadline March of each year.

[403]
MARY ELLEN RUSSELL MEMORIAL SCHOLARSHIP

Society of Women Engineers-Pacific Northwest Section
Attn: Scholarship Committee
P.O. Box 1601
Bellevue, WA 98009
E-mail: pnw@swe.org
Web: www.swe-pnw.org/scholarship.html

Summary To provide financial assistance to women from any state studying engineering at a university in Montana or western Washington.

Eligibility This program is open to women from any state who, at the time of application, have completed at least 50% of the requirements toward college graduation in an engineering field. Applicants must be attending an ABET-accredited engineering school in Montana or western Washington. They must be U.S. citizens and members of the Society of Women Engineers (SWE) student section at their school or, if no student section exists, of the national SWE organization. Along with their application, they must submit 1) a 300-word essay on their educational and career goals; and 2) a 500-word essay describing why they have chosen their particular field of engineering; the person, event, or job experience influencing their decision to work on an engineering degree; and the most and least favorite courses they have taken and which course they are most looking forward to and why. Selection is based on the essays, academic achievement, extracurricular and community service activities, and financial need.

Financial data The stipend is $1,800.

Duration 1 year.

Number awarded 1 each year.

Deadline April of each year.

[404]
MARY LAUGHLIN BEARDMORE-ANDERSON FUND

American Association of University Women-Honolulu Branch
Attn: Scholarship Committee
1802 Ke'eaumoku Street
Honolulu, HI 96822
(808) 537-4702   Fax: (808) 537-4702
E-mail: Edu@aauw-honolulu.org
Web: aauw.xodev01.com

Summary To provide financial assistance to women in Hawaii who are interested in working on an undergraduate degree, especially in the arts, at a college in the state.

Eligibility This program is open to female residents of Hawaii who have completed at least 2 semesters of undergraduate study at an accredited college or university in the state. Preference is given to women majoring in the arts. Applicants must submit a 500-word biographical statement that includes information on their family, work, school, community service, and future goals. Selection is based on academic excellence, demonstrated leadership in school and community activities, and financial need. U.S. citizenship is required.

Financial data A stipend is awarded (amount not specified).

Duration 1 year.

Number awarded 1 or more each year.

Deadline May of each year.

[405]
MARY LILY RESEARCH GRANTS

Duke University
Rare Book, Manuscript, and Special Collections Library
Attn: Sallie Bingham Center for Women's History and Culture
P.O. Box 90185
Durham, NC 27708-0185
(919) 660-5828   Fax: (919) 660-5934
E-mail: cwhc@duke.edu
Web: library.duke.edu

Summary To provide funding to scholars at all levels who wish to use the resources of the Sallie Bingham Center for Women's History and Culture in the Special Collections Library at Duke University.

Eligibility This program is open to undergraduates, graduate students, faculty members, and independent scholars in any academic field who wish to use the resources of the center for their research in women's studies. Applicants must reside outside a 50-mile radius of Durham, North Carolina. Undergraduate and graduate students must be currently enrolled, be working on a degree, and enclose a letter of recommendation from their adviser or thesis director. Faculty members must be working on a research project and enclose a curriculum vitae. Independent scholars must be working on a nonprofit project and enclose a curriculum vitae.

Financial data Grants up to $1,000 are available; funds may be used for travel, costs of copying pertinent resources, and living expenses while conducting the research.

Additional information The library's collections are especially strong in the history of feminist activism and theory, prescriptive literature, girls' literature, artists' books by women, lay and ordained church women, gender expression, women's sexuality, and the history and culture of women in the South. A number of prominent women writers have placed their personal and professional papers in the collections.

Number awarded Varies each year; recently, 8 of these grants were awarded.

Deadline January of each year.

[406]
MARY MACON MCGUIRE SCHOLARSHIP

General Federation of Women's Clubs of Virginia
Attn: Scholarship Committee
513 Forest Avenue
P.O. Box 8750
Richmond, VA 23226
(804) 288-3724   Toll Free: (800) 699-8392
Fax: (804) 288-0341
E-mail: headquarters@gfwcvirginia.org
Web: www.gfwcvirginia.org/forms/scholarships.htm

Summary To provide financial assistance to women heads of households in Virginia who have returned to school.

Eligibility This program is open to women residents of Virginia who are heads of households. Applicants must be currently enrolled in a course of study (vocational or academic) at an accredited Virginia school. They must have returned to school to upgrade their education and employment skills in order to better provide for their families. Selection is based on 3 letters of recommendation (1 of a general nature, 2 from recent professors, teachers, counselors, or advisers); a resume of educational and employment history, financial circumstances, and community activities; and an essay up to 2,000 words that outlines the financial need for the grant as well as the reasons for entering the field of study selected.

Financial data The stipend is $2,500. Funds are paid directly to the recipient's college or university.

Duration 1 year.

Additional information This program began in 1929 as a loan fund. It was converted to its current form in 2000.

Number awarded 2 each year.

Deadline March of each year.

[407]
MARY PAOLOZZI MEMBER'S SCHOLARSHIP

Navy Wives Clubs of America
P.O. Box 54022
Millington, TN 38053-6022
Toll Free: (866) 511-NWCA
E-mail: nwca@navywivesclubsofamerica.org
Web: www.navywivesclubsofamerica.org/scholarinfo.htm

Summary To provide financial assistance for undergraduate or graduate study to members of the Navy Wives Clubs of America (NWCA).

Eligibility This program is open to NWCA members who can demonstrate financial need. Applicants must be 1) a high school graduate or senior planning to attend college full time next year; 2) currently enrolled in an undergraduate program and planning to continue as a full-time undergraduate; 3) a college graduate or senior planning to be a full-time graduate student next year; or 4) a high school graduate or GED recipient planning to attend vocational or business school next year. Along with their application, they must submit a brief statement on why they feel they should be awarded this scholarship and any special circumstances (financial or other) they wish to have considered. Financial need is also considered in the selection process.

Financial data Stipends range from $500 to $1,000 each year (depending upon the donations from the NWCA chapters).

Duration 1 year.

Additional information Membership in the NWCA is open to spouses of enlisted personnel serving in the Navy, Marine Corps, Coast Guard, and the active Reserve units of those services; spouses of enlisted personnel who have been honorably discharged, retired, or transferred to the Fleet Reserve on completion of duty; and widows of enlisted personnel in those services.

Number awarded 1 or more each year.

Deadline May of each year.

[408]
MARY R. NORTON MEMORIAL SCHOLARSHIP AWARD

ASTM International
100 Barr Harbor Drive
P.O. Box C700
West Conshohocken, PA 19428-2959
(610) 832-9500
Web: www.astm.org/studentmember/Student_Awards.html

Summary To provide financial assistance to female undergraduate and graduate students working on a degree related to physical metallurgy.

Eligibility This program is open to women entering their senior year of college or first year of graduate study. Applicants must be working on a degree in physical metallurgy or materials science, with an emphasis on relationship of microstructure and properties.

Financial data The stipend is $1,000.

Duration 1 year.

Additional information This program, established in 1975, is administered by ASTM Committee CO4 on Metallography. ASTM International was formerly the American Society for Testing and Materials.

Number awarded 1 or more each year.

Deadline Deadline not specified.

[409]
MARY V. MUNGER MEMORIAL SCHOLARSHIP

Society of Women Engineers
Attn: Scholarship Selection Committee
120 South LaSalle Street, Suite 1515
Chicago, IL 60603-3572
(312) 596-5223   Toll Free: (877) SWE-INFO
Fax: (312) 644-8557
E-mail: scholarshipapplication@swe.org
Web: societyofwomenengineers.swe.org

Summary To provide financial assistance to undergraduate members of the Society of Women Engineers (SWE) who are majoring in computer science or engineering.

Eligibility This program is open to members of the society who are entering their sophomore, junior, or senior year at a 4-year ABET-accredited college or university. Applicants must be majoring in computer science or engineering and have a GPA of 3.0 or higher. Selection is based on merit. U.S. citizenship is required.

Financial data The stipend is $3,000.

Duration 1 year.

Number awarded 1 each year.

Deadline February of each year.

[410]
MARYLAND CAPITAL CHAPTER ABWA EDUCATION GRANTS

American Business Women's Association-Maryland
  Capital Chapter
Attn: Ann Broduer, Vice President
P.O. Box 1955
Edgewater, MD 21037
E-mail: abrodeur@verizon.net
Web: www.abwamdcap.org/mc/page.do?sitePageID=45248

Summary To provide financial assistance to female residents of Maryland who are working on an undergraduate or graduate degree at a college or university in any state.

Eligibility This program is open to women who are residents of Maryland and enrolled as juniors, seniors, or graduate students at a college or university in any state. Applicants must be U.S. citizens and have a GPA of 2.5 or higher. Along with their application, they must submit a 1-page biographical essay that includes the degree they plan to earn, how they are currently contributing to the community, the kind of salaried work they currently do (if any), their entrepreneurial plan for applying the knowledge and skills gained through their degree, and why they need financial support to continue their education.

Financial data The stipend ranges from $1,500 to $2,000.

Duration 1 year; nonrenewable.

Number awarded 1 or more each year.

Deadline April of each year.

[411]
MARYLAND LEGION AUXILIARY CHILDREN AND YOUTH FUND SCHOLARSHIP

American Legion Auxiliary
Department of Maryland
1589 Sulphur Spring Road, Suite 105
Baltimore, MD 21227
(410) 242-9519   Fax: (410) 242-9553
E-mail: hq@alamd.org
Web: www.alamd.org

Summary To provide financial assistance for college to the daughters of veterans who are Maryland residents and wish to study arts, sciences, business, public administration, education, or a medical field at a school in the state.

Eligibility This program is open to Maryland senior high school girls with a veteran parent who wish to study arts, sciences, business, public administration, education, or a medical field other than nursing at a college or university in the state. Preference is given to children of members of the American Legion or American Legion Auxiliary. Selection is based on character (30%), Americanism (20%), leadership (10%), scholarship (20%), and financial need (20%).

Financial data The stipend is $2,000.

Duration 1 year; may be renewed up to 3 additional years.

Number awarded 1 each year.

Deadline April of each year.

[412]
MARYLAND LEGION AUXILIARY PAST PRESIDENTS' PARLEY NURSING SCHOLARSHIP

American Legion Auxiliary
Department of Maryland
1589 Sulphur Spring Road, Suite 105
Baltimore, MD 21227
(410) 242-9519   Fax: (410) 242-9553
E-mail: hq@alamd.org
Web: www.alamd.org

Summary To provide financial assistance to the female descendants of Maryland veterans who wish to study nursing at a school in any state.

Eligibility This program is open to Maryland residents who are the daughters, granddaughters, great-granddaughters, step-daughters, step-granddaughters, or step-great-granddaughters of ex-servicewomen (or of ex-servicemen, if there are no qualified descendants of ex-servicewomen). Applicants must be interested in attending a school in any state to become a registered nurse and be able to show financial need. They must submit a 300-word essay on the topic "What a Nursing Career Means to Me."

Financial data The stipend is $2,000. Funds are sent directly to the recipient's school.

Duration 1 year; may be renewed for up to 3 additional years if the recipient remains enrolled full time.

Number awarded 1 each year.

Deadline April of each year.

[413]
MASWE SCHOLARSHIPS

Society of Women Engineers
Attn: Scholarship Selection Committee
120 South LaSalle Street, Suite 1515
Chicago, IL 60603-3572
(312) 596-5223   Toll Free: (877) SWE-INFO
Fax: (312) 644-8557
E-mail: scholarshipapplication@swe.org
Web: societyofwomenengineers.swe.org

Summary To provide financial assistance to undergraduate women majoring in computer science or engineering.

Eligibility This program is open to women who are entering their sophomore, junior, or senior year at a 4-year ABET-accredited college or university. Applicants must be majoring in computer science or engineering and have a GPA of 3.0 or higher. Financial need is considered in the selection process.

Financial data The stipend is $1,500.

Duration 1 year.

Additional information These scholarships were established by the Men's Auxiliary of the Society of Women Engineers (MASWE) in 1971 and are continued through a fund established by the organization when it disbanded in 1976 (effective with the opening of Society of Women Engineer's membership to men).

Number awarded 4 each year.

Deadline February of each year.

[414]
MEDTRONIC SWENET SCHOLARSHIP

Society of Women Engineers-Minnesota Section
Attn: Scholarship Committee
P.O. Box 582813
Minneapolis, MN 55458-2813
E-mail: scholarships@swe-mn.org
Web: swe-mn.org/scholarships.html

Summary To provide financial assistance to women from any state working on an undergraduate or graduate degree in specified fields of engineering at colleges and universities in Minnesota, North Dakota, and South Dakota.

Eligibility This program is open to female undergraduate and graduate students at ABET-accredited engineering programs in Minnesota, North Dakota, or South Dakota. Applicants must be working full time on a degree in biomedical, chemical, electrical, or mechanical engineering. Along with their application, they must submit a short paragraph describing how they plan to utilize their engineering skills after they graduate. Selection is based on potential to succeed as an engineer (20 points), communication skills (10 points), extracurricular or community involvement and leadership skills (10 points), demonstrated successful work experience (10 points), and academic success (5 points).

Financial data   The stipend is $1,000.

Duration   1 year.

Additional information   This program is sponsored by Medtronic, Inc.

Number awarded   2 each year.

Deadline   March of each year.

[415]
MERIDITH THOMS MEMORIAL SCHOLARSHIPS

Society of Women Engineers
Attn: Scholarship Selection Committee
120 South LaSalle Street, Suite 1515
Chicago, IL 60603-3572
(312) 596-5223   Toll Free: (877) SWE-INFO
Fax: (312) 644-8557
E-mail: scholarshipapplication@swe.org
Web: societyofwomenengineers.swe.org

Summary   To provide financial assistance to undergraduate women majoring in computer science or engineering.

Eligibility   This program is open to women who are entering their sophomore, junior, or senior year at a 4-year ABET-accredited college or university. Applicants must be majoring in computer science or engineering and have a GPA of 3.0 or higher. Selection is based on merit.

Financial data   The stipend is $2,000.

Duration   1 year.

Additional information   This program was established in 2001.

Number awarded   5 each year.

Deadline   February of each year.

[416]
MICHAEL BAKER CORPORATION SCHOLARSHIP PROGRAM FOR DIVERSITY IN ENGINEERING

Association of Independent Colleges and Universities of
  Pennsylvania
101 North Front Street
Harrisburg, PA 17101-1405
(717) 232-8649   Fax: (717) 233-8574
E-mail: info@aicup.org
Web: www.aicup.org/fundraising

Summary   To provide financial assistance to women and minority students from any state enrolled at member institutions of the Association of Independent Colleges and Universities of Pennsylvania (AICUP) who are majoring in designated fields of engineering.

Eligibility   This program is open to full-time undergraduate students from any state enrolled at designated AICUP colleges and universities who are women and/or members of the following minority groups: American Indians, Alaska Natives, Asians, Blacks/African Americans, Hispanics/Latinos, Native Hawaiians, or Pacific Islanders. Applicants must be juniors majoring in architectural, civil, or environmental engineering with a GPA of 3.0 or higher. Along with their application, they must submit a 2-page essay on what they believe will be the

greatest challenge facing the engineering profession over the next decade, and why.

Financial data   The stipend is $2,500 per year.

Duration   1 year; may be renewed 1 additional year if the recipient maintains appropriate academic standards.

Additional information   This program, sponsored by the Michael Baker Corporation, is available at the 83 private colleges and universities in Pennsylvania that comprise the AICUP.

Number awarded   1 each year.

Deadline   April of each year.

[417]
MICHELE L. MCDONALD SCHOLARSHIP

Educational Foundation for Women in Accounting
Attn: Foundation Administrator
136 South Keowee Street
Dayton, OH 45402
(937) 424-3391   Fax: (937) 222-5749
E-mail: info@efwa.org
Web: www.efwa.org/scholarships_McDonald.php

Summary   To provide financial support to women who are returning to college from the workforce or after raising their family to work on a degree in accounting.

Eligibility   This program is open to women who are returning to college from the workforce or after raising children. Applicants must be planning to begin a program of study for a college degree in accounting. Selection is based on aptitude for accounting and business, commitment to the goal of working on a degree in accounting (including evidence of continued commitment after receiving this award), clear evidence that the candidate has established goals and a plan for achieving those goals (both personal and professional), and financial need. U.S. citizenship is required.

Financial data   The stipend is $1,000 per year.

Duration   1 year; may be renewed 1 additional year if the recipient completes at least 12 hours each semester.

Additional information   This program was established by the Albuquerque Chapter of the American Society of Women Accountants (ASWA) and transferred to the Educational Foundation for Women in Accounting in 2006.

Number awarded   1 each year.

Deadline   April of each year.

[418]
MICHIGAN JOB'S DAUGHTERS SCHOLARSHIPS

International Order of Job's Daughters-Grand Guardian
  Council of Michigan
c/o Pam Van Duinen, Educational Trustee Board Chair
218 First Street
Menominee, MI 49858
(906) 863-6923
Web: www.michiganiojd.org/scholarships.htm

Summary   To provide financial assistance to members of Job's Daughters in Michigan who are interested in attending college in any state.

Eligibility   This program is open to members of Job's Daughters in Michigan who are high school seniors or graduates under 25 years of age. Applicants must be attending or planning to attend a college or university in any state. Along with their application, they must submit a brief summary of their personal goals and financial situation.

Financial data A stipend is awarded (amount not specified).

Duration 1 year; may be renewed.

Number awarded Varies each year.

Deadline April of each year.

[419]
MICKEY LELAND ENERGY FELLOWSHIPS

Department of Energy
Attn: Office of Fossil Energy
19901 Germantown Road, FE-6
Germantown, MD 20874
(301) 903-4293   E-mail: MLEF@hq.doe.gov
Web: fossil.energy.gov

Summary To provide summer work experience at fossil energy sites of the Department of Energy (DOE) to women and underrepresented minority students.

Eligibility This program is open to U.S. citizens currently enrolled full time at an accredited college or university. Applicants must be undergraduate, graduate, or postdoctoral students in mathematics, physical sciences, technology, or engineering and have a GPA of 3.0 or higher. They must be interested in a summer work experience at a DOE fossil energy research facility. Along with their application, they must submit a 100-word statement on why they want to participate in this program. A goal of the program is to recruit women and underrepresented minorities into careers related to fossil energy.

Financial data Weekly stipends are $500 for undergraduates, $650 for master's degree students, or $750 for doctoral and postdoctoral students. Travel costs for a round trip to and from the site and for a trip to a designated place for technical presentations are also paid.

Duration 10 weeks during the summer.

Additional information This program began as 3 separate activities: the Historically Black Colleges and Universities Internship Program established in 1995, the Hispanic Internship Program established in 1998, and the Tribal Colleges and Universities Internship Program, established in 2000. Those 3 programs were merged into the Fossil Energy Minority Education Initiative, renamed the Mickey Leland Energy Fellowship Program in 2000. Sites to which interns may be assigned include the Albany Research Center (Albany, Oregon), the National Energy Technology Laboratory (Morgantown, West Virginia and Pittsburgh, Pennsylvania), Pacific Northwest National Laboratory (Richland, Washington), Rocky Mountain Oilfield Testing Center (Casper, Wyoming), Strategic Petroleum Reserve Project Management Office (New Orleans, Louisiana), or U.S. Department of Energy Headquarters (Washington, D.C.).

Number awarded Varies each year; recently, 30 students participated in this program.

Deadline January of each year.

[420]
MID-HUDSON SECTION SCHOLARSHIP

Society of Women Engineers
Attn: Scholarship Selection Committee
120 South LaSalle Street, Suite 1515
Chicago, IL 60603-3572
(312) 596-5223   Toll Free: (877) SWE-INFO
Fax: (312) 644-8557
E-mail: scholarshipapplication@swe.org
Web: societyofwomenengineers.swe.org

Summary To provide financial assistance to women, especially those from New York, who are working on an undergraduate or graduate degree in engineering or computer science.

Eligibility This program is open to women who will be sophomores, juniors, seniors, or graduate students at ABET-accredited colleges and universities. Applicants must be working on a degree in computer science or engineering and have a GPA of 3.0 or higher. Selection is based on merit. Preference is given to applicants who reside and attend school in New York.

Financial data The stipend is $1,000.

Duration 1 year.

Number awarded 2 each year.

Deadline February of each year.

[421]
MIKE SHINN DISTINGUISHED MEMBER OF THE YEAR AWARDS

National Society of Black Engineers
Attn: Programs Department
205 Daingerfield Road
Alexandria, VA 22314
(703) 549-2207   Fax: (703) 683-5312
E-mail: scholarships@nsbe.org
Web: www.nsbe.org

Summary To provide financial assistance to members of the National Society of Black Engineers (NSBE) who are working on a degree in engineering (females and males are judged separately).

Eligibility This program is open to members of the society who are undergraduate or graduate engineering students. Applicants must have a GPA of 3.2 or higher. Selection is based on an essay; NSBE and university academic achievement; professional development; service to the society at the chapter, regional, and/or national level; and campus and community activities. The male and female applicants for the NSBE Fellows Scholarship Program who are judged most outstanding receive these awards.

Financial data The stipend is $7,500. Travel, hotel accommodations, and registration to the national convention are also provided.

Duration 1 year.

Number awarded 2 each year: 1 male and 1 female.

Deadline November of each year.

[422]
MILITARY NONRESIDENT TUITION WAIVER AFTER ASSIGNMENT IN TEXAS

Texas Higher Education Coordinating Board
Attn: Grants and Special Programs
1200 East Anderson Lane
P.O. Box 12788
Austin, TX 78711-2788
(512) 427-6340   Toll Free: (800) 242-3062
Fax: (512) 427-6420   E-mail: grantinfo@thecb.state.tx.us
Web: www.collegeforalltexans.com

Summary To provide educational assistance to the spouses and children of Texas military personnel assigned elsewhere.

Eligibility This program is open to the spouses and dependent children of members of the U.S. armed forces or commissioned officers of the Public Health Service who remain in Texas when the member is reassigned to duty outside of the state. The spouse or dependent child must reside continuously in Texas. Applicants must be attending or planning to attend a Texas public college or university.

Financial data Eligible students are entitled to pay tuition and fees at the resident rate at publicly-supported colleges and universities in Texas.

Duration The waiver remains in effect for the duration of the member's first assignment outside of Texas.

Additional information This program became effective in 2003.

Number awarded Varies each year.

Deadline Deadline not specified.

[423]
MILITARY NONRESIDENT TUITION WAIVER FOR MEMBERS, SPOUSES OR CHILDREN ASSIGNED TO DUTY IN TEXAS

Texas Higher Education Coordinating Board
Attn: Grants and Special Programs
1200 East Anderson Lane
P.O. Box 12788
Austin, TX 78711-2788
(512) 427-6340   Toll Free: (800) 242-3062
Fax: (512) 427-6420   E-mail: grantinfo@thecb.state.tx.us
Web: www.collegeforalltexans.com

Summary To exempt military personnel stationed in Texas and their spouses or children from the payment of nonresident tuition at public institutions of higher education in the state.

Eligibility Eligible for these waivers are members of the U.S. armed forces and commissioned officers of the Public Health Service from states other than Texas, their spouses, and dependent children. Applicants must be assigned to Texas and attending or planning to attend a public college or university in the state.

Financial data Although persons eligible under this program are classified as nonresidents, they are entitled to pay the resident tuition at Texas institutions of higher education, regardless of their length of residence in Texas.

Duration 1 year; may be renewed.

Number awarded Varies each year.

Deadline Deadline not specified.

[424]
MILITARY NONRESIDENT TUITION WAIVER FOR MEMBERS, SPOUSES OR CHILDREN WHO REMAIN CONTINUOUSLY ENROLLED IN HIGHER EDUCATION IN TEXAS

Texas Higher Education Coordinating Board
Attn: Grants and Special Programs
1200 East Anderson Lane
P.O. Box 12788
Austin, TX 78711-2788
(512) 427-6340   Toll Free: (800) 242-3062
Fax: (512) 427-6420   E-mail: grantinfo@thecb.state.tx.us
Web: www.collegeforalltexans.com

Summary To waive nonresident tuition at Texas public colleges and universities for members of the armed forces and their spouses or children who are no longer in the military.

Eligibility Eligible for these waivers are members of the U.S. armed forces, commissioned officers of the Public Health Service (PHS), their spouses, and their children. Applicants must have previously been eligible to pay tuition at the resident rate while enrolled in a degree or certificate program at a Texas public college or university because they were a member, spouse, or child of a member of the armed forces or PHS. This waiver is available after the servicemember, spouse, or parent is no longer a member of the armed forces or a commissioned officer of the PHS. The student must remain continuously enrolled in the same degree or certificate program in subsequent terms or semesters.

Financial data The student's eligibility to pay tuition and fees at the rate provided for Texas students does not terminate because the member, spouse, or parent is no longer in the service.

Duration 1 year.

Additional information This program became effective in September 2003.

Number awarded Varies each year.

Deadline Deadline not specified.

[425]
MILLIE GONZALEZ MEMORIAL SCHOLARSHIPS

Factor Support Network Pharmacy
Attn: Scholarship Committee
900 Avenida Acaso, Suite A
Camarillo, CA 93012-8749
(805) 388-9336   Toll Free: (877) FSN-4-YOU
Fax: (805) 482-6324
E-mail: Scholarships@FactorSupport.com
Web: www.factorsupport.com/scholarships.htm

Summary To provide financial assistance to women entering or attending college who have a bleeding disorder.

Eligibility This program is open to women with hemophilia or von Willebrand Disease who are entering or attending a college, university, juniors college, or vocational school. Applicants must submit 3 short essays: 1) their career goals; 2) how hemophilia or von Willebrand Disease has affected their life; and 3) their efforts to be involved in the bleeding disorder community and what they can do to education their peers and others outside their family about bleeding disorders. Selection is based on academic goals, volunteer work, school activities, other pertinent experience and achievements, and financial need.

Financial data The stipend is $1,000. Funds are paid directly to the recipient.

Duration 1 year.

Number awarded 5 each year.

Deadline April of each year.

[426]
MINNESOTA CHAPTER WTS SCHOLARSHIPS

Women's Transportation Seminar-Minnesota Chapter
c/o Nikki Farrington, Scholarship and Recognitions
  Director
CH2M Hill
1295 Northland Drive, Suite 200
Mendota Heights, MN 55120
(651) 365-8536   Fax: (651) 688-8844
E-mail: nfarring@ch2m.com
Web: www.wtsinternational.org/Chapters.aspx?ID=6964

Summary To provide financial assistance to women working on an undergraduate or graduate degree in a transportation-related field at colleges and universities in Minnesota.

Eligibility This program is open to women currently enrolled in an undergraduate or graduate degree program at a college or university in Minnesota. Applicants must be preparing for a career in transportation or a transportation-related field and be majoring in such fields as transportation engineering, planning, finance, or logistics. They must have a GPA of 3.0 or higher. Along with their application, they must submit a 750-word statement on their career goals after graduation and why they think they should receive this award. Selection is based on transportation goals, academic record, and transportation-related activities or job skills. Minority candidates are encouraged to apply.

Financial data The stipend is $2,000 or $500.

Duration 1 year.

Additional information Winners are also nominated for scholarships offered by the national organization of the Women's Transportation Seminar.

Number awarded 3 each year: 2 undergraduates and 1 graduate student.

Deadline November of each year.

[427]
MINNESOTA CHILD CARE GRANT PROGRAM

Minnesota Office of Higher Education
Attn: Manager of State Financial Aid Programs
1450 Energy Park Drive, Suite 350
St. Paul, MN 55108-5227
(651) 642-0567   Toll Free: (800) 657-3866
Fax: (651) 642-0675   TDD: (800) 627-3529
E-mail: Ginny.Dodds@state.mn.us
Web: www.ohe.state.mn.us

Summary To provide financial assistance for child care to college students in Minnesota who are not receiving Minnesota Family Investment Program (MFIP) benefits.

Eligibility Minnesota residents who are working on an undergraduate degree or vocational certificate in the state and who have children age 12 and under (14 and under if disabled) may receive this assistance to help pay child care expenses. Recipients must demonstrate financial need but must not be receiving MFIP benefits. U.S. citizenship or eligible noncitizen status is required.

Financial data The amount of the assistance depends on the income of applicant and spouse, number of day care hours necessary to cover education and work obligations, student's enrollment status, and number of eligible children in applicant's family. The maximum available is $2,600 per eligible child per academic year.

Duration 1 year; may be renewed as long as the recipient remains enrolled on at least a half-time basis in an undergraduate program.

Additional information Assistance may cover up to 40 hours per week per eligible child.

Number awarded Varies each year; recently, a total of $1.1 million was provided for this program.

Deadline Deadline not specified.

[428]
MINNESOTA LEGION AUXILIARY PAST PRESIDENTS PARLEY HEALTH CARE SCHOLARSHIP

American Legion Auxiliary
Department of Minnesota
State Veterans Service Building
20 West 12th Street, Room 314
St. Paul, MN 55155-2069
(651) 224-7634   Toll Free: (888) 217-9598
Fax: (651) 224-5243   E-mail: deptoffice@mnala.org
Web: www.mnala.org/ala/scholarship.asp

Summary To provide financial assistance for education in health care fields to members of the American Legion Auxiliary in Minnesota.

Eligibility This program is open to residents of Minnesota who have been members of the American Legion Auxiliary for at least 3 years. Applicants must have a GPA of 2.0 or higher and be planning to study in Minnesota. Their proposed major may be in any phase of health care, including nursing assistant, registered nursing, licensed practical nurse, X-ray or other technician, physical or other therapist, dental hygienist, or dental assistant.

Financial data The stipend is $1,000. Funds are sent directly to the recipient's school after satisfactory completion of the first quarter.

Duration 1 year.

Number awarded Up to 10 each year.

Deadline March of each year.

[429]
MINNESOTA NATIONAL GUARD SURVIVOR ENTITLEMENT TUITION REIMBURSEMENT PROGRAM

Department of Military Affairs
Attn: Education Services Officer
JFMN-J1-ARED
20 West 12th Street
St. Paul, MN 55155-2098
(651) 282-4125   Toll Free: (800) 657-3848
Fax: (651) 282-4694 E-mail: education@mn.ngb.army.mil
Web: www.minnesotanationalguard.org

Summary To provide financial assistance for college or graduate school to widows and children of members of the Minnesota National Guard who were killed on active duty.

Eligibility This program is open to surviving spouses and children of members of the Minnesota Army or Air National Guard who were killed while performing military duty. Spouses remain eligible unless they remarry; dependent children are eligible until their 24th birthday. The Guard member's death must have occurred within the scope of assigned duties while in a federal duty status or on state active service. Applicants must be enrolled as undergraduate or graduate students at colleges or universities in Minnesota. Reimbursement is provided only for undergraduate courses completed with a grade of "C" or better or for graduate courses completed with a grade of "B" or better.

Financial data The maximum reimbursement rate is 100% of the undergraduate tuition rate at the University of Minnesota Twin Cities campus (currently, $326.92 per credit to a maximum of $4,250 per term).

Duration 1 academic term, to a maximum of 18 credits per term; may be renewed for a total of 144 semester credits or 208 quarter credits.

Number awarded Varies each year.

Deadline Participants must request reimbursement within 60 days of the last official day of the term.

[430]
MINNESOTA SECTION SWE SCHOLARSHIP

Society of Women Engineers-Minnesota Section
Attn: Scholarship Committee
P.O. Box 582813
Minneapolis, MN 55458-2813
E-mail: scholarships@swe-mn.org
Web: swe-mn.org/scholarships.html

Summary To provide financial assistance to upper-division women from any state studying engineering or computer science at colleges and universities in Minnesota, North Dakota, and South Dakota.

Eligibility This program is open to women entering their junior or senior year at an ABET-accredited engineering program in Minnesota, North Dakota, or South Dakota. Applicants must be full-time students majoring in engineering or computer science. Along with their application, they must submit a short paragraph describing how they plan to utilize their engineering skills after they graduate. Preference is given to student members of the Society of Women Engineers (SWE). Selection is based on potential to succeed as an engineer (20 points), communication skills (10 points), extracurricular or community involvement and leadership skills (10 points), demonstrated successful work experience (10 points), and academic success (5 points).

Financial data The stipend is $1,500.

Duration 1 year.

Number awarded 1 each year.

Deadline March of each year.

[431]
MINNESOTA SWE LOCKHEED MARTIN SCHOLARSHIPS

Society of Women Engineers-Minnesota Section
Attn: Scholarship Committee
P.O. Box 582813
Minneapolis, MN 55458-2813
E-mail: scholarships@swe-mn.org
Web: swe-mn.org/scholarships.html

Summary To provide financial assistance to women from any state working on an undergraduate or graduate degree in electrical, systems, or mechanical engineering at colleges and universities in Minnesota, North Dakota, and South Dakota.

Eligibility This program is open to female undergraduate and graduate students at ABET-accredited engineering programs in Minnesota, North Dakota, or South Dakota. Applicants must be working full time on a degree in electrical, systems, or mechanical engineering. Along with their application, they must submit a short paragraph describing how they plan to utilize their engineering skills after they graduate. Selection is based on potential to succeed as an engineer (20 points), communication skills (10 points), extracurricular or community involvement and leadership skills (10 points), demonstrated successful work experience (10 points), and academic success (5 points).

Financial data The stipend is $1,500 for electrical or systems engineering or $1,000 for mechanical engineering.

Duration 1 year.

Additional information This program is sponsored by Lockheed Martin Corporation.

Number awarded 2 each year: 1 for electrical or systems engineering and 1 for mechanical engineering.

Deadline March of each year.

[432]
MINNESOTA VETERANS' DEPENDENTS ASSISTANCE PROGRAM

Minnesota Office of Higher Education
Attn: Manager of State Financial Aid Programs
1450 Energy Park Drive, Suite 350
St. Paul, MN 55108-5227
(651) 642-0567   Toll Free: (800) 657-3866
Fax: (651) 642-0675   TDD: (800) 627-3529
E-mail: Ginny.Dodds@state.mn.us
Web: www.ohe.state.mn.us

Summary To provide financial assistance for college to the spouses and children of Minnesota veterans and military personnel listed as POWs or MIAs.

Eligibility Eligible for this assistance are 1) spouses of a prisoner of war or person missing in action, or 2) children born before or during the period of time the parent served as a POW or was declared MIA, or 3) children legally adopted or in the legal custody of a parent prior to and during the time the parent served as a POW or was declared to be MIA. Veteran parents must have been residents of Minnesota at the time of entry into service or at the time declared to be a POW or MIA, which must have occurred after August 1, 1958.

Financial data Students who attend private postsecondary institutions receive up to $250 per year for tuition and fees. Students who attend a Minnesota public postsecondary institution are exempt from all tuition charges.

Duration Assistance continues until the student completes a bachelor's degree or receives a certificate of completion.

Number awarded Varies each year.

Deadline Deadline not specified.

[433]
MISS AMERICA COMPETITION AWARDS

Miss America Pageant
Attn: Scholarship Department
222 New Road, Suite 700
Linwood, NJ 08221
(609) 653-8700, ext. 127   Fax: (609) 653-8740
E-mail: info@missamerica.org
Web: www.missamerica.org/scholarships

Summary To provide educational scholarships to participants in the Miss America Pageant on local, state, and national levels.

Eligibility To enter an official Miss America Preliminary Pageant, candidates must meet certain basic requirements and agree to abide by all the rules of the local, state, and national Miss America Pageants. Among the qualifications required are that the applicant be female, between the ages of 17 and 24, a resident of the town or state in which they first compete, in good health, of good moral character, and a citizen of the United States. A complete list of all eligibility requirements is available from each local and state pageant. Separate scholarships are awarded to the winners of the talent competition and the lifestyle and fitness in swimsuit competition. In addition, the Charles and Theresa Brown Scholarships are awarded to Miss America, the top 4 runners-up, Miss Alaska, Miss Hawaii, Miss Illinois, Miss Ohio, and 1 other state representative.

Financial data More than $45 million in cash and tuition assistance is awarded annually at the local, state, and national Miss America Pageants. At the national level, nearly $500,000 is awarded: Miss America receives $50,000 in scholarship money, the first runner-up $25,000, second runner-up $20,000, third runner-up $15,000, fourth runner-up $10,000, the top finalist $8,000, 4 other finalists $6,000 each, the top 2 semifinalists $5,000 each, 3 other semifinalists $4,000 each, and other national contestants $3,000 each. Other awards include those for the 3 preliminary talent winners at $2,000 each, the 3 preliminary lifestyle and fitness in swimsuit winners at $1,000 each, and the 5 non-finalist talent winners at $1,000 each. The Charles and Theresa Brown Scholarships are $2,500 each.

Duration The pageants are held every year.

Additional information The Miss America Pageant has been awarding scholarships since 1945. Scholarships are to be used for tuition, room, board, supplies, and other college expenses. Use of the scholarships must begin within 4 years from the date of the award (5 years if the recipient is Miss America), unless a reasonable extension is requested and granted. Training under the scholarship should be continuous and completed within 10 years from the date the scholarship is activated; otherwise, the balance of the scholarship may be canceled without further notice.

Number awarded At the national level, 52 contestants (1 from each state, the District of Columbia, and the Virgin Islands) share the awards.

Deadline Varies, depending upon the date of local pageants leading to the state and national finals.

[434]
MISS BLACK AMERICA

Miss Black America Pageant
P.O. Box 25668
Philadelphia, PA 19144
(215) 844-8872 E-mail: Contact@MissBlackAmerica.com
Web: www.missblackamerica.com

Summary To recognize and reward beautiful and talented Black American women.

Eligibility All African American women between 17 and 29 years of age, including married contestants and contestants with children, are eligible. Finalists who compete in the national pageant are selected after competitions on the local and state levels. The winner at the national pageant is chosen by a panel of judges on the basis of beauty, talent, and personality.

Financial data Miss Black America receives a cash award and an array of prizes.

Duration The competition is held annually.

Additional information This competition began in 1968. There is a $50 application fee and an $800 sponsorship fee.

Number awarded 1 each year.

Deadline December of each year.

[435]
MISS DEAF AMERICA AMBASSADOR PROGRAM

National Association of the Deaf
8630 Fenton Street, Suite 820
Silver Spring, MD 20910-3819
(301) 587-1788   Fax: (301) 587-1791
TDD: (301) 587-1789   E-mail: nadinfo@nad.org
Web: www.nad.org/youth-leadership-programs

Summary To recognize and reward outstanding young deaf women.

Eligibility This is a 2-tiered competition. Young deaf women between the ages of 18 and 30 compete first on the state level; winners take part in the national pageant. Winners are selected on the basis of artistic expression, community service, academics, current events, deaf culture, and more.

Financial data The national winner receives an educational scholarship (amount not specified).

Duration The competition is held biennially during the summer of even-numbered years, in conjunction with the National Association of the Deaf conventions.

Deadline The deadline dates of the state competitions vary; check with the sponsor in your area.

[436]
MISS INDIAN USA SCHOLARSHIP PROGRAM

American Indian Heritage Foundation
P.O. Box 750
Pigeon Forge, TN 37868
(703) 819-0979   E-mail: MissIndianUSA@indians.org
Web: www.indians.org/miss-indian-usa-program.html

Summary   To recognize and reward the most beautiful and talented Indian women.

Eligibility   American Indian women between the ages of 18 and 26 are eligible to enter this national contest if they are high school graduates and have never been married, cohabited with the opposite sex, been pregnant, or had children. U.S. citizenship is required. Selection is based on public appearance (20%), a traditional interview (15%), a contemporary interview (15%), beauty of spirit (15%), a cultural presentation (10%), scholastic achievement (10%), a platform question (10%), and a finalist question (5%).

Financial data   Awards vary each year; recently, Miss Indian USA received an academic scholarship of $4,000 plus a cash grant of $6,500, a wardrobe allowance of $2,000, appearance fees of $3,000, a professional photo shoot worth $500, gifts worth more than $4,000, honoring gifts worth more than $2,000, promotional materials worth more than $2,000, and travel to Washington, D.C. with a value of approximately $2,000; the total value of the prize was more than $26,000. Members of her court received scholarships of $2,000 for the first runner-up, $1,500 for the second runner-up, $1,000 for the third runner-up, and $500 for the fourth runner-up.

Duration   This competition is held annually.

Additional information   The program involves a week-long competition in the Washington, D.C. metropolitan area that includes seminars, interviews, cultural presentations, and many public appearances. The application fee is $100 if submitted prior to mid-April or $200 if submitted later. In addition, a candidate fee of $750 is required.

Number awarded   1 winner and 4 runners-up are selected each year.

Deadline   May of each year.

[437]
MISS LATINA WORLD

Dawn Rochelle Models Agency
129 South Tennessee Street
McKinney, TX 75069
(469) 396-5670   E-mail: contact@dawnrochelle.com
Web: www.misslatina.com

Summary   To recognize and reward young Latina women who compete in a national beauty pageant.

Eligibility   This program is open to women between 18 and 28 years of age who are at least 25% Hispanic. Applicants may be single, married, or divorced, and they may have children. They appear in a nationally-televised pageant where selection is based on 3 categories: beauty/evening gown, fashion wear, and photogenic. Judges also interview each participant; the interview score may replace the fashion wear score. Height and weight are not factors, but contestants should be proportionate. Pageant experience and fluency in Spanish are not required.

Financial data   Each year, prizes vary. The overall winner receives a $10,000 bond.

Duration   The pageant is held annually.

Number awarded   1 overall winner is selected each year.

Deadline   April of each year.

[438]
MISS TEEN AMERICA

Miss Teen America, Inc.
P.O. Box 37
Getzville, NY 14068
(716) 629-3990   E-mail: info@missteenamerica.com
Web: www.missteenamerica.com

Summary   To recognize and reward, with college scholarships, teenage women who participate in a talent and beauty competition.

Eligibility   This competition is open to females between 15 and 18 years of age who have never been to college, been married, or given birth to a child. Applicants must first apply for state or metropolitan area competitions by submitting a 1-page essay on why they want to represent their state. At the national level, they participate in talent, modeling, and photogenic competitions. Selection is based on a personal interview with judges (20%), talent or spokesmodel presentation (20%), physical fitness, in recommended swimsuit (20%), a formal evening wear presentation (10%), a 30-second commercial or public service announcement about their state (10%), the photogenic competition (10%), and modeling (10%).

Financial data   Cash scholarships, for use at an accredited college or university, range up to $5,000 for Miss Teen America. Other awards vary each year.

Duration   The competition is held annually.

Additional information   All participants are required to pay a total sponsorship fee of $1,195, including a deposit of $50 to accompany the application. They are also required to sell $400 worth of ads for the national program.

Number awarded   5 winners receive national scholarships each year.

Deadline   Deadline not specified.

[439]
MISSISSIPPI NATIONAL GUARD NONCOMMISSIONED OFFICERS ASSOCIATION SCHOLARSHIPS

Mississippi National Guard Noncommissioned Officers Association
Attn: Executive Director
P.O. Box 699
Brandon, MS 39043-0699
(601) 824-0304   Toll Free: (800) 205-5797
Fax: (601) 824-4970   E-mail: msngnco@bellsouth.net
Web: www.msncoa.org/Scholorships.htm

Summary   To provide financial assistance to spouses and other dependents of members of the Mississippi National Guard Noncommissioned Officers Association who are interested in attending college in any state.

Eligibility   This program is open to the unmarried dependent children and spouses of annual, enlisted, retired, and life members of the association. Applicants must be high school seniors or undergraduate students with at least 1 full semester remaining before graduation. They must be attending or planning to attend an accredited university, college, community college, vocational/technical, business, or trade school in any state. Along with their application, they must submit a personal letter about themselves, letters of recommendation, transcripts, a copy of their sponsor's association membership card, and a copy of their ACT score.

Financial data The stipend depends on the availability of funds.

Duration 1 year.

Number awarded Varies each year.

Deadline January of each year.

[440]
MISSOURI GENERAL BPW SCHOLARSHIPS

Missouri Business and Professional Women's
  Foundation, Inc.
P.O. Box 28243
Kansas City, MO 64188
(816) 333-6959   Fax: (816) 333-6959
E-mail: jo.mofedbpw@gmail.com
Web: www.mofedbpw.org/files/index.php?id=14

Summary To provide financial assistance to women in Missouri who plan to attend college in any state.

Eligibility This program is open to women in Missouri who have been accepted into an accredited program or course of study in any state to upgrade their skills and/or complete education for career advancement. Along with their application, they must submit brief statements on the following: their achievements and/or specific recognitions in their field of endeavor; professional and/or civic affiliations; present and long-range career goals; how they plan to participate in and contribute to their community upon completion of their program of study; why they feel they would make a good recipient; and any special circumstances that may have influenced their ability to continue or complete their education. They must also demonstrate financial need and U.S. citizenship.

Financial data A stipend is awarded (amount not specified).

Duration 1 year.

Number awarded Varies each year; recently, 3 of these scholarships were awarded.

Deadline December of each year.

[441]
MISSOURI JOB'S DAUGHTERS SCHOLARSHIPS

International Order of Job's Daughters-Grand Bethel of
  Missouri
c/o Donna Brown, Scholarship and Loan Committee
2022 Bainbridge Road
Jackson, MO 63755
(573) 243-8689
Web: www.missouriiojd.org/Scholarships/index.htm

Summary To provide financial assistance to members of Job's Daughters in Missouri who are interested in attending college in any state.

Eligibility This program is open to residents of Missouri who have been an active member of a Missouri Job's Daughter Bethel for at least 1 year or are majority members younger than 25 years of age. Applicants must be attending or planning to attend a college or university in any state. Along with their application, they must submit 1) an essay describing how Job's Daughters has helped them develop leadership abilities and explaining how those relate to their everyday life; 2) an essay on the ways in which Job's Daughters has helped them to grow as an individual; 3) brief statements on their

awards and honors in Job's Daughters, high school activities, church activities, community activities, and volunteer work. Their Executive Bethel Council must submit a letter of recommendation on why they believe they are qualified to receive this scholarship and the contributions they have made to their Bethel. Selection is based on the applicant's essays and statements, the letter of recommendation, academic standing in high school or college, and contributions to Bethel and community.

Financial data A stipend is awarded (amount not specified).

Duration 1 year; recipients may reapply.

Number awarded Several each year.

Deadline March of each year.

[442]
MISSOURI STATE KNIGHTS OF COLUMBUS LADIES AUXILIARY SCHOLARSHIP

Knights of Columbus-Missouri State Council
c/o J.Y. Miller, Scholarship Committee Chair
322 Second Street
Glasgow, MO 65254
(660) 338-2105   E-mail: j.y.miller@sbcglobal.net
Web: www.mokofc.org/youth.htm

Summary To provide financial assistance to members of the Ladies Auxiliary of the Knights of Columbus in Missouri who are interested in attending college in the state.

Eligibility This program is open to residents of Missouri who are enrolled or planning to enroll at an accredited college, university, or trade school in the state. Applicants must be a member of the Ladies Auxiliary of the Knights of Columbus. Along with their application, they must submit a 200-word statement explaining their goals for the future, their professional ambitions, and how this scholarship will help them to achieve their goals. Selection is based on Catholic citizenship, community service, scholarship, and financial need.

Financial data The stipend is $1,000.

Duration 1 year.

Additional information This program was originally established in 1971.

Number awarded 1 each year.

Deadline February of each year.

[443]
MISSOURI VIETNAM VETERAN SURVIVOR GRANT PROGRAM

Missouri Department of Higher Education
Attn: Student Financial Assistance
3515 Amazonas Drive
Jefferson City, MO 65109-5717
(573) 751-2361   Toll Free: (800) 473-6757
Fax: (573) 751-6635   E-mail: info@dhe.mo.gov
Web: www.dhe.mo.gov/vietnamveterans.html

Summary To provide financial assistance to the spouses and children of certain deceased Missouri Vietnam veterans who plan to attend college in the state.

Eligibility This program is open to surviving spouses and children of veterans who served in the military in Vietnam or the war zone in southeast Asia, who were residents of Missouri when first entering military service and at the time of death, whose death was attributed to or caused by exposure to toxic chemicals during the Vietnam conflict, and who served in the Vietnam Theater between 1961 and 1972. Applicants must be Missouri residents enrolled in a program leading to a certificate, associate degree, or baccalaureate degree at an approved postsecondary institution in the state. Students working on a degree or certificate in theology or divinity are not eligible. U.S. citizenship or permanent resident status is required.

Financial data The maximum annual grant is the lesser of 1) the actual tuition charged at the school where the recipient is enrolled, or 2) the amount of tuition charged to a Missouri undergraduate resident enrolled full time in the same class level and in the same academic major as an applicant at the Missouri public 4-year regional institutions.

Duration 1 semester; may be renewed until the recipient has obtained a baccalaureate degree or has completed 150 semester credit hours, whichever comes first.

Additional information Awards are not available for summer study.

Number awarded Up to 12 each year.

Deadline There is no application deadline, but early submission of the completed application is encouraged.

[444]
MISSOURI WARTIME VETERAN'S SURVIVOR GRANT PROGRAM

Missouri Department of Higher Education
Attn: Student Financial Assistance
3515 Amazonas Drive
Jefferson City, MO 65109-5717
(573) 751-2361   Toll Free: (800) 473-6757
Fax: (573) 751-6635   E-mail: info@dhe.mo.gov
Web: www.dhe.mo.gov/wartimevetsurvivor.html

Summary To provide financial assistance to the spouses and children of deceased or disabled Missouri post-September 11, 2001 veterans who plan to attend college or graduate school in the state.

Eligibility This program is open to spouses and children of veterans whose deaths or injuries were a result of combat action or were attributed to an illness that was contracted while serving in combat action, or who became 80% disabled as a result of injuries or accidents sustained in combat action since September 11, 2001. The veteran must have been a Missouri resident when first entering military service or at the time of death or injury. The spouse or child must be a U.S. citizen or permanent resident or otherwise lawfully present in the United States; children of veterans must be younger than 25 years of age. All applicants must be enrolled or accepted for enrollment at least half time at an approved public college or university in Missouri and working on an associate, baccalaureate, master's, or doctoral degree.

Financial data The maximum annual grant is the lesser of 1) the actual tuition charged at the school where the recipient is enrolled, or 2) the amount of tuition charged to a Missouri resident enrolled in the same number of hours at the University of Missouri Columbia. Additional allowances provide up to $2,000 per semester for room and board and the lesser of the actual cost for books or $500.

Duration 1 year. May be renewed, provided the recipient maintains a GPA of 2.5 or higher and makes satisfactory academic progress; children of veterans are eligible until they turn 25 years of age or receive their first bachelor's degree, whichever occurs first.

Number awarded Up to 25 each year.

Deadline There is no application deadline, but early submission of the completed application is encouraged.

[445]
MOSS ADAMS FOUNDATION SCHOLARSHIP

Educational Foundation for Women in Accounting
Attn: Foundation Administrator
136 South Keowee Street
Dayton, OH 45402
(937) 424-3391   Fax: (937) 222-5749
E-mail: info@efwa.org
Web: www.efwa.org/scholarships_MossAdams.php

Summary To provide financial support to women, including minority women, who are working on an accounting degree.

Eligibility This program is open to women who are enrolled in an accounting degree program at an accredited college or university. Applicants must meet 1 of the following criteria: 1) women pursuing a fifth-year requirement either through general studies or within a graduate program; 2) women returning to school as current or reentry juniors or seniors; or 3) minority women. Selection is based on aptitude for accounting and business, commitment to the goal of working on a degree in accounting (including evidence of continued commitment after receiving this award), clear evidence that the candidate has established goals and a plan for achieving those goals (both personal and professional), financial need, and a demonstration of how the scholarship will impact her life. U.S. citizenship is required.

Financial data The stipend is $1,000.

Duration 1 year.

Additional information This program was established by Rowling, Dold & Associates LLP, a woman-owned C.P.A. firm based in San Diego. It was renamed when that firm merged with Moss Adams LLP.

Number awarded 1 each year.

Deadline April of each year.

[446]
MTS SYSTEMS CORPORATION SCHOLARSHIP

Society of Women Engineers-Minnesota Section
Attn: Scholarship Committee
P.O. Box 582813
Minneapolis, MN 55458-2813
E-mail: scholarships@swe-mn.org
Web: swe-mn.org/scholarships.html

Summary To provide financial assistance to women from any state working on an undergraduate or graduate degree in software or mechanical engineering at colleges and universities in Minnesota, North Dakota, and South Dakota.

Eligibility This program is open to female undergraduate and graduate students at ABET-accredited engineering programs in Minnesota, North Dakota, or South Dakota. Applicants must be working full time on a degree in software or mechanical engineering. Along with their application, they must submit a short paragraph describing how they plan to utilize their engineering skills after they graduate. Selection is based on potential to succeed as an engineer (20 points), communication skills (10 points), extracurricular or community involvement and leadership skills (10 points), demonstrated successful work experience (10 points), and academic success (5 points).

Financial data   The stipend is $1,500.

Duration   1 year.

Additional information   This program is sponsored by MTS Systems Corporation.

Number awarded   1 each year.

Deadline   March of each year.

[447]
MURIEL ANDERSON STEED SCHOLARSHIP

Kappa Alpha Theta Foundation
Attn: Scholarships
8740 Founders Road
Indianapolis, IN 46268-1337
(317) 876-1870   Toll Free: (800) KAO-1870
Fax: (317) 876-1925
E-mail: FDNmail@kappaalphatheta.org
Web: www.kappaalphathetafoundation.org

Summary   To provide financial assistance to undergraduate and graduate members of Kappa Alpha Theta who are preparing for a career as a teacher.

Eligibility   This program is open to members of Kappa Alpha Theta who are full-time undergraduate or graduate students at a college or university in Canada or the United States. Applicants must be preparing for a career as a teacher. Along with their application, they must submit an official transcript, personal essays on assigned topics related to their involvement in Kappa Alpha Theta, and 2 letters of reference. Financial need is not considered in the selection process.

Financial data   The stipend is $1,550.

Duration   1 year.

Number awarded   1 each year.

Deadline   January of each year.

[448]
MUSIC THERAPY SCHOLARSHIP

Sigma Alpha Iota Philanthropies, Inc.
One Tunnel Road
Asheville, NC 28805
(828) 251-0606   Fax: (828) 251-0644
E-mail: nh@sai-national.org
Web: www.sigmaalphaiota.org

Summary   To provide financial assistance to members of Sigma Alpha Iota (an organization of women musicians) who are working on an undergraduate or graduate degree in music therapy.

Eligibility   This program is open to members of the organization who have completed at least 2 years of study for an undergraduate or graduate degree in music therapy. Applicants must submit an essay that includes their personal definition of music therapy, their career plans and professional goals as a music therapist, and why they feel they are deserving of this scholarship. Selection is based on music therapy skills, musicianship, fraternity service, community service, leadership, self-reliance, and dedication to the field of music therapy as a career.

Financial data   The stipend is $1,500.

Duration   1 year.

Number awarded   1 each year.

Deadline   March of each year.

[449]
MUSICAL THEATER SCHOLARSHIP

Sigma Alpha Iota Philanthropies, Inc.
One Tunnel Road
Asheville, NC 28805
(828) 251-0606   Fax: (828) 251-0644
E-mail: nh@sai-national.org
Web: www.sigmaalphaiota.org

Summary   To provide financial assistance to members of Sigma Alpha Iota (an organization of women musicians) who are working on an undergraduate degree with an emphasis on musical theater.

Eligibility   This program is open to members of the organization who are enrolled in an undergraduate degree program in music with an emphasis on musical theater. Applicants must be endorsed or recommended by a director of musical theater or major professor with whom they have worked for at least 6 months. Along with their application, they must submit a 15-minute performance DVD that includes a variety of styles and at least 2 monologues; a brief resume, including their musical experience; current academic transcripts; and a brief statement of their career goals and aspirations. Financial need is not considered in the selection process.

Financial data   The stipend is $1,500.

Duration   1 year.

Additional information   This program was established in 2010.

Number awarded   1 each year.

Deadline   March of each year.

[450]
MUSICIANS WITH SPECIAL NEEDS SCHOLARSHIP

Sigma Alpha Iota Philanthropies, Inc.
One Tunnel Road
Asheville, NC 28805
(828) 251-0606   Fax: (828) 251-0644
E-mail: nh@sai-national.org
Web: www.sigmaalphaiota.org

Summary   To provide financial assistance for college or graduate school to members of Sigma Alpha Iota (an organization of women musicians) who have a disability and are working on a degree in music.

Eligibility   This program is open to members of the organization who either 1) have a sensory or physical impairment and are enrolled in a graduate or undergraduate degree program in music, or 2) are preparing to become a music teacher or therapist for people with disabilities. Performance majors must submit a 15-minute DVD of their work; non-performance majors must submit evidence of work in their area of specialization, such as composition, musicology, or research.

Financial data   The stipend is $1,500.

Duration   1 year.

Number awarded   1 each year.

Deadline   March of each year.

[451]
MYRT WILLEY SCHOLARSHIP

Zonta Club of Bangor
c/o Barbara A. Cardone
P.O. Box 1904
Bangor, ME 04402-1904
Web: www.zontaclubofbangor.org/?area=scholarship

Summary To provide financial assistance to women attending or planning to attend college in Maine and major in a business-related field.

Eligibility This program is open to women who are attending or planning to attend an accredited 2- or 4-year college in Maine. Applicants must major in a business-related field. Along with their application, they must submit brief essays on 1) their goals in seeking higher education and their plans for the future, and 2) any school and community activities that have been of particular importance to them and why they found them worthwhile. Financial need may be considered in the selection process.

Financial data The stipend is $1,000.

Duration 1 year.

Number awarded 1 each year.

Deadline March of each year.

[452]
NABA 20 PEARLS SCHOLARSHIP

National Association of Black Accountants
Attn: National Scholarship Program
7474 Greenway Center Drive, Suite 1120
Greenbelt, MD 20770
(301) 474-NABA, ext. 114   Fax: (301) 474-3114
E-mail: customerservice@nabainc.org
Web: www.nabainc.org

Summary To provide financial assistance to student members of the National Association of Black Accountants (NABA) who are also members of Alpha Kappa Alpha sorority and working on an undergraduate or graduate degree in a field related to accounting.

Eligibility This program is open to NABA members who are also Alpha Kappa Alpha members and enrolled full time as 1) an undergraduate freshman, sophomore, junior, or first-semester senior majoring in accounting, business, or finance at a 4-year college or university; or 2) a graduate student working on a master's degree in accounting. High school seniors are not eligible. Applicants must have a GPA of 3.5 or higher in their major and 3.3 or higher overall. Selection is based on grades, financial need, and a 500-word autobiography that discusses career objectives, leadership abilities, community activities, and involvement in NABA.

Financial data The stipend is $1,500.

Duration 1 year.

Number awarded 1 each year.

Deadline January of each year.

[453]
NANCY LORRAINE JENSEN MEMORIAL SCHOLARSHIP FUND

Sons of Norway
Attn: Foundation
1455 West Lake Street
Minneapolis, MN 55408-2666
(612) 821-4632   Toll Free: (800) 945-8851
Fax: (612) 827-0658   E-mail: foundation@sofn.com
Web: www.sofn.com

Summary To provide financial assistance to women who have a connection to the Sons of Norway and are interested in studying chemistry, physics, or engineering in college.

Eligibility This program is open to women who are U.S. citizens between 17 and 35 years of age and members (or daughters or granddaughters of members) of the Sons of Norway; they must have been a member for at least 3 years. Applicants must have a combined SAT score of 1800 or higher, a mathematics score of 600 or higher, or an ACT score of 26 or higher. They must be full-time undergraduate students and have completed at least 1 quarter or semester of study in chemistry, physics, or chemical, electrical, or mechanical engineering. Selection is based on long-term career goals, clarity of study plan, academic potential, evidence of ability to succeed, and letters of recommendation attesting to good character, eagerness, earnestness, and ambition in the field of science or engineering.

Financial data Stipends range from 50% of tuition for 1 quarter or semester to 100% for 1 year. Grants are issued jointly to the recipient and her institution.

Duration Awards are made for either 1 term (quarter or semester) or 1 year; a student may receive up to 3 awards as an undergraduate.

Additional information This fund was established in 1995 by Dr. and Mrs. Arthur S. Jensen in memory of their daughter, a chemical engineer whose work resulted in advances in the field of weather satellite photography and who died at the age of 35.

Number awarded Varies each year; recently, 4 of these scholarships were awarded.

Deadline March of each year.

[454]
NANNIE W. NORFLEET SCHOLARSHIP

American Legion Auxiliary
Department of North Carolina
P.O. Box 25726
Raleigh, NC 27611-5726
(919) 832-4051   Fax: (919) 832-1888
E-mail: ala1_nc@bellsouth.net
Web: nclegion.org/auxil.htm

Summary To provide financial assistance to members of the American Legion Auxiliary in North Carolina and their children and grandchildren who plan to attend college in any state.

Eligibility This program is open to North Carolina residents who are either adult members of the American Legion Auxiliary or high school seniors (with preference to the children and grandchildren of members). Applicants must be interested in attending college in any state. They must be able to demonstrate financial need.

Financial data   The stipend is $1,000.
Duration   1 year.
Number awarded   1 each year.
Deadline   March of each year.

[455]
NAOMI BERBER MEMORIAL SCHOLARSHIP

Print and Graphics Scholarship Foundation
Attn: Scholarship Competition
200 Deer Run Road
Sewickley, PA 15143-2600
(412) 259-1740   Toll Free: (800) 910-GATF
Fax: (412) 741-2311   E-mail: pgsf@printing.org
Web: www.printing.org/pgsf

Summary   To provide financial assistance for college to women who want to prepare for a career in the printing or publishing industry.

Eligibility   This program is open to women who are high school seniors or full-time college students. Applicants must be interested in preparing for a career in graphic communications or printing. This is a merit-based program; financial need is not considered.

Financial data   The stipend ranges from $1,000 to $5,000, depending upon the funds available each year.

Duration   1 year; may be renewed for up to 3 additional years, provided the recipient maintains a GPA of 3.0 or higher.

Additional information   This program was established in 1983 to honor Naomi Berber, the first woman elected to the Graphic Arts Technical Foundation Society of Fellows.

Number awarded   1 or more each year.

Deadline   February of each year for high school seniors; March of each year for students already in college.

[456]
NASA MOTIVATING UNDERGRADUATES IN SCIENCE AND TECHNOLOGY (MUST) SCHOLARSHIP PROGRAM

National Aeronautics and Space Administration
Attn: Vanessa R. Webbs, MUST Project Manager
NASA John H. Glenn Research Center at Lewis Field
2100 Brookpark Road, M.S. 500-107
Cleveland, OH 44135
(216) 433-3768   Fax: (216) 433-3344
E-mail: vanessa.r.webbs@nasa.gov
Web: www.nasa.gov

Summary   To provide financial assistance to women and members of other underrepresented groups who are working on an undergraduate degree in a field of science, technology, engineering, or mathematics (STEM).

Eligibility   This program is open to U.S. citizens from an underrepresented group, including women, African Americans, Hispanic Americans, Native Americans, and persons with disabilities. Applicants must be entering their sophomore or junior year at an accredited college or university in the 50 states or Puerto Rico as a full-time student. They must have a GPA of 3.0 or higher and a major in a STEM field of study.

Financial data   Stipends provide payment of 50% of the tuition and fees at the recipient's institution, to a maximum of $10,000.

Duration   1 year; may be renewed 1 additional year.
Deadline   January of each year.

[457]
NASA SCIENCE AND TECHNOLOGY INSTITUTE (NSTI) SUMMER SCHOLARS PROGRAM

United Negro College Fund Special Programs Corporation
Attn: NASA Science and Technology Institute
6402 Arlington Boulevard, Suite 600
Falls Church, VA 22042
(703) 677-3400   Toll Free: (800) 530-6232
Fax: (703) 205-7645   E-mail: portal@uncfsp.org
Web: www.uncfsp.org

Summary   To provide an internship opportunity for women and other underrepresented undergraduate students to work on a summer research project at designated research centers of the U.S. National Aeronautics and Space Administration (NASA).

Eligibility   This program is open to current college freshmen, sophomores, and juniors at accredited institutions who are members of underrepresented groups, including women, ethnic minorities, and persons with disabilities. Applicants must be working on a degree in a science, technology, engineering, or mathematics (STEM) field and have a GPA of 3.0 or higher. They must be interested in working on a research project during the summer at Ames Research Center (Moffett Field, California), Johnson Space Center (Houston, Texas), or Glenn Research Center (Cleveland, Ohio). U.S. citizenship is required.

Financial data   A stipend is provided (amount not specified).

Duration   10 weeks during the summer.

Additional information   This program, which began in 2006, is funded by NASA and administered by the United Negro College Fund Special Programs Corporation.

Number awarded   Varies each year.

Deadline   January of each year.

[458]
NATIONAL HISPANIC BUSINESS WOMEN ASSOCIATION EDUCATIONAL SCHOLARSHIPS

National Hispanic Business Women Association
2024 North Broadway, Suite 100
Santa Ana, CA 92706
(714) 836-4042
Web: nationalhbwa.com

Summary   To provide financial assistance to women in California who are working on an undergraduate or graduate degree at a school in any state and submit an essay related to Latinas in education.

Eligibility   This program is open to female residents of California who are currently enrolled as undergraduate or graduate students at a school in any state. Applicants must have a GPA of 3.0 or higher and be able to demonstrate financial need. They must also have a record of participation in some form of community service. Along with their application, they must submit 2 essays of 2 pages each on 1) their academic and professional goals; and 2) their choice of the importance or value of obtaining a higher education, the potential impacts or influences of a growing Latino population in relation to their field of interest, or the specific challenges faced by Latinas in pursuit of higher education.

Financial data Stipends range from $500 to $1,000.

Duration 1 year.

Number awarded Varies each year; recently, 12 of these scholarships were awarded.

Deadline March of each year.

[459]
NATIONAL ORGANIZATION OF ITALIAN AMERICAN WOMEN SCHOLARSHIPS

National Organization of Italian American Women
25 West 43rd Street, Suite 1005
New York, NY 10036
(212) 642-2003   Fax: (212) 642-2006
E-mail: noiaw@noiaw.org
Web: www.noiaw.org

Summary To provide financial assistance for college or graduate school to women of Italian descent.

Eligibility This program is open to women who have at least 1 parent of Italian American descent and are working on an associate, bachelor's, or master's degree. Applicants must be enrolled full time and have a GPA of 3.5 or higher. Along with their application, they must submit a 2-page essay on how being an Italian American has impacted them personally and professionally. Financial need is considered in the selection process.

Financial data The stipend is $2,000.

Duration 1 year; nonrenewable.

Number awarded 4 each year, including 1 reserved for an undergraduate or graduate student at the City University of New York system.

Deadline April of each year.

[460]
NATIONAL PATHFINDER SCHOLARSHIPS

National Federation of Republican Women
Attn: Scholarships and Internships
124 North Alfred Street
Alexandria, VA 22314-3011
(703) 548-9688   Fax: (703) 548-9836
E-mail: mail@nfrw.org
Web: www.nfrw.org/programs/scholarships.htm

Summary To provide financial assistance for college or graduate school to Republican women.

Eligibility This program is open to women currently enrolled as college sophomores, juniors, seniors, or master's degree students. Recent high school graduates and first-year college women are not eligible. Applicants must submit 3 letters of recommendation, an official transcript, a 1-page essay on why they should be considered for the scholarship, and a 1-page essay on career goals. Applications must be submitted to the Republican federation president in the applicant's state. Each president chooses 1 application from her state to submit for scholarship consideration. Financial need is not a factor in the selection process. U.S. citizenship is required.

Financial data The stipend is $2,500.

Duration 1 year; nonrenewable.

Additional information This program, previously named the Nancy Reagan Pathfinder Scholarships, was established in 1985.

Number awarded 3 each year.

Deadline Applications must be submitted to the state federation president by May of each year.

[461]
NATIONAL SORORITY OF PHI DELTA KAPPA SCHOLARSHIPS

National Sorority of Phi Delta Kappa, Inc.
Attn: Perpetual Scholarship Foundation
8233 South King Drive
Chicago, IL 60619
(773) 783-7379   Fax: (773) 783-7354
E-mail: nspdkhdq@aol.com
Web: www.sororitynpdk.org/scholarships.html

Summary To provide financial assistance to African American high school seniors who are interested in studying education in college (females and males are judged separately).

Eligibility This program is open to African American high school seniors who are interested in working on a 4-year college degree in education. Men and women compete separately. Financial need is considered in the selection process.

Financial data The stipend is $1,250 per year.

Duration 4 years, provided the recipient maintains a GPA of 3.0 or higher and a major in education.

Additional information The sponsor was founded in 1923 as an organization of female African American educators.

Number awarded 10 each year: 1 male and 1 female in each of the organization's 5 regions.

Deadline Applications must be submitted to a local chapter of the organization by January of each year.

[462]
NATIONAL SPACE GRANT COLLEGE AND FELLOWSHIP PROGRAM

National Aeronautics and Space Administration
Attn: Office of Education
300 E Street, S.W.
Mail Suite 6M35
Washington, DC 20546-0001
(202) 358-1069   Fax: (202) 358-7097
E-mail: Diane.D.DeTroye@nasa.gov
Web: www.nasa.gov

Summary To provide financial assistance to undergraduate and graduate students (especially women and members of other underrepresented groups) who are interested in preparing for a career in a space-related field.

Eligibility This program is open to undergraduate and graduate students at colleges and universities that participate in the National Space Grant program of the U.S. National Aeronautics and Space Administration (NASA) through their state consortium. Applicants must be interested in a program of study and/or research in a field of science, technology, engineering, or mathematics (STEM) related to space. A specific goal of the program is to increase preparation by members of underrepresented groups (minorities, women, and persons with disabilities) for STEM space-related careers. Financial need is not considered in the selection process.

Financial data Each consortium establishes the terms of the fellowship program in its state.

Additional information NASA established the Space Grant program in 1989. It operates through 52 consortia in each state, the District of Columbia, and Puerto Rico. Each consortium includes selected colleges and universities in that state as well as other affiliates from industry, museums, science centers, and state and local agencies.

Number awarded Varies each year.

Deadline Each consortium sets its own deadlines.

[463]
NATIVE AMERICAN PROJECT GRANTS

Delta Kappa Gamma Society International-Mu State
  Organization
c/o Beverly Staff, Native American Project
7407 Lillie Lane
Pensacola, FL 32526
(850) 944-3302   E-mail: leannjax@yahoo.com
Web: www.orgsites.com/fl/mustatedeltakappagamma

Summary To provide financial assistance to female Native Americans from Florida who are working on a degree in education or conducting research into the history of Native Americans at a college or university in the state.

Eligibility This program is open to women who are members of a recognized Native American tribe in Florida. Applicants must be enrolled at an accredited college or university in the state and either working on a degree in education or conducting research into the history of Native Americans in Florida. Along with their application, they must submit a brief statement with details of the purpose of the grant, a letter of recommendation from a tribal official, and a copy of high school or college transcripts.

Financial data The stipend is $1,000.

Duration 1 year.

Number awarded 6 each year: 1 in each of the districts of the sponsoring organization in Florida.

Deadline May of each year.

[464]
NATIVE AMERICAN WOMEN'S HEALTH EDUCATION RESOURCE CENTER INTERNSHIPS

Native American Women's Health Education Resource
  Center
Attn: Internship Coordinator
P.O. Box 572
Lake Andes, SD 57356-0572
(605) 487-7072   Fax: (605) 487-7964
E-mail: charon@charles-mix.com
Web: www.nativeshop.org

Summary To provide work experience to students and recent graduates interested in working at the Native American Women's Health Education Resource Center and its Domestic Violence Shelter.

Eligibility This program is open to college students, graduate students, and recent graduates. Applicants must have a background of work in Native American rights and health issues to promote civil rights, women's rights, and a healthy environment. They must be interested in working at the Native American Women's Health Education Resource Center and its Domestic Violence Shelter.

Financial data Interns receive a stipend of $500 per month, free room at the shelter, and partial board from the resource center's food pantry.

Duration 3 months to 1 year; priority is given for internships of 6 months or longer.

Additional information The Native American Women's Health Education Resource Center is a project of the Native American Community Board. It is located in Lake Andes, South Dakota in a rural area of the Yankton Sioux Reservation. The Domestic Violence Shelter is 4 blocks away. Past intern projects have included domestic violence advocacy at the shelter, counseling on the youth crisis hotline, environmental activism, Native women's reproductive health and rights, indigenous people's rights projects, web site development, organizing the annual community health fair, producing a Dakota language CD-ROM, and AIDS education.

Number awarded Varies each year.

Deadline Deadline not specified.

[465]
NAVY/MARINE CORPS/COAST GUARD ENLISTED DEPENDENT SPOUSE SCHOLARSHIP

Navy Wives Clubs of America
P.O. Box 54022
Millington, TN 38053-6022
Toll Free: (866) 511-NWCA
E-mail: nwca@navywivesclubsofamerica.org
Web: www.navywivesclubsofamerica.org/scholarinfo.htm

Summary To provide financial assistance for undergraduate or graduate study to spouses of naval personnel.

Eligibility This program is open to the spouses of active-duty Navy, Marine Corps, or Coast Guard members who can demonstrate financial need. Applicants must be 1) a high school graduate or senior planning to attend college full time next year; 2) currently enrolled in an undergraduate program and planning to continue as a full-time undergraduate; 3) a college graduate or senior planning to be a full-time graduate student next year; or 4) a high school graduate or GED recipient planning to attend vocational or business school next year. Along with their application, they must submit a brief statement on why they feel they should be awarded this scholarship and any special circumstances (financial or other) they wish to have considered. Financial need is also considered in the selection process.

Financial data The stipends range from $500 to $1,000 each year (depending upon the donations from chapters of the Navy Wives Clubs of America).

Duration 1 year.

Number awarded 1 or more each year.

Deadline May of each year.

[466]
NCAIAW SCHOLARSHIP

North Carolina Alliance for Athletics, Health, Physical
  Education, Recreation and Dance
Attn: Executive Director
727 West Hargett Street, Suite 111
P.O. Box 27751
Raleigh, NC 27611
(919) 833-1219   Toll Free: (888) 840-6500
Fax: (919) 833-7700   E-mail: ncaahperd@ncaahperd.org
Web: www.ncaahperd.org

Summary To provide financial assistance to women who
are college seniors involved in sports at an institution that is a
member of the former North Carolina Association of Intercollegiate Athletics for Women (NCAIAW).

Eligibility This program is open to women who have been
a participant on 1 or more varsity athletic teams either as a
player or in the support role of manager, trainer, etc. Appli-
cants must be attending 1 of the following former NCAIAW
colleges or universities in North Carolina: Appalachian State,
Belmont Abbey, Bennett, Campbell, Davidson, Duke, East
Carolina, Gardner-Webb, High Point, Mars Hill, Meredith,
North Carolina A&T, North Carolina State, Pembroke State,
Salem, University of North Carolina at Ashville, University of
North Carolina at Chapel Hill, University of North Carolina at
Charlotte, University of North Carolina at Wilmington, Wake
Forest, or Western Carolina. They must be college seniors at
the time of application, be able to demonstrate high stan-
dards of scholarship, and show evidence of leadership poten-
tial (as indicated by participation in school and community
activities).

Financial data The stipend is $1,000. Funds are sent to
the recipient's school.

Duration 1 year.

Additional information This scholarship was established
in 1983.

Number awarded 1 each year.

Deadline June of each year.

[467]
NCCE SCHOLARSHIPS

National Commission for Cooperative Education
360 Huntington Avenue, 384 CP
Boston, MA 02115-5096
(617) 373-3770   Fax: (617) 373-3463
E-mail: ncce@co-op.edu
Web: www.co-op.edu/scholarships.htm

Summary To provide financial assistance to students
(especially women and minorities) who are participating or
planning to participate in cooperative education projects at
designated colleges and universities.

Eligibility This program is open to high school seniors and
community college transfer students entering 1 of the 7 partner colleges and universities. Applicants must be planning to
participate in college cooperative education. They must have
a GPA of 3.5 or higher. Along with their application, they must
submit a 1-page essay describing why they have chosen to
enter a college cooperative education program. Applications
are especially encouraged from minorities, women, and students interested in science, mathematics, engineering, and

technology. Selection is based on merit; financial need is not
considered.

Financial data The stipend is $6,000 per year.

Duration 1 year; may be renewed up to 3 additional years
or (for some programs) up to 4 additional years.

Additional information The schools recently participat-
ing in this program were Drexel University (Philadelphia,
Pennsylvania), Johnson & Wales University (Providence,
Rhode Island; Charleston, South Carolina; Norfolk, Virginia;
North Miami, Florida; Denver, Colorado; and Charlotte, North
Carolina), Kettering University (Flint, Michigan), Rochester
Institute of Technology (Rochester, New York), University of
Cincinnati (Cincinnati, Ohio), University of Toledo (Toledo,
Ohio), and Wentworth Institute of Technology (Boston, Mas-
sachusetts). Applications must be sent directly to the college
or university.

Number awarded Varies each year; recently, 155 of these
scholarships were awarded: 30 at Drexel, 30 at Johnson &
Wales, 20 at Kettering, 15 at Rochester Tech, 15 at Cincinnati, 15 at Toledo, and 30 at Wentworth Tech.

Deadline February of each year.

[468]
NEBRASKA WAIVER OF TUITION FOR
VETERANS' DEPENDENTS

Department of Veterans' Affairs
State Office Building
301 Centennial Mall South, Sixth Floor
P.O. Box 95083
Lincoln, NE 68509-5083
(402) 471-2458   Fax: (402) 471-2491
E-mail: john.hilgert@nebraska.gov
Web: www.vets.state.ne.us

Summary To provide financial assistance for college to the
spouses, widows, and children of deceased and disabled veterans and military personnel in Nebraska.

Eligibility Eligible are spouses, widow(er)s, and children
who are residents of Nebraska and whose parent, steppar-
ent, or spouse was a member of the U.S. armed forces and 1)
died of a service-connected disability; 2) died subsequent to
discharge as a result of injury or illness sustained while in
service; 3) is permanently and totally disabled as a result of
military service; or 4) is classified as missing in action or as a
prisoner of war during armed hostilities after August 4, 1964.
Applicants must be attending or planning to attend a branch
of the University of Nebraska, a state college, or a community
college in Nebraska.

Financial data Tuition is waived at public institutions in
Nebraska.

Duration The waiver is valid for 1 degree, diploma, or certificate from a community college and 1 baccalaureate
degree.

Additional information Applications may be submitted
through 1 of the recognized veterans' organizations or any
county service officer.

Number awarded Varies each year; recently, 311 of these
grants were awarded.

Deadline Deadline not specified.

[469]
NEED-BASED SCHOLARSHIPS

Delta Gamma Foundation
Attn: Director of Scholarships, Fellowships and Loans
3250 Riverside Drive
P.O. Box 21397
Columbus, OH 43221-0397
(614) 481-8169   Toll Free: (800) 644-5414
Fax: (614) 481-0133
E-mail: FNScholarFellow@deltagamma.org
Web: www.deltagamma.org

Summary To provide financial assistance to undergraduate members of Delta Gamma sorority who can demonstrate financial need.

Eligibility This program is open to initiated members of a collegiate chapter of Delta Gamma in the United States or Canada who have proven financial need or who find themselves in a sudden or unexpected financial crisis. Applicants must have a GPA of 2.5 or higher. Along with their application, they must submit 1) a 500-word essay explaining their financial need or crisis; 2) a copy of any financial aid award letters from their school; and 3) a letter of recommendation from an official of their chapter.

Financial data The stipend is $2,500. Funds are sent directly to the recipient's university or college to be used for tuition, books, laboratory fees, room, and board. They may not be used for sorority dues, house fees, or other chapter expenses.

Duration 1 year.

Number awarded Varies each year.

Deadline Applications may be submitted at any time.

[470]
NETWORK OF EXECUTIVE WOMEN SCHOLARSHIP

Network of Executive Women
c/o Nathalia Granger, Director of Operations
Accenture
161 North Clark Street, 37th Floor
Chicago, IL 60601
(312) 693-6855   Fax: (312) 726-4704
E-mail: ngranger@newonline.org
Web: www.newonline.org/?page=scholarships

Summary To provide financial assistance to upper-division and graduate student women preparing for a career in the consumer products and retail industry.

Eligibility This program is open to women enrolled full time as juniors, seniors, or graduate students in a retail, food, or consumer packaged goods-related program at a U.S. college or university. Applicants must have a GPA of 3.0 or higher. Along with their application, they must submit a 1-page essay explaining why they merit this scholarship and outlining their food, retail, or consumer packaged goods industry interests. Selection is based on that essay, a current resume, a transcript, and 2 letters of recommendation; financial need is not considered. U.S. citizenship is required.

Financial data A stipend is awarded (amount not specified).

Duration 1 year.

Number awarded 1 or more each year.

Deadline April of each year.

[471]
NEW HORIZONS LEADER SCHOLARSHIP

Royal Neighbors of America
Attn: Fraternal Services
230 16th Street
Rock Island, IL 61201-8645
(309) 788-4561   Toll Free: (800) 627-4762
E-mail: contact@royalneighbors.org
Web: www.royalneighbors.org

Summary To provide financial assistance to women who are members of the Royal Neighbors of America and interested in attending college.

Eligibility This program is open to female beneficial members of the society who are 18 years of age or older and planning to enroll as a full- or part-time student at an accredited college, university, or junior college. They must have previously graduated from high school.

Financial data The stipend is $5,000 per year.

Duration 1 year; may be renewed up to 3 additional years.

Number awarded 1 each year.

Deadline Requests for applications must be submitted by December of each year.

[472]
NEW JERSEY BANKERS EDUCATION FOUNDATION SCHOLARSHIPS

New Jersey Bankers Association
Attn: New Jersey Bankers Education Foundation, Inc.
411 North Avenue East
Cranford, NJ 07016-2436
(908) 272-8500, ext. 614   Fax: (908) 272-6626
E-mail: j.meredith@njbankers.com
Web: www.njbankers.com

Summary To provide financial assistance to spouses, widows, and descendants of deceased and disabled military personnel who have a connection to New Jersey and are interested in attending college in any state.

Eligibility This program is open to the spouses, children, stepchildren, and grandchildren of members of the armed services who died or became disabled while on active duty; it is not required that the military person died in combat. Applicants must have a high school or equivalency diploma and be attending college in any state. Adult dependents who wish to obtain a high school equivalency diploma are also eligible. Either the dependent or the servicemember must have a connection to New Jersey; the applicant's permanent address must be in New Jersey or the servicemember's last permanent address or military base must have been in the state. Financial need is considered in the selection process.

Financial data A stipend is awarded (amount not specified).

Duration 1 year; may be renewed if the recipient maintains a "C" average.

Additional information This program was established in 2005.

Number awarded 1 or more each year.

Deadline June of each year.

[473]
NEW JERSEY STATE ELKS SPECIAL CHILDREN'S SCHOLARSHIP

New Jersey State Elks
Attn: Special Children's Committee
665 Rahway Avenue
P.O. Box 1596
Woodbridge, NJ 07095-1596
(732) 326-1300   E-mail: info@njelks.org
Web: www.njelks.org

Summary   To provide financial assistance to high school seniors in New Jersey who have a disability and plan to attend college in any state (females and males are judged separately).

Eligibility   This program is open to seniors graduating from high schools in New Jersey who have a disability. Applicants must be planning to attend a college or university in any state. Selection is based on academic standing, general worthiness, and financial need. Boys and girls are judged separately.

Financial data   The stipend is $2,500 per year. Funds are paid directly to the recipient's college or university.

Duration   4 years.

Number awarded   2 each year: 1 to a boy and 1 to a girl.

Deadline   April of each year.

[474]
NEW JERSEY SWE SCHOLARSHIP

Society of Women Engineers
Attn: Scholarship Selection Committee
120 South LaSalle Street, Suite 1515
Chicago, IL 60603-3572
(312) 596-5223   Toll Free: (877) SWE-INFO
Fax: (312) 644-8557
E-mail: scholarshipapplication@swe.org
Web: societyofwomenengineers.swe.org

Summary   To provide financial assistance to women from New Jersey who will be entering freshmen at a college in any state and are interested in studying engineering or computer science.

Eligibility   This program is open to women who are entering college in any state as freshmen with a GPA of 3.5 or higher. Applicants must be residents of New Jersey planning to enroll full time at an ABET-accredited 4-year college or university and major in computer science or engineering. Selection is based on merit.

Financial data   The stipend is $2,000.

Duration   1 year.

Additional information   This program was established in 1998 by the New Jersey Section of the Society of Women Engineers (SWE).

Number awarded   1 each year.

Deadline   May of each year.

[475]
NEW JERSEY UTILITIES ASSOCIATION EQUAL EMPLOYMENT OPPORTUNITY SCHOLARSHIPS

New Jersey Utilities Association
50 West State Street, Suite 1117
Trenton, NJ 08608
(609) 392-1000   Fax: (609) 396-4231
Web: www.njua.org/html/njua_eeo_scholarship.cfm

Summary   To provide financial assistance to female, minority, and disabled high school seniors in New Jersey interested in attending college in any state.

Eligibility   This program is open to seniors graduating from high schools in New Jersey who are women, minorities (Black or African American, Hispanic or Latino, American Indian or Alaska Native, Asian, Native Hawaiian or Pacific Islander, or 2 or more races), and persons with disabilities. Applicants must be planning to work on a bachelor's degree at a college or university in any state. They must be able to demonstrate financial need. Children of employees of any New Jersey Utilities Association-member company are ineligible. Selection is based on overall academic excellence and demonstrated financial need. U.S. citizenship or permanent resident status is required.

Financial data   The stipend is $1,500 per year.

Duration   4 years.

Number awarded   2 each year.

Deadline   March of each year.

[476]
NEW MEXICO ELKS ASSOCIATION CHARITABLE AND BENEVOLENT TRUST SCHOLARSHIPS

New Mexico Elks Association
Attn: Charitable and Benevolent Trust Commission
c/o Michael Stewart, Scholarship Committee
199 Old El Paso Highway
Alamagordo, NM 87123
Fax: (575) 921-5597
E-mail: michaelstewart.per@Live.com
Web: www.nmelks.org/scholarships.htm

Summary   To provide financial assistance for college to high school seniors in New Mexico (females and males are judged separately).

Eligibility   Applicants must be seniors graduating from a high school in New Mexico. They must have exhibited outstanding scholastic and leadership ability, including extracurricular and civic activities. High school class rank, GPA, and standardized test scores must be validated by a school official. An endorsement from the local Elks Lodge is required. Financial need is also considered in the selection process. Some awards are designated for females and some for males.

Financial data   Stipends are either $2,000 or $1,000 per year.

Duration   1 or 4 years.

Additional information   Recipients may attend any level of academic institution and may major in any field. This program includes the following named awards: the Charles Mahr Memorial Scholarship, the Evelyn Boney Memorial Scholarships, the Howard Medlin Memorial Scholarship, and the Robert E. Boney Memorial Scholarship.

Number awarded Varies each year; recently, 26 of these scholarships were awarded: 1 at $2,000 per year for 4 years to the top female applicant, 1 at $2,000 per year for 4 years to the top male applicant, 12 at $2,000 for 1 year (6 for females and 6 for males), and 12 at $1,000 for 1 year (6 for females and 6 for males).

Deadline Applications must be submitted to local Elks Lodges by March of each year.

[477]
NFWL/NRA BILL OF RIGHTS ESSAY CONTEST

National Foundation for Women Legislators, Inc.
910 16th Street, N.W., Suite 100
Washington, DC 20006
(202) 293-3040   Fax: (202) 293-5430
E-mail: events@womenlegislators.org
Web: www.womenlegistors.org

Summary To recognize and reward, with college scholarships the best essays written by female high school juniors or seniors on a topic related to the Bill of Rights.

Eligibility This competition is open to female high school juniors or seniors. Applicants are invited to write an essay of 400 to 600 words on a topic (changes annually) related to the Bill of Rights; recently, the topic related to the impact of the first amendment on women leaders and social media. In addition to the essay, candidates must submit 2 personal reference letters.

Financial data Each winner receives a $3,000 unrestricted scholarship to use toward college tuition at any U.S. college or university and an all-expense paid trip to the foundation's annual conference.

Duration The competition is held annually.

Additional information This essay competition is sponsored jointly by the National Foundation of Women Legislators (NFWL) and the National Rifle Association (NRA).

Number awarded Varies each year; recently, 9 of these scholarships were awarded.

Deadline June of each year.

[478]
NINETY-NINES, INC. AMELIA EARHART MEMORIAL SCHOLARSHIPS

Ninety-Nines, Inc.
4300 Amelia Earhart Road
Oklahoma City, OK 73159
(405) 685-7969   Toll Free: (800) 994-1929
Fax: (405) 685-7985   E-mail: AEChair@ninety-nines.org
Web: www.ninety-nines.org/index.cfm/scholarships.htm

Summary To provide funding to members of the Ninety-Nines (an organization of women pilots) who are interested in advanced flight training or academic study related to aviation.

Eligibility This program is open to women who have been members of the organization for at least 1 year. Applicants must be interested in 1 of the following 4 types of scholarships: 1) flight training, to complete an additional pilot certificate or rating or pilot training course; 2) jet type rating, to complete type rating certification in any jet; 3) technical certification, to complete an aviation or aerospace technical training or certification course; or 4) academic, to work on an associate, bachelor's, master's, or doctoral degree in such fields as aerospace engineering, aviation technology, aviation

business management, air traffic management, or professional pilot. They must submit their application to their Ninety-Nines scholarship chair, who forwards it to the appropriate Amelia Earhart Scholarship Trustee. Applicants for flight training scholarships must be a current pilot with the appropriate medical certification and approaching the flight time requirement for the rating or certificate. Applicants for jet type rating scholarships must be a current airline transport pilot with a first-class medical certificate and at least 100 hours of multi-engine flight time or combined multi-engine and turbine time. Applicants for academic scholarships must be currently enrolled; associate or bachelor's degree students must have a GPA of 3.0 or higher. Financial need is considered in the selection process.

Financial data Flight training, jet type rating, and technical certification scholarships provide payment of all costs to complete the appropriate rating or certificate. Academic scholarships provide a stipend of up to $5,000 per year.

Duration Support is provided until completion of the rating, certificate, or degree.

Additional information This program was established in 1941. It includes the following endowed scholarships: the Jane Zieber Kelley Memorial Scholarship of the Aeons (established in 1979), the Gerda Ruhnke Memorial Flight Instructor Scholarship (established in 1988), the Geraldine Mickelsen Memorial Scholarship (established in 1993), the Alice Hammond Memorial Scholarship (established in 1995), the Lydiellen M. Hagan Memorial Scholarship (established in 1997), the Katherine A. Menges Brick Scholarship (established in 1998), the Betty DeWitt Witmer Scholarship (established in 1999), the Virginia S. Richardson Memorial Scholarship (established in 2000), the Darlene Sanders Memorial Scholarship (established in 2000), the Milton and Bonnie Seymour Memorial Scholarship (established in 2000), the Marion Barnick Memorial Scholarship (established in 2001), the Evelyn Bryan Johnson Memorial Scholarship (established in 2002), and the Mary Kelley Memorial Scholarship (established in 2003).

Number awarded Varies each year; recently, 14 of these scholarships were awarded.

Deadline Applications must be submitted to the chapter scholarship chair by November of each year; they must forward the applications from their chapter to the designated trustee by December of each year.

[479]
NONRESIDENT TUITION WAIVERS FOR VETERANS AND THEIR DEPENDENTS WHO MOVE TO TEXAS

Texas Higher Education Coordinating Board
Attn: Grants and Special Programs
1200 East Anderson Lane
P.O. Box 12788
Austin, TX 78711-2788
(512) 427-6340   Toll Free: (800) 242-3062
Fax: (512) 427-6420   E-mail: grantinfo@thecb.state.tx.us
Web: www.collegeforalltexans.com

Summary To exempt veterans who move to Texas and their spouses or children from the payment of nonresident tuition at public institutions of higher education in the state.

Eligibility Eligible for these waivers are former members of the U.S. armed forces and commissioned officers of the Public Health Service who are retired or have been honorably discharged, their spouses, and dependent children. Applicants must have moved to Texas upon separation from the service and be attending or planning to attend a public college or university in the state. They must have indicated their intent to become a Texas resident by registering to vote and doing 1 of the following: owning real property in Texas, registering an automobile in Texas, or executing a will indicating that they are a resident of the state.

Financial data Although persons eligible under this program are still classified as nonresidents, they are entitled to pay the resident tuition at Texas institutions of higher education on an immediate basis.

Duration 1 year.

Number awarded Varies each year.

Deadline Deadline not specified.

[480]
NORMA ROSS WALTER SCHOLARSHIP PROGRAM

Willa Cather Pioneer Memorial and Educational
   Foundation
Attn: Scholarship Program
413 North Webster
Red Cloud, NE 68970
(402) 746-2653   Toll Free: (866) 731-7304
Fax: (402) 746-2652
Web: www.willacather.org/education/scholarships

Summary To provide financial assistance to female graduates of Nebraska high schools who are or will be majoring in English at an accredited college or university in any state.

Eligibility This program is open to women who have graduated or plan to graduate from a Nebraska high school and enter a college or university in any state as a first-year student. Applicants must plan to continue their education as English majors (journalism is not acceptable). Along with their application, they must submit a 1,500-word essay on several of the short stories or a novel written by Willa Cather. Selection is based on intellectual promise, creativity, and character.

Financial data Stipends are $1,000, $750, or $500.

Duration 1 year; nonrenewable.

Number awarded 3 each year: 1 each at $1,000, $750, and $500.

Deadline January of each year.

[481]
NORTH CAROLINA BUSINESS AND PROFESSIONAL WOMEN'S FOUNDATION SCHOLARSHIPS

North Carolina Federation of Business and Professional
   Women's Club, Inc.
Attn: BPW/NC Foundation
P.O. Box 276
Carrboro, NC 27510
Web: www.bpw-nc.org/Default.aspx?pageId=837230

Summary To provide financial assistance to women attending North Carolina colleges, community colleges, or graduate schools.

Eligibility This program is open to women who are currently enrolled in a community college, 4-year college, or graduate school in North Carolina. Applicants must be

endorsed by a local BPW unit. Along with their application, they must submit a 1-page statement that summarizes their career goals, previous honors, or community activities and justifies their need for this scholarship. U.S. citizenship is required.

Financial data The stipend is $1,000. Funds are paid directly to the recipient's school.

Duration 1 year; recipients may reapply.

Additional information This program was established in 1996.

Number awarded 2 each year.

Deadline April of each year.

[482]
NORTH DAKOTA EDUCATIONAL ASSISTANCE FOR DEPENDENTS OF VETERANS

Department of Veterans Affairs
4201 38th Street S.W., Suite 104
P.O. Box 9003
Fargo, ND 58106-9003
(701) 239-7165   Toll Free: (866) 634-8387
Fax: (701) 239-7166
Web: www.nd.gov/veterans/benefits/waiver.html

Summary To provide financial assistance for college to the spouses, widows, and children of disabled and other North Dakota veterans and military personnel.

Eligibility This program is open to the spouses, widow(er)s, and dependent children of veterans who are totally disabled as a result of service-connected causes, or who were killed in action, or who have died as a result of wounds or service-connected disabilities, or who were identified as prisoners of war or missing in action. Veteran parents must have been born in and lived in North Dakota until entrance into the armed forces (or must have resided in the state for at least 6 months prior to entrance into military service) and must have served during wartime.

Financial data Eligible dependents receive free tuition and are exempt from fees at any state-supported institution of higher education, technical school, or vocational school in North Dakota.

Duration Up to 45 months or 10 academic semesters.

Number awarded Varies each year.

Deadline Deadline not specified.

[483]
NORTH DAKOTA WOMEN'S OPPORTUNITY SCHOLARSHIP FUND

North Dakota Council on Abused Women's Services
Attn: Scholarship Review Committee
525 North Fourth Street
Bismarck, ND 58501
(701) 255-6240   Toll Free: (888) 255-6240
Fax: (701) 255-1904
Web: www.ndcaws.org/what_we_do/scholarships

Summary To provide financial assistance to women in North Dakota who are interested in attending a college or university in the state.

Eligibility This program is open to female residents of North Dakota who plan to enroll full time at a college, university, or certification program in the state. Applicants must be able to demonstrate income lower than established financial guidelines (currently less than $13,612 for a single person, rising to $47,035 for a family of 8). Along with their application, they must submit an essay of 500 to 1,000 words on their motivation for attending college and their plans for the future. Priority is given to 1) first-time students and current students in special circumstances that may prevent them from completing a pending degree or program; and 2) students who may not be eligible for sources of funding normally available to low-income applicants.

Financial data A stipend is awarded (amount not specified).

Duration 1 year; may be renewed.

Number awarded Varies each year.

Deadline June of each year.

[484]
NORTHROP GRUMMAN FOUNDATION SCHOLARSHIP

Society of Women Engineers
Attn: Scholarship Selection Committee
120 South LaSalle Street, Suite 1515
Chicago, IL 60603-3572
(312) 596-5223   Toll Free: (877) SWE-INFO
Fax: (312) 644-8557
E-mail: scholarshipapplication@swe.org
Web: societyofwomenengineers.swe.org

Summary To provide financial assistance to female undergraduates interested in studying specified fields of engineering in college.

Eligibility This program is open to women who entering their sophomore, junior, or senior year as a full time student at an ABET-accredited 4-year college or university. Applicants must have a GPA of 3.0 or higher and be majoring in computer science or aerospace, computer, electrical, industrial, mechanical, or systems engineering. Selection is based on merit. U.S. citizenship is required.

Financial data The stipend is $5,000.

Duration 1 year.

Additional information This program, established in 1983, is sponsored by Northrup Grumman.

Number awarded 5 each year.

Deadline February of each year.

[485]
NORTHWEST WOMEN IN EDUCATIONAL ADMINISTRATION SCHOLARSHIP

Confederation of Oregon School Administrators
Attn: Youth Development Program
707 13th Street, S.E., Suite 100
Salem, OR 97301-4035
(503) 581-3141   Fax: (503) 581-9840
Web: www.cosa.k12.or.us

Summary To provide financial assistance to women who are high school seniors in Oregon and interested in preparing for a teaching career at a community college, college, or university in the state.

Eligibility This program is open to women who are graduating from high schools in Oregon. Applicants must be interested in attending a community college, college, or university in the state to major in education. They must have been active in community and school affairs, have a GPA of 3.5 or higher,

and be able to enroll in the fall term after graduating from high school. Along with their application, they must submit a 1-page autobiography (that includes their personal goals), the name of the school they plan to attend, and the endorsement of a member of the Confederation of Oregon School Administrators (COSA). Financial need is not considered in the selection process.

Financial data The stipend is $1,000. Funds are paid directly to the recipient.

Duration 1 year; nonrenewable.

Additional information This program is offered through Northwest Women in Educational Administration.

Number awarded 2 each year.

Deadline February of each year.

[486]
NSPE AUXILIARY LEGACY SCHOLARSHIP

National Society of Professional Engineers
Attn: NSPE Educational Foundation
1420 King Street
Alexandria, VA 22314-2794
(703) 684-2833   Toll Free: (888) 285-NSPE
Fax: (703) 836-4875   E-mail: education@nspe.org
Web: www.nspe.org/Students/Scholarships/index.html

Summary To provide financial assistance to female members of the National Society of Professional Engineers (NSPE) who are entering their junior year at a college or university in any state.

Eligibility This program is open to women who are NSPE student members entering their junior year in an ABET-accredited engineering program. Applicants must submit a 500-word essay on their engineering career goals and aspirations and their plans to achieve them. Selection is based on that essay, GPA, internship and co-op experience, involvement in other activities, 2 faculty recommendations, and honors and awards since high school. U.S. citizenship is required.

Financial data The stipend is $2,000; funds are paid directly to the recipient's institution.

Duration 1 year.

Number awarded 1 each year.

Deadline February of each year.

[487]
NYWICI FOUNDATION SCHOLARSHIPS

New York Women in Communications, Inc.
Attn: NYWICI Foundation
355 Lexington Avenue, 15th Floor
New York, NY 10017-6603
(212) 297-2133   Fax: (212) 370-9047
E-mail: nywicipr@nywici.org
Web: www.nywici.org/foundation/scholarships

Summary To provide financial assistance to female residents of designated eastern states who are interested in preparing for a career in communications at a college or graduate school in any state.

Eligibility This program is open to women who are seniors graduating from high schools in New York, New Jersey, Connecticut, or Pennsylvania or undergraduate or graduate students who are permanent residents of those states; they must be attending or planning to attend a college or university in any state. Graduate students must be members of New York Women in Communications, Inc. (NYWICI). Also eligible are women who reside outside the 4 states but are currently enrolled at a college or university within 1 of the 5 boroughs of New York City. All applicants must be working on a degree in a communications-related field (e.g., advertising, broadcasting, communications, English, film, journalism, marketing, new media, public relations) and have a GPA of 3.2 or higher. Along with their application, they must submit a 2-page resume that includes school and extracurricular activities, significant achievements, academic honors and awards, and community service work; a personal essay of 300 to 500 words on their choice of an assigned topic that changes annually; 2 letters of recommendation; and an official transcript. Selection is based on academic record, need, demonstrated leadership, participation in school and community activities, honors, work experience, goals and aspirations, and unusual personal and/or family circumstances. U.S. citizenship is required.

Financial data   The maximum stipend is $10,000.

Duration   1 year; recipients may reapply.

Number awarded   Varies each year; recently, 19 of these scholarships, with a total value of $103,000, were awarded.

Deadline   January of each year.

[488]
OHIO NEWSPAPER WOMEN'S SCHOLARSHIP

Ohio Newspapers Foundation
1335 Dublin Road, Suite 216-B
Columbus, OH 43215-7038
(614) 486-6677   Fax: (614) 486-4940
E-mail: ariggs@ohionews.org
Web: www.ohionews.org/students/scholarships

Summary   To provide financial assistance to women majoring in journalism at a college or university in Ohio.

Eligibility   This program is open to female juniors and seniors at Ohio colleges and universities who are majoring in journalism or an equivalent degree program. Applicants must be preparing for a career as a print journalist. Along with their application, they must submit a 2-page essay that covers their inspiration to get involved in the field of journalism, why they selected print journalism as their area of interest, why they need a scholarship, what qualifies them for a scholarship, and what they hope to accomplish during their career as a professional journalist.

Financial data   The stipend is $1,500.

Duration   1 year.

Additional information   The Ohio Newspaper Women's Association (ONWA) offered this scholarship until 2004 when it disbanded and transferred the program to the Ohio Newspapers Foundation.

Number awarded   1 each year.

Deadline   March of each year.

[489]
OKLAHOMA BW FOUNDATION SCHOLARSHIPS

Oklahoma Federation of Business Women, Inc.
Attn: Oklahoma Business Women's Foundation
P.O. Box 160
Maud, OK 74854-0160
(405) 374-2866   Fax: (405) 374-2316
E-mail: askkathy@oklahomabusinesswomen.org
Web: www.oklahomabusinesswomen/obw_foundation.htm

Summary   To provide financial assistance to women from any state who are working on an undergraduate or graduate degree in any field at a school in Oklahoma.

Eligibility   This program is open to women from any state who are working on an undergraduate or graduate degree at a college, university, or technical school in Oklahoma. Applicants must submit a 500-word essay on their career goals and how receiving this scholarship will help them to accomplish those goals and make a difference in their professional career. Selection is based on that essay, academic record, employment and volunteer record, and financial need.

Financial data   Stipends are $1,000, $750, or $500.

Duration   1 year.

Additional information   This program includes the following named scholarships: the Jewell Russell Mann Scholarship, the Dorothy Dickerson Scholarship, the Ann Garrison/Delores Schofield Scholarship, and the Dr. Ann Marie Benson Scholarship.

Number awarded   Varies each year; recently, 9 of these scholarships were awarded.

Deadline   February of each year.

[490]
OKLAHOMA CITY CHAPTER SCHOLARSHIPS

Association for Women in Communications-Oklahoma City Chapter
c/o Mandi Briggs, Byliner Committee Co-Chair
Heritage Trust
2802 West Country Club Drive
P.O. Box 21708
Oklahoma City, OK 73156
(405) 848-8899   Toll Free: (877) 887-8899
Fax: (405) 848-8805   E-mail: mandi@heritagetrust.com
Web: www.okcawc.org/p/2399/Default.aspx

Summary   To provide financial assistance to women from any state studying journalism or a related field at a school in Oklahoma.

Eligibility   This program is open to women who are residents of any state working on a degree in a communications-related field (e.g., public relations, journalism, advertising, photography) at a 2- or 4-year college or university in Oklahoma. Applicants must submit a 250-word statement explaining why they are applying for the scholarship, why they chose to study communications, their goals after graduation, and related topics. Selection is based on aptitude, interest in preparing for a career in journalism or communications, academic achievement, community service, extracurricular activities, and financial need. Preference is given to student or professional members of the Association of Women in Communications.

Financial data   Stipends range from $1,000 to $1,500.

Duration   1 year.

Additional information Recipients must enroll full time.

Number awarded Varies each year; recently, 5 of these scholarships were awarded: 1 at $1,500, 2 at $1,250, and 2 at $1,000.

Deadline April of each year.

[491]
OLIVE LYNN SALEMBIER MEMORIAL REENTRY SCHOLARSHIP

Society of Women Engineers
Attn: Scholarship Selection Committee
120 South LaSalle Street, Suite 1515
Chicago, IL 60603-3572
(312) 596-5223   Toll Free: (877) SWE-INFO
Fax: (312) 644-8557
E-mail: scholarshipapplication@swe.org
Web: societyofwomenengineers.swe.org

Summary To provide financial assistance to women interested in returning to college or graduate school to study engineering or computer science.

Eligibility This program is open to women who are planning to enroll at an ABET-accredited 4-year college or university. Applicants must have been out of the engineering workforce and school for at least 2 years and must be planning to return as an undergraduate or graduate student to major in computer science or engineering. Selection is based on merit.

Financial data The award is $1,500.

Duration 1 year; may be renewed up to 3 additional years.

Additional information This program was established in 1979.

Number awarded 1 each year.

Deadline February of each year.

[492]
OLIVE WHITMAN MEMORIAL SCHOLARSHIP

Daughters of the American Revolution-New York State
  Organization
c/o Theresa Willemsen, Recording Secretary
1248 McKoons Road
Richfield Springs, NY 13438-4101
E-mail: sportster_harley@hotmail.com
Web: www.nydar.org/education.html

Summary To provide financial assistance for college to Native American women in New York.

Eligibility This program is open to women who are at least 50% Native American and graduating seniors at high schools in New York. Applicants must be planning to attend an accredited 4-year college or university in the state.

Financial data The stipend is $2,000.

Duration 1 year.

Number awarded 1 each year.

Deadline January of each year.

[493]
OLIVER AND ESTHER R. HOWARD SCHOLARSHIP

Fleet Reserve Association
Attn: Scholarship Administrator
125 North West Street
Alexandria, VA 22314-2754
(703) 683-1400   Toll Free: (800) FRA-1924
Fax: (703) 549-6610   E-mail: fra@fra.org
Web: www.fra.org

Summary To provide financial assistance for college to female and male dependents (considered separately) of members of the Fleet Reserve Association or its Ladies Auxiliary.

Eligibility This program is open to dependent children of members of the association or its ladies auxiliary who are in good standing (or were at the time of death, if deceased). Applicants must be interested in working on an undergraduate degree. Along with their application, they must submit an essay on their life experiences, their career objectives, and what motivated them to select those objectives. Awards alternate annually between female dependents (in even-numbered years) and male dependents (in odd-numbered years). Selection is based on academic record, financial need, extracurricular activities, leadership skills, and participation in community activities. U.S. citizenship is required.

Financial data The amount awarded varies, depending upon the needs of the recipient and the funds available.

Duration 1 year; may be renewed.

Additional information Membership in the Fleet Reserve Association is restricted to active-duty, retired, and Reserve members of the Navy, Marine Corps, and Coast Guard.

Number awarded 1 each year.

Deadline April of each year.

[494]
ON THE ROAD TO MATRIX SCHOLARSHIP

New York Women in Communications, Inc.
Attn: NYWICI Foundation
355 Lexington Avenue, 15th Floor
New York, NY 10017-6603
(212) 297-2133   Fax: (212) 370-9047
E-mail: nywicipr@nywici.org
Web: www.nywici.org/foundation/scholarships

Summary To provide financial assistance to upper-division and graduate student members of New York Women in Communications, Inc. (NYWICI) who reside in designated eastern states and are interested in preparing for a career in communications at a college or graduate school in any state.

Eligibility This program is open to residents of New York, New Jersey, Connecticut, or Pennsylvania who are members of NYWICI and attending a college or university in any state. Also eligible are women who reside outside the 4 states but are currently enrolled at a college or university within 1 of the 5 boroughs of New York City. Applicants must be college juniors, seniors, or graduate students and working on a degree in a communications-related field (e.g., advertising, broadcasting, communications, English, film, journalism, marketing, new media, public relations). They must have a GPA of 3.2 or higher. Along with their application, they must submit a 2-page resume that includes school and extracurricular activities, significant achievements, academic honors and awards, and community service work; a personal essay of 300 to 500 words on their choice of an assigned topic that changes annually; 2 letters of recommendation; and an official transcript. Selection is based on academic record, need, demonstrated leadership, participation in school and community activities, honors, work experience, goals and aspirations, and unusual personal and/or family circumstances. U.S. citizenship is required.

Financial data The stipend ranges up to $10,000.

Duration 1 year.

Additional information This program is sponsored by the Matrix Hall of Fame, an organization of women who have received special recognition from NYWICI.

Number awarded 1 each year.

Deadline January of each year.

[495]
ONE FAMILY SCHOLARS PROGRAM

One Family, Inc.
Attn: Field Services Director
186 South Street, Fourth Floor
Boston, MA 02111
(617) 423-0504, ext. 226 E-mail: ypere@onefamilyinc.org
Web: www.onefamilyinc.org/scholars

Summary To provide financial assistance for college to women in Massachusetts who are homeless or formerly homeless.

Eligibility This program is open to women in Massachusetts who are homeless or have been homeless. Applicants must be attempting to enter or reenter college to work on an associate or bachelor's degree. They must apply through 1 of 5 participating social service organizations at sites in Massachusetts. Along with their application, they must submit a personal essay and 3 letters of reference. They must also apply for financial aid and participate in an interview. Selection is based on financial need (family earnings below 200% of the federal poverty level), clear and realistic academic and career goals, potential for success in chosen academic program, and desire to participate actively in all aspects of the program.

Financial data Scholars receive grants up to $11,000 per year. They are also reimbursed for reasonable childcare, transportation, and lost wages incurred to participate in mandatory activities.

Duration 1 year; may be renewed until completion of a degree, provided the scholar successfully completes 6 to 9 credits per semester; participates in mandatory leadership development retreats, seminars, and activities; maintains a GPA of 3.0 or higher; remains a Massachusetts resident; and maintains contact with site coordinators.

Additional information This program was established in 2000 by the Paul and Phyllis Fireman Charitable Foundation, with administration by Wellspring House in Gloucester and Project Hope in Dorchester. For academic year 2004-05, additional support from the Richard and Susan Smith Foundation resulted in adding Housing Families in Malden and Mainspring House in Brockton. In academic year 2005-06, Community Teamwork Inc. of Lowell was added as a fifth site. Additional support is provided by Putnam Investments.

Number awarded Varies each year; recently, 125 scholars received support from this program.

Deadline March of each year.

[496]
OPTIMIST INTERNATIONAL ORATORICAL CONTEST

Optimist International
Attn: Programs Department
4494 Lindell Boulevard
St. Louis, MO 63108
(314) 371-6000   Toll Free: (800) 500-8130, ext. 235
Fax: (314) 371-6009   E-mail: programs@optimist.org
Web: www.optimist.org/e/member/scholarships4.cfm

Summary To recognize and reward, with college scholarships, outstanding female or male orators (judged separately) at the high school or younger level.

Eligibility All students in public, private, or parochial elementary, junior high, and senior high schools in the United States, Canada, or the Caribbean who are under 16 years of age may enter. All contestants must prepare their own orations of 4 to 5 minutes, but they may receive advice and make minor changes or improvements in the oration at any time. Each year a different subject is selected for the orations; a recent topic was "Cyber Communication: Progress or Problem?" The orations may be delivered in a language other than English if that language is an official language of the country in which the sponsoring club is located. Selection is based on poise (20 points), content of speech (35 points), delivery and presentation (35 points), and overall effectiveness (10 points). Competition is first conducted at the level of individual clubs, with winners advancing to zone and then district competitions. At the discretion of the district, boys may compete against boys and girls against girls in separate contests.

Financial data Each district awards either 2 scholarships of $2,500 (1 for a boy and 1 for a girl) or (if the district chooses to have a combined gender contest) a first-place scholarship of $2,500, a second-place scholarship of $1,500, and a third-place scholarship of $1,000.

Duration The competition is held annually.

Additional information This competition was first held in 1928. Nearly 2,000 Optimist International local clubs participate in the program each year. Entry information is available only from local Optimist Clubs.

Number awarded Each year, more than $150,000 is awarded in scholarships.

Deadline Each local club sets its own deadline. The district deadline is the end of June.

[497]
ORDER OF THE AMARANTH IN PENNSYLVANIA SCHOLARSHIP PROGRAM

Pennsylvania Masonic Youth Foundation
Attn: Educational Endowment Fund
1244 Bainbridge Road
Elizabethtown, PA 17022-9423
(717) 367-1536   Toll Free: (800) 266-8424 (within PA)
Fax: (717) 367-0616   E-mail: pmyf@pagrandlodge.org
Web: www.pmyf.org/scholar/index.html

Summary To provide financial assistance to females in Pennsylvania who have a connection to Masonry and are interested in attending college in any state.

Eligibility This program is open to 1) daughters and granddaughters of members of the Order of the Amaranth in Pennsylvania, and 2) active Pennsylvania Rainbow Girls and Job's Daughters. Applicants must be between 18 and 21 years of age, high school graduates, and enrolled at an institution of higher learning in any state.

Financial data The stipend depends on the availability of funds.

Duration 1 year.

Additional information This program is sponsored by the Grand Court of Pennsylvania of the Order of the Armaranth.

Number awarded 1 or more each year.

Deadline June of each year.

[498]
ORDER OF THE EASTERN STAR OF PENNSYLVANIA SCHOLARSHIPS

Pennsylvania Masonic Youth Foundation
Attn: Educational Endowment Fund
1244 Bainbridge Road
Elizabethtown, PA 17022-9423
(717) 367-1536   Toll Free: (800) 266-8424 (within PA)
Fax: (717) 367-0616   E-mail: pmyf@pagrandlodge.org
Web: www.pmyf.org/scholar/index.html

Summary To provide financial assistance to students from Pennsylvania who are members of the Rainbow Girls, Job's Daughters, or other Masonic youth organizations (judged separately) and are attending college in any state.

Eligibility This program is open to active Pennsylvania DeMolays, Rainbow Girls, and Job's Daughters who have completed at least 1 year in an accredited college or university in any state. Applicants must be enrolled full time in a program of at least 3 years' duration or an accredited nursing program leading to an R.N. degree. They must have a GPA of 2.5 or higher, good moral character, limited financial resources, and a willingness to help themselves.

Financial data The stipend is $1,000 per year.

Duration 1 year; may be renewed 1 additional year.

Additional information This program is sponsored by the Grand Chapter of Pennsylvania of the Order of the Eastern Star.

Number awarded 3 each year: 1 each to a member of DeMolay, Rainbow Girls, and Job's Daughters.

Deadline March of each year.

[499]
OREGON FARM BUREAU WOMEN'S ADVISORY COUNCIL SCHOLARSHIP

Oregon Farm Bureau
Attn: Women's Advisory Council
3415 Commercial Street S.E.
Salem, OR 97302-5169
(503) 399-1701   Toll Free: (800) 334-6323
Fax: (503) 399-8082   E-mail: annemarie@oregonfb.org
Web: www.oregonfb.org/programs/scholarships.shtml

Summary To provide financial assistance to women who are members of the Oregon Farm Bureau (OFB) and interested in returning to college in any state to study agriculture or forestry.

Eligibility This program is open to women who are members or relatives of members of OFB. Applicants must have completed at least 1 year of education beyond high school and be interested in returning to school in any state to study agriculture, forestry, or a related subject. Along with their application, they must submit a brief statement on their reasons for choosing their major or field of study and how it can relate to or benefit agriculture. Financial need is not considered in the selection process.

Financial data The stipend is $1,000 for full-time students or $500 for part-time students.

Duration 1 year; recipients may reapply.

Number awarded At least 1 full-time and 1 part-time scholarship are awarded each year.

Deadline April of each year.

[500]
OREGON LEGION AUXILIARY DEPARTMENT SCHOLARSHIPS

American Legion Auxiliary
Department of Oregon
30450 S.W. Parkway Avenue
P.O. Box 1730
Wilsonville, OR 97070-1730
(503) 682-3162   Fax: (503) 685-5008
E-mail: alaor@pcez.com

Summary To provide financial assistance to the wives, widows, and children of Oregon veterans who are interested in attending college in any state.

Eligibility This program is open to Oregon residents who are children or wives of disabled veterans or widows of veterans. Applicants must be interested in obtaining education beyond the high school level at a college, university, business school, vocational school, or any other accredited postsecondary school in the state of Oregon. Selection is based on ability, aptitude, character, seriousness of purpose, and financial need.

Financial data The stipend is $1,000.

Duration 1 year; nonrenewable.

Number awarded 3 each year; 1 of these is to be used for vocational or business school.

Deadline March of each year.

[501]
OREGON LEGION AUXILIARY NURSES SCHOLARSHIP

American Legion Auxiliary
Department of Oregon
30450 S.W. Parkway Avenue
P.O. Box 1730
Wilsonville, OR 97070-1730
(503) 682-3162   Fax: (503) 685-5008
E-mail: alaor@pcez.com

Summary To provide financial assistance to the wives, widows, and children of Oregon veterans who are interested in studying nursing at a school in any state.

Eligibility This program is open to Oregon residents who are the wives or children of veterans with disabilities or the widows of deceased veterans. Applicants must have been accepted by an accredited hospital or university school of nursing in any state. Selection is based on ability, aptitude, character, determination, seriousness of purpose, and financial need.

Financial data   The stipend is $1,500.

Duration   1 year; may be renewed.

Number awarded   1 each year.

Deadline   May of each year.

[502]
OUTPUTLINKS WOMAN OF DISTINCTION AWARD

Electronic Document Systems Foundation
Attn: EDSF Scholarship Awards
1845 Precinct Line Road, Suite 212
Hurst, TX 76054
(817) 849-1145   Fax: (817) 849-1185
E-mail: info@edsf.org
Web: www.edsf.org/what_we_do/scholarships/index.html

Summary   To provide financial assistance to female undergraduate and graduate students from any country interested in preparing for a career in document management and graphic communications.

Eligibility   This program is open to full-time female undergraduate and graduate students from any country who demonstrate a strong interest in preparing for a career in the document management and graphic communications industry, including computer science and engineering (e.g., web design, webmaster, software development, materials engineer, applications specialist, information technology designer, systems analyst); graphic and media communications (e.g., graphic designer, illustrator, color scientist, print production, prepress imaging specialist, workflow specialist, document preparation, production and/or document distribution, content management, e-commerce, imaging science, printing, web authoring, electronic publishing, archiving, security); or business (e.g., sales, marketing, trade shows, customer service, project or product development, management). Preference is given to graduate students and upper-division undergraduates, but freshmen and sophomores who can show interest, experience, and/or commitment to the document management and graphic communication industry are encouraged to apply. Applicants must have a GPA of 3.0 or higher. Along with their application, they must submit 2 essays on assigned topics that change annually but relate to the document management and graphic communication industries. Selection is based on the essays, academic excellence, participation in school activities, community service, honors and organizational affiliations, education goals, and recommendations; financial need is not considered.

Financial data   The stipend is $5,000.

Duration   1 year.

Additional information   This program is sponsored by OutputLinks.

Number awarded   1 each year.

Deadline   April of each year.

[503]
PAM BARTON STAPLES SCHOLARSHIP

Kappa Delta Sorority
Attn: Foundation Manager
3205 Players Lane
Memphis, TN 38125
(901) 748-1897   Toll Free: (800) 536-1897
Fax: (901) 748-0949 E-mail: kappadelta@kappadelta.org
Web: www.kappadelta.org/scholarships

Summary   To provide financial assistance to members of Kappa Delta Sorority who have served their campus Panhellenic association and are interested in continuing their undergraduate education.

Eligibility   This program is open to undergraduate members of Kappa Delta Sorority. Applicants must submit a personal statement giving their reasons for applying for this scholarship, an official undergraduate transcript, and 2 letters of recommendation. They must have a GPA of 3.0 or higher and a record of outstanding service to the campus Panhellenic association. Selection is based on academic excellence; service to the chapter, alumnae association, or national Kappa Delta; service to the campus and community; personal objectives and goals; potential; recommendations; and financial need.

Financial data   The stipend is $2,000 per year. Funds may be used only for tuition, fees, and books, not for room and board.

Duration   1 year; may be renewed.

Number awarded   1 each year.

Deadline   January of each year.

[504]
PATRICIA CREED SCHOLARSHIP

Connecticut Women's Golf Association
c/o Judy Gamble, Scholarship Committee
27 Cold Spring Circle
Shelton, CT 06484
(203) 929-0435   E-mail: scholarships@cwga.org
Web: www.cwga.org/CWGA/index.php?section=16

Summary   To provide financial assistance to female high school seniors from Connecticut who are golfers and planning to attend college in any state.

Eligibility   This program is open to female high school seniors who are residents of Connecticut planning to attend a public college or university in any state. Applicants must be active golfers with a handicap. Along with their application, they must submit a 200-word essay on how golf has made an impact on their life. Selection is based on character, academic achievement, interest in golf, and financial need.

Financial data   A stipend is awarded (amount not specified).

Duration   1 year.

Additional information   This program was established in 1997.

Number awarded   1 or 2 each year.

Deadline   April of each year.

[505]
PATSY TAKEMOTO MINK EDUCATION FOUNDATION EDUCATION SUPPORT AWARD

Patsy Takemoto Mink Education Foundation for Low-
Income Women and Children
P.O. Box 479
Honolulu, HI 96809
E-mail: admin@ptmfoundation.net
Web: www.patsyminkfoundation.org/edsupport.html

Summary To provide financial assistance for college or graduate school to low-income women.

Eligibility This program is open to women who are at least 17 years of age and are from a low-income family (less than $17,500 annually for a family of 2, $22,000 for a family of 3, or $26,500 for a family of 4). Applicants must be mothers with minor children. They must be 1) enrolled in a skills training, ESL, or GED program; or 2) working on an associate, bachelor's, master's, professional, or doctoral degree. Along with their application, they must submit brief essays on what this award will help them accomplish, the program in which they are or will be enrolled, how they decided on that educational pursuit, their educational goals, their educational experience, and their personal and educational history.

Financial data The stipend is $2,000.

Duration 1 year.

Additional information This foundation was established in 2003.

Number awarded 5 each year.

Deadline July of each year.

[506]
PAULINE EILBER KEELER SCHOLARSHIP

Kappa Alpha Theta Foundation
Attn: Scholarships
8740 Founders Road
Indianapolis, IN 46268-1337
(317) 876-1870   Toll Free: (800) KAO-1870
Fax: (317) 876-1925
E-mail: FDNmail@kappaalphatheta.org
Web: www.kappaalphathetafoundation.org

Summary To provide financial assistance to undergraduate members of Kappa Alpha Theta who are majoring in liberal arts or engineering.

Eligibility This program is open to members of Kappa Alpha Theta who are full-time undergraduates at a college or university in Canada or the United States. Applicants must be majoring in liberal arts or engineering. Along with their application, they must submit an official transcript, personal essays on assigned topics related to their involvement in Kappa Alpha Theta, and 2 letters of reference. Financial need is not considered in the selection process.

Financial data The stipend is $1,100.

Duration 1 year.

Number awarded 1 each year.

Deadline January of each year.

[507]
PEGGY VATTER MEMORIAL SCHOLARSHIPS

Washington Science Teachers Association
c/o Patricia MacGowan, Washington MESA
University of Washington
P.O. Box 352181
Seattle, WA 98195-2181
(206) 543-0562   Fax: (206) 685-0666
E-mail: macgowan@engr.washington.edu
Web: www.wsta.net

Summary To provide financial assistance to upper-division students and teachers in Washington (preference given to women and minorities) who are interested in training in science education.

Eligibility This program is open to 1) juniors and seniors at colleges and universities in Washington who are working on certification in science education or in elementary education with an emphasis on science; and 2) certified teachers in Washington interested in improving their skills in providing equitable science education through professional development. In the student category, preference is given to African Americans, Hispanics, Native Americans, and women. Applicants must submit a 1-page essay on why they are applying for this scholarship.

Financial data The stipend is $1,500.

Duration 1 year; nonrenewable.

Additional information This program was established in 2003.

Number awarded 1 or more each year.

Deadline April of each year.

[508]
PENNSYLVANIA BPW FOUNDATION SCHOLARSHIPS

Business and Professional Women of Pennsylvania
Attn: Pennsylvania BPW Foundation
c/o Teresa A. Miller, Vice Chair
8 West Front Street
Media, PA 19063
(610) 566-5035   Fax: (610) 566-2954
E-mail: tmiller@frontrowlaw.com
Web: www.bpwpa.org

Summary To provide financial assistance to women from Pennsylvania who are interested in attending college in any state.

Eligibility This program is open to female residents of Pennsylvania who are attending or planning to attend a college or university in any state. Applicants must submit an essay that 1) discusses their specific short-term career goals and how the proposed training will help them accomplish those goals; 2) explains how those short-term goals apply to their long-range career goals; and 3) includes a summary of issues that are important to working women in today's world. In the selection process, strong emphasis is placed on financial need.

Financial data The stipend is $2,500.

Duration 1 year.

Number awarded 6 each year: 3 in the fall semester and 3 in the spring semester.

Deadline April of each year for fall semester; September of each year for spring semester.

[509]
PENNSYLVANIA BUSINESS AND PROFESSIONAL WOMEN SCHOLARSHIP

Pennsylvania Federation of Business and Professional
  Women's Clubs, Inc.
c/o Carol L. Bowman, Education and Service Funds Chair
577 Sunnyside Road
Bedford, PA 15522
E-mail: info@bpwpa.org
Web: www.bpwpa.org

Summary To provide financial assistance for continuing education to women in Pennsylvania.

Eligibility This program is open to women in Pennsylvania who have been accepted into an accredited educational institution. Applicants must be able to demonstrate financial need. They must submit an essay that discusses their specific short-term career goals, how the proposed training will help them to accomplish those goals, and how those apply to their long-range career goals. The essay should include a summary of the following topics: self, educational goals, and issues that are important to working women in today's world.

Financial data A stipend is awarded (amount not specified).

Number awarded Varies each year.

Deadline April of each year for fall semester; September of each year for spring semester.

[510]
PENNSYLVANIA FEDERATION OF DEMOCRATIC WOMEN MEMORIAL SCHOLARSHIP

Pennsylvania Federation of Democratic Women
c/o Bonita Hannis, Scholarship Chair
36 Betts Lane
Lock Haven, PA 17745
(570) 769-7175   E-mail: behannis@kcnet.org
Web: www.pfdw.org

Summary To provide financial assistance to women from Pennsylvania who are registered Democrats and attending college in any state.

Eligibility This program is open to women who are residents of Pennsylvania and currently enrolled as juniors at an accredited college or university in any state. Applicants must be registered Democrats and an active participant in the Democratic Party with a Democratic Party family background. Along with their application, they must submit a 1-page essay describing their need for this scholarship, their professional goals, their Democratic Party activities, and their family Democratic Party involvement.

Financial data The stipend is $5,000.

Duration 1 year (the senior year of college).

Number awarded Varies each year; recently, 4 of these scholarships were awarded.

Deadline April of each year.

[511]
PENNSYLVANIA RAINBOW NURSING SCHOLARSHIP

Pennsylvania Masonic Youth Foundation
Attn: Educational Endowment Fund
1244 Bainbridge Road
Elizabethtown, PA 17022-9423
(717) 367-1536   Toll Free: (800) 266-8424 (within PA)
Fax: (717) 367-0616   E-mail: pmyf@pagrandlodge.org
Web: www.pmyf.org/scholar/index.html

Summary To provide financial assistance to members of Rainbow Girls in Pennsylvania who are attending nursing school in any state.

Eligibility This program is open to active Pennsylvania Rainbow Girls in good standing. Applicants must have completed at least 1 year at an accredited nursing school in any state.

Financial data The stipend depends on the availability of funds.

Duration 1 year; may be renewed.

Number awarded Varies each year, depending on the availability of funds.

Deadline Requests for applications must be submitted by January of each year. Completed applications are due by the end of February.

[512]
PENNSYLVANIA RAINBOW SCHOLARSHIP

Pennsylvania Masonic Youth Foundation
Attn: Educational Endowment Fund
1244 Bainbridge Road
Elizabethtown, PA 17022-9423
(717) 367-1536   Toll Free: (800) 266-8424 (within PA)
Fax: (717) 367-0616   E-mail: pmyf@pagrandlodge.org
Web: www.pmyf.org/scholar/index.html

Summary To provide financial assistance to members of Rainbow Girls in Pennsylvania who are attending college in any state.

Eligibility This program is open to active Pennsylvania Rainbow Girls in good standing. Applicants must have completed at least 1 year at an accredited college, university, or nursing school in any state.

Financial data The stipend depends on the availability of funds.

Duration 1 year; may be renewed.

Number awarded Varies each year, depending on the availability of funds.

Deadline Requests for applications must be submitted by January of each year. Completed applications are due by the end of February.

[513]
PENTAGON ASSISTANCE FUND

Navy-Marine Corps Relief Society
Attn: Education Division
875 North Randolph Street, Suite 225
Arlington, VA 22203-1757
(703) 696-4960   Fax: (703) 696-0144
E-mail: education@hq.nmcrs.org
Web: www.nmcrs.org/goldstar.html

Summary To provide financial assistance for college to the spouses and children of deceased military personnel who died at the Pentagon on September 11, 2001.

Eligibility This program is open to the children and spouses of deceased military personnel who died at the Pentagon as a result of the terrorist attack of September 11, 2001. Applicants must be enrolled or planning to enroll full time (spouses may enroll part time) at a college, university, or vocational/technical school. They must have a GPA of 2.0 or higher and be able to demonstrate financial need. Children must be 23 years of age or younger. Spouses may be eligible if the service member became disabled as a result of the attack.

Financial data Stipends range from $500 to $2,500 per year. Funds are disbursed directly to the financial institution.

Duration 1 year; may be renewed up to 3 additional years.

Number awarded Varies each year.

Deadline Children must apply by February of each year. Spouses must apply at least 2 months prior to the start of their studies.

[514]
P.E.O. PROGRAM FOR CONTINUING EDUCATION

P.E.O. Sisterhood
Attn: Executive Office
3700 Grand Avenue
Des Moines, IA 50312-2899
(515) 255-3153   Fax: (515) 255-3820
Web: www.peointernational.org/peo-projectsphilanthropies

Summary To provide financial assistance to mature women interested in resuming or continuing their academic or technical education.

Eligibility This program is open to mature women who are citizens of the United States or Canada and have experienced an interruption in their education that has lasted at least 24 consecutive months during their adult life. Applicants are frequently single parents who must acquire marketable skills to support their families. They must be within 2 years of completing an academic or technical course of study. Applicants must be sponsored by a local P.E.O. chapter. Students enrolled in a doctoral degree program are not eligible.

Financial data The maximum stipend is $3,000.

Duration 1 year; nonrenewable.

Additional information This program was established in 1973 by the Women's Philanthropic Educational Organization (P.E.O.).

Number awarded Varies each year; for a recent biennium, 3,242 of these awards, with a total value of nearly $4.3 million, were granted.

Deadline Applications may be submitted at any time.

[515]
P.E.O. STAR SCHOLARSHIPS

P.E.O. Sisterhood
Attn: Scholar Awards Office
3700 Grand Avenue
Des Moines, IA 50312-2899
(515) 255-3153   Fax: (515) 255-3820
E-mail: psa@peodsm.org
Web: www.peointernational.org/peo-projectsphilanthropies

Summary To provide financial assistance for college to female high school seniors in the United States or Canada.

Eligibility This program is open to women who are graduating from high schools in the United States or Canada and planning to enroll full or part time at an accredited postsecondary educational institution. Applicants must have an unweighted GPA of 3.0 or higher. They must be sponsored by a local P.E.O. chapter. Selection is based on leadership, extracurricular activities, community service, and potential for success; financial need is not considered. U.S. or Canadian citizenship or permanent resident status is required.

Financial data The stipend is $2,500.

Duration 1 year; nonrenewable.

Additional information This program was established in 2009 by the Women's Philanthropic Educational Organization (P.E.O.).

Number awarded Varies each year.

Deadline November of each year.

[516]
PEPSI USBC YOUTH BOWLING CHAMPIONSHIPS

United States Bowling Congress
Attn: Pepsi-Cola Youth Bowling Event Manager
621 Six Flags Drive
Arlington, TX 76011
(817) 385-8426   Toll Free: (800) 514-BOWL, ext. 8426
E-mail: Gary.Schmit@bowl.com
Web: www.bowl.com/tournaments/pepsichamp

Summary To recognize and reward (with college scholarships) members of the United States Bowling Congress (USBC) who achieve high scores in an international competition (females and males are judged separately).

Eligibility This competition is open to USBC members in the United States, Puerto Rico, U.S. military zones, and Canada. Applicants enter in 1 of 6 categories: 11 and under boys' handicap, 12 and above boys' handicap, 12 and above boys' scratch, 11 and under girls' handicap, 12 and above girls' handicap, and 12 and above girls' scratch. Based on their bowling scores in state and zone competitions, the top bowlers in the 12 and above boys' and girls' handicap categories advance to the international finals. Also advancing to the international finals are the state and zone winners in the 12 and above boys' and girls' scratch categories who are also USBC Junior Gold members (boys must have an average of 175 or above, girls must have an average of 165 or above). All selected finalists (more than 200 qualify each year), are then assigned to Division I or Division II for the international competition, held annually at a site in the United States; assignment is based on their adjusted score from year-end averages and state and zone competitions. Bowlers whose scores are in the top half are assigned to Division I and bowlers whose scores are in the bottom half are assigned to Division II. Scholarships are awarded solely on the basis of bowling performance in the international finals.

Financial data At the international finals, the top finishers in each division receive scholarships of $3,000, $2,000, $1,500, and $1,000, respectively.

Duration The competition is held annually.

Additional information This competition is sponsored by the Pepsi-Cola Company, presented by Brunswick, and conducted by the USBC. More than $500,000 in scholarships is awarded at state and zone competitions for all 6 categories.

Number awarded Each year, 16 scholarships are awarded: 8 are set aside for girls (4 in each division) and 8 for boys (4 in each division).

Deadline Qualifying tournaments are held in bowling centers from October through February of each year. Center and section qualifying takes place in March and April. State and zone competitions take place through the end of May. The international finals are held in July.

[517]
PHIPPS MEMORIAL SCHOLARSHIP

General Federation of Women's Clubs of Connecticut
c/o JoAnn Calnen, President
74 Spruceland Road
Enfield, CT 06082-2359
E-mail: gfwcct@yahoo.com
Web: www.gfwcct.org

Summary To provide financial assistance to women in Connecticut who are working on an undergraduate or graduate degree.

Eligibility This program is open to female residents of Connecticut who have completed at least 2 years of college. Applicants must have a GPA of 3.0 or higher and be working on a bachelor's or master's degree. Selection is based on academic ability, future promise, and financial need.

Financial data The stipend is $1,000.

Duration 1 year.

Number awarded 1 each year.

Deadline February of each year.

[518]
PHOENIX SECTION FRESHMAN SCHOLARSHIPS

Society of Women Engineers
Attn: Scholarship Selection Committee
120 South LaSalle Street, Suite 1515
Chicago, IL 60603-3572
(312) 596-5223　　　　　　Toll Free: (877) SWE-INFO
Fax: (312) 644-8557
E-mail: scholarshipapplication@swe.org
Web: societyofwomenengineers.swe.org

Summary To provide financial assistance to women from Arizona who will be entering college as freshmen and are interested in studying engineering or computer science.

Eligibility This program is open to women who are entering college as freshmen with a GPA of 3.5 or higher. Applicants must be residents of Arizona or attending school in the state and planning to enroll full time at an ABET-accredited 4-year college or university and major in computer science or engineering. Selection is based on merit.

Financial data The stipend is $1,000.

Duration 1 year.

Additional information This program was established in 2001 by the Phoenix Section of the Society of Women Engineers (SWE).

Number awarded 2 each year.

Deadline May of each year.

[519]
PHYLLIS DOBBYN HOLT SCHOLARSHIPS

Sigma Alpha Iota Philanthropies, Inc.
One Tunnel Road
Asheville, NC 28805
(828) 251-0606　　　　　　Fax: (828) 251-0644
E-mail: nh@sai-national.org
Web: www.sigmaalphaiota.org

Summary To provide financial assistance for undergraduate study to members of Sigma Alpha Iota (an organization of women musicians).

Eligibility This program is open to members of the organization in the first 3 years of undergraduate study. Candidates must be nominated by their chapter and their chapter adviser must submit a letter of recommendation. Nominees must submit a brief statement of career goals and aspirations. Selection is based on financial need, musical ability, scholarship, potential leadership, contribution to campus and community life, and exemplification of the ideals of the organization.

Financial data The stipend is $2,000.

Duration 1 year.

Number awarded 3 each year.

Deadline March of each year.

[520]
PHYLLIS G. MEEKINS SCHOLARSHIP

Ladies Professional Golf Association
Attn: LPGA Foundation
100 International Golf Drive
Daytona Beach, FL 32124-1082
(386) 274-6200　　　　　　Fax: (386) 274-1099
E-mail: foundation.scholarships@lpga.com
Web: www.lpgafoundation.org

Summary To provide financial assistance to minority female graduating high school seniors who played golf in high school and plan to continue to play in college.

Eligibility This program is open to female high school seniors who are members of a recognized minority group. Applicants must have a GPA of 3.0 or higher and a background in golf. They must be planning to enroll full time at a college or university in the United States and play competitive golf. Along with their application, they must submit a letter that describes how golf has been an integral part of their lives and includes their personal, academic, and professional goals; their chosen discipline of study; and how this scholarship will be of assistance. Financial need is considered in the selection process. U.S. citizenship or legal resident status is required.

Financial data The stipend is $1,250.

Duration 1 year.

Additional information This program was established in 2006.

Number awarded 1 each year.

Deadline May of each year.

[521]
PHYLLIS SANDERS SCHOLARSHIP

Missouri Business and Professional Women's
 Foundation, Inc.
P.O. Box 28243
Kansas City, MO 64188
(816) 333-6959   Fax: (816) 333-6959
E-mail: jo.mofedbpw@gmail.com
Web: www.mofedbpw.org/files/index.php?id=14

Summary To provide financial assistance to members of the Missouri Federation of Business and Professional Women (BPW Missouri) who plan to attend college in any state.

Eligibility This program is open to BPW Missouri members who have been accepted into an accredited program or course of study in any state to upgrade their skills and/or complete education for career advancement. Along with their application, they must submit brief statements on the following: their achievements and/or specific recognitions in their field of endeavor; professional and/or civic affiliations; present and long-range career goals; how they plan to participate in and contribute to their community upon completion of their program of study; why they feel they would make a good recipient; and any special circumstances that may have influenced their ability to continue or complete their education They must also demonstrate financial need and U.S. citizenship.

Financial data A stipend is awarded (amount not specified).

Duration 1 year.

Number awarded Varies each year; recently, 2 of these scholarships were awarded.

Deadline December of each year.

[522]
PI BETA PHI UNDERGRADUATE SCHOLARSHIPS

Pi Beta Phi
Attn: Pi Beta Phi Foundation
1154 Town and Country Commons Drive
Town and Country, MO 63017
(636) 256-8124   Fax: (636) 256-8124
E-mail: fndn@pibetaphi.org
Web: www.pibetaphifoundation.org/scholarship-program

Summary To provide financial assistance for college to members of Pi Beta Phi.

Eligibility This program is open to women who are officially enrolled at a college or university where there is a Pi Beta Phi chapter. They must be active members in good standing in the sorority and have a GPA of 3.0 or higher (70% or higher for Canadian members). Selection is based on financial need, academic record, and service to the sorority, campus, and community.

Financial data Stipends range from $1,000 to $10,000.

Duration 1 year.

Additional information This program includes approximately 50 named scholarships. Many of those specify additional eligibility requirements, such as chapter, residence, or academic major. Recipients must use the funds during the immediately succeeding academic year and must be willing to write a brief report of their academic progress at the end of the school year.

Number awarded Varies each year.
Deadline February of each year.

[523]
PI STATE NATIVE AMERICAN GRANTS-IN-AID

Delta Kappa Gamma Society International-Pi State
 Organization
c/o Harlene Gilbert
5338 East Lake Road
Romulus, NY 14541
(315) 585-6691   E-mail: hgilbert@happiness.org
Web: www.deltakappagamma.org/NY/ASaGiA.html

Summary To provide funding to Native American women from New York who plan to work in education or another service field.

Eligibility This program is open to Native American women from New York who are attending a 2- or 4-year college in the state. Applicants must be planning to work in education or another service field, but preference is given to those majoring in education. Both undergraduate and graduate students are eligible.

Financial data The grant is $500 per semester ($1,000 per year). Funds may be used for any career-related purpose, including purchase of textbooks.

Duration 1 semester; may be renewed for a total of 5 years and a total of $5,000 over a recipient's lifetime.

Number awarded Up to 5 each year.

Deadline July or December of each year.

[524]
PILOTMALL.COM AVIATION SUPERSTORE CFI SCHOLARSHIP

Women in Aviation, International
Attn: Scholarships
Morningstar Airport
3647 State Route 503 South
West Alexandria, OH 45381-9354
(937) 839-4647   Fax: (937) 839-4645
E-mail: scholarships@wai.org
Web: www.wai.org/education/scholarships.cfm

Summary To provide financial assistance to members of Women in Aviation, International (WAI) who are interested in attending college or flight school to become a Certified Flight Instructor (CFI).

Eligibility This program is open to WAI members who are enrolled at a flight school, college, or university to earn certification as a CFI. Applicants should have their Instrument Rating and Commercial Certificate and hold a second class medical. Along with their application, they must submit 2 letters of recommendation, a 500-word essay on their aviation history and goals, a resume, copies of all aviation licenses and medical certificates, and the last 3 pages of their pilot logbook (if applicable). Selection is based on achievements, attitude toward self and others, commitment to success, dedication to career, financial need, motivation, reliability, responsibility, and teamwork.

Financial data The stipend is $1,250. Funds are paid directly to the flight school, college, or university.

Duration Funds must be used within 1 year.

Additional information WAI is a nonprofit professional organization dedicated to encouraging women to consider an aviation career and to providing educational outreach activities and networking resources to women active in the industry. This program was established in 2011 by PilotMall.com Aviation Superstore.

Number awarded 1 each year.

Deadline November of each year.

[525]
PIONEERS SCHOLARSHIP

Society of Women Engineers
Attn: Scholarship Selection Committee
120 South LaSalle Street, Suite 1515
Chicago, IL 60603-3572
(312) 596-5223   Toll Free: (877) SWE-INFO
Fax: (312) 644-8557
E-mail: scholarshipapplication@swe.org
Web: societyofwomenengineers.swe.org

Summary To provide financial assistance to members of the Society of Women Engineers (SWE) from any state interested in working on an undergraduate degree in engineering or computer science at a college or university in New Mexico.

Eligibility This program is open to women who are sophomores, juniors, or seniors at an ABET-accredited college, university, or 4-year engineering technology program in New Mexico. Applicants must be working on a degree in computer science or engineering and have a GPA of 3.0 or higher. They must be U.S. citizens and members of the society. Selection is based on merit.

Financial data The stipend is $1,250 per year.

Duration 1 year; may be renewed up to 2 additional years.

Additional information This program was established in 2005 by the Central New Mexico section of SWE.

Number awarded 1 each year.

Deadline February of each year.

[526]
P.O. PISTILLI SCHOLARSHIPS

Design Automation Conference
c/o Cherrice Traver
Union College
Steinmetz Hall, Room 202
Schenectady, NY 12308
(518) 388-6326   Fax: (518) 388-6789
E-mail: traverc@union.edu
Web: doc.union.edu/acsee.html

Summary To provide financial assistance to female, minority, or disabled high school seniors who are interested in preparing for a career in computer science or electrical engineering.

Eligibility This program is open to graduating high school seniors who are members of underrepresented groups: women, African Americans, Hispanics, Native Americans, and persons with disabilities. Applicants must be interested in preparing for a career in electrical engineering, computer engineering, or computer science. They must have at least a 3.0 GPA, have demonstrated high achievements in math and science courses, have demonstrated involvement in activities associated with the underrepresented group they represent, and be able to demonstrate significant financial need. U.S. citizenship is not required, but applicants must be U.S. residents when they apply and must plan to attend an accredited

U.S. college or university. Along with their application, they must submit 3 letters of recommendation, official transcripts, ACT/SAT and/or PSAT scores, a personal statement outlining future goals and why they think they should receive this scholarship, and documentation of financial need.

Financial data Stipends are $4,000 per year. Awards are paid each year in 2 equal installments.

Duration 1 year; renewable for up to 4 additional years.

Additional information This program is funded by the Design Automation Conference of the Association for Computing Machinery's Special Interest Group on Design Automation.

Number awarded 2 to 7 each year.

Deadline January of each year.

[527]
PORTLAND CHAPTER WOMEN'S TRANSPORTATION SEMINAR LEADERSHIP SCHOLARSHIP

Women's Transportation Seminar-Portland Chapter
c/o Lisa Diercksen, Scholarship Chair
DKS Associates
1400 S.W. Fifth Avenue, Suite 500
Portland, OR 97201-5502
(503) 243-3500
E-mail: wts_portland-chapter@yahoo.com
Web: www.wtsinternational.org/Chapters.aspx?ID=7080

Summary To provide financial assistance to women from Oregon and southwestern Washington who have demonstrated leadership and are working on an undergraduate or graduate degree in a transportation-related field at a school in any state.

Eligibility This program is open to women who are residents of Oregon or southwestern Washington and currently enrolled as an undergraduate or graduate student at a college or university in any state. Applicants must be preparing for a career in a transportation-related field and be working on a degree in transportation engineering, planning, finance, logistics, or a related field. They must have a GPA of 3.0 or higher and be able to demonstrate leadership qualities. Along with their application, they must submit a 500-word personal statement about their career goals after graduation, how they demonstrate leadership in the transportation industry, and why they think they should receive this scholarship. Minority candidates are encouraged to apply. Selection is based on transportation goals, academic record, and transportation-related activities or job skills.

Financial data The stipend is $5,000.

Duration 1 year.

Number awarded 1 each year.

Deadline March of each year.

[528]
PORTLAND CHAPTER WOMEN'S TRANSPORTATION SEMINAR SCHOLARSHIPS

Women's Transportation Seminar-Portland Chapter
c/o Lisa Diercksen, Scholarship Chair
DKS Associates
1400 S.W. Fifth Avenue, Suite 500
Portland, OR 97201-5502
(503) 243-3500
E-mail: wts_portland-chapter@yahoo.com
Web: www.wtsinternational.org/Chapters.aspx?ID=7080

Summary To provide financial assistance to women from Oregon and southwestern Washington who are working on an undergraduate or graduate degree in a transportation-related field at a school in any state.

Eligibility This program is open to women who are residents of Oregon or southwestern Washington and currently enrolled as an undergraduate or graduate student at a college or university in any state. Applicants must be preparing for a career in a transportation-related field and be working on a degree in transportation engineering, planning, finance, logistics, or a related field. They must have a GPA of 3.0 or higher. Along with their application, they must submit a 500-word personal statement about their career goals after graduation and why they think they should receive this scholarship. Minority candidates are encouraged to apply. Selection is based on transportation goals, academic record, and transportation-related activities or job skills.

Financial data The stipend is $3,500.

Duration 1 year.

Number awarded 3 each year.

Deadline March of each year.

[529]
PORTLAND WOMEN'S CLUB SCHOLARSHIP

Oregon Student Assistance Commission
Attn: Grants and Scholarships Division
1500 Valley River Drive, Suite 100
Eugene, OR 97401-2146
(541) 687-7395   Toll Free: (800) 452-8807, ext. 7395
Fax: (541) 687-7414   TDD: (800) 735-2900
E-mail: awardinfo@osac.state.or.us
Web: www.osac.state.or.us/osac_programs.html

Summary To provide financial assistance for college to high school seniors and recent graduates, especially women, who are from Oregon and plan to attend college in any state.

Eligibility This program is open to graduating seniors and recent graduates from high schools in Oregon who had a cumulative high school GPA of 3.0 or higher. Preference is given to women. Applicants must be attending or planning to attend a college or university in any state. Along with their application, they must submit an essay of 250 to 350 words on how their struggle with a life challenge has influenced their commitment to community involvement.

Financial data The stipend is at least $1,500 per year.

Duration 1 year; may be renewed if the recipient shows satisfactory academic progress and continued financial need.

Number awarded Varies each year; recently, 5 of these scholarships were awarded.

Deadline February of each year.

[530]
PRISCILLA CARNEY JONES SCHOLARSHIP

American Chemical Society
Attn: Department of Diversity Programs
1155 16th Street, N.W.
Washington, DC 20036
(202) 872-6334   Toll Free: (800) 227-5558, ext. 6334
Fax: (202) 776-8003   E-mail: diversity@acs.org
Web: womenchemists.sites.acs.org/attracting.htm

Summary To provide financial assistance to female upper-division students majoring in chemistry.

Eligibility This program is open to women entering their junior or senior year of full-time study with a major in chemistry or chemistry-related science. Students in pre-med programs who intend to go to medical school are not eligible. Applicants must have a GPA of 3.25 or higher and be able to demonstrate financial need. They must have completed research or plan to conduct research during their undergraduate years. Along with their application, they must submit brief statements on why they are a good candidate to receive this scholarship, their community service activities and related responsibilities, the key leadership roles they have fulfilled, any research presentations or publications, and their future plans and goals. U.S. citizenship or permanent resident status is required.

Financial data The stipend is at least $1,500.

Duration 1 year.

Number awarded 1 each year.

Deadline April of each year.

[531]
PRISCILLA MAXWELL ENDICOTT SCHOLARSHIPS

Connecticut Women's Golf Association
c/o Judy Gamble, Scholarship Committee
27 Cold Spring Circle
Shelton, CT 06484
(203) 929-0435   E-mail: scholarships@cwga.org
Web: www.cwga.org/CWGA/index.php?section=16

Summary To provide financial assistance to women golfers from Connecticut who are interested in attending college in any state.

Eligibility This program is open to high school seniors and college students who are residents of Connecticut attending or planning to attend a 4-year college or university in any state. Applicants must be active women golfers with a handicap. Along with their application, they must submit a 200-word essay on how golf has made an impact on their life. Selection is based on participation in golf programs, academic achievement, and financial need.

Financial data The maximum stipend is $3,000 per year.

Duration Up to 4 years.

Additional information This program was established in 1977.

Number awarded Varies each year; recently, 5 of these scholarships were awarded.

Deadline April of each year.

[532]
PROFESSIONAL GOLF MANAGEMENT DIVERSITY SCHOLARSHIP

Professional Golfers' Association of America
Attn: PGA Foundation
100 Avenue of the Champions
Palm Beach Gardens, FL 33418
Toll Free: (888) 532-6661
Web: www.pgafoundation.com

Summary To provide financial assistance to women and minorities interested in attending a designated college or university to prepare for a career as a golf professional.

Eligibility This program is open to women and minorities interested in becoming a licensed PGA Professional. Applicants must be interested in attending 1 of 20 colleges and universities that offer the Professional Golf Management (PGM) curriculum sanctioned by the PGA.

Financial data The stipend is $3,000 per year.

Duration 1 year; may be renewed.

Additional information This program began in 1993. Programs are offered at Arizona State University (Mesa, Arizona), Campbell University (Buies Creek, North Carolina), Clemson University (Clemson, South Carolina), Coastal Carolina University (Conway, South Carolina), Eastern Kentucky University (Richmond, Kentucky), Ferris State University (Big Rapids, Michigan), Florida Gulf Coast University (Fort Myers, Florida), Florida State University (Tallahassee, Florida), Methodist College (Fayetteville, North Carolina), Mississippi State University (Mississippi State, Mississippi), New Mexico State University (Las Cruces, New Mexico), North Carolina State University (Raleigh, North Carolina), Pennsylvania State University (University Park, Pennsylvania), Sam Houston State University (Huntsville, Texas), University of Central Oklahoma (Edmond, Oklahoma), University of Colorado (Colorado Springs, Colorado), University of Idaho (Moscow, Idaho), University of Maryland Eastern Shore (Princess Anne, Maryland), University of Nebraska (Lincoln, Nebraska), and University of Nevada (Las Vegas, Nevada).

Number awarded Varies each year; recently, 20 of these scholarships were awarded.

Deadline Deadline not specified.

[533]
PROJECT RED FLAG ACADEMIC SCHOLARSHIP FOR WOMEN WITH BLEEDING DISORDERS

National Hemophilia Foundation
Attn: Manager of Education
P.O. Box 971483
Ypsilanti, MI 48197
(734) 890-2504   E-mail: pflax@hemophilia.org
Web: www.projectredflag.org/scholarship.htm

Summary To provide financial assistance for college or graduate school to women who have a bleeding disorder.

Eligibility This program is open to women who are entering or already enrolled in an undergraduate or graduate program at a university, college, or accredited vocational school. Applicants must have von Willebrand Disease, hemophilia or other clotting factor deficiency, or carrier status. Along with their application, they must submit a 250-word essay that describes how their education and future career plans will

benefit others in the bleeding disorders community. Financial need is not considered in the selection process.

Financial data The stipend is $2,500.

Duration 1 year.

Additional information The program was established in 2005 in partnership with the Centers for Disease Control and Prevention (CDC) and with support from CSL Behring.

Number awarded 2 each year.

Deadline May of each year.

[534]
PROVIDENCE ALUMNAE CHAPTER COLLEGE AWARDS

Delta Sigma Theta Sorority, Inc.-Providence Alumnae Chapter
Attn: Financial Awards Review Committee
P.O. Box 40175
Providence, RI 02940-0175
E-mail: providencealumnae@hotmail.com
Web: www.dstprovidencealumnae.com

Summary To provide financial assistance to African American female residents of Rhode Island who are attending college in any state.

Eligibility This program is open to African American women who are residents of Rhode Island. Applicants must be attending a 4-year college or university in any state and have a GPA of 3.0 or higher. Along with their application, they must submit a current official transcript, a letter of recommendation, and an essay describing their career goals, community service activities, educational accomplishments, and personal interests and talents.

Financial data A stipend is awarded (amount not specified).

Duration 1 year.

Number awarded 1 or more each year.

Deadline February of each year.

[535]
PROVIDENCE MEMORIAM AWARD

Delta Sigma Theta Sorority, Inc.-Providence Alumnae Chapter
Attn: Financial Awards Review Committee
P.O. Box 40175
Providence, RI 02904-0175
E-mail: providencealumnae@hotmail.com
Web: www.dstprovidencealumnae.com

Summary To provide financial assistance to African American female high school seniors from Rhode Island who are planning to attend college in any state.

Eligibility This program is open to African American women who are seniors graduating from high schools in Rhode Island. Applicants must be planning to enroll at a college in any state. Along with their application, they must submit a current official transcript, a letter of recommendation, and an essay describing their career goals, community service activities, educational accomplishments, and personal interests and talents.

Financial data A stipend is awarded (amount not specified).

Duration 1 year.

Number awarded 1 or more each year.

Deadline February of each year.

[536]
PUGET SOUND CHAPTER SHARON D. BANKS MEMORIAL UNDERGRADUATE SCHOLARSHIP

Women's Transportation Seminar-Puget Sound Chapter
c/o Jennifer Barnes, Scholarship Co-Chair
Heffron Transportation, Inc.
6544 N.E. 61st Street
Seattle, WA 98115
(206) 523-3939   Fax: (206) 523-4949
E-mail: jennifer@hefftrans.com
Web: www.wtsinternational.org/Chapters.aspx?ID=7166

Summary To provide financial assistance to women undergraduate students from Washington working on an undergraduate degree related to transportation.

Eligibility This program is open to women who are residents of Washington, studying at a college in the state, or working as an intern in the state. Applicants must be currently enrolled in an undergraduate degree program in a transportation-related field, such as engineering, planning, finance, or logistics. They must have a GPA of 3.0 or higher and plans to prepare for a career in a transportation-related field. Minority women are especially encouraged to apply. Along with their application, they must submit a 500-word statement about their career goals after graduation and why they think they should receive this scholarship award. Selection is based on that statement, academic record, and transportation-related activities or job skills. Financial need is not considered.

Financial data The stipend is $4,000.

Duration 1 year.

Additional information The winner is also nominated for scholarships offered by the national organization of the Women's Transportation Seminar.

Number awarded 1 each year.

Deadline November of each year.

[537]
QUALITY OF LIFE AWARDS

Miss America Pageant
Attn: Scholarship Department
222 New Road, Suite 700
Linwood, NJ 08221
(609) 653-8700, ext. 127   Fax: (609) 653-8740
E-mail: info@missamerica.org
Web: www.missamerica.org/scholarships/quality.aspx

Summary To recognize and reward, with college scholarships, women who participate in the Miss America Pageant at the national level and demonstrate outstanding community service.

Eligibility This program is open to women who compete at the national level of the Miss America Pageant and demonstrate a commitment to enhancing the quality of life for others through volunteerism and community service. Applicants must demonstrate that they have fulfilled a legitimate need in their community through the creation, development, and/or participation in a community service project. Selection is based on the depth of service, creativity of the project, and effects on the lives of others.

Financial data The awards are college scholarships of $6,000 for the winner, $4,000 for the first runner-up, and $2,000 for the second runner-up.

Duration The awards are presented annually.

Additional information This program was established in 1988.

Number awarded 3 each year.

Deadline Deadline not specified.

[538]
RACHEL E. LEMIEUX YOUTH SCHOLARSHIP

Maine Federation of Business and Professional Women's Clubs
Attn: BPW/Maine Futurama Foundation
c/o Susan Tardie, Co-President
25 Hall Street
Fort Kent, ME 04743
E-mail: susan.tardie@maine.edu
Web: www.bpwmefoundation.org/files/index.php?id=10

Summary To provide financial assistance to female high school seniors and recent graduates in Maine who plan to attend college in any state.

Eligibility This program is open to women who are seniors graduating from high schools in Maine or recent graduates of those schools. Applicants must be planning to attend an accredited college or university in any state. They must have a realistic goal for their education. Along with their application, they must submit a statement describing their educational and personal goals, including their financial need.

Financial data The stipend is $1,200. Funds are paid directly to the recipient's school.

Duration 1 year.

Number awarded 1 or more each year.

Deadline April of each year.

[539]
RECOGNITION SCHOLARSHIPS

Zeta Tau Alpha Foundation, Inc.
Attn: Director of Foundation Administration
3450 Founders Road
Indianapolis, IN 46268
(317) 872-0540   Fax: (317) 876-3948
E-mail: zetataualpha@zetataualpha.org
Web: www.zetataualpha.org

Summary To provide financial assistance for college to women who are members of Zeta Tau Alpha.

Eligibility This program is open to undergraduate women who are enrolled at a 4-year college or university and student members of the school's Zeta Tau Alpha chapter. These scholarships have been established with endowment monies and annual gifts in memory or honor of a member of the sorority. Selection is based on academic achievement (GPA of 2.75 or higher), involvement in campus and community activities, recommendations, current class status, and financial need.

Financial data The stipend is $1,500.

Duration 1 year; renewable.

Number awarded Varies each year; recently, the foundation awarded a total of more than $600,000 to 235 undergraduate and graduate members for all of its scholarship programs.

Deadline   February of each year.

[540]
RED RIVER VALLEY FIGHTER PILOTS ASSOCIATION SCHOLARSHIP GRANT PROGRAM

Red River Valley Association Foundation
Attn: Executive Director
P.O. Box 1553
Front Royal, VA 22630-0033
(540) 639-9798   Toll Free: (866) 401-7287
Fax: (540) 636-9776
E-mail: ExecutiveOffice@river-rats.org
Web: www.river-rats.org/about_us/scholarship.php

Summary   To provide financial assistance for college or graduate school to the spouses and children of selected service personnel and members of the Red River Valley Fighter Pilots Association.

Eligibility   This program is open to the spouses and children of 1) servicemembers missing in action (MIA) or killed in action (KIA) in combat situations involving U.S. military forces from August 1964 through the present; 2) U.S. military aircrew members killed in a non-combat aircraft accident in which they were performing aircrew duties; and 3) current members of the association and deceased members who were in good standing at the time of their death. Scholarships are also available to students in fields related to aviation and space, even if they have no kinship relationship to a deceased aviator or member of the association. Applicants must be interested in attending an accredited college or university to work on an undergraduate or graduate degree. Selection is based on demonstrated academic achievement, college entrance examination scores, financial need, and accomplishments in school, church, civic, and social activities.

Financial data   The amount awarded varies, depending upon the need of the recipient. Recently, undergraduate stipends have ranged from $500 to $3,500 and averaged $1,725; graduate stipends have ranged from $500 to $2,000 and averaged $1,670. Funds are paid directly to the recipient's institution and are to be used for tuition, fees, books, and room and board for full-time students.

Duration   1 year; may be renewed if the recipient maintains a GPA of 2.0 or higher.

Additional information   This program was established in 1970, out of concern for the families of aircrews (known as "River Rats") who were killed or missing in action in the Red River Valley of North Vietnam.

Number awarded   Varies each year; since this program was established, it has awarded more than 1,000 scholarships worth more than $1,700,000.

Deadline   May of each year.

[541]
REDI-TAG CORPORATION SCHOLARSHIP

American Health Information Management Association
Attn: AHIMA Foundation
233 North Michigan Avenue, 21st Floor
Chicago, IL 60601-5809
(312) 233-1175   Fax: (312) 233-1475
E-mail: info@ahimafoundation.org
Web: www.ahimafoundation.org

Summary   To provide financial assistance to members of the American Health Information Management Association (AHIMA) who are single parents and interested in working on an undergraduate degree in health information administration or technology.

Eligibility   This program is open to AHIMA members who are single parents and enrolled at least half time in a program accredited by the Commission on Accreditation of Allied Health Education Programs. Applicants must be working on an associate degree in health information technology or a bachelor's degree in health information administration. They must have a GPA of 3.0 or higher and at least 1 full semester remaining after the date of the award. Financial need is not considered in the selection process.

Financial data   Stipends are $1,000 for students working on an associate degree or $1,200 for students working on a bachelor's degree.

Duration   1 year; nonrenewable.

Additional information   Funding for this program is provided by the Redi-Tag Corporation.

Number awarded   1 each year.

Deadline   April or October of each year.

[542]
REED AND GLORIA PENNINGTON SCHOLARSHIP

Kappa Delta Sorority
Attn: Foundation Manager
3205 Players Lane
Memphis, TN 38125
(901) 748-1897   Toll Free: (800) 536-1897
Fax: (901) 748-0949 E-mail: kappadelta@kappadelta.org
Web: www.kappadelta.org/scholarships

Summary   To provide financial assistance to members of Kappa Delta Sorority who are majoring in journalism or communications.

Eligibility   This program is open to undergraduate members of Kappa Delta Sorority. Applicants must submit a personal statement giving their reasons for applying for this scholarship, an official undergraduate transcript, and 2 letters of recommendation. They must be majoring in journalism or communications. Selection is based on academic excellence; service to the chapter, alumnae association, or national Kappa Delta; service to the campus and community; personal objectives and goals; potential; recommendations; and financial need.

Financial data   The stipend is $2,000 per year. Funds may be used only for tuition, fees, and books, not for room and board.

Duration   1 year; may be renewed.

Number awarded   1 each year.

Deadline   January of each year.

[543]
REGION F SCHOLARSHIP

Society of Women Engineers
Attn: Scholarship Selection Committee
120 South LaSalle Street, Suite 1515
Chicago, IL 60603-3572
(312) 596-5223   Toll Free: (877) SWE-INFO
Fax: (312) 644-8557
E-mail: scholarshipapplication@swe.org
Web: societyofwomenengineers.swe.org

Summary To provide financial assistance to members of the Society of Women Engineers (SWE) working on an undergraduate or graduate degree in engineering or computer science at a school in its Region F (New England and eastern New York).

Eligibility This program is open to members of the society who will be sophomores, juniors, seniors, or graduate students at ABET-accredited colleges and universities in the New England states or eastern New York. Applicants must be majoring in computer science or engineering and have a GPA of 3.0 or higher. Financial need is considered in the selection process. U.S. citizenship is required.

Financial data The stipend is $1,000.

Duration 1 year.

Number awarded 1 each year.

Deadline February of each year.

[544]
REGION H SCHOLARSHIP

Society of Women Engineers
Attn: Scholarship Selection Committee
120 South LaSalle Street, Suite 1515
Chicago, IL 60603-3572
(312) 596-5223   Toll Free: (877) SWE-INFO
Fax: (312) 644-8557
E-mail: scholarshipapplication@swe.org
Web: societyofwomenengineers.swe.org

Summary To provide financial assistance to members of the Society of Women Engineers (SWE) working on an undergraduate or graduate degree in engineering or computer science at a school in the upper Midwest (Region H).

Eligibility This program is open to members of the society who will be sophomores, juniors, seniors, or graduate students at ABET-accredited colleges and universities in Illinois, Indiana, Iowa, Michigan, Minnesota, North Dakota, South Dakota, or Wisconsin. Applicants must be majoring in computer science or engineering and have a GPA of 3.0 or higher. Selection is based on merit and participation in SWE activities.

Financial data The stipend is $1,000.

Duration 1 year.

Number awarded 1 each year.

Deadline February of each year.

[545]
REGIONAL SUMMER MUSIC SCHOLARSHIPS

Sigma Alpha Iota Philanthropies, Inc.
One Tunnel Road
Asheville, NC 28805
(828) 251-0606   Fax: (828) 251-0644
E-mail: nh@sai-national.org
Web: www.sigmaalphaiota.org

Summary To provide financial assistance for summer study in music, in the United States or abroad, to members of Sigma Alpha Iota (an organization of women musicians).

Eligibility This program is open to undergraduate and graduate student members of the organization who are planning to study at a summer music program in the United States or abroad. Applicants must submit a complete resume (including musical studies and activities, academic GPA, community service record, and record of participation in Sigma Alpha Iota), supporting materials (recital and concert programs, reviews, repertoire list, etc.), a statement of why they chose this program and how it will aid their musical growth, a full brochure of information on the program (including cost and payment due dates), a copy of the completed summer school application and acceptance letter (when available), and a letter of recommendation from their major teacher.

Financial data The stipend is $1,000.

Duration Summer months.

Number awarded 10 each year: 2 from each region of Sigma Alpha Iota.

Deadline March of each year.

[546]
RENEE FELDMAN SCHOLARSHIPS

Blinded Veterans Association Auxiliary
c/o Barbara Stocking, Scholarship Chair
3801 Coco Grove Avenue
Miami, FL 33133
(305) 446-8008

Summary To provide financial assistance for college to spouses and children of blinded veterans.

Eligibility This program is open to children and spouses of blinded veterans who are attending or planning to attend a college, university, community college, or vocational school. The veteran is not required to be a member of the Blinded Veterans Association. Applicants must submit a 300-word essay on their career goals and aspirations. Selection is based on that essay, academic achievement, and letters of reference.

Financial data Stipends are $2,000 or $1,000. Funds are paid directly to the recipient's school to be applied to tuition, books, and general fees.

Duration 1 year.

Number awarded 5 each year: 3 at $2,000 and 2 at $1,000.

Deadline April of each year.

[547]
RESOURCES FOR THE FUTURE SUMMER INTERNSHIPS

Resources for the Future
Attn: Internship Coordinator
1616 P Street, N.W., Suite 600
Washington, DC 20036-1400
(202) 328-5008   Fax: (202) 939-3460
E-mail: IC@rff.org
Web: www.rff.org

Summary   To provide internships to undergraduate and graduate students (especially women and minorities) who are interested in working on research projects in public policy during the summer.

Eligibility   This program is open to undergraduate and graduate students (with priority to graduate students) interested in an internship at Resources for the Future (RFF). Applicants must be working on a degree in the social and natural sciences and have training in economics and quantitative methods or an interest in public policy. They should display strong writing skills and a desire to analyze complex environmental policy problems amenable to interdisciplinary methods. The ability to work without supervision in a careful and conscientious manner is essential. Women and minority candidates are strongly encouraged to apply. Both U.S. and non-U.S. citizens are eligible, if the latter have proper work and residency documentation.

Financial data   The stipend is $375 per week for graduate students or $350 per week for undergraduates. Housing assistance is not provided.

Duration   10 weeks during the summer; beginning and ending dates can be adjusted to meet particular student needs.

Deadline   March of each year.

[548]
RHODA D. HOOD MEMORIAL SCHOLARSHIP

Northwest Baptist Convention
Attn: Woman's Missionary Union
3200 N.E. 109th Avenue
Vancouver, WA 98682
(360) 882-2100   Fax: (360) 882-2295
Web: www.nwbaptist.org

Summary   To provide financial assistance to women from the Northwest who are attending college or seminary in any state to prepare for a career in vocational ministry, preferably with a Southern Baptist Convention church.

Eligibility   This program is open to women who have been active members of a church affiliated with the Northwest Baptist Convention and a member of the Woman's Missionary Union within their church. Special consideration is given to children of ministers from the Northwest. Applicants must be attending or planning to attend an accredited college, university, or Southern Baptist seminary in any state with the intention of serving in a vocational ministry position through a church or denomination; priority is given to applicants going into a mission vocation affiliated with the Southern Baptist Convention. Along with their application, they must submit 1) a written account of their conversion experience and their call to vocational ministry; and 2) a written endorsement from their church.

Financial data   A stipend is awarded (amount not specified).

Duration   1 year; may be renewed if the recipient maintains a GPA of 2.5 or higher.

Additional information   The Northwest Baptist Convention serves Oregon, Washington, and northern Idaho.

Number awarded   1 or more each year.

Deadline   May of each year for fall term; October of each year for spring term.

[549]
RHODE ISLAND COMMISSION ON WOMEN/ FREDA H. GOLDMAN EDUCATION AWARDS

Rhode Island Foundation
Attn: Funds Administrator
One Union Station
Providence, RI 02903
(401) 427-4017   Fax: (401) 331-8085
E-mail: lmonahan@rifoundation.org
Web: www.rifoundation.org

Summary   To provide supplemental funding to women in Rhode Island who are working on a degree or job training beyond high school.

Eligibility   This program is open to women in Rhode Island who are 1) preparing for a nontraditional job or career through an educational program; 2) needing skills to reenter the job market; 3) seeking skills to improve their job status; 4) ex-offenders wishing to undertake vocational or career education and training; or 5) displaced homemakers and single mothers wishing to further their education. Applicants must be enrolled or registered in an educational or job skills training program and be able to demonstrate financial need. Preference is given to highly motivated, self-supporting, low-income women who are completing their first undergraduate degree or certificate program. Along with their application, they must submit an essay (up to 300 words) in which they explain their reasons for returning to school, how they chose their intended career or job training, how this scholarship can help them achieve their goals, and specifically how the money will be used.

Financial data   Stipends range from $500 to $1,000; funds may be used for transportation, child care, introductory courses to a program, tutoring, educational materials, and related costs (not including tuition).

Duration   1 year; may be renewed.

Additional information   This program, established in 1983 and transferred to the foundation in 1997, is supported by the Rhode Island Commission on Women.

Number awarded   2 each year.

Deadline   June of each year.

[550]
RHODE ISLAND WOMEN'S GOLF ASSOCIATION SCHOLARSHIPS

Rhode Island Women's Golf Association
c/o Pat Davitt
17 Oak Manor Drive
Barrington, RI 02806
(401) 245-4959   E-mail: pdavitt@lincolnschool.org
Web: www.riwga.org/scholarships.html

Summary To provide financial assistance for college to women golfers from Rhode Island.

Eligibility This program is open to women who have participated in the program of the Rhode Island Women's Golf Association. Applicants must be high school seniors or current undergraduates and attending or planning to attend a college or university in any state. They must submit information on their community service experiences; special recognition received at school (e.g., athletic, academic, clubs); financial need; and involvement with golf.

Financial data A stipend is awarded (amount not specified).

Duration 1 year; may be renewed up to 3 additional years, provided the recipient maintains a "C" average.

Additional information This program began in 1981.

Number awarded Varies each year; recently, 20 of these scholarships were awarded.

Deadline May of each year.

[551]
R.L. GILLETTE SCHOLARSHIPS

American Foundation for the Blind
Attn: Scholarship Committee
11 Penn Plaza, Suite 300
New York, NY 10001
(212) 502-7661   Toll Free: (800) AFB-LINE
Fax: (212) 502-7771   TDD: (212) 502-7662
E-mail: afbinfo@afb.net
Web: www.afb.org/Section.asp?Documentid=2962

Summary To provide financial assistance to legally blind undergraduate women who are studying literature or music.

Eligibility This program is open to women who are legally blind, U.S. citizens, and enrolled full time in a 4-year baccalaureate degree program in literature or music. Along with their application, they must submit a 200-word essay that includes their past and recent achievements and accomplishments; their intended field of study and why they have chosen it; and the role their visual impairment has played in shaping their life. They must also submit a sample performance tape/CD (not to exceed 30 minutes) or a creative writing sample. Financial need is considered in the selection process.

Financial data The stipend is $1,000.

Duration 1 academic year.

Number awarded 2 each year.

Deadline April of each year.

[552]
ROBERT SMILEY SCHOLARSHIP

Iowa Girls High School Athletic Union
Attn: Scholarships
2900 Grand Avenue
P.O. Box 10348
Des Moines, IA 50306-0348
(515) 288-9741   Fax: (515) 284-1969
E-mail: lisa@ighsau.org
Web: www.ighsau.org

Summary To provide financial assistance to female high school seniors in Iowa who have participated in athletics and plan to attend college in the state.

Eligibility This program is open to women graduating from high schools in Iowa who have lettered in 1 varsity sport sponsored by the Iowa Girls High School Athletic Union (IGHSAU) each year of high school and have a GPA of 2.5 or higher. Applicants must be planning to attend a college or university in Iowa. Each high school in the state may nominate 1 student. Selection is based on academic achievements, athletic accomplishments, non-sports extracurricular activities, and community involvement.

Financial data The stipend is $1,000.

Duration 1 year.

Number awarded 1 each year.

Deadline March of each year.

[553]
ROCKWELL AUTOMATION SCHOLARSHIPS

Society of Women Engineers
Attn: Scholarship Selection Committee
120 South LaSalle Street, Suite 1515
Chicago, IL 60603-3572
(312) 596-5223   Toll Free: (877) SWE-INFO
Fax: (312) 644-8557
E-mail: scholarshipapplication@swe.org
Web: societyofwomenengineers.swe.org

Summary To provide financial assistance to upper-division women majoring in computer science or selected engineering specialties.

Eligibility This program is open to women who are entering their junior year at an ABET-accredited college or university. Applicants must be majoring in computer science or computer, electrical, industrial, manufacturing, mechanical, or software engineering and have a GPA of 3.0 or higher. Selection is based on merit and demonstrated leadership potential. Preference is given to students attending designated universities and to members of groups underrepresented in computer science and engineering.

Financial data The stipend is $2,500.

Duration 1 year.

Additional information This program, established in 1991, is supported by Rockwell Automation, Inc. For a list of the preferred universities, contact the sponsor.

Number awarded 2 each year.

Deadline February of each year.

[554]
ROCKWELL COLLINS SWE SCHOLARSHIPS

Society of Women Engineers
Attn: Scholarship Selection Committee
120 South LaSalle Street, Suite 1515
Chicago, IL 60603-3572
(312) 596-5223   Toll Free: (877) SWE-INFO
Fax: (312) 644-8557
E-mail: scholarshipapplication@swe.org
Web: societyofwomenengineers.swe.org

Summary To provide financial assistance to undergraduate members of the Society of Women Engineers (SWE) majoring in computer science or selected engineering specialties.

Eligibility This program is open to members of the society who are entering their sophomore or junior year at a 4-year ABET-accredited college or university. Applicants must be majoring in computer science or computer, electrical, or software engineering and have a GPA of 3.0 or higher. Selection is based on merit. Preference is given to members of groups underrepresented in computer science and engineering.

Financial data   The stipend is $2,250.

Duration   1 year.

Additional information   This program, established in 1991, is supported by Rockwell Collins, Inc.

Number awarded   3 each year.

Deadline   February of each year.

[555]
ROCKY MOUNTAIN SECTION COLLEGE SCHOLARSHIPS

Society of Women Engineers-Rocky Mountain Section
Attn: Collegiate Scholarship Committee Chair
P.O. Box 260692
Lakewood, CO 80226-0692
(303) 751-0741   Fax: (303) 751-2581
E-mail: Christina.wisleder@merrick.copm
Web: www.societyofwomenengineers.org

Summary   To provide financial assistance to women from any state who are working on an undergraduate or graduate degree in engineering at colleges and universities in Colorado and Wyoming.

Eligibility   This program is open to women from any state who are enrolled as an undergraduate or graduate engineering student in an ABET-accredited engineering or computer science program in Colorado or Wyoming (excluding zip codes 80800-81599). Applicants must have a GPA of 3.0 or higher. Along with their application, they must submit an essay on why they have chosen an engineering major, what they will accomplish or how they believe they will make a difference as an engineer, and who or what influenced them to study engineering. Selection is based on merit.

Financial data   The stipend is $1,250.

Duration   1 year.

Additional information   This program includes the following named scholarships: the Dorolyn Lines Scholarship, the Lottye Miner Scholarship, and the Rocky Mountain Section Pioneer Scholarship.

Number awarded   3 each year.

Deadline   January of each year.

[556]
ROGER J. SHERIDAN MEMORIAL SCHOLARSHIPS

Vermont Elks Association, Inc.
c/o John A. Cutler, Scholarship Chair
16 Second Street
Barre, VT 05641-2411
E-mail: JohnCutler1@msn.com

Summary   To provide financial assistance to high school seniors in Vermont who are interested in studying physical education at a college in any state (females and males are judged separately).

Eligibility   This program is open to seniors graduating from high schools in Vermont who plan to attend a college or university in any state. Applicants must be planning to major in physical education to prepare for a career as a teacher of physical education. Along with their application, they must submit transcripts, copies of their SAT or ACT scores, letters of recommendation, documentation of financial need, and an

essay on their plans after graduation from college. Selection is based on commitment to chosen career and field of study, academic achievement, school and community involvement and/or service, and financial need. Females and males are considered separately.

Financial data   Stipends range up to $1,000.

Duration   1 year.

Number awarded   2 each year: 1 to a female and 1 to a male.

Deadline   January of each year.

[557]
ROLLIE HOPGOOD FUTURE TEACHERS HIGH SCHOOL SENIOR SCHOLARSHIPS

AFT Michigan
Attn: Scholarship Committee
2661 East Jefferson Avenue
Detroit, MI 48207
(313) 393-2200   Toll Free: (800) MFT-8868
Fax: (313) 393-2236
Web: aftmichigan.org/members/scholarships.html

Summary   To provide financial assistance to high school seniors in Michigan who are interested in attending college in any state to prepare for a career as a teacher (females and males are judged separately).

Eligibility   This program is open to seniors graduating from high schools that are represented by AFT Michigan. Applicants must be planning to attend a college or university in any state to prepare for a career as a teacher. Along with their application, they must submit a 500-word essay on why they want to become a teacher, why they should be considered for this scholarship, and the correlation between education and politics. Selection is based on the essay, GPA, extracurricular activities, community-related activities, and financial need. Female and male applicants compete separately.

Financial data   The stipend is $1,000.

Duration   1 year.

Additional information   AFT Michigan was formerly the Michigan Federation of Teachers & School Related Personnel. Recipients must enroll as full-time students.

Number awarded   2 each year: 1 female and 1 male.

Deadline   May of each year.

[558]
RURAL MUTUAL INSURANCE COMPANY SCHOLARSHIPS

Wisconsin Towns Association
Attn: Scholarship Program
W7686 County Road MMM
Shawano, WI 54166-6086
(715) 526-3157   Fax: (715) 524-3917
E-mail: wtowns@frontiernet.net
Web: www.wisctowns.com/home/scholarship-program

Summary   To provide financial assistance to high seniors in Wisconsin who submit outstanding essays on town government and plan to attend college in the state (females and males are judged separately).

Eligibility   This program is open to seniors graduating from high schools in Wisconsin who plan to attend a college, university, or vocational/technical institute in the state. Applicants must live in a town or village that has insurance from

Rural Mutual Insurance Company for its municipal government. Along with their application, they must submit an essay of 500 to 1,000 words on a topic that changes annually but relates to local government in Wisconsin; recently, students were asked to write on "How can towns and villages best protect their infrastructure and still provide other needed services such as fire and emergency services in tough economic times?" Selection is based primarily on the essay's originality and subject matter in relationship to the topic; financial need is not considered. Boys and girls are judged separately.

Financial data The stipend is $1,000.

Duration 1 year.

Additional information This program is supported by Rural Mutual Insurance Company, 1241 John Q. Hammons Drive, Suite 200, P.O. Box 5555, Madison, WI 53705-0555.

Number awarded 2 each year: 1 to a boy and 1 to a girl.

Deadline May of each year.

[559]
RUTH BILLOW MEMORIAL EDUCATION FUND

Delta Gamma Foundation
Attn: Director, Service for Sight
3250 Riverside Drive
P.O. Box 21397
Columbus, OH 43221-0397
(614) 481-8169   Toll Free: (800) 644-5414
Fax: (614) 481-0133   E-mail: fngrants@deltagamma.org
Web: www.deltagamma.org

Summary To provide financial assistance to undergraduate or graduate members of Delta Gamma sorority who are visually impaired or preparing for a career in working with the visually impaired.

Eligibility This program is open to undergraduate and graduate members of the sorority who are either 1) blind or visually impaired; or 2) pursuing professional training in areas related to working with persons who are blind or visually impaired or in sight preservation. Applicants must be pursuing a program of postsecondary education in the United States or Canada.

Financial data The stipend is $1,000 for undergraduates or $2,500 for graduate students.

Duration 1 year or more.

Number awarded 2 each year: 1 to an undergraduate and 1 to a graduate student.

Deadline Applications may be submitted at any time.

[560]
RUTH E. BLACK SCHOLARSHIP FUND

American Association of University Women-Honolulu
   Branch
Attn: Scholarship Committee
1802 Ke'eaumoku Street
Honolulu, HI 96822
(808) 537-4702   Fax: (808) 537-4702
E-mail: Edu@aauw-honolulu.org
Web: aauw.xodev01.com

Summary To provide financial assistance to undergraduate women in Hawaii.

Eligibility This program is open to female residents of Hawaii who are currently enrolled at an accredited college, university, or vocational/technical institute in the state. Appli-

cants must have completed at least 2 semesters of college or university study. Selection is based on academic achievement, demonstrated leadership in school and community activities, and financial need. First-time applicants receive priority. U.S. citizenship is required.

Financial data Stipends vary, but generally range from $500 to $1,000.

Duration 1 year.

Additional information This program was established in 1969 and given its current name in 1975.

Number awarded Varies each year; recently, 5 of these scholarships were awarded.

Deadline May of each year.

[561]
RUTH WHITNEY SCHOLARSHIP

New York Women in Communications, Inc.
Attn: NYWICI Foundation
355 Lexington Avenue, 15th Floor
New York, NY 10017-6603
(212) 297-2133   Fax: (212) 370-9047
E-mail: nywicipr@nywici.org
Web: www.nywici.org/foundation/scholarships

Summary To provide financial assistance to female residents of designated eastern states who are interested in preparing for a career in magazine journalism or publishing at a college or graduate school in any state.

Eligibility This program is open to women who are residents of New York, New Jersey, Connecticut, or Pennsylvania and enrolled as undergraduate or graduate students at a college or university in any state. Graduate students must be members of New York Women in Communications, Inc. (NYWICI). Also eligible are women who reside outside the 4 states but are currently enrolled at a college or university within 1 of the 5 boroughs of New York City. Applicants must have some experience in writing, reporting, or design and be preparing for a career in magazine journalism or publishing. Along with their application, they must submit a 2-page resume that includes school and extracurricular activities, significant achievements, academic honors and awards, and community service work; a personal essay of 300 to 500 words on their choice of an assigned topic that changes annually; 2 letters of recommendation; and an official transcript. Selection is based on academic record, need, demonstrated leadership, participation in school and community activities, honors, work experience, goals and aspirations, and unusual personal and/or family circumstances. U.S. citizenship is required.

Financial data The stipend ranges up to $10,000.

Duration 1 year.

Additional information This program is sponsored by *Glamour* magazine, which invites the recipient to visit its offices and spend a week with its editorial team.

Number awarded 1 each year.

Deadline January of each year.

[562]
S. EVELYN LEWIS MEMORIAL SCHOLARSHIP IN MEDICAL HEALTH SCIENCES

Zeta Phi Beta Sorority, Inc.
Attn: National Education Foundation
1734 New Hampshire Avenue, N.W.
Washington, DC 20009
(202) 387-3103   Fax: (202) 232-4593
E-mail: scholarship@ZPhiBNEF.org
Web: www.zphib1920.org/nef

Summary To provide financial assistance to women interested in studying medicine or health sciences on the undergraduate or graduate school level.

Eligibility This program is open to women enrolled full time in a program on the undergraduate or graduate school level leading to a degree in medicine or health sciences. Proof of enrollment is required. Applicants need not be members of Zeta Phi Beta Sorority. Along with their application, they must submit a 150-word essay on their educational goals and professional aspirations, how this award will help them to achieve those goals, and why they should receive the award. Financial need is not considered in the selection process.

Financial data The stipend ranges from $500 to $1,000. Funds are paid directly to the college or university.

Duration 1 academic year.

Number awarded 1 or more each year.

Deadline January of each year.

[563]
SANDRA SEBRELL BAILEY SCHOLARSHIP

Delta Zeta Sorority
Attn: Foundation Coordinator
202 East Church Street
Oxford, OH 45056
(513) 523-7597   Fax: (513) 523-1921
E-mail: DZFoundation@dzshq.com
Web: www.deltazeta.org

Summary To provide financial assistance for continued undergraduate study to members of Delta Zeta Sorority, especially those planning to major in education.

Eligibility This program is open to members of the sorority who are entering their junior or senior year and have been an initiated member for at least 1 year. Applicants must submit an official transcript, a statement of their career goals, information on their service to the sorority, documentation of campus activities and/or community involvement, a list of academic honors, and an explanation of their financial need. Preference may be given to students entering the field of education, but that is not required.

Financial data The stipend ranges from $500 to $2,500, depending on the availability of funds.

Duration 1 year; nonrenewable.

Number awarded 1 each year.

Deadline February of each year.

[564]
SARAH E. HUNEYCUTT SCHOLARSHIP

Florida Women's State Golf Association
Attn: Executive Director
1314 East Venice Avenue, Suite B
Venice, FL 34285-7160
(941) 308-4635   Fax: (941) 237-4179
E-mail: info@fwsga.org
Web: www.fwsga.org/juniors

Summary To provide financial assistance to women in Florida who have an interest in golf and are attending or planning on attending college in the state.

Eligibility This program is open to women in Florida who have an interest in golf but are not skilled enough to qualify for an athletic scholarship. Applicants must be attending or planning to attend a junior college, college, university, or technical school in Florida. They must have a GPA of 3.0 or higher and be able to document financial need. Along with their application, they must submit transcripts, SAT and/or ACT scores, and a copy of their FAFSA.

Financial data Stipends range from $1,000 to $2,000. Funds are paid directly to the recipient's school.

Duration 1 year.

Additional information This program was established in 1994.

Number awarded Varies each year; recently, 3 of these scholarships were awarded.

Deadline April of each year.

[565]
SARAH JANE HOUSTON SCHOLARSHIP

Delta Zeta Sorority
Attn: Foundation Coordinator
202 East Church Street
Oxford, OH 45056
(513) 523-7597   Fax: (513) 523-1921
E-mail: DZFoundation@dzshq.com
Web: www.deltazeta.org

Summary To provide financial assistance for continued undergraduate study to members of Delta Zeta Sorority who are majoring in English or a related field.

Eligibility This program is open to members of the sorority who are entering their junior or senior year and have a GPA of 3.0 or higher. Applicants must be working on a degree in English or a related field (e.g., speech, debate, drama, theater, education). Along with their application, they must submit an official transcript, a statement of their career goals, information on their service to the sorority, documentation of campus activities and/or community involvement, a list of academic honors, and an explanation of their financial need. Preference is given to members of chapters in Illinois.

Financial data The stipend ranges from $500 to $2,500, depending on the availability of funds.

Duration 1 year; nonrenewable.

Number awarded 1 each year.

Deadline February of each year.

[566]
SCHOLAR AWARDS

Miss America Pageant
Attn: Scholarship Department
222 New Road, Suite 700
Linwood, NJ 08221
(609) 653-8700, ext. 127   Fax: (609) 653-8740
E-mail: info@missamerica.org
Web: www.missamerica.org/scholarships/missstate.aspx

Summary To recognize and reward, with college scholarships, women who participate in the Miss America Pageant at the state level and demonstrate academic excellence.

Eligibility This competition is open to women who compete at the state level of the Miss America Pageant. Selection is based on academic excellence (grades, course content, and academic standing of the institution).

Financial data The stipend is $1,000.

Duration 1 year.

Additional information This program, established in 1998, is administered by Scholarship Management Services, a division of Scholarship America, One Scholarship Way, P.O. Box 297, St. Peter, MN 56082, (507) 931-1682, (800) 537-4180, Fax: (507) 931-9168, E-mail: smsinfo@csfa.org.

Number awarded Up to 52 each year: 1 for each of the states, the District of Columbia, and the Virgin Islands.

Deadline Varies, depending upon the date of local pageants leading to the state finals.

[567]
SCHOLARSHIPS FOR ALL MILITARY SPOUSES

National Military Family Association, Inc.
Attn: Spouse Scholarship Program
2500 North Van Dorn Street, Suite 102
Alexandria, VA 22302-1601
(703) 931-NMFA   Toll Free: (800) 260-0218
Fax: (703) 931-4600
E-mail: scholarships@militaryfamily.org
Web: www.militaryfamily.org

Summary To provide financial assistance for postsecondary study to spouses of active and retired military personnel.

Eligibility This program is open to the spouses of military personnel (active, retired, Reserve, Guard, or survivor). Applicants must be attending or planning to attend an accredited postsecondary institution to work on an undergraduate or graduate degree, professional certification, vocational training, GED or ESL, or other postsecondary training. They may enroll part or full time and in-class or online. Along with their application, they must submit an essay on a question that changes annually; recently, applicants were asked to write about what they like most about the health care they are receiving as a military family member, what they like the least, and what they would recommend to change it. Selection is based on that essay, community involvement, and academic achievement.

Financial data The stipend is $1,000. Funds are paid directly to the educational institution to be used for tuition, fees, and school room and board. Support is not provided for books, rent, or previous education loans.

Duration 1 year; recipients may reapply.

Additional information This program, is a component of the Joanne Holbrook Patton Military Spouse Scholarship Program, which began in 2004.

Number awarded Varies each year; recently, the program awarded a total of 293 scholarships.

Deadline January of each year.

[568]
SCHOLARSHIPS FOR ELCA SERVICE ABROAD

Women of the Evangelical Lutheran Church in America
Attn: Scholarships
8765 West Higgins Road
Chicago, IL 60631-4101
(773) 380-2736   Toll Free: (800) 638-3522, ext. 2736
Fax: (773) 380-2419   E-mail: Women.elca@elca.org
Web: www.elca.org

Summary To provide financial assistance to lay women who are members of Evangelical Lutheran Church of America (ELCA) congregations and interested in pursuing postsecondary education for service abroad, either in general or in health fields.

Eligibility This program is open to ELCA lay women who are at least 21 years of age and have experienced an interruption of at least 2 years in their education since high school. Applicants must have been admitted to an academic institution to prepare for a career other than the ordained ministry. This program is available only to women studying for ELCA service abroad, either in general or in health professions associated with ELCA projects abroad. U.S. citizenship is required.

Financial data The stipend ranges from $800 to $1,000 per year.

Duration Up to 2 years.

Additional information This program includes the following named scholarships: the Belmer Scholarship, the Flora Prince Scholarship, the Kahler Scholarship, the Vickers/Raup Scholarship, and the Emma Wettstein Scholarship.

Number awarded 1 or more each year.

Deadline February of each year.

[569]
SCHOLARSHIPS FOR SPOUSES OF THE FALLEN

National Military Family Association, Inc.
Attn: Spouse Scholarship Program
2500 North Van Dorn Street, Suite 102
Alexandria, VA 22302-1601
(703) 931-NMFA   Toll Free: (800) 260-0218
Fax: (703) 931-4600
E-mail: scholarships@militaryfamily.org
Web: www.militaryfamily.org

Summary To provide financial assistance for undergraduate or graduate study to spouses of military personnel who have been killed as a result of service since September 11, 2001.

Eligibility This program is open to the spouses of military personnel who have been killed as a result of active-duty service since September 11, 2001. Applicants must be able to verify that the death was a result of service in support of the Global War on Terror. They must be attending or planning to attend an accredited postsecondary institution to work on an undergraduate or graduate degree, professional certification, vocational training, GED or ESL, or other postsecondary training. They may enroll part or full time and in-class or online. Along with their application, they must submit an essay on a question that changes annually; recently, applicants were asked to write about what they like most about the health care they are receiving as a military family member, what they like the least, and what they would recommend to change it. Selection is based on that essay, community involvement, and academic achievement.

Financial data The stipend is $1,000. Funds are paid directly to the educational institution to be used for tuition, fees, and school room and board. Support is not provided for books, rent, or previous education loans.

Duration 1 year; recipients may reapply.

Additional information This program, is a component of the Joanne Holbrook Patton Military Spouse Scholarship Program, which began in 2004.

Number awarded Varies each year; recently, the program awarded a total of 293 scholarships.

Deadline January of each year.

[570]
SCHOLARSHIPS FOR SPOUSES OF THE WOUNDED

National Military Family Association, Inc.
Attn: Spouse Scholarship Program
2500 North Van Dorn Street, Suite 102
Alexandria, VA 22302-1601
(703) 931-NMFA   Toll Free: (800) 260-0218
Fax: (703) 931-4600
E-mail: scholarships@militaryfamily.org
Web: www.militaryfamily.org

Summary To provide financial assistance for undergraduate or graduate study to spouses of military personnel who have been wounded as a result of service since September 11, 2001.

Eligibility This program is open to the spouses of military personnel who have been wounded as a result of active-duty service since September 11, 2001. Applicants must be able to verify that the wound or injury was a result of service in support of the Global War on Terror. They must be attending or planning to attend an accredited postsecondary institution to work on an undergraduate or graduate degree, professional certification, vocational training, GED or ESL, or other postsecondary training. They may enroll part or full time and in-class or online. Along with their application, they must submit an essay on a question that changes annually; recently, applicants were asked to write about what they like most about the health care they are receiving as a military family member, what they like the least, and what they would recommend to change it. Selection is based on that essay, community involvement, and academic achievement.

Financial data The stipend is $1,000. Funds are paid directly to the educational institution to be used for tuition, fees, and school room and board. Support is not provided for books, rent, or previous education loans.

Duration 1 year; recipients may reapply.

Additional information This program, is a component of the Joanne Holbrook Patton Military Spouse Scholarship Program, which began in 2004.

Number awarded Varies each year; recently, the program awarded a total of 293 scholarships.

Deadline January of each year.

[571]
SCHOLARSHIPS FOR UNDERGRADUATE PERFORMANCE

Sigma Alpha Iota Philanthropies, Inc.
One Tunnel Road
Asheville, NC 28805
(828) 251-0606   Fax: (828) 251-0644
E-mail: nh@sai-national.org
Web: www.sigmaalphaiota.org

Summary To recognize and reward, with scholarships for additional study, outstanding performances in vocal and instrumental categories by undergraduate members of Sigma Alpha Iota (an organization of women musicians).

Eligibility This competition is open to undergraduate student members of the organization who are vocalists or instrumentalists. Entrants must be younger than 25 years of age. Selection is based on taped auditions in 4 categories: voice, piano or percussion, strings or harp, and winds or brass.

Financial data The awards are $1,500. Funds must be used for continued study.

Duration The competition is held triennially.

Additional information This program consists of the following named awards: the Blanche Z. Hoffman Memorial Award for Voice, the Mary Ann Starring Memorial Award for Piano and Percussion, the Dorothy E. Morris Memorial Award for Strings or Harp, and the Mary Ann Starring Memorial Award for Woodwinds or Brass.

Number awarded 4 every 3 years: 1 in each of the 4 categories.

Deadline March of the year of the awards (2012, 2015, etc.).

[572]
SCHOLARSHIPS FOR WOMEN RESIDENTS OF THE STATE OF DELAWARE

American Association of University Women-Wilmington Branch
Attn: Scholarship Committee
1800 Fairfax Boulevard
Wilmington, DE 19803-3106
(302) 428-0939   Fax: (775) 890-9043
E-mail: aauwwilm@gmail.com
Web: www.aauwwilmington.org/procedure.html

Summary To provide financial assistance to female residents of Delaware who plan to attend college or graduate school in any state.

Eligibility This program is open to women who are U.S. citizens and 1) a Delaware resident and a high school graduate; 2) a Delaware resident and a senior at a high school in New Castle County; or 3) a resident of New Castle County, Delaware and a home-schooled student who can meet the admission requirements of the University of Delaware. Applicants must be attending or planning to attend a college or university in any state. Along with their application, they must submit a 150-word essay on what they plan to study and why. High school seniors must also submit a 150-word essay on either 1) what they would do and where they would do it if they had

4 hours to spend any place, either now or in history; or 2) the famous person, past or present, who appeals to them most and why. Selection is based on scholastic standing, contributions to school and community, SAT scores, and financial need. An interview is required.

Financial data A stipend is awarded (amount not specified).

Duration 1 year.

Number awarded Varies each year; recently, 17 of these scholarships, worth $55,000, were awarded.

Deadline February of each year.

[573]
SCOTTS COMPANY SCHOLARS PROGRAM

Golf Course Superintendents Association of America
Attn: Environmental Institute for Golf
1421 Research Park Drive
Lawrence, KS 66049-3859
(785) 832-4445   Toll Free: (800) 472-7878, ext. 4445
Fax: (785) 832-4448   E-mail: mwright@gcsaa.org
Web: www.gcsaa.org/students/Scholarships.aspx

Summary To provide financial assistance and summer work experience to high school seniors and college students (particularly women, minorities and individuals with disabilities) who are preparing for a career in golf management.

Eligibility This program is open to high school seniors and college students (freshmen, sophomores, and juniors) who are interested in preparing for a career in golf management (the "green industry"). Applicants should come from diverse ethnic, cultural, or socioeconomic backgrounds, defined to include women, minorities, and people with disabilities. Selection is based on cultural diversity, academic achievement, extracurricular activities, leadership, employment potential, essay responses, and letters of recommendation. Financial need is not considered. Finalists are selected for summer internships and then compete for scholarships.

Financial data The finalists receive a $500 award to supplement their summer internship income. Scholarship stipends are $2,500.

Duration 1 year.

Additional information The program is funded from a permanent endowment established by Scotts Company. Finalists are responsible for securing their own internships.

Number awarded 5 finalists, of whom 2 receive scholarships, are selected each year.

Deadline February of each year.

[574]
SEATTLE CHAPTER AWIS SCHOLARSHIPS

Association for Women in Science-Seattle Chapter
c/o Fran Solomon, Scholarship Committee Chair
5805 16th Avenue, N.E.
Seattle, WA 98105
(206) 522-6441   E-mail: scholarship@seattleawis.org
Web: www.seattleawis.org/programs/scholarship.html

Summary To provide financial assistance to women undergraduates from any state majoring in science, mathematics, or engineering at colleges and universities in Washington.

Eligibility This program is open to women from any state entering their junior or senior year at a 4-year college or university in Washington. Applicants must have a declared major

in science (e.g., biological sciences, environmental science, biochemistry, chemistry, pharmacy, geology, computer science, physics), mathematics, or engineering. Along with their application, they must submit essays on the events that led to their choice of a major, their current career plans and long-term goals, and their volunteer and community activities. Financial need is considered in the selection process. At least 1 scholarship is reserved for a woman from a group that is underrepresented in science, mathematics, and engineering careers, including Native American Indians and Alaska Natives, Black/African Americans, Mexican Americans/Chicanas/Latinas, Native Pacific Islanders (Polynesians, Melanesians, and Micronesians), and women with disabilities.

Financial data Stipends range from $1,000 to $1,500.

Duration 1 year.

Additional information This program includes the following named awards: the Virginia Badger Scholarship, the Angela Paez Memorial Scholarship, and the Fran Solomon Scholarship. Support for the program is provided by several sponsors, including the American Chemical Society, Iota Sigma Pi, Rosetta Inpharmatics, and ZymoGenetics, Inc.

Number awarded 5 to 8 each year.

Deadline April of each year.

[575]
SEATTLE PROFESSIONAL CHAPTER SCHOLARSHIPS

Association for Women in Communications-Seattle
  Professional Chapter
c/o Pam Love, Scholarship Chair
3417 30th Avenue West
Seattle, WA 98199
(425) 280-1968   E-mail: pamlove@grappanetwork.og
Web: www.seattleawc.org/about/student-chapter

Summary To provide financial assistance to female upper-division and graduate students in Washington who are preparing for a career in the communications industry.

Eligibility This program is open to female Washington state residents who are enrolled at a 4-year college or university in the state as a junior, senior, or graduate student (sophomores at 2-year colleges applying to a 4-year institution are also eligible). Applicants must be majoring, or planning to major, in a communications program, including print and broadcast journalism, television and radio production, film, advertising, public relations, marketing, graphic design, multimedia design, photography, or technical communication. Selection is based on demonstrated excellence in communications; contributions made to communications on campus and in the community; scholastic achievement; financial need; and writing samples from journalism, advertising, public relations, or broadcasting.

Financial data The stipend is $1,500. Funds are paid directly to the recipient's school and must be used for tuition and fees.

Duration 1 year.

Number awarded 2 each year.

Deadline April of each year.

[576]
SEVENTEEN MAGAZINE ANNUAL FICTION CONTEST

Seventeen Magazine
Attn: Fiction Contest
300 West 57th Street, 17th Floor
New York, NY 10019-1798
(212) 649-2000   E-mail: mail@seventeen.com
Web: www.seventeen.com

Summary To recognize and reward female teenagers who write fiction that would interest the readers of *Seventeen* magazine.

Eligibility This competition is open to female residents of the United States and Canada who are between 13 and 21 years of age. Applicants must submit a fiction short story, up to 500 words in length, that has not been published previously in any form (except in school publications). Contestants may submit as many stories as they like. Selection is based on creativity (33%), originality (33%), and writing ability (34%).

Financial data The prize is $5,000 and publication of the story in *Seventeen* magazine.

Duration The competition is held annually.

Number awarded 1 each year.

Deadline December of each year.

[577]
SHANNON FUND

Episcopal Diocese of Bethlehem
Attn: Archdeacon Howard Stringfellow
333 Wyandotte Street
Bethlehem, PA 18015
(610) 691-5655, ext. 222
Toll Free: (800) 358-5655 (within PA)
E-mail: archdeacon@diobeth.org
Web: www.diobeth.org

Summary To provide financial assistance to residents of Pennsylvania who are the daughters of Episcopal clergy and interested in working on a degree at a college in any state.

Eligibility Applicants must be 1) residents of 1 of the 5 dioceses of Pennsylvania; 2) daughters of an Episcopal priest; 3) younger than 20 years of age; and 4) interested in working on a degree at a college in any state. The clergy parent must live in the Commonwealth of Pennsylvania and must be canonically resident in 1 of its dioceses. Preference is given to daughters of clergy in the diocese of Bethlehem; if there are surplus funds, then scholarships can be awarded to daughters of clergy in the other 4 Pennsylvania dioceses. Financial need is considered in the selection process.

Financial data Stipends up to $1,500, depending on need, are available.

Duration 1 year; may be renewed until the recipient reaches the age of 20.

Number awarded Varies each year.

Deadline April of each year.

[578]
SHARON D. BANKS MEMORIAL UNDERGRADUATE SCHOLARSHIP

Women's Transportation Seminar
Attn: WTS Foundation
1701 K Street, N.W., Suite 800
Washington, DC 20006
(202) 955-5085   Fax: (202) 955-5088
E-mail: wts@wtsinternational.org
Web: www.wtsinternational.org

Summary To provide financial assistance to undergraduate women interested in a career in transportation.

Eligibility This program is open to women who are working on an undergraduate degree in transportation or a transportation-related field (e.g., transportation engineering, planning, finance, or logistics). Applicants must have a GPA of 3.0 or higher and be interested in a career in transportation. Along with their application, they must submit a 500-word statement about their career goals after graduation and why they think they should receive the scholarship award. Applications must be submitted first to a local chapter; the chapters forward selected applications for consideration on the national level. Minority women are especially encouraged to apply. Selection is based on transportation involvement and goals, job skills, and academic record; financial need is not considered.

Financial data The stipend is $3,000.

Duration 1 year.

Additional information This program was established in 1992. Local chapters may also award additional funding to winners in their area.

Number awarded 1 each year.

Deadline Applications must be submitted by November to a local WTS chapter.

[579]
SHAWN MARGARET DONNELLEY SCHOLARSHIP

Alpha Chi Omega Foundation
Attn: Foundation Programs Coordinator
5939 Castle Creek Parkway North Drive
Indianapolis, IN 46250-4343
(317) 579-5050, ext. 262   Fax: (317) 579-5051
E-mail: foundation@alphachiomega.org
Web: www.alphachiomega.org/index.aspx?id=1030

Summary To provide financial assistance for college or graduate school to undergraduate or graduate members of Alpha Chi Omega.

Eligibility This program is open to undergraduate and graduate members of Alpha Chi Omega. Preference is given to applicants affiliated with Zeta Psi Chapter (Loyola University of New Orleans). If there are no qualified applicants from that chapter, the grant is then opened to all undergraduate and graduate members of the sorority. Selection is based on academic achievement, chapter involvement, community and campus involvement, and financial need.

Financial data A stipend is awarded (amount not specified).

Duration 1 year.

Number awarded 1 or more each year.

Deadline March of each year.

[580]
SHAWNA MULHALL MEMORIAL SCHOLARSHIP

Women's Transportation Seminar-Puget Sound Chapter
c/o Jennifer Barnes, Scholarship Co-Chair
Heffron Transportation, Inc.
6544 N.E. 61st Street
Seattle, WA 98115
(206) 523-3939   Fax: (206) 523-4949
E-mail: jennifer@hefftrans.com
Web: www.wtsinternational.org/Chapters.aspx?ID=7166

Summary   To provide financial assistance to women undergraduate and graduate students from Washington working on a degree related to transportation.

Eligibility   This program is open to women who are residents of Washington, studying at a college in the state, or working as an intern in the state. Applicants must be currently enrolled in an undergraduate or graduate degree program in a transportation-related field, such as engineering, planning, finance, or logistics. They must have a GPA of 3.0 or higher and plans to prepare for a career in a transportation-related field. Minority women are especially encouraged to apply. Along with their application, they must submit a 500-word statement about their career goals after graduation and why they think they should receive this scholarship award. Selection is based on that statement, academic record, financial need, and transportation-related activities or job skills.

Financial data   The stipend is $4,000.

Duration   1 year.

Number awarded   1 each year.

Deadline   November of each year.

[581]
SHERYL KRATZ MEMORIAL SCHOLARSHIP

California Groundwater Association
P.O. Box 14369
Santa Rosa, CA 95402
(707) 578-4408   Fax: (707) 546-4906
E-mail: wellguy@groundh2o.org
Web: www.groundh2o.org/programs/scholarship.html

Summary   To provide financial assistance to women in California who are interested in attending college in the state and either have a relationship to the California Groundwater Association (CGA) or plan to major in a field related to ground water.

Eligibility   This program is open to female residents of California currently enrolled or accepted at a college or university in the state. Applicants must either 1) have a family affiliation with a CGA member (including employees of business members) and be interested in working on a degree in any field; or 2) be interested in working on a degree in a field of study related to ground water. Along with their application, they must submit a 500-word essay demonstrating their interest in either their chosen field of interest or in ground water technology. Financial need is not considered in the selection process.

Financial data   The stipend is $1,000.

Duration   1 year.

Number awarded   1 each year.

Deadline   March of each year.

[582]
SHIRLEY HOLMGREEN MEMORIAL SCHOLARSHIP

Society of Women Engineers-Pacific Northwest Section
Attn: Scholarship Committee
P.O. Box 1601
Bellevue, WA 98009
E-mail: pnw@swe.org
Web: www.swe-pnw.org/scholarship.html

Summary   To provide financial assistance to women from any state studying engineering at a university in Montana or western Washington.

Eligibility   This program is open to women from any state who have, at the time of application, completed at least 50% of the requirements toward college graduation in an engineering field. Applicants must be attending an ABET-accredited engineering school in Montana or western Washington. They must be U.S. citizens and members of the Society of Women Engineers (SWE) student section at their school or, if no student section exists, of the national SWE organization. Along with their application, they must submit 1) a 300-word essay on their educational and career goals; and 2) a 500-word essay describing why they have chosen their particular field of engineering; the person, event, or job experience influencing their decision to work on an engineering degree; and the most and least favorite courses they have taken and which course they are most looking forward to and why. Selection is based on the essays, academic achievement, extracurricular and community service activities, and financial need.

Financial data   The stipend is $1,200.

Duration   1 year.

Number awarded   1 each year.

Deadline   April of each year.

[583]
SIGMA ALPHA IOTA UNDERGRADUATE SCHOLARSHIPS

Sigma Alpha Iota Philanthropies, Inc.
One Tunnel Road
Asheville, NC 28805
(828) 251-0606   Fax: (828) 251-0644
E-mail: nh@sai-national.org
Web: www.sigmaalphaiota.org

Summary   To provide financial assistance for undergraduate study to members of Sigma Alpha Iota (an organization of women musicians).

Eligibility   This program is open to members of the organization in the first 3 years of undergraduate study. Candidates must be nominated by their chapter and their chapter adviser must submit a letter of recommendation. Nominees must submit a brief statement of career goals and aspirations. Selection is based on financial need, musical ability, scholarship, potential leadership, contribution to campus and community life, and exemplification of the ideals of the organization.

Financial data   The stipend is $1,500.

Duration   1 year.

Number awarded   12 each year.

Deadline   March of each year.

[584]
SIGMA KAPPA FOUNDERS' SCHOLARSHIPS

Sigma Kappa Foundation Inc.
Attn: Scholarship Committee
8733 Founders Road
Indianapolis, IN 46268
(317) 381-5531   Fax: (317) 872-0716
E-mail: foundation@sigmakappa.org
Web: www.sigmakappafoundation.org/scholaravail.asp

Summary To provide financial assistance to undergraduate members of Sigma Kappa sorority who have been demonstrated leadership.

Eligibility This program is open to undergraduate members of the sorority who have a GPA of 3.0 or higher. Applicants must be able to demonstrate a leadership role on campus (e.g., student government, chapter officer, Panhellenic). Along with their application, they must submit an essay describing themselves, their future career goals after graduation, and why they are qualified for this scholarship. Financial need is considered in the selection process. Preference is given to sophomores and juniors with at least 1 year's study remaining.

Financial data The stipend is $1,000.

Duration 1 year.

Number awarded 4 each year.

Deadline March of each year.

[585]
SIGN OF THE ARROW MELISSA SCHOLARSHIP

Pi Beta Phi
Attn: Pi Beta Phi Foundation
1154 Town and Country Commons Drive
Town and Country, MO 63017
(636) 256-1357   Fax: (636) 256-8124
E-mail: fndn@pibetaphi.org
Web: www.pibetaphifoundation.org/scholarship-program

Summary To provide financial assistance to members of Pi Beta Phi who are working on an undergraduate degree.

Eligibility This program is open to women who are officially enrolled at a college or university where there is a Pi Beta Phi chapter. They must be active members in good standing in the sorority and entering their senior year as a full-time student with a GPA of 3.1 or higher. Applicants must commit to 1) continue a program of community service for the year the scholarship is applicable; 2) promote and inspire others to community service; and 3) write a reflective piece summarizing community service efforts during the award year. Financial need is not considered.

Financial data Stipends up to $10,000 are available.

Duration 1 year.

Additional information This scholarship was first awarded in 2001.

Number awarded 1 each year.

Deadline February of each year.

[586]
SISTER ELIZABETH CANDON SCHOLARSHIP

Vermont Student Assistance Corporation
Attn: Scholarship Programs
10 East Allen Street
P.O. Box 2000
Winooski, VT 05404-2601
(802) 654-3798   Toll Free: (888) 253-4819
Fax: (802) 654-3765   TDD: (800) 281-3341 (within VT)
E-mail: info@vsac.org
Web: services.vsac.org/wps/wcm/connect/vsac/VSAC

Summary To provide financial assistance to single mothers in Vermont who plan to attend college in any state.

Eligibility This program is open to female residents of Vermont who are single parents with primary custody of at least 1 child 12 years of age or younger. Applicants must be enrolled at least half time in an accredited undergraduate degree program in any state. Along with their application, they must submit 1) a 250-word essay on their short- and long-term academic, educational, career, vocational, and/or employment goals; 2) a 100-word essay on how the program in which they will be enrolled will enhance their career or vocation; and 3) a 250-word essay on what they believe distinguishes their application from others that may be submitted. Selection is based on those essays, a letter of recommendation, and financial need.

Financial data The stipend is $1,000 per year.

Duration 1 year; may be renewed up to 3 additional years.

Number awarded 1 each year.

Deadline March of each year.

[587]
SOCIETY OF DAUGHTERS OF THE UNITED STATES ARMY SCHOLARSHIPS

Society of Daughters of the United States Army
c/o Janet B. Otto, Scholarship Chair
7717 Rockledge Court
Springfield, VA 21152

Summary To provide financial assistance for college to daughters and granddaughters of active, retired, or deceased career Army warrant and commissioned officers.

Eligibility This program is open to the daughters, adopted daughters, stepdaughters, or granddaughters of career commissioned officers or warrant officers of the U.S. Army (active, regular, or Reserve) who 1) are currently on active duty, 2) retired after 20 years of active duty or were medically retired, or 3) died while on active duty or after retiring from active duty with 20 or more years of service. Applicants must have at least a 3.0 GPA and be studying or planning to study at the undergraduate level. Selection is based on depth of character, leadership, seriousness of purpose, academic achievement, and financial need.

Financial data Scholarships, to a maximum of $1,000, are paid directly to the college or school for tuition, laboratory fees, books, or other expenses.

Duration 1 year; may be renewed up to 4 additional years if the recipient maintains at least a 3.0 GPA.

Additional information Recipients may attend any accredited college, professional, or vocational school. This program includes named scholarships from the following funds: the Colonel Hayden W. Wagner Memorial Fund, the

Eugenia Bradford Roberts Memorial Fund, the Daughters of the U.S. Army Scholarship Fund, the Gladys K. and John K. Simpson Scholarship Fund, and the Margaret M. Prickett Scholarship Fund. Requests for applications must be accompanied by a self-addressed stamped envelope.

Number awarded Varies each year.

Deadline February of each year.

[588]
SOCIETY OF WOMEN ENGINEERS/ADA I. PRESSMAN SCHOLARSHIP

Society of Women Engineers
Attn: Scholarship Selection Committee
120 South LaSalle Street, Suite 1515
Chicago, IL 60603-3572
(312) 596-5223   Toll Free: (877) SWE-INFO
Fax: (312) 644-8557
E-mail: scholarshipapplication@swe.org
Web: societyofwomenengineers.swe.org

Summary To provide financial assistance to women working on an undergraduate or graduate degree in engineering or computer science.

Eligibility This program is open to women who will be sophomores, juniors, seniors, or graduate students at ABET-accredited colleges and universities. Applicants must be U.S. citizens working on a degree in engineering or computer science and have a GPA of 3.0 or higher. Selection is based on merit.

Financial data The stipend is $5,000.

Duration 1 year.

Number awarded 6 each year.

Deadline February of each year.

[589]
SOLAR TURBINES SCHOLARSHIP

Society of Women Engineers
Attn: Scholarship Selection Committee
120 South LaSalle Street, Suite 1515
Chicago, IL 60603-3572
(312) 596-5223   Toll Free: (877) SWE-INFO
Fax: (312) 644-8557
E-mail: scholarshipapplication@swe.org
Web: societyofwomenengineers.swe.org

Summary To provide financial assistance to women who will be entering college as freshmen and are interested in studying computer science or specified fields of engineering.

Eligibility This program is open to women who are entering college as freshmen with a GPA of 3.5 or higher. Applicants must be planning to enroll full time at an ABET-accredited 4-year college or university and major in computer science or aeronautical, computer, electrical, manufacturing, materials, or mechanical engineering. Selection is based on merit.

Financial data The stipend is $1,000. The award includes a travel grant for the recipient to attend the national conference of the Society of Women Engineers.

Duration 1 year.

Number awarded 1 each year.

Deadline May of each year.

[590]
SOPHIA SCHOLAR AND ELISE LIPSCOMB FERGUSON SCHOLARSHIP

Kappa Alpha Theta Foundation
Attn: Scholarships
8740 Founders Road
Indianapolis, IN 46268-1337
(317) 876-1870   Toll Free: (800) KAO-1870
Fax: (317) 876-1925
E-mail: FDNmail@kappaalphatheta.org
Web: www.kappaalphathetafoundation.org

Summary To provide financial assistance to members of Kappa Alpha Theta who are working on an undergraduate or graduate degree in the arts.

Eligibility This program is open to members of Kappa Alpha Theta who are full-time juniors, seniors, or graduate students at a college or university in Canada or the United States. Applicants must be working on a degree in the arts and be able to demonstrate creative ability. Along with their application, they must submit an official transcript, personal essays on assigned topics related to their involvement in Kappa Alpha Theta, and 2 letters of reference. Financial need is not considered in the selection process.

Financial data The stipend is $2,225.

Duration 1 year.

Number awarded 1 each year.

Deadline January of each year.

[591]
SOUTH DAKOTA JOB'S DAUGHTERS SCHOLARSHIPS

International Order of Job's Daughters-Grand Guardian Council of South Dakota
c/o Dawn Erk
3720 Elm Avenue
Rapid City, SD 57701
(605) 721-4459   E-mail: hdskerk@rushmore.com
Web: www.sdjd.org/scholarship.html

Summary To provide financial assistance to members of Job's Daughters in South Dakota who are interested in attending college in any state.

Eligibility This program is open to members of Job's Daughters in South Dakota who are graduating high school seniors or students currently attending college or technical school in any state. Applicants must submit a brief statement on why they chose their planned field of study and a resume that includes extracurricular activities, honors they have received, church and community activities and honors, and involvement in Job's Daughters. Selection is based on academic status and merit and on participation in Job's Daughters and other activities.

Financial data A stipend is awarded (amount not specified).

Duration 1 year.

Number awarded Varies each year; recently, 4 of these scholarships were awarded.

Deadline March of each year.

[592]
SOUTH DAKOTA REDUCED TUITION FOR DEPENDENTS OF PRISONERS OF WAR OR MISSING IN ACTION

South Dakota Board of Regents
Attn: Scholarship Committee
306 East Capitol Avenue, Suite 200
Pierre, SD 57501-2545
(605) 773-3455   Fax: (605) 773-2422
E-mail: info@sdbor.edu
Web: www.sdbor.edu/students/redtuit_deppowmia.htm

Summary To provide free tuition at South Dakota public colleges and universities to spouses and children of prisoners of war (POWs) and persons missing in action (MIAs).

Eligibility This program is open to residents of South Dakota who are the dependents of POWs or of MIAs who are officially listed as residents of the state. Dependents include 1) children born before or during the period of time when the parent was declared MIA or POW; 2) children legally adopted or in legal custody of the parent during the period of time when the parent was declared MIA or POW; and 3) the spouse (if not legally separated) of the individual who is MIA or POW. Applicants must be attending or planning to attend a state-supported school in South Dakota.

Financial data For those who qualify, tuition and mandatory fees are waived.

Duration 8 semesters or 12 quarters of either full- or part-time study.

Number awarded Varies each year.

Deadline Deadline not specified.

[593]
SOUTH EASTERN REGION FELLOWSHIP FOR LIFE-LONG LEARNING

Alpha Kappa Alpha Sorority, Inc.
Attn: Educational Advancement Foundation
5656 South Stony Island Avenue
Chicago, IL 60637
(773) 947-0026   Toll Free: (800) 653-6528
Fax: (773) 947-0277   E-mail: akaeaf@akaeaf.net
Web: www.akaeaf.org/fellowships_endowments.htm

Summary To provide financial assistance to residents of southeastern states (especially African American women) who are engaged in a program of lifelong learning at a college in any state.

Eligibility This program is open to students who are enrolled full time as sophomores or higher in an accredited degree-granting institution and are planning to continue their program of education. Applicants must be residents of Alabama, Mississippi, or Tennessee and enrolled in a program of lifelong learning at a college or university in any state. Along with their application, they must submit 1) a list of honors, awards, and scholarships received; 2) a list of organizations in which they have memberships, especially minority organizations; and 3) a statement of their personal and career goals, including how this scholarship will enhance their ability to attain those goals. The sponsor is a traditionally African American women's sorority.

Financial data A stipend is awarded (amount not specified).

Duration 1 year.

Number awarded 1 or more each even-numbered year.

Deadline April of each even-numbered year.

[594]
SOUTHWEST IDAHO SECTION SWE SCHOLARSHIPS

Society of Women Engineers-Southwest Idaho Section
c/o Scholarship Committee Chair
11548 West Rader Drive
Boise, ID 83713
(208) 396-4458   E-mail: idahoswe@gmail.com
Web: www.swiswe.org/scholarships.html

Summary To provide financial assistance to female high school seniors in Idaho planning to enter an engineering school in any state.

Eligibility This program is open to women graduating from high schools in Idaho who plan to attend an ABET-accredited 4- or 5-year engineering program in any state. Applicants must submit an essay of 500 to 1,000 words on their desire to enter an engineering or engineering-related field, transcripts, SAT/ACT scores, and a letter of recommendation from a high school science or mathematics teacher. Selection is based on that essay, academic accomplishments (especially in science and mathematics), extracurricular accomplishments, and the letter of recommendation. Financial need is not considered.

Financial data Stipends are generally $2,000.

Duration 1 year.

Number awarded Varies each year; recently, 7 of these scholarships were awarded.

Deadline February of each year.

[595]
SPACE COAST SECTION SWE FIRST FRESHMAN SCHOLARSHIP PROGRAM

Society of Women Engineers-Space Coast Section
Attn: Scholarship Committee
P.O. Box 1297
Cape Canaveral, FL 32920
E-mail: spacecoast@swe.org
Web: swe-sc.org/Scholarship

Summary To provide financial assistance to female high school seniors in Florida who have participated in a For Inspiration and Recognition of Science and Technology (FIRST) competition and plan to study engineering at a college in any state.

Eligibility This program is open to women graduating from high schools in Florida who have participated in at least 1 regional FIRST competition. Applicants must be planning to enroll as a freshman and major in an engineering discipline at an ABET-accredited 4-year college or university in any state. Along with their application, they must submit a 1-page statement on why they would like to be an engineer, why they believe they will make a difference as an engineer, and what influenced them to study engineering. Selection is based on merit, but optional financial information may be considered as a determining factor in case of a tie.

Financial data The stipend is $1,000.

Duration 1 year; nonrenewable.

Number awarded 1 or more each year.

Deadline March of each year.

[596]
SPIRIT OF YOUTH SCHOLARSHIP FOR JUNIOR MEMBERS

American Legion Auxiliary
8945 North Meridian Street
Indianapolis, IN 46260
(317) 569-4500   Fax: (317) 569-4502
E-mail: alahq@legion-aux.org
Web: www.legion-aux.org

Summary To provide financial assistance for college to junior members of the American Legion Auxiliary.

Eligibility Applicants for this scholarship must have been junior members of the Auxiliary for at least the past 3 years. They must be seniors at an accredited high school in the United States, have a GPA of 3.0 or higher, and be planning to enroll full time at a college, university, or professional or technical school that awards a certificate upon completion of an accredited course. Along with their application, they must submit a 1,000-word essay on a topic that changes annually; recently, students were asked to write on "The Future-Serving My Community and Our Veterans." Selection is based on that essay (30%), character and leadership (30%), and academic record (40%). Each unit of the Auxiliary may select a candidate for application to the department level, and each department submits a candidate for the national award.

Financial data The stipend is $1,000 per year.

Duration 4 years.

Additional information Applications are available from the president of the candidate's own unit or from the secretary or education chair of the department.

Number awarded 5 each year: 1 in each division of the American Legion Auxiliary.

Deadline Applications must be submitted to the unit president by February of each year.

[597]
SPORTS ILLUSTRATED SCHOLARSHIP

National Association of Black Journalists
Attn: Program Coordinator
8701-A Adelphi Road
Adelphi, MD 20783-1716
(301) 445-7100, ext. 108   Toll Free: (866) 479-NABJ
Fax: (301) 445-7101   E-mail: nabj@nabj.org
Web: www.nabj.org/programs/scholarships/si

Summary To provide financial assistance to female student members of the National Association of Black Journalists (NABJ) who are preparing for a career in sports journalism.

Eligibility This program is open to female African American students who are entering their senior year of college. Applicants must be preparing for a career in sports journalism. They must be NABJ members. Along with their application, they must submit samples of their work, an official college transcript, 2 letters of recommendation, a resume, and a 500- to 800-word essay describing their accomplishments as a student journalist, their career goals, and their financial need.

Financial data The stipend is $5,000. Funds are paid directly to the recipient's college or university.

Duration 1 year; nonrenewable.

Additional information This program is sponsored by Sports Illustrated.

Number awarded 1 each year.

Deadline February of each year.

[598]
STEPHEN BUFTON MEMORIAL EDUCATION FUND OUTRIGHT GRANTS PROGRAM

American Business Women's Association
Attn: Stephen Bufton Memorial Educational Fund
11050 Roe Avenue, Suite 200
Overland Park, KS 66211
Toll Free: (800) 228-0007
Web: www.sbmef.org/Opportunities.cfm

Summary To provide financial assistance to women undergraduate and graduate students in any field who are sponsored by a chapter of the American Business Women's Association (ABWA).

Eligibility This program is open to women who are at least juniors at an accredited college or university. Applicants must be working on an undergraduate or graduate degree and have a GPA of 2.5 or higher. They are not required to be ABWA members, but they must be sponsored by an ABWA chapter that has contributed to the fund in the previous chapter year. U.S. citizenship is required.

Financial data The maximum grant is $1,500. Funds are paid directly to the recipient's institution to be used only for tuition, books, and fees.

Duration 1 year. Grants are not automatically renewed, but recipients may reapply.

Additional information This program was established in 1953. The ABWA does not provide the names and addresses of local chapters; it recommends that applicants check with their local Chamber of Commerce, library, or university to see if any chapter has registered a contact's name and number.

Number awarded Varies each year; since the inception of this program, it has awarded more than $14 million to more than 14,000 students.

Deadline May of each year.

[599]
SUE AND VIRGINIA HESTER SPECIAL EDUCATION SCHOLARSHIP

Alabama Federation of Women's Clubs
Attn: Scholarship Chair
2728 Niazuma Avenue
Birmingham, AL 35205
(205) 323-2392   Fax: (205) 323-8443
Web: www.gfwc-alabama.org/Scholarships.html

Summary To provide financial assistance to women who are residents of Alabama and interested in studying special education at a public university in the state.

Eligibility This program is open to female residents of Alabama who are attending or planning to attend a public university in the state. Applicants must be interested in majoring in special education. Along with their application, they must submit a personal letter on their educational goals, 3 letters of recommendation, and transcripts. Financial need is not considered in the selection process.

Financial data The stipend is $1,000.

Duration 1 year.

Number awarded   1 each year.

Deadline   Deadline not specified.

[600]
SUMMER TRANSPORTATION INTERNSHIP PROGRAM FOR DIVERSE GROUPS

Department of Transportation
Attn: Summer Transportation Internship Program for
    Diverse Groups
HAHR-40, Room E63-433
1200 New Jersey Avenue, S.E.
Washington, DC 20590
(202) 366-2907   E-mail: lafayette.melton@dot.gov
Web: www.fhwa.dot.gov/education/stipdg.htm

Summary   To enable female, minority, and disabled undergraduate, graduate, and law students to gain work experience during the summer at facilities of the U.S. Department of Transportation (DOT).

Eligibility   This program is open to all qualified applicants, but it is designed to provide women, persons with disabilities, and members of diverse social and ethnic groups with summer opportunities in transportation. Applicants must be U.S. citizens currently enrolled in a degree-granting program of study at an accredited institution of higher learning at the undergraduate (community or junior college, university, college, or Tribal College or University) or graduate level. Undergraduates must be entering their junior or senior year; students attending a Tribal or community college must have completed their first year of school; law students must be entering their second or third year of school. Students who will graduate during the spring or summer are not eligible unless they have been accepted for enrollment in graduate school. The program accepts applications from students in all majors who are interested in working on transportation-related topics and issues. Preference is given to students with a GPA of 3.0 or higher. Undergraduates must submit a 1-page essay on their transportation interests and how participation in this program will enhance their educational and career plans and goals. Graduate students must submit a writing sample representing their educational and career plans and goals. Law students must submit a legal writing sample.

Financial data   The stipend is $4,000 for undergraduates or $5,000 for graduate and law students. The program also provides housing and reimbursement of travel expenses from interns' homes to their assignment location.

Duration   10 weeks during the summer.

Additional information   Assignments are at the DOT headquarters in Washington, D.C., a selected modal administration, or selected field offices around the country.

Number awarded   80 to 100 each year.

Deadline   January of each year.

[601]
SURVIVORS' AND DEPENDENTS' EDUCATIONAL ASSISTANCE PROGRAM

Department of Veterans Affairs
Attn: Veterans Benefits Administration
810 Vermont Avenue, N.W.
Washington, DC 20420
(202) 418-4343   Toll Free: (888) GI-BILL1
Web: www.gibill.va.gov/GI_Bill_Info/benefits.htm

Summary   To provide financial assistance for undergraduate or graduate study to spouses and children of deceased and disabled veterans, MIAs, and POWs.

Eligibility   Eligible for this assistance are spouses and children of 1) veterans who died or are permanently and totally disabled as the result of active service in the armed forces; 2) veterans who died from any cause while rated permanently and totally disabled from a service-connected disability; 3) servicemembers listed as missing in action or captured in the line of duty by a hostile force; 4) servicemembers listed as forcibly detained or interned by a foreign government or power; and 5) servicemembers who are hospitalized or receiving outpatient treatment for a service-connected permanent and total disability and are likely to be discharged for that disability. Children must be between 18 and 26 years of age, although extensions may be granted. Spouses and children over 14 years of age with physical or mental disabilities are also eligible.

Financial data   Monthly stipends from this program for study at an academic institution are $925 for full time, $694 for three-quarter time, or $461 for half-time. For farm cooperative work, the monthly stipends are $745 for full-time, $559 for three-quarter time, or $372 for half-time. For an apprenticeship or on-the-job training, the monthly stipend is $674 for the first 6 months, $505 for the second 6 months, $333 for the third 6 months, and $168 for the remainder of the program. For special restorative training by beneficiaries with a physical or mental disability, the monthly stipend for full-time training is $925.

Duration   Up to 45 months (or the equivalent in part-time training). Spouses must complete their training within 10 years of the date they are first found eligible. For spouses of servicemembers who died on active duty, benefits end 20 years from the date of death.

Additional information   Benefits may be used to work on associate, bachelor, or graduate degrees at colleges and universities, including independent study, cooperative training, and study abroad programs. Courses leading to a certificate or diploma from business, technical, or vocational schools may also be taken. Other eligible programs include apprenticeships, on-the-job training programs, farm cooperative courses, correspondence courses (for spouses only), secondary school programs (for recipients who are not high school graduates), tutorial assistance, remedial deficiency and refresher training, or work-study (for recipients who are enrolled at least three-quarter time). Eligible children who are handicapped by a physical or mental disability that prevents pursuit of an educational program may receive special restorative training that includes language retraining, lip reading, auditory training, Braille reading and writing, and similar programs. Eligible spouses and children over 14 years of age who are handicapped by a physical or mental disability that prevents pursuit of an educational program may receive specialized vocational training that includes specialized courses, alone or in combination with other courses, leading to a vocational objective that is suitable for the person and required by reason of physical or mental handicap. Ineligible courses include bartending; audited courses; non-accredited independent study courses; any course given by radio; self-improvement courses, such as reading, speaking, woodworking, basic seamanship, and English as a second language; audited courses; any course that is avocational or recreational in character; courses not leading to an educational, professional, or vocational objective; courses taken and successfully completed previously; courses taken by a federal government employee and paid for under the Government Employees' Training Act; and courses taken while in receipt of benefits for the same program from the Office of Workers' Compensation Programs.

Number awarded Varies each year.

Deadline Applications may be submitted at any time.

[602]
SUSAN EKDALE MEMORIAL SCHOLARSHIP

Association for Women Geoscientists
Attn: AWG Foundation
12000 North Washington Street, Suite 285
Thornton, CO 80241
(303) 412-6219   Fax: (303) 253-9220
E-mail: office@awg.org
Web: www.awg.org/EAS/scholarships.html

Summary To provide financial assistance for a summer field camp to women who have a Utah connection and are majoring in geoscience.

Eligibility This program is open to women majoring in geoscience at a college or university in Utah who must attend a summer field camp as part of their graduation requirements. Women geoscience students from Utah attending college in other states are also eligible. Applicants must submit a 1- to 2-page essay in which they describe their personal and academic highlights, their reasons for applying for the scholarship, and what they, as women, can contribute to the geosciences. Selection is based on merit and need.

Financial data The stipend is $2,000. Funds must be used to help pay field camp expenses.

Duration Summer months.

Additional information This program is sponsored by the Salt Lake Chapter of the Association for Women Geoscientists.

Number awarded 1 each year.

Deadline April of each year.

[603]
SUSAN MISZKOWICZ MEMORIAL SCHOLARSHIP

Society of Women Engineers
Attn: Scholarship Selection Committee
120 South LaSalle Street, Suite 1515
Chicago, IL 60603-3572
(312) 596-5223   Toll Free: (877) SWE-INFO
Fax: (312) 644-8557
E-mail: scholarshipapplication@swe.org
Web: societyofwomenengineers.swe.org

Summary To provide financial assistance to undergraduate women majoring in computer science or engineering.

Eligibility This program is open to women who are entering their sophomore, junior, or senior year at a 4-year ABET-accredited college or university. Applicants must be majoring in computer science or engineering and have a GPA of 3.0 or higher. Selection is based on merit.

Financial data The stipend is $1,500.

Duration 1 year.

Additional information This program was established in 2002 to honor a member of the Society of Women Engineers who was killed in the New York World Trade Center on September 11, 2001.

Number awarded 1 each year.

Deadline February of each year.

[604]
SUSAN STEIN SCHOLARSHIP

American College of Nurse-Midwives
Attn: ACNM Foundation, Inc.
8403 Colesville Road, Suite 1550
Silver Spring, MD 20910-6374
(240) 485-1850   Fax: (240) 485-1818
Web: www.midwife.org/foundation_award.cfm

Summary To provide financial assistance for midwifery education to student members of the American College of Nurse-Midwives (ACNM) who have had a personal experience with breast cancer.

Eligibility This program is open to ACNM members who are currently enrolled in an accredited basic midwife education program and have successfully completed 1 academic or clinical semester/quarter or clinical module. Applicants must have had or currently have a personal experience with breast cancer, either their own or a family member's. Along with their application, they must submit a 300-word essay on the effect of breast cancer on their identity as a midwife. Selection is based primarily on the quality of the application, although leadership potential, financial need, academic achievement, and personal goals may also be considered.

Financial data The stipend is $3,000.

Duration 1 year.

Additional information This program was established in 2010.

Number awarded 1 each year.

Deadline May of each year.

[605]
SUSIE HOLMES MEMORIAL SCHOLARSHIP

International Order of Job's Daughters
c/o Anna Rhoads, Educational Scholarships Committee
  Chair
35 Ridgewood Drive
Troy, MO 63379
(636) 462-6834   E-mail: alrhoad@centurytel.net
Web: www.iojd.org/Scholarships/index.htm

Summary To provide financial assistance for college to members of Job's Daughters.

Eligibility This program is open to high school graduates who are members of Job's Daughters. Applicants must be able to demonstrate dedicated, continuous, and joyful service to Job's Daughters; regular attendance at Supreme and/or Grand Sessions; participation in competitions at Supreme and/or Grand Sessions; friendship and impartiality in their Bethel; good character and integrity; and a GPA of 2.5 or higher.

Financial data The stipend is $1,000.

Duration 1 year.

Number awarded 1 or more each year.

Deadline April of each year.

[606]
SWE PAST PRESIDENTS SCHOLARSHIPS

Society of Women Engineers
Attn: Scholarship Selection Committee
120 South LaSalle Street, Suite 1515
Chicago, IL 60603-3572
(312) 596-5223   Toll Free: (877) SWE-INFO
Fax: (312) 644-8557
E-mail: scholarshipapplication@swe.org
Web: societyofwomenengineers.swe.org

Summary   To provide financial assistance to women working on an undergraduate or graduate degree in engineering or computer science.

Eligibility   This program is open to women who will be sophomores, juniors, seniors, or graduate students at ABET-accredited colleges and universities. Applicants must be U.S. citizens majoring in computer science or engineering and have a GPA of 3.0 or higher. Along with their application, they must submit a 1-page essay on why they want to be an engineer or computer scientist, how they believe they will make a difference as an engineer or computer scientist, and what influenced them to study engineering or computer science. Selection is based on merit.

Financial data   The stipend is $1,500.

Duration   1 year.

Additional information   This program was established in 1999 by an anonymous donor to honor the commitment and accomplishments of past presidents of the Society of Women Engineers (SWE).

Number awarded   2 each year.

Deadline   February of each year.

[607]
SYMANTEC SCHOLARSHIPS

Society of Women Engineers
Attn: Scholarship Selection Committee
120 South LaSalle Street, Suite 1515
Chicago, IL 60603-3572
(312) 596-5223   Toll Free: (877) SWE-INFO
Fax: (312) 644-8557
E-mail: scholarshipapplication@swe.org
Web: societyofwomenengineers.swe.org

Summary   To provide financial assistance to undergraduate women majoring in designated engineering specialties.

Eligibility   This program is open to women who are entering their junior or senior year at a 4-year ABET-accredited college or university. Applicants must be majoring in computer science or computer or electrical engineering. They must have a GPA of 3.0 or higher. Preference is given to members of groups underrepresented in engineering or computer science. Selection is based on merit.

Financial data   The stipend is $5,000.

Duration   1 year.

Additional information   This program is sponsored by Symantec Corporation.

Number awarded   3 each year.

Deadline   February of each year.

[608]
TALBOTS WOMEN'S SCHOLARSHIP FUND

Talbots Charitable Foundation
c/o Scholarship America
Scholarship Management Services
One Scholarship Way
P.O. Box 297
St. Peter, MN 56082
(507) 931-1682   Toll Free: (800) 537-4180
Fax: (507) 931-9168
E-mail: talbotswomen@scholarshipamerica.org
Web: www1.talbots.com

Summary   To provide financial assistance to women returning to college after an absence of at least 10 years.

Eligibility   This program is open to women who earned their high school diploma or GED at least 10 years ago and are now enrolled or planning to enroll full or part time at an accredited 2- or 4-year college, university, or vocational/technical school. Applicants must have at least 2 full-time semesters remaining to complete their undergraduate degree. They must be currently residing in the United States or Canada. Along with their application, they must submit an essay on their plans as they relate to their educational and career objectives and long-term goals. Selection is based on the essay, academic record, leadership and participation in community activities, honors, work experience, an outside appraisal, and financial need.

Financial data   Stipends are either $30,000 or $15,000. Checks are mailed to the recipient's home address and are made payable jointly to the student and the school.

Duration   1 year; nonrenewable.

Additional information   This program was established in 1997. Applications are available at Talbots' stores in the United States. The program is administered by Scholarship Management Services, a division of Scholarship America, One Scholarship Way, P.O. Box 297, St. Peter, MN 56082, (507) 931-1682. Only the first 5,000 eligible applications received are processed.

Number awarded   11 each year: 1 at $30,000 (named the Nancy Talbot Scholarship Award in honor of the firm's founder) and 10 at $15,000.

Deadline   December of each year.

[609]
TARGETED OPPORTUNITY PROGRAM (TOPJOBS)

Wisconsin Office of State Employment Relations
Attn: Division of Affirmative Action Workforce Planning
101 East Wilson Street, Fourth Floor
P.O. Box 7855
Madison, WI 53707-7855
(608) 267-1005   Fax: (608) 267-1020
E-mail: Claire.Dehnert@wisconsin.gov
Web: oser.state.wi.us/category.asp?linkcatid=342

Summary   To provide an opportunity for women, minorities, and persons with disabilities to gain summer work experience with agencies of the state of Wisconsin.

Eligibility   This program is open to women, ethnic/racial minorities (Black or African American, Asian, Native Hawaiian or other Pacific Islander, American Indian or Alaska Native, or Hispanic or Latino), and persons with disabilities. Applicants must be juniors, seniors, or graduate students at an accredited 4-year college or university or second-year students in the second year of a 2-year technical or vocational school program. They must be 1) Wisconsin residents enrolled full time at a school in Wisconsin or any other state, or 2) residents of other states who are enrolled full time at a school in Wisconsin.

Financial data Most internships provide a competitive stipend.

Duration Summer months.

Additional information This program was established in 1974. Relevant fields of study include, but are not limited to, the liberal arts and sciences (e.g., history, mathematics, library science, political science, philosophy, physics, psychology, social services, social work, sociology, women's studies); agriculture and natural resources (e.g., animal and dairy science, biology, botany, chemistry, geography, entomology, environmental studies, horticulture, landscape architecture, microbiology, plant pathology, soil science, urban planning, water resources management, wildlife ecology); business (e.g., accounting, business management, economics, finance, human resources, marketing, public administration, real estate); criminal justice; education; health care (including nursing); engineering; information systems and computers; journalism and communications; and law.

Number awarded Varies each year. Since the program was established, it has placed more than 2,500 students with more than 30 different agencies and universities throughout the state.

Deadline February of each year.

[610]
TEACHING INDIANA'S FUTURE SCHOLARSHIP

Indiana Women's Education Foundation, Inc.
P.O. Box 33
Knightstown, IN 46148-0033
(765) 345-9812   Fax: (765) 345-9812
E-mail: bpwin@msn.com
Web: indianawomensfoundation.org/scholarships.htm

Summary To provide financial assistance to female residents of Indiana who are engaged in student teaching through a college in the state.

Eligibility This program is open to women who are at least 21 years of age and have been residents of Indiana for at least 1 year. Applicants must be doing their student teaching at a school in the state. Along with their application, they must submit a statement (up to 200 words) on their career goals and how their education relates to those goals. Financial need is considered in the selection process.

Financial data A stipend is awarded (amount not specified). Funds are paid directly to the recipient's school.

Duration 1 year; recipients may reapply.

Additional information The Indiana Women's Education Foundation was formerly named the Indiana Business and Professional Women's Foundation.

Number awarded 1 each year.

Deadline March of each year.

[611]
TEEN LATINA WORLD

Dawn Rochelle Models Agency
129 South Tennessee Street
McKinney, TX 75069
(469) 396-5670   E-mail: contact@dawnrochelle.com
Web: www.misslatina.com

Summary To recognize and reward teenage Latinas who compete in a national beauty pageant.

Eligibility This program is open to girls between 13 and 17 years of age who are at least 25% Hispanic. Applicants must be single and they may not have children. They appear in a nationally-televised pageant where selection is based on 3 categories: beauty/evening gown, fashion wear, and photogenic. Judges also interview each participant; the interview score may replace the fashion wear score. Height and weight are not factors, but contestants should be proportionate. Pageant experience and fluency in Spanish are not required.

Financial data Each year, prizes vary. The overall winner receives a $10,000 bond.

Duration The pageant is held annually.

Number awarded 1 overall winner is selected each year.

Deadline April of each year.

[612]
TENNESSEE ACTEENS SCHOLARSHIP

Tennessee Baptist Convention
Attn: WMU Scholarships
5001 Maryland Way
P.O. Box 728
Brentwood, TN 37024-9728
(615) 373-2255   Toll Free: (800) 558-2090, ext. 2038
Fax: (615) 371-2014   E-mail: jferguson@tnbaptist.org
Web: www.tnbaptist.org/page.asp?page=92

Summary To provide financial assistance to members of Baptist churches in Tennessee who have been active in the Acteens program for girls and plan to attend college in any state.

Eligibility This program is open to high school seniors who are members and active participants in mission programs and ministry of a Tennessee Baptist church. Applicants must be able to demonstrate active involvement in Acteens in at least 2 of the following ways: 1) participation in local ministry for at least 2 years; 2) completion of at least 2 levels of MissionsQuest or an approved individual achievement plan; 3) selection as a state or national Acteen advisory panelist or Top Teen; or 4) participation on 2 Acteens Activator Teams. They must have a GPA of 2.6 or higher and be planning to enroll full time at a college or university in any state.

Financial data A stipend is awarded (amount not specified).

Duration 1 year.

Number awarded 1 or more each year.

Deadline January of each year.

[613]
TESA GIRL SCOUT GOLD AWARD SCHOLARSHIP

Texas Elks State Association
c/o Carol Castlebury, Youth Activities Committee
P.O. Box 13538
Austin, TX 78711-3538
E-mail: ccastlebur@aol.com
Web: www.texaselks.org/scholarships.htm

Summary To provide financial assistance to high school seniors in Texas who earned the Girl Scout Gold Award and plan to attend college in the state.

Eligibility This program is open to seniors at high schools in Texas who have earned a Girl Scout Gold Award. Applicants must be planning to attend a college or university in the state. Selection is based on leadership, achievement, recommendations, and financial need.

Financial data The stipend is $2,500. Funds are paid directly to the recipient's school.

Duration 1 year.

Number awarded 1 each year.

Deadline Applications must be submitted to the state chairperson by April of each year.

[614]
TESA SCHOLARSHIP PROGRAM

Texas Elks State Association
c/o Robert R. Weems, Youth Activities Committee
4511 Goodnight Trail
Amarillo, TX 79109-5909
E-mail: Robert.weems@suddenlink.net
Web: www.texaselks.org/scholarships.htm

Summary To provide financial assistance to high school seniors in Texas who are not at the top of their class and plan to attend college in the state (females and males are judged separately).

Eligibility This program is open to seniors at high schools in Texas who are not in the top 5% of their class. Candidates are nominated by their high school counselors; up to 3 boys and 3 girls may be nominated per school. Nominees must be U.S. citizens, residents of Texas, and planning to enroll full time at an accredited junior college, college, or university in the state. The names of these nominees are submitted to the local lodge; each lodge then selects 1 boy and 1 girl and submits their applications to the state scholarship chair. Those students must submit 1) a 300-word statement on their professional goals and how their past, present, and future activities make attainment of those goals probable; 2) a transcript; 3) a 200-word parent statement on the family's financial situation; and 4) SAT and/or ACT scores. Females and males compete separately. Final selection at the state level is based on leadership and extracurricular activities (200 points), character (200 points), scholarship (300 points), and financial need (300 points).

Financial data The stipend is $1,250 per year.

Duration 4 years.

Number awarded 6 each year: 3 boys and 3 girls.

Deadline School nominations must be submitted to the local lodges by March of each year.

[615]
TEXAS CONFERENCE FOR WOMEN SCHOLARSHIPS

Texas Conference for Women
Attn: Scholarship Program
98 San Jacinto Boulevard, Suite 1200
Austin, TX 78701
Toll Free: (866) 375-1785   Fax: (866) 747-2857
E-mail: info@txconferenceforwomen.org
Web: www.txconferenceforwomen.org/scholarships.htm

Summary To provide financial assistance to women in Texas interested in studying specified areas at a college in the state.

Eligibility This program is open to women who are residents of Texas and enrolled or accepted for enrollment at an institution of higher education in the state as a full- or part-time student. Applicants must be majoring or planning to major in the following 6 categories: the arts, business, education, nursing, mathematics and science, or public service. Along with their application, they must submit a 1,200-word autobiographical essay with information on their financial need, personal challenges they have experienced and how they have overcome or plan to overcome them, their plans for the future, and why they deserve this scholarship. Selection is based on that essay, academic record, volunteer community service, demonstrated leadership and participation in school and community activities, honors, work experience, and unusual personal or family circumstances and/or financial need. Top candidates may be asked to participate in a brief telephone interview.

Financial data The stipend is $5,000.

Duration 1 year.

Additional information Recipients are expected to accept their awards at the annual Texas Conference for Women in November.

Number awarded 6 each year: 1 in each category.

Deadline June of each year.

[616]
TEXAS DISTRICT LUTHERAN WOMEN'S MISSIONARY LEAGUE SCHOLARSHIP

Lutheran Women's Missionary League-Texas District
c/o Carolyn Culbertson, Scholarship Committee Chair
1615 Allison Drive
New Braunfels, TX 78130
(830) 606-1477   E-mail: schirm007@satx.rr.com
Web: www.lwmltxdist.org/officers/schol.html

Summary To provide financial assistance to female members of the Lutheran Church-Missouri Synod (LCMS) in Texas who are interested in preparing for a career within the denomination.

Eligibility This program is open to women who are communicant members of a congregation of the Texas District of the LCMS. Applicants must be full-time undergraduate students enrolled or planning to enroll at a recognized institution of higher learning in a course of study leading to full-time professional church work in the LCMS. Selection is based primarily on overall aptitude for professional church work. Financial need is also considered.

Financial data A stipend is awarded (amount not specified).

Duration 1 year.
Additional information This program was established in 1990.
Number awarded 1 or more each year.
Deadline March of each year.

[617]
TEXAS KAPPA DELTA ALUMNAE SCHOLARSHIP

Kappa Delta Sorority
Attn: Foundation Manager
3205 Players Lane
Memphis, TN 38125
(901) 748-1897   Toll Free: (800) 536-1897
Fax: (901) 748-0949 E-mail: kappadelta@kappadelta.org
Web: www.kappadelta.org/scholarships

Summary To provide financial assistance for undergraduate education to members of Kappa Delta Sorority chapters in Texas.

Eligibility This program is open to full-time undergraduate members of Kappa Delta Sorority at chapters in Texas. Applicants must submit a personal statement giving their reasons for applying for this scholarship, an official undergraduate transcript, and 2 letters of recommendation. They must have a GPA of 3.0 or higher. Selection is based on academic excellence; service to the chapter, alumnae association, or national Kappa Delta; service to the campus and community; personal objectives and goals; potential; recommendations; and financial need.

Financial data The stipend is $1,000. Funds may be used only for tuition, fees, and books, not for room and board.
Duration 1 year.
Number awarded 1 each year.
Deadline January of each year.

[618]
TEXAS STATE FIRE FIGHTERS COLLEGE SCHOLARSHIP FUND

Texas State Association of Fire Fighters
Attn: Emergency Relief and College Scholarship Fund
627 Radam Lane
Austin, TX 78745-1121
(512) 326-5050   Fax: (512) 326-5040
Web: www.tsaff.org

Summary To provide financial assistance to children of certified Texas fire fighters who plan to attend college in any state (daughters and sons are judged separately).

Eligibility This program is open to dependents under 24 years of age of current, retired, or deceased certified fire fighters in Texas. Applicants must be first-time students enrolled full time at an accredited college, university, or junior college in any state. Along with their application, they must submit a brief essay about their life and school years. Financial need is considered in the selection process. Males and females compete separately for scholarships.

Financial data The stipend is at least $500 for the first 2 terms or semesters of college (a total of $1,000). Funds are paid directly to the recipient's school.
Duration Freshman year.
Additional information This fund was established in 1997.

Number awarded At least 2 each year: 1 is set aside specifically for a female and 1 for a male. If additional funds are available, the program may award additional scholarships to equal numbers of female and male applicants.
Deadline April of each year.

[619]
TEXAS WAIVERS OF NONRESIDENT TUITION FOR MILITARY SURVIVORS

Texas Higher Education Coordinating Board
Attn: Grants and Special Programs
1200 East Anderson Lane
P.O. Box 12788
Austin, TX 78711-2788
(512) 427-6340   Toll Free: (800) 242-3062
Fax: (512) 427-6420 E-mail: grantinfo@thecb.state.tx.us
Web: www.collegeforalltexans.com

Summary To provide a partial tuition exemption to the surviving spouses and dependent children of deceased military personnel who move to Texas following the servicemember's death.

Eligibility Eligible for these waivers are the surviving spouses and dependent children of members of the U.S. armed forces and commissioned officers of the Public Health Service who died while in service. Applicants must move to Texas within 60 days of the date of the death of the servicemember. They must be attending or planning to attend a public college or university in the state. Children are eligible even if the surviving parent does not accompany them to Texas.

Financial data Although persons eligible under this program are still classified as nonresidents, they are entitled to pay the resident tuition at Texas institutions of higher education on an immediate basis.
Duration 1 year.
Additional information This program became effective in 2003.
Number awarded Varies each year.
Deadline Deadline not specified.

[620]
THADDEUS COLSON AND ISABELLE SAALWAECHTER FITZPATRICK MEMORIAL SCHOLARSHIP

Community Foundation of Louisville
Attn: Community Leadership Officer
Waterfront Plaza, Suite 1110
325 West Main Street
Louisville, KY 40202-4251
(502) 585-4649, ext. 1025   Fax: (502) 587-7484
E-mail: info@cflouisville.org
Web: www.cflouisville.org/page13940.cfm

Summary To provide financial assistance to women from Kentucky studying fields related to the environment at colleges and universities in the state.

Eligibility This program is open to female residents of Kentucky who are entering their sophomore, junior, or senior year at a 4-year public college or university in the state. Applicants must be majoring in an environmentally-related program (e.g., agriculture, biology, horticulture, environmental studies, environmental engineering). They must be enrolled full time with a GPA of 3.0 or higher. Along with their application, they must submit a 200-word essay describing their interest, leadership, volunteer efforts, and work experience in the environmental field; their future plans and goals in the environmental field; and what they hope to accomplish with their college degree. Financial need is also considered in the selection process.

Financial data The stipend ranges up to $5,000. Funds are paid directly to the college or university.

Duration 1 year; nonrenewable.

Number awarded 1 each year.

Deadline March of each year.

[621]
THANKSUSA SCHOLARSHIPS

ThanksUSA
1390 Chain Bridge Road, Suite 260
McLean, VA 22101
Toll Free: (877) THX-USAS
Web: www.thanksusa.org/main/scholarships.html

Summary To provide financial assistance for college to spouses and children of military personnel who served after September 11, 2001.

Eligibility This program is open to spouses of active-duty military personnel and dependent children 24 years of age or younger. The parent or spouse must 1) have served on active duty for at least 180 days since September 11, 2001; 2) have been killed or wounded in action since that date; 3) be a member of the military Reserves activated to full-time duty; or 4) be a member of the National Guard who have been federalized. Applicants must be entering or attending an accredited 2- or 4-year college, university, vocational school, or technical school as a full-time student. They must have a GPA of 2.0 or higher. Selection is based on financial need, academic record, and demonstrated leadership and participation in school and community activities.

Financial data The stipend is $3,000.

Duration 1 year.

Additional information This program was established in 2006. Selection of recipients is made by Scholarship Management Services, a division of Scholarship America.

Number awarded Varies each year; recently, more than 250 of these scholarship were awarded. Since the program was established, it has awarded 2,200 scholarships with a value of nearly $6.5 million.

Deadline May of each year.

[622]
THEODORE AND MARY JANE RICH MEMORIAL SCHOLARSHIPS

Slovak Catholic Sokol
Attn: Membership Memorial Scholarship Fund
205 Madison Street
P.O. Box 899
Passaic, NJ 07055-0899
(973) 777-2605   Toll Free: (800) 886-7656
Fax: (973) 779-8245 E-mail: life@slovakcatholicsokol.org
Web: www.slovakcatholicsokol.org

Summary To provide financial assistance to female and male members (judged separately) of the Slovak Catholic Sokol who are working on a medically-related degree at a college or graduate school in any state.

Eligibility This program is open to members of the Slovak Catholic Sokol who have completed at least 1 semester of college and are currently enrolled full time as an undergraduate or graduate student at an accredited college, university, or professional school in any state. Applicants must have been a member for at least 5 years, have at least $3,000 permanent life insurance coverage, and have at least 1 parent who is a member and is of Slovak ancestry. They must be studying a medical program. Males and females compete for scholarships separately.

Financial data The stipend is $2,500 per year.

Duration 1 year; may be renewed 1 additional year.

Additional information Slovak Catholic Sokol was founded as a fraternal benefit society in 1905. It is licensed to operate in the following states: Connecticut, Illinois, Indiana, Massachusetts, Michigan, New Jersey, New York, Ohio, Pennsylvania, and Wisconsin. This program was established in 2003.

Number awarded 2 each year: 1 for a male and 1 for a female.

Deadline March of each year.

[623]
THOMAS M. HRICIK MEMORIAL SCHOLARSHIP AWARD FOR FEMALES

First Catholic Slovak Union of the United States and
    Canada
Jednota Benevolent Foundation, Inc.
Attn: Scholarship Program
6611 Rockside Road, Suite 300
Independence, OH 44131
(216) 642-9406   Toll Free: (800) JEDNOTA
Fax: (216) 642-4310   E-mail: FCSU@aol.com
Web: www.fcsu.com

Summary To provide financial assistance for college to female high school seniors who are of Slovak descent and the Catholic faith.

Eligibility This program is open to women graduating from high schools in the United States and Canada and planning to attend an approved institution of higher education. Applicants must be of Slovak descent and the Catholic faith. Along with their application, they must submit 1) a transcript of grades that includes ACT or SAT scores; 2) a list of volunteer community activities in which they have participated; 3) a list of awards received for academic excellence and leadership ability; 4) a description of their career objectives; 5) an essay on why they think they should receive this scholarship; and 6) information on their financial need.

Financial data The stipend is $1,000. The winner also receives a $3,000 single premium life insurance policy upon proof of graduation from college.

Duration 1 year; nonrenewable.

Number awarded 1 each year.

Deadline September of each year.

[624]
THORNBERG/HAVENS SCHOLARSHIP
Delta Zeta Sorority
Attn: Foundation Coordinator
202 East Church Street
Oxford, OH 45056
(513) 523-7597   Fax: (513) 523-1921
E-mail: DZFoundation@dzshq.com
Web: www.deltazeta.org

Summary   To provide financial assistance for continued undergraduate or graduate study to members of Delta Zeta Sorority.

Eligibility   This program is open to undergraduate and graduate members of the sorority who have a GPA of 3.0 or higher. Applicants must submit an official transcript, a statement of their career goals, information on their service to the sorority, documentation of campus activities and/or community involvement, a list of academic honors, and an explanation of their financial need.

Financial data   The stipend ranges from $500 to $2,500 for undergraduates or from $1,000 to $15,000 for graduate students, depending on the availability of funds.

Duration   1 year; nonrenewable.

Number awarded   1 each year.

Deadline   February of each year.

[625]
TRAUB-DICKER RAINBOW SCHOLARSHIPS
Stonewall Community Foundation
Attn: Bee's Fund
446 West 33rd Street, Sixth Floor
New York, NY 10001
(212) 367-1155   Fax: (212) 367-1157
E-mail: stonewall@stonewallfoundation.org
Web: stonewallfoundation.org

Summary   To provide financial assistance for college or graduate school to lesbians.

Eligibility   This program is open to lesbian-identified students who are 1) graduating high school seniors planning to attend a recognized college or university; 2) currently-enrolled undergraduates; and 3) graduate students. Applicants must submit 400-word essays on 1) their personal history, including a significant challenge or achievement in terms of community service, academic excellence, or dynamic leadership; 2) a particularly important experience they have had as a lesbian and how it has affected them; and 3) their plans or goals to give back to or focus on the lesbian, gay, bisexual, and transgender (LGBT) community while in school or after graduating. Selection is based on academic excellence, community service, and commitment to impacting LGBT issues. Financial need is not considered.

Financial data   The stipend is $3,000. Funds are paid directly to the recipient's school to help pay for tuition, books, or room and board.

Duration   1 year.

Additional information   This program was established in 2004.

Number awarded   3 each year.

Deadline   April of each year.

[626]
TREWA SCHOLARSHIPS
Texas Rural Electric Women's Association
1122 Colorado Street, 24th Floor
Austin, TX 78701
(512) 454-0311   E-mail: postmaster@trewa.org
Web: www.trewa.org

Summary   To provide financial assistance to members and children of members of the Texas Rural Electric Women's Association (TREWA) who plan to study a field related to energy or electricity at a college in any state.

Eligibility   This program is open to current members of the association and their children. Applicants may be enrolled or planning to enroll full time at an accredited college, university, junior or community college, trade/technical school, or business school in any state to work on a degree, certificate, diploma, or license. Along with their application, they must submit a 250-word essay on their planned field of study and how it relates to energy or electricity, their goals (educational, professional, and personal), their plans for the future, and why they have chosen their particular field of study. Grades received in high school are not the deciding factor in the selection process; leadership qualities, career focus, energy awareness, the essay, general knowledge of the rural electric program, and financial need are considered.

Financial data   The stipend is $1,500. Funds are paid directly to the recipient's institution, half at the beginning of the first semester and half upon verification of completion of the first semester with passing grades.

Duration   1 year; nonrenewable.

Additional information   This scholarship is sponsored by TREWA and administered by Texas Electric Cooperatives, Inc. Membership in TREWA is open to rural electric employees, directors, and co-op members. The organization is run by women, but men are also eligible to join.

Number awarded   15 each year.

Deadline   March of each year.

[627]
TWEET COLEMAN AVIATION SCHOLARSHIP
American Association of University Women-Honolulu
   Branch
Attn: Scholarship Committee
1802 Ke'eaumoku Street
Honolulu, HI 96822
(808) 537-4702   Fax: (808) 537-4702
E-mail: Edu@aauw-honolulu.org
Web: aauw.xodev01.com

Summary   To provide financial assistance to women in Hawaii who are interested in a career in aviation.

Eligibility   This program is open to women who are residents of Hawaii, at least 17 years of age, and attending an accredited college in the state. Applicants must be interested in obtaining a private pilot license. They must be able to pass a First Class FAA medical examination and to speak, read, write, and understand the English language. Along with their application, they must include a 2-page statement on "Why I Want to be a Pilot." Selection is based on the merit of the applicant and a personal interview.

Financial data The stipend ranges up to $3,000. Funds may be used for flight training, ground school training, and aviation study manuals.

Duration 1 year.

Additional information This scholarship was first awarded in 1990.

Number awarded 1 each year.

Deadline May of each year.

[628]
TWISTER SCHOLARSHIP

Women in Technology of Tennessee
c/o Barbara Webb
330 Franklin Road, Suite 135A-538
Brentwood, TN 37027
(615) 202-5840   E-mail: barbara.webb@level3.com
Web: www.wittn.org

Summary To provide financial assistance to female high school seniors in Tennessee who are interested in attending college in any state to prepare for a career in science, technology, engineering, or research.

Eligibility This program (Tennessee Women in Science, Technology, Engineering & Research) is open to women who are graduating from a Tennessee public high school, approved private high school, or home school. Applicants must be interested in attending college in any state to prepare for a career in science, technology, engineering, or research. They must have a GPA of 3.0 or higher. Along with their application, they must submit a 2-page essay on a topic that changes annually but relates to science, technology, or engineering. Financial need is not considered in the selection process.

Financial data Stipends are $2,500 and $1,000.

Duration 1 year.

Additional information This program, established in 2006, is offered in partnership with the Adventure Science Center of Nashville.

Number awarded 2 each year: 1 at $2,500 and 1 at $1,000.

Deadline February of each year.

[629]
UNDERGRADUATE LEADERSHIP SCHOLARSHIP

Women's Transportation Seminar-Greater Dallas/Fort
  Worth Chapter
c/o Amanda Wilson, Scholarship Chair
North Central Texas COG
616 Six Flags Drive
P.O. Box 5888
Arlington, TX 76005-5888
(817) 695-9284   Fax: (817) 640-3028
E-mail: awilson@nctcog.org
Web: www.wtsinternational.org/Chapters.aspx?ID=6888

Summary To provide financial assistance to women from any state who have demonstrated an interest in leadership and are working on an undergraduate degree in a field related to transportation at specified colleges and universities in Oklahoma or Texas.

Eligibility This program is open to women from any state who are enrolled at a college or university in Oklahoma or Texas that has been selected to participate. Applicants must

be working on an undergraduate degree in a transportation-related field, such as transportation engineering, planning, finance, or logistics and have a GPA of 3.0 or higher. They must be preparing for a career in a transportation-related field, especially in a leadership role. Along with their application, they must submit a 500-word statement about their career goals after graduation, why they think they should receive this scholarship, the importance of leadership in a transportation career, and their leadership achievements. Selection is based on transportation involvement and goals, job skills, academic record, and leadership potential; financial need is not considered. Minority women are especially encouraged to apply.

Financial data The stipend is $1,000.

Duration 1 year; nonrenewable.

Additional information The winner is also nominated for scholarships offered by the national organization of the Women's Transportation Seminar (WTS). For a list of the eligible Oklahoma and Texas schools, contact the sponsor.

Number awarded 1 each year.

Deadline November of each year.

[630]
UNITED PARCEL SERVICE SCHOLARSHIP FOR FEMALE STUDENTS

Institute of Industrial Engineers
Attn: Scholarship Coordinator
3577 Parkway Lane, Suite 200
Norcross, GA 30092
(770) 449-0461, ext. 105   Toll Free: (800) 494-0460
Fax: (770) 441-3295   E-mail: bcameron@iienet.org
Web: www.iienet2.org/Details.aspx?id=857

Summary To provide financial assistance to female undergraduates who are studying industrial engineering at a school in the United States, Canada, or Mexico.

Eligibility Eligible to be nominated are female undergraduate students enrolled at any school in the United States or its territories, Canada, or Mexico, provided the school's engineering program is accredited by an agency recognized by the Institute of Industrial Engineers (IIE) and the student is pursuing a full-time course of study in industrial engineering with a GPA of at least 3.4. Nominees must have at least 5 full quarters or 3 full semesters remaining until graduation. Students may not apply directly for these awards; they must be nominated by the head of their industrial engineering department. Nominees must be IIE members. Selection is based on scholastic ability, character, leadership, potential service to the industrial engineering profession, and need for financial assistance.

Financial data The stipend is $4,000.

Duration 1 year.

Additional information Funding for this program is provided by the UPS Foundation.

Number awarded 1 each year.

Deadline Schools must submit nominations by November of each year.

[631]
UNITED STATES STEEL CORPORATION SCHOLARSHIPS

Society of Women Engineers
Attn: Scholarship Selection Committee
120 South LaSalle Street, Suite 1515
Chicago, IL 60603-3572
(312) 596-5223   Toll Free: (877) SWE-INFO
Fax: (312) 644-8557
E-mail: scholarshipapplication@swe.org
Web: societyofwomenengineers.swe.org

Summary To provide financial assistance to members of the Society of Women Engineers (SWE) majoring in computer science or engineering.

Eligibility This program is open to members of the society who are entering their junior year or fourth year of a 5-year program at an ABET-accredited college or university. Applicants must be U.S. citizens who are majoring in computer science or engineering and have a GPA of 3.0 or higher. Selection is based on merit and interest in manufacturing.

Financial data The stipend is $5,000.

Duration 1 year.

Additional information This program is supported by the United States Steel Corporation.

Number awarded 5 each year.

Deadline February of each year.

[632]
U.S. ARMY WOMEN'S FOUNDATION LEGACY SCHOLARSHIPS

U.S. Army Women's Foundation
Attn: Scholarship Committee
P.O. Box 5030
Fort Lee, VA 23801-0030
(804) 734-3078   E-mail: info@awfdn.org
Web: www.awfdn.org/programs/legacyscholarships.shtml

Summary To provide financial assistance for college to women who are serving or have served in the Army and their children.

Eligibility This program is open to 1) women who have served or are serving honorably in the U.S. Army, U.S. Army Reserve, or Army National Guard; and 2) children of women who served honorably in the U.S. Army, U.S. Army Reserve, or Army National Guard. Applicants must be entering their junior or senior year at an accredited college or university and have a GPA of 3.0 or higher. Along with their application, they must submit a 2-page essay on why they should be considered for this scholarship, their future plans as related to their program of study, and information about their community service, activities, and work experience. Selection is based on merit, academic potential, community service, and financial need.

Financial data The stipend is $2,500.

Duration 1 year.

Additional information This program includes scholarships named after Lt. Col. Juanita L. Warman, Sgt. Amy Krueger, and Pvt. Francheska Velez, all of whom lost their lives in the tragedy at Fort Hood, Texas on November 5, 2009.

Number awarded 5 to 10 each year.

Deadline February of each year.

[633]
USBC YOUTH AMBASSADOR OF THE YEAR AWARDS

United States Bowling Congress
Attn: Youth Department
621 Six Flags Drive
Arlington, TX 76011
Toll Free: (800) 514-BOWL, ext. 3168
Fax: (817) 385-8262
E-mail: beoff@ibcyouth.com
Web: www.bowl.com/scholarships

Summary To recognize and reward, with college scholarships, outstanding bowlers (females and males are judged separately).

Eligibility These awards are presented to members of the United States Bowling Congress (USBC) who are 18 years of age or older. Males and females are considered in separate competitions. Selection is based on contributions to the sport of bowling (excluding league or tournament play), academic accomplishment, and community involvement.

Financial data The awards consist of $1,500 college scholarships.

Duration The awards are presented annually.

Additional information The winners may also be selected to serve on the USBC Youth Committee for 3 years. This program was formerly named the USBC Youth Leader of the Year Awards.

Number awarded 2 each year: 1 for a female and 1 for a male.

Deadline Nominations must be submitted by October of each year.

[634]
USO DESERT STORM EDUCATION FUND

USO World Headquarters
Attn: Scholarship Program
Washington Navy Yard, Building 198
901 M Street, S.E.
Washington, DC 20374
(202) 610-5700   Fax: (202) 610-5699
Web: www.desert-storm.com/soldiers/uso.html

Summary To provide financial assistance for academic or vocational education to spouses and children of military personnel who died in the Persian Gulf War.

Eligibility This program is open to the spouses and children of armed service personnel killed, either through accidental causes or in combat, during Operations Desert Shield and Desert Storm. Department of Defense guidelines will be used to determine those service personnel who were taking part in either of these operations at the time of their deaths. This is an entitlement program; neither financial need nor academic achievement are factors in allocating support from the fund. All eligible candidates are contacted directly.

Financial data It is the purpose of the fund to provide as much financial support as possible to all eligible persons. To this end, USO will distribute all of the funds to the eligible persons in equal amounts.

Duration There will be a 1-time distribution of these funds.

Number awarded All eligible survivors will receive funding.

Deadline Deadline not specified.

[635]
USS STARK MEMORIAL SCHOLARSHIP FUND

Navy-Marine Corps Relief Society
Attn: Education Division
875 North Randolph Street, Suite 225
Arlington, VA 22203-1757
(703) 696-4960   Fax: (703) 696-0144
E-mail: education@hq.nmcrs.org
Web: www.nmcrs.org/goldstar.html

Summary To provide financial assistance for college to the spouses and children of deceased or disabled crewmembers of the *USS Stark* (FFG 31).

Eligibility This program is open to the spouses and children of crewmembers of the *USS Stark* (FFG 31) who died as a result of the missile attack on the ship in the Persian Gulf on May 17, 1987. Applicants must be enrolled or planning to enroll full time at a college, university, or vocational/technical school. They must have a GPA of 2.0 or higher and be able to demonstrate financial need. Children must be 23 years of age or younger. Spouses may be eligible if the service member became disabled as a result of the attack.

Financial data Stipends range from $500 to $2,500 per year. Funds are disbursed directly to the financial institution.

Duration 1 year; may be renewed up to 3 additional years.

Number awarded Varies each year.

Deadline February of each year.

[636]
USTA/DWIGHT MOSLEY SCHOLARSHIPS

United States Tennis Association
Attn: USTA Serves
70 West Red Oak Lane
White Plains, NY 10604
(914) 696-7223   E-mail: foundation@usta.com
Web: www.usta.com

Summary To provide financial assistance for college to female and male high school seniors (judged separately) from diverse ethnic backgrounds who have participated in an organized community tennis program.

Eligibility This program is open to high school seniors from diverse ethnic backgrounds who have excelled academically, demonstrated achievements in leadership, and participated extensively in an organized community tennis program. Applicants must be planning to enroll as a full-time undergraduate student at a 4-year college or university. They must have a GPA of 3.0 or higher and be able to demonstrate financial need and sportsmanship. Along with their application, they must submit an essay of 1 to 2 pages about how their participation in a tennis and education program has influenced their life, including examples of special mentors, volunteer service, and future goals. Males and females are considered separately.

Financial data The stipend is $2,500 per year. Funds are paid directly to the recipient's college or university.

Duration 4 years.

Number awarded 2 each year: 1 male and 1 female.

Deadline February of each year.

[637]
VANESSA RUDLOFF SCHOLARSHIP PROGRAM

Texas Women in Law Enforcement
Attn: Scholarship Awards Chair
P.O. Box 542376
Dallas, TX 75354-2376
E-mail: suggestions@twle.net
Web: www.twle.net

Summary To provide financial assistance to members of Texas Women in Law Enforcement (TWLE) and their relatives who are interested in attending college in any state.

Eligibility This program is open to 1) members of TWLE who have been active for the past 2 years, are currently in good standing with their department, are enrolled at an accredited college or university in any state, and submit a 1-page essay stating why they deserve the scholarship; 2) dependents of TWLE members who are entering a college or university in any state; are the spouse, child, brother, sister, niece, nephew, or grandchild of the member; are in the top 25% of their graduating class; have a cumulative high school GPA of 3.0 or higher; submit 2 letters of recommendation; and submit a 500-word essay on an assigned topic that changes annually; and 3) dependents of TWLE members who are already enrolled full time at a college or university in any state, have a college GPA of 3.0 or higher, and submit a 500-word essay on an assigned topic that changes annually. For dependents, the sponsor must have been an active member of TWLE for the past 2 years. Financial need is not considered in the selection process.

Financial data The stipend is $1,000.

Duration 1 year.

Number awarded At least 4 each year.

Deadline March of each year.

[638]
VANGUARD WOMEN IN INFORMATION TECHNOLOGY SCHOLARSHIP PROGRAM

Scholarship America
Attn: Scholarship Management Services
One Scholarship Way
P.O. Box 297
St. Peter, MN 56082
(507) 931-1682   Toll Free: (800) 537-4180
Fax: (507) 931-9168
Web: sms.scholarshipamerica.org

Summary To provide financial assistance to women working on an undergraduate degree in fields related to information technology.

Eligibility This program is open to women who are U.S. citizens or permanent residents. Applicants must be entering their junior or senior year as a full-time student at an accredited 4-year college or university in the United States and have a GPA of 3.0 or higher. They must be working on a degree in computer science, computer engineering, web design, or other field related to information technology. Selection is based on academic record, demonstrated leadership and participation in school and community activities, honors, work experience, a statement of goals and aspirations, unusual personal or family circumstances, recommendations, and a resume; financial need is not considered.

Financial data The stipend ranges up to $10,000.

Duration 1 year; nonrenewable.

Additional information This program, established in 2004, is sponsored by Vanguard Group, Inc.

Number awarded Up to 10 each year.

Deadline November of each year.

[639]
VERIZON SCHOLARSHIPS OF THE SOCIETY OF WOMEN ENGINEERS

Society of Women Engineers
Attn: Scholarship Selection Committee
120 South LaSalle Street, Suite 1515
Chicago, IL 60603-3572
(312) 596-5223   Toll Free: (877) SWE-INFO
Fax: (312) 644-8557
E-mail: scholarshipapplication@swe.org
Web: societyofwomenengineers.swe.org

Summary To provide financial assistance to women working on an undergraduate or graduate degree in designated engineering specialties.

Eligibility This program is open to women who are enrolling as freshmen, sophomores, juniors, seniors, or graduate students at an ABET-accredited 4-year college or university. Applicants must be majoring in computer science or computer, electrical, industrial, or mechanical engineering and have a GPA of 3.0 or higher. Preference is given to students attending specified colleges and universities. Selection is based on merit.

Financial data The stipend is $3,500.

Duration 1 year.

Additional information This program is sponsored by Verizon. For a list of the specified colleges and universities, contact the Society of Women Engineers.

Number awarded 2 each year.

Deadline February of each year for entering freshmen; May of each year for continuing undergraduate and graduate students.

[640]
VERMONT ARMED SERVICES SCHOLARSHIPS

Office of Veterans Affairs
118 State Street
Montpelier, VT 05620-4401
(802) 828-3379   Toll Free: (888) 666-9844 (within VT)
Fax: (802) 828-5932   E-mail: rhonda.boyce@state.vt.us
Web: www.va.state.vt.us

Summary To provide financial assistance for college to the spouses and children of deceased members of the armed services in Vermont.

Eligibility This program is open to the children and spouses of 1) members of the Vermont National Guard who have been killed since 1955 or who since January 1, 2001 have died while on active or inactive duty; 2) members in good standing of the active Reserve forces of the United States who since January 1, 2001 have died while on active or inactive duty and who were Vermont residents at the time of death; and 3) members of the active armed forces of the United States who since January 1, 2001 have died while on active duty and who, at the time of death, were Vermont residents, nonresident members of the Vermont National Guard mobilized to active duty, or nonresident active Reserve force members of a Vermont-based Reserve unit mobilized to active duty. Applicants must be residents of Vermont and attending or planning to attend a Vermont public university, college, or technical institute.

Financial data Full tuition, in excess of any funds the student receives from a federal Pell Grant, is paid at Vermont public institutions.

Duration 1 year; may be renewed until completion of 130 academic credits.

Number awarded Varies each year.

Deadline Deadline not specified.

[641]
VHSL-ALLSTATE ACHIEVEMENT AWARDS

Virginia High School League
1642 State Farm Boulevard
Charlottesville, VA 22911
(434) 977-8475   Fax: (434) 977-5943
E-mail: info@vhsl.org
Web: www.vhsl.org/about_vhsl/scholarships

Summary To provide financial assistance to high school seniors (females and males are judged separately) who have participated in activities of the Virginia High School League (VHSL) and plan to attend college in any state.

Eligibility This program is open to seniors graduating from high schools that are members of the VHSL and planning to attend a college or university in any state. Applicants must have participated in 1 or more VHSL athletic activities (baseball, basketball, cheer, cross country, field hockey, football, golf, gymnastics, soccer, softball, swimming, tennis, indoor and outdoor track, volleyball, wrestling) and/or academic activities (student publications, creative writing, theater, forensics, debate, scholastic bowl). They must have a GPA of 3.0 or higher. Each school may nominate up to 4 students: 1 female athlete, 1 male athlete, 1 academic participant, and 1 courageous achievement candidate. The courageous achievement category is reserved for students who have overcome serious obstacles to make significant contributions to athletic and/or academic activities. The obstacles may include a serious illness, injury, or disability; a challenging social or home situation; or another extraordinary situation where the student has displayed tremendous courage against overwhelming odds. Along with their application, students must submit a 500-word essay describing how extracurricular activities have enhanced their educational experience. Candidates are judged separately in the 3 VHSL groups (A, AA, and AAA). Selection is based on the essay; involvement in other school-sponsored activities; involvement in activities outside of school; and 2 letters of support.

Financial data The stipend is $1,000.

Duration 1 year.

Additional information This program, which began in 1992, is currently supported by the Allstate Foundation. The courageous achievement category, designated the Andrew Mullins Courageous Achievement Award, was added in 2002.

Number awarded 10 each year. For each of the 3 groups (A, AA, and AAA), 1 female athlete, 1 male athlete, and 1 academic participant are selected. In addition, 1 courageous achievement candidate is selected statewide.

Deadline March of each year.

[642]
VIP WOMEN IN TECHNOLOGY SCHOLARSHIPS

Visionary Integration Professionals
80 Iron Point Circle, Suite 100
Folsom, CA 95630
(916) 985-9625   Toll Free: (800) 434-2673
Fax: (916) 985-9632   E-mail: WITS@vipconsulting.com
Web: www.vipconsulting.com

Summary To provide financial assistance to women preparing for a career in information technology.

Eligibility This program is open to women who are enrolled at or accepted into a 2- or 4-year college or university to prepare for a career in information technology or a related field. Applicants must have a cumulative GPA of 3.0 or higher. Along with their application, they must submit a 1,000-word essay in which they define a specific problem that they see in their community related to information technology and recommend a solution that is thoughtful and likely to make an impact on the problem. Selection is based on that essay, academic performance, and participation in community service and/or extracurricular activities.

Financial data The stipend is $2,500.

Duration 1 year.

Number awarded Varies each year; recently, 9 of these scholarships were awarded.

Deadline March of each year.

[643]
VIRGINIA GOLF FOUNDATION SCHOLARSHIP PROGRAM

Virginia State Golf Association
Attn: Virginia Golf Foundation, Inc.
600 Founders Bridge Boulevard
Midlothian, VA 23113
(804) 378-2300, ext. 11   Fax: (804) 378-8216
E-mail: info@vsga.org
Web: www.vsga.org/about/scholarship-program

Summary To provide financial assistance to high school seniors in Virginia who have an interest in golf and plan to attend college in the state (females and males are judged separately).

Eligibility This program is open to high school seniors in Virginia who are interested in golf and wish to attend a college or university in the state. Applicants must submit an essay of 500 words or less on how golf has influenced their life, the role it will play in their future plans, why they are applying for this scholarship, and their career plans following graduation. Selection is based on the essay, interest in golf (excellence and ability are not considered), academic achievement, citizenship, character, and financial need. Applications must be made on behalf of the candidate by a member club of the Virginia State Golf Association (VSGA). Some scholarships are reserved for women, for men, and for students working on graduate degrees in turfgrass management at Virginia Polytechnic Institute and State University.

Financial data Stipends range from $1,000 to $5,000. Funds may be used only for tuition, room, and other approved educational expenses.

Duration The program includes 4-year scholarships and 1-year merit awards.

Additional information This program was established in 1984. Since then, more than 700 students have received more than $1.6 million in scholarships.

Number awarded Varies each year; recently, 36 of these scholarships were awarded: 2 at $5,000 (the Spencer-Wilkinson Award for a woman and the C. Dan Keffer Award for a man), 9 at $3,500 (including the David A. King Merit Award and the Red Speigle Award reserved for a golfer from the Peninsula area), 2 at $3,000 (both designated Spencer-Wilkinson Awards for women), 3 at $2,500, 8 at $1,500, 10 at $1,000, and 2 at $1,500 each for turfgrass management graduate students at Virginia Tech. The 34 golf scholarships included 12 for 4 years and 22 merit awards for 1 year.

Deadline February of each year.

[644]
VIRGINIA M. WAGNER EDUCATIONAL GRANT

Soroptimist International of the Americas-Midwestern
  Region
c/o Alexandra Nicholis
2117 Quayle Drive
Akron, OH 44312-2332
(330) 524-7113   E-mail: soroptimist@simwr.org
Web: simwr.org/id61.html

Summary To provide financial assistance to women working on an undergraduate or graduate degree at a college or university in midwestern states.

Eligibility This program is open to women who reside in Illinois, Indiana, Kentucky, Michigan, Ohio, or Wisconsin and are attending college or graduate school in any state. Applicants must be working on a bachelor's, master's, or doctoral degree in the field of their choice. Awards are first presented at the club level, then in districts, and finally for the entire region. Selection is based on the effort toward education by the applicant and her family, cumulative GPA, extracurricular activities, general impression, and financial need.

Financial data Club level awards vary at the discretion of the club. District finalists receive a $500 award and are then judged at the regional level. The regional winner receives a $3,000 award.

Duration 1 year.

Additional information This program was established in 1972 and given its current name in 2004.

Number awarded 4 district winners are selected each year; 1 of those receives the regional award.

Deadline January of each year.

[645]
VIRGINIA PEACE MACKEY-ALTHOUSE VOICE AWARD

National Federation of Music Clubs
1646 Smith Valley Road
Greenwood, IN 46142
(317) 882-4003   Fax: (317) 882-4019
E-mail: info@nfmc-music.org
Web: www.nfmc-music.org

Summary To recognize and reward outstanding female student singers who are members of the National Federation of Music Clubs (NFMC).

Eligibility This award is presented to female singers between 19 and 26 years of age. Student membership in the federation and U.S. citizenship are required. Candidates for the NFMC Biennial Student Audition Awards competition are automatically considered for this award; no separate application is necessary.

Financial data The prize is $1,750. Funds must be used for continued study.

Duration The competition is held biennially, in odd-numbered years.

Additional information The entry fee is $30.

Number awarded 1 every other year.

Deadline January of odd-numbered years.

[646]
WAI/AIRTRAN AIRWAYS MAINTENANCE SCHOLARSHIP

Women in Aviation, International
Attn: Scholarships
Morningstar Airport
3647 State Route 503 South
West Alexandria, OH 45381-9354
(937) 839-4647   Fax: (937) 839-4645
E-mail: scholarships@wai.org
Web: www.wai.org/education/scholarships.cfm

Summary To provide financial assistance to members of Women in Aviation, International (WAI) who are interested in earning a degree or certificate in a field related to aviation maintenance.

Eligibility This program is open to WAI members who are interested in preparing for a career in aviation maintenance, engineering, or technical management. Applicants must be enrolled or planning to enroll in an aviation maintenance technician program, an avionics training program, or a degree program in aviation maintenance technology. They must have a GPA of 3.0 or higher. Along with their application, they must submit 2 letters of recommendation, a 500-word essay on their aviation history and goals, another essay of 500 to 1,000 words on how this scholarship will benefit their education and chosen career path, a resume, copies of all aviation licenses and medical certificates, and the last 3 pages of their pilot logbook (if applicable). Selection is based personal accomplishments, community involvement, academic standing, and career goals.

Financial data The stipend is $2,500.

Duration Funds must be used within 1 year.

Additional information WAI is a nonprofit professional organization dedicated to encouraging women to consider an aviation career and to providing educational outreach activities and networking resources to women active in the industry. This program was established in 2011 by AirTran Airways.

Number awarded 1 each year.

Deadline November of each year.

[647]
WAI/BOEING COMPANY CAREER ENHANCEMENT SCHOLARSHIP

Women in Aviation, International
Attn: Scholarships
Morningstar Airport
3647 State Route 503 South
West Alexandria, OH 45381-9354
(937) 839-4647   Fax: (937) 839-4645
E-mail: scholarships@wai.org
Web: www.wai.org/education/scholarships.cfm

Summary To provide financial assistance to members of Women in Aviation, International (WAI) who are active in aerospace and need financial support to advance their career.

Eligibility This program is open to WAI members who wish to advance their career in the aerospace industry in the fields of engineering, technology development, or management. Applicants may be 1) full-time or part-time employees working in the aerospace industry or a related field, or 2) students working on an aviation-related degree who are at least sophomores and have a GPA of 2.5 or higher. Along with their application, they must submit a 500-word essay on their aviation history and goals, 2 letters of recommendation, a resume, copies of all aviation licenses and medical certificates, and the last 3 pages of their pilot logbook, if applicable. Selection is based on achievements, attitude toward self and others, commitment to success, dedication to career, financial need, motivation, reliability, responsibility, and teamwork.

Financial data The stipend is $2,500.

Duration 1 year.

Additional information WAI is a nonprofit professional organization dedicated to encouraging women to consider an aviation career and to providing educational outreach activities and networking resources to women active in the industry. This program is sponsored by the Boeing Company.

Number awarded 2 each year.

Deadline November of each year.

[648]
WAIVERS OF NONRESIDENT TUITION FOR DEPENDENTS OF MILITARY PERSONNEL MOVING TO TEXAS

Texas Higher Education Coordinating Board
Attn: Grants and Special Programs
1200 East Anderson Lane
P.O. Box 12788
Austin, TX 78711-2788
(512) 427-6340   Toll Free: (800) 242-3062
Fax: (512) 427-6420   E-mail: grantinfo@thecb.state.tx.us
Web: www.collegeforalltexans.com

Summary To exempt spouses and children of military personnel who move to Texas from the payment of nonresident tuition at public institutions of higher education in the state.

Eligibility Eligible for these waivers are the spouses and dependent children of members of the U.S. armed forces and commissioned officers of the Public Health Service who move to Texas while the servicemember remains assigned to another state. Applicants must be attending or planning to attend a public college or university in the state. They must indicate their intent to become a Texas resident. For dependent children to qualify, the spouse must also move to Texas.

Financial data Although persons eligible under this program are still classified as nonresidents, they are entitled to pay the resident tuition at Texas institutions of higher education on an immediate basis.

Duration 1 year.

Additional information This program became effective in 2003.

Number awarded Varies each year.

Deadline Deadline not specified.

[649]
WAIVERS OF NONRESIDENT TUITION FOR DEPENDENTS OF MILITARY PERSONNEL WHO PREVIOUSLY LIVED IN TEXAS

Texas Higher Education Coordinating Board
Attn: Grants and Special Programs
1200 East Anderson Lane
P.O. Box 12788
Austin, TX 78711-2788
(512) 427-6340   Toll Free: (800) 242-3062
Fax: (512) 427-6420   E-mail: grantinfo@thecb.state.tx.us
Web: www.collegeforalltexans.com

Summary To provide a partial tuition exemption to the spouses and dependent children of military personnel who are Texas residents but are not assigned to duty in the state.

Eligibility Eligible for these waivers are the spouses and dependent children of members of the U.S. armed forces who are not assigned to duty in Texas but have previously resided in the state for at least 6 months. Servicemembers must verify that they remain Texas residents by designating Texas as their place of legal residence for income tax purposes, registering to vote in the state, and doing 1 of the following: owning real property in Texas, registering an automobile in Texas, or executing a will indicating that they are a resident of the state. The spouse or dependent child must be attending or planning to attend a Texas public college or university.

Financial data Although persons eligible under this program are classified as nonresidents, they are entitled to pay the resident tuition at Texas institutions of higher education, regardless of their length of residence in Texas.

Duration 1 year.

Number awarded Varies each year.

Deadline Deadline not specified.

[650]
WALDO AND ALICE AYER MUSIC SCHOLARSHIP

Citizens Bank New Hampshire
Attn: Scholarship Department
875 Elm Street, Fourth Floor
Manchester, NH 03101-2104
(603) 634-7719
E-mail: ayerscholarship@citizensbank.com
Web: www.citizensbank.com/scholarships

Summary To provide financial assistance to New Hampshire residents (particularly women) who are interested in majoring in music or music education at a college in any state.

Eligibility This program is open to New Hampshire residents who are interested in attending college in any state to

become professional musicians or music teachers. Applicants must have a GPA of 2.5 or higher and be able to demonstrate financial need. Preference is given to female applicants.

Financial data A stipend is awarded (amount not specified).

Duration 1 year.

Number awarded 1 or more each year.

Deadline May of each year.

[651]
WALTER REED SMITH SCHOLARSHIP PROGRAM

United Daughters of the Confederacy
Attn: Education Director
328 North Boulevard
Richmond, VA 23220-4057
(804) 355-1636   Fax: (804) 353-1396
E-mail: hqudc@rcn.com
Web: www.hqudc.org/scholarships/scholarships.html

Summary To provide financial assistance to mature women who are lineal descendants of Confederate veterans and plan to major in selected fields in college.

Eligibility Eligible to apply for these scholarships are women over the age of 30 who are lineal descendants of worthy Confederates or collateral descendants and members of the Children of the Confederacy or the United Daughters of the Confederacy. Applicants must intend to study business administration, computer science, home economics, nutrition, or nursing. They must submit certified proof of the Confederate record of 1 ancestor, with the company and regiment in which he served, and must have had at least a 3.0 GPA in high school.

Financial data The amount of this scholarship depends on the availability of funds.

Duration 1 year; may be renewed.

Additional information Members of the same family may not hold scholarships simultaneously, and only 1 application per family will be accepted within any 1 year. All requests for applications must be accompanied by a self-addressed stamped envelope.

Number awarded 1 each year.

Deadline April of each year.

[652]
WANDA MUNN SCHOLARSHIP

Society of Women Engineers-Eastern Washington Section
Attn: Sandy Brower, Scholarship Committee Chair
P.O. Box 364
Richland, WA 99352
(509) 375-3112   E-mail: embrower@aol.com
Web: www.eastwashingtonswe.org/Scholarships/WM.html

Summary To provide financial assistance to nontraditional women engineering students who live in the northwestern United States and plan to attend school in any state.

Eligibility This program is open to female residents of Alaska, Idaho, Montana, Oregon, and Washington who are nontraditional students attempting to reenter the workforce or enhance career growth and potential. Applicants must have completed at least 2 years of full-time study at an ABET-accredited college or university in any state (do not have to be in an engineering curriculum) and be able to enter an undergraduate or graduate engineering program in the following year. Along with their application, they must submit 2 essays of 100 to 300 words on 1) their short-term and long-term career goals and their plan to reach those goals; and 2) a major obstacle they have encountered in their life, how they responded to it, and how they overcame it. Financial need and academic success are considered in the selection process, but greater weight is given to the applicant's motivation, leadership potential, and ability to follow projects through to completion. All other factors being equal, preference is given to residents of eastern Washington.

Financial data The stipend is $1,000.

Duration 1 year.

Number awarded 1 each year.

Deadline February of each year.

[653]
WASHINGTON STATE BUSINESS AND PROFESSIONAL WOMEN'S FOUNDATION MATURE WOMAN EDUCATIONAL SCHOLARSHIP

Washington State Business and Professional Women's
Foundation
Attn: Virginia Murphy, Scholarship Committee Chair
P.O. Box 631
Chelan, WA 98816-0631
(509) 682-4747   E-mail: vamurf@nwi.net
Web: www.bpwwa.org/scholarships.htm

Summary To provide financial assistance to mature women from Washington interested in attending postsecondary school in the state for retraining or continuing education.

Eligibility This program is open to women over 35 years of age who have been residents of Washington for at least 2 years. Applicants must be planning to enroll at a college or university in the state for a program of retraining or continuing education. Along with their application, they must submit a 500-word essay on their specific short-term goals and how the proposed training will help them accomplish those goals and make a difference in their professional career. Financial need is considered in the selection process. U.S. citizenship is required.

Financial data The stipend is $1,000.

Duration 1 year.

Number awarded 1 or more each year.

Deadline March of each year.

[654]
WASHINGTON STATE BUSINESS AND PROFESSIONAL WOMEN'S FOUNDATION SINGLE PARENT SCHOLARSHIP

Washington State Business and Professional Women's
Foundation
Attn: Virginia Murphy, Scholarship Committee Chair
P.O. Box 631
Chelan, WA 98816-0631
(509) 682-4747   E-mail: vamurf@nwi.net
Web: www.bpwwa.org/scholarships.htm

Summary To provide financial assistance to women from Washington who are single parents interested in returning to college to continue their education.

Eligibility This program is open to women of any age who have been residents of Washington for at least 2 years. Applicants must have at least 1 dependent child, under 18 years of age, living at home. They must be interested in returning to school in the state to continue their education beyond the high school level. Along with their application, they must submit a 500-word essay on their specific short-term goals and how the proposed training will help them accomplish those goals and make a difference in their professional career. Financial need is considered in the selection process. U.S. citizenship is required.

Financial data The stipend is $1,000.

Duration 1 year.

Number awarded 1 or more each year.

Deadline March of each year.

[655]
WASHINGTON UNIVERSITY AMGEN SCHOLARS PROGRAM

Washington University
Division of Biology and Biomedical Sciences
Attn: Summer Research Admissions
660 South Euclid Avenue
Campus Box 8226
St. Louis, MO 63110-1093
(314) 362-7963   Toll Free: (800) 852-9074
E-mail: DBBS-summerresearch@wusm.wustl.edu
Web: dbbssummerresearch.wustl.edu/amgen

Summary To provide undergraduate students (particularly women, minorities, and disabled students) with a summer research experience at Washington University in St. Louis in biological and biomedical sciences.

Eligibility This program is open to sophomores, juniors, and non-graduating seniors at 4-year colleges and universities in the United States, Puerto Rico, and U.S. territories. Applicants must be interested in a summer research experience at Washington University in biochemistry, bioengineering, bioinformatics, biology (molecular, cell, and developmental), biopsychology, biotechnology, chemical and biomedical engineering, chemistry, immunology, medical pharmacology, microbiology, molecular genetics, molecular medicine, molecular pharmacology, neurobiology, neuroscience, pathology, physiological psychology, physiological science, statistics, or toxicology. They must have a GPA of 3.2 or higher and an interest in continuing on to a Ph.D. or M.D./Ph.D. (but not M.D.) program. Applications are especially encouraged from residents of rural and inner-city areas and from members of groups traditionally underrepresented in biomedical research (African Americans, Hispanic Americans, Native Americans, Pacific Islanders, women, and people with disabilities). U.S. citizenship or permanent resident status is required.

Financial data Housing, travel to and from St. Louis, meals, and a stipend of $4,000 are provided.

Duration 10 weeks during the summer.

Additional information This program serves as the Washington University component of the Amgen Scholars Program, which operates at 9 other U.S. universities and is funded by the Amgen Foundation.

Number awarded 25 each year.

Deadline January of each year.

[656]
WASHINGTON WOMEN IN NEED EDUCATIONAL GRANTS

Washington Women in Need
700 108th Avenue, N.E., Suite 207
Bellevue, WA 98004
(425) 451-8838   Toll Free: (888) 440-WWIN
Fax: (425) 451-8845   E-mail: wwininfo@wwin.org
Web: www.wwin.org/how-to-apply/programs

Summary To provide financial assistance to low-income women who reside in Washington and are interested in attending college in the state.

Eligibility This program is open to low-income women who are at least 18 years of age and residents of Washington. Applicants must be interested in attending an accredited institution in the state. They must first apply for all available federal and private grants and scholarships. If all available assistance does not fully cover the costs of tuition and books, they may apply for these grants. Any field of study is eligible, at any level of degree or vocational certification through a bachelor's degree, including GED completion and college transfer.

Financial data Stipends range up to $5,000 per year.

Duration 1 year; renewal is possible if the recipient maintains a GPA of 2.5 or higher and remains eligible for in-state tuition at their institution.

Number awarded Varies each year.

Deadline Deadline not specified.

[657]
WATSON MIDWIVES OF COLOR SCHOLARSHIP

American College of Nurse-Midwives
Attn: ACNM Foundation, Inc.
8403 Colesville Road, Suite 1550
Silver Spring, MD 20910-6374
(240) 485-1850   Fax: (240) 485-1818
Web: www.midwife.org/foundation_award.cfm

Summary To provide financial assistance for midwifery education to students of color who belong to the American College of Nurse-Midwives (ACNM).

Eligibility This program is open to ACNM members of color who are currently enrolled in an accredited basic midwife education program and have successfully completed 1 academic or clinical semester/quarter or clinical module. Applicants must submit a 150-word essay on their 5-year midwifery career plans and a 100-word essay on their intended future participation in the local, regional, and/or national activities of the ACNM. Selection is based on leadership potential, financial need, academic history, and potential for future professional contribution to the organization.

Financial data The stipend is $3,000.

Duration 1 year.

Number awarded Varies each year; recently, 3 of these scholarships were awarded.

Deadline March of each year.

[658]
WILLA HAVERSTICK DIAL SCHOLARSHIP

Kappa Alpha Theta Foundation
Attn: Scholarships
8740 Founders Road
Indianapolis, IN 46268-1337
(317) 876-1870   Toll Free: (800) KAO-1870
Fax: (317) 876-1925
E-mail: FDNmail@kappaalphatheta.org
Web: www.kappaalphathetafoundation.org

Summary To provide financial assistance to members of Kappa Alpha Theta who are working on an undergraduate degree in finance or business.

Eligibility This program is open to members of Kappa Alpha Theta who are full-time sophomores or juniors at a college or university in Canada or the United States. Applicants must be working on a degree in finance or business. Along with their application, they must submit an official transcript, personal essays on assigned topics related to their involvement in Kappa Alpha Theta, and 2 letters of reference. Financial need is not considered in the selection process.

Financial data The stipend is $1,000.

Duration 1 year.

Number awarded 1 each year.

Deadline January of each year.

[659]
WILLIAM BRIDGE SCHOLARSHIP

Ninety-Nines, Inc.-Eastern New England Chapter
c/o Olga Mitchell
10 Glory Lane
East Falmouth, MA 02536
E-mail: ene99s@comcast.net
Web: www.womenpilotsene.org/scholarships.html

Summary To provide financial assistance to female residents of New England who are interested in preparing for a career in aviation.

Eligibility This program is open to women who are high school seniors or beyond and reside or study in 1 of the following states: Maine, New Hampshire, Rhode Island, Vermont, Massachusetts, or Connecticut. Applicants must be studying or planning to study in an area of aviation at an accredited college or flight school or with a private instructor. Selection is based on involvement in aviation activities (e.g., flying, aviation employment, model airplane building, science fair projects), recommendations, academic achievement, interest and dedication to a career in aviation, and financial need.

Financial data The stipend is $1,000. Funds may be applied to academic tuition, technical school, or flight training.

Duration 1 year.

Number awarded 1 each year.

Deadline January of each year.

[660]
WILLIAM J. POLISSINO MEMORIAL SCHOLARSHIP

Pennsylvania Masonic Youth Foundation
Attn: Educational Endowment Fund
1244 Bainbridge Road
Elizabethtown, PA 17022-9423
(717) 367-1536   Toll Free: (800) 266-8424 (within PA)
Fax: (717) 367-0616   E-mail: pmyf@pagrandlodge.org
Web: www.pmyf.org/scholar/index.html

Summary   To provide financial assistance to members of Rainbow Girls in Pennsylvania who are attending college in any state.

Eligibility   This program is open to active Pennsylvania Rainbow Girls in good standing. Applicants must have completed at least 1 year in an accredited college, university, or nursing school in any state.

Financial data   The stipend depends on the availability of funds.

Duration   1 year; may be renewed.

Number awarded   1 each year.

Deadline   Requests for applications must be submitted by January of each year. Completed applications are due by the end of February.

[661]
WILLIAM RUCKER GREENWOOD SCHOLARSHIP

Association for Women Geoscientists
Attn: AWG Foundation
12000 North Washington Street, Suite 285
Thornton, CO 80241
(303) 412-6219   Fax: (303) 253-9220
E-mail: office@awg.org
Web: www.awg.org/EAS/scholarships.html

Summary   To provide financial assistance to minority women from any state working on an undergraduate or graduate degree in the geosciences at a college in the Potomac Bay region.

Eligibility   This program is open to minority women who are residents of any state and currently enrolled as full-time undergraduate or graduate geoscience majors at an accredited, degree-granting college or university in Delaware, the District of Columbia, Maryland, Virginia, or West Virginia. Selection is based on the applicant's 1) participation in geoscience or earth science educational activities, and 2) potential for leadership as a future geoscience professional.

Financial data   The stipend is $1,000. The recipient also is granted a 1-year membership in the Association for Women Geoscientists (AWG).

Duration   1 year.

Additional information   This program is sponsored by the AWG Potomac Area Chapter.

Number awarded   1 each year.

Deadline   April of each year.

[662]
WINGS OVER AMERICA SCHOLARSHIPS

Wings Over America Scholarship Foundation
Attn: Scholarship Administrator
4966 Euclid Road, Suite 109
Virginia Beach, VA 23462
(757) 671-3200, ext. 118
E-mail: scholarship@wingsoveramerica.us
Web: www.wingsoveramerica.us

Summary   To provide financial assistance for college to spouses and children of naval aviators.

Eligibility   This program is open to 1) children of a military sponsor who are graduating high school seniors planning to enroll in college full time to work on a bachelor's degree or who are already enrolled in such a program; and 2) spouses of a military sponsor currently enrolled full or part time and working on an associate or bachelor's degree at an accredited college or university. Children must be unmarried and younger than 23 years of age. The military sponsor must have completed at least 8 years of active-duty service in a Naval air forces or subordinate command and be currently on active duty, retired, or deceased. Also eligible are children of members of the U.S. Navy who died while on active duty serving with a Naval air force unit, regardless of the length of service of the deceased parent. Selection is based on academic proficiency, extracurricular activities, community contributions, and life experience and character of the applicant. The highest ranked applicant receives the CAPT Neil Kinnear Scholarship.

Financial data   The CAPT Neil Kinnear Scholarship is $3,000 per year. Other stipend amounts depend on the availability of funds.

Duration   1 year; may be renewed.

Additional information   This program was established in 1987.

Number awarded   Varies each year; recently, 43 of these scholarships were awarded: 20 high school seniors, 16 college students, and 7 spouses. Since the program was established, it has awarded more than $440,000 in scholarships.

Deadline   March of each year.

[663]
WISCONSIN JOB RETRAINING GRANTS

Wisconsin Department of Veterans Affairs
30 West Mifflin Street
P.O. Box 7843
Madison, WI 53707-7843
(608) 266-1311   Toll Free: (800) WIS-VETS
Fax: (608) 267-0403   E-mail: WDVAInfo@dva.state.wi.us
Web: www.dva.state.wi.us/Ben_retraininggrants.asp

Summary   To provide funds to recently unemployed Wisconsin veterans or their spouses and children who need financial assistance while being retrained for employment.

Eligibility   This program is open to current residents of Wisconsin who 1) were residents of the state when they entered or reentered active duty in the U.S. armed forces, or 2) have moved to the state and have been residents for any consecutive 12-month period after entry or reentry into service. Applicants must have served on active duty for at least 2 continuous years or for at least 90 days during specified wartime periods. Unremarried spouses and minor or dependent children of deceased veterans who would have been eligible for the grant if they were living today may also be eligible. The applicant must, within the year prior to the date of application, have become unemployed (involuntarily laid off or discharged, not due to willful misconduct) or underemployed (experienced an involuntary reduction of income). Underemployed applicants must have current annual income from employment that does not exceed federal poverty guidelines. All applicants must be retraining at accredited schools in Wisconsin or in a structured on-the-job program. Course work toward a college degree does not qualify. Training does not have to be full time, but the program must be completed within 2 years and must reasonably be expected to lead to employment.

Financial data   The maximum grant is $3,000 per year; the actual amount varies, depending upon the amount of the applicant's unmet need. In addition to books, fees, and tuition, the funds may be used for living expenses.

Duration   1 year; may be renewed 1 additional year.

Number awarded   Varies each year.

Deadline   Applications may be submitted at any time.

[664]
WISCONSIN LEGION AUXILIARY DEPARTMENT PRESIDENT'S SCHOLARSHIP

American Legion Auxiliary
Department of Wisconsin
Attn: Education Chair
2930 American Legion Drive
P.O. Box 140
Portage, WI 53901-0140
(608) 745-0124   Toll Free: (866) 664-3863
Fax: (608) 745-1947   E-mail: alawi@amlegionauxwi.org
Web: www.amlegionauxwi.org/Scholarships.htm

Summary   To provide financial assistance to Wisconsin residents who are members or children of members of the American Legion Auxiliary and interested in attending college in any state.

Eligibility   This program is open to members and children of members of the American Legion Auxiliary. Applicants must be high school seniors or graduates with a GPA of 3.5 or higher and be able to demonstrate financial need. They must be Wisconsin residents, although they are not required to attend school in the state. Along with their application, they must submit a 300-word essay on "Education—An Investment in the Future."

Financial data   The stipend is $1,000.

Duration   1 year.

Number awarded   3 each year.

Deadline   March of each year.

[665]
WISCONSIN LEGION AUXILIARY MERIT AND MEMORIAL SCHOLARSHIPS

American Legion Auxiliary
Department of Wisconsin
Attn: Education Chair
2930 American Legion Drive
P.O. Box 140
Portage, WI 53901-0140
(608) 745-0124   Toll Free: (866) 664-3863
Fax: (608) 745-1947   E-mail: alawi@amlegionauxwi.org
Web: www.amlegionauxwi.org/Scholarships.htm

Summary   To provide financial assistance to Wisconsin residents who are the wives, widows, and children of veterans or related to members of the American Legion Auxiliary and interested in working on an undergraduate degree at a school in any state.

Eligibility   This program is open to the children, wives, and widows of veterans who are high school seniors or graduates and have a GPA of 3.5 or higher. Grandchildren and great-grandchildren of members of the American Legion Auxiliary are also eligible. Applicants must be residents of Wisconsin and interested in working on an undergraduate degree at a school in any state. Along with their application, they must submit a 300-word essay on "Education-An Investment in the Future." Financial need is considered in the selection process.

Financial data   The stipend is $1,000.

Duration   1 year; nonrenewable.

Additional information   This program includes the following named scholarships: the Harriet Hass Scholarship, the Adalin Macauley Scholarship, the Eleanor Smith Scholarship, the Pearl Behrend Scholarship, the Barbara Kranig Scholarship, and the Jan Pulvermacher-Ryan Scholarship.

Number awarded   7 each year.

Deadline   March of each year.

[666]
WISCONSIN LEGION AUXILIARY PAST PRESIDENTS PARLEY HEALTH CAREER SCHOLARSHIPS

American Legion Auxiliary
Department of Wisconsin
Attn: Education Chair
2930 American Legion Drive
P.O. Box 140
Portage, WI 53901-0140
(608) 745-0124   Toll Free: (866) 664-3863
Fax: (608) 745-1947   E-mail: alawi@amlegionauxwi.org
Web: www.amlegionauxwi.org/Scholarships.htm

Summary   To provide financial assistance for health-related education at a school in any state to the wives, widows, and descendants of veterans in Wisconsin.

Eligibility   This program is open to the children, wives, and widows of veterans who are attending or entering a hospital, university, or technical school in any state to prepare for a health-related career. Grandchildren and great-grandchildren of veterans are eligible if they are members of the American Legion Auxiliary. Applicants must be residents of Wisconsin and have a GPA of 3.5 or higher. Along with their application, they must submit a 300-word essay on "The Importance of

Health Careers Today." Financial need is considered in the selection process.

Financial data The stipend is $1,200.

Duration 1 year; nonrenewable.

Number awarded 2 each year.

Deadline March of each year.

[667]
WISCONSIN LEGION AUXILIARY PAST PRESIDENTS PARLEY REGISTERED NURSE SCHOLARSHIPS

American Legion Auxiliary
Department of Wisconsin
Attn: Education Chair
2930 American Legion Drive
P.O. Box 140
Portage, WI 53901-0140
(608) 745-0124   Toll Free: (866) 664-3863
Fax: (608) 745-1947   E-mail: alawi@amlegionauxwi.org
Web: www.amlegionauxwi.org/Scholarships.htm

Summary To provide financial assistance to the wives, widows, and children of Wisconsin veterans who are interested in studying nursing at a school in any state.

Eligibility This program is open to the wives, widows, and children of Wisconsin veterans who are enrolled or have been accepted in an accredited school of nursing in any state to prepare for a career as a registered nurse. Grandchildren and great-grandchildren of veterans are also eligible if they are American Legion Auxiliary members. Applicants must be Wisconsin residents and have a GPA of 3.5 or higher. Along with their application, they must submit a 300-word essay on "The Need for Trained Nurses Today." Financial need is considered in the selection process.

Financial data The stipend is $1,200.

Duration 1 year.

Number awarded 3 each year.

Deadline March of each year.

[668]
WISCONSIN PUBLIC SERVICE FOUNDATION BUSINESS AND TECHNOLOGY SCHOLARSHIPS

Wisconsin Public Service Corporation
Attn: Wisconsin Public Service Foundation
c/o Scholarship Assessment Service
P.O. Box 997
Appleton, WI 54912-0997
(920) 832-8322
Web: www.wisconsinpublicservice.com

Summary To provide financial assistance to women and minority upper-division students who are majoring in business or engineering at universities in selected states.

Eligibility This program is open to women and African American, Native American, Asian American, and Hispanic students from any state who are enrolled full time as a junior or senior with a GPA of 2.8 or higher. Applicants must be attending a college or university in Illinois, Indiana, Iowa, Michigan, Minnesota, or Wisconsin. They must be majoring in business or engineering (chemical, civil, computer, electrical, environmental, industrial, or mechanical). Along with their application, they must submit 250-word essays on 1) their

educational goals and why they have chosen their major; and 2) how they have demonstrated their leadership skills.

Financial data The stipend is $1,500 per year.

Duration 1 year; may be renewed if the recipient remains in good academic standing.

Number awarded Varies each year; recently, 15 of these scholarships were awarded.

Deadline February of each year.

[669]
WISCONSIN TOWNS ASSOCIATION SCHOLARSHIPS

Wisconsin Towns Association
Attn: Scholarship Program
W7686 County Road MMM
Shawano, WI 54166-6086
(715) 526-3157   Fax: (715) 524-3917
E-mail: wtowns@frontiernet.net
Web: www.wisctowns.com/home/scholarship-program

Summary To provide financial assistance to high school seniors in Wisconsin who submit outstanding essays on town government and plan to attend college in the state (females and males are judged separately).

Eligibility This program is open to seniors graduating from high schools in Wisconsin who plan to attend a college, university, or vocational/technical institute in the state. Applicants must submit an essay of 500 to 1,000 words on a topic that changes annually but relates to local government in Wisconsin; recently, students were asked to write on "How can towns and villages best protect their infrastructure and still provide other needed services such as fire and emergency services in tough economic times?" Selection is based primarily on the essay's originality and subject matter in relationship to the topic; financial need is not considered. Boys and girls are judged separately.

Financial data The stipend is $1,000.

Duration 1 year.

Additional information This program is supported by Rural Mutual Insurance Company, 1241 John Q. Hammons Drive, Suite 200, P.O. Box 5555, Madison, WI 53705-0555, and by Scott Construction, Inc., P.O. Box 340, Lake Delton, WI 53940.

Number awarded 5 each year: 2 to boys, 2 to girls, and 1 to a boy or girl who has the next highest ranking.

Deadline May of each year.

[670]
WISCONSIN WOMEN IN GOVERNMENT UNDERGRADUATE SCHOLARSHIPS

Wisconsin Women in Government, Inc.
Attn: Scholarship Committee
P.O. Box 2543
Madison, WI 53701
(608) 848-2321
E-mail: info@wiscwomeningovernment.org
Web: www.wiscwomeningovernment.org/scholarships.cfm

Summary To provide financial assistance to women in Wisconsin interested in attending a college or university in the state to prepare for a career in public service.

Eligibility This program is open to women in Wisconsin who are enrolled full or part time at an institution that is a member of the University of Wisconsin system, the Wisconsin Technical College System, or the Wisconsin Association of Independent Colleges and Universities. Applicants must have a grade average of "C" or higher and be able to demonstrate financial need. They must possess leadership potential, initiative, and excellent communication skills and have an interest in public service, government, and the political process. Juniors and seniors must have declared a major. Selection is based on leadership, demonstrated ability to handle responsibility, initiative, communication skills, academic achievement, community involvement, and commitment to public service.

Financial data   The stipend is $3,000 per year. Funds may be used for tuition, school supplies, child care, or to reduce loan burden.

Duration   1 year; may be renewed.

Number awarded   6 each year.

Deadline   April of each year.

[671]
WOKSAPE OYATE: "WISDOM OF THE PEOPLE" KEEPERS OF THE NEXT GENERATION AWARD

American Indian College Fund
Attn: Scholarship Department
8333 Greenwood Boulevard
Denver, CO 80221
(303) 426-8900   Toll Free: (800) 776-FUND
Fax: (303) 426-1200
E-mail: scholarships@collegefund.org
Web: www.collegefund.org/scholarships/schol_tcu.html

Summary   To provide financial assistance to Native Americans who are single parents and attending or planning to attend a Tribal College or University (TCU).

Eligibility   This program is open to American Indians or Alaska Natives who are single parents and enrolled or planning to enroll full time at an eligible TCU. Applicants must have a GPA of 3.5 or higher. Applications are available only online and include required essays on specified topics. Selection is based on exceptional academic achievement.

Financial data   The stipend is $8,000.

Duration   1 year.

Additional information   This program was established in 2006 with an endowment grant from the Lilly Foundation.

Number awarded   1 each year.

Deadline   May of each year.

[672]
WOMEN CHEFS & RESTAURATEURS SCHOLARSHIP PROGRAM

Women Chefs & Restaurateurs
Attn: Scholarship Program Coordinator
P.O. Box 1875
Madison, AL 35758
(256) 975-1346   Toll Free: (877) 927-7787
E-mail: Admin@womenchefs.org
Web: www.womenchefs.org

Summary   To provide financial assistance to members of Women Chefs & Restaurateurs (WCR) who are interested in preparing for a culinary or related career.

Eligibility   This program is open to women who are members of WCR, interested in attending a culinary or related

school, and at least 18 years of age (21 for the wine scholarships). Recently, support was offered for the bachelor of science degree in culinary arts, culinary nutrition, or baking and pastry arts at Johnson & Wales University (Charlotte, North Carolina; Denver, Colorado; North Miami, Florida; and Providence, Rhode Island); the mastering wine program and the ProChef Certification program at the Culinary Institute of America at Greystone (St. Helena, California) and at Hyde Park, New York; the pastry arts career evening program and the culinary arts career evening program at the French Culinary Institute (New York, New York); the Le Cordon Bleu culinary management program at Le Cordon Bleu (Secaucus, New Jersey); and the pastry and baking diploma program and the culinary management diploma program at the Institute of Culinary Education (New York, New York). Applicants must submit a 1-page essay about their food service career, their culinary interests, what inspires them professionally, and how the scholarship will contribute to their career.

Financial data   In general, scholarships provide payment of full or partial tuition, or stipends of $5,000 or $7,500 per year.

Duration   Program lengths vary; scholarships must be used during the calendar year in which they are awarded.

Additional information   Students may apply for only 1 program on a single application; the fee is $25 for the first application and (if they wish to apply for more than 1 program) $15 for each additional application.

Number awarded   Varies each year; recently, 18 of these scholarships were awarded.

Deadline   April of each year.

[673]
WOMEN CHEMISTS COMMITTEE/ELI LILLY TRAVEL AWARDS

American Chemical Society
Attn: Department of Diversity Programs
1155 16th Street, N.W.
Washington, DC 20036
(202) 872-6334   Toll Free: (800) 227-5558, ext. 6334
Fax: (202) 776-8003   E-mail: diversity@acs.org
Web: womenchemists.sites.acs.org/attracting.htm

Summary   To provide funding to women chemists or chemistry students who are interested in traveling to scientific meetings.

Eligibility   This program is open to undergraduate, graduate, and postdoctoral women chemists who wish to travel to scientific meetings to present the results of their research. Only U.S. citizens and permanent residents are eligible. Preference is given to those who have not made a previous presentation at a national or major meeting. Women who have received a prior award under this program are ineligible.

Financial data   Awards apply to registration, travel, and accommodations only.

Additional information   Funding for this program is provided by Eli Lilly and Company. Grants are restricted to travel within the United States.

Number awarded   Varies each year.

Deadline   September of each year for meetings between January and June; February of each year for meetings between July and December.

[674]
WOMEN ENGINEERS COMMITTEE SCHOLARSHIP

Society of Automotive Engineers
Attn: Scholarship Administrator
400 Commonwealth Drive
Warrendale, PA 15096-0001
(724) 776-4970   Fax: (724) 776-3049
E-mail: scholarships@sae.org
Web: students.sae.org/awdscholar/scholarships/wec

Summary To provide financial support to female graduating high school seniors interested in studying engineering in college.

Eligibility This program is open to female U.S. citizens who intend to earn an ABET-accredited degree in engineering. Applicants must be high school seniors with a GPA of 3.0 or higher. Selection is based on high school transcripts; SAT or ACT scores; school-related extracurricular activities; non-school related activities; academic honors, civic honors, and awards; and a 250-word essay on their goals, plans, experiences, and interests in mobility engineering. Financial need is not considered.

Financial data The stipend is $2,000.

Duration 1 year; nonrenewable.

Additional information Funds for this scholarship are provided by Mercedes-Benz USA.

Number awarded 1 each year.

Deadline January of each year.

[675]
WOMEN IN AVIATION, INTERNATIONAL ACHIEVEMENT AWARDS

Women in Aviation, International
Attn: Scholarships
Morningstar Airport
3647 State Route 503 South
West Alexandria, OH 45381-9354
(937) 839-4647   Fax: (937) 839-4645
E-mail: scholarships@wai.org
Web: www.wai.org/education/scholarships.cfm

Summary To provide financial assistance to members of Women in Aviation, International (WAI) who are working on a college degree or other training in the aviation field.

Eligibility This program is open to WAI members who are 1) full-time college or university students working on an aviation or aviation-related degree; or 2) non-college students preparing for an aviation or aviation-related career. Applicants must submit 2 letters of recommendation, a 500-word essay on their aviation history and goals, a resume, copies of all aviation licenses and medical certificates, and the last 3 pages of their pilot logbook (if applicable). Selection is based on achievements, attitude toward self and others, commitment to success, dedication to career, financial need, motivation, reliability, responsibility, and teamwork.

Financial data The stipend is $1,000.

Duration 1 year.

Additional information WAI is a nonprofit professional organization dedicated to encouraging women to consider an aviation career and to providing educational outreach activities and networking resources to women active in the industry.

Number awarded 2 each year: 1 college scholarship and 1 non-college scholarship.

Deadline November of each year.

[676]
WOMEN IN FEDERAL LAW ENFORCEMENT MEMBERS-ONLY SCHOLARSHIP

Women in Federal Law Enforcement
Attn: Scholarship Coordinator
2200 Wilson Boulevard, Suite 102
PMB 204
Arlington, VA 22201-3324
(703) 548-9211   Toll Free: (866) 399-4353
Fax: (410) 451-7373   E-mail: WIFLE@comcast.net
Web: www.wifle.com/scholarshipprogram.htm

Summary To provide financial assistance for college or graduate school to women who are interested in preparing for a career in law enforcement and are members of Women in Federal Law Enforcement (WIFLE) or sponsored by a member.

Eligibility This program is open to women who are members of WIFLE or sponsored by a member and have completed at least 1 academic year of full-time study at an accredited 4-year college or university (or at a community college with the intention of transferring to a 4-year school). Applicants must be majoring in criminal justice or a related field (e.g., social sciences, public administration, computer science, finance, linguistic arts, chemistry, physics). They must have a GPA of 3.0 or higher. Students in graduate and postgraduate programs are also eligible, but those working on an associate degree are not. Along with their application, they must submit a letter demonstrating their financial need and describing their career objectives. U.S. citizenship is required.

Financial data The stipend is $1,500.

Duration 1 year; may be renewed automatically for 1 additional year.

Number awarded 1 each year.

Deadline April of each year.

[677]
WOMEN IN FEDERAL LAW ENFORCEMENT SCHOLARSHIP

Women in Federal Law Enforcement
Attn: Scholarship Coordinator
2200 Wilson Boulevard, Suite 102
PMB 204
Arlington, VA 22201-3324
(703) 548-9211   Toll Free: (866) 399-4353
Fax: (410) 451-7373   E-mail: WIFLE@comcast.net
Web: www.wifle.com/scholarshipprogram.htm

Summary To provide financial assistance for college or graduate school to women interested in preparing for a career in law enforcement.

Eligibility This program is open to women who have completed at least 1 academic year of full-time study at an accredited 4-year college or university (or at a community college with the intention of transferring to a 4-year school). Applicants must be majoring in criminal justice or a related field (e.g., social sciences, public administration, computer science, finance, linguistic arts, chemistry, physics). They must have a GPA of 3.0 or higher. Students in graduate and postgraduate programs are also eligible, but those working on an associate degree are not. Along with their application, they must submit a 500-word essay describing a community project in which they have been involved and the results or impact to the community. Selection is based on academic potential, achievement, and commitment to serving communities in the field of law enforcement. U.S. citizenship is required.

Financial data   The stipend is $2,500.

Duration   1 year; may be renewed.

Number awarded   Several each year.

Deadline   April of each year.

[678]
WOMEN IN FILM/DALLAS COLLEGE/ UNIVERSITY STUDENT TUITION SCHOLARSHIP

Women in Film/Dallas
Attn: Scholarships and Grants
15110 Dallas Parkway, Suite 440
Dallas, TX 75248
(214) 379-1171   Toll Free: (800) 724-0767
Fax: (214) 379-1172   E-mail: education@wifdallas.org
Web: www.wifdallas.org/Default.aspx?pageId=950618

Summary   To provide financial assistance to women from any state who are studying film and video at colleges and universities in Texas.

Eligibility   This program is open to women who are residents of any state majoring or with a primary field of study in film or video at an accredited college or university in the north Texas area. Applicants must have consistently maintained a GPA of 3.0 or higher. Along with their application, they must submit a 3-page essay on what inspired them to study film or video, 2 letters of recommendation, a letter from the college or university verifying their enrollment, and a short sample of their work. Financial need is not considered in the selection process.

Financial data   The stipend is $2,500.

Duration   1 year.

Number awarded   1 each year.

Deadline   September of each year.

[679]
WOMEN IN NEED SCHOLARSHIP

Educational Foundation for Women in Accounting
Attn: Foundation Administrator
136 South Keowee Street
Dayton, OH 45402
(937) 424-3391   Fax: (937) 222-5749
E-mail: info@efwa.org
Web: www.efwa.org/scholarships_women_in_need.php

Summary   To provide financial support to women who are the sole source of support for themselves and their families and are in the junior year of an accounting degree program.

Eligibility   This program is open to women who, either through divorce or death of a spouse, have become the sole source of support for themselves and their families. Women who are single parents as a result of other circumstances are also considered. Applicants must be working on a degree in accounting as incoming, current, or reentry juniors. Selection is based on aptitude for accounting and business, commitment to the goal of working on a degree in accounting (including evidence of continued commitment after receiving this

award), clear evidence that the candidate has established goals and a plan for achieving those goals (both personal and professional), and financial need. U.S. citizenship is required.

Financial data   The stipend is $2,000 per year.

Duration   1 year; may be renewed 1 additional year if the recipient completes at least 12 hours each semester.

Additional information   This program was established in 2000.

Number awarded   1 or more each year.

Deadline   April of each year.

[680]
WOMEN IN SCIENCE SCHOLARSHIP

Zonta Club of Milwaukee
Attn: Scholarship Team
P.O. Box 1494
Milwaukee, WI 53201
E-mail: zcscholarship@zontamilwaukee.org
Web: www.zontamilwaukee.org/OurScholarships.htm

Summary   To provide financial assistance to women, especially residents of Wisconsin, who are upper-division students working on a degree in a field of science, technology, engineering or mathematics (STEM) at a college in any state.

Eligibility   This program is open to women who are entering the third or fourth year of an undergraduate degree program in a STEM-related field at a college, university, or institute in any state. Preference is given to residents of Wisconsin. Applicants must submit a 300-word essay that describes their academic and professional goals, the relevance of their program of study to STEM, and how the scholarship will assist them in reaching their goals. Financial need is not considered in the selection process.

Financial data   The stipend is $1,000.

Duration   1 year.

Additional information   This program was established in 2005.

Number awarded   1 each year.

Deadline   May of each year.

[681]
WOMEN IN TRANSITION ACCOUNTING SCHOLARSHIP

Educational Foundation for Women in Accounting
Attn: Foundation Administrator
136 South Keowee Street
Dayton, OH 45402
(937) 424-3391   Fax: (937) 222-5749
E-mail: info@efwa.org
Web: www.efwa.org/scholarships_women_in_transition.php

Summary   To provide financial support to women who have become the sole support of their family and wish to begin work on an undergraduate accounting degree.

Eligibility   This program is open to women who, either through divorce or death of a spouse, have become the sole source of support for themselves and their family. Women who are single parents as a result of other circumstances are also considered. Applicants should be incoming or current freshmen, or they may be returning to school with sufficient credits to qualify for freshman status. Selection is based on aptitude for accounting, commitment to the goal of working on a degree in accounting (including evidence of continued commitment after receiving this award), clear evidence that the candidate has established goals and a plan for achieving those goals (both personal and professional), and financial need. U.S. citizenship is required.

Financial data The stipend is $4,000 per year.

Duration 1 year; may be renewed 3 additional years if the recipient completes at least 12 hours each semester and maintains a GPA of 3.0 or higher.

Additional information This program, established in 1990, was formerly called the Displaced Homemaker's Scholarship.

Number awarded 1 each year.

Deadline April of each year.

[682]
WOMEN MILITARY AVIATORS DREAM OF FLIGHT SCHOLARSHIP

Women in Aviation, International
Attn: Scholarships
Morningstar Airport
3647 State Route 503 South
West Alexandria, OH 45381-9354
(937) 839-4647   Fax: (937) 839-4645
E-mail: scholarships@wai.org
Web: www.wai.org/education/scholarships.cfm

Summary To provide financial assistance to members of Women in Aviation, International (WAI) who are interested in flight training or academic study.

Eligibility This program is open to WAI members who are students in high school, an accredited flight program, or an accredited college or university. Applicants must submit 2 letters of recommendation, a 500-word essay on their aviation history and goals, a resume, and copies of all aviation licenses and medical certificates, and the last 3 pages of their pilot logbook (if applicable). Selection is based on the applicant's ambition to further women in aviation, demonstrated persistence and determination, financial need, ability to complete training, and ability to bring honor to the women of Women Military Aviators, Inc. (WMA).

Financial data The stipend is $2,500.

Duration Recipients must be able to complete training within 1 year.

Additional information WAI is a nonprofit professional organization dedicated to encouraging women to consider an aviation career and to providing educational outreach activities and networking resources to women active in the industry. WMA established this program in 2005 to honor the women aviators who are serving or have served in Iraq and Afghanistan.

Number awarded 1 each year.

Deadline November of each year.

[683]
WOMEN OF ALPFA DELOITTE STUDENT ESSAY COMPETITION

Association of Latino Professionals in Finance and
   Accounting
Attn: Student Essay Contest
801 South Grand Avenue, Suite 650
Los Angeles, CA 90017
(213) 243-0004   Fax: (213) 243-0006
Web: alpfa.org

Summary To recognize and reward, with scholarships for further study, female members of the Association of Latino Professionals in Finance and Accounting (ALPFA) who submit outstanding essays on topics related to business.

Eligibility This competition is open to women who are members of ALPFA and working full time on an undergraduate or master's degree in accounting, business, finance, or a related field at a college or university in the United States or Puerto Rico. Applicants must have a GPA of 3.0 or higher. They must submit an essay, approximately 800 words in length, in response to an assigned problem related to professional development in business-related fields. Their essay should include descriptions and explanations of their ability to demonstrate leadership, strategize and problem solve effectively, overcome team doubt, and show strength derived from their culture. U.S. citizenship or permanent resident status is required.

Financial data The award is a $1,250 scholarship. The winner also receives complimentary registration, airfare, and accommodations for the ALPFA annual convention.

Duration The competition is held annually.

Additional information This competition is sponsored by Deloitte & Touche LLP.

Number awarded 1 each year.

Deadline May of each year.

[684]
WOMEN OF THE ELCA SCHOLARSHIP PROGRAM

Women of the Evangelical Lutheran Church in America
Attn: Scholarships
8765 West Higgins Road
Chicago, IL 60631-4101
(773) 380-2736   Toll Free: (800) 638-3522, ext. 2736
Fax: (773) 380-2419   E-mail: Women.elca@elca.org
Web: www.elca.org

Summary To provide financial assistance to lay women who are members of Evangelical Lutheran Church of America (ELCA) congregations and who wish to take classes on the undergraduate, graduate, professional, or vocational school level.

Eligibility This program is open to ELCA lay women who are at least 21 years of age and have experienced an interruption of at least 2 years in their education since high school. Applicants must have been admitted to an educational institution to prepare for a career in other than the ordained ministry. They may be working on an undergraduate, graduate, professional, or vocational school degree. U.S. citizenship is required.

Financial data The maximum stipend is $1,000.

Duration Up to 2 years.

Additional information These scholarships are supported by several endowment funds: the Cronk Memorial Fund, the First Triennial Board Scholarship Fund, the General Scholarship Fund, the Mehring Fund, the Paepke Scholarship Fund, the Piero/Wade/Wade Fund, and the Edwin/Edna Robeck Scholarship.

Number awarded Varies each year; recently, 15 of these scholarships were awarded.

Deadline February of each year.

[685]
WOMEN WHO MADE A DIFFERENCE SCHOLARSHIPS

Arizona Business and Professional Women's Foundation
Attn: Administrator
P.O. Box 32596
Phoenix, AZ 85064
Web: www.arizonabpwfoundation.com/scholarships.html

Summary To provide financial assistance to women in Arizona who are attending or interested in attending a community college or university in the state.

Eligibility This program is open to women, at least 25 years of age, who are attending a community college or university in Arizona. Applicants must fall into 1 of the following categories: women who have been out of the workforce and wish to upgrade their skills; women with no previous experience in the workforce who are seeking a marketable skill, and women who are currently employed who are interested in career advancement or change. Along with their application, they must submit 2 letters of recommendation, a statement of financial need (latest income tax return must be provided), a career goal statement, and their most recent transcript (when available). Preference is given to women who have been members of Arizona Business and Professional Women for 2 or more years.

Financial data The stipend is $1,000.

Duration 1 year.

Additional information This program was established in 1992 with proceeds from the book, *Women Who Made a Difference.* It was originally limited to BPW members only, but is now open to all students.

Number awarded 1 or more each year.

Deadline February of each year.

[686]
WOMEN'S ART STUDIO INTERNSHIPS

Women's Studio Workshop
722 Binnewater Lane
P.O. Box 489
Rosendale, NY 12472
(845) 658-9133   Fax: (845) 658-9031
E-mail: info@wsworkshop.org
Web: www.wsworkshop.org/_art_opp/intern_sixmo.htm

Summary To provide internship opportunities in the arts at the Women's Studio Workshop (WSW) in Rosendale, New York.

Eligibility This program is open to young women artists interested in working with the staff at the studio on projects including papermaking, book arts, and arts administration. Applicants should send a resume, 10 to 20 images of recent works, 3 letters of reference, and a letter of interest. They

should have studio experience, be hard-working, and have a desire and ability to live in a close-knit community of women artists. Along with their application, they must submit a letter of interest explaining why an internship at WSW is important to them and why type of experiences they would bring to the position, 3 letters of reference, a resume, and a CD with 10 images of recent work.

Financial data Interns receive on-site housing and a stipend of $250 per month.

Duration Approximately 6 months, either as winter-spring interns (beginning in January) or as summer-fall interns (beginning in June). Interns may reapply for a second 6-month assignment.

Additional information Tasks include (but are not limited to) preparing the studios; assisting in the production of artists' books; administrative duties (including data entry and web maintenance); designing, printing, and distributing brochures and posters; assisting in all aspects of the exhibition program; preparing the apartments for visiting artists; setting up evening programs; managing the set up and break down of lunch each day; assisting with preparations for fundraising events; and assisting in the day-to-day running of the studios (including general maintenance and cleaning).

Number awarded 2 to 3 each term (winter-spring or summer-fall).

Deadline October of each year for winter-spring internships; February of each year for summer-fall internships.

[687]
WOMEN'S BUSINESS ALLIANCE SCHOLARSHIP PROGRAM

Choice Hotels International
Attn: Women's Business Alliance
4225 East Windrose Drive
Phoenix, AZ 85032
(602) 953-4478
Web: www.choicehotels.com/en/about-choice/wba

Summary To provide financial assistance to women interested in preparing for a career in the hospitality industry.

Eligibility This program is open to female high school seniors, undergraduates, and graduate students. Applicants must be U.S. citizens or permanent residents interested in preparing for a career in the hospitality industry. They must submit an essay of 500 words or less on why they are interested in a career in the hospitality industry, the area of the industry that appeals to them the most, and some of their major accomplishments and/or personal characteristics that will benefit their work in the hospitality industry. Selection is based on that essay, academic record, and 2 letters of recommendation.

Financial data The stipend is $2,000.

Duration 1 year; recipients may reapply.

Additional information This program was established in 2004.

Number awarded 2 or more each year.

Deadline January of each year.

[688]
WOMEN'S ENVIRONMENTAL COUNCIL SCHOLARSHIPS

Women's Environmental Council
Attn: Scholarship Chair
P.O. Box 36
Solano Beach, CA 92075
E-mail: sarah.anunsen@gmail.com
Web: www.wecweb.org/Scholarships/scholarships.html

Summary To provide financial assistance to women from any state working on an undergraduate or graduate degree in an environmental field at colleges and universities in southern California.

Eligibility This program is open to female undergraduate and graduate students from any state who are enrolled at colleges and universities in Los Angeles, Orange, and San Diego counties in California. Applicants must be studying such environmental fields as architecture, biology, chemistry, environmental science, ecology, environmental engineering, forestry, geography, geology/hydrology, marine studies, or urban planning. They must have a GPA of 3.0 or higher. Along with their application, they must submit a personal statement that includes a description of their academic professional, and environmental achievements and goals; how they became interested in preparing for a career in the environmental field; and how this scholarship will help them achieve their professional and personal goals. Selection is based on that statement (50%); personal incentive, volunteerism, and extracurricular activities (20%); grades and course work (10%); a letter of references (15%); and thoroughness and presentation of the application packet (5%).

Financial data The stipend is $1,000. Recipients are also given a 1-year membership in the Women's Environmental Council (WEC).

Duration 1 year.

Additional information The WEC, founded in 1993, currently has chapters in Los Angeles, Orange County, and San Diego. Recipients are expected to attend the WEC annual meeting in the spring to receive their awards.

Number awarded Varies each year; recently, 6 of these scholarships were awarded.

Deadline December of each year.

[689]
WOMEN'S GOLF ASSOCIATION OF MASSACHUSETTS JUNIOR SCHOLAR PROGRAM

Women's Golf Association of Massachusetts, Inc.
Attn: WGAM Junior Scholarship Fund, Inc.
William F. Connell Golf House & Museum
300 Arnold Palmer Boulevard
Norton, MA 02766
(774) 430-9010   Fax: (774) 430-9011
E-mail: info@wgam.org
Web: www.wgam.org/Pages/junior/jrscholarship.aspx

Summary To provide financial assistance to female golfers from Massachusetts who plan to attend college in any state.

Eligibility This program is open to female golfers who have participated in the Women's Golf Association of Massachusetts (WGAM) junior golf program. Applicants must be attending or planning to attend a college or university in any state.

Selection is based on high school academic record and performance, leadership qualities, community and civic involvement, character, personality, and extent of participation in the WGAM junior golf program. Financial need may determine the size of the stipend, but it is not considered in the selection process. An interview is required.

Financial data A stipend is awarded (amount not specified).

Duration 1 year; may be renewed.

Additional information This program was established in 1985.

Number awarded Varies each year; recently, 7 of these scholarships were awarded.

Deadline May of each year.

[690]
WOMEN'S INDEPENDENCE SCHOLARSHIP PROGRAM

Women's Independence Scholarship Program, Inc.
Attn: WISP Program
4900 Randall Parkway, Suite H
Wilmington, NC 28403
(910) 397-7742   Toll Free: (866) 255-7742
Fax: (910) 397-0023   E-mail: nancy@wispinc.org
Web: www.wispinc.org

Summary To provide financial assistance for college or graduate school to women who are victims of partner abuse.

Eligibility This program is open to women who are victims of partner abuse and have worked for at least 6 months with a nonprofit domestic violence victim services provider that is willing to sponsor them. Applicants must be interested in attending a vocational school, community college, 4-year college or university, or (in exceptional circumstances) graduate school as a full- or part-time student. They should have left an abusive partner at least 1 year previously; women who have been parted from their batterer for more than 5 years are also eligible but funding for such applicants may be limited. Preference is given to single mothers with young children. Special consideration is given to applicants who plan to use their education to further the rights of, and options for, women and girls. Selection is based primarily on financial need. U.S. citizenship or permanent resident status is required.

Financial data Stipends depend on the need of the recipient, but they are at least $250 and average $2,000 per academic term. First priority is given to funding for direct educational expenses (tuition, books, and fees), which is paid directly to the educational institution. Second priority is for assistance in reducing indirect financial barriers to education (e.g., child care, transportation), which is paid directly to the sponsoring agency.

Duration 1 year; may be renewed if the recipient maintains a GPA of 2.75 or higher.

Additional information This program was established in 1999 when the sponsor was known as the Sunshine Lady Foundation.

Number awarded Varies each year.

Deadline Applications may be submitted at any time, but they must be received at least 2 months before the start of the intended program.

[691]
WOMEN'S JEWELRY ASSOCIATION SCHOLARSHIP

Women's Jewelry Association
Attn: Scholarship Committee
52 Vanderbilt Avenue, 19th Floor
New York, NY 10017-3827
(212) 687-2722   Toll Free: (877) 224-5421
Fax: (212) 355-0219   E-mail: info@womensjewelry.org
Web: wjamarion.memberlodge.com

Summary To provide financial assistance for college to women who are interested in careers in jewelry.

Eligibility This program is open to women who are enrolled at a college or university and taking classes in fine jewelry and watch design. Applicants in the designer category must submit images of finished work they have created. Applicants in the designer/creator category must submit images of finished pieces that they have designed and created. Applicants in the non-designer category must be interested in preparing for a career as a bench jeweler, appraiser, gemologist, watch-maker, or retailer; they must submit a 2-page essay on the program for which they are applying, what motivated them to attend this program, why they think they deserve a scholarship, why they wish to prepare for a career in jewelry or watches, their goals and aspirations for the future, and how the jewelry industry will benefit from their receiving this scholarship. Financial need is not considered in the selection process.

Financial data Stipends range from $250 to $4,000.

Duration 1 year.

Additional information This program includes the June Herman Scholarship of $5,000, awarded for the first time in 2001.

Number awarded Varies each year; recently, 6 of these scholarships were awarded: 1 at $5,000, 3 at $3,500, 1 at $2,500, and 1 at $2,000.

Deadline April of each year.

[692]
WOMEN'S MUSIC COMMISSION

Broadcast Music Inc.
Attn: BMI Foundation, Inc.
7 World Trade Center
250 Greenwich Street
New York, NY 10007-0030
(212) 220-3000   E-mail: info@bmifoundation.org
Web: www.bmifoundation.org

Summary To recognize and reward, with a commission for production of a new work, outstanding young female composers.

Eligibility This competition is open to women between 20 and 30 years of age who are citizens or permanent residents of the United States. Applicants must submit samples of their original compositions.

Financial data The winner receives a $5,000 commission to create a new work.

Duration The competition is held annually.

Additional information This program began in 2006. Each year, the sponsor partners with a different world-class performer, ensemble, or presenter to present the premier performance.

Number awarded 1 each year.

Deadline May of each year.

[693]
WOMEN'S OPPORTUNITY AWARDS PROGRAM

Soroptimist International of the Americas
Attn: Program Department
1709 Spruce Street
Philadelphia, PA 19103-6103
(215) 893-9000   Fax: (215) 893-5200
E-mail: siahq@soroptimist.org
Web: www.soroptimist.org/awards/awards.html

Summary To provide financial assistance to women reentering the job market to upgrade their employment status through education.

Eligibility This program is open to women who provide the primary financial support for their family. Applicants must have been accepted to a vocational/skills training program or an undergraduate degree program. They must reside in 1 of the 20 countries or territories (divided into 28 regions) that are part of Soroptimist International of the Americas. Along with their application, they must submit 1) a 300-word description of their career goals and how their education and/or skills training support those goals; 2) a 750-word essay on the economic and personal hardships they have faced and their plans to gain additional skills, training, and education; and 3) documentation of financial need.

Financial data The award is $10,000.

Duration The awards are issued each year and are nonrenewable.

Additional information This program, established in 1972, was formerly known as the Training Awards Program. The awards may not be used for graduate study or international travel. Applications are to be processed through the local Soroptimist club. Countries that are part of Soroptimist International of the Americas include Argentina, Bolivia, Brazil, Canada, Chile, Colombia, Costa Rica, Ecuador, Guam, Japan, Republic of Korea, Mexico, Panama, Paraguay, Peru, Philippines, Puerto Rico, Taiwan, United States, and Venezuela.

Number awarded In each of the 28 regions, the winner receives an award of $5,000; most regions grant additional $3,000 awards. From among the regional winners, 3 receive an additional award of $10,000 from Soroptimist International of the Americas. Since the program was established, it has awarded approximately $20 million in scholarships to more than 25,000 women.

Deadline Applications must be submitted to regional contacts by November of each year.

[694]
WOMEN'S OVERSEAS SERVICE LEAGUE SCHOLARSHIPS FOR WOMEN

Women's Overseas Service League
Attn: Scholarship Committee
P.O. Box 7124
Washington, DC 20044-7124
E-mail: carolhabgood@sbcglobal.net
Web: www.wosl.org/scholarships.htm

Summary To provide financial assistance for college to women who are committed to a military or another public service career.

Eligibility This program is open to women who are committed to a military or other public service career. Applicants must have completed at least 12 semester or 18 quarter hours of postsecondary study with a GPA of 2.5 or higher. They must be working on an academic degree (the program may be professional or technical in nature) and must agree to enroll for at least 6 semester or 9 quarter hours of study each academic period. Along with their application, they must submit an official transcript, a 1-page essay on their career goals, 3 current letters of reference, and a brief statement describing sources of financial support and the need for scholarship assistance. They must also provide information on their educational background, employment experience, civic and volunteer activities, and expected degree completion date.

Financial data Stipends range from $500 to $1,000 per year.

Duration 1 year; may be renewed 1 additional year.

Additional information The Women's Overseas Service League is a national organization of women who have served overseas in or with the armed forces.

Deadline February of each year.

[695]
WOMEN'S SECOND CHANCE COLLEGE SCHOLARSHIP

Community Foundation of Louisville
Attn: Community Leadership Officer
Waterfront Plaza, Suite 1110
325 West Main Street
Louisville, KY 40202-4251
(502) 585-4649, ext. 1025   Fax: (502) 587-7484
E-mail: info@cflouisville.org
Web: www.cflouisville.org/page13940.cfm

Summary To provide financial assistance for college to mature female residents of Kentucky and southern Indiana.

Eligibility This program is open to women between 25 and 40 years of age who reside in Kentucky or the Indiana counties of Clark, Crawford, Floyd, Harrison, Scott, or Washington. Applicants must have a high school diploma or GED certificate and may have some college credits. They must commit to attend a participating college or university and complete a baccalaureate degree within an agreed upon period of time. Selection is based on financial need and desire to learn.

Financial data The stipend is at least $1,000 per year.

Duration 1 year; renewable until completion of a baccalaureate degree if the recipient maintains a GPA of 2.5 or higher.

Number awarded 1 or more each year.

Deadline March of each year.

[696]
WOMEN'S SOUTHERN GOLF ASSOCIATION SCHOLARSHIP

Women's Southern Golf Association
c/o Marci Likens, Scholarship Committee Chair
827 Bentley Green Circle
Winter Springs, FL 32708
(407) 366-0204
E-mail: scholarship@womens-southerngolfassociation.org
Web: www.womens-southerngolfassociation.org

Summary To provide financial assistance to women golfers in the southern states who plan to attend college in any state.

Eligibility This program is open to amateur female golfers who are residents of 1 of the 15 southern states (Alabama, Arkansas, Florida, Georgia, Kentucky, Louisiana, Maryland, Mississippi, North Carolina, Oklahoma, South Carolina, Tennessee, Texas, Virginia, and West Virginia) or the District of Columbia. Applicants must be graduating high school seniors planning to work on an undergraduate degree at an accredited institution of higher learning in any state. Along with their application, they must submit a 200-word personal statement on their goals for college and their future. Selection is based on academic excellence, citizenship, sportsmanship, and financial need. U.S. citizenship is required.

Financial data The stipend is $3,500 per year. Funds are paid directly to the recipient's college.

Duration 1 year; may be renewed up to 3 additional years, provided the recipient maintains a GPA of 3.0 or higher.

Additional information This scholarship was first awarded in 1973.

Number awarded 1 each year.

Deadline April of each year.

[697]
WOMEN'S TRANSPORTATION SEMINAR CHAPTER OF COLORADO ANNUAL SCHOLARSHIPS

Women's Transportation Seminar-Colorado Chapter
c/o Nyssa Beach, Scholarship Chair
Jacobs Engineering Group Inc.
707 17th Street, Suite 2300
Denver, CO 80202-5131
(303) 820-5240   Fax: (303) 820-2402
E-mail: nyssa.beach@jacobs.com
Web: www.wtsinternational.org/Chapters.aspx?ID=6842

Summary To provide financial assistance to female undergraduate and graduate students in Colorado and Wyoming preparing for a career in transportation.

Eligibility This program is open to women at colleges and universities in Colorado and Wyoming who are working on a bachelor's or graduate degree in a field related to transportation. Those fields may include transportation or civil engineering, urban planning, finance, architecture, or logistics. Applicants must submit an essay on their career goals after graduation and why they should receive this scholarship. They must have a GPA of 3.0 or higher. Minority women are especially encouraged to apply.

Financial data Undergraduate stipends are $2,000 or $1,000. Graduate stipends are $3,000.

Duration 1 year.

Additional information Winners are also nominated for scholarships offered by the national organization of the Women's Transportation Seminar.

Number awarded 4 each year: 2 to undergraduates and 2 to graduate students.

Deadline November of each year.

[698]
WOMEN'S WESTERN GOLF FOUNDATION SCHOLARSHIP

Women's Western Golf Foundation
c/o Mrs. Richard Willis
393 Ramsay Road
Deerfield, IL 60015
Web: www.wwga.org/scholarship_info.htm

Summary To provide financial assistance to high school senior girls who are interested in the sport of golf and plan to attend college.

Eligibility Applicants must be high school senior girls who intend to graduate in the year they submit their application. They must meet entrance requirements of, and plan to enroll at, an accredited college or university. Selection is based on academic achievement, financial need, excellence of character, and involvement with the sport of golf. Skill or excellence in the game is not a criterion. U.S. citizenship is required.

Financial data The stipend is $2,000 per year. The funds are to be used to pay for room, board, tuition, and other university fees or charges.

Duration 1 year; may be renewed up to 3 additional years if the recipient maintains a GPA of 3.0 or higher.

Number awarded 15 each year.

Deadline February of each year.

[699]
WOMEN'S WILDLIFE MANAGEMENT/ CONSERVATION SCHOLARSHIP

National Rifle Association of America
Attn: Women's Program Department
11250 Waples Mill Road
Fairfax, VA 22030-7400
(703) 267-1399   Toll Free: (800) 861-1166
E-mail: rherr@nrahq.org
Web: www.nrahq.org/women/awards/wmc-scholarship.asp

Summary To provide financial assistance to women who are upper-division students working on a degree in wildlife management or conservation.

Eligibility This program is open to women currently enrolled full time as college juniors or seniors. Applicants must be working on a degree in wildlife management or conservation. They must have a GPA of 3.0 or higher. Financial need is not considered in the selection process.

Financial data The stipend is $1,000 per year.

Duration 1 year; may be renewed 1 additional year.

Additional information This scholarship was first awarded in 2006.

Number awarded 1 each year.

Deadline November of each year.

[700]
WYOMING COMBAT VETERAN SURVIVING SPOUSE TUITION BENEFIT

Wyoming Veterans Commission
Attn: Executive Director
5500 Bishop Boulevard
Cheyenne, WY 82009
(307) 772-5145   Toll Free: (866) 992-7641, ext. 5145
Fax: (307) 772-5202   E-mail: lbartt@state.wy.us
Web: www.wy.ngb.army.mil/benefits

Summary To provide financial assistance to surviving spouses of deceased, POW, or MIA Wyoming veterans who are interested in attending college in the state.

Eligibility This program is open to spouses of veterans whose spouse had been a resident of Wyoming for at least 1 year at the time of entering service and received the armed forces expeditionary medal or a campaign medal for service in an armed conflict in a foreign country. The veteran spouse must 1) have died during active service during armed conflict in a foreign country; 2) be listed officially as being a POW or MIA as a result of active service with the military forces of the United States; or 3) have been honorably discharged from the military and subsequently died of an injury or disease incurred while in service and was a Wyoming resident at the time of death. Applicants must enroll at the University of Wyoming or a community college in the state within 10 years following the death of the combat veteran.

Financial data Qualifying veterans' spouses are eligible for free resident tuition at the University of Wyoming or at any of the state's community colleges.

Duration Up to 10 semesters.

Additional information Applications may be obtained from the institution the applicant is attending or planning to attend.

Number awarded Varies each year.

Deadline Applications may be submitted at any time, but they should be received 2 or 3 weeks before the beginning of the semester.

[701]
WYOMING VIETNAM VETERAN SURVIVING SPOUSE TUITION BENEFIT

Wyoming Veterans Commission
Attn: Executive Director
5500 Bishop Boulevard
Cheyenne, WY 82009
(307) 772-5145   Toll Free: (866) 992-7641, ext. 5145
Fax: (307) 772-5202   E-mail: lbartt@state.wy.us
Web: www.wy.ngb.army.mil/benefits

Summary To provide financial assistance to surviving spouses of deceased, POW, or MIA Wyoming veterans of the Vietnam era who are interested in attending college in the state.

Eligibility This program is open to spouses of veterans whose spouse had been a resident of Wyoming for at least 1 year at the time of entering service, served between August 5, 1964 and May 7, 1975, and received the Vietnam service medal. The veteran spouse must 1) have died as a result of service-connected causes; 2) be listed officially as being a POW or MIA as a result of active service with the military forces of the United States; or 3) have been honorably discharged from the military and subsequently died of an injury or disease incurred while in service and was a Wyoming resident at the time of death. Applicants must be attending or planning to attend the University of Wyoming or a community college in the state.

Financial data Qualifying veterans' surviving spouses are eligible for free resident tuition at the University of Wyoming or at any of the state's community colleges.

Duration Up to 10 semesters.

Additional information Applications may be obtained from the institution the applicant is attending or planning to attend.

Number awarded Varies each year.

Deadline Applications may be submitted at any time, but they should be received 2 or 3 weeks before the beginning of the semester.

[702]
XI PSI OMEGA CHAPTER SCHOLARSHIPS

Alpha Kappa Alpha Sorority, Inc.-Xi Psi Omega Chapter
Attn: President
P.O. Box 140894
Anchorage, AK 99514
(907) 346-3998
Web: xipsiomega.com/scholarship.html

Summary To provide financial assistance to high school seniors (especially African American women) from Alaska who plan to attend college in any state.

Eligibility This program is open to seniors graduating from high schools in Alaska who are planning to attend a 2- or 4-year accredited college or university in any state. Applicants must have a GPA of 2.5 or higher and a record of active participation in school and community activities. Alpha Kappa Alpha (AKA) is currently 1 of the largest social sororities whose membership is predominantly African American women.

Financial data A stipend is awarded (amount not specified).

Duration 1 year; nonrenewable.

Additional information The Xi Psi Omega chapter of AKA serves alumnae members in Alaska.

Number awarded 1 or more each year.

Deadline March of each year.

[703]
YOUNG LADIES' RADIO LEAGUE SCHOLARSHIP

Foundation for Amateur Radio, Inc.
Attn: Scholarship Committee
P.O. Box 911
Columbia, MD 21044-0911
(410) 552-2652   Fax: (410) 981-5146
E-mail: dave.prestel@gmail.com
Web: www.farweb.org/scholarships

Summary To provide funding to licensed radio amateurs (especially women) who are interested in earning a bachelor's or graduate degree in the United States.

Eligibility This program is open to radio amateurs who have at least an FCC Technician Class license or equivalent foreign authorization. Applicants must intend to work full time on a bachelor's or graduate degree at a college or university in the United States. There are no restrictions on the course

of study or residency location. Non-U.S. amateurs are eligible. Preference is given to female applicants and to those studying communications, electronics, or related arts and sciences. Financial need is considered in the selection process.

Financial data The stipend is $1,500.

Duration 1 year.

Additional information This program is sponsored by the Young Ladies' Radio League. It includes the following named scholarships: the Ethel Smith-K4LMB Memorial Scholarship and the Mary Lou Brown-NM7N Memorial Scholarship.

Number awarded 2 each year.

Deadline March of each year.

[704]
YOUNG WOMEN'S ALLIANCE HIGHER EDUCATION SCHOLARSHIPS

Young Women's Alliance
Attn: Foundation
P.O. Box 1503
Austin, TX 78767
(512) 553-6176
E-mail: foundationpresident@youngwomensalliance.org
Web: www.youngwomensalliance.org/scholarships

Summary To provide financial assistance to women from any state enrolled as upper-division or graduate students at a college or university in Texas.

Eligibility This program is open to women from any state who are younger than 40 years of age. Applicants must have completed at least 60 undergraduate semester hours or be working on a graduate degree at an accredited institution of higher learning in central Texas. They must have devoted at least 40 hours of work on a Community Impact Project during the current semester. Along with their application, they must submit a description of their Community Impact Project and a personal statement about why they should be chosen to receive this scholarship. Selection is based on academic achievement, demonstrated leadership, commitment to both past community service and the Community Impact Project, and financial need.

Financial data The stipend is $2,500.

Duration 1 year.

Additional information This foundation was established in 1997.

Number awarded 1 or more each year.

Deadline March of each year.

[705]
YOUTH PARTNERS IN ACCESS TO CAPITAL PROGRAM

Alpha Kappa Alpha Sorority, Inc.
Attn: Educational Advancement Foundation
5656 South Stony Island Avenue
Chicago, IL 60637
(773) 947-0026   Toll Free: (800) 653-6528
Fax: (773) 947-0277   E-mail: akaeaf@akaeaf.net
Web: www.akaeaf.org/undergraduate_scholarships.htm

Summary To provide funding to undergraduate members of Alpha Kappa Alpha sorority interested in conducting a project to support the platform of the sorority.

Eligibility This program is open to members of the organization, a traditionally African American women's sorority, who are working at least as sophomores on an undergraduate degree at an accredited degree-granting institution. Applicants must have a GPA of 3.0 or higher and a record of demonstrated participation in leadership, volunteer, and civic services. They must be proposing to conduct a community service project that will implement 1 of the platforms of the sorority: emerging young leaders, health, global poverty, economic security, social justice and human rights, or internal leadership training for external service. Along with their application, they must submit a personal goal statement on how they promote healing, nurturing, learning, and uplifting of youth by assisting in developing lifelong learning skills.

Financial data Grants range from $500 to $1,000.

Duration 1 year; nonrenewable.

Additional information This program began in 1997.

Number awarded Varies each year; recently, 13 of these grants were awarded.

Deadline April of each year.

[706]
ZANNONI INDIVIDUAL SUMMER UNDERGRADUATE RESEARCH FELLOWSHIPS

American Society for Pharmacology and Experimental
  Therapeutics
9650 Rockville Pike
Bethesda, MD 20814-3995
(301) 634-7060   Fax: (301) 634-7061
E-mail: info@aspet.org
Web: www.aspet.org/awards/SURF

Summary To provide funding to undergraduate students (particularly women and underrepresented minorities) who are interested in participating in a summer research project at a laboratory affiliated with the American Society for Pharmacology and Experimental Therapeutics (ASPET).

Eligibility This program is open to undergraduate students interested in working during the summer in the laboratory of a society member who must agree to act as a sponsor. Applications must be submitted jointly by the student and the sponsor, and they must include 1) a letter from the sponsor with a brief description of the proposed research, a statement of the qualifications of the student, the degree of independence the student will have, a description of complementary activities available to the student, and a description of how the student will report on the research results; 2) a letter from the student indicating the nature of his or her interest in the project and a description of future plans; 3) a copy of the sponsor's updated curriculum vitae; and 4) copies of all the student's undergraduate transcripts. Selection is based on the nature of the research opportunities provided, student and sponsor qualifications, and the likelihood the student will prepare for a career in pharmacology. Applications from underrepresented minorities and women are particularly encouraged.

Financial data The stipend is $2,800. Funds are paid directly to the institution but may be used only for student stipends.

Duration 10 weeks during the summer.

Additional information Some of these awards are funded through the Glenn E. Ullyot Fund; those recipients are designated as the Ullyot Fellows.

Number awarded Varies each year; recently, 4 of these fellowships were awarded.

Deadline February of each year.

[707]
ZETA TAU ALPHA ENDOWED SCHOLARSHIPS

Zeta Tau Alpha Foundation, Inc.
Attn: Director of Foundation Administration
3450 Founders Road
Indianapolis, IN 46268
(317) 872-0540   Fax: (317) 876-3948
E-mail: zetataualpha@zetataualpha.org
Web: www.zetataualpha.org

Summary To provide financial assistance to undergraduate women who are members of Zeta Tau Alpha.

Eligibility This program is open to undergraduate women who are enrolled at a 4-year college or university and student members of the school's Zeta Tau Alpha chapter. These scholarships have been established for specific chapters, with preference for the award going to a member of that particular chapter. Selection is based on academic achievement (GPA of 2.75 or higher), involvement in campus and community activities, recommendations, current class status, and financial need.

Financial data The stipend is at least $1,000.

Duration 1 year; renewable.

Number awarded Varies each year; recently, the foundation awarded a total of more than $600,000 to 235 undergraduate and graduate members for all of its scholarship programs.

Deadline February of each year.

[708]
ZOE CAVALARIS HELLENIC ATHLETIC WOMEN'S AWARD

Daughters of Penelope
1909 Q Street, N.W., Suite 500
Washington, DC 20009-1007
(202) 234-9741   Fax: (202) 483-6983
E-mail: dophq@ahepa.org
Web: www.ahepa.org/dop

Summary To recognize and reward women of Greek descent who demonstrate excellence in high school or college athletics.

Eligibility This award is presented to a young woman of Hellenic descent who has unusually high quality athletic ability and a record of accomplishment in any sport or any series of sports. Nominees must be outstanding high school or college amateur female athletes recognized for their accomplishments during their high school and/or college years. Along with a letter of nomination from a sponsoring chapter of Daughters of Penelope, they must submit documentation of their current overall GPA, academic honors, other honors, participation in sports activities, extracurricular activities (other than sports), church and/or community activities, and special achievements (other than sports).

Financial data The award includes a college scholarship (amount not specified), an engraved plaque, public recognition through Daughters of Penelope events and publications, and reimbursement of transportation and hotel accommodations to attend the organization's national convention.

Duration The award is presented annually.
Number awarded 1 each year.
Deadline May of each year.

[709]
ZONTA CLUB OF BANGOR SCHOLARSHIPS

Zonta Club of Bangor
c/o Barbara A. Cardone
P.O. Box 1904
Bangor, ME 04402-1904
Web: www.zontaclubofbangor.org/?area=scholarship

Summary To provide financial assistance to women attending or planning to attend college in Maine and major in any field.

Eligibility This program is open to women who are attending or planning to attend an accredited 2- or 4-year college in Maine. Applicants may major in any field. Along with their application, they must submit brief essays on 1) their goals in seeking higher education and their plans for the future, and 2) any school and community activities that have been of particular importance to them and why they found them worthwhile. Financial need may be considered in the selection process.

Financial data The stipend is $1,000.

Duration 1 year.

Number awarded 2 each year.

Deadline March of each year.

[710]
ZONTA CLUB OF MILWAUKEE TECHNICAL SPECIALTY SCHOLARSHIP AWARD

Zonta Club of Milwaukee
Attn: Scholarship Team
P.O. Box 1494
Milwaukee, WI 53201
E-mail: zcscholarship@zontamilwaukee.org
Web: www.zontamilwaukee.org/OurScholarships.htm

Summary To provide financial assistance to women, especially residents of Wisconsin, who are interested in working on an associate degree or certificate at a technical college or institute in any state.

Eligibility This program is open to women who are interested in working on an associate degree or certificate in a nontraditional technical field, including (but not limited to) health occupations, computer, electronic, mechanical, or other technological fields. Preference is given to residents of Wisconsin and to low income or otherwise disadvantaged women. Applicants must be currently enrolled at an accredited technical college or institute in any state. They must have a GPA of 2.5 or higher. Along with their application, they must submit a description of their anticipated course of study and current career interests, including how they plan to continue to advance the status of women through their career.

Financial data The stipend is $1,000.

Duration 1 year.

Number awarded 1 or more each year.

Deadline May of each year.

[711]
ZONTA INTERNATIONAL YOUNG WOMEN IN PUBLIC AFFAIRS AWARDS

Zonta International
Attn: Foundation
1211 West 22nd Street, Suite 900
Oak Brook, IL 60523-3384
(630) 928-1400   Fax: (630) 928-1559
E-mail: programs@zonta.org
Web: www.zonta.org

Summary To recognize and reward women in secondary schools who are interested in a career in public policy, government, or volunteer organizations.

Eligibility This program is open to young women, 16 to 19 years of age, who are currently living or studying in a district or region of Zonta International. Applicants must be interested in preparing for a career in public affairs, public policy, or community organization. Along with their application, they must submit essays on their student activities and leadership roles (200 words), their community service activities (200 words), their efforts to understand other countries (150 words), and the status of women in their country and worldwide (300 words). Selection is based on commitment to volunteerism, experience in local or student government, volunteer leadership achievements, knowledge of Zonta International and its programs, and advocating in Zonta International's mission of advancing the status of women worldwide. Winners are selected at the club level and forwarded for a district competition; district winners are entered in the international competition.

Financial data District awardees receive $1,000 and international awardees receive $3,000.

Duration The competition is held annually.

Additional information This program was established in 1990.

Number awarded Varies each year; recently, 24 district winners and 5 international winners were selected. Since the program began, it has presented 565 awards to 503 young women from 49 countries.

Deadline Clubs set their own deadlines but must submit their winners to the district governor by March of each year.

Graduate Students

Listed alphabetically by program title and described in detail here are 481 fellowships, grants, awards, internships, and other sources of "free money" set aside for women who are incoming, continuing, or returning graduate students working on a master's. doctoral, or professional degree. This funding is available to support study, training, research, and/or creative activities in the United States.

[712]
ABWA PRESIDENT'S SCHOLARSHIP

American Business Women's Association
Attn: Stephen Bufton Memorial Educational Fund
11050 Roe Avenue, Suite 200
Overland Park, KS 66211
Toll Free: (800) 228-0007
Web: www.sbmef.org/Opportunities.cfm

Summary To provide financial assistance to female graduate students who are working on a degree in a specified field (the field changes each year).

Eligibility This program is open to women who are working on a graduate degree and have a cumulative GPA of 3.0 or higher. Applicants are not required to be members of the American Business Women's Association. Along with their application, they must submit a 250-word biographical sketch that includes information about their background, activities, honors, work experience, and long-term educational and professional goals. Financial need is not considered in the selection process. Each year, the trustees designate an academic discipline for which the scholarship will be presented that year; recently, eligibility was limited to women working on a graduate degree in business administration. U.S. citizenship is required.

Financial data The stipend is $3,000. Funds are paid directly to the recipient's institution to be used only for tuition, books, and fees.

Duration 1 year.

Additional information This program was created in 1969 as part of ABWA's Stephen Bufton Memorial Education Fund. The ABWA does not provide the names and addresses of local chapters; it recommends that applicants check with their local Chamber of Commerce, library, or university to see if any chapter has registered a contact's name and number.

Number awarded 1 each year.

Deadline May of each year.

[713]
ACHIEVEMENT SCHOLARSHIPS

Zeta Tau Alpha Foundation, Inc.
Attn: Director of Foundation Administration
3450 Founders Road
Indianapolis, IN 46268
(317) 872-0540   Fax: (317) 876-3948
E-mail: zetataualpha@zetataualpha.org
Web: www.zetataualpha.org

Summary To provide financial assistance for college or graduate school to women who are members of Zeta Tau Alpha.

Eligibility This program is open to undergraduate and graduate women who are enrolled at a 4-year college or university and student members of the school's Zeta Tau Alpha chapter. Applicants must demonstrate leadership qualities within their chapter or in campus activities while maintaining a high scholastic average. Selection is based on academic achievement (GPA of 2.75 or higher), involvement in campus and community activities, recommendations, current class status, and financial need.

Financial data The stipend is at least $1,000.

Duration 1 year; renewable.

Number awarded Varies each year; recently, the foundation awarded a total of more than $600,000 to 235 undergraduate and graduate members for all of its scholarship programs.

Deadline February of each year.

[714]
ACT SUMMER INTERNSHIP PROGRAM

American College Testing
Attn: Human Resources Department
500 ACT Drive
P.O. Box 168
Iowa City, IA 52243-0168
(319) 337-1763   E-mail: working@act.org
Web: www.act.org/humanresources/jobs/intern.html

Summary To provide work experience during the summer to doctoral students interested in careers in assessment and educational studies, especially those (including women) who will increase diversity in the field.

Eligibility This program is open to doctoral students enrolled in such fields as educational psychology, measurement, program evaluation, counseling psychology, educational policy, mathematical and applied statistics, industrial or organizational psychology, and counselor education. Applicants must be interested in working at American College Testing (ACT) in 1 of the following categories: 1) psychometrics and statistics; 2) education and workforce research services; 3) industrial-organizational psychology; or 4) career and vocational psychology. Along with their application, they must submit a description of their interests and experiences. They must be able to demonstrate the ability to function both independently and as a team member in a professional work environment and must possess excellent written and oral communication skills. The program is also intended to assist in increasing the diversity of professionals in measurement and related fields.

Financial data Interns receive a stipend of $5,000 and round-trip transportation between their graduate institution and Iowa City. A supplemental housing allowance of $1,000 is provided if the intern lives outside a 50-mile radius.

Duration 8 weeks during the summer.

Number awarded Varies each year.

Deadline February of each year.

[715]
ADELE LOBRACIO LOWE LEADERSHIP GRANT

Lambda Kappa Sigma Pharmacy Fraternity
Attn: Executive Director
S77 W16906 Casey Drive
P.O. Box 570
Muskego, WI 53150-0570
Toll Free: (800) LKS-1913   Fax: (262) 679-4558
E-mail: lks@lks.org
Web: www.lks.org

Summary To provide financial assistance to members of Lambda Kappa Sigma who are interested in working on a Pharm.D. degree and can demonstrate leadership.

Eligibility This program is open to collegiate or alumnae members of Lambda Kappa Sigma who are enrolled in a licensure-eligible pharmacy degree program. (In the United States, the Pharm.D. degree is the only qualifying program at schools or colleges of pharmacy recognized by the Accreditation Council on Pharmacy Education.) Applicants must rank in the top half of their class and be able to demonstrate financial need. Along with their application, they must submit a brief essay on their leadership qualities and the importance of leadership.

Financial data   The stipend is $1,000.

Duration   1 year.

Additional information   This program was established in 1998. Lambda Kappa Sigma was founded in 1913 to promote the profession of pharmacy among women.

Number awarded   1 each year.

Deadline   October of each year.

[716]
AGNES MISSIRIAN SCHOLARSHIP

Armenian International Women's Association
65 Main Street, Room 3A
Watertown, MA 02472
(617) 926-0171   E-mail: aiwainc@aol.com
Web: www.aiwa-net.org/scholarshipinfo.html

Summary   To provide financial assistance to Armenian women who are upper-division and graduate students.

Eligibility   This program is open to full-time women students of Armenian descent attending an accredited college or university. Applicants must be full-time juniors, seniors, or graduate students with a GPA of 3.2 or higher. They must submit an essay, up to 500 words, describing their planned academic program, their career goals, and the reasons why they believe they should be awarded this scholarship. Selection is based on financial need and merit.

Financial data   The stipend is $2,000.

Duration   1 year.

Number awarded   1 or more each year.

Deadline   April of each year.

[717]
AIR FORCE OFFICERS' WIVES' CLUB OF WASHINGTON, D.C. CONTINUING EDUCATION SCHOLARSHIPS FOR NON-MILITARY AIR FORCE SPOUSES

Air Force Officers' Wives' Club of Washington, D.C.
Attn: Scholarship Committee
P.O. Box 8490
Washington, DC 20032
E-mail: scholarship@afowc.com
Web: www.afowc.com/making-difference.html

Summary   To provide financial assistance for undergraduate or graduate study in any state to the non-military spouses of Air Force members in the Washington, D.C. area.

Eligibility   This program is open to the non-military spouses of Air Force members residing in the Washington, D.C. metropolitan area in the following categories: active duty, retired, MIA/POW, or deceased. Spouses whose Air Force sponsor is assigned remote from the area or reassigned during the current school year are also eligible if they remained behind to continue their education. Applicants must be enrolled or planning to enroll as an undergraduate or graduate student at a college or university in any state. Along with their application, they must submit a 500-word essay on a topic that changes annually; recently, applicants were asked to write on which book is required reading for all students and why. Selection is based on academic and citizenship achievements; financial need is not considered.

Financial data   A stipend is awarded (amount not specified). Funds may be used only for payment of tuition or academic fees.

Duration   1 year.

Number awarded   Varies each year.

Deadline   February of each year.

[718]
ALABAMA G.I. DEPENDENTS' SCHOLARSHIP PROGRAM

Alabama Department of Veterans Affairs
770 Washington Avenue, Suite 530
Montgomery, AL 36102-1509
(334) 242-5077   Fax: (334) 242-5102
E-mail: willie.moore@va.state.al.us
Web: www.va.state.al.us/scholarship.htm

Summary   To provide educational benefits to spouses and other dependents of Alabama veterans.

Eligibility   Eligible are spouses, children, stepchildren, and unremarried widow(er)s of veterans who served honorably for 90 days or more and 1) are currently rated as 20% or more service-connected disabled or were so rated at time of death; 2) were a former prisoner of war; 3) have been declared missing in action; 4) died as the result of a service-connected disability; or 5) died while on active military duty in the line of duty. The veteran must have been a permanent civilian resident of Alabama for at least 1 year prior to entering active military service; veterans who were not Alabama residents at the time of entering active military service may also qualify if they have a 100% disability and were permanent residents of Alabama for at least 5 years prior to filing the application for this program or prior to death, if deceased. Children and stepchildren must be under the age of 26, but spouses and unremarried widow(er)s may be of any age.

Financial data   Eligible dependents may attend any state-supported Alabama institution of higher learning or enroll in a prescribed course of study at any Alabama state-supported trade school without payment of any tuition, book fees, or laboratory charges.

Duration   This is an entitlement program for 4 years of full-time undergraduate or graduate study or part-time equivalent. Spouses and unremarried widow(er)s whose veteran spouse is rated between 20% and 90% disabled, or 100% disabled but not permanently so, may attend only 2 standard academic years.

Additional information   Benefits for children, spouses, and unremarried widow(er)s are available in addition to federal government benefits. Assistance is not provided for non-credit courses, placement testing, GED preparation, continuing educational courses, pre-technical courses, or state board examinations.

Number awarded   Varies each year.

Deadline   Applications may be submitted at any time.

[719]
ALICE PAUL FEMINIST JURISPRUDENCE ESSAY CONTEST

American University
Washington College of Law
Attn: Women and the Law Program
4801 Massachusetts Avenue, N.W., Suite 418
Washington, DC 20016-8184
(202) 274-4089
E-mail: apessaycontest@wcl.american.edu
Web: www.wcl.american.edu

Summary To recognize and reward the best unpublished work on feminist jurisprudence written by law students in the United States or Canada.

Eligibility This competition is open to law students in the United States and Canada. They are invited to submit an original, unpublished work (up to 50 pages) on any issue within the category of feminist jurisprudence. Co-authored essays are allowed.

Financial data The prize is $1,000.

Duration The competition is held annually.

Additional information This competition, previously sponsored by the University of Notre Dame Law School, was first held in 1994.

Number awarded 1 each year.

Deadline May of each year.

[720]
ALPHA CHI OMEGA EDUCATIONAL ASSISTANCE GRANTS

Alpha Chi Omega Foundation
Attn: Educational Assistance Grants Committee
5939 Castle Creek Parkway North Drive
Indianapolis, IN 46250-4343
(317) 579-5050, ext. 262   Fax: (317) 579-5051
E-mail: foundation@alphachiomega.org
Web: www.alphachiomega.org/index.aspx?id=1031

Summary To provide financial assistance to members of Alpha Chi Omega sorority who are interested in continuing education, including study abroad.

Eligibility This program is open to members of the sorority at the undergraduate and graduate school levels. Applicants must be seeking funding for continuing education and related expenses. They may be interested in studying abroad if the credits earned will be included with credits needed to earn a degree. Along with their application, they must submit documentation of financial need, an outline of their future career goals, a description of their participation in sorority activities, transcripts, and (if studying abroad) confirmation that credits earned will be included with credits needed to earn a degree.

Financial data Grants range from $500 to $2,000.

Duration 1 year.

Additional information This program includes the Alpha Zeta Undergraduate Member Assistance Grant in Memory of Kay Roh, the Carol Edmundson Hutcheson Education Assistance Fund, the Florence Staiger Lonn Educational Grants, the Lisa Hancock Rehrig Educational Assistance Grants, and the Mary Frances-Guilbert Mariani-Bigler Continuing Education Grant.

Number awarded Varies each year; recently, 51 of these grants, with $13,372, were awarded.

Deadline May or October of each year.

[721]
ALPHA CHI OMEGA FOUNDERS FELLOWSHIP

Alpha Chi Omega Foundation
Attn: Foundation Programs Coordinator
5939 Castle Creek Parkway North Drive
Indianapolis, IN 46250-4343
(317) 579-5050, ext. 262   Fax: (317) 579-5051
E-mail: foundation@alphachiomega.org
Web: www.alphachiomega.org/index.aspx?id=1030

Summary To provide financial assistance to graduating Alpha Chi Omega members who are interested in studying on the graduate school level.

Eligibility This program is open to women college seniors or graduates who are members of the sorority. Applicants must be interested in attending graduate school. They may study any field. Financial need is considered in the selection process.

Financial data A stipend is awarded (amount not specified).

Duration 1 year.

Number awarded 1 each year.

Deadline March of each year.

[722]
ALPHA EPSILON PHI FOUNDATION SCHOLARSHIPS

Alpha Epsilon Phi
Attn: AEPhi Foundation
11 Lake Avenue Extension, Suite 1A
Danbury, CT 06811
(203) 748-0029   Fax: (203) 748-0039
E-mail: aephifoundation@aephi.org
Web: www.aephi.org/foundation/scholarships

Summary To provide financial assistance for undergraduate or graduate education to Alpha Epsilon Phi members or alumnae.

Eligibility This program is open to active and alumnae members of the sorority who are either full-time rising juniors or seniors or graduate students who have completed at least 1 year of graduate study. Applicants must have a GPA of 3.0 or higher. Along with their application, they must submit a letter describing 1) their activities in their chapter, on campus, and in the general community; 2) what they have done to supplement their parents' contribution toward their education; and 3) their need for scholarship consideration.

Financial data Stipends range from $1,000 to $2,000 per year.

Duration 1 year; may be renewed.

Additional information This program includes the following named scholarships: the Judith Resnik Memorial Scholarship (preference to those working on a degree in engineering, science, or a related field and have a GPA of 3.5 or higher), the Anne Klauber Berson Memorial Scholarship, the Edith Hirsch Miller Memorial Scholarship (preference to Jewish applicants who are members of Nu Chapter at the University of Pittsburgh or residents of Pittsburgh), the Irma Loeb Cohen Scholarship (preference to members of Rho Chapter at Ohio

State University), the Ruth Rosenbaum Goldfeder Memorial Scholarship (preference to students at universities in California), the Constance Bauman Abraham Scholarship (preference to members of Eta Chapter at SUNY Albany or at universities in other northeastern states, the Ruth Bader Ginsburg Scholarship (preference to members entering their second year of law school), and the Shonnette Meyer Kahn Scholarship (preference to members of Rho Chapter at Ohio State University or Epsilon Chapter at Tulane University). Recipients must be willing to remain active in the sorority and live in the sorority house (if any) for the entire year the scholarship covers.

Number awarded Several each year.

Deadline March of each year.

[723]
ALPHA KAPPA ALPHA ENDOWMENT AWARDS

Alpha Kappa Alpha Sorority, Inc.
Attn: Educational Advancement Foundation
5656 South Stony Island Avenue
Chicago, IL 60637
(773) 947-0026   Toll Free: (800) 653-6528
Fax: (773) 947-0277   E-mail: akaeaf@akaeaf.net
Web: www.akaeaf.org/fellowships_endowments.htm

Summary To provide financial assistance to undergraduate and graduate students (especially African American women) who meet designated requirements.

Eligibility This program is open to undergraduate and graduate students who are enrolled full time as sophomores or higher in an accredited degree-granting institution and are planning to continue their program of education. Applicants may apply for scholarships that include specific requirements established by the donor of the endowment that supports it. Along with their application, they must submit 1) a list of honors, awards, and scholarships received; 2) a list of organizations in which they have memberships, especially minority organizations; and 3) a statement of their personal and career goals, including how this scholarship will enhance their ability to attain those goals. The sponsor is a traditionally African American women's sorority.

Financial data Award amounts are determined by the availability of funds from the particular endowment. Recently, stipends averaged more than $1,700 per year.

Duration 1 year or longer.

Additional information Each endowment establishes its own requirements. Examples of requirements include residence of the applicant, major field of study, minimum GPA, attendance at an Historically Black College or University (HBCU) or member institution of the United Negro College Fund (UNCF), or other personal feature. For further information on all endowments, contact the sponsor.

Number awarded Varies each year; recently, 30 of these scholarships, with a total value of $52,082, were awarded.

Deadline April of each year.

[724]
ALPHA KAPPA ALPHA GRADUATE SCHOLARSHIPS

Alpha Kappa Alpha Sorority, Inc.
Attn: Educational Advancement Foundation
5656 South Stony Island Avenue
Chicago, IL 60637
(773) 947-0026   Toll Free: (800) 653-6528
Fax: (773) 947-0277   E-mail: akaeaf@akaeaf.net
Web: www.akaeaf.org/graduate_scholarships.htm

Summary To provide financial assistance for study or research to graduate students (especially African American women).

Eligibility This program is open to students who are working full time on a graduate degree in any state. Applicants may apply either for a scholarship based on merit (requires a GPA of 3.0 or higher) or on financial need (requires a GPA of 2.5 or higher). Along with their application, they must submit 1) a list of honors, awards, and scholarships received; 2) a list of organizations in which they have memberships, especially minority organizations; 3) a description of the project or research on which they are currently working, or (if they are not involved in a project or research) the aspects of their field that interest them; and 4) a statement of their personal and career goals, including how this scholarship will enhance their ability to attain those goals. The sponsor is a traditionally African American women's sorority.

Financial data Stipends range from $750 to $1,500 per year.

Duration 1 year; nonrenewable.

Number awarded Varies each year; recently, 60 of these scholarships, with a total value of $47,550, were awarded.

Deadline August of each year.

[725]
ALPHA OMICRON PI FOUNDATION NAMED SCHOLARSHIPS

Alpha Omicron Pi Foundation
Attn: Scholarship Committee
5390 Virginia Way
Brentwood, TN 37027
(615) 370-0920   Fax: (615) 370-4424
E-mail: foundation@alphaomicronpi.org
Web: www.aoiifoundation.org/scholarship.php

Summary To provide financial assistance for college or graduate school to collegiate and alumnae members of Alpha Omicron Pi who meet specified requirements.

Eligibility This program is open to collegiate members of Alpha Omicron Pi who are classified by their institutions at least as sophomores and alumnae members who wish to work on a graduate degree. Applicants must be able to qualify for specified awards by meeting extra requirements of each named award. They must be enrolled full time. Along with their application, they must submit the following 50-word statements: 1) the circumstances that have created their need for this scholarship; 2) their immediate and long-term life objectives; and 3) a letter of recommendation that they would write about themselves. Selection is based on those statements; academic achievement; Alpha Omicron Pi service, leadership, and involvement; college and community involvement; letters of recommendation; and financial need and evidence of self-help.

Financial data Stipend amounts vary; recently, the average value of each scholarship provided by this foundation was approximately $1,200.

Duration 1 year.

Additional information These named awards include the Muriel T. McKinney Scholarship for the highest-ranked undergraduate; the Helen Haller Scholarship for the highest-ranked graduate applicant; several for which membership in a particular chapter of the sorority is required or preferred; others which may be open to members in designated regions or states (the Angels of Kappa Theta Memorial Scholarship for collegiate members of southern California chapters, the Carey Griner Memorial Scholarship for collegiate members of Indiana colleges, the Jasmine Queen Scholarship for collegiate members of Maryland colleges, the Kappa Gamma Chapter Scholarship for collegiate members of Florida colleges, the Kerri Keith Memorial Scholarship for collegiate members of Georgia colleges, the Martha McKinney Wilhoite Scholarship for juniors or seniors who reside or attend college in Indiana, the Rho Omicron Chapter Scholarship for collegiate or alumna members who reside or attend college in Tennessee, and the San Diego Alumnae Chapter Honor Scholarship for alumna members who reside in California); the Caroline Craig Lazzara Scholarship for a member of a chapter that has been installed or re-colonized within the past 5 years; and a number of scholarships available to all Alpha Omicron Pi members (Karen Tucker Centennial Scholarship, Laura Gilliam McDowell Scholarship, Nancy McCain Memorial Scholarship, Nu Iota Scholarship in Memory of Julia V. Nelson and in Honor of Elaine Nelson Mackenzie, the Rho Chapter Scholarship, and the Robert and Eleanore MacCurdy Scholarship).

Number awarded Varies each year; recently, 23 of these scholarships were awarded (17 to undergraduates and 6 to graduate students).

Deadline February of each year.

[726]
ALPHA SIGMA TAU SCHOLARSHIPS

Alpha Sigma Tau National Foundation
Attn: Office Manager
P.O. Box 476
Gardendale, AL 35071
(205) 978-4512
E-mail: melinda@alphasigmataufoundation.org
Web: www.alphasigmataufoundation.org/scholarships

Summary To provide financial assistance to members of Alpha Sigma Tau sorority interested in continuing undergraduate or graduate study.

Eligibility This program is open to members of Alpha Sigma Tau who are sophomores, juniors, seniors, or graduate students. Applicants must have a GPA of 3.0 or higher. Along with their application, they must submit a 1-page essay on why they should receive this scholarship. Selection is based on academic achievement, service to Alpha Sigma Tau, academic honors, university or community service, and financial need.

Financial data Stipends range from $275 to $2,250.

Duration 1 year.

Number awarded Varies each year.

Deadline January of each year.

[727]
ALPHA THETA STATE SCHOLARSHIP AWARDS

Delta Kappa Gamma Society International-Alpha Theta State Organization
c/o Liz Naccarato, Scholarship Chair
4429 South 1025 East, Number B
Salt Lake City, UT 84124
Web: www.deltakappagamma.org/UT/scholarshipx.html

Summary To provide funding to members of Delta Kappa Gamma Society International in Utah who are interested in working on a graduate degree in education at a school in any state.

Eligibility This program is open to residents of Utah who have been members of Delta Kappa Gamma (an honorary society of women educators) for at least 3 years. Applicants must be engaged in graduate work leading to an advanced degree or a special certificate at an accredited institution of higher learning in any state. Selection is based on involvement and service to Delta Kappa Gamma, leadership, and professional promise. Recipients of Delta Kappa Gamma international scholarships are not eligible.

Financial data A stipend is awarded (amount not specified).

Duration 1 year.

Additional information Recipients are expected to remain members for at least 3 years following completion of the proposed program.

Number awarded 1 or more each year.

Deadline April of each year.

[728]
AMELIA EARHART FELLOWSHIP AWARDS

Zonta International
Attn: Foundation
1211 West 22nd Street, Suite 900
Oak Brook, IL 60523-3384
(630) 928-1400   Fax: (630) 928-1559
E-mail: programs@zonta.org
Web: www.zonta.org

Summary To provide financial assistance to women interested in doctoral study in scientific or engineering areas related to aerospace.

Eligibility This program is open to women who have a bachelor's degree in an area of science or engineering related to aerospace. Applicants must be registered as a full-time student at an accredited Ph.D. program at a recognized institution of higher learning and be able to provide evidence of a well-defined research and development program. They may be citizens of any country and studying in any country. Along with their application, they must submit a 500-word statement on their academic research program, their professional goals, and the relevance of their research program to aerospace-related sciences or engineering.

Financial data The stipend is $10,000, paid in 2 installments. Funds may be used for tuition, books, and fees.

Duration 1 year; renewable.

Additional information The fellowship may be used at any institution offering accredited courses in the applicant's field of study in the United States or abroad. Fellows may receive financial assistance from other programs. This program, established in 1938, is named for Amelia Earhart, famed air pioneer and Zontian, who disappeared over the Pacific in 1937.

Number awarded 35 each year. Since the program began, it has awarded nearly 1,300 of these fellowships, worth $7 million, to women from 64 countries.

Deadline November of each year.

[729]
AMELIA EARHART RESEARCH SCHOLAR GRANT

Ninety-Nines, Inc.
Attn: Chair, Research Scholar Grants
4300 Amelia Earhart Road
Oklahoma City, OK 73159
(405) 685-7969   Toll Free: (800) 994-1929
Fax: (405) 685-7985   E-mail: AEChair@ninety-nines.org
Web: www.ninety-nines.org/index.cfm/scholarships.htm

Summary To provide funding to scholars interested in expanding knowledge about women in aviation and space.

Eligibility This program is open to scholars who are conducting research on the role of women in aviation and space. Disciplines may include, but are not limited to, biology, business administration, economics, ergonomics, history, human engineering, psychology, and sociology. Applicants may be seeking funding to be used in conjunction with other research activities, such as completion of requirements for an advanced degree or matching funds with other grants to support a program larger than either grant could sponsor independently.

Financial data The amount awarded varies; generally, the grant is at least $1,000.

Duration The grant is awarded periodically.

Number awarded 1 each granting period.

Deadline Deadline not specified.

[730]
AMELIA KEMP MEMORIAL SCHOLARSHIP

Women of the Evangelical Lutheran Church in America
Attn: Scholarships
8765 West Higgins Road
Chicago, IL 60631-4101
(773) 380-2736   Toll Free: (800) 638-3522, ext. 2736
Fax: (773) 380-2419   E-mail: Women.elca@elca.org
Web: www.elca.org

Summary To provide financial assistance to lay women of color who are members of Evangelical Lutheran Church of America (ELCA) congregations and who wish to study on the undergraduate, graduate, professional, or vocational school level.

Eligibility This program is open to ELCA lay women of color who are at least 21 years of age and have experienced an interruption of at least 2 years in their education since high school. Applicants must have been admitted to an educational institution to prepare for a career in other than a church-certified profession. U.S. citizenship is required.

Financial data The maximum stipend is $1,000.

Duration Up to 2 years.

Number awarded 1 or more each year.

Deadline February of each year.

[731]
AMERICAN ASSOCIATION OF JAPANESE UNIVERSITY WOMEN SCHOLARSHIP PROGRAM

American Association of Japanese University Women
c/o Scholarship Committee
3543 West Boulevard
Los Angeles, CA 90016
E-mail: scholarship@aajuw.org
Web: www.aajuw.org/Scholarship.htm

Summary To provide financial assistance to female students currently enrolled in upper-division or graduate classes in California.

Eligibility This program is open to women enrolled at accredited colleges or universities in California as juniors, seniors, or graduate students. Applicants must be involved in U.S.-Japan relations, cultural exchanges, and leadership development in the areas of their designated field of study. Along with their application, they must submit a current resume, an official transcript of the past 2 years of college work, 2 letters of recommendation, and an essay (up to 2 pages in English or 1,200 characters in Japanese) on what they hope to accomplish in their field of study and how that will contribute to better U.S.-Japan relations.

Financial data The stipend is $2,000.

Duration 1 year.

Additional information The association was founded in 1970 to promote the education of women as well as to contribute to U.S.-Japan relations, cultural exchanges, and leadership development.

Number awarded 2 or 3 each year. Since this program was established, it has awarded nearly $100,000 worth of scholarships to more than 90 women.

Deadline October of each year.

[732]
AMERICAN ASSOCIATION OF UNIVERSITY WOMEN DISSERTATION FELLOWSHIPS

American Association of University Women
Attn: AAUW Educational Foundation
301 ACT Drive, Department 60
P.O. Box 4030
Iowa City, IA 52243-4030
(319) 337-1716, ext. 60   Fax: (319) 337-1204
E-mail: aauw@act.org
Web: www.aauw.org/learn/fellowships_grants/american.cfm

Summary To provide funding to women in the final year of writing their dissertation.

Eligibility This program is open to U.S. citizens and permanent residents who are women and intend to pursue professional careers in the United States. They should have successfully completed all required course work for their doctorate, passed all preliminary examinations, and received written acceptance of their prospectus. Applicants may propose research in any field. Selection is based on scholarly excellence, quality of project design, originality of project, scholarly significance of project to discipline, feasibility of project and proposed schedule, qualifications of applicant, potential of applicant to make a significant contribution to field, applicant's teaching experience, applicant's commitment to women's issues in profession and community, and applicant's mentoring of other women.

Financial data The stipend is $20,000.

Duration 1 year, beginning in July.

Additional information The filing fee is $40. It is expected that the fellowship will be used for the final year of doctoral work and that the degree will be received at the end of the fellowship year. The fellowship is not intended to fund extended field research. The recipient should be prepared to devote full time to the dissertation during the fellowship year.

Number awarded Varies each year; recently, 44 of these fellowships were awarded.

Deadline November of each year.

[733]
AMERICAN BAPTIST WOMEN'S MINISTRIES OF COLORADO STUDENT GRANTS

American Baptist Churches of the Rocky Mountains
Attn: American Baptist Women's Ministries
9085 East Mineral Circle, Suite 170
Centennial, CO 80112
(303) 988-3900   E-mail: web@abcrm.org
Web: www.abcrm.org

Summary To provide financial assistance to women who are members of churches affiliated with the American Baptist Churches (ABC) USA in Colorado, New Mexico, and Utah and interested in attending an ABC college or seminary in any state.

Eligibility This program is open to women older than 26 years of age who are active members of churches cooperating with ABC in Colorado, New Mexico, or Utah. Applicants must be enrolled or planning to enroll at an ABC college, university, or seminary in any state. Along with their application, they must submit a personal letter describing their Christian experience; their participation in the life of their church, school, and community; and their goals for the future. Selection is based on academic performance, Christian participation in church and school, and financial need.

Financial data A stipend is awarded (amount not specified). Funds are sent directly to the recipient's school.

Duration 1 year; recipients may reapply.

Number awarded 1 or more each year.

Deadline March of each year.

[734]
AMERICAN BAPTIST WOMEN'S MINISTRIES OF MASSACHUSETTS SCHOLARSHIP PROGRAM

American Baptist Women's Ministries of Massachusetts
c/o Penny Mulloy, Scholarship Committee Chair
27 Ox Road
Billerica, MA 01821-4439
(978) 667-7496   E-mail: pennymulloy@gmail.com
Web: www.abwmofma.org

Summary To provide financial assistance to American Baptist women in Massachusetts interested in church-related vocations.

Eligibility This program is open to women who intend to offer Christian service in their chosen vocation, have been active members of an American Baptist Church in Massachusetts for at least 1 year prior to submitting an application, and

are able to supply satisfactory references. They must be nominated by their pastor. Applicants should include a written statement of faith and a separate letter of life purpose that clearly indicates how they intend to serve in the Christian community after their education is completed. Selection is based on dedication, need, and scholastic ability.

Financial data A stipend is awarded (amount not specified).

Duration 1 year; may be renewed.

Additional information Of the scholarships awarded, 2 are designated as the Lenore S. Bigelow Scholarships, for graduate study at Andover Newton Theological School in Newton Centre, Massachusetts and/or Colgate-Rochester Divinity School in Rochester, New York. An interview with the committee or designated members is required of first-time applicants.

Number awarded Varies each year.

Deadline April of each year.

[735]
AMERICAN BAPTIST WOMEN'S MINISTRIES OF NEW YORK STATE SCHOLARSHIPS

American Baptist Women's Ministries of New York State
Attn: Scholarship Committee
5865 East Seneca Turnpike
Jamesville, NY 13078
(315) 469-4236   Fax: (315) 492-2369
E-mail: isingram@rochester.rr.com
Web: www.abwm-nys.org/M_M/scholarship.html

Summary To provide financial assistance to women who are members of American Baptist Churches in New York and interested in attending college in any state.

Eligibility This program is open to women who are residents of New York and active members of an American Baptist Church. Applicants must be enrolled or planning to enroll full time at a college or university in any state. While in college, they must maintain Christian fellowship, preferably with the American Baptist Church (although any Protestant church or campus ministry is acceptable). Along with their application, they must submit a 1-page essay on an event that occurred in their life during the past year and how it has impacted their faith. Women may be of any age; graduate students are considered on an individual basis. Financial need is considered in the selection process.

Financial data A stipend is awarded (amount not specified).

Duration 1 year.

Number awarded Varies each year.

Deadline February of each year.

[736]
AMERICAN BAPTIST WOMEN'S MINISTRIES OF WISCONSIN ADULT WOMEN SEMINARY SCHOLARSHIP

American Baptist Women's Ministries of Wisconsin
c/o Lois A. Horsman, Scholarship Committee Chair
P.O. Box 68
Wyocena, WI 53969
(608) 429-2483
Web: www.abcofwi.org/abwinfo.htm

Summary To provide financial assistance to female members of American Baptist Churches in Wisconsin who are interested in attending a seminary in any state that is affiliated with the denomination.

Eligibility This program is open to adult women who are residents of Wisconsin and attending or planning to attend an American Baptist seminary in any state. Applicants must have been an active member of an American Baptist Church in Wisconsin for the preceding 3 years. They must have graduated from a college affiliated with the American Baptist Churches USA.

Financial data A stipend is awarded (amount not specified).

Duration 1 year.

Number awarded 1 or more each year.

Deadline Deadline not specified.

[737]
AMERICAN COLLEGE OF NURSE-MIDWIVES FOUNDATION FELLOWSHIP FOR GRADUATE EDUCATION

American College of Nurse-Midwives
Attn: ACNM Foundation, Inc.
8403 Colesville Road, Suite 1550
Silver Spring, MD 20910-6374
(240) 485-1850   Fax: (240) 485-1818
Web: www.midwife.org/foundation_award.cfm

Summary To provide financial assistance for midwifery education to graduate student members of the American College of Nurse-Midwives (ACNM).

Eligibility This program is open to ACNM members who are currently enrolled in a doctoral or postdoctoral midwife education program. Applicants must be a certified nurse midwife (CNM) or a certified midwife (CM). Along with their application, they must submit a curriculum vitae; a sample of up to 30 pages of scholarly work; and brief essays on their 5-year academic career plans, intended use of the fellowship money, and intended future participation in the local, regional, and/or national activities of ACNM or other activities that contribute to midwifery research, education, or practice.

Financial data A stipend is awarded (amount not specified).

Duration 1 year.

Additional information This program was established in 1997.

Number awarded 1 each year.

Deadline March of each year.

[738]
AMERICAN MEDICAL WOMEN'S ASSOCIATION SCHOLARSHIPS

American Medical Women's Association
Attn: National Student Leadership
100 North 20th Street, Fourth Floor
Philadelphia, PA 19103
(215) 320-3716   Toll Free: (866) 564-2483
Fax: (215) 564-2175   E-mail: awards@amwa-student.org
Web: www.amwa-doc.org/page3-112/AwardsScholarships

Summary To provide financial assistance for medical education to student members of the American Medical Women's Association (AMWA).

Eligibility This program is open to student members of the association currently enrolled in medical school. Applicants must submit brief statements on a situation in which they demonstrated leadership, their involvement in AMWA, their plans for future AMWA involvement, and their goals for women in medicine. Financial need is considered but is not required.

Financial data The stipend is $1,000.

Duration 1 year.

Number awarded 2 each year.

Deadline January or September of each year.

[739]
AMERICAN METEOROLOGICAL SOCIETY GRADUATE FELLOWSHIP IN THE HISTORY OF SCIENCE

American Meteorological Society
Attn: Fellowship/Scholarship Program
45 Beacon Street
Boston, MA 02108-3693
(617) 227-2426, ext. 246   Fax: (617) 742-8718
E-mail: scholar@ametsoc.org
Web: www.ametsoc.org

Summary To provide funding to women, minority, and other graduate student members of the American Meteorological Society (AMS) who are interested in conducting dissertation research on the history of meteorology.

Eligibility This program is open to AMS members and student members who are planning to complete a doctoral dissertation on the history of the atmospheric or related oceanic or hydrologic sciences. Applicants must be U.S. citizens or permanent residents and working on a degree at a U.S. institution. Fellowships may be used to support research at a location away from the student's institution, provided the plan is approved by the student's thesis adviser. In such an instance, an effort is made to place the student into a mentoring relationship with a member of the society at an appropriate institution. The sponsor specifically encourages applications from women, minorities, and students with disabilities who are traditionally underrepresented in the atmospheric and related oceanic sciences.

Financial data The stipend is $15,000.

Duration 1 year.

Number awarded 1 each year.

Deadline February of each year.

[740]
ANDREW W. MELLON FOUNDATION/ACLS DISSERTATION COMPLETION FELLOWSHIPS

American Council of Learned Societies
Attn: Office of Fellowships and Grants
633 Third Avenue
New York, NY 10017-6795
(212) 697-1505   Fax: (212) 949-8058
E-mail: fellowships@acls.org
Web: www.acls.org/programs/dcf

Summary To provide research funding to women, minority, and other doctoral candidates in all disciplines of the humanities and the humanities-related social sciences who are ready to complete their dissertations.

Eligibility This program is open to doctoral candidates in a humanities or humanities-related social science discipline at a U.S. institution. Applicants must have completed all requirements for the Ph.D. except the dissertation. They must not have completed more than 6 years in the degree program. Research may be conducted at the home institution, abroad, or another appropriate site. Appropriate fields of specialization include, but are not limited to, American studies; anthropology; archaeology; art and architectural history; classics; economics; film; geography; history; languages and literatures; legal studies; linguistics; musicology; philosophy; political science; psychology; religious studies; rhetoric, communication, and media studies; sociology; and theater, dance, and performance studies. Proposals in the social sciences are eligible only if they employ predominantly humanistic approaches (e.g., economic history, law and literature, political philosophy). Proposals in interdisciplinary and cross-disciplinary studies are welcome, as are proposals focused on a geographic region or on a cultural or linguistic group. Applications are particularly invited from women and members of minority groups.

Financial data Grants provide a stipend of $25,000, funds for research costs up to $3,000, and payment of university fees up to $5,000.

Duration 1 academic year. Grantees may accept this fellowship no later than their seventh year.

Additional information This program, which began in 2006, is supported by funding from the Andrew W. Mellon Foundation and administered by the American Council of Learned Societies (ACLS).

Number awarded 65 each year.

Deadline November of each year.

[741]
ANITA BORG MEMORIAL SCHOLARSHIPS

Google Inc.
Attn: Scholarships
1600 Amphitheatre Parkway
Mountain View, CA 94043-8303
(650) 253-0000   Fax: (650) 253-0001
E-mail: anitaborgscholarship@google.com
Web: www.google.com/intl/en/anitaborg/us

Summary To provide financial assistance to women working on a bachelor's or graduate degree in a computer-related field.

Eligibility This program is open to women who are entering their senior year of undergraduate study or are enrolled in a graduate program in computer science, computer engineering, or a closely-related field. Applicants must be full-time students at a university in the United States and have a GPA of 3.5 or higher. They must submit essays of 400 to 600 words on 1) a significant technical project on which they have worked; 2) their leadership abilities; 3) what they would do if someone gave them the funding and resources for a 3- to 12-month project to investigate a technical topic of their choice; and 4) what they would do if someone gave them $1,000 to plan an event or project to benefit women in technical fields. Citizens, permanent residents, and international students are eligible. Selection is based on academic background and demonstrated leadership.

Financial data The stipend is $10,000 per year.

Duration 1 year; recipients may reapply.

Additional information These scholarships were first offered in 2004.

Number awarded Varies each year; recently, 25 of these scholarships were awarded.

Deadline January of each year.

[742]
ANN CLARK NURSING SCHOLARSHIP

American Association of University Women-Honolulu Branch
Attn: Scholarship Committee
1802 Ke'eaumoku Street
Honolulu, HI 96822
(808) 537-4702   Fax: (808) 537-4702
E-mail: Edu@aauw-honolulu.org
Web: aauw.xodev01.com

Summary To provide financial assistance to women in Hawaii who are interested in working on an advanced degree in nursing at a school in the state.

Eligibility This program is open to female residents of Hawaii who are currently enrolled in an R.N. to B.S.N., M.S.N., or nursing doctoral program in the state. Applicants must submit a 500-word biographical statement that includes information on their family, work, school, community service, and future goals. Financial need is not considered in the selection process.

Financial data A stipend is awarded (amount not specified).

Duration 1 year.

Number awarded 1 or more each year.

Deadline May of each year.

[743]
ANN E. DICKERSON SCHOLARSHIPS

Christian Church (Disciples of Christ)
Attn: Higher Education and Leadership Ministries
11477 Olde Cabin Road, Suite 310
St. Louis, MO 63141-7130
(314) 991-3000   Fax: (314) 991-2957
E-mail: helm@helmdisciples.org
Web: www.helmdisciples.org/aid/dickerson.htm

Summary To provide financial assistance to female members of the Christian Church (Disciples of Christ) who are working on a Ph.D. degree in religion.

Eligibility This program is open to women working on a Ph.D. degree in religion. Applicants must members of the Christian Church (Disciples of Christ). Along with their application, they must submit a 300-word essay describing their vocational goals, their academic interests, and how they envision being of service to the church.

Financial data The stipend is $2,000.

Duration 1 year.

Number awarded 3 each year.

Deadline April of each year.

[744]
ANN HERSHFANG/HELENE M. OVERLY MEMORIAL SCHOLARSHIP

Women's Transportation Seminar-Boston Chapter
c/o Sasha Wood
Tetra Tech Rizzo
One Grant Street
Framingham, MA 01701
(508) 902-2000   E-mail: sasha.wood@tetratech.com
Web: www.wtsinternational.org/Chapters.aspx/ID=6758

Summary   To provide financial assistance to women working on a transportation-related graduate degree at a college or university in Massachusetts.

Eligibility   This program is open to women enrolled at colleges and universities in Massachusetts who are working on a graduate degree in a transportation-related field, including transportation engineering, planning, finance, or logistics. Applicants must have a GPA of 3.0 or higher and plans to prepare for a career in a transportation-related field. Along with their application, they must submit a 750-word personal statement about their career goals after graduation and why they think they should receive this scholarship. Selection is based on the applicant's specific transportation involvement and goals, job skills, and academic record. Minority women are especially encouraged to apply.

Financial data   The stipend is $4,000.

Duration   1 year.

Additional information   This program was established in 2007.

Number awarded   1 or more each year.

Deadline   November of each year.

[745]
ANNE C. CARTER STUDENT LEADERSHIP AWARD

American Medical Women's Association
Attn: National Student Leadership
100 North 20th Street, Fourth Floor
Philadelphia, PA 19103
(215) 320-3716   Toll Free: (866) 564-2483
Fax: (215) 564-2175   E-mail: awards@amwa-student.org
Web: www.amwa-doc.org/page3-112/AwardsScholarships

Summary   To recognize and reward student members of the American Medical Women's Association (AMWA) who have demonstrated exceptional leadership skills.

Eligibility   This program is open to student members of the association who are nominated by their chapter. Nominees must have demonstrated exceptional leadership skills through vision, inspiration, innovation, and coordination of local projects that further the mission of AMWA by improving women's health and/or supporting women in medicine.

Financial data   The award is $1,000. The nominating chapter also receives an award of $1,000 to be used at its discretion.

Duration   The award is presented annually.

Additional information   This award was first presented in 2004.

Number awarded   1 each year.

Deadline   December of each year.

[746]
ANNETTE URSO RICKEL DISSERTATION AWARD FOR PUBLIC POLICY

American Psychological Foundation
750 First Street, N.E.
Washington, DC 20002-4242
(202) 336-5843   Fax: (202) 336-5812
E-mail: foundation@apa.org
Web: www.apa.org/apf/funding/rickel.aspx

Summary   To provide funding to women, minority, and other psychology doctoral students interested in conducting dissertation research related to public policy on services for children and families.

Eligibility   This program is open to graduate students who are enrolled full time in a graduate program in psychology at an accredited college or university in the United States or Canada. Applicants must be interested in conducting dissertation research on public policy that has the potential to improve services for children and families facing psychological issues. Examples of eligible topics include, but are not limited to, issues with at-risk populations, prevention of child abuse, services for youth in the criminal justice system, effectiveness of school programs for children with psychological issues, using psychology in public policy to improve mathematics and science education, and promoting health parenting. The sponsor encourages applications from individuals who represent diversity in race, ethnicity, gender, age, disability, and sexual orientation.

Financial data   The stipend is $1,000.

Duration   1 year.

Number awarded   1 each year.

Deadline   October of each year.

[747]
AOS/NORMAN'S ORCHIDS MASTERS SCHOLARSHIP

American Orchid Society
16700 AOS Lane
Delray Beach, FL 33446-4351
(561) 404-2000   Fax: (561) 404-2045
E-mail: TheAOS@aos.org
Web: www.aos.org

Summary   To provide funding for research to students (particularly women, minorities, and students with disabilities) who are working on a master's degree in a field related to orchids.

Eligibility   This program is open to students working on a master's degree at an accredited institution. Applicants must have a thesis project that deals with an aspect of orchid education, applied science, or orchid biology in the disciplines of physiology, molecular biology, structure, systematics, cytology, ecology, or evolution. They must submit a current curriculum vitae, transcripts of all college course work, a synopsis of the proposed project or research, a 1-page statement of the value of their project and importance to the future of orchid education or orchidology, and a letter of recommendation from their chairperson. Women, minorities, and persons with disabilities are especially encouraged to apply.

Financial data   The grant is $5,000 per year. Funds are paid through the recipient's college or university, but institutional overhead is not allowed.

Duration 2 years.

Additional information This program, established in 2005, is supported by Norman's Orchids of Montclair, California.

Number awarded 1 each year.

Deadline February of each year.

[748]
APF/COGDOP GRADUATE RESEARCH SCHOLARSHIPS

American Psychological Foundation
750 First Street, N.E.
Washington, DC 20002-4242
(202) 336-5843   Fax: (202) 336-5812
E-mail: foundation@apa.org
Web: www.apa.org/apf/funding/cogdop.aspx

Summary To provide funding for research to graduate students in psychology, particularly those who are women, minorities, or disabled.

Eligibility Each department of psychology that is a member in good standing of the Council of Graduate Departments of Psychology (COGDOP) may nominate up to 3 candidates for these scholarships. Nominations must include a completed application form, a letter of nomination from the department chair or director of graduate studies, a letter of recommendation from the nominee's graduate research adviser, a transcript of all graduate course work completed by the nominee, a curriculum vitae, and a brief outline of the nominee's thesis or dissertation research project. Selection is based on the context for the research, the clarity and comprehensibility of the research question, the appropriateness of the research design, the general importance of the research, and the use of requested funds. The sponsor encourages applications from individuals who represent diversity in race, ethnicity, gender, age, disability, and sexual orientation.

Financial data Awards range from $1,000 to $5,000 per year. A total of $20,000 is available for these scholarships each year.

Duration 1 year.

Additional information The highest rated nominee receives the Harry and Miriam Levinson Scholarship of $5,000. The second highest rated nominee receives the Ruth G. and Joseph D. Matarazzo Scholarship of $3,000. The third highest rated nominee receives the Clarence Rosecrans Scholarship of $2,000. The other scholarships include the Peter and Malina James and Dr. Louis P. James Legacy Scholarship of $1,000.

Number awarded 13 each year: 1 at $5,000, 1 at $3,000, 1 at $2,000, and 10 at $1,000.

Deadline June of each year.

[749]
AREVA NP SCHOLARSHIP

Society of Women Engineers-Eastern Washington Section
Attn: Sandy Brower, Scholarship Committee Chair
P.O. Box 364
Richland, WA 99352
(509) 375-3112   E-mail: embrower@aol.com
Web: www.eastwashingtonswe.org

Summary To provide financial assistance to female residents of the northwestern United States who are working on an undergraduate or graduate degree in nuclear engineering at a school in any state.

Eligibility This program is open to female residents of Alaska, Idaho, Montana, Oregon, and Washington who have completed at least 1 year of study at an ABET-accredited school in any state. Applicants must be planning to work on an undergraduate or graduate degree in nuclear engineering in the following year. Along with their application, they must submit an essay of 100 to 300 words on their short-term and long-term career goals, their plan to reach those goals, how they decided on their course of study, their interest in a career in nuclear energy, and anything else about themselves or their situation that could affect the evaluation of their application. Financial need and academic success are considered in the selection process, but greater weight is given to the applicant's affiliation with AREVA NP (e.g., internship, summer job, family member employed by the company), intention to enter the nuclear energy industry, motivation, leadership potential, and ability to follow projects through to completion. All other factors being equal, preference is given to residents of eastern Washington.

Financial data The stipend is $1,000.

Duration 1 year.

Additional information This program is sponsored by AREVA NP Inc.

Number awarded 1 each year.

Deadline February of each year.

[750]
ARFORA/MARTHA GAVRILA SCHOLARSHIP FOR WOMEN

Association of Romanian Orthodox Ladies Auxiliaries of North America
Attn: Scholarship Committee
222 Orchard Park Drive
New Castle, PA 16105
(724) 652-4313   E-mail: adelap@verizon.net
Web: www.arfora.org/scholarships.htm

Summary To provide financial assistance to women who are members of a parish of the Romanian Orthodox Episcopate of America and interested in working on a graduate degree.

Eligibility This program is open to women who have been voting communicant members of a parish of the Romanian Orthodox Episcopate of America for at least 1 year. Applicants must have completed a baccalaureate degree and been accepted as a graduate student at a college or university in any state. Along with their application, they must submit a 300-word statement describing their personal goals; high school, university, church, and community involvement; honors and awards; and why they should be considered for this award. Selection is based on academic achievement, character, worthiness, and participation in religious life.

Financial data The stipend is $1,000.

Duration 1 year.

Additional information This scholarship was first awarded in 1985. The Association of Romanian Orthodox Ladies Auxiliaries (ARFORA) was established in 1938 as a women's organization within the Romanian Orthodox Episcopate of America.

Number awarded   1 each year.

Deadline   May of each year.

[751]
ARMY JUDGE ADVOCATE GENERAL CORPS SUMMER INTERN PROGRAM

U.S. Army
Attn: Judge Advocate Recruiting Office
1777 North Kent Street, Suite 5200
Rosslyn, VA 22209-2194
(703) 696-2822   Toll Free: (866) ARMY-JAG
Fax: (703) 588-0100
Web: www.goarmy.com/jag/summer_intern_program.jsp

Summary   To provide an opportunity for law students (particularly women and minorities) to gain work experience during the summer in Army legal offices throughout the United States and overseas.

Eligibility   This program is open to full-time students enrolled in law schools accredited by the American Bar Association. Applications are accepted both from students who are completing the first year of law school and those completing the second year. Students must be interested in a summer internship with the Army Judge Advocate General's Corps (JAGC). U.S. citizenship is required. The program actively seeks applications from women and minority group members. Selection is based on academic ability and demonstrated leadership potential.

Financial data   Interns who have completed the first year of law school are paid at the GS-5 scale, starting at $474 per week. Interns who have completed the second year of law school are paid at the GS-7 scale, starting at $588 per week.

Duration   Approximately 60 days, beginning in May or June.

Additional information   Interns work under the supervision of an attorney and perform legal research, write briefs and opinions, conduct investigations, interview witnesses, and otherwise assist in preparing civil or criminal cases. Positions are available at Department of the Army legal offices in Washington, D.C. and at Army installations throughout the United States and overseas. These are not military positions. No military obligation is incurred by participating in the summer intern program.

Number awarded   100 per year: 25 first-year students and 75 second-year students.

Deadline   February of each year for first-year students; October of each year for second-year students.

[752]
ARNE ADMINISTRATIVE LEADERSHIP SCHOLARSHIP

Women of the Evangelical Lutheran Church in America
Attn: Scholarships
8765 West Higgins Road
Chicago, IL 60631-4101
(773) 380-2736   Toll Free: (800) 638-3522, ext. 2736
Fax: (773) 380-2419   E-mail: Women.elca@elca.org
Web: www.elca.org

Summary   To provide financial assistance to women members of congregations of the Evangelical Lutheran Church of America (ELCA) who wish to train for administrative positions.

Eligibility   This program is open to women members of the ELCA who have completed a bachelor's degree or its equivalent and have taken some academic or professional courses since completing that degree. Applicants must have been admitted to an academic institution as a full-time student to take regular classes, night courses, or summer session. U.S. citizenship is required. Selection is based on records of graduate academic or professional courses, examples of being a decision-maker, and evidence of ability and willingness to study.

Financial data   The maximum stipend is $1,000.

Duration   Up to 2 years.

Additional information   This program was established in 1998.

Number awarded   Varies each year.

Deadline   February of each year.

[753]
ASSOCIATION FOR WOMEN IN SPORTS MEDIA SCHOLARSHIP/INTERNSHIP PROGRAM

Association for Women in Sports Media
Attn: President
3899 North Front Street
Harrisburg, PA 17110
(717) 703-3086   E-mail: internships@awsmonline.org
Web: awsmonline.org/intern-scholarship

Summary   To provide financial assistance and work experience to women undergraduate and graduate students who are interested in preparing for a career in sports writing.

Eligibility   This program is open to women who are enrolled in college or graduate school full time and preparing for a career in sports writing, sports copy editing, sports broadcasting, or sports public relations. Applicants must submit a 750-word essay describing their most memorable experience in sports or sports media, a 1-page resume highlighting their journalism experience, a letter of recommendation, up to 5 samples of their work, and a $20 application fee. They must apply for and accept an internship with a sports media organization.

Financial data   The highest-ranked applicant receives a $1,000 scholarship and a paid trip to the sponsor's convention (including hotel stay, reimbursement for travel, and free convention registration). Other winners receive a $500 scholarship. Half of the funds are paid at the beginning of the internship and half after its completion.

Duration   1 year; nonrenewable.

Additional information   This program, which began in 1990, includes the Jackie and Gene Autry Memorial Scholarship, the Jim Brennan Scholarship, and the Betty Brennan Scholarship.

Number awarded   At least 12 each year.

Deadline   October of each year.

[754]
ASSOCIATION FOR WOMEN LAWYERS FOUNDATION SCHOLARSHIPS

Association for Women Lawyers
Attn: AWL Foundation
3322 North 92nd Street
Milwaukee, WI 53222
(414) 463-0758   Fax: (414) 463-0759
E-mail: dana@barefoot-marketing.com
Web: www.wisbar.org

Summary   To provide financial assistance to women who are attending law school in Wisconsin.

Eligibility   This program is open to women from any state currently enrolled at law schools in Wisconsin. Applicants must be able to demonstrate academic achievement, service to others, diversity, unique life experience or circumstance, commitment to advancement of women in the profession, and financial need.

Financial data   The stipend varies; recently, awards averaged $2,500.

Duration   1 year.

Additional information   This program was established in 1998.

Number awarded   Varies each year; recently, 2 of these scholarships were awarded.

Deadline   June of each year.

[755]
AT&T LABORATORIES FELLOWSHIP PROGRAM

AT&T Laboratories
Attn: Fellowship Administrator
180 Park Avenue, Room C103
P.O. Box 971
Florham Park, NJ 07932-0971
(973) 360-8109   Fax: (973) 360-8881
E-mail: recruiting@research.att.com
Web: www.research.att.com

Summary   To provide financial assistance and work experience to women and underrepresented minority students who are working on a doctoral degree in computer and technology-related fields.

Eligibility   This program is open to minorities underrepresented in the sciences (African Americans, Hispanics, and Native Americans) and to women. Applicants must be U.S. citizens or permanent residents who are graduating college seniors or graduate students enrolled in their first or second year. They must be working on or planning to work on a Ph.D. in a field of study relevant to the business of AT&T; currently, those include computer science, electrical engineering, industrial engineering, mathematics, operations research, systems engineering, statistics, and related fields. Along with their application, they must submit a personal statement on why they are enrolled in their present academic program and how they intend to use their technical training, official transcripts, 3 academic references, and GRE scores. Selection is based on potential for success in scientific research.

Financial data   This program covers all educational expenses during the school year, including tuition, books, fees, and approved travel expenses; educational expenses for summer study or university research; a stipend for living expenses (recently, $2,380 per month); and support for attending approved scientific conferences.

Duration   1 year; may be renewed for up to 2 additional years, as long as the fellow continues making satisfactory progress toward the Ph.D.

Additional information   The AT&T Laboratories Fellowship Program (ALFP) provides a mentor who is a staff member at AT&T Labs as well as a summer research internship within AT&T Laboratories during the first summer. The ALFP replaces the Graduate Research Program for Women (GRPW) and the Cooperative Research Fellowship Program (CRFP) run by the former AT&T Bell Laboratories. If recipients accept other support, the tuition payment and stipend received from that fellowship will replace that provided by this program. The other provisions of this fellowship will remain in force and the stipend will be replaced by an annual grant of $2,000.

Number awarded   Approximately 8 each year.

Deadline   January of each year.

[756]
AWHONN NOVICE RESEARCHER AWARD

Association of Women's Health, Obstetric and Neonatal Nurses
Attn: Research Grants Program
2000 L Street, N.W., Suite 740
Washington, DC 20036
(202) 261-2431   Toll Free: (800) 673-8499, ext. 2431
Fax: (202) 728-0575
E-mail: ResearchPrograms@awhonn.org
Web: www.awhonn.org

Summary   To provide funding for small research projects to members of the Association of Women's Health, Obstetric and Neonatal Nurses (AWHONN) who qualify as novice researchers.

Eligibility   This program is open to members of the association who have at least a master's degree or are currently enrolled in a master's program and completing a thesis or clinical research project. Applicants must be interested in beginning areas of study, investigating clinical issues, and/or launching a pilot study. They must identify a senior researcher who has agreed to serve as mentor and who submits a letter of support describing the role he or she will be implementing.

Financial data   The grant is $5,000. Funds may not be used for indirect costs, tuition, computer hardware or printers, conference attendance, or salary for the principal investigator or other investigators.

Duration   1 year.

Number awarded   1 each year.

Deadline   November of each year.

[757]
BAKER HUGHES SCHOLARSHIPS

Society of Women Engineers
Attn: Scholarship Selection Committee
120 South LaSalle Street, Suite 1515
Chicago, IL 60603-3572
(312) 596-5223   Toll Free: (877) SWE-INFO
Fax: (312) 644-8557
E-mail: scholarshipapplication@swe.org
Web: societyofwomenengineers.swe.org

Summary To provide financial assistance to women working on an undergraduate or graduate degree in designated engineering specialties.

Eligibility This program is open to women who are sophomores, juniors, seniors, or graduate students at 4-year ABET-accredited colleges and universities. Applicants must be working on a degree in computer science or chemical, electrical, mechanical, or petroleum engineering and have a GPA of 3.0 or higher. Preference is given to members of groups underrepresented in engineering or computer science. Selection is based on merit.

Financial data The stipend is $5,000 per year.

Duration 1 year; may be renewed up to 2 additional years.

Additional information This program is sponsored by Baker Hughes Incorporated.

Number awarded 3 each year.

Deadline February of each year.

[758]
BANNER ENGINEERING MINNESOTA SWE SCHOLARSHIP

Society of Women Engineers-Minnesota Section
Attn: Scholarship Committee
P.O. Box 582813
Minneapolis, MN 55458-2813
E-mail: scholarships@swe-mn.org
Web: swe-mn.org/scholarships.html

Summary To provide financial assistance to women from any state working on an undergraduate or graduate degree in electrical or mechanical engineering at colleges and universities in Minnesota, North Dakota, and South Dakota.

Eligibility This program is open to female undergraduate and graduate students at ABET-accredited engineering programs in Minnesota, North Dakota, or South Dakota. Applicants must be working full time on a degree in electrical or mechanical engineering. Along with their application, they must submit a short paragraph describing how they plan to utilize their engineering skills after they graduate. Selection is based on potential to succeed as an engineer (20 points), communication skills (10 points), extracurricular or community involvement and leadership skills (10 points), demonstrated successful work experience (10 points), and academic success (5 points).

Financial data The stipend is $2,000.

Duration 1 year.

Additional information This program is sponsored by Banner Engineering Corporation.

Number awarded 1 each year.

Deadline March of each year.

[759]
BAPTIST WOMEN IN MINISTRY OF NORTH CAROLINA STUDENT SCHOLARSHIPS

Baptist Women in Ministry of North Carolina
Attn: Geneva Metzger, Convener
2604 Overbrook Drive
Greensboro, NC 27408-5313
(336) 288-1877   E-mail: mizzometzger@yahoo.com
Web: www.bwimnc.org/Scholarships.html

Summary To provide financial assistance to women ministerial students enrolled at North Carolina Baptist institutions.

Eligibility This program is open to women working on a graduate degree in theological education at North Carolina Baptist institutions. Applicants must be able to demonstrate a clear call and commitment to vocational Christian ministry, academic excellence, leadership skills, and expressed support of inclusiveness in all dimensions of life.

Financial data The stipend is $1,000.

Duration 1 year.

Additional information The eligible schools include Duke Divinity School, Campbell University Divinity School, M. Christopher White School of Divinity at Gardner-Webb University, and the Wake Forest University Divinity School.

Number awarded 4 each year: 1 at each of the eligible schools.

Deadline Deadline not specified.

[760]
BARBARA ALICE MOWER MEMORIAL SCHOLARSHIP

Barbara Alice Mower Memorial Scholarship Committee
c/o Nancy A. Mower
1536 Kamole Street
Honolulu, HI 96821-1424
(808) 373-2901   E-mail: nmower@hawaii.edu

Summary To provide financial assistance to female residents of Hawaii who are interested in women's studies and are attending studying on the undergraduate or graduate level in the United States or abroad.

Eligibility This program is open to female residents of Hawaii who are at least juniors in college, are interested in and committed to women's studies, and have worked or studied in the field. Selection is based on interest in studying about and commitment to helping women, previous work and/or study in that area, previous academic performance, character, personality, and future plans to help women (particularly women in Hawaii). If there are several applicants who meet all these criteria, then financial need may be taken into consideration.

Financial data The stipend ranges from $1,000 to $3,500.

Duration 1 year; may be renewed.

Additional information Recipients may use the scholarship at universities in Hawaii, on the mainland, or in foreign countries. They must focus on women's studies or topics that relate to women in school.

Number awarded 1 or more each year.

Deadline April of each year.

[761]
BARBARA GIBSON FROEMMING SCHOLARSHIP

Kappa Delta Sorority
Attn: Foundation Manager
3205 Players Lane
Memphis, TN 38125
(901) 748-1897   Toll Free: (800) 536-1897
Fax: (901) 748-0949 E-mail: kappadelta@kappadelta.org
Web: www.kappadelta.org/scholarships

Summary To provide financial assistance to members of Kappa Delta Sorority who are working on a graduate degree in education.

Eligibility This program is open to graduate members of Kappa Delta Sorority. Applicants must submit a personal statement giving their reasons for applying for this scholarship, official undergraduate and graduate transcripts, and 2 letters of recommendation. They must be working on a graduate degree in education. Selection is based on academic excellence; service to the chapter, alumnae association, or national Kappa Delta; service to the campus and community; personal objectives and goals; potential; recommendations; and financial need.

Financial data The stipend is $2,000 per year. Funds may be used only for tuition, fees, and books, not for room and board.

Duration 1 year; may be renewed.

Additional information This program was established in 2007.

Number awarded 1 each year.

Deadline January of each year.

[762]
BARBARA MCBRIDE SCHOLARSHIP

Society of Exploration Geophysicists
Attn: SEG Foundation
8801 South Yale, Suite 500
P.O. Box 702740
Tulsa, OK 74170-2740
(918) 497-5500   Fax: (918) 497-5557
E-mail: scholarships@seg.org
Web: www.seg.org/web/foundation/programs/scholarship

Summary To provide financial assistance to women who are interested in studying applied geophysics or a related field on the undergraduate or graduate school level.

Eligibility This program is open to women who are 1) high school students planning to enter college in the fall, or 2) undergraduate or graduate students whose grades are above average. Applicants must intend to work on a degree directed toward a career in applied geophysics or a closely-related field (e.g., geosciences, physics, geology, or earth and environmental sciences). Along with their application, they must submit a 150-word essay on how they plan to use geophysics in their future. Financial need is not considered in the selection process.

Financial data Stipends provided by this sponsor average $2,500 per year.

Duration 1 academic year; may be renewable, based on scholastic standing, availability of funds, and continuance of a course of study leading to a career in applied geophysics.

Number awarded 1 each year.

Deadline February of each year.

[763]
BARBARA ROSENBLUM CANCER DISSERTATION SCHOLARSHIP

Sociologists for Women in Society
Attn: Executive Officer
University of Rhode Island
Department of Sociology
10 Chafee Road
Kingston, RI 02881
(401) 874-9510   Fax: (401) 874-2588
E-mail: swseo@socwomen.org
Web: www.socwomen.org

Summary To provide funding to women interested in conducting doctoral research on the social science aspects of women and cancer.

Eligibility This program is open to women doctoral students with a feminist orientation who are interested in studying breast cancer and its impact on women of color, lesbians, and other women from diverse social classes and cultural backgrounds. The research may be conducted in the areas of sociology, anthropology, psychology, or other social science fields concerned with women's experiences with breast cancer and the prevention of breast cancer. Priority is given to research that is not only useful academically but will have pragmatic and practical applications.

Financial data The grant is $1,500.

Duration 1 year.

Additional information This program was established in 1991.

Number awarded 1 each year.

Deadline March of each year.

[764]
BARNUM FESTIVAL FOUNDATION/JENNY LIND COMPETITION FOR SOPRANOS

Barnum Festival Foundation
Attn: Director
1070 Main Street
Bridgeport, CT 06604
(203) 367-8495   Toll Free: (866) 867-8495
Fax: (203) 367-0212   E-mail: barnumfestival@aol.com
Web: www.barnumfestival.com

Summary To recognize and reward (with scholarships and a concert trip to Sweden) outstanding young female singers who have not yet reached professional status.

Eligibility This program is open to sopranos between 20 and 30 years of age who have not yet attained professional status. They must be U.S. citizens. Past finalists may reapply, but former first-place winners and mezzo-sopranos are not eligible. Applicants must submit a CD or audio cassette tape with 2 contrasting arias and 1 art song. Based on the CD or tape, 12 semifinalists are selected for an audition at the Barnum Festival in Bridgeport, Connecticut every April. From that audition, 6 finalists are chosen. Selection of the winner is based on technique, musicianship, diction, interpretation, and stage presence.

Financial data The winner of the competition is presented with a $2,000 scholarship award to further her musical education at a recognized voice training school, academy, or college or with a recognized voice teacher or coach. She is featured in a concert in June with the Swedish Jenny Lind at a locale in Connecticut and is sent to Sweden with her Swedish counterpart to perform in concerts for 2 weeks in July and August. The runner-up receives a $500 scholarship.

Duration The competition is held annually.

Additional information The winner of this competition serves as the American Jenny Lind, a 21st-century counterpart of the Swedish Nightingale brought to the United States for a successful concert tour in 1850 by P.T. Barnum. There is a $35 application fee.

Number awarded 2 each year: 1 winner and 1 runner-up.

Deadline March of each year.

[765]
BASIC MIDWIFERY STUDENT SCHOLARSHIPS

American College of Nurse-Midwives
Attn: ACNM Foundation, Inc.
8403 Colesville Road, Suite 1550
Silver Spring, MD 20910-6374
(240) 485-1850   Fax: (240) 485-1818
Web: www.midwife.org/foundation_award.cfm

Summary To provide financial assistance for midwifery education to student members of the American College of Nurse-Midwives (ACNM).

Eligibility This program is open to ACNM members who are currently enrolled in an accredited basic midwife education program and have successfully completed 1 academic or clinical semester/quarter or clinical module. Applicants must submit a 150-word essay on their midwifery career plans and a 100-word essay on their intended future participation in the local, regional, and/or national activities of the ACNM. Selection is based on leadership potential, financial need, academic history, and potential for future professional contribution to the organization.

Financial data The stipend is $3,000.

Duration 1 year.

Additional information This program includes the following named scholarships: the A.C.N.M. Foundation Memorial Scholarship, the TUMS Calcium for Life Scholarship (presented by GlaxoSmithKline), the Edith B. Wonnell CNM Scholarship, and the Margaret Edmundson Scholarship.

Number awarded Varies each year; recently, 4 of these scholarships were awarded.

Deadline March of each year.

[766]
BENTON-MEIER NEUROPSYCHOLOGY SCHOLARSHIPS

American Psychological Foundation
750 First Street, N.E.
Washington, DC 20002-4242
(202) 336-5843   Fax: (202) 336-5812
E-mail: foundation@apa.org
Web: www.apa.org/apf/funding/benton-meier.aspx

Summary To provide research funding to graduate students (especially women, minorities, and individuals with disabilities) who are completing a dissertation related to neuropsychology.

Eligibility This program is open to students who have been admitted to candidacy for a doctoral degree in the area of neuropsychology. Applicants must submit statements documenting their research competence and area commitment, a budget and justification, and how the scholarship money will be used. Selection is based on conformance with stated program goals and the applicant's demonstrated scholarship and research competence. The sponsor encourages applications from individuals who represent diversity in race, ethnicity, gender, age, disability, and sexual orientation.

Financial data The grant is $2,500.

Duration 1 year.

Additional information This program replaces the Henry Hécaen Scholarship, first awarded in 1994, and the Manfred Meier Scholarship, first awarded in 1997.

Number awarded 2 each year.

Deadline May of each year.

[767]
BERKSHIRE CONFERENCE OF WOMEN HISTORIANS GRADUATE STUDENT FELLOWSHIP

Coordinating Council for Women in History
c/o Sandra Dawson, Executive Director
Northern Illinois University
Department of History and Women's Studies
715 Zulauf Hall
DeKalb, IL 60115
(815) 895-2624   E-mail: execdir@theccwh.org
Web: theccwh.org/awards.htm

Summary To provide funding to women graduate students in history for completion of their doctoral dissertations.

Eligibility This program is open to women graduate students in history departments at U.S. institutions who are members of the Coordinating Council for Women in History (CCWH). Applicants must have passed to A.B.D. status. They may be specializing in any field of history.

Financial data The grant is $1,000.

Duration 1 year.

Additional information This program, established in 1991, is administered by the CCWH and the Berkshire Conference of Women Historians. The award is presented at the CCWH luncheon at the annual meeting of the American Historical Association, although the recipient does not need to be present to accept the award.

Number awarded 1 each year.

Deadline September of each year.

[768]
BERNADINE JOHNSON MARSHALL-MARTHA BELLE SCHOLARSHIPS

Association of Black Women Lawyers of New Jersey, Inc.
P.O. Box 22524
Trenton, NJ 08607
E-mail: abwlnj@yahoo.com
Web: www.abwlnj.org

Summary To provide financial assistance to African American women from New Jersey attending law school in any state.

Eligibility This program is open to African American women who are 1) residents of New Jersey and currently enrolled in their first, second, or third year at an accredited law school in any state; or 2) residents of other states enrolled at a law school in New Jersey. Selection is based on a writing sample, community service, and financial need.

Financial data   The stipend is $1,000.

Duration   1 year.

Number awarded   At least 3 each year.

Deadline   February of each year.

[769]
BERNICE F. ELLIOTT MEMORIAL SCHOLARSHIP

Baptist Convention of New Mexico
Attn: Missions Mobilization Team
5325 Wyoming Boulevard, N.E.
P.O. Box 94485
Albuquerque, NM 87199-4485
(505) 924-2315   Toll Free: (800) 898-8544
Fax: (505) 924-2320   E-mail: cpairett@bcnm.com
Web: www.bcnm.com

Summary   To provide financial assistance to women who are Southern Baptists from New Mexico and interested in attending a college or seminary in any state.

Eligibility   This program is open to women college and seminary students who are members of churches affiliated with the Baptist Convention of New Mexico. Preference is given to applicants who are committed to full-time Christian service, have a background in the Woman's Missionary Union, and can demonstrate financial need.

Financial data   A stipend is awarded (amount not specified).

Duration   1 year; may be renewed.

Number awarded   1 or more each year.

Deadline   March of each year.

[770]
BESSIE BELLAMY PARKER SCHOLARSHIPS

South Carolina United Methodist Foundation
P.O. Box 5087
Columbia, SC 29250-5087
(803) 771-9125   Fax: (803) 771-9135
E-mail: scumf@bellsouth.net
Web: www.umcsc.org/scholarships.html

Summary   To provide financial assistance to female Methodist seminary students from South Carolina.

Eligibility   This program is open to women from South Carolina who are certified candidates for ministry in the United Methodist Church. Applicants must have completed at least 1 year of full-time enrollment in an approved United Methodist seminary with a grade average of "C" or higher. They must be planning to work in a local church setting. Selection is based (in descending order of importance) on self-understanding of ministry and intended future direction, promise for ministry, financial need, and academic performance in seminary.

Financial data   A stipend is awarded (amount not specified).

Duration   1 year.

Additional information   This scholarship was established by the South Carolina Conference of the United Methodist Church in 1986.

Number awarded   1 or more each year.

Deadline   April of each year.

[771]
BETA STATE LONG-TERM SCHOLARSHIP

Delta Kappa Gamma Society International-Beta State Organization
c/o Dr. Jeane B. Lee, Scholarships and World Fellowship Committee Chair
P.O. Box 241972
Montgomery, AL 36124
(334) 229-6956   E-mail: jeaneblee@gmail.com
Web: www.deltakappagamma.org/AL

Summary   To provide financial assistance to members of Delta Kappa Gamma Society International in Alabama who are interested in working on an advanced degree or certificate at a school in any state.

Eligibility   This program is open to residents of Alabama who have been members of Delta Kappa Gamma (an honorary society of women educators) for at least 5 years. Applicants must be enrolled in a program of graduate study, including a doctoral program, advanced certification program, or educational specialist program. Along with their application, they must submit a 1-page narrative that covers their educational and professional goals, personal goals, and philosophy of education. Selection is based primarily on participation in the society. Finalists are interviewed.

Financial data   The stipend is $3,100.

Duration   1 year.

Number awarded   1 or more each year.

Deadline   January of each year.

[772]
BETSY B. AND GAROLD A. LEACH SCHOLARSHIP FOR MUSEUM STUDIES

Delta Zeta Sorority
Attn: Foundation Coordinator
202 East Church Street
Oxford, OH 45056
(513) 523-7597   Fax: (513) 523-1921
E-mail: DZFoundation@dzshq.com
Web: www.deltazeta.org

Summary   To provide financial assistance to members of Delta Zeta Sorority working on an undergraduate or graduate degree to prepare for a career in museum work.

Eligibility   This program is open to upper-division and graduate members of the sorority who have a GPA of 3.0 or higher. Applicants must be working on a degree in a field that will prepare them for a career in museum work, including library science, archaeology, geology, or art history. Along with their application, they must submit an official transcript, a statement of their career goals, information on their service to the sorority, documentation of campus activities and/or community involvement, a list of academic honors, and an explanation of their financial need.

Financial data   The stipend ranges from $500 to $2,500 for undergraduates or from $1,000 to $15,000 for graduate students, depending on the availability of funds.

Duration   1 year; nonrenewable.

Number awarded   1 each year.

Deadline   February of each year.

[773]
BETTY B. AND JAMES B. LAMBERT SCHOLARSHIPS

Kappa Alpha Theta Foundation
Attn: Scholarships
8740 Founders Road
Indianapolis, IN 46268-1337
(317) 876-1870   Toll Free: (800) KAO-1870
Fax: (317) 876-1925
E-mail: FDNmail@kappaalphatheta.org
Web: www.kappaalphathetafoundation.org

Summary   To provide financial assistance to members of Kappa Alpha Theta who are working on a graduate degree in any field.

Eligibility   This program is open to members of Kappa Alpha Theta who are working on a graduate degree at a college or university in Canada or the United States. Along with their application, they must submit an official transcript, personal essays on assigned topics related to their involvement in Kappa Alpha Theta, and 2 letters of reference. Financial need is not considered in the selection process.

Financial data   Stipends range from $1,000 to $3,250.

Duration   1 year.

Number awarded   Varies each year; recently, nearly 80 of these scholarships, with a total value of $119,000, were awarded.

Deadline   January of each year.

[774]
BETTY HANSEN NATIONAL SCHOLARSHIPS

Danish Sisterhood of America
Attn: Donna Hansen, Scholarship Chair
1605 South 58th Street
Lincoln, NE 68506
(402) 488-5820   E-mail: djhansen@windstream.net
Web: www.danishsisterhood.org/DanishHTML/rschol.asp

Summary   To provide financial assistance for educational purposes in the United States or Denmark to members or relatives of members of the Danish Sisterhood of America.

Eligibility   This program is open to members or the family of members of the sisterhood who are interested in attending an accredited 4-year college or university as a full-time undergraduate or graduate student. Members must have belonged to the sisterhood for at least 1 year. They must have a GPA of 2.5 or higher. Selection is based on academics (including ACT or SAT scores), academic awards or honors, other special recognition and awards, employment record, special talents or hobbies, and participation in Danish Sisterhood and other civic activities. Upon written request, the scholarship may be used for study in Denmark.

Financial data   The stipend is $1,000.

Duration   1 year; nonrenewable.

Number awarded   Up to 8 each year.

Deadline   February of each year.

[775]
BIENNIAL STUDENT AUDITION AWARDS

National Federation of Music Clubs
1646 Smith Valley Road
Greenwood, IN 46142
(317) 882-4003   Fax: (317) 882-4019
E-mail: info@nfmc-music.org
Web: www.nfmc-music.org

Summary   To recognize and reward outstanding student musicians (including a separate competition for women singers) who are members of the National Federation of Music Clubs (NFMC).

Eligibility   This competition is open to instrumentalists and vocalists between 19 and 26 years of age. Student membership in the federation and U.S. citizenship are required. Competition categories include: women's voice, men's voice, piano, organ, harp, classical guitar, violin, viola, cello, double bass, orchestral woodwinds, orchestral brass, and percussion. Awards are presented at the national level after auditions at the state and district levels.

Financial data   The winner in each category is awarded $1,200.

Duration   The competition is held biennially, in odd-numbered years.

Additional information   Students who enter this competition are also automatically considered for a number of supplemental awards. The entry fee is $30 for each category.

Deadline   January of odd-numbered years.

[776]
BISHOP CHARLES P. GRECO GRADUATE FELLOWSHIPS

Knights of Columbus
Attn: Committee on Fellowships
P.O. Box 1670
New Haven, CT 06507-0901
(203) 752-4332   Fax: (203) 772-2696
E-mail: info@kofc.org
Web: www.kofc.org/un/en/scholarships/greco.html

Summary   To provide financial assistance to members of the Knights of Columbus and their wives, widows, or children who are interested in working on a graduate degree to prepare for a career as a teacher of people with intellectual disabilities.

Eligibility   This program is open to members as well as to their wives, sons, and daughters and to the widows and children of deceased members. Applicants must be working full time on a master's degree to prepare for a career as a teacher of people with intellectual disabilities. They must be at the beginning of their graduate program. Special consideration is given to applicants who select a Catholic graduate school.

Financial data   The stipend is $500 per semester ($1,000 per year), payable to the university.

Duration   1 semester; may be renewed for up to 3 additional semesters.

Additional information   This program was established in 1973.

Deadline   April of each year.

[777]
BISHOP FRANK MURPHY SCHOLARSHIP FOR WOMEN IN MINISTRY

Women's Ordination Conference
Attn: Scholarship Committee
P.O. Box 15057
Washington, DC 20003
(202) 675-1006   Fax: (202) 675-1008
E-mail: woc@womensordination.org
Web: www.womensordination.org/content/view/38/66

Summary To provide financial assistance to members of the Women's Ordination Conference (WOC) who are working on a graduate degree to prepare for Catholic ministry.

Eligibility This program is open to women who are members of the WOC. Applicants must be enrolled or accepted in a graduate program at a seminary or a diocesan certificate program preparing for Catholic priestly ministry. They must submit a letter of recommendation from a mentor who can testify to their commitment to WOC's goals, a personal statement of how their future ministry supports WOC's mission, a resume or curriculum vitae, and proof of enrollment.

Financial data The stipend is $1,000. Funds must be used for educational expenses.

Duration 1 year.

Additional information The WOC is an organization "working locally and nationally in collaboration with the worldwide movement for women's ordination." In pursuit of its goals, it "works for justice and equality for women in our church; strives to eliminate all forms of domination and discrimination in the Catholic church; advocates inclusive church structures; supports and affirms women's talents, gifts and calls to ministry." Recipients are required to submit a report at the end of the grant period explaining how the award impacted their study and growth.

Number awarded 1 or 2 each year.

Deadline January of each year.

[778]
B.J. DEAN SCHOLARSHIP

Community Foundation of Middle Tennessee
Attn: Scholarship Committee
3833 Cleghorn Avenue, Suite 400
Nashville, TN 37215-2519
(615) 321-4939   Toll Free: (888) 540-5200
Fax: (615) 327-2746   E-mail: mail@cfmt.org
Web: www.cfmt.org/scholarships

Summary To provide financial assistance to women from Tennessee or Texas preparing for a career in the ministry at a seminary in any state.

Eligibility This program is open to women from Tennessee or Texas interested in entering the ministry; students enrolled at Yale Divinity School are also eligible. Applicants must be preparing for full-time ministry but not necessarily seeking ordination. They must be planning to enroll full time at a seminary in any state. There are no denominational restrictions. Along with their application, they must submit an essay describing their educational plans and how those plans will help them reach their career goals. Financial need is considered in the selection process.

Financial data Stipends range from $500 to $2,500 per year. Funds are paid to the recipient's school and must be

used for tuition, fees, books, supplies, room, board, or miscellaneous expenses.

Duration 1 year; recipients may reapply.

Additional information This fund was established in 1995.

Number awarded 1 or more each year.

Deadline March of each year.

[779]
B.K. KRENZER MEMORIAL REENTRY SCHOLARSHIP

Society of Women Engineers
Attn: Scholarship Selection Committee
120 South LaSalle Street, Suite 1515
Chicago, IL 60603-3572
(312) 596-5223   Toll Free: (877) SWE-INFO
Fax: (312) 644-8557
E-mail: scholarshipapplication@swe.org
Web: societyofwomenengineers.swe.org

Summary To provide financial assistance to women (particularly women engineers) who are interested in returning to college or graduate school to continue their study of engineering or computer science.

Eligibility This program is open to women who are planning to enroll at an ABET-accredited 4-year college or university. Applicants must have been out of the engineering workforce and school for at least 2 years and must be planning to return as an undergraduate or graduate student to work on a degree in computer science or engineering. They must have a GPA of 3.0 or higher. Selection is based on merit. Preference is given to engineers who already have a degree and are planning to reenter the engineering workforce after a period of temporary retirement.

Financial data The stipend is $2,000.

Duration 1 year.

Additional information This program was established in 1996.

Number awarded 1 each year.

Deadline February of each year.

[780]
BLACK WOMEN IN ENTERTAINMENT LAW STUDENT SCHOLARSHIP

Black Women in Entertainment Law
c/o Angela M. Rogers
James E. McMillan, P.C.
19 Fulton Street, Suite 400
New York, NY 10038-2110
(212) 986-6262
Web: www.bwelfoundation.org/scholarships.html

Summary To provide financial assistance to women of color who are enrolled in law school and have an interest in entertainment law.

Eligibility This program is open to women of color who have completed at least 1 semester of law school as a full- or part-time student. Applicants must list the entertainment law courses they have taken and write a 1,500-word essay on a question related to entertainment law. They must have a GPA of 2.5 or higher. Financial need is considered in the selection process.

Financial data The stipend is $5,000.

Duration 1 year.
Number awarded 2 each year.
Deadline October of each year.

[781]
BOBBIE BURK CONDUCTING SCHOLARSHIP FOR GRADUATE STUDENTS

Sigma Alpha Iota Philanthropies, Inc.
One Tunnel Road
Asheville, NC 28805
(828) 251-0606   Fax: (828) 251-0644
E-mail: nh@sai-national.org
Web: www.sigmaalphaiota.org

Summary To provide financial assistance to members of Sigma Alpha Iota (an organization of women musicians) who are working on a graduate degree in conducting.

Eligibility This program is open to members of the organization who are currently enrolled in a graduate degree program with an emphasis on conducting. Applicants must include a videotape of a performance they conducted.

Financial data The stipend is $2,500.
Duration 1 year.
Number awarded 1 each year.
Deadline March of each year.

[782]
BOOZ ALLEN HAMILTON IT SCHOLARSHIP

Society of Women Engineers
Attn: Scholarship Selection Committee
120 South LaSalle Street, Suite 1515
Chicago, IL 60603-3572
(312) 596-5223   Toll Free: (877) SWE-INFO
Fax: (312) 644-8557
E-mail: scholarshipapplication@swe.org
Web: societyofwomenengineers.swe.org

Summary To provide financial assistance to members of the Society of Women Engineers (SWE) working on a graduate degree in computer science or civil engineering.

Eligibility This program is open to women who are enrolled in graduate school at a designated ABET-accredited college or university. Applicants must be working on a degree in computer science or civil engineering and have a GPA of 3.8 or higher. They must be U.S. citizens and members of the society. Selection is based on merit.

Financial data The stipend is $2,000.
Duration 1 year.
Additional information This program is sponsored by Booz Allen Hamilton.
Number awarded 1 each year.
Deadline February of each year.

[783]
BOOZ ALLEN HAMILTON SYSTEMS ENGINEERING SCHOLARSHIP

Society of Women Engineers
Attn: Scholarship Selection Committee
120 South LaSalle Street, Suite 1515
Chicago, IL 60603-3572
(312) 596-5223   Toll Free: (877) SWE-INFO
Fax: (312) 644-8557
E-mail: scholarshipapplication@swe.org
Web: societyofwomenengineers.swe.org

Summary To provide financial assistance to members of the Society of Women Engineers (SWE) working on a graduate degree in systems engineering or a related field.

Eligibility This program is open to women who are enrolled in graduate school at a designated ABET-accredited college or university. Applicants must be working on a degree in systems engineering or a related field (e.g., security engineering, information assurance, computer engineering) and have a GPA of 3.8 or higher. They must be U.S. citizens and members of the society. Selection is based on merit.

Financial data The stipend is $2,000.
Duration 1 year.
Additional information This program is sponsored by Booz Allen Hamilton.
Number awarded 1 each year.
Deadline February of each year.

[784]
BOSTON AFFILIATE AWSCPA SCHOLARSHIP

American Woman's Society of Certified Public
  Accountants-Boston Affiliate
c/o Andrea Costantino
Oxford Bioscience Partners
222 Berkeley Street, Suite 1650
Boston, MA 02116
(617) 357-7474   E-mail: acostantino@oxbio.com
Web: www.awscpa.org/affiliate_scholarships/boston.html

Summary To provide financial assistance to women from any state who are working on an undergraduate or graduate degree in accounting at a college or university in New England.

Eligibility This program is open to women from any state who are attending a college in New England and majoring in accounting. Applicants must have completed at least 12 semester hours of accounting or tax courses and have a cumulative GPA of 3.0 or higher. They must be planning to graduate between May of next year and May of the following year or, for the 15-month graduate program, before September of the current year. Along with their application, they must submit a brief essay on why they feel they would be a good choice for this award. Selection is based on that essay, academic achievement, work experience, extracurricular activities, scholastic honors, career plans, and financial need.

Financial data The stipend is $1,000.
Duration 1 year.
Number awarded 2 each year.
Deadline September of each year.

[785]
BOSTON SCIENTIFIC MINNESOTA SWE SCHOLARSHIP

Society of Women Engineers-Minnesota Section
Attn: Scholarship Committee
P.O. Box 582813
Minneapolis, MN 55458-2813
E-mail: scholarships@swe-mn.org
Web: swe-mn.org/scholarships.html

Summary To provide financial assistance to women from any state working on an undergraduate or graduate degree in biomedical or mechanical engineering at colleges and universities in Minnesota, North Dakota, and South Dakota.

Eligibility This program is open to female undergraduate and graduate students at ABET-accredited engineering programs in Minnesota, North Dakota, or South Dakota. Applicants must be working full time on a degree in biomedical or mechanical engineering. Along with their application, they must submit a short paragraph describing how they plan to utilize their engineering skills after they graduate. Selection is based on potential to succeed as an engineer (20 points), communication skills (10 points), extracurricular or community involvement and leadership skills (10 points), demonstrated successful work experience (10 points), and academic success (5 points).

Financial data The stipend is $1,500.

Duration 1 year.

Additional information This program is sponsored by Boston Scientific.

Number awarded 1 each year.

Deadline March of each year.

[786]
CALIFORNIA P.E.O. SELECTED SCHOLARSHIPS

P.E.O. Foundation-California State Chapter
c/o Carol Born, Scholarship Committee Chair
718 Via La Paloma
Riverside, CA 92507-6403
(951) 686-2728
Web: www.peocalifornia.org/ssc.html

Summary To provide financial assistance to female residents of California attending college or graduate school in any state.

Eligibility This program is open to female residents of California who have completed 4 years of high school (or the equivalent); are enrolled at or accepted by an accredited college, university, vocational school, or graduate school in any state; and have an excellent academic record. Selection is based on financial need, character, academic ability, and school and community activities. Some awards include additional requirements.

Financial data Stipends recently ranged from $400 to $2,500.

Duration 1 year; may be renewed for up to 3 additional years.

Additional information This program includes the following named scholarships: the Barbara Furse Mackey Scholarship (for women whose education has been interrupted); the Beverly Dye Anderson Scholarship (for the fields of teaching or health care); the Marjorie M. McDonald P.E.O. Scholarship (for women who are continuing their education after a long hiatus from school); the Ora Keck Scholarship (for women who are preparing for a career in music or the fine arts); the Phyllis J. Van Deventer Scholarship (for women who are preparing for a career in music performance or music education); the Jean Gower Scholarship (for women preparing for a career in education); the Helen D. Thompson Memorial Scholarship (for women studying music or fine arts); the Stella May Nau Scholarship (for women who are interested in reentering the job market); the Linda Jones Memorial Fine Arts Scholarship (for women studying fine arts); the Polly Thompson Memorial Music Scholarship (for women studying music); the Ruby W. Henry Scholarship; the Jean W. Gratiot Scholarship; the Pearl Prime Scholarship; the Helen Beardsley Scholarship; the Chapter GA Scholarship; and the Nearly New Scholarship.

Number awarded Varies each year; recently, 43 of these scholarships were awarded.

Deadline January of each year.

[787]
CALIFORNIA STATE UNIVERSITY CHANCELLOR'S DOCTORAL INCENTIVE PROGRAM

California State University
Office of the Chancellor
Attn: Human Resources
401 Golden Shore, Fourth Floor
Long Beach, CA 90802-4210
(562) 951-4425   Fax: (562) 951-4954
E-mail: forgivableloan@calstate.edu
Web: www.calstate.edu/hr/cdip/index.shtml

Summary To provide funding to women and other graduate students who can help increase the diversity of persons qualified to compete for instructional faculty positions at campuses of the California State University (CSU) system.

Eligibility This program is open to new and continuing full-time students enrolled in a doctoral program anywhere in the United States, whether affiliated with a CSU campus or not. Applicants must present a plan of support from a full-time CSU faculty sponsor who has agreed to advise and support the candidate throughout doctoral study. Selection is based on the applicant's academic record; professional qualifications; and relevant background, experience, skills, and motivation to educate a diverse student body in the CSU system. The factors considered include experience working with persons with a wide range of backgrounds and perspectives, research interests related to educating an increasingly diverse student body, and experience in a variety of cultural environments. Primary consideration is given to candidates who proposed area of study falls where CSU campuses anticipate the greatest difficulty in filling instructional faculty positions.

Financial data Participants receive up to $10,000 per year or a maximum of $30,000 over 5 years. The loans are converted to fellowships at the rate of 20% of the total loan amount for each postdoctoral year that the program participant teaches, for up to 5 years. Thus, the entire loan will be forgiven after the recipient has taught full time for 5 years on a CSU campus. Recipients who do not teach on a CSU campus or who discontinue full-time studies will be required to repay the total loan amount within a 15-year period at the rate established for other student loans.

Duration   Up to 5 years.

Additional information   This program began in 1987 as the California State University Forgivable Loan Program. It has loaned $39.9 million to 1,682 doctoral students enrolled in universities throughout the nation and abroad. Participants included 66.9% who were female, 20.8% African American, 13.8% Asian, 29.2% Hispanic, and 3.5% American Indian.

Number awarded   Varies each year; recently, 81 new participants were admitted to the program.

Deadline   The deadline varies at different CSU campuses but typically falls in February of each year.

[788]
CAREER DEVELOPMENT GRANTS

American Association of University Women
Attn: AAUW Educational Foundation
301 ACT Drive, Department 60
P.O. Box 4030
Iowa City, IA 52243-4030
(319) 337-1716, ext. 60   Fax: (319) 337-1204
E-mail: aauw@act.org
Web: www.aauw.org

Summary   To provide financial assistance to women who are seeking career advancement, career change, or reentry into the workforce.

Eligibility   This program is open to women who are U.S. citizens or permanent residents, have earned a bachelor's degree, received their most recent degree more than 4 years ago, and are making career changes, seeking to advance in current careers, or reentering the work force. Applicants must be interested in working toward a master's degree, second bachelor's or associate degree, professional degree (e.g., M.D., J.D.), certification program, or technical school certificate. They must be planning to undertake course work at an accredited 2- or 4-year college or university (or a technical school that is licensed, accredited, or approved by the U.S. Department of Education). Special consideration is given to women of color and women pursuing credentials in nontraditional fields. Support is not provided for prerequisite course work or for Ph.D. course work or dissertations. Selection is based on demonstrated commitment to education and equity for women and girls, reason for seeking higher education or technical training, degree to which study plan is consistent with career objectives, potential for success in chosen field, documentation of opportunities in chosen field, feasibility of study plans and proposed time schedule, validity of proposed budget and budget narrative (including sufficient outside support), and quality of written proposal.

Financial data   Grants range from $2,000 to $12,000. Funds may be used for tuition, fees, books, supplies, local transportation, dependent child care, or purchase of a computer required for the study program.

Duration   1 year, beginning in July; nonrenewable.

Additional information   The filing fee is $35.

Number awarded   Varies each year; recently, 47 of these grants, with a value of $500,000, were awarded.

Deadline   December of each year.

[789]
CAROL TYLER AWARD

International Precious Metals Institute
5101 North 12th Avenue, Suite C
Pensacola, FL 32504
(850) 476-1156   Fax: (850) 476-1548
E-mail: mail@ipmi.org
Web: www.ipmi.org/awards/index.cfm

Summary   To recognize and reward women who have made outstanding contributions to the field of precious metals.

Eligibility   This award is available to women who are graduate students or currently employed in industry or academia. Nominees must have made outstanding theoretical and experimental contributions to the science and technology of precious metals. They may be residents of any country.

Financial data   The award is $5,000 and a certificate.

Duration   The award is presented annually.

Additional information   This award was first presented in 2011.

Number awarded   1 each year.

Deadline   January of each year.

[790]
CAROLYN WEATHERFORD SCHOLARSHIP FUND

Woman's Missionary Union
Attn: WMU Foundation
100 Missionary Ridge
Birmingham, AL 35242
(205) 408-5525   Toll Free: (877) 482-4483
Fax: (205) 408-5508   E-mail: wmufoundation@wmu.org
Web: www.wmufoundation.com

Summary   To provide an opportunity for women to work on a graduate degree or an internship so they can engage in activities of the Woman's Missionary Union (WMU).

Eligibility   This program is open to women who are members of the Baptist Church and are attending or planning to attend a Southern Baptist seminary or divinity school at the graduate level or participate in an internship. Applicants must be interested in 1) field work experience as interns or in women's missionary work in the United States; or 2) service in women's missionary work in the United States. They must arrange for 3 letters of endorsement, from a recent professor, a state or associational WMU official, and a recent pastor. Selection is based on current active involvement in WMU, previous activity in WMU, plans for long-term involvement in WMU and/or home missions, academic strength, leadership skills, and personal and professional characteristics.

Financial data   A stipend is awarded (amount not specified).

Duration   1 year.

Number awarded   1 or more each year.

Deadline   February of each year.

[791]
CARRIE CHAPMAN CATT PRIZE FOR RESEARCH ON WOMEN AND POLITICS

Iowa State University
Attn: Carrie Chapman Catt Center for Women and Politics
309 Carrie Chapman Catt Hall
Ames, IA 50011-1305
(515) 294-3181   Fax: (515) 294-3741
E-mail: cattcntr@iastate.edu
Web: www.iastate.edu/CattCenter/cattprize.shtml

Summary To recognize and reward outstanding research in the area of women and politics.

Eligibility This competition is open to scholars at all levels, including graduate students and junior faculty, who are planning to conduct research in the area of women and politics. Applicants must submit a detailed description of their research project, including 1) its purpose and content; 2) a discussion of relevant theory, contributions to literature in the field, and methodology; 3) a statement on how this prize will contribute to the research project; and 4) a timetable for completion of the project. They also must submit a 1-page biographical statement, highlighting their research interests, significant publications and/or presentations, and professional interests and experiences. Research projects can address the annual conference theme or any other topic related to women and politics.

Financial data Prizes are $1,000 for winners or $500 for honorable mention. All prize-winners may also receive travel expenses to Des Moines, Iowa where awards are presented at the annual conference of the Carrie Chapman Catt Center for Women and Politics.

Duration The prizes are awarded annually.

Number awarded Up to 2 winners and up to 2 honorable mentions are selected each year.

Deadline November of each year.

[792]
CATERPILLAR SWE SCHOLARSHIPS

Society of Women Engineers
Attn: Scholarship Selection Committee
120 South LaSalle Street, Suite 1515
Chicago, IL 60603-3572
(312) 596-5223   Toll Free: (877) SWE-INFO
Fax: (312) 644-8557
E-mail: scholarshipapplication@swe.org
Web: societyofwomenengineers.swe.org

Summary To provide financial assistance to women who are working on an undergraduate or graduate degree in selected fields of engineering or computer science.

Eligibility This program is open to women who are sophomores, juniors, seniors, or graduate students at ABET-accredited 4-year colleges and universities. Applicants must be working on a degree in computer science or agricultural, chemical, electrical, industrial, manufacturing, materials, or mechanical engineering. They must be U.S. citizens or authorized to work in the United States and have a GPA of 3.0 or higher. Selection is based on merit.

Financial data The stipend is $2,400.

Duration 1 year.

Additional information This program is sponsored by Caterpillar, Inc.

Number awarded 3 each year.

Deadline February of each year.

[793]
CATHERINE PRELINGER AWARD

Coordinating Council for Women in History
c/o Sandra Dawson, Executive Director
Northern Illinois University
Department of History and Women's Studies
715 Zulauf Hall
DeKalb, IL 60115
(815) 895-2624   E-mail: execdir@theccwh.org
Web: theccwh.org/awards.htm

Summary To provide funding to members of the Coordinating Council for Women in History (CCWH) for a project that focuses on women's roles in history.

Eligibility This program is open to members of CCWH whose academic path has not followed the traditional pattern of uninterrupted study. Applicants must hold either A.B.D. status or a Ph.D. and be engaged in scholarship that is historical in nature, although their degree may be in related fields. They must submit a description of a project they propose to undertake with this award, including the work they intend to complete, the schedule they have developed, the sources they intend to use, and the contribution the work will make to women in history. Independent and non-academic scholars are encouraged to apply.

Financial data The grant is $20,000.

Duration 1 year.

Additional information This program was established in 1998.

Number awarded 1 each year.

Deadline September of each year.

[794]
CENTRAL NEW MEXICO RE-ENTRY SCHOLARSHIP

Society of Women Engineers
Attn: Scholarship Selection Committee
120 South LaSalle Street, Suite 1515
Chicago, IL 60603-3572
(312) 596-5223   Toll Free: (877) SWE-INFO
Fax: (312) 644-8557
E-mail: scholarshipapplication@swe.org
Web: societyofwomenengineers.swe.org

Summary To provide financial assistance to members of the Society of Women Engineers (SWE) from any state who are reentering college or graduate school in New Mexico to work on a degree in engineering or computer science.

Eligibility This program is open to members of the society who are sophomores, juniors, seniors, or graduate students at an ABET-accredited college, university, or 4-year engineering technology program in New Mexico. Applicants must be returning to college or graduate school after an absence of several years to work on a degree in computer science or engineering. They must have a GPA of 3.0 or higher. Selection is based on merit. U.S. citizenship is required.

Financial data The stipend is $1,250 per year.

Duration 1 year; may be renewed up to 5 additional years.

Additional information This program was established in 2005 by the Central New Mexico section of SWE.

Number awarded 1 each year.

Deadline February of each year.

[795]
CHARLES T. STONER LAW SCHOLARSHIP AWARD

Women's Basketball Coaches Association
Attn: Manager of Events and Awards
4646 Lawrenceville Highway
Lilburn, GA 30047-3620
(770) 279-8027, ext. 105   Fax: (770) 279-8473
E-mail: dtrujillo@wbca.org
Web: www.wbca.org/stoneraward.asp

Summary To provide financial assistance for law school to women's basketball players.

Eligibility This program is open to women's college basketball players who are seniors planning to attend law school. Applicants must be nominated by a member of the Women's Basketball Coaches Association (WBCA). Selection is based on a letter of recommendation, academic major and GPA, basketball statistics for all 4 years of college, academic and athletic honors, and campus activities.

Financial data The stipend is $1,000.

Duration 1 year; nonrenewable.

Additional information This program began in 2001.

Number awarded 1 each year.

Deadline Deadline not specified.

[796]
CHARLINE CHILSON SCHOLARSHIPS

Delta Zeta Sorority
Attn: Foundation Coordinator
202 East Church Street
Oxford, OH 45056
(513) 523-7597   Fax: (513) 523-1921
E-mail: DZFoundation@dzshq.com
Web: www.deltazeta.org

Summary To provide financial assistance to members of Delta Zeta Sorority working on an undergraduate or graduate degree in science.

Eligibility This program is open to upper-division and graduate members of the sorority who have a high GPA in their major. Applicants must be working on a degree in science. Along with their application, they must submit an official transcript, a statement of their career goals, information on their service to the sorority, documentation of campus activities and/or community involvement, a list of academic honors, and an explanation of their financial need.

Financial data The stipend ranges from $500 to $2,500 for undergraduates or from $1,000 to $15,000 for graduate students, depending on the availability of funds.

Duration 1 year; nonrenewable.

Number awarded Varies each year; recently, 12 of these scholarships were awarded: 6 to undergraduates and 6 to graduate students.

Deadline February of each year.

[797]
CHARLOTTE BRENT MEMORIAL SCHOLARSHIP

United Methodist Church-Louisiana Conference
Attn: Coordinator, Conference Board of Ordained Ministry
527 North Boulevard
Baton Rouge, LA 70802-5700
(225) 346-1646, ext. 230
Toll Free: (888) 239-5286, ext. 230
Fax: (225) 383-2652   E-mail: johneddd@bellsouth.net
Web: www.la-umc.org

Summary To provide financial assistance to women from Louisiana who are attending a Methodist seminary in any state to prepare for a career in ordained ministry.

Eligibility This program is open to female members of United Methodist Churches in Louisiana who are enrolled or planning to enroll full time at a Methodist seminary in any state. Applicants must be beginning a second career as an ordained minister. Along with their application, they must submit an essay on their vocational goals and plans for ministry.

Financial data The stipend is $1,000.

Duration 1 year.

Number awarded 1 each year.

Deadline February of each year.

[798]
CHARLOTTE FIELDS SILVERSTEEN SCHOLARSHIP

Delta Zeta Sorority
Attn: Foundation Coordinator
202 East Church Street
Oxford, OH 45056
(513) 523-7597   Fax: (513) 523-1921
E-mail: DZFoundation@dzshq.com
Web: www.deltazeta.org

Summary To provide financial assistance to members of Delta Zeta Sorority working on a graduate degree in education.

Eligibility This program is open to graduate members of the sorority who are working on a degree in education. Applicants must submit an official transcript, a statement of their career goals, information on their service to the sorority, documentation of campus activities and/or community involvement, a list of academic honors, and an explanation of their financial need. Preference is given to applicants from the Delta Tau chapter at Temple University.

Financial data The stipend ranges from $1,000 to $15,000, depending on the availability of funds.

Duration 1 year; nonrenewable.

Number awarded 1 each year.

Deadline February of each year.

[799]
CHERYL A. RUGGIERO SCHOLARSHIP

Rhode Island Society of Certified Public Accountants
45 Royal Little Drive
Providence, RI 02904
(401) 331-5720   Fax: (401) 454-5780
E-mail: info@riscpa.org
Web: student.riscpa.org/index.html

Summary To provide financial assistance to female undergraduate and graduate students from any state who are working on a degree in accounting at a school in Rhode Island.

Eligibility This program is open to female students at Rhode Island colleges and universities who have expressed an interest in public accounting during their undergraduate and/or graduate years. Applicants must be U.S. citizens who have a GPA of 3.0 or higher. They are not required to be residents of Rhode Island. Selection is based on demonstrated potential to become a valued member of the public accounting profession. Finalists are interviewed.

Financial data The stipend is $1,250.

Duration 1 year.

Additional information This program was established in 2005.

Number awarded 1 each year.

Deadline January of each year.

[800]
CHI OMEGA FOUNDATION ALUMNAE EDUCATIONAL GRANTS

Chi Omega Fraternity
Attn: Chi Omega Foundation
3395 Players Club Parkway
Memphis, TN 38125
(901) 748-8600   Fax: (901) 748-8686
E-mail: foundation@chiomega.com
Web: www.chiomega.com/students/default.aspx

Summary To provide financial assistance for graduate school to women who are members of Chi Omega Fraternity and have been out of college for a period of time.

Eligibility This program is open to women over 24 years of age who are alumnae members of Chi Omega Fraternity. Applicants must be planning to enter graduate school as a full- or part-time student for career qualification or advancement. Along with their application, they must submit a personal letter describing their reasons and need for the grant. Selection is based on academic achievement, aptitude, service to Chi Omega, contributions to the university and community, personal and professional goals, and financial need.

Financial data The stipend is $1,000.

Duration 1 year.

Additional information This program was established in 1997.

Number awarded 10 each year.

Deadline February of each year.

[801]
CHRYSALIS SCHOLARSHIP

Association for Women Geoscientists
Attn: AWG Foundation
12000 North Washington Street, Suite 285
Thornton, CO 80241
(303) 412-6219   Fax: (303) 253-9220
E-mail: chrysalis@awg.org
Web: www.awg.org/EAS/scholarships.html

Summary To provide assistance to women who have returned to graduate school to earn a degree in the geosciences and need funding to complete their thesis.

Eligibility This program is open to women geoscience graduate students whose education has been interrupted for at least 1 year for personal or financial reasons. Applicants must submit a letter describing their background, career goals and objectives, how the scholarship will be used, and nature and length of the interruption to their education.

Financial data The stipend is $2,000. The funds may be used for typing, drafting, child care, or anything necessary to allow a degree candidate to finish her thesis and enter a geoscience profession.

Duration 1 year.

Number awarded 2 each year.

Deadline March of each year.

[802]
CHURCH TRAINING AND DEACONESS HOUSE SCHOLARSHIP

Episcopal Diocese of Pennsylvania
Attn: Church Training and Deaconess House Scholarship Fund
240 South Fourth Street
Philadelphia, PA 19106
(215) 627-6434, ext. 101   Fax: (215) 627-7550
E-mail: diopa@libertynet.org
Web: www.diopa.org/leadership/transition/deaconess

Summary To provide financial assistance for graduate school to women preparing for a career in religious or benevolent work for the Episcopal Church.

Eligibility This program is open to women at the graduate level who are training for religious and benevolent work for the Episcopal Church. Preference is given to women in the Diocese of Pennsylvania. Applicants must have an earned bachelor's degree and acceptance into 1) a seminary; 2) an accredited college or university advanced degree program in education, religion, social work, medicine, or allied fields; or 3) a degree credit program of continuing education in their present field of work. Along with their application, they must submit a 250-word essay on how they expect to use this graduate educational training to advance their ordained or lay ministry within the Episcopal Church or the church at large. Selection is based on the quality of the essay, academic record, and financial need.

Financial data Stipends range from $2,000 to $3,000.

Duration 1 year; may be renewed up to 2 additional years.

Number awarded 1 or more each year.

Deadline March of each year.

[803]
CITRUS DISTRICT 2 DAUGHTERS OF PENELOPE SCHOLARSHIPS

Daughters of Penelope-District 2
c/o Nicole P. Sackedis
9003 Spring Garden Way
Tampa, FL 33626
(813) 749-6000   E-mail: chickref@hotmail.com
Web: www.ahepad2.org

Summary To provide financial assistance to women from Florida who are members of organizations affiliated with the American Hellenic Educational Progressive Association (AHEPA) and interested in attending college or graduate school in any state.

Eligibility This program is open to women who are residents of AHEPA Citrus District 2 (Florida) and high school seniors, undergraduates, or graduate students. Applicants must have been a member of the Maids of Athena for at least 2 years or have an immediate family member who has belonged to the Daughters of Penelope or Order of AHEPA for at least 2 years. They must have an unweighted high school or college GPA of 3.0 or higher. Along with their application, they must submit a personal essay of 300 to 600 words on how the AHEPA family has influenced their goals, personal effort, and/or educational experiences. Selection is based on merit and financial need. Only single women are eligible.

Financial data A stipend is awarded (amount not specified).

Duration 1 year; may be renewed.

Additional information This program includes the Past District Governors/Julie P. Microutsicos Scholarship, awarded to the runner-up.

Number awarded 2 each year.

Deadline April of each year.

[804]
CLAIRE BARRETT MEMORIAL SCHOLARSHIP

Women's Transportation Seminar-Boston Chapter
c/o Sasha Wood
Tetra Tech Rizzo
One Grant Street
Framingham, MA 01701
(508) 902-2000   E-mail: sasha.wood@tetratech.com
Web: www.wtsinternational.org/Chapters.aspx/ID=6758

Summary To provide financial assistance to women who have an interest in public policy issues and are working on a transportation-related graduate degree at a college or university in Massachusetts.

Eligibility This program is open to women enrolled at colleges and universities in Massachusetts who are working on a graduate degree in a transportation-related field, including transportation engineering, planning, finance, or logistics. Applicants must be able to demonstrate 1) plans to prepare for a career in a transportation-related field; 2) excellent communication skills; 3) a belief in the power of public dialogue in communicating and improving the goals of public institutions and public projects; and 4) current involvement in a research or thesis project that incorporates use of public transportation, environmental awareness, use of public art, awareness of diversity, and use of landscape architecture. Along with their application, they must submit a 750-word personal statement about their career goals after graduation and why they think they should receive this scholarship. Selection is based on the applicant's specific transportation involvement and goals, job skills, and academic record. Minority women are especially encouraged to apply.

Financial data The stipend is $4,000.

Duration 1 year.

Additional information This program was established in 2005.

Number awarded 1 or more each year.

Deadline November of each year.

[805]
CLAUDIA STEELE BAKER GRADUATE FELLOWSHIP

Alpha Chi Omega Foundation
Attn: Foundation Programs Coordinator
5939 Castle Creek Parkway North Drive
Indianapolis, IN 46250-4343
(317) 579-5050, ext. 262   Fax: (317) 579-5051
E-mail: foundation@alphachiomega.org
Web: www.alphachiomega.org/index.aspx?id=1030

Summary To provide financial assistance to Alpha Chi Omega members who are interested in studying social services in graduate school.

Eligibility Women college seniors and graduates who are members of the sorority are eligible to apply if they have majored in a social service field, are committed to peace and understanding, and plan to attend graduate school. Selection is based on campus, community, and chapter service.

Financial data A stipend is awarded (amount not specified).

Duration 1 year.

Number awarded 1 each year.

Deadline March of each year.

[806]
COLLEGE SCHOLARSHIPS FOUNDATION WOMEN'S SCHOLARSHIP

College Scholarships Foundation
5506 Red Robin Road
Raleigh, NC 27613
(919) 630-4895   Toll Free: (888) 501-9050
E-mail: info@collegescholarships.org
Web: www.collegescholarships.org

Summary To provide financial assistance to women working on an undergraduate or graduate degree.

Eligibility This program is open to women who are working full time on an undergraduate or graduate degree. Applicants must have a GPA of 3.0 or higher. Along with their application, they must submit a 300-word essay on how their education plans have affected their plans of starting a family, what trends they foresee occurring for women in the workforce, and where they see themselves in 10 years. U.S. citizenship is required.

Financial data The stipend is $1,000.

Duration 1 year.

Additional information This scholarship was first awarded in 2006. The sponsor was formerly known as the Daniel Kovach Scholarship Foundation.

Number awarded 1 each year.

Deadline December of each year.

[807]
COLUMBUS CHAPTER WOMEN'S TRANSPORTATION SEMINAR SCHOLARSHIPS

Women's Transportation Seminar-Columbus Chapter
c/o Tracey Nixon, Scholarship Committee Chair
Parsons Brinckerhoff
2545 Farmers Drive, Suite 350
Columbus, OH 43235
(614) 791-5181   E-mail: ixon@pbworld.com
Web: www.wtsinternational.org/Chapters.aspx?ID=14102

Summary To provide financial assistance to women from Ohio who are working on an undergraduate or graduate degree in a transportation-related field.

Eligibility This program is open to women who are residents of Ohio or currently enrolled as an undergraduate or graduate student at a college or university in the state. Applicants must be preparing for a career in a transportation-related field and be working on a degree in transportation engineering, planning, aviation, finance, public policy, logistics, or a related field. They must have a GPA of 3.0 or higher. Along with their application, they must submit a personal statement about their career goals after graduation and why they think they should receive this scholarship. Minority candidates are encouraged to apply. Selection is based on transportation goals, academic record, and transportation-related activities or job skills.

Financial data Stipends are $1,000 for undergraduates or $1,200 for graduate students.

Duration 1 year.

Number awarded 3 each year: 2 for undergraduates and 1 for a graduate student.

Deadline November of each year.

[808]
CONGRESSIONAL FELLOWSHIPS ON WOMEN AND PUBLIC POLICY

Women's Research and Education Institute
Attn: Education and Training Programs
714 G Street, S.E., Suite 200
Washington, DC 20003
(202) 280-2720   E-mail: wrei@wrei.org
Web: www.wrei.org

Summary To provide graduate students and young professionals with an opportunity to work as a Congressional aide on policy issues affecting women.

Eligibility This program is open to women and men who are currently enrolled in a master's or doctoral program at an accredited institution in the United States or who have completed such a program within the past 18 months. Applicants should have completed at least 9 hours of graduate course work or the equivalent and have a demonstrated interest in research or political activity relating to women's social and political status. They may be of any age, gender, race, religion, sexual orientation, experience, or academic field, but they must be articulate and adaptable and have strong writing skills. Selection is based on academic competence and demonstrated interest in the public policy process. Interviews are required of semifinalists.

Financial data Fellows receive a stipend of $1,450 per month, $500 for health insurance, and up to $1,500 for reimbursement of 3 hours of tuition at their home institutions.

Duration 8 months, from January through August; nonrenewable.

Additional information This program began in 1977. Fellows are assigned to Congressional or committee offices to work for at least 30 hours per week as a legislative assistant monitoring, researching, and providing information on policy issues affecting women.

Number awarded At least 5 each year; since the program began, 277 fellows (all women) have been appointed to these positions.

Deadline June of each year.

[809]
COOLEY DIVERSITY FELLOWSHIP PROGRAM

Cooley LLP
Attn: Attorney Recruiting Manager
4401 Eastgate Mall
San Diego, CA 92121-1909
(858) 550-6000   E-mail: diversityfellowship@cooley.com
Web: www.cooley.com/diversityfellowship

Summary To provide financial assistance and work experience to women and other law students who are committed to promoting diversity in their community and are interested in a summer associateship at an office of Cooley LLP.

Eligibility This program is open to students enrolled full time at an ABA-accredited law school and planning to graduate 2 years after applying. Applicants must submit a 3-page personal statement describing their demonstrated commitment to promoting diversity (e.g., ethnicity, gender, physical disability, and/or sexual orientation) in their community. Selection is based on undergraduate and law school academic performance, personal achievements, leadership abilities, community service, demonstrated commitment to promoting diversity, and commitment to joining Cooley's summer associate program following their second year of law school.

Financial data The award includes a stipend of $15,000 to assist with law school tuition and a paid summer associate position.

Duration 1 year.

Additional information Summer associates may work in any of the firm's offices in California (Palo Alto, San Diego, or San Francisco), Colorado (Broomfield), Massachusetts (Boston), New York (New York), Virginia (Reston), Washington (Seattle), or Washington, D.C.

Number awarded 1 or more each year.

Deadline June of each year.

[810]
CORA E. CRAVEN EDUCATIONAL GRANT

Lambda Kappa Sigma Pharmacy Fraternity
Attn: Executive Director
S77 W16906 Casey Drive
P.O. Box 570
Muskego, WI 53150-0570
Toll Free: (800) LKS-1913   Fax: (262) 679-4558
E-mail: lks@lks.org
Web: www.lks.org

Summary To provide financial assistance to members of Lambda Kappa Sigma who are interested in working on a Pharm.D. degree.

Eligibility This program is open to collegiate or alumnae members of Lambda Kappa Sigma who are enrolled in a licensure-eligible pharmacy degree program. (In the United States, the Pharm.D. degree is the only qualifying program at schools or colleges of pharmacy recognized by the Accreditation Council on Pharmacy Education.) Applicants must rank in the top half of their class and be able to demonstrate financial need.

Financial data The stipend is $1,000.

Duration 1 year.

Additional information This program was established in 1962. Lambda Kappa Sigma was founded in 1913 to promote the profession of pharmacy among women.

Number awarded Varies each year; recently, 3 of these grants were awarded.

Deadline October of each year.

[811]
CUMMINS SCHOLARSHIPS

Society of Women Engineers
Attn: Scholarship Selection Committee
120 South LaSalle Street, Suite 1515
Chicago, IL 60603-3572
(312) 596-5223   Toll Free: (877) SWE-INFO
Fax: (312) 644-8557
E-mail: scholarshipapplication@swe.org
Web: societyofwomenengineers.swe.org

Summary To provide financial assistance to women working on an undergraduate or graduate degree in designated engineering specialties.

Eligibility This program is open to women who are sophomores, juniors, seniors, or graduate students at 4-year ABET-accredited colleges and universities. Applicants must be working on a degree in computer science or automotive, chemical, computer, electrical, industrial, manufacturing, materials, or mechanical engineering and have a GPA of 3.5 or higher. Preference is given to members of groups underrepresented in engineering or computer science. Selection is based on merit. U.S. citizenship is required.

Financial data The stipend is $1,000.

Duration 1 year.

Additional information This program is sponsored by Cummins, Inc.

Number awarded 2 each year.

Deadline February of each year.

[812]
D. ANITA SMALL SCIENCE AND BUSINESS SCHOLARSHIP

Business and Professional Women of Maryland
Attn: BPW Foundation of Maryland
c/o Joyce Draper, Chief Financial Officer
615 Fairview Avenue
Frederick, MD 21701
Web: www.bpwmaryland.org

Summary To provide financial assistance to women in Maryland who are interested in working on an undergraduate or graduate degree in a science or business-related field.

Eligibility This program is open to women who are at least 21 years of age and have been accepted to a bachelor's or advanced degree program at an accredited Maryland academic institution. Applicants must be preparing for a career in 1 of the following or a related field: accounting, aeronautics, business administration, computer sciences, engineering, finance, information technology, mathematics, medical sciences (including nursing, laboratory technology, therapy, etc.), oceanography, or physical sciences. They must have a GPA of 3.0 or higher and be able to demonstrate financial need.

Financial data The stipend is $1,000 per year.

Duration 1 year.

Number awarded 1 or more each year.

Deadline July of each year.

[813]
DANIEL LADNER SCHOLARSHIPS

New York Women in Communications, Inc.
Attn: NYWICI Foundation
355 Lexington Avenue, 15th Floor
New York, NY 10017-6603
(212) 297-2133   Fax: (212) 370-9047
E-mail: nywicipr@nywici.org
Web: www.nywici.org/foundation/scholarships

Summary To provide financial assistance to female upper-division and graduate students who reside in designated eastern states and are interested in preparing for a career in financial or political communications at a college or graduate school in any state.

Eligibility This program is open to female residents of New York, New Jersey, Connecticut, or Pennsylvania who are attending a college or university in any state. Also eligible are women who reside outside the 4 states but are currently enrolled at a college or university within 1 of the 5 boroughs of New York City. Applicants must be college juniors, seniors, or graduate students who are preparing for a career in either 1) financial communications (e.g., marketing, advertising, investor relations, public relations, corporate communications, media/journalism); or 2) political communications (e.g., political journalism; advertising; analysis; consulting; public, government, or international affairs; diplomacy; speechwriting; advocacy). They must have a GPA of 3.2 or higher. Graduate students must be members of New York Women in Communications, Inc. (NYWICI). Along with their application, they must submit a 2-page resume that includes school and extra-curricular activities, significant achievements, academic honors and awards, and community service work; a personal essay of 300 to 500 words on their choice of an assigned topic that changes annually; 2 letters of recommendation; and an official transcript. Selection is based on academic record, need, demonstrated leadership, participation in school and community activities, honors, work experience, goals and aspirations, and unusual personal and/or family circumstances. U.S. citizenship is required.

Financial data The stipend ranges up to $10,000.

Duration 1 year.

Number awarded 2 each year.

Deadline January of each year.

[814]
DASSAULT FALCON JET CORPORATION SCHOLARSHIP

Women in Aviation, International
Attn: Scholarships
Morningstar Airport
3647 State Route 503 South
West Alexandria, OH 45381-9354
(937) 839-4647   Fax: (937) 839-4645
E-mail: scholarships@wai.org
Web: www.wai.org/education/scholarships.cfm

Summary To provide financial assistance to women who are working on an undergraduate or graduate degree in a field related to aviation.

Eligibility This program is open to women who are working on an undergraduate or graduate degree in an aviation-related field. Applicants must be U.S. citizens, be fluent in English, and have a GPA of 3.0 or higher. Along with their application, they must submit 2 letters of recommendation; a 1-page essay on their current educational status, what they hope to achieve by working on a degree in aviation, and their aspirations in the field; a resume; copies of all aviation licenses and medical certificates; and the last 3 pages of their pilot logbook (if applicable). Selection is based on achievements, attitude toward self and others, commitment to success, dedication to career, financial need, motivation, reliability, responsibility, and teamwork.

Financial data The stipend is $1,000.

Duration 1 year.

Additional information WAI is a nonprofit professional organization dedicated to encouraging women to consider an aviation career and to providing educational outreach activities and networking resources to women active in the industry. This program is sponsored by Dassault Falcon Jet Corporation.

Number awarded 1 each year.

Deadline November of each year.

[815]
DAUGHTERS OF PENELOPE GRADUATE STUDENT SCHOLARSHIPS

Daughters of Penelope
Attn: Daughters of Penelope Foundation, Inc.
1909 Q Street, N.W., Suite 500
Washington, DC 20009-1007
(202) 234-9741   Fax: (202) 483-6983
E-mail: dophq@ahepa.org
Web: www.dopfoundationinc.com/?page_id=382

Summary To provide financial assistance for graduate school to women of Greek descent.

Eligibility This program is open to women who have been members of the Daughters of Penelope or the Maids of Athena for at least 2 years, or whose parents or grandparents have been members of the Daughters of Penelope or the Order of AHEPA for at least 2 years. Applicants must be accepted or currently enrolled for a minimum of 9 units per academic year in an M.A., M.S., M.B.A., Ph.D., D.D.S., M.D., or other university graduate degree program. They must have taken the GRE or other entrance examination (or Canadian, Greek, or Cypriot equivalent) and must write an essay (in

English) about their educational and vocational goals. Selection is based on academic merit.

Financial data Stipends are $2,500 or $1,000.

Duration 1 year; nonrenewable.

Additional information This program includes the Dorothy Lillian Quincey Memorial Graduate Scholarship, the Big Five Graduate Scholarship, and the Sonja Stefanadis Graduate Scholarship.

Number awarded Varies each year; recently, 3 of these scholarships (1 at $2,500 and 2 at $1,000) were awarded.

Deadline April of each year.

[816]
DAVID HILLIARD EATON SCHOLARSHIP

Unitarian Universalist Association
Attn: Ministerial Credentialing Office
25 Beacon Street
Boston, MA 02108-2800
(617) 948-6403   Fax: (617) 742-2875
E-mail: mco@uua.org
Web: www.uua.org

Summary To provide financial assistance to minority women preparing for the Unitarian Universalist (UU) ministry.

Eligibility This program is open to women from historically marginalized groups who are currently enrolled or planning to enroll full or at least half time in a UU ministerial training program with aspirant or candidate status. Applicants must be citizens of the United States or Canada. Priority is given first to those who have demonstrated outstanding ministerial ability and secondarily to students with the greatest financial need (especially persons of color).

Financial data The stipend ranges from $1,000 to $11,000 per year.

Duration 1 year.

Number awarded Varies each year; recently, 2 of these scholarships were awarded.

Deadline April of each year.

[817]
DEALER DEVELOPMENT SCHOLARSHIP PROGRAM

General Motors Corporation
Women's Retail Network
Attn: GM Scholarship Administration Center
700 West Fifth Avenue
Mail Code 2001
Naperville, IL 60563
Toll Free: (888) 377-5233
E-mail: wrnscholarshipinfo@gmsac.com
Web: www.gmsac.com

Summary To provide financial assistance to women attending college or graduate school to prepare for a retail automotive career.

Eligibility This program is open to women who are enrolled full time in undergraduate, graduate, and nontraditional continuing education institutions that offer degrees in the automotive retail field. Applicants must be interested in preparing for a career in automotive retail and/or service management. They must be citizens of the United States or have the ability to accept permanent employment in the United States without the need for visa sponsorship now or in the future. Current and former enrollees in the General Motors National Candidate Program are not eligible, but applications are accepted from female employees and female employee dependents working at GM dealerships. Selection is based on academic performance, community service and volunteerism, work experience, and a personal statement. Financial need is not considered.

Financial data The stipend is $5,000 per year.

Duration 1 year; recipients may reapply.

Additional information This program was established in 2011.

Number awarded Several each year.

Deadline April of each year.

[818]
DELAYED EDUCATION SCHOLARSHIP FOR WOMEN

American Nuclear Society
Attn: Scholarship Coordinator
555 North Kensington Avenue
La Grange Park, IL 60526-5592
(708) 352-6611   Toll Free: (800) 323-3044
Fax: (708) 352-0499   E-mail: outreach@ans.org
Web: www.ans.org/honors/scholarships

Summary To provide financial assistance to mature women whose formal studies in nuclear science or nuclear engineering have been delayed or interrupted.

Eligibility Applicants must be mature women who have experienced at least a 1-year delay or interruption of their undergraduate studies and are returning to school to work on an undergraduate or graduate degree in nuclear science or nuclear engineering. They must be members of the American Nuclear Society (ANS), but they may be citizens of any country. Along with their application, they must submit an essay on their academic and professional goals, experiences that have affected those goals, and other relevant information. Selection is based on that essay, academic achievement, letters of recommendation, and financial need.

Financial data The stipend is $5,000. Funds may be used by the student to cover any educational expense, including tuition, books, room, and board.

Duration 1 year; nonrenewable.

Number awarded 1 each year.

Deadline January of each year.

[819]
DELTA DELTA DELTA UNRESTRICTED GRADUATE SCHOLARSHIPS

Delta Delta Delta
Attn: Tri Delta Foundation
2331 Brookhollow Plaza Drive
P.O. Box 5987
Arlington, TX 76005-5987
(817) 633-8001   Fax: (817) 652-0212
E-mail: foundation@trideltaeo.org
Web: www.tridelta.org/Document/Foundation/Scholarships

Summary To provide financial assistance for graduate study to women students who are members of Delta Delta Delta.

Eligibility This program is open to members of the sorority who are entering or already engaged in graduate study. Appli-

cants must submit a personal statement outlining their educational and vocational goals, 2 academic recommendations, a Tri Delta recommendation, academic transcripts, and documentation of financial need. Selection is based on academic merit, chapter and campus activities, and community activities.

Financial data The stipend is $3,000.

Duration 1 year.

Additional information This program, originally established in 1938, includes the following named awards: the Mary Margaret Hafter Fellowship, the Luella Akins Key Graduate Scholarship, the Second Century Graduate Scholarship, the Margaret Stafford Memorial Scholarship, and the Sarah Shinn Marshall Graduate Scholarship.

Number awarded Varies each year; recently, a total of 10 graduate scholarships were awarded.

Deadline February of each year.

[820]
DELTA GAMMA FELLOWSHIPS

Delta Gamma Foundation
Attn: Director of Scholarships, Fellowships and Loans
3250 Riverside Drive
P.O. Box 21397
Columbus, OH 43221-0397
(614) 481-8169   Toll Free: (800) 644-5414
Fax: (614) 481-0133
E-mail: FNScholarFellow@deltagamma.org
Web: www.deltagamma.org

Summary To provide financial assistance to members of Delta Gamma sorority who are interested in working on a graduate degree.

Eligibility This program is open to dues-paying members of Delta Gamma who are currently enrolled in graduate school or will have completed their undergraduate work by June 30 of the year in which the fellowship is granted and will begin graduate study in the following fall. Applicants may attend an accredited university in the United States or Canada and work on a degree in any field. Along with their application, they must submit a 1- to 2-page essay in which they introduce themselves, including their career goals, their reasons for applying, and the impact Delta Gamma has had upon their life. Selection is based on scholastic excellence, contributions to their chosen field, past and current Delta Gamma activities, and campus and community involvement.

Financial data The stipend is $2,500.

Duration 1 year.

Number awarded Varies each year; recently, 14 of these fellowships were awarded.

Deadline March of each year.

[821]
DELTA KAPPA GAMMA SCHOLARSHIP PROGRAM

Delta Kappa Gamma Society International
Attn: Scholarships Committee
416 West 12th Street
P.O. Box 1589
Austin, TX 78767-1589
(512) 478-5748   Toll Free: (888) 762-4685
Fax: (512) 478-3961   E-mail: societyoper@dkg.org
Web: www.dkg.org

Summary To provide financial assistance to members of Delta Kappa Gamma Society International from any country interested in graduate study or research.

Eligibility Applicants must have been members in good standing of the Delta Kappa Gamma Society International (an honorary society of women educators) for at least 3 years, have completed a master's degree or equivalent, and have been accepted and enrolled in a graduate program at a nationally accredited institution of higher education, preferably working on a doctoral degree. Along with their application, they must submit a 500-word impact statement that describes the area of their intended study or major interest, the potential benefits of the degree to them professionally, and the potential benefits of the degree to Delta Kappa Gamma. Selection is based on that statement (30 points), active participation and demonstrated leadership in Delta Kappa Gamma (20 points), recognitions for achievement (10 points), professional work experience (10 points), current status of program (10 points), prior education (10 points), and recommendations (10 points).

Financial data The stipend is $6,000.

Duration 1 year.

Additional information Delta Kappa Gamma Society International has 170,000 members in 13 countries and is the largest organization of its kind. This program includes the following named awards: the Marjorie Jeanne Allen Scholarship, the Mamie Sue Bastian Scholarship, the Dr. Annie Webb Blanton Scholarship, the Blanton Centennial Scholarship, the A. Margaret Boyd Scholarship, the Dr. Eula Lee Carter Scholarship, the Delta Kappa Gamma Founders Scholarship, the Delta Kappa Gamma Golden Anniversary Scholarship, the Delta Kappa Gamma 60th Anniversary Scholarship, the Delta Kappa Gamma 70th Anniversary Scholarship, the Zora Ellis Scholarship, the Emma Giles Scholarship, the Carolyn Guss Scholarship, the Dr. Ola B. Hiller Scholarship, the Eunah Temple Holden Scholarship, the Hazel Johnson Memorial Scholarship, the Dr. Evelyn Milam Scholarships, the Berneta Minkwitz Scholarship, the Dr. Catherine Nutterville Scholarship, the Alida W. Parker Scholarship, the J. Maria Pierce Scholarship, the Dr. Emma Reinhart Scholarship, the Norma Bristow Salter Scholarship, the Mary Katherine Shoup Scholarship, the Dr. Maycie K. Southall Scholarship, the M. Margaret Stroh Scholarship, the Letti P. Trefz Scholarship, and the Dr. Mary Frances White Scholarship. Recipients must remain active members of Delta Kappa Gamma, work full time on the study or research outlined in their applications, submit reports requested by the society, and acknowledge assistance of the society in any publication that results from data gathered while the award was being used.

Number awarded Up to 30 each year.

Deadline January of each year.

[822]
DELTA PHI EPSILON SCHOLARSHIPS

Delta Phi Epsilon Educational Foundation
Attn: Executive Director
251 South Carnac Street
Philadelphia, PA 19107
(215) 732-5901   Fax: (215) 732-5906
E-mail: info@dphie.org
Web: www.dphie.org

Summary To provide financial assistance for college or graduate school to Delta Phi Epsilon Sorority members, alumnae, and relatives.

Eligibility This program is open to undergraduate Delta Phi Epsilon sorority sisters (not pledges) and alumnae who are returning to college or graduate school. Sons and daughters of Delta Phi Epsilon members or alumnae are also eligible for some of the programs. Selection is based on service and involvement, academics, and financial need.

Financial data The stipend is $1,000.

Duration 1 year or longer, depending upon the scholarship awarded.

Number awarded Varies each year; recently, 8 of these scholarships were awarded.

Deadline March of each year.

[823]
DELTA SIGMA THETA SORORITY GENERAL SCHOLARSHIPS

Delta Sigma Theta Sorority, Inc.
Attn: Scholarship and Standards Committee Chair
1707 New Hampshire Avenue, N.W.
Washington, DC 20009
(202) 986-2400   Fax: (202) 986-2513
E-mail: dstemail@deltasigmatheta.org
Web: www.deltasigmatheta.org

Summary To provide financial assistance to members of Delta Sigma Theta who are working on an undergraduate or graduate degree in any field.

Eligibility This program is open to active, dues-paying members of Delta Sigma Theta who are currently enrolled in college or graduate school. Applicants must submit an essay on their major goals and educational objectives, including realistic steps they foresee as necessary for the fulfillment of their plans. Financial need is considered in the selection process.

Financial data The stipends range from $1,000 to $2,000. The funds may be used to cover tuition, fees, and living expenses.

Duration 1 year; may be renewed for 1 additional year.

Additional information This sponsor is a traditionally-African American social sorority. The application fee is $20.

Deadline April of each year.

[824]
DEPARTMENT OF STATE STUDENT INTERN PROGRAM

Department of State
Attn: HR/REE
2401 E Street, N.W., Suite 518 H
Washington, DC 20522-0108
(202) 261-8888   Toll Free: (800) JOB-OVERSEAS
Fax: (301) 562-8968   E-mail: Careers@state.gov
Web: www.careers.state.gov/students/programs

Summary To provide a work/study opportunity to undergraduate and graduate students (especially women and minority students) who are interested in foreign service.

Eligibility This program is open to full- and part-time continuing college and university juniors, seniors, and graduate students. Applications are encouraged from students with a broad range of majors, such as business or public administration, social work, economics, information management, journalism, and the biological, engineering, and physical sciences, as well as those majors more traditionally identified with international affairs. U.S. citizenship is required. The State Department particularly encourages eligible women and minority students with an interest in foreign affairs to apply.

Financial data Most internships are unpaid. A few paid internships are granted to applicants who can demonstrate financial need. If they qualify for a paid internship, they are placed at the GS-4 step 5 level (currently with an annual rate of $27,786). Interns placed abroad may also receive housing, medical insurance, a travel allowance, and a dependents' allowance.

Duration Paid internships are available only for 10 weeks during the summer. Unpaid internships are available for 1 semester or quarter during the academic year, or for 10 weeks during the summer.

Additional information About half of all internships are in Washington, D.C., or occasionally in other large cities in the United States. The remaining internships are at embassies and consulates abroad. Depending upon the needs of the department, interns are assigned junior-level professional duties, which may include research, preparing reports, drafting replies to correspondence, working in computer science, analyzing international issues, financial management, intelligence, security, or assisting in cases related to domestic and international law. Interns must agree to return to their schooling immediately upon completion of their internship.

Number awarded Approximately 800 internships are offered each year, but only about 5% of those are paid positions.

Deadline February of each year for fall internships; June of each year for spring internships; October of each year for a summer internships.

[825]
DIAMOND JUBILEE FOUNDATION SCHOLARSHIPS

Alpha Omicron Pi Foundation
Attn: Scholarship Committee
5390 Virginia Way
Brentwood, TN 37027
(615) 370-0920   Fax: (615) 370-4424
E-mail: foundation@alphaomicronpi.org
Web: www.aoiifoundation.org/scholarship.php

Summary To provide financial assistance for college or graduate school to collegiate and alumnae members of Alpha Omicron Pi.

Eligibility This program is open to collegiate members of Alpha Omicron Pi who are classified by their institutions at least as sophomores and alumnae members who wish to work on a graduate degree. Applicants must be enrolled full time. Along with their application, they must submit the following 50-word statements: 1) the circumstances that have created their need for this scholarship; 2) their immediate and long-term life objectives; and 3) a letter of recommendation that they would write about themselves. Selection is based on those statements; academic achievement; Alpha Omicron Pi service, leadership, and involvement; college and community involvement; letters of recommendation; and financial need and evidence of self-help.

Financial data Stipend amounts vary; recently, the average value of each scholarship provided by this foundation was approximately $1,200.

Duration 1 year.

Additional information This program was established in 1962.

Number awarded Varies each year; recently, 35 of these scholarships were awarded (25 to undergraduates and 10 to graduate students).

Deadline February of each year.

[826]
DISSERTATION FELLOWSHIPS IN EAST EUROPEAN STUDIES

American Council of Learned Societies
Attn: Office of Fellowships and Grants
633 Third Avenue
New York, NY 10017-6795
(212) 697-1505   Fax: (212) 949-8058
E-mail: fellowships@acls.org
Web: www.acls.org/grants/Default.aspx?id=532

Summary To provide funding to doctoral candidates (particularly women and minorities) who are interested in conducting dissertation research in the social sciences and humanities relating to eastern Europe.

Eligibility This program is open to U.S. citizens or permanent residents who are working on a dissertation in the humanities or social sciences as related to eastern Europe, including Albania, Bosnia and Herzegovina, Bulgaria, Croatia, Czech Republic, Estonia, Hungary, Latvia, Lithuania, Former Yugoslav Republic of Macedonia, Kosovo, Montenegro, Poland, Romania, Serbia, Slovakia, and Slovenia. Applicants may be proposing projects comparing more than 1 country of eastern Europe or relating eastern European societies to those of other parts of the world. They may be seeking support for research fellowships (for use in eastern Europe to conduct fieldwork or archival investigations) or writing fellowships (for use in the United States, after all research is complete, to write the dissertation). Selection is based on the scholarly potential of the applicant, the quality and scholarly importance of the proposed work, and its importance to the development of scholarship on eastern Europe. Applications are particularly invited from women and members of minority groups.

Financial data The maximum stipend is $18,000. Recipients' home universities are required (consistent with their policies and regulations) to provide or to waive normal academic year tuition payments or to provide alternative cost-sharing support.

Duration 1 year. Students may apply for 1-year research and writing fellowships in sequence, but they may not apply for a second year of funding in either category.

Additional information This program is sponsored jointly by the American Council of Learned Societies, (ACLS) and the Social Science Research Council, funded by the U.S. Department of State under the Research and Training for Eastern Europe and the Independent States of the Former Soviet Union Act of 1983 (Title VIII) but administered by ACLS.

Number awarded Varies each year; recently, 8 of these fellowships were awarded.

Deadline November of each year.

[827]
DISSERTATION PROPOSAL DEVELOPMENT FELLOWSHIP PROGRAM

Social Science Research Council
Attn: DPDF Program
One Pierrepont Plaza, 15th Floor
Brooklyn, NY 11201
(212) 377-2700   Fax: (212) 377-2727
E-mail: dpdf@ssrc.org
Web: www.ssrc.org/fellowships/dpdf-fellowship

Summary To provide an opportunity for women, minorities, and other doctoral students in the social sciences and humanities to formulate their dissertation proposals and conduct predissertation research.

Eligibility This program is open to full-time graduate students in the second or third year of a doctoral program who have not yet had their dissertation proposals accepted by their thesis directors and their home institutions. Each year, the program selects 6 subdisciplinary and interdisciplinary fields within the social sciences and humanities, and students apply to participate in 1 of those fields. They must be able to attend a workshop in the spring to prepare to undertake predissertation research, spend the summer conducting that research, and then attend another workshop in the fall to synthesize their summer research and draft proposals for dissertation funding. Workshop participants are selected on the basis of the originality and appropriateness of their dissertation topic, the preparation of the student, and the quality of the summer predissertation research plan. Minorities and women are particularly encouraged to apply.

Financial data For all fellows, expenses to attend the workshops (airfare, hotel, meals, ground transport) are paid. Those fellows who are selected for summer predissertation research receive $5,000 grants.

Duration The program extends over 1 calendar year.

Additional information Funding for this program is provided by the Andrew W. Mellon Foundation. Recently, the designated research fields were: new approaches to religion and modernity; discrimination studies; interdisciplinary approaches to the study of contentious politics; multiculturalism, immigration, and identity in western Europe and the United States; spaces of inquiry; and virtual worlds.

Number awarded Each research field accepts 10 to 12 graduate students.

Deadline January of each year.

[828]
DISSERTATION SUPPORT PROGRAM

National Physical Science Consortium
c/o University of Southern California
3716 South Hope Street, Suite 348
Los Angeles, CA 90007-4344
(213) 743-2409   Toll Free: (800) 854-NPSC
Fax: (213) 743-2407   E-mail: npschq@npsc.org
Web: www.npsc.org

Summary To provide funding to women and underrepresented minorities who are conducting dissertation research in designated science and engineering fields.

Eligibility This program is open to U.S. citizens who are enrolled in a doctoral program and about to begin dissertation research. Eligible fields of study are generally limited to astronomy, chemistry, computer science, geology, materials science, mathematical sciences, physics, their subdisciplines, and related engineering fields (chemical, computer, electrical, environmental, and mechanical). The program welcomes applications from all qualified students and continues to emphasize the recruitment of underrepresented minority (African American, Hispanic, Native American Indian, Eskimo, Aleut, and Pacific Islander) and women physical science and engineering students. Fellowships are provided to students at the 119 universities that are members of the consortium. Selection is based on academic standing (GPA), undergraduate and graduate course work and grades, university and/or industry research experience, letters of recommendation, and GRE scores.

Financial data The fellowship pays tuition and fees plus an annual stipend of $20,000.

Duration Up to 4 years.

Number awarded Varies each year.

Deadline November of each year.

[829]
DIVERSITY IN PSYCHOLOGY AND LAW RESEARCH AWARD

American Psychological Association
Attn: Division 41 (American Psychology-Law Society)
c/o Jennifer Hunt, Minority Affairs Committee Chair
Buffalo State University of New York, Psychology
  Department
Classroom Building C308
1300 Elmwood Avenue
Buffalo, NY 14222
(716) 878-3421   E-mail: huntjs@buffalostate.edu
Web: www.ap-ls.org

Summary To provide funding to women and other student members of the American Psychology-Law Society (AP-LS) who are interested in conducting a research project related to diversity.

Eligibility This program is open to undergraduate and graduate student members of AP-LS who are interested in conducting research on issues related to psychology, law, multiculturalism, and/or diversity (e.g., research pertaining to psycholegal issues on race, gender, culture, sexual orientation). Students from underrepresented groups are strongly encouraged to apply; underrepresented groups include, but are not limited to: racial and ethnic minorities; first-generation college students; lesbian, gay, bisexual, and transgender students; and physically disabled students. Applicants must submit a project description that includes a statement of the research problem, the project's likely impact on the field of psychology and law broadly, methodology, budget, and an overview of relevant literature. Selection is based on the impact of the project on diversity and multiculturalism and the expected completion within the allocated time.

Financial data The grant is $1,000.

Duration The project must be completed within 1 year.

Number awarded 3 each year.

Deadline November of each year.

[830]
DOLORES E. FISHER AWARD

Mel Fisher Maritime Heritage Society and Museum
Attn: Curator, Department of Education
200 Greene Street
Key West, FL 33040
(305) 294-2633   Fax: (305) 294-5671
E-mail: office@melfisher.org
Web: www.melfisher.org/deoaward.htm

Summary To recognize and reward, with funding for college or graduate school, women who submit outstanding essays on the oceans.

Eligibility This competition is open to women in 2 age groups: 16 to 21 and 22 to 30. Candidates must submit a 1,000-word essay on how they hope to make a difference in the world through their passion for the oceans, their career goals, where they currently stand along that career path, and how this award will help them achieve those goals. They must also include 3 letters of recommendation and a brief statement on the personality characteristics they value most in themselves and why. If they are currently enrolled in school, they must identify their program, but school enrollment is not required. Finalists in each age group compete for the award.

Financial data The award is $1,000.

Duration The award is presented annually.

Number awarded 1 each year.

Deadline March of each year.

[831]
DONALD W. BANNER DIVERSITY SCHOLARSHIP

Banner & Witcoff, Ltd.
Attn: Christopher Hummel
1100 13th Street, N.W., Suite 1200
Washington, DC 20005-4051
(202) 824-3000   Fax: (202) 824-3001
E-mail: chummel@bannerwitcoff.com
Web: www.bannerwitcoff.com

Summary To provide financial assistance to female and other law students who come from groups historically underrepresented in intellectual property law.

Eligibility This program is open to students enrolled in the first or second year of a J.D. program at an ABA-accredited law school in the United States. Applicants must come from a group historically underrepresented in intellectual property law; that underrepresentation may be the result of race, sex, ethnicity, sexual orientation, or disability. Selection is based on academic merit, commitment to the pursuit of a career in intellectual property law, written communication skills, oral communication skills (determined through an interview), leadership qualities, and community involvement.

Financial data The stipend is $5,000 per year.

Duration 1 year (the second or third year of law school); students who accept and successfully complete the firm's summer associate program may receive an additional $5,000 for a subsequent semester of law school.

Number awarded 2 each year.

Deadline October of each year.

[832]
DONNA HEIKEN DOCTORAL GRANT

Sigma Alpha Iota Philanthropies, Inc.
One Tunnel Road
Asheville, NC 28805
(828) 251-0606   Fax: (828) 251-0644
E-mail: nh@sai-national.org
Web: www.sigmaalphaiota.org

Summary To provide funding for doctoral research in music to members of Sigma Alpha Iota (an organization of women musicians).

Eligibility This program is open to members of the organization who are enrolled in a program leading to a doctoral degree. They must be conducting doctoral research on music education, music therapy, musicology, ethnomusicology, music theory, psychology of music, or applied research (including performance or pedagogy).

Financial data The grant is $2,500 per year.

Duration 1 year.

Number awarded 1 each year.

Deadline March of each year.

[833]
DONNA REIFSCHNEIDER SCHOLARSHIP

Delta Zeta Sorority
Attn: Foundation Coordinator
202 East Church Street
Oxford, OH 45056
(513) 523-7597   Fax: (513) 523-1921
E-mail: DZFoundation@dzshq.com
Web: www.deltazeta.org

Summary To provide financial assistance for continued undergraduate or graduate study in music or music education to members of Delta Zeta Sorority.

Eligibility This program is open to upper-division and graduate members of the sorority who have a GPA of 3.0 or higher. Applicants must be working on a degree in music or music education. Along with their application, they must submit an official transcript, a statement of their career goals, information on their service to the sorority, documentation of campus activities and/or community involvement, a list of academic honors, and an explanation of their financial need. Preference is given to members of the Iota Upsilon chapter at California State University at Fullerton or Iota Iota chapter at Middle Tennessee State University.

Financial data The stipend ranges from $500 to $2,500 for undergraduates or from $1,000 to $15,000 for graduate students, depending on the availability of funds.

Duration 1 year; nonrenewable.

Number awarded 1 each year.

Deadline February of each year.

[834]
DORIS BALLANCE ORMAN, '25, FELLOWSHIP

Gallaudet University Alumni Association
Attn: Graduate Fellowship Fund Committee
Peikoff Alumni House
Gallaudet University
800 Florida Avenue, N.E.
Washington, DC 20002-3695
(202) 651-5060   Fax: (202) 651-5062
TDD: (202) 651-5060
E-mail: alumni.relations@gallaudet.edu
Web: alumni.gallaudet.edu/GFF_Info.xml

Summary To provide financial assistance to deaf women who wish to work on a graduate degree at universities for people who hear normally.

Eligibility This program is open to deaf or hard of hearing women graduates of Gallaudet University or other accredited academic institutions who have been accepted for graduate study at colleges or universities for people who hear normally. Applicants must be working on a doctorate or other terminal degree. They must have a particular interest in the arts, the humanities, or community leadership. Financial need is considered in the selection process.

Financial data The amount awarded varies, depending upon the needs of the recipient and the availability of funds.

Duration 1 year; may be renewed.

Additional information This program is 1 of 12 designated funds within the Graduate Fellowship Fund of the Gallaudet University Alumni Association. Recipients must carry a full-time semester load.

Number awarded Up to 1 each year.

Deadline April of each year.

[835]
DOROTHY E. SCHOELZEL MEMORIAL SCHOLARSHIP

General Federation of Women's Clubs of Connecticut
c/o JoAnn Calnen, President
74 Spruceland Road
Enfield, CT 06082-2359
E-mail: gfwcct@yahoo.com
Web: www.gfwcct.org

Summary To provide financial assistance to women in Connecticut who are working on an undergraduate or graduate degree in education.

Eligibility This program is open to female residents of Connecticut who have completed at least 3 years of college. Applicants must have a GPA of 3.0 or higher and be working on a bachelor's or master's degree in education. Selection is based on academic ability, future promise, and financial need.

Financial data The stipend is $2,000.

Duration 1 year.

Number awarded 1 each year.

Deadline February of each year.

[836]
DOROTHY L. WELLER PEO SCHOLARSHIP

P.E.O. Foundation-California State Chapter
c/o Carol Born, Scholarship Committee Chair
718 Via La Paloma
Riverside, CA 92507-6403
(951) 686-2728
Web: www.peocalifornia.org/dlw.html

Summary To provide financial assistance for law school or paralegal studies to women in California.

Eligibility This program is open to female residents of California who have been admitted to an accredited law school or a licensed paralegal school. Applicants must have completed 4 years of high school and be able to demonstrate excellence in academic ability, character, integrity, and school activities. Financial need is also considered in the selection process.

Financial data Recently, the stipend was $2,500.

Duration 1 year.

Number awarded Varies each year; recently, 4 of these scholarships were awarded.

Deadline January of each year.

[837]
DOROTHY WORDEN RONKEN SCHOLARSHIP

Delta Zeta Sorority
Attn: Foundation Coordinator
202 East Church Street
Oxford, OH 45056
(513) 523-7597   Fax: (513) 523-1921
E-mail: DZFoundation@dzshq.com
Web: www.deltazeta.org

Summary To provide financial assistance to members of Delta Zeta Sorority working on a graduate degree in education or business.

Eligibility This program is open to graduate members of the sorority who are working on a degree in education or business. Applicants must be preparing for a career in the purchase of academic books. Along with their application, they must submit an official transcript, a statement of their career goals, information on their service to the sorority, documentation of campus activities and/or community involvement, a list of academic honors, and an explanation of their financial need. Preference is given to applicants from the Alpha Alpha chapter at Northwestern University.

Financial data The stipend ranges from $1,000 to $15,000, depending on the availability of funds.

Duration 1 year; nonrenewable.

Number awarded 1 each year.

Deadline February of each year.

[838]
DOYNE M. GREEN SCHOLARSHIP

Seattle Foundation
Attn: Scholarship Administrator
1200 Fifth Avenue, Suite 1300
Seattle, WA 98101-3151
(206) 622-2294   Fax: (206) 622-7673
E-mail: scholarships@seattlefoundation.org
Web: www.seattlefoundation.org

Summary To provide financial assistance to women in Washington working on a graduate degree in law, medicine, or social and public services.

Eligibility This program is open to female residents of Washington who have completed the first year of a graduate program in law, medicine, or social and public services. Applicants must be able to demonstrate financial need. Along with their application, they must submit a brief statement on their plans as they relate to their educational and career objectives and long-term goals.

Financial data The stipend is $4,000.

Duration 1 year; nonrenewable.

Additional information This program is administered by Scholarship Management Services, a division of Scholarship America, One Scholarship Way, P.O. Box 297, St. Peter, MN 56082, (507) 931-1682.

Number awarded 2 each year.

Deadline February of each year.

[839]
DR. ALEXANDRA KIRKLEY TRAVELING FELLOWSHIP

Ruth Jackson Orthopaedic Society
6300 North River Road, Suite 727
Rosemont, IL 60018-4226
(847) 698-1626   Fax: (847) 823-0536
E-mail: rjos@aaos.org
Web: www.rjos.org/web/awards/index.htm

Summary To provide funding to female orthopedic medical students who are interested in traveling to enrich their academic career.

Eligibility This program is open to female medical students who are members of the Ruth Jackson Orthopaedic Society (RJOS). Applicants must be Board Eligible orthopedic surgeons and citizens of the United States or Canada. They must be interested in a program of travel to enrich their academic career.

Financial data Grants up to $6,000 are available.

Additional information Funding for this program is provided by Zimmer, Inc.

Number awarded 1 each year.

Deadline September of each year.

[840]
DR. AND MRS. DAVID B. ALLMAN MEDICAL SCHOLARSHIPS

Miss America Pageant
Attn: Scholarship Department
222 New Road, Suite 700
Linwood, NJ 08221
(609) 653-8700, ext. 127   Fax: (609) 653-8740
E-mail: info@missamerica.org
Web: www.missamerica.org

Summary To provide financial assistance to medical students who have competed or are competing in the Miss America contest at any level.

Eligibility This program is open to women who have competed in the Miss America competition at least once, at any level of competition, within the past 10 years. Applicants do not have to apply during the year they competed; they may apply any year following as long as they are attending or accepted by a medical school and plan to become a medical doctor. They must submit an essay, up to 500 words, on why they wish to become a medical doctor and how this scholarship can help them attain that goal. Selection is based on GPA, class rank, MCAT score, extracurricular activities, financial need, and level of participation within the system.

Financial data The stipend is 4,600.

Duration 1 year.

Additional information This scholarship was established in 1974.

Number awarded 1 each year.

Deadline June of each year.

[841]
DR. B. OLIVE COLE GRADUATE EDUCATIONAL GRANT

Lambda Kappa Sigma Pharmacy Fraternity
Attn: Executive Director
S77 W16906 Casey Drive
P.O. Box 570
Muskego, WI 53150-0570
Toll Free: (800) LKS-1913   Fax: (262) 679-4558
E-mail: lks@lks.org
Web: www.lks.org

Summary To provide financial assistance to members of Lambda Kappa Sigma who are interested in working on an advanced degree.

Eligibility This program is open to members of Lambda Kappa Sigma who are enrolled in a program of graduate study and research that will advance their career. Eligible programs include master's or doctoral degrees (e.g., M.S., M.A., M.B.A., M.P.H., Ph.D., J.D., Dr.P.H.) as well as joint degree programs that combine the Pharm.D. degree with master's or doctoral studies. Applicants must have an initial degree in pharmacy. They must rank in the upper half of their class and be able to demonstrate financial need. Studies may be at institutions that do not offer the Pharm.D. or have a chapter of Lambda Kappa Sigma.

Financial data The stipend is $1,000.

Duration 1 year.

Additional information This program was established in 1972. Lambda Kappa Sigma was founded in 1913 to promote the profession of pharmacy among women.

Number awarded 1 each year.

Deadline October of each year.

[842]
DR. BESSIE ELIZABETH DELANEY FELLOWSHIP

National Dental Association
Attn: National Dental Association Foundation, Inc.
3517 16th Street, N.W.
Washington, DC 20010
(202) 588-1697   Fax: (202) 588-1244
E-mail: admin@ndaonline.org
Web: www.ndaonline.org

Summary To provide financial assistance to female dental postdoctoral students who are members of underrepresented minority groups.

Eligibility This program is open to female members of underrepresented minority groups who are working on a postdoctoral degree in subspecialty areas of dentistry, public health, administration, research, or law. Students working on a master's degree beyond their residency may be considered. Applicants must be members of the National Dental Association (NDA) and U.S. citizens or permanent residents. Along with their application, they must submit a letter explaining why they should be considered for this scholarship, 2 letters of recommendation, a curriculum vitae, a description of the program, nomination by their program director, and documentation of financial need.

Financial data The stipend is $10,000.

Duration 1 year.

Additional information This program, established in 1990, is supported by the Colgate-Palmolive Company.

Number awarded 1 each year.

Deadline May of each year.

[843]
DR. CAROLANN S. NAJARIAN SCHOLARSHIPS

Armenian International Women's Association
65 Main Street, Room 3A
Watertown, MA 02472
(617) 926-0171   E-mail: aiwainc@aol.com
Web: www.aiwa-net.org/scholarshipinfo.html

Summary To provide financial assistance to Armenian women who are upper-division and graduate students.

Eligibility This program is open to full-time women students of Armenian descent attending an accredited college or university. Applicants must be full-time juniors, seniors, or graduate students with a GPA of 3.2 or higher. They must submit an essay, up to 500 words, describing their planned academic program, their career goals, and the reasons why they believe they should be awarded this scholarship. Selection is based on financial need and merit.

Financial data The stipend is $1,000.

Duration 1 year.

Number awarded 5 each year.

Deadline April of each year.

[844]
DR. DORRI PHIPPS FELLOWSHIPS

Alpha Kappa Alpha Sorority, Inc.
Attn: Educational Advancement Foundation
5656 South Stony Island Avenue
Chicago, IL 60637
(773) 947-0026   Toll Free: (800) 653-6528
Fax: (773) 947-0277   E-mail: akaeaf@akaeaf.net
Web: www.akaeaf.org/fellowships_endowments.htm

Summary To provide financial assistance to students (especially African American women) working on a degree in medicine or conducting research related to lupus.

Eligibility This program is open to students currently enrolled in a medical or related program in any state. Applicants must be working on a degree in medicine or conducting research related to lupus. Along with their application, they must submit 1) a list of honors, awards, and scholarships received; 2) a list of organizations in which they have memberships, especially minority organizations; 3) a description of the project or research on which they are currently working, of (if they are not involved in a project or research) the aspects of their field that interest them; and 4) a statement of their personal and career goals, including how this scholarship will enhance their ability to attain those goals. The sponsor is a traditionally African American women's sorority.

Financial data A stipend is awarded (amount not specified).

Duration 1 year.

Number awarded 1 each even-numbered year.

Deadline April of each even-numbered year.

[845]
DR. PRENTICE GAUTT POSTGRADUATE SCHOLARSHIPS

Big 12 Conference
2201 Stemmons Freeway, 28th Floor
Dallas, TX 75207
(214) 742-1212   Fax: (214) 753-0145
Web: www.big12sports.com

Summary To provide financial assistance for graduate school to student athletes who are completing their undergraduate study at a Big 12 university (females and males are judged separately).

Eligibility This program is open to students graduating from a Big 12 university who have participated in at least 2 years of intercollegiate athletics. Applicants must have a GPA of 3.2 or higher and be planning to enroll full time in a program of professional or graduate study. Male and female athletes are considered separately.

Financial data The stipend is $9,000. Funds are paid directly to the student.

Duration 1 year.

Additional information This program began with the inception of the league in 1996-97. Members of the Big 12 include Baylor, Colorado, Iowa State, Kansas, Kansas State, Missouri, Nebraska, Oklahoma, Oklahoma State, Texas, Texas A&M, and Texas Tech. Recipients must graduate from their Big 12 university within 15 months of their selection for this scholarship and must enroll in a graduate or professional school within 2 years of graduation.

Number awarded 24 each year: 2 (1 male and 1 female) at each member institution.

Deadline Deadline not specified.

[846]
DRI LAW STUDENT DIVERSITY SCHOLARSHIP

DRI-The Voice of the Defense Bar
Attn: Deputy Executive Director
55 West Monroe Street, Suite 2000
Chicago, IL 60603
(312) 795-1101   Fax: (312) 795-0747
E-mail: dri@dri.org
Web: www.dri.org/open/About.aspx

Summary To provide financial assistance to women and minority law students.

Eligibility This program is open to students entering their second or third year of law school who are African American, Hispanic, Asian, Pan Asian, Native American, or female. Applicants must submit an essay, up to 1,000 words, on a topic that changes annually but relates to the work of defense attorneys. Selection is based on that essay, demonstrated academic excellence, service to the profession, service to the community, and service to the cause of diversity. Students affiliated with the American Association for Justice as members, student members, or employees are not eligible. Finalists are invited to participate in personal interviews.

Financial data The stipend is $10,000.

Duration 1 year.

Additional information This program was established in 2004.

Number awarded 2 each year.

Deadline May of each year.

[847]
DURNING SISTERS FELLOWSHIP

Delta Delta Delta
Attn: Tri Delta Foundation
2331 Brookhollow Plaza Drive
P.O. Box 5987
Arlington, TX 76005-5987
(817) 633-8001   Fax: (817) 652-0212
E-mail: foundation@trideltaeo.org
Web: www.trideltao.org/Document/Foundation/Scholarships

Summary To provide financial assistance for graduate study to unmarried women who are members of Delta Delta Delta.

Eligibility This program is open to members of the sorority who have completed at least 12 hours of graduate study. Applicants must be unmarried. Along with their application, they must submit a personal statement outlining their educational and vocational goals, 2 academic recommendations, a Tri Delta recommendation, academic transcripts, and documentation of financial need. Selection is based on academic merit, chapter and campus activities, and community activities.

Financial data The stipend is $3,000.

Duration 1 year.

Number awarded 1 each year.

Deadline February of each year.

[848]
EAST EUROPEAN LANGUAGE GRANTS TO INDIVIDUALS FOR SUMMER STUDY

American Council of Learned Societies
Attn: Office of Fellowships and Grants
633 Third Avenue
New York, NY 10017-6795
(212) 697-1505   Fax: (212) 949-8058
E-mail: fellowships@acls.org
Web: www.acls.org/grants/Default.aspx?id=540

Summary To provide financial support to graduate students, professionals, and postdoctorates (particularly women and minorities) who are interested in studying eastern European languages during the summer.

Eligibility Applicants must have completed at least a 4-year college degree. They must be interested in a program of training in the languages of eastern Europe, including Albanian, Bosnian-Croatian-Serbian, Bulgarian, Czech, Estonian, Hungarian, Latvian, Lithuanian, Macedonian, Polish, Romanian, Slovak, or Slovene. The language course may be at the beginning, intermediate, or advanced level. Normally, requests for beginning and intermediate level training should be for attendance at intensive courses offered by institutions in the United States; proposals for study at the advanced level are ordinarily for courses in eastern Europe. Applications are particularly encouraged from women and members of minority groups.

Financial data Grants up to $2,500 are available.

Duration Summer months.

Additional information This program, reinstituted in 2002, is supported by the U.S. Department of State under the Research and Training for Eastern Europe and the Independent States of the Former Soviet Union Act of 1983 (Title VIII).

Number awarded Approximately 15 each year.

Deadline January of each year.

[849]
EDITH HEAD SCHOLARSHIP

Delta Zeta Sorority
Attn: Foundation Coordinator
202 East Church Street
Oxford, OH 45056
(513) 523-7597   Fax: (513) 523-1921
E-mail: DZFoundation@dzshq.com
Web: www.deltazeta.org

Summary To provide financial assistance for continued undergraduate or graduate study in fashion design to members of Delta Zeta Sorority.

Eligibility This program is open to upper-division and graduate members of the sorority who have a GPA of 3.0 or higher. Applicants must be working on a degree in a field related to the design, production, or merchandising of textile and apparel products and/or costume design. Along with their application, they must submit an official transcript, a statement of their career goals, information on their service to the sorority, documentation of campus activities and/or community involvement, a list of academic honors, and an explanation of their financial need.

Financial data The stipend ranges from $500 to $2,500 for undergraduates or from $1,000 to $15,000 for graduate students, depending on the availability of funds.

Duration 1 year; nonrenewable.

Number awarded 1 each year.

Deadline February of each year.

[850]
EDITH HUNTINGTON ANDERSON SCHOLARSHIP

Alpha Omicron Pi Foundation
Attn: Scholarship Committee
5390 Virginia Way
Brentwood, TN 37027
(615) 370-0920   Fax: (615) 370-4424
E-mail: foundation@alphaomicronpi.org
Web: www.aoiifoundation.org/scholarship.php

Summary To provide financial assistance to alumnae members of Alpha Omicron Pi who are interested in preparing for a medical career.

Eligibility This program is open to alumnae members of Alpha Omicron Pi who have a bachelor's degree and are preparing for a career in medicine or a medical-related field. Applicants must be enrolled full time. Along with their application, they must submit the following 50-word statements: 1) the circumstances that have created their need for this scholarship; 2) their immediate and long-term life objectives; and 3) a letter of recommendation that they would write about themselves. Selection is based on those statements; academic achievement; Alpha Omicron Pi service, leadership, and involvement; college and community involvement; letters of recommendation; and financial need and evidence of self-help.

Financial data Stipend amounts vary; recently, the average value of each scholarship provided by this foundation was approximately $1,200.

Duration 1 year.

Number awarded 1 each odd-numbered year.

Deadline February of each odd-numbered year.

[851]
EDUCATIONAL FOUNDATION FOR WOMEN IN ACCOUNTING MASTERS SCHOLARSHIP

Educational Foundation for Women in Accounting
Attn: Foundation Administrator
136 South Keowee Street
Dayton, OH 45402
(937) 424-3391   Fax: (937) 222-5749
E-mail: info@efwa.org
Web: www.efwa.org/scholarships_masters.php

Summary To provide financial support to women who are working on a master's degree in accounting.

Eligibility This program is open to women who are working full time on a master's degree in accounting at an accredited college or university. Applicants may be working on an M.B.A. degree with an accounting concentration or a master's degree in an area of accounting. Selection is based on aptitude for accounting and business as demonstrated by prior course work and/or work experience, commitment to the goal of working on a master's degree in accounting in preparation for a career as an accounting or finance professional (including evidence of continued commitment after receiving this

award), clear evidence that the candidate has established goals and a plan for achieving those goals (both personal and professional), financial need, and a demonstration of how the scholarship will impact her life. U.S. citizenship is required.

Financial data The stipend is $1,000.

Duration 1 year.

Number awarded 1 each year.

Deadline April of each year.

[852]
EFWA SEATTLE CHAPTER ASWA SCHOLARSHIP

Educational Foundation for Women in Accounting
Attn: Foundation Administrator
136 South Keowee Street
Dayton, OH 45402
(937) 424-3391   Fax: (937) 222-5749
E-mail: info@efwa.org
Web: www.efwa.org/scholarships_seattle.php

Summary To provide financial support to women who are enrolled in an undergraduate or graduate accounting degree program at a school in Washington.

Eligibility This program is open to women from any state who are working on a bachelor's or master's degree in accounting at an accredited school in Washington. Selection is based on aptitude for accounting and business, commitment to the goal of working on a degree in accounting (including evidence of continued commitment after receiving this award), clear evidence that the candidate has established goals and a plan for achieving those goals (both personal and professional), and financial need. U.S. citizenship is required.

Financial data The stipend is $2,000 per year.

Duration 1 year; may be renewed 1 additional year if the recipient completes at least 12 hours each semester.

Additional information This program was established in 2007 with funds provided by the Seattle Chapter of the American Society of Women Accountants (ASWA).

Number awarded 1 each year.

Deadline April of each year.

[853]
E.K. WISE SCHOLARSHIP FUND

American Occupational Therapy Association
Attn: Membership Department
4720 Montgomery Lane
P.O. Box 31220
Bethesda, MD 20824-1220
(301) 652-2682   Toll Free: (800) 729-2682, ext. 2769
Fax: (301) 652-7711   TDD: (800) 377-8555
E-mail: ekwise@aota.org
Web: www.aota.org

Summary To provide financial assistance to female members of the American Occupational Therapy Association (AOTA) who are working on a master's degree in occupational therapy.

Eligibility This program is open to women who are AOTA members working full time on a professional post-baccalaureate occupational therapy degree. Applicants must be able to demonstrate a sustained record of outstanding scholastic performance, demonstrated leadership, and community service. Along with their application, they must submit an essay (up to 1,000 words) on how they can contribute to meeting the

AOTA objective of developing a well-prepared, diverse workforce. Financial need is considered in the selection process. U.S. citizenship or permanent resident status is required.

Financial data The stipend is $5,000 per year.

Duration 1 year; may be renewed 1 additional year.

Additional information This fund was established in 1969 as the E.K. Wise Loan Program. In 2008, the AOTA converted it to a scholarship program.

Number awarded 3 each year.

Deadline May of each year.

[854]
ELA FOUNDATION SCHOLARSHIPS

Ethel Louise Armstrong Foundation, Inc.
Attn: Chairman
1482 East Valley Road, Suite 504
Santa Barbara, CA 93108
Web: www.ela.org/scholarships/scholarships.html

Summary To provide financial assistance for graduate school to women with disabilities.

Eligibility This program is open to women with disabilities who are currently enrolled in or actively applying to a graduate program at an accredited college or university in the United States. Applicants must be a member of the American Association of People with Disabilities (AAPD). Along with their application, they must submit a 1,000-word essay on "How I will change the face of disability on the planet." Selection is based on academic and leadership merit.

Financial data The stipend ranges from $500 to $2,000 per year.

Duration 1 year.

Additional information The sponsoring foundation was founded in 1994 by Margaret Staton, who was disabled by a spinal cord tumor at 2 years of age. Recipients must agree to 1) network with the sponsor's board of directors and current and alumni scholarship recipients, and 2) update the sponsor on their progress in their academic and working career.

Number awarded Varies each year; recently, 14 of these scholarships were awarded.

Deadline May of each year.

[855]
ELAINE OSBORNE JACOBSON AWARD FOR WOMEN WORKING IN HEALTH CARE LAW

American Association for Justice
Attn: Manager, Law Student Services
777 Sixth Street, N.W., Suite 200
Washington, DC 20001
(202) 965-3500, ext. 8302
Toll Free: (800) 424-2725, ext. 8302
Fax: (202) 965-0355
E-mail: brandon.grubesky@justice.org
Web: www.justice.org/cps/rde/xchg/justice/hs.xsl/1737.htm

Summary To recognize and reward women who are interested in preparing for a career in health care law.

Eligibility This competition is open to women currently enrolled in an accredited North American law school. Candidates are selected if they, through their law school academic and clinical work and other related activities, demonstrate their aptitude for and a long-term commitment to a legal career of advocacy on behalf of the health care needs of chil-

dren, women, the elderly, or the disabled. Only nominations are accepted (multiple nominations per school are accepted); candidates may not apply directly. Nominees must submit a 1-page statement on their view of the civil justice system as a means of achieving a safe society.

Financial data The award is $3,000.

Duration The award is presented annually.

Additional information This award was established in 1991.

Number awarded 1 each year.

Deadline May of each year.

[856]
ELEANORE KLINE MEMORIAL SCHOLARSHIP

Michigan Association of Certified Public Accountants
Attn: Michigan Accountancy Foundation
5480 Corporate Drive, Suite 200
Troy, MI 48098-2642
(248) 267-3723   Toll Free: (888) 877-4CPE (within MI)
Fax: (248) 267-3737   E-mail: maf@michcpa.org
Web: www.michcpa.org/Content/22461.aspx

Summary To provide financial assistance to single mothers at Michigan colleges and universities who are working on a degree in accounting.

Eligibility This program is open to single mothers enrolled full time at accredited Michigan colleges and universities with a declared concentration in accounting. Applicants must be seniors planning to enter the fifth or graduate year of their school's program. They must intend to or have successfully passed the Michigan C.P.A. examination and intend to practice public accounting in the state. Along with their application, they must submit a 500-word statement about their educational and career aspirations, including internships and/or other employment, volunteer and community activities, professional affiliations, and full-time employment. Documentation of financial need may also be included. U.S. citizenship or eligibility for permanent employment in the United States is required.

Financial data The stipend is $4,000 per year; funds are disbursed directly to the recipient's college or university.

Duration 1 year.

Number awarded 1 each year.

Deadline January of each year.

[857]
ELECTRONICS FOR IMAGING SCHOLARSHIPS

Society of Women Engineers
Attn: Scholarship Selection Committee
120 South LaSalle Street, Suite 1515
Chicago, IL 60603-3572
(312) 596-5223   Toll Free: (877) SWE-INFO
Fax: (312) 644-8557
E-mail: scholarshipapplication@swe.org
Web: societyofwomenengineers.swe.org

Summary To provide financial assistance to women working on an undergraduate or graduate degree in engineering or computer science.

Eligibility This program is open to women who will be sophomores, juniors, seniors, or graduate students at ABET-accredited colleges and universities. Applicants must be working on a degree in computer science or engineering and have a GPA of 3.0 or higher. Selection is based on merit. Preference is given to students at designated colleges and universities; for a list, contact the sponsor.

Financial data The stipend is $4,000.

Duration 1 year.

Additional information This program, established in 2001, is sponsored by Electronics for Imaging, Inc.

Number awarded 4 each year.

Deadline February of each year.

[858]
ELIZABETH FURBUR FELLOWSHIP

American Indian Graduate Center
Attn: Executive Director
4520 Montgomery Boulevard, N.E., Suite 1-B
Albuquerque, NM 87109-1291
(505) 881-4584   Toll Free: (800) 628-1920
Fax: (505) 884-0427   E-mail: aigc@aigc.com
Web: www.aigc.com/02scholarships/scholarships.htm

Summary To provide financial assistance to female Native American graduate students interested in working on a degree related to the arts.

Eligibility This program is open to women who are enrolled members of federally-recognized American Indian tribes and Alaska Native groups or who can document one-fourth degree federally-recognized Indian blood. Applicants must be enrolled full time in a graduate program in the creative fine arts, visual works, crafts, music, performing, dance, literary arts, creative writing, or poetry. Along with their application, they must submit a 500-word essay on their extracurricular activities as they relate to American Indian programs at their institution, volunteer and community work as related to American Indian communities, tribal and community involvement, and plans to make positive changes in the American Indian community with their college education. Financial need is also considered in the selection process.

Financial data Stipends range from $1,000 to $5,000 per academic year, depending on the availability of funds and the recipient's unmet financial need.

Duration 1 year; may be renewed.

Additional information The application fee is $15. Since this a supplemental program, students must apply in a timely manner for federal financial aid and campus-based aid at the college they are attending to be considered for this program. Failure to apply will disqualify an applicant.

Number awarded 1 each year.

Deadline May of each year.

[859]
ELIZABETH M. GRUBER SCHOLARSHIPS

Delta Zeta Sorority
Attn: Foundation Coordinator
202 East Church Street
Oxford, OH 45056
(513) 523-7597   Fax: (513) 523-1921
E-mail: DZFoundation@dzshq.com
Web: www.deltazeta.org

Summary To provide financial assistance to members of Delta Zeta Sorority working on a graduate degree in the liberal arts.

Eligibility This program is open to graduate members of the sorority who are working on a degree in the liberal arts. Applicants must have a GPA of 3.0 or higher. Along with their application, they must submit an official transcript, a statement of their career goals, information on their service to the sorority, documentation of campus activities and/or community involvement, a list of academic honors, and an explanation of their financial need. Preference is given to applicants from the Alpha Beta chapter at the University of Illinois at Urbana-Champaign or at a university in the Midwest, in that order.

Financial data The stipend ranges from $1,000 to $15,000, depending on the availability of funds.

Duration 1 year; nonrenewable.

Number awarded Varies each year; recently, 3 of these scholarships were awarded.

Deadline February of each year.

[860]
ELIZABETH MUNSTERBERG KOPPITZ CHILD PSYCHOLOGY GRADUATE FELLOWSHIPS

American Psychological Foundation
750 First Street, N.E.
Washington, DC 20002-4242
(202) 336-5843   Fax: (202) 336-5812
E-mail: foundation@apa.org
Web: www.apa.org/apf/funding/koppitz.aspx

Summary To provide funding to doctoral students (especially women, minorities, and individuals with disabilities) who are interested in conducting research in child psychology.

Eligibility This program is open to graduate students who have progressed academically through the qualifying examinations, usually after the third or fourth year of doctoral study. Applicants must be interested in conducting psychological research that promotes the advancement of knowledge and learning in the field of child psychology. Selection is based on conformance with stated program goals, magnitude of incremental contribution, quality of proposed work, and applicant's demonstrated scholarship and research competence. The sponsor encourages applications from individuals who represent diversity in race, ethnicity, gender, age, disability, and sexual orientation.

Financial data The grant is $25,000 for fellows or $5,000 for runners-up.

Duration 1 year.

Additional information This fellowship was first awarded in 2003.

Number awarded Up to 4 fellows and up to 2 runners-up are selected each year.

Deadline November of each year.

[861]
ELLEN CUSHING SCHOLARSHIPS

American Baptist Churches USA
National Ministries
Attn: Office of Financial Aid for Studies
P.O. Box 851
Valley Forge, PA 19482-0851
(610) 768-2067   Toll Free: (800) ABC-3USA, ext. 2067
Fax: (610) 768-2453
E-mail: Financialaid.Web@abc-usa.org
Web: www.nationalministries.org

Summary To provide financial assistance to Baptist women interested in working on a graduate degree in human service fields.

Eligibility This program is open to female Baptists in graduate programs who are preparing for a human service career in the secular world. Applicants must be U.S. citizens who have been a member of a church affiliated with American Baptist Churches USA for at least 1 year. M.Div. and D.Min. students are not eligible. Preference is given to students active in their school, church, or region.

Financial data The stipend is $2,000.

Duration 1 year.

Number awarded Up to 3 each year.

Deadline May of each year.

[862]
ELLIOTT G. HEARD JR. MEMORIAL SCHOLARSHIP

Elliott G. Heard Jr. Memorial Scholarship Committee
P.O. Box 214
Mullica Hill, NJ 08062
(609) 202-0061   Fax: (856) 223-0888
E-mail: yhbautista@yahoo.com

Summary To provide financial assistance to students enrolled or planning to enroll at an accredited law school, especially women, minorities, and students with disabilities.

Eligibility This program is open to college seniors who have been accepted to an accredited law school and students currently enrolled in law school who are not in their final semester. Applicants must be U.S. citizens. Along with their application, they must submit a 500-word essay describing why they should be considered for this scholarship and why they decided on a career in the law. Minorities, women, and the physically challenged are especially encouraged to apply. Finalists are invited to an interview. Selection is based on academic achievement, community service, leadership, citizenship, and financial need.

Financial data The stipend is $1,000.

Duration 1 year; nonrenewable.

Additional information This program is named after the first African American jurist in Gloucester County, New Jersey.

Number awarded 1 or more each year.

Deadline October of each year.

[863]
ELOISE GERRY FELLOWSHIPS

Sigma Delta Epsilon-Graduate Women in Science, Inc.
c/o Julie Gros-Louis, Fellowships Coordinator
University of Iowa-Department of Psychology
11 Seashore Hall E
Iowa City, IA 52242-1407
(319) 384-1816   Fax: (319) 335-0191
E-mail: Julie-gros-louis@uiowa.edu
Web: www.gwis.org/programs.htm

Summary To provide funding to women interested in conducting research in the natural sciences anywhere in the world.

Eligibility This program is open to women from any country currently enrolled as a graduate student, engaged in post-doctoral research, or holding a junior faculty position. Applicants must be interested in conducting research anywhere in the world in the natural sciences (including physical, environmental, mathematical, computer, or life sciences), anthropology, psychology, or statistics. Along with their application, they must submit 2-paragraph essays on 1) how the proposed research relates to their degree program and/or career development; 2) initiatives in which they are participating to promote the careers of scientists, particularly women, within their institution, program, or peer group; and 3) relevant personal factors, including financial need, that should be considered in evaluating their proposal. Appointments are made without regard to race, religion, nationality, creed, national origin, sexual orientation, or age.

Financial data The grant currently is $2,500. Funds may be used for such research expenses as expendable supplies, small equipment, publication of research findings, travel and subsistence while performing field studies, or travel to another laboratory for collaborative research. They may not be used for tuition, child care, travel to professional meetings or to begin a new appointment, administrative overhead or indirect costs, personal computers, living allowances, or equipment for general use.

Duration 1 year.

Additional information This fellowship was first awarded in 1975. An application processing fee of $30 is required.

Number awarded Varies each year; recently, 2 of these grants were awarded.

Deadline January of each year.

[864]
ELSA LUDEKE GRADUATE SCHOLARSHIPS

Delta Zeta Sorority
Attn: Foundation Coordinator
202 East Church Street
Oxford, OH 45056
(513) 523-7597   Fax: (513) 523-1921
E-mail: DZFoundation@dzshq.com
Web: www.deltazeta.org

Summary To provide financial assistance for graduate school to members of Delta Zeta Sorority.

Eligibility This program is open to members of the sorority who are working on a graduate degree. Applicants may be either continuing students who are entering graduate school immediately after completing their bachelor's degree or alumnae returning to graduate school after an absence of more than 3 years. They must have a GPA of 3.0 or higher. Along with their application, they must submit an official transcript, a statement of their career goals, information on their service to the sorority, documentation of campus activities and/or community involvement, a list of academic honors, and an explanation of their financial need.

Financial data The stipend ranges from $1,000 to $15,000, depending on the availability of funds.

Duration 1 year; nonrenewable.

Number awarded 2 each year: 1 to a continuing student and 1 to a returning alumna.

Deadline February of each year.

[865]
ELSIE G. RIDDICK SCHOLARSHIP

North Carolina Federation of Business and Professional
  Women's Club, Inc.
Attn: BPW/NC Foundation
P.O. Box 276
Carrboro, NC 27510
Web: www.bpw-nc.org/Default.aspx?pageId=837230

Summary To provide financial assistance to women attending North Carolina colleges, community colleges, or graduate schools.

Eligibility This program is open to women who are currently enrolled in a community college, 4-year college, or graduate school in North Carolina. Applicants must be endorsed by a local BPW unit. Along with their application, they must submit a 1-page statement that summarizes their career goals, previous honors, or community activities and justifies their need for this scholarship. U.S. citizenship is required.

Financial data The stipend is $1,000. Funds are paid directly to the recipient's school.

Duration 1 year; recipients may reapply.

Additional information This program was established in 1925 as a loan fund. Since 1972 it has been administered as a scholarship program.

Number awarded 1 each year.

Deadline April of each year.

[866]
EMILY SCHOENBAUM RESEARCH AND COMMUNITY DEVELOPMENT GRANTS

Tulane University
Newcomb College Center for Research on Women
Attn: Executive Director
200 Caroline Richardson Hall
New Orleans, LA 70118
(504) 865-5238   Fax: (504) 862-8948
E-mail: nccrow@tulane.edu
Web: tulane.edu/nccrow/programs/schoenbaum-grant.cfm

Summary To provide funding to scholars and students in Louisiana interested in conducting research or other projects related to women and girls.

Eligibility This program is open to students, faculty, and staff of primary and secondary schools, colleges, and universities in Louisiana, as well as community scholars and activists. Applicants must be interested in conducting a project with potential to bring about change in women's lives or effect

public policy so as to improve the well-being of women and girls, particularly those in the New Orleans area.

Financial data The grant is $1,500.

Duration 1 year.

Additional information This program was established in 1999.

Number awarded 1 each year.

Deadline March of each year.

[867]
ESPERANZA SCHOLARSHIP

New York Women in Communications, Inc.
Attn: NYWICI Foundation
355 Lexington Avenue, 15th Floor
New York, NY 10017-6603
(212) 297-2133   Fax: (212) 370-9047
E-mail: nywicipr@nywici.org
Web: www.nywici.org/foundation/scholarships

Summary To provide financial assistance to Hispanic women who are residents of designated eastern states and interested in preparing for a career in communications at a college or graduate school in any state.

Eligibility This program is open to Hispanic women who are seniors graduating from high schools in New York, New Jersey, Connecticut, or Pennsylvania or undergraduate or graduate students who are permanent residents of those states; they must be attending or planning to attend a college or university in any state. Graduate students must be members of New York Women in Communications, Inc. (NYWICI). Also eligible are Hispanic women who reside outside the 4 states but are currently enrolled at a college or university within 1 of the 5 boroughs of New York City. All applicants must be working on a degree in a communications-related field (e.g., advertising, broadcasting, communications, English, film, journalism, marketing, new media, public relations) and have a GPA of 3.2 or higher. Along with their application, they must submit a 2-page resume that includes school and extracurricular activities, significant achievements, academic honors and awards, and community service work; a personal essay of 300 to 500 words on their choice of an assigned topic that changes annually; 2 letters of recommendation; and an official transcript. Selection is based on academic record, need, demonstrated leadership, participation in school and community activities, honors, work experience, goals and aspirations, and unusual personal and/or family circumstances. U.S. citizenship is required.

Financial data The stipend ranges up to $10,000.

Duration 1 year.

Additional information This program is funded by Macy's and Bloomingdale's.

Number awarded 1 each year.

Deadline January of each year.

[868]
ESTHER EDWARDS GRADUATE SCHOLARSHIP

United Methodist Church
Attn: General Board of Higher Education and Ministry
Office of Loans and Scholarships
1001 19th Avenue South
P.O. Box 340007
Nashville, TN 37203-0007
(615) 340-7344   Fax: (615) 340-7367
E-mail: umscholar@gbhem.org
Web: www.gbhem.org/loansandscholarships

Summary To provide financial assistance to female graduate students who are working on a degree in higher education administration to prepare for a career with a United Methodist school.

Eligibility This program is open to women who are working on a graduate degree to prepare for an executive management career in higher education administration with a United Methodist school, college, or university. Applicants must have been active, full members of a United Methodist Church for at least 1 year prior to applying. They must have a GPA of 2.5 or higher. First preference is given to students currently employed by a United Methodist school, college, or university and to full-time students.

Financial data The stipend is $5,000.

Duration 1 year; nonrenewable.

Number awarded 1 each year.

Deadline February of each year.

[869]
ESTHER KATZ ROSEN FELLOWSHIPS

American Psychological Foundation
750 First Street, N.E.
Washington, DC 20002-4242
(202) 336-5843   Fax: (202) 336-5812
E-mail: foundation@apa.org
Web: www.apa.org/apf/funding/rosen.aspx

Summary To provide funding to graduate students (especially women, minorities, and students with disabilities) who are interested in conducting research on psychological issues relevant to giftedness in children.

Eligibility This program is open to graduate students at universities in the United States and Canada who have advanced to candidacy. Applicants must be interested in conducting research on the psychological understanding of gifted and talented children and adolescents. Selection is based on conformance with stated program goals, magnitude of incremental contribution, quality of proposed work, and applicant's demonstrated scholarship and research competence. The sponsor encourages applications from individuals who represent diversity in race, ethnicity, gender, age, disability, and sexual orientation.

Financial data The grant is $25,000. The fellow's home institution is expected to provide a tuition waiver.

Duration 1 year.

Additional information This fund was established in 1974.

Number awarded Up to 3 each year.

Deadline February of each year.

[870]
ESTHER NGAN-LING CHOW AND MAREYJOYCE GREEN SCHOLARSHIP

Sociologists for Women in Society
Attn: Executive Officer
University of Rhode Island
Department of Sociology
10 Chafee Road
Kingston, RI 02881
(401) 874-9510   Fax: (401) 874-2588
E-mail: swseo@socwomen.org
Web: www.socwomen.org/page.php?sss=115

Summary To provide funding to women of color who are conducting dissertation research in sociology.

Eligibility This program is open to women from a racial/ethnic group that faces racial discrimination in the United States. Applicants must be in the early stages of writing a doctoral dissertation in sociology on a topic relating to the concerns that women of color face domestically and/or internationally. They must be able to demonstrate financial need. Both domestic and international students are eligible to apply. Along with their application, they must submit a personal statement that details their short- and long-term career and research goals; a resume or curriculum vitae; 2 letters of recommendation; and a 5-page dissertation proposal that includes the purpose of the research, the work to be accomplished through support from this scholarship, and a time line for completion.

Financial data The stipend is $15,000. An additional grant of $500 is provided to enable the recipient to attend the winter meeting of Sociologists for Women in Society (SWS), and travel expenses to attend the summer meeting are reimbursed.

Duration 1 year.

Additional information This program was established in 2007 and originally named the Women of Color Dissertation Scholarship.

Number awarded 1 each year.

Deadline March of each year.

[871]
ETHEL F. LORD AWARD

Soroptimist International of the Americas-North Atlantic Region
c/o Patti Cullen, Governor
426 Beechwood Avenue
Feasterville, PA 19053
(215) 355-5472   E-mail: eflordaward@soroptimistnar.org
Web: www.soroptimistnar.org

Summary To provide financial assistance to women who reside in the north Atlantic region and are working on a graduate degree in gerontology at a university in the region.

Eligibility This program is open to female residents of Delaware, New Jersey, New York, Pennsylvania, and the panhandle area of West Virginia who are enrolled full time at a college or university in the region. Applicants must be working on a master's or doctoral degree in gerontology. Selection is based on academic excellence and financial need.

Financial data The stipend is $5,000.

Duration 1 year.

Number awarded 1 each year.

Deadline March of each year.

[872]
ETHEL K. ALLEN FELLOWSHIP

Sigma Delta Epsilon-Graduate Women in Science, Inc.
c/o Julie Gros-Louis, Fellowships Coordinator
University of Iowa-Department of Psychology
11 Seashore Hall E
Iowa City, IA 52242-1407
(319) 384-1816   Fax: (319) 335-0191
E-mail: Julie-gros-louis@uiowa.edu
Web: www.gwis.org/programs.htm

Summary To provide funding to women interested in conducting research anywhere in the world in the natural sciences.

Eligibility This program is open to women from any country currently enrolled as a graduate student, engaged in postdoctoral research, or holding a junior faculty position. Applicants must be interested in conducting research anywhere in the world in the natural sciences (including physical, environmental, mathematical, computer, or life sciences), anthropology, psychology, or statistics. Along with their application, they must submit 2-paragraph essays on 1) how the proposed research relates to their degree program and/or career development; 2) initiatives in which they are participating to promote the careers of scientists, particularly women, within their institution, program, or peer group; and 3) relevant personal factors, including financial need, that should be considered in evaluating their proposal. Appointments are made without regard to race, religion, nationality, creed, national origin, sexual orientation, or age.

Financial data The grant currently is $3,000. Funds may be used for such research expenses as expendable supplies, small equipment, publication of research findings, travel and subsistence while performing field studies, or travel to another laboratory for collaborative research. They may not be used for tuition, child care, travel to professional meetings or to begin a new appointment, administrative overhead or indirect costs, personal computers, living allowances, or equipment for general use.

Duration 1 year.

Additional information This program was established in 1994. An application processing fee of $30 is required.

Number awarded 1 each year.

Deadline January of each year.

[873]
ETHEL O. GARDNER PEO SCHOLARSHIP

P.E.O. Foundation-California State Chapter
c/o Carol Born, Scholarship Committee Chair
718 Via La Paloma
Riverside, CA 92507-6403
(951) 686-2728
Web: www.peocalifornia.org/eog.html

Summary To provide financial assistance to women from California who are upper-division or graduate students at a school in any state.

Eligibility This program is open to female residents of California who have completed at least 2 years at a college or university in any state. Applicants must be enrolled as full-

time undergraduate or graduate students. Selection is based on financial need, character, and a record of academic and extracurricular activities achievement.

Financial data Stipends range from $500 to $1,500.

Duration 1 year.

Number awarded Varies each year; recently, 69 of these scholarships were awarded.

Deadline January of each year.

[874]
EUGENIA VELLNER FISCHER AWARD FOR THE PERFORMING ARTS

Miss America Pageant
Attn: Scholarship Department
222 New Road, Suite 700
Linwood, NJ 08221
(609) 653-8700, ext. 127   Fax: (609) 653-8740
E-mail: info@missamerica.org
Web: www.missamerica.org/scholarships/eugenia.aspx

Summary To provide financial assistance to women who are working on an undergraduate or graduate degree in the performing arts and who, in the past, competed at some level in the Miss America competition.

Eligibility This program is open to women who are working on an undergraduate, master's, or higher degree in the performing arts and who competed at the local, state, or national level in a Miss America competition within the past 10 years. Applicants may be studying dance, instrumental, monologue, or vocal. They must submit an essay, up to 500 words, on the factors that influenced their decision to enter the field of performing arts, what they consider to be their major strengths in the field, and how they plan to use their degree in the field. Selection is based on GPA, class rank, extracurricular activities, financial need, and level of participation within the system.

Financial data The stipend is $1,000.

Duration 1 year; renewable.

Additional information This scholarship was established in 1999.

Number awarded 2 each year.

Deadline June of each year.

[875]
EULA MAE HENDERSON SCHOLARSHIPS

Baptist General Convention of Texas
Attn: Woman's Missionary Union of Texas
333 North Washington, Suite 160
Dallas, TX 75246-1716
(214) 828-5150   Toll Free: (888) 968-6389
Fax: (214) 828-5179   E-mail: wmutx@bgct.org
Web: www.bgct.org/texasbaptists/Page.aspx?&pid=2975

Summary To provide financial assistance to women members of Baptist churches in Texas who are preparing for a career in ministry at a Texas Baptist institution.

Eligibility This program is open to women who are active members of Southern Baptist churches in Texas. Applicants must be full-time students in at least their second semester of graduate work in preparation for a career in vocational Christian ministry through the International Mission Board, the North American Mission Board, or the Woman's Missionary Union (all of the Southern Baptist Convention). Along with their application, they must submit brief statements on when they became a Christian, their call to vocational Christian ministry, the field of Christian mission they plan to enter following graduation, the factors and influences that led them to select that field, and their involvement in Women's Missionary Union organizations. They must have a GPA of 3.0 or higher and be able to document financial need.

Financial data The stipend is $500 per semester ($1,000 per year).

Duration 1 semester; may be renewed up to 7 additional semesters if the recipient continues to meet the requirements.

Additional information This program was established in 1986. The eligible schools are Southwestern Baptist Theological Seminary, George W. Truett Seminary at Baylor University, Logsdon School of Theology at Hardin-Simmons University, and Baylor University's School of Social Work.

Number awarded Varies each year; recently, 3 of these scholarships were awarded.

Deadline February of each year.

[876]
EURASIA DISSERTATION SUPPORT FELLOWSHIPS

Social Science Research Council
Attn: Eurasia Program
One Pierrepont Plaza, 15th Floor
Brooklyn, NY 11201
(212) 377-2700   Fax: (212) 377-2727
E-mail: eurasia@ssrc.org
Web: www.ssrc.org/fellowships/Eurasia-fellowship

Summary To provide funding to women, minority, and other graduate students completing a dissertation dealing with Eurasia.

Eligibility This program is open to students who have completed field research for their doctoral dissertation and who plan to work on writing it during the next academic year. Applicants must have been conducting research in a discipline of the social sciences or humanities that deals with the Russian Empire, the Soviet Union, or the New States of Eurasia. Research related to the non-Russian states, regions, and peoples is particularly encouraged. Regions and countries currently supported by the program include Armenia, Azerbaijan, Belarus, Georgia, Kazakhstan, Kyrgyzstan, Moldova, Russian Federation, Tajikistan, Turkmenistan, Ukraine, and Uzbekistan; funding is not presently available for research on the Baltic states. U.S. citizenship or permanent resident status is required. Minorities and women are particularly encouraged to apply.

Financial data Grants up to $25,000 are available.

Duration Up to 1 year.

Additional information Funding for this program is provided by the U.S. Department of State under the Program for Research and Training on Eastern Europe and the Independent States of the Former Soviet Union (Title VIII).

Number awarded Varies each year; recently, 7 of these fellowships were awarded.

Deadline December of each year.

[877]
EVA LOIS EVANS MATHEMATICS AND SCIENCE FELLOWSHIPS

Alpha Kappa Alpha Sorority, Inc.
Attn: Educational Advancement Foundation
5656 South Stony Island Avenue
Chicago, IL 60637
(773) 947-0026   Toll Free: (800) 653-6528
Fax: (773) 947-0277   E-mail: akaeaf@akaeaf.net
Web: www.akaeaf.org/fellowships_endowments.htm

Summary To provide funding to pre- and postdoctoral scholars (especially African American women) who are engaged in research in mathematics, science, or technology.

Eligibility This program is open to graduate students and more advanced scholars who are interested in conducting research in the area of mathematics, science, or technology. Applicants must submit 1) a list of honors, awards, and scholarships received; 2) a list of organizations in which they have memberships, especially minority organizations; 3) a description of the project or research on which they are currently working, or (if they are not involved in a project or research) the aspects of their field that interest them; and 4) a statement of their personal and career goals, including how this scholarship will enhance their ability to attain those goals. The sponsor is a traditionally African American women's sorority.

Financial data A stipend is awarded (amount not specified).

Duration These fellowships are awarded biennially, in even-numbered years.

Number awarded Varies each biennium; recently, 2 of these fellowships were awarded.

Deadline April of even-numbered years.

[878]
EXEMPTION FROM TUITION FEES FOR DEPENDENTS OF KENTUCKY VETERANS

Kentucky Department of Veterans Affairs
Attn: Division of Field Operations
321 West Main Street, Room 390
Louisville, KY 40202
(502) 595-4447   Toll Free: (800) 928-4012 (within KY)
Fax: (502) 595-4448   E-mail: Pamela.Cypert@ky.gov
Web: www.veterans.ky.gov/benefits/tuitionwaiver.htm

Summary To provide financial assistance for undergraduate or graduate studies to the unremarried widow(er)s or children of deceased Kentucky veterans.

Eligibility This program is open to the children, stepchildren, adopted children, and unremarried widow(er)s of veterans who were residents of Kentucky when they entered military service or joined the Kentucky National Guard. The qualifying veteran must have been killed in action during a wartime period or died as a result of a service-connected disability incurred during a wartime period. Applicants must be attending or planning to attend a state-supported college or university in Kentucky to work on an undergraduate or graduate degree.

Financial data Eligible dependents and survivors are exempt from tuition and matriculation fees at any state-supported institution of higher education in Kentucky.

Duration There are no age or time limits on the waiver.

Number awarded Varies each year.

Deadline Deadline not specified.

[879]
FEDERATION OF HOUSTON PROFESSIONAL WOMEN EDUCATIONAL FOUNDATION SCHOLARSHIPS

Federation of Houston Professional Women
Attn: Educational Foundation
P.O. Box 27621
Humble, TX 77227-7621
E-mail: scholarshipapps@fhpw.org
Web: www.fhpw.org/scholarship_application.html

Summary To provide financial assistance for college or graduate school to women from Texas.

Eligibility This program is open to women who are residents of Texas and have completed at least 30 semesters hours of work on an associate, bachelor's, or graduate degree at an accredited college or university in the state. Applicants must be U.S. citizens or permanent residents and have a GPA of 3.0 or higher. They must submit a 200-word statement on their reasons for applying for this scholarship, a 200-word statement on their short- and long-term goals, their most recent transcript, 2 letters of recommendation, and a 100-word biographical sketch. Financial need is considered in the selection process.

Financial data Stipends are $2,000 for students at 4-year colleges and universities or $1,000 for students at community colleges. Funds are issued payable jointly to the student and the educational institution.

Duration 1 year.

Number awarded 2 each year.

Deadline May of each year.

[880]
FELLOWSHIPS IN SCIENCE AND INTERNATIONAL AFFAIRS

Harvard University
John F. Kennedy School of Government
Belfer Center for Science and International Affairs
Attn: Fellowship Coordinator
79 John F. Kennedy Street
Cambridge, MA 02138
(617) 495-8806   Fax: (617) 495-8963
E-mail: bcsia_fellowships@ksg.harvard.edu
Web: belfercenter.ksg.harvard.edu/fellowships

Summary To provide funding to professionals, postdoctorates, and doctoral students (particularly women and minorities) who are interested in conducting research in areas of concern to the Belfer Center for Science and International Affairs at Harvard University in Cambridge, Massachusetts.

Eligibility The postdoctoral fellowship is open to recent recipients of the Ph.D. or equivalent degree, university faculty members, and employees of government, military, international, humanitarian, and private research institutions who have appropriate professional experience. Applicants for predoctoral fellowships must have passed their general examinations. Lawyers, economists, political scientists, those in the natural sciences, and others of diverse disciplinary backgrounds are also welcome to apply. The program especially encourages applications from women, minorities, and

citizens of all countries. All applicants must be interested in conducting research in 1 of the 3 major program areas of the center: 1) the International Security Program (ISP), including Religion in International Affairs; 2) the Science, Technology, and Public Policy Program (STPP), including information and communications technology, energy and water policy, managing the atom project, and the energy technology innovation policy research group; 3) and the Dubai initiative.

Financial data The stipend is $34,000 for postdoctoral research fellows or $20,000 for predoctoral research fellows. Health insurance is also provided.

Duration 10 months.

Number awarded A limited number each year.

Deadline January of each year.

[881]
FICHTER RESEARCH GRANT COMPETITION

Association for the Sociology of Religion
Attn: Executive Officer
618 S.W. Second Avenue
Galva, IL 61434-1912
(309) 932-2727   Fax: (309) 932-2282
Web: www.sociologyofreligion.com

Summary To provide funding to scholars interested in conducting research on women and religion.

Eligibility This program is open to scholars involved in research on women and religion, gender issues, and feminist perspectives on religion. Scholars at the beginning of their careers are particularly encouraged to apply; dissertation research qualifies for funding. Applicants must be members of the association at the time the application is submitted. The proposal must not be more than 5 double-spaced pages and should outline the rationale and plan of the research, previous research, methodology proposed, timeline, and budget; a curriculum vitae should also be included. Simultaneous submissions to other grant competitions are permissible if the applicant is explicit about which budget items in the Fichter grant proposal do not overlap items in other submitted proposals.

Financial data Each year, a total of $24,000 is available to be awarded.

Duration 1 year.

Number awarded Varies each year; recently, 6 of these grants were awarded.

Deadline April of each year.

[882]
FINANCIAL WOMEN INTERNATIONAL OF HAWAII SCHOLARSHIP

Hawai'i Community Foundation
Attn: Scholarship Department
827 Fort Street Mall
Honolulu, HI 96813
(808) 537-6333   Toll Free: (888) 731-3863
Fax: (808) 521-6286
E-mail: scholarships@hcf-hawaii.org
Web: www.hawaiicommunityfoundation.org/scholarships

Summary To provide financial assistance to women in Hawaii who are studying business on the upper-division or graduate school level at a school in any state.

Eligibility This program is open to female residents of Hawaii who are working on a degree in business or a business-related field as a junior, senior, or graduate student at a school in any state. Applicants must be able to demonstrate academic achievement (GPA of 3.5 or higher), good moral character, and financial need. Along with their application, they must submit a short statement indicating their reasons for attending college, their planned course of study, their career goals, and what community service means to them.

Financial data The amounts of the awards depend on the availability of funds and the need of the recipient. Recently, the average value of each of the scholarships awarded by the foundation was more than $2,000.

Duration 1 year.

Additional information This program was established in 1998.

Number awarded 1 or more each year.

Deadline February of each year.

[883]
F.J. MCGUIGAN DISSERTATION AWARD

American Psychological Foundation
750 First Street, N.E.
Washington, DC 20002-4242
(202) 336-5843   Fax: (202) 336-5812
E-mail: foundation@apa.org
Web: www.apa.org/apf/funding/mcguigan-dissertation.aspx

Summary To provide funding to doctoral candidates (especially women, minorities, and students with disabilities) who are interested in conducting research on the materialistic understanding of the human mind.

Eligibility This program is open to graduate students enrolled full time in a psychology program at an accredited college or university in the United States or Canada. Applicants must be interested in conducting dissertation research on the materialistic understanding of the human mind, both empirically and theoretically. Selection is based on conformance with stated program goals, quality of proposed work, and applicant's demonstrated scholarship and research competence. The sponsor encourages applications from individuals who represent diversity in race, ethnicity, gender, age, disability, and sexual orientation.

Financial data The grant is $2,000.

Duration 1 year.

Additional information This grant was first awarded in 2009.

Number awarded 1 each year.

Deadline May of each year.

[884]
FLETCHER MAE HOWELL SCHOLARSHIP

Woman's Missionary Union of Virginia
2828 Emerywood Parkway
Richmond, VA 23294
(804) 915-5000, ext. 8267
Toll Free: (800) 255-2428 (within VA)
Fax: (804) 672-8008   E-mail: wmuv@wmuv.org
Web: wmuv.org/developing-future-leaders/scholarships

Summary To provide financial assistance to African American women from Virginia who are working on a graduate degree in Christian education.

Eligibility This program is open to African American women from Virginia who are interested in full-time graduate study in Christian education. An interview is required.

Financial data The stipend is $1,000.

Duration 1 year.

Number awarded Up to 2 each year.

Deadline January of each year.

[885]
FLORIDA LEGION AUXILIARY MASTER'S PROGRAM GRANT

American Legion Auxiliary
Department of Florida
1912A Lee Road
P.O. Box 547917
Orlando, FL 32854-7917
(407) 293-7411   Fax: (407) 299-6522
E-mail: contact@alafl.org
Web: alafl.org

Summary To provide financial assistance to members of the Florida American Legion Auxiliary who are interested in working on a master's degree in any field at a university in any state.

Eligibility This program is open to residents of Florida who have been members of the American Legion Auxiliary for at least 5 consecutive years. Applicants must be planning to enroll in an accredited master's degree program in any field at a college or university in any state. They must be sponsored by the local American Legion Auxiliary unit. Selection is based on academic record and financial need.

Financial data The stipend is $2,500 per year. All funds are paid directly to the institution.

Duration 1 year; may be renewed 1 additional year if the recipient needs further financial assistance and has maintained at least a 2.5 GPA.

Number awarded 1 each year.

Deadline January of each year.

[886]
FOCUS PROFESSIONS GROUP FELLOWSHIPS

American Association of University Women
Attn: AAUW Educational Foundation
301 ACT Drive, Department 60
P.O. Box 4030
Iowa City, IA 52243-4030
(319) 337-1716, ext. 60   Fax: (319) 337-1204
E-mail: aauw@act.org
Web: www.aauw.org/learn/fellowships_grants/selected.cfm

Summary To aid women of color who are in their final year of graduate training in the fields of business administration, law, or medicine.

Eligibility This program is open to women who are working full time on a degree in fields in which women of color have been historically underrepresented: business administration (M.B.A.), law (J.D.), or medicine (M.D., D.O.). They must be African Americans, Mexican Americans, Puerto Ricans and other Hispanics, Native Americans, Alaska Natives, Asian Americans, or Pacific Islanders. U.S. citizenship or permanent resident status is required. Applicants in business administration must be entering their second year of study; applicants in law must be entering their third year of study;

applicants in medicine may be entering their third or fourth year of study. Special consideration is given to applicants who 1) demonstrate their intent to enter professional practice in disciplines in which women are underrepresented, to serve underserved populations and communities, or to pursue public interest areas; and 2) are nontraditional students. Selection is based on professional promise and personal attributes (50%), academic excellence and related academic success indicators (40%), and financial need (10%).

Financial data   Stipends range from $5,000 to $18,000.

Duration   1 academic year, beginning in September.

Additional information   The filing fee is $35.

Number awarded   Varies each year.

Deadline   January of each year.

[887]
FOUNDATION FOR THE HISTORY OF WOMEN IN MEDICINE FELLOWSHIPS

Foundation for the History of Women in Medicine
P.O. Box 543
Pottstown, PA 19464
(610) 970-9143   Fax: (610) 970-7520
Web: www.fhwim.org/programs/fellowships.php

Summary   To provide funding to students and scholars interested in short-term use of resources in the Boston area to conduct research on the history of women and medicine.

Eligibility   This program is open to doctoral candidates and other advanced scholars interested in using the Archives for Women in Medicine at the Countway Library's Center for the History of Medicine in Boston. Applicants must be interested in conducting research on the history of women in medicine. Preference is given to projects that deal specifically with women as physicians or other health workers, but proposals dealing with the history of women's health issues are also considered. Preference is given to applicants who live beyond commuting distance of the Countway.

Financial data   The grant is $5,000.

Duration   Recipients may conduct research on a flexible schedule during 1 academic year.

Additional information   The Francis A. Countway Library of Medicine, the largest academic medical library in the United States, was established in 1960 as the result of an alliance between the Boston Medical Library and the Harvard Medical School Library. Information is available from the Countway Library, Center for the History of Medicine, Archives for Women in Medicine, 10 Shattuck Street, Boston, MA 02115, (617) 432-6206, Fax: (617) 432-4737, E-mail: arm@hms.harvard.edu.

Number awarded   1 each year.

Deadline   February of each year.

[888]
FOUNDER REGION SOROPTIMIST FELLOWSHIPS

Soroptimist International of the Americas-Founder Region
c/o Joyce Strand
781 Franklin Drive
Brentwood, CA 94513
(510) 410-1931   Fax: (510) 217-3916
E-mail: jstrand@onemain.com
Web: www.sifounderregion.org/fellowship/index.html

Summary   To provide financial assistance to women from any state who are completing a doctoral degree at a university in the Founder Region of Soroptimist International of the Americas.

Eligibility   This program is open to women from any state who are attending graduate school in the Founder Region of Soroptimist International of the Americas (which includes designated counties in northern California, the state of Hawaii, and the U.S. possessions of Guam and the Marianas). Applicants must have been advanced to candidacy for a doctoral degree and should be entering the final year of their program. Along with their application, they must submit documentation of financial need, transcripts, verification of their advancement in their doctoral program, a 5-page autobiographical sketch, a 3- to 5-page description of their dissertation, and 2 letters of recommendation. A personal interview is required.

Financial data   Recently, stipends have been approximately $10,000.

Duration   1 year.

Additional information   This program began in 1948. The designated northern California counties are Alameda, Contra Costa, Del Norte, Humboldt, Lake, Marin, Mendocino, Napa, Solano, and Sonoma.

Number awarded   Varies each year; recently, 5 of these fellowships have been awarded.

Deadline   January of each year.

[889]
FRANCES C. ALLEN FELLOWSHIPS

Newberry Library
Attn: McNickle Center for American Indian History
60 West Walton Street
Chicago, IL 60610-3305
(312) 255-3564   Fax: (312) 255-3696
E-mail: mcnickle@newberry.org
Web: www.newberry.org/mcnickle/frances.html

Summary   To provide funding to Native American women who are graduate students and wish to use the resources of the D'Arcy McNickle Center for the History of the American Indian at the Newberry Library.

Eligibility   This program is open to women of American Indian heritage who are interested in using the library for a project appropriate to its collections. Applicants must be enrolled in a graduate or pre-professional program, especially in the humanities or social sciences. Recommendations are required; at least 2 must come from academic advisers or instructors who can comment on the significance of the applicant's proposed project and explain how it will help in the achievement of professional goals.

Financial data   The basic stipend is $1,600 per month; supplemental funding may be available on a case by case basis.

Duration   From 1 month to 1 year.

Additional information   These grants were first awarded in 1983. Fellows must spend a significant portion of their time at the library's D'Arcy McNickle Center.

Number awarded   Varies each year; recently, 2 of these fellowships were awarded.

Deadline   February of each year.

[890]
FRANCIS M. KEVILLE MEMORIAL SCHOLARSHIP

Construction Management Association of America
Attn: CMAA Foundation
7926 Jones Branch Drive, Suite 800
McLean, VA 22101-3303
(703) 356-2622   Fax: (703) 356-6388
E-mail: foundation@cmaanet.org
Web: www.cmaafoundation.org

Summary   To provide financial assistance to female and minority undergraduate and graduate students working on a degree in construction management.

Eligibility   This program is open to women and members of minority groups who are enrolled as full-time undergraduate or graduate students. Applicants must have completed at least 1 year of study and have at least 1 full year remaining for a bachelor's or master's degree in construction management or a related field. Along with their application, they must submit essays on why they are interested in a career in construction management and why they should be awarded this scholarship. Selection is based on that essay (20%), academic performance (40%), recommendation of the faculty adviser (15%), and extracurricular activities (25%).

Financial data   The stipend is $3,000. Funds are disbursed directly to the student's university.

Duration   1 year.

Number awarded   1 each year.

Deadline   June of each year.

[891]
FURNISS FOUNDATION/AOS GRADUATE FELLOWSHIP

American Orchid Society
16700 AOS Lane
Delray Beach, FL 33446-4351
(561) 404-2000   Fax: (561) 404-2045
E-mail: TheAOS@aos.org
Web: www.aos.org

Summary   To provide funding to doctoral candidates (especially women, minorities, and students with disabilities) who are conducting dissertation research related to orchids.

Eligibility   This program is open to graduate students whose doctoral dissertation relates to orchids within the disciplines of physiology, molecular biology, structure, systematics, cytology, ecology, and/or evolution. Applicants must submit an outline of their project, their college transcript, a letter of recommendation from their chair, and a 1-page statement on why their project should be considered and the impact it will have on the future of orchidology. Women, minorities, and persons with disabilities are especially encouraged to apply.

Financial data   The grant is $9,000 per year. Funds are paid directly to the recipient's college or university, but indirect overhead is not allowed.

Duration   Up to a maximum of 3 years.

Additional information   This fellowship was first awarded in 1990.

Number awarded   1 each year.

Deadline   February of each year.

[892]
GABWA FOUNDATION SCHOLARSHIPS

Georgia Association of Black Women Attorneys
Attn: GABWA Foundation
P.O. Box 4381
Atlanta, GA 30302
(404) 292-3567   E-mail: contact@gabwa.org
Web: www.gabwa.org/foundation.php

Summary   To provide financial assistance to Black women from any state enrolled at law schools in Georgia.

Eligibility   This program is open to Black women from any state enrolled in the second or third year at a law school in Georgia. Applicants must be able to demonstrate academic achievement, leadership, and commitment to the profession and their community. Along with their application, they must submit a 300-word personal statement that discusses their experience as a Black woman law student, how they expect their legal career to benefit the community at large, and how this scholarship will benefit their quest for a legal education and future career goals. Financial need is considered in the selection process but is not required.

Financial data   Stipend amounts vary, depending on the availability of funds; recently, they averaged $5,000.

Duration   1 year.

Additional information   This program was established in 2002.

Number awarded   Varies each year. Since the program was established, it has awarded $80,000 to 21 African American women law students.

Deadline   October of each year.

[893]
GAIL PATRICK CHARITABLE TRUST "WOMEN OF DISTINCTION" SCHOLARSHIPS

Delta Zeta Sorority
Attn: Foundation Coordinator
202 East Church Street
Oxford, OH 45056
(513) 523-7597   Fax: (513) 523-1921
E-mail: DZFoundation@dzshq.com
Web: www.deltazeta.org

Summary   To provide financial assistance for graduate school to alumnae members of Delta Zeta Sorority.

Eligibility   This program is open to alumnae members of the sorority who are returning to graduate school after an absence of up to 10 years. Applicants must have an undergraduate GPA of 3.1 or higher. Along with their application, they must submit an official transcript, a statement of their career goals, information on their service to the sorority, documentation of campus activities and/or community involvement, a list of academic honors, and an explanation of their financial need.

Financial data   The stipend ranges from $15,000 to $20,000.

Duration   1 year; nonrenewable.

Number awarded   2 each year.

Deadline   February of each year.

[894]
GAIUS CHARLES BOLIN DISSERTATION AND POST-MFA FELLOWSHIPS

Williams College
Attn: Dean of the Faculty
Hopkins Hall, Third Floor
P.O. Box 141
Williamstown, MA 01267
(413) 597-4351   Fax: (413) 597-3553
E-mail: gburda@williams.edu
Web: dean-faculty.williams.edu/graduate-fellowships

Summary To provide financial assistance to women and members of other underrepresented groups who are interested in teaching courses at Williams College while working on their doctoral dissertation or building their post-M.F.A. professional portfolio.

Eligibility This program is open to members of underrepresented groups, including ethnic minorities, first-generation college students, women in predominantly male fields, and scholars with disabilities. Applicants must be 1) doctoral candidates in any field who have completed all work for a Ph.D. except for the dissertation; or 2) artists who completed an M.F.A. degree within the past 2 years and are building their professional portfolio. They must be willing to teach a course at Williams College. Along with their application, they must submit a full curriculum vitae, a graduate school transcript, 3 letters of recommendation, a copy of their dissertation prospectus or samples of their artistic work, and a description of their teaching interests within a department or program at Williams College. U.S. citizenship or permanent resident status is required.

Financial data Fellows receive $33,000 for the academic year, plus housing assistance, office space, computer and library privileges, and a research allowance of up to $4,000.

Duration 2 years.

Additional information Bolin fellows are assigned a faculty adviser in the appropriate department. This program was established in 1985. Fellows are expected to teach a 1-semester course each year. They must be in residence at Williams College for the duration of the fellowship.

Number awarded 3 each year.

Deadline November of each year.

[895]
GENERAL DYNAMICS AIS SCHOLARSHIP

Society of Women Engineers-Minnesota Section
Attn: Scholarship Committee
P.O. Box 582813
Minneapolis, MN 55458-2813
E-mail: scholarships@swe-mn.org
Web: swe-mn.org/scholarships.html

Summary To provide financial assistance to women from any state working on an undergraduate or graduate degree in electrical or computer engineering at colleges and universities in Minnesota, North Dakota, or South Dakota.

Eligibility This program is open to female undergraduate and graduate students at ABET-accredited engineering programs in Minnesota, North Dakota, or South Dakota. Applicants must be working full time on a degree in electrical or computer engineering. Along with their application, they must submit a short paragraph describing how they plan to utilize

their engineering skills after they graduate. Selection is based on potential to succeed as an engineer (20 points), communication skills (10 points), extracurricular or community involvement and leadership skills (10 points), demonstrated successful work experience (10 points), and academic success (5 points). U.S. citizenship is required.

Financial data The stipend is $1,000.

Duration 1 year.

Additional information This program is sponsored by General Dynamics-Advanced Information Systems.

Number awarded 1 each year.

Deadline March of each year.

[896]
GEOLOGICAL SOCIETY OF AMERICA GRADUATE STUDENT RESEARCH GRANTS

Geological Society of America
Attn: Program Officer-Grants, Awards and Recognition
3300 Penrose Place
P.O. Box 9140
Boulder, CO 80301-9140
(303) 357-1028   Toll Free: (800) 472-1988, ext. 1028
Fax: (303) 357-1070   E-mail: awards@geosociety.org
Web: www.geosociety.org/grants/gradgrants.htm

Summary To provide funding to graduate student members of the Geological Society of America (GSA), especially women, minorities, and students with disabilities who are interested in conducting research at universities in the United States, Canada, Mexico, or Central America.

Eligibility This program is open to GSA members working on a master's or doctoral degree at a university in the United States, Canada, Mexico, or Central America. Applicants must be interested in conducting geological research. Minorities, women, and persons with disabilities are strongly encouraged to apply. Selection is based on the scientific merits of the proposal, the capability of the investigator, and the reasonableness of the budget.

Financial data Grants range up to $4,000 and recently averaged $2,411. Funds can be used for the cost of travel, room and board in the field, services of a technician or field assistant, funding of chemical and isotope analyses, or other expenses directly related to the fulfillment of the research contract. Support is not provided for the purchase of ordinary field equipment, for maintenance of the families of the grantees and their assistants, as reimbursement for work already accomplished, for institutional overhead, for adviser participation, or for tuition costs.

Duration 1 year.

Additional information In addition to general grants, GSA awards a number of specialized grants: the Gretchen L. Blechschmidt Award for women (especially in the fields of biostratigraphy and/or paleoceanography); the John T. Dillon Alaska Research Award for earth science problems particular to Alaska; the Robert K. Fahnestock Memorial Award for the field of sediment transport or related aspects of fluvial geomorphology; the Lipman Research Award for volcanology and petrology; the Bruce L. "Biff" Reed Award for studies in the tectonic and magmatic evolution of Alaska; the Alexander Sisson Award for studies in Alaska and the Caribbean; the Harold T. Stearns Fellowship Award for work on the geology of the Pacific Islands and the circum-Pacific region; the Parke

D. Snavely, Jr. Cascadia Research Fund Award for studies of the Pacific Northwest convergent margin; the Alexander and Geraldine Wanek Fund Award for studies of coal and petroleum; the Charles A. and June R.P. Ross Research Fund Award for stratigraphy; and the John Montagne Fund Award for research in the field of quaternary geology or geomorphology.

Number awarded Varies each year; recently, the society awarded 220 grants worth more than $530,000 through this and all of its specialized programs.

Deadline January of each year.

[897]
GEOPHYSICAL FLUID DYNAMICS FELLOWSHIPS

Woods Hole Oceanographic Institution
Attn: Academic Programs Office
Clark Laboratory, MS 31
266 Woods Hole Road
Woods Hole, MA 02543-1541
(508) 289-2950   Fax: (508) 457-2188
E-mail: gfd@whoi.edu
Web: www.whoi.edu/gfd

Summary To provide summer research and study opportunities at Woods Hole Oceanographic Institution (WHOI) to pre- and postdoctoral scholars (particularly women and minorities) who are interested in geophysical fluid dynamics.

Eligibility This program is open to pre- and postdoctorates who are interested in pursuing research or study opportunities in a field that involves nonlinear dynamics of rotating, stratified fluids. Fields of specialization include classical fluid dynamics, physical oceanography, meteorology, geophysical fluid dynamics, astrophysics, planetary atmospheres, hydromagnetics, physics, and applied mathematics. Applications from women and members of underrepresented groups are particularly encouraged.

Financial data Participants receive a stipend of $5,400 and an allowance for travel expenses within the United States.

Duration 10 weeks during the summer.

Additional information Each summer, the program at WHOI revolves around a central theme. A recent theme related to shear turbulence. The main components of the summer program are a series of principal lectures, a set of supplementary research seminars, and research projects conducted by the student fellows with the active support of the staff. Funding for this program, which began in 1959, is provided by the National Science Foundation and Office of Naval Research.

Number awarded Up to 10 graduate students are supported each year.

Deadline February of each year.

[898]
GEORGIA ASSOCIATION FOR WOMEN LAWYERS SCHOLARSHIPS

Georgia Association for Women Lawyers
Attn: GAWL Foundation, Inc.
3855 Spalding Bluff Drive
Norcross, GA 30092
(770) 446-1517   Fax: (770) 446-7721
E-mail: info@gawl.org
Web: www.gawl.org

Summary To provide financial assistance to women enrolled at law schools in Georgia.

Eligibility This program is open to women entering the second or third year at a law school in Georgia. Applicants must submit a 200-word statement describing their career objectives and expectations with respect to the practice of law. Selection is based on academic achievement, leadership, community service, philanthropic potential, and commitment to the profession. Students who can demonstrate involvement in programs that affect and/or promote the advancement of women in the profession and in the community receive special consideration.

Financial data The stipend is generally $2,000.

Duration 1 year.

Number awarded 1 or more each year.

Deadline February of each year.

[899]
GEORGIA HARKNESS SCHOLARSHIP AWARDS

United Methodist Church
Attn: General Board of Higher Education and Ministry
Division of Ordained Ministry
1001 19th Avenue South
P.O. Box 340007
Nashville, TN 37203-0007
(615) 340-7409   Fax: (615) 340-7367
E-mail: gharkness@gbhem.org
Web: www.gbhem.org/loansandscholarships

Summary To provide financial assistance to women over 35 years of age who are preparing for a second career in ordained ministry as an elder in the United Methodist Church.

Eligibility This program is open to women over 35 years of age who have a bachelor's degree. Applicants must be enrolled full time in a school of theology approved by the University Senate of the United Methodist Church and working on an M.Div. degree. They must be currently certified as candidates for ordained ministry as an elder in the United Methodist Church. The award is not available for undergraduate, D.Min., or Ph.D. work. Selection is based on financial need, academic scholarship, spiritual leadership, and commitment to social justice.

Financial data The stipend is $5,000.

Duration 1 year; recipients may reapply.

Number awarded Varies each year.

Deadline February of each year.

[900]
GERTRUDE BOYD CRANE SCHOLARSHIP

United Methodist Church-Oregon-Idaho Conference
Attn: United Methodist Women
1505 S.W. 18th Avenue
Portland, OR 97201-2524
(503) 226-7031   Toll Free: (800) J-WESLEY
Web: www.umoi.org/pages/detail/45

Summary To provide financial assistance to female Methodists from Oregon and Idaho who are interested in attending seminary in any state to prepare for a church-related career.

Eligibility This program is open to women who are members of congregations affiliated with the Oregon-Idaho Conference of the United Methodist Church (UMC). Applicants must be enrolled or planning to enroll at an accredited graduate school or seminary in any state to prepare for a church-related vocation within the Conference. Selection is based primarily on financial need.

Financial data The stipend, which depends on the availability of funds, has ranged from $200 to $1,900.

Duration 1 year.

Number awarded 1 each year.

Deadline April of each year.

[901]
GERTRUDE M. COX SCHOLARSHIP IN STATISTICS

American Statistical Association
Attn: Executive Secretary
732 North Washington Street
Alexandria, VA 22314-1943
(703) 684-1221, ext. 134   Toll Free: (888) 231-3473
Fax: (703) 684-2037   E-mail: awards@amstat.org
Web: www.amstat.org/education/coxscholarship.cfm

Summary To provide funding to women who wish to earn a graduate degree in order to enter statistically-oriented professions.

Eligibility This program is open to women who are citizens or permanent residents of the United States or Canada and admitted to full-time study in a graduate statistical program. Women in or entering the early stages of graduate training are especially encouraged to apply. Applicants must submit a 1-page personal essay on why they are enrolled in their present academic program and how they intend to use their technical training, along with examples of acts of leadership, community service, and/or mentoring they have performed. Selection is based on academic record, employment history, references, and a personal statement of interest.

Financial data The stipend is $2,000.

Duration 1 year.

Additional information This program was established in 1989.

Number awarded 2 each year: 1 to a woman in or entering the early stages of graduate training and 1 to a woman in a more advanced stage of training.

Deadline March of each year.

[902]
GLADYS C. ANDERSON MEMORIAL SCHOLARSHIP

American Foundation for the Blind
Attn: Scholarship Committee
11 Penn Plaza, Suite 300
New York, NY 10001
(212) 502-7661   Toll Free: (800) AFB-LINE
Fax: (212) 502-7771   TDD: (212) 502-7662
E-mail: afbinfo@afb.net
Web: www.afb.org/Section.asp?Documentid=2962

Summary To provide financial assistance to legally blind women who are studying classical or religious music on the undergraduate or graduate school level.

Eligibility This program is open to women who are legally blind, U.S. citizens, and enrolled in an undergraduate or graduate degree program in classical or religious music. Along with their application, they must submit a 200-word essay that includes their past and recent achievements and accomplishments; their intended field of study and why they have chosen it; and the role their visual impairment has played in shaping their life. They must also submit a sample performance tape or CD of up to 30 minutes. Financial need is considered in the selection process.

Financial data The stipend is $1,000.

Duration 1 academic year.

Number awarded 1 each year.

Deadline April of each year.

[903]
GLOBAL CHANGE GRADUATE RESEARCH ENVIRONMENTAL FELLOWSHIPS (GREF)

Oak Ridge Institute for Science and Education
Attn: Global Change Education Program
120 Badger Avenue, M.S. 36
P.O. Box 117
Oak Ridge, TN 37831-0117
(865) 576-7009   Fax: (865) 241-9445
E-mail: gcep@orau.gov
Web: www.atmos.anl.gov/GCEP/GREF/index.html

Summary To provide doctoral students (particularly women and minorities) with an opportunity to conduct research on global change.

Eligibility This program is open to students who have completed their first year of graduate school, unless they previously participated in the Global Change Summer Undergraduate Research Experience (SURE). Applicants must be proposing to conduct research at a national laboratory in a program area within the Department of Energy's Office of Biological and Environmental Research (DOE-BER): the atmospheric science program, the environmental meteorology program, the atmospheric radiation measurement program, the terrestrial carbon processes effort, the program for ecosystem research, and studies carried out under the direction of the National Institute for Global Environmental Change. Minority and female students are particularly encouraged to apply. U.S. citizenship is required.

Financial data Participants receive an annual stipend of $19,500 ($1,500 per month plus a $600 research education supplement in March and October); reimbursement of tuition and fees at the college or university they attend; and transportation, per diem, and lodging for summer activities.

Duration Up to 3 years.

Additional information This program, funded by DOE-BER, began in 1999. Fellows are encouraged to participate in the Summer Undergraduate Research Experience (SURE) orientation and focus sessions at a participating university.

Number awarded 10 to 15 each year.

Deadline December of each year.

[904]
GLORINE TUOHEY MEMORIAL SCHOLARSHIP

American Business Women's Association
Attn: Stephen Bufton Memorial Educational Fund
11050 Roe Avenue, Suite 200
Overland Park, KS 66211
Toll Free: (800) 228-0007
Web: www.sbmef.org/Opportunities.cfm

Summary To provide financial assistance to female graduate students who are working on a degree in a specified field (the field changes each year).

Eligibility This program is open to women who are working on a graduate degree and have a cumulative GPA of 3.0 or higher. Applicants are not required to be members of the American Business Women's Association. Along with their application, they must submit a 250-word biographical sketch that includes information about their background, activities, honors, work experience, and long-term educational and professional goals. Financial need is not considered in the selection process. Annually, the trustees designate an academic discipline for which the scholarship will be presented that year; recently, eligibility was limited to women working on a graduate degree in nursing. U.S. citizenship is required.

Financial data The stipend is $3,000. Funds are paid directly to the recipient's institution to be used only for tuition, books, and fees.

Duration 1 year.

Additional information This program was created in 1997 as part of ABWA's Stephen Bufton Memorial Education Fund.

Number awarded 1 each year.

Deadline May of each year.

[905]
GRACE LEGENDRE FELLOWSHIP FOR ADVANCED GRADUATE STUDY

Business and Professional Women's Clubs of New York
   State
Attn: Mary Ellen Morgan, Fellowship Chair
901 East Lake Road
Dundee, NY 14837
(315) 536-8440   E-mail: dmmea@aol.com
Web: www.gracelegendre.org

Summary To provide financial assistance to women in New York who wish to continue their education on the graduate level.

Eligibility This program is open to women who are permanent residents of New York and citizens of the United States, have a bachelor's degree, and are currently registered full time or have completed 1 year in an advanced graduate degree program at a recognized college or university in New York. Applicants must show evidence of scholastic ability and need for financial assistance. They should be within 2 years of completing their degree.

Financial data Stipends are $2,000 or $1,500.

Duration 1 year; recipients may reapply.

Additional information This program was established in 1969. Requests for applications must be accompanied by a self-addressed stamped envelope.

Number awarded Varies each year; recently, 4 of these fellowships were awarded: 2 at $2,000 and 2 at $1,500.

Deadline February of each year.

[906]
GRETCHEN L. BLECHSCHMIDT AWARD

Geological Society of America
Attn: Program Officer-Grants, Awards and Recognition
3300 Penrose Place
P.O. Box 9140
Boulder, CO 80301-9140
(303) 357-1028   Toll Free: (800) 472-1988, ext. 1028
Fax: (303) 357-1070   E-mail: awards@geosociety.org
Web: www.geosociety.org/grants/gradgrants.htm

Summary To provide support to female members of the Geological Society of America (GSA) interested in conducting doctoral research in geology.

Eligibility This program is open to GSA members working on a doctoral degree at a university in the United States, Canada, Mexico, or Central America. Applicants must be women interested in a career in academic research. Special consideration may be given to women 1) whose proposals are in the fields of biostratigraphy and/or paleoceanography and 2) who have an interest in sequence stratigraphy analysis, particularly in conjunction with research into deep-sea sedimentology. Disabled and minority women are particularly encouraged to submit research proposals. Selection is based on the scientific merits of the proposal, the capability of the investigator, and the reasonableness of the budget.

Financial data Grants range up to $4,000. Funds can be used for the cost of travel, room and board in the field, services of a technician or field assistant, funding of chemical and isotope analyses, or other expenses directly related to the fulfillment of the research contract. Support is not provided for the purchase of ordinary field equipment, for maintenance of the families of the grantees and their assistants, as reimbursement for work already accomplished, for institutional overhead, for adviser participation, or for tuition costs.

Duration 1 year.

Number awarded 1 each year.

Deadline January of each year.

[907]
GROTTO/JOB'S DAUGHTERS SCHOLARSHIP

International Order of Job's Daughters
c/o Anna Rhoads, Educational Scholarships Committee
   Chair
35 Ridgewood Drive
Troy, MO 63379
(636) 462-6834   E-mail: alrhoad@centurytel.net
Web: www.iojd.org/Scholarships/index.htm

Summary To provide financial assistance to members of Job's Daughters who are working on an undergraduate or graduate degree in a dental field.

Eligibility This program is open to high school seniors and graduates; students in early graduation programs; junior college, technical, and vocational students; and college and graduate students. Applicants must be Job's Daughters in good standing in their Bethels; unmarried majority members under 30 years of age are also eligible. They must be working on a degree in a dental field, preferably with some training in the field of disabilities. Selection is based on scholastic standing, Job's Daughters activities, the applicant's self-help plan, recommendation by the Executive Bethel Guardian Council, faculty recommendations, achievements outside Job's Daughters, and financial need.

Financial data The stipend is $1,500.

Duration 1 year.

Number awarded 1 or more each year.

Deadline April of each year.

[908]
HADASSAH-BRANDEIS INSTITUTE RESEARCH AWARDS

Brandeis University
Hadassah-Brandeis Institute
Attn: Program Manager
515 South Street
Mailstop 079
Waltham, MA 02454-9110
(781) 736-2064　　　　　　Fax: (781) 736-2078
E-mail: hbi@brandeis.edu
Web: www.brandeis.edu/hbi/grants/res_awards.html

Summary To provide funding to scholars, graduate students, writers, activists, and artists conducting research in the field of Jewish women's studies.

Eligibility This program offers senior grants (for established scholars and professionals) and junior grants (for graduate students and scholars within 3 years of receiving a Ph.D.). All applicants must be interested in conducting interdisciplinary research on Jewish women and gender issues, although there are no gender or religious limitations. Graduate students in recognized master's and Ph.D. programs are encouraged to apply. Applications from outside the United States are welcome. Grants are awarded in 10 categories: history; the Yishuv and Israel; Diaspora studies; families, children, and the Holocaust; gender, culture, religion, and the law; women's health; Judaism; biography; the arts (performance arts, visual arts, creative writing); and film and video. Applications must specify the category and may be for only 1 category. Selection is based on excellence.

Financial data Senior grants are $5,000 and junior grants are $2,000.

Duration 1 year.

Additional information The Hadassah-Brandeis Institute was formerly the Hadassah International Research Institute on Jewish Women at Brandeis University.

Number awarded Between 20 and 30 each year.

Deadline September of each year.

[909]
HARRIETT G. JENKINS PRE-DOCTORAL FELLOWSHIP PROGRAM

United Negro College Fund Special Programs
  Corporation
6402 Arlington Boulevard, Suite 600
Falls Church, VA 22042
(703) 677-3400　　　　　Toll Free: (800) 530-6232
Fax: (703) 205-7645　　　E-mail: portal@uncfsp.org
Web: www.uncfsp.org

Summary To provide financial assistance and work experience to women, minorities, and people with disabilities working on a graduate degree in a field of interest to the National Aeronautics and Space Administration (NASA).

Eligibility This program is open to members of groups underrepresented in science, technology, engineering, or mathematics (STEM), including women, minorities, and people with disabilities. Applicants must be full-time graduate students in a program leading to a master's or doctoral degree in a NASA-related discipline (aeronautics, aerospace engineering, astronomy, atmospheric science, bioengineering, biology, chemistry, computer science, earth sciences, engineering, environmental sciences, life sciences, materials sciences, mathematics, meteorology, neuroscience, physics, or robotics). They must be U.S. citizens and have a GPA of 3.0 or higher. Doctoral students who have advanced to candidacy are ineligible.

Financial data The stipend is $22,000 per year for doctoral fellows or $16,000 per year for master's degree students. The tuition offset is at least $8,500. Fellows who are also selected for a mini research award at a NASA Center or the Jet Propulsion Laboratory receive an additional grant of $7,000.

Duration 3 years.

Additional information This program, established in 2001, is funded by NASA and administered by the United Negro College Fund Special Programs Corporation. Fellows may also compete for a mini research award to engage in a NASA research experience that is closely aligned with the research conducted at the fellow's institution. The participating NASA facilities are Ames Research Center (Moffett Field, California), Jet Propulsion Laboratory (Pasadena, California), Dryden Flight Research Center (Edwards, California), Johnson Space Center (Houston, Texas), Stennis Space Center (Stennis Space Center, Mississippi), Marshall Space Flight Center (Marshall Space Flight Center, Alabama), Glenn Research Center (Cleveland, Ohio), Kennedy Space Center (Kennedy Space Center, Florida), Langley Research Center (Hampton, Virginia), and Goddard Space Flight Center (Greenbelt, Maryland).

Number awarded Approximately 20 each year.

Deadline April of each year.

[910]
HAZEL BEARD LEASE SCHOLARSHIP

Kappa Alpha Theta Foundation
Attn: Scholarships
8740 Founders Road
Indianapolis, IN 46268-1337
(317) 876-1870   Toll Free: (800) KAO-1870
Fax: (317) 876-1925
E-mail: FDNmail@kappaalphatheta.org
Web: www.kappaalphathetafoundation.org

Summary To provide financial assistance to members of Kappa Alpha Theta who are working on an undergraduate or graduate degree in speech therapy or speech communication.

Eligibility This program is open to members of Kappa Alpha Theta who are full-time sophomores, juniors, seniors, or graduate students at a college or university in Canada or the United States. Applicants must be working on a degree in speech therapy or speech communication. Along with their application, they must submit an official transcript, personal essays on assigned topics related to their involvement in Kappa Alpha Theta, and 2 letters of reference. Financial need is not considered in the selection process.

Financial data The stipend is $1,175.

Duration 1 year.

Number awarded 1 each year.

Deadline January of each year.

[911]
HEALTH SCIENCES STUDENT FELLOWSHIPS IN EPILEPSY

Epilepsy Foundation
Attn: Research Department
8301 Professional Place
Landover, MD 20785-2237
(301) 459-3700   Toll Free: (800) EFA-1000
Fax: (301) 577-2684   TDD: (800) 332-2070
E-mail: grants@efa.org
Web: www.epilepsyfoundation.org

Summary To provide financial assistance to medical and health science graduate students (particularly women, minorities, and students with disabilities) who are interested in working on an epilepsy project during the summer.

Eligibility This program is open to students enrolled, or accepted for enrollment, in a medical school, a doctoral program, or other graduate program. Applicants must have a defined epilepsy-related study or research plan to be carried out under the supervision of a qualified mentor. Because the program is designed as a training opportunity, the quality of the training plans and environment are considered in the selection process. Other selection criteria include the quality of the proposed project, the relevance of the proposed work to epilepsy, the applicant's interest in the field of epilepsy, the applicant's qualifications, the mentor's qualifications (including his or her commitment to the student and the project), and the quality of the training environment for research related to epilepsy. U.S. citizenship is not required, but the project must be conducted in the United States. Applications from women, members of minority groups, and people with disabilities are especially encouraged. The program is not intended for students working on a dissertation research project.

Financial data Stipends are $3,000.

Duration 3 months during the summer.

Additional information Support for this program is provided by many individuals, families, and corporations, especially the American Epilepsy Society, Abbott Laboratories, Ortho-McNeil Pharmaceutical, and Pfizer Inc.

Number awarded Varies each year; recently, 3 of these fellowships were awarded.

Deadline March of each year.

[912]
HEART OF TEXAS CHAPTER HELENE M. OVERLY MEMORIAL SCHOLARSHIP

Women's Transportation Seminar-Heart of Texas Chapter
c/o Lindsay Liggett, Scholarship Chair
Jacobs Engineering Group Inc.
2705 Bee Cave Road, Suite 300
Austin, TX 78746-5688
(512) 314-3100   Fax: (512) 314-3135
E-mail: lindsay.liggett@jacobs.com
Web: www.wtsinternational.org/Chapters.aspx?ID=8336

Summary To provide financial assistance to women graduate students from any state preparing for a career in transportation at selected colleges and universities in Arkansas, New Mexico, or Texas.

Eligibility This program is open to women from any state enrolled in a graduate program at selected colleges and universities in Arkansas, New Mexico, or Texas. Applicants must be working on a degree in a field related to transportation (e.g., engineering, finance, planning, logistics) and be planning for a career in the field. They must have a GPA of 3.0 or higher. Minority women are especially encouraged to apply.

Financial data The stipend is $2,000.

Duration 1 year.

Additional information The winner is also nominated for scholarships offered by the national organization of the Women's Transportation Seminar. For a list of the eligible schools in Arkansas, New Mexico, and Texas, contact the sponsor.

Number awarded 1 each year.

Deadline April of each year.

[913]
HEART OF TEXAS CHAPTER WTS PRESIDENT'S LEGACY SCHOLARSHIP

Women's Transportation Seminar-Heart of Texas Chapter
c/o Lindsay Liggett, Scholarship Chair
Jacobs Engineering Group Inc.
2705 Bee Cave Road, Suite 300
Austin, TX 78746-5688
(512) 314-3100   Fax: (512) 314-3135
E-mail: lindsay.liggett@jacobs.com
Web: www.wtsinternational.org/Chapters.aspx?ID=8336

Summary To provide financial assistance to women graduate students from any state who are interested in global transportation issues and are preparing for a career in transportation at designated colleges and universities in Arkansas, New Mexico, or Texas.

Eligibility This program is open to women from any state enrolled in a graduate program at designated colleges and universities in Arkansas, New Mexico, and Texas. Applicants must be working on a degree in a field related to transportation (e.g., engineering, finance, planning, logistics) and be planning for a career in the field. They must have a GPA of 3.0 or higher and a demonstrated interest in addressing global transportation issues. Along with their application, they must submit a 1,000-word statement on their interest in a transportation-related field, relevant international experiences and interests, and how this award will contribute to their ability to make a meaningful contribution to the transportation arena. Minority women are especially encouraged to apply.

Financial data The stipend is $2,000.

Duration 1 year.

Additional information The winner is also nominated for scholarships offered by the national organization of the Women's Transportation Seminar. For a list of the eligible schools in Arkansas, New Mexico, and Texas, contact the sponsor.

Number awarded 1 each year.

Deadline April of each year.

[914]
HELEN ANN MINS ROBBINS FELLOWSHIP

University of Rochester
Attn: Rossell Hope Robbins Library
Rush Rhees 416
Rochester, NY 14627-0055
(585) 275-0110   E-mail: alupack@library.rochester.edu
Web: www.library.rochester.edu/robbins/fellowship

Summary To provide funding to women interested in using the resources of the Rossell Hope Robbins Library at the University of Rochester to conduct research for a dissertation in medieval studies.

Eligibility This program is open to women working on a doctoral dissertation in medieval studies, especially English literature, British history and culture, and the relations between England and France in the Middle Ages. Applicants must be interested in using the resources of the Rossell Hope Robbins Library while remaining in residence in Rochester, New York for the academic year. Along with their application, they must submit a narrative of 750 to 1,000 words describing their dissertation, outlining the appropriateness of the library to the work they are doing, and commenting on the benefit of the period of research free of other obligations that the fellowship would allow.

Financial data The grant is $20,000.

Duration 1 academic year (up to 12 months).

Additional information The fellow is expected to engage in the academic life of the university and, towards the end of her residency, to give a lecture based on her research.

Number awarded 1 each even-numbered year.

Deadline March of each even-numbered year.

[915]
HELEN W. NIES SCHOLARSHIP

Federal Circuit Bar Association
1620 I Street, N.W., Suite 900
Washington, DC 20006
(202) 466-3923   Fax: (202) 833-1061
Web: www.fedcirbar.org

Summary To provide financial assistance to female law students who are interested in intellectual property law.

Eligibility This program is open to women who are currently enrolled in ABA-accredited law schools and are interested in intellectual property law. Applicants must submit a 450-word essay on their financial need, interest in particular areas of the law, and any other qualifications for this particular scholarship. Selection is based on academic excellence, financial need, and interest in intellectual property law.

Financial data The stipend is $10,000.

Duration 1 year.

Additional information This scholarship was first presented in 2007.

Number awarded 1 each year.

Deadline April of each year.

[916]
HELEN WOODRUFF NOLOP SCHOLARSHIP IN AUDIOLOGY AND ALLIED FIELDS

Delta Zeta Sorority
Attn: Foundation Coordinator
202 East Church Street
Oxford, OH 45056
(513) 523-7597   Fax: (513) 523-1921
E-mail: DZFoundation@dzshq.com
Web: www.deltazeta.org

Summary To provide financial assistance to women who are working on a graduate degree in audiology or a related field.

Eligibility This program is open to women working on a graduate degree in audiology or a related field of speech and hearing. Membership in Delta Zeta Sorority is not required. Applicants must submit an official transcript, a statement of their career goals, documentation of campus activities and/or community involvement, a list of academic honors, and an explanation of their financial need.

Financial data The stipend ranges from $1,000 to $15,000, depending on the availability of funds.

Duration 1 year; nonrenewable.

Number awarded 1 each year.

Deadline February of each year.

[917]
HELENE M. OVERLY MEMORIAL GRADUATE SCHOLARSHIP

Women's Transportation Seminar
Attn: WTS Foundation
1701 K Street, N.W., Suite 800
Washington, DC 20006
(202) 955-5085   Fax: (202) 955-5088
E-mail: wts@wtsinternational.org
Web: www.wtsinternational.org

Summary To provide financial assistance to women graduate students interested in preparing for a career in transportation.

Eligibility This program is open to women who are enrolled in a graduate degree program in a transportation-related field (e.g., transportation engineering, planning, finance, or logistics). Applicants must have at least a 3.0 GPA and be interested in a career in transportation. Along with their application, they must submit a 750-word statement about their career goals after graduation and why they think they should receive the scholarship award. Applications must be submitted first to a local chapter; the chapters forward selected applications for consideration on the national level. Minority women are particularly encouraged to apply. Selection is based on transportation involvement and goals, job skills, and academic record.

Financial data The stipend is $6,000.

Duration 1 year.

Additional information This program was established in 1981. Local chapters may also award additional funding to winners in their area.

Number awarded 1 each year.

Deadline Applications must be submitted by November to a local WTS chapter.

[918]
HENRY DAVID RESEARCH GRANT IN HUMAN REPRODUCTIVE BEHAVIOR AND POPULATION STUDIES

American Psychological Foundation
750 First Street, N.E.
Washington, DC 20002-4242
(202) 336-5843   Fax: (202) 336-5812
E-mail: foundation@apa.org
Web: www.apa.org/apf/funding/david.aspx

Summary To provide funding to young psychologists (particularly women, minorities, and individuals with disabilities) who are interested in conducting research on reproductive behavior.

Eligibility This program is open to doctoral students in psychology working on a dissertation and young psychologists who have no more than 7 years of postgraduate experience. Applicants must be interested in conducting research on human reproductive behavior or an area related to population concerns. Along with their application, they must submit a current curriculum vitae, 2 letters of recommendation, and an essay of 1 to 2 pages on their interest in human reproductive behavior or in population studies. The sponsor encourages applications from individuals who represent diversity in race, ethnicity, gender, age, disability, and sexual orientation.

Financial data The grant is $1,500.

Duration The grant is presented annually.

Number awarded 1 each year.

Deadline February of each year.

[919]
HENRY LUCE FOUNDATION/ACLS DISSERTATION FELLOWSHIPS IN AMERICAN ART

American Council of Learned Societies
Attn: Office of Fellowships and Grants
633 Third Avenue
New York, NY 10017-6795
(212) 697-1505   Fax: (212) 949-8058
E-mail: fellowships@acls.org
Web: www.acls.org/programs/American-art

Summary To provide funding to women, minority, and other doctoral students interested in conducting dissertation research anywhere in the world on the history of American art.

Eligibility This program is open to Ph.D. candidates in departments of art history whose dissertations are focused on the history of the visual arts in the United States and are object-oriented. Applicants may be proposing to conduct research at their home institution, abroad, or at another appropriate site. U.S. citizenship or permanent resident status is required. Students preparing theses for a Master of Fine Arts degree are not eligible. Applications are particularly invited from women and members of minority groups.

Financial data The grant is $25,000. Fellowship funds may not be used to pay tuition costs.

Duration 1 year; nonrenewable.

Additional information This program is funded by the Henry Luce Foundation and administered by the American Council of Learned Societies (ACLS).

Number awarded 10 each year.

Deadline November of each year.

[920]
HERBERT AND BETTY CARNES FUND

American Ornithologists' Union
c/o Executive Officer
5405 Villa View Drive
Farmington, NM 87402
(505) 326-1579   E-mail: aou@aou.org
Web: www.aou.org/awards/research

Summary To provide funding to female graduate students and scholars who are members of the American Ornithologists' Union (AOU) and interested in conducting research on avian biology.

Eligibility This program is open to female AOU members who are graduate students, postdoctorates, or other researchers without access to major funding agencies. Applicants must be interested in conducting research on avian biology. They must be nonsmokers (have not smoked in at least the previous 6 months). Along with their application, they should send a cover letter (about 5 pages) describing their proposed project, a budget, and 1 letter of reference. Selection is based on significance and originality of the research question, clarity of the objectives, feasibility of the plan of research, and appropriateness of the budget.

Financial data The maximum award is $2,500 per year.

Duration 1 year; recipients may reapply for 1 additional award.

Number awarded The sponsor awards a total of 28 to 30 grants each year.

Deadline January of each year.

[921]
HERBERT W. AND CORRINE CHILSTROM SCHOLARSHIP

Women of the Evangelical Lutheran Church in America
Attn: Scholarships
8765 West Higgins Road
Chicago, IL 60631-4101
(773) 380-2736   Toll Free: (800) 638-3522, ext. 2736
Fax: (773) 380-2419   E-mail: Women.elca@elca.org
Web: www.elca.org

Summary To provide financial assistance to mature women who are studying for a second career in the ordained ministry in the Evangelical Lutheran Church of America (ELCA).

Eligibility Applicants for this scholarship must be women who have experienced an interruption of at least 5 years in their education since college graduation and are currently entering the final year of an M.Div. program at an ELCA seminary. They must have been endorsed by the Synodical Candidacy Committee. Selection is based on academic achievement, personal commitment and determination to serve as a pastor in the ELCA, and financial need. U.S. citizenship is required.

Financial data The maximum stipend is $2,000.

Duration 1 year.

Additional information This scholarship was established in 1995 to honor Rev. Herbert W. Chilstrom and Rev. Corrine Chilstrom during the 25th anniversary year of the ordination of women in the predecessor bodies of the ELCA. Recipients must agree to serve for at least 3 years as an ELCA pastor after graduation from seminary.

Number awarded 1 each year.

Deadline February of each year.

[922]
HERMINE DALKOWITZ TOBOLOWSKY SCHOLARSHIP

Texas Business Women
Attn: Texas Business and Professional Women's
  Foundation
P.O. Box 70
Round Rock, TX 78680-0070
(806) 922-7090   Toll Free: (877) 225-4TBW
E-mail: info@texasbusinesswomen.org
Web: www.texasbpwfoundation.org/scholarships.php

Summary To provide financial assistance to women from any state who are attending college in Texas to prepare for a career in selected professions.

Eligibility This program is open to women from any state who are interested in preparing for a career in law, public service, government, political science, or women's history. Applicants must have completed at least 2 semesters of study at an accredited college or university in Texas, have a GPA of 3.0 or higher, and be U.S. citizens. Selection is based on academic achievement and financial need.

Financial data A stipend is awarded (amount not specified).

Duration 1 year.

Additional information This program was established in 1995 when Texas Business Women was named Texas Federation of Business and Professional Women's Clubs.

Number awarded 1 or more each year.

Deadline December of each year.

[923]
HERMIONE GRANT CALHOUN SCHOLARSHIP

National Federation of the Blind
Attn: Scholarship Committee
1800 Johnson Street
Baltimore, MD 21230
(410) 659-9314, ext. 2415   Fax: (410) 685-5653
E-mail: scholarships@nfb.org
Web: www.nfb.org/nfb/scholarship_program.asp

Summary To provide financial assistance to female blind students interested in working on an undergraduate or graduate degree.

Eligibility This program is open to legally blind women who are working on or planning to work full time on an undergraduate or graduate degree. Along with their application, they must submit transcripts, standardized test scores, proof of legal blindness, 2 letters of recommendation, and a letter of endorsement from their National Federation of the Blind state president or designee. Selection is based on academic excellence, service to the community, and financial need.

Financial data The stipend is $3,000.

Duration 1 year; recipients may resubmit applications up to 2 additional years.

Additional information Scholarships are awarded at the federation convention in July. Recipients attend the convention at federation expense; that funding is in addition to the scholarship grant.

Number awarded 1 each year.

Deadline March of each year.

[924]
HILARY A. BUFTON JR. SCHOLARSHIP

American Business Women's Association
Attn: Stephen Bufton Memorial Educational Fund
11050 Roe Avenue, Suite 200
Overland Park, KS 66211
Toll Free: (800) 228-0007
Web: www.sbmef.org/Opportunities.cfm

Summary To provide financial assistance to female graduate students who are working on a degree in a specified field (the field changes each year).

Eligibility This program is open to women who are working on a graduate degree and have a cumulative GPA of 3.0 or higher. Applicants are not required to be members of the American Business Women's Association. Along with their application, they must submit a 250-word biographical sketch that includes information about their background, activities, honors, work experience, and long-term educational and professional goals. Financial need is not considered in the selection process. Annually, the trustees designate an academic discipline for which the scholarship will be presented that year. U.S. citizenship is required.

Financial data The stipend is $10,000 (paid over a 2-year period). Funds are paid directly to the recipient's institution to be used only for tuition, books, and fees.

Duration 2 years.

Additional information This program was created in 1986 as part of ABWA's Stephen Bufton Memorial Education Fund. The ABWA does not provide the names and addresses of local chapters; it recommends that applicants check with their local Chamber of Commerce, library, or university to see if any chapter has registered a contact's name and number.

Number awarded 1 each even-numbered year.

Deadline May of each even-numbered year.

[925]
HOLLAND & HART SUMMER ASSOCIATES PROGRAM DIVERSITY INITIATIVE

Holland & Hart LLP
Attn: Manager of Attorney Recruitment and Professional
  Development
555 17th Street, Suite 3200
Denver, CO 80202
(303) 295-8509   Fax: (303) 295-8261
E-mail: meconnor@hollandhart.com
Web: www.hhjobs.com/diversityinitiative.html

Summary   To provide summer work experience at Holland & Hart in Denver, Colorado to female and minority law students.

Eligibility   This program is open to second-year students at top-tier law schools who are interested in a summer clerkship at the firm. Applicants must be women or people of color. They must submit a resume, transcript, and cover letter.

Financial data   The current stipend is $2,308 per week.

Duration   Summer months.

Number awarded   1 each year.

Deadline   September of each year.

[926]
HOLLY A. CORNELL SCHOLARSHIP

American Water Works Association
Attn: Scholarship Coordinator
6666 West Quincy Avenue
Denver, CO 80235-3098
(303) 347-6201   Toll Free: (800) 926-7337
Fax: (303) 795-7603   E-mail: lmoody@awwa.org
Web: www.awwa.org

Summary   To provide financial assistance to outstanding female and minority students interested in working on an master's degree in the field of water supply and treatment.

Eligibility   <EG>This program is open to minority and female students working on a master's degree in the field of water supply and treatment at a college or university in Canada, Guam, Mexico, Puerto Rico, or the United States. Students who have been accepted into graduate school but have not yet begun graduate study are encouraged to apply. Applicants must submit a 2-page resume, official transcripts, 3 letters of recommendation, a proposed curriculum of study, a 1-page statement of educational plans and career objectives demonstrating an interest in the drinking water field, and a 3-page proposed plan of research. Selection is based on academic record and potential to provide leadership in the field of water supply and treatment.

Financial data   The stipend is $7,500.

Duration   1 year; nonrenewable.

Additional information   Funding for this program comes from the consulting firm CH2M Hill.

Number awarded   1 each year.

Deadline   January of each year.

[927]
HON. GERALDINE A. FERRARO ENDOWED SCHOLARSHIP

National Organization of Italian American Women
25 West 43rd Street, Suite 1005
New York, NY 10036
(212) 642-2003   Fax: (212) 642-2006
E-mail: noiaw@noiaw.org
Web: www.noiaw.org

Summary   To provide financial assistance for law school to women of Italian descent.

Eligibility   This program is open to women who have at least 1 parent of Italian American descent and are working on a law degree. Applicants must be enrolled full time and have a GPA of 3.5 or higher. Along with their application, they must submit a 2-page essay on how being an Italian American has impacted them personally and professionally. Financial need is considered in the selection process.

Financial data   The stipend is $2,000.

Duration   1 year; nonrenewable.

Number awarded   1 each year.

Deadline   April of each year.

[928]
HONORABLE HARRISON W. EWING FELLOWSHIPS

Alpha Chi Omega Foundation
Attn: Foundation Programs Coordinator
5939 Castle Creek Parkway North Drive
Indianapolis, IN 46250-4343
(317) 579-5050, ext. 262   Fax: (317) 579-5051
E-mail: foundation@alphachiomega.org
Web: www.alphachiomega.org/index.aspx?id=1030

Summary   To provide financial assistance to graduating Alpha Chi Omega members who are interested in attending law school.

Eligibility   Women college seniors or college graduates who are members of the sorority are eligible to apply if they are interested in attending law school. Selection is based on academic achievement, chapter involvement, campus and community service, and financial need.

Financial data   A stipend is awarded (amount not specified).

Duration   1 year.

Number awarded   Up to 5 each year.

Deadline   March of each year.

[929]
HORIZONS FOUNDATION SCHOLARSHIP PROGRAM

Women in Defense
c/o National Defense Industrial Association
2111 Wilson Boulevard, Suite 400
Arlington, VA 22201-3061
(703) 247-2552   Fax: (703) 522-1885
E-mail: wid@ndia.org
Web: wid.ndia.org/horizons/Pages/default.aspx

Summary   To provide financial assistance to women (including those already working in national security fields) who are upper-division or graduate students working on a degree related to the national security interests of the United States.

Eligibility This program is open to women who are already working in national security fields as well as women planning such careers. Applicants must 1) be currently enrolled at an accredited college or university, either full time or part time, as graduate students or upper-division undergraduates; 2) demonstrate financial need; 3) be U.S. citizens; 4) have a GPA of 3.25 or higher; and 5) demonstrate interest in preparing for a career related to national security. The preferred fields of study include business (as it relates to national security or defense), computer science, economics, engineering, government relations, international relations, law (as it relates to national security or defense), mathematics, military history, political science, physics, and security studies; others are considered if the applicant can demonstrate relevance to a career in national security or defense. Selection is based on academic achievement, participation in defense and national security activities, field of study, work experience, statements of objectives, recommendations, and financial need.

Financial data The stipend ranges up to $12,000.

Duration 1 year; renewable.

Additional information This program was established in 1988.

Number awarded Varies each year; recently, 3 of these scholarships were awarded: 1 at $12,000, 1 at $10,000, and 1 at $3,000. Since the program was established, 104 women have received more than $119,000 in support.

Deadline June of each year.

[930]
HORIZONS-MICHIGAN SCHOLARSHIP

Women in Defense-Michigan Chapter
Attn: Scholarship Director
P.O. Box 4744
Troy, MI 48099
E-mail: scholarships@wid-mi.org
Web: www.wid-mi.org/scholarships.aspx

Summary To provide financial assistance to women in Michigan who are upper-division or graduate students working on a degree related to national defense.

Eligibility This program is open to women who are residents of Michigan and enrolled either full or part time at a college or university in the state. Applicants must be juniors, seniors, or graduate students and have a GPA of 3.25 or higher. They must be interested in preparing for a career related to national security or defense. Relevant fields of study include security studies, military history, government relations, engineering, computer science, physics, mathematics, business (as related to national security or defense), law (as related to national security or defense), international relations, political science, or economics; other fields may be considered if the applicant can demonstrate relevance to a career in national security or defense. Along with their application, they must submit brief statements on their interest in a career in national security or defense, the principal accomplishments in their life that relate to their professional goals, and the objectives of their educational program. Selection is based on those statements, academic achievement, participation in defense and national security activities, field of study, work experience, recommendations, and financial need. U.S. citizenship is required.

Financial data Stipends have averaged at least $3,000.

Duration 1 year.

Additional information This program was established in 2009.

Number awarded Varies each year; recently, 6 of these scholarships were awarded.

Deadline September of each year.

[931]
HOUSTON CHAPTER HELENE M. OVERLY MEMORIAL SCHOLARSHIP

Women's Transportation Seminar-Houston Chapter
c/o Tracy Rudder, Scholarship Chair
Parsons Brinckerhoff, Inc.
16285 Park Ten Place, Suite 400
Houston, TX 77084
(281) 589-5900   Fax: (281) 759-5164
E-mail: rudder@pbworld.com
Web: www.wtsinternational.org/Chapters.aspx?ID=10172

Summary To provide financial assistance to women graduate students from any state preparing for a career in transportation at selected colleges and universities in Louisiana or Texas.

Eligibility This program is open to women from any state enrolled in a graduate program at selected colleges and universities in Louisiana or Texas. Applicants must be working on a degree in a field related to transportation (e.g., engineering, finance, planning, logistics) and be planning for a career in the field. They must have a GPA of 3.0 or higher. Along with their application, they must submit a 750-word statement about their career goals after graduation and why they think they should receive this scholarship. Minority women are especially encouraged to apply.

Financial data The stipend is $1,500.

Duration 1 year.

Additional information The winner is also nominated for scholarships offered by the national organization of the Women's Transportation Seminar. For a list of the eligible schools in Louisiana and Texas, contact the sponsor.

Number awarded 1 each year.

Deadline November of each year.

[932]
HOWARD HUGHES MEDICAL INSTITUTE RESEARCH TRAINING FELLOWSHIPS FOR MEDICAL STUDENTS

Howard Hughes Medical Institute
Attn: Office of Grants and Special Programs
4000 Jones Bridge Road
Chevy Chase, MD 20815-6789
(301) 215-8889   Toll Free: (800) 448-4882, ext. 8889
Fax: (301) 215-8888   E-mail: fellows@hhmi.org
Web: www.hhmi.org/grants/individuals/medfellows.html

Summary To provide financial assistance to medical, dental, and veterinary students (particularly women and minorities) who are interested in pursuing research training.

Eligibility Applicants must be enrolled in a medical, dental, or veterinary school in the United States, although they may be citizens of any country with a visa authorizing them to work in this country. They must describe a proposed research project to be conducted at an academic or nonprofit research institution in the United States, other than a facility of the National Institutes of Health in Bethesda, Maryland. Research proposals should reflect the interests of the Howard Hughes Medical Institute (HHMI), especially in biochemistry, bioinformatics, biomedical engineering, biophysics, biostatistics, cell biology, developmental biology, epidemiology, genetics, immunology, mathematical and computational biology, microbiology, molecular biology, neuroscience, pharmacology, physiology, structural biology, or virology. Applications from women and minorities underrepresented in the sciences (Blacks or African Americans, Hispanics, American Indians, Native Alaskans, and Native Pacific Islanders) are especially encouraged. Students enrolled in M.D./Ph.D., Ph.D., or Sc.D. programs and those who have completed a Ph.D. or Sc.D. in a laboratory-based science are not eligible. Selection is based on the applicant's ability and promise for a research career as a physician-scientist and the quality of training that will be provided.

Financial data Fellows receive a stipend of $28,000 per year. Indirect costs are not covered, but the institution receives an institutional allowance of $5,500 and a research allowance of $5,500. If fellows are conducting research at an institution other than their own, a travel and moving allowance of $1,500 is provided.

Duration 12 months, beginning any time between June and August.

Additional information This program complements the HHMI-NIH Research Scholars Program; students may not apply to both programs in the same year. HHMI has entered into partnership agreements with designated sponsors to support fellows in certain areas; those include the Burroughs Wellcome Fund for veterinary students, the Foundation Fighting Blindness for ophthalmology research (particularly in the area of inherited retinal degenerative diseases), the GM Trust for research in a field related to Duchenne Muscular Dystrophy, and the Society of Interventional Radiology Foundation for preclinical research in interventional radiology.

Number awarded Up to 66 each year.

Deadline January of each year.

[933]
H.S. AND ANGELINE LEWIS SCHOLARSHIPS

American Legion Auxiliary
Department of Wisconsin
Attn: Education Chair
2930 American Legion Drive
P.O. Box 140
Portage, WI 53901-0140
(608) 745-0124   Toll Free: (866) 664-3863
Fax: (608) 745-1947   E-mail: alawi@amlegionauxwi.org
Web: www.amlegionauxwi.org/Scholarships.htm

Summary To provide financial assistance to Wisconsin residents who are related to veterans or are members of the American Legion Auxiliary and interested in working on an undergraduate or graduate degree at a school in any state.

Eligibility This program is open to the children, wives, and widows of veterans who are high school seniors or graduates and have a GPA of 3.5 or higher. Grandchildren and great-grandchildren of members of the American Legion Auxiliary are also eligible. Applicants must be residents of Wisconsin and interested in working on an undergraduate or graduate degree at a school in any state. Along with their application,

they must submit a 300-word essay on "Education-An Investment in the Future." Financial need is considered in the selection process.

Financial data The stipend is $1,000.

Duration 1 year; nonrenewable.

Number awarded 6 each year: 1 to a graduate student and 5 to undergraduates.

Deadline March of each year.

[934]
IADES FELLOWSHIP AWARD

International Alumnae of Delta Epsilon Sorority
c/o Virginia Borggaard
2453 Bear Den Road
Frederick, MD 21701-9321
Fax: (301) 663-3231   TDD: (301) 663-9235
E-mail: vborggaard@juno.com

Summary To provide financial assistance to deaf women who are working on a doctoral degree.

Eligibility Eligible to apply are deaf women who have completed 12 or more units in a doctoral-level program with a GPA of 3.0 or more. They need not be members of Delta Epsilon. Along with their application, they must submit official transcripts, a recent copy of their audiogram, and 2 letters of recommendation.

Financial data The stipend is $1,000.

Duration 1 year.

Number awarded 1 or more each year.

Deadline April of each year.

[935]
IBM PHD FELLOWSHIP PROGRAM

IBM Corporation
Attn: University Relations
1133 Westchester Avenue
White Plains, NY 10604
Toll Free: (800) IBM-4YOU   TDD: (800) IBM-3383
E-mail: phdfellow@us.ibm.com
Web: www.ibm.com

Summary To provide funding and work experience to women, minority, and other students from any country working on a Ph.D. in a research area of broad interest to IBM.

Eligibility Students nominated for this fellowship should be enrolled full time at an accredited college or university in any country and should have completed at least 1 year of graduate study in the following fields: business sciences (including financial services, risk management, marketing, communication, and learning/knowledge management); computer science and engineering; electrical and mechanical engineering; management; mathematical sciences (including analytics, statistics, operations research, and optimization); physical sciences (including chemistry, materials sciences, and physics); or service science, management, and engineering (SSME). They should be planning a career in research. Nominations must be made by a faculty member and endorsed by the department head. The program values diversity, and encourages nominations of women, minorities, and others who contribute to that diversity. Selection is based on the applicants' potential for research excellence, the degree to which their technical interests align with those of IBM, and academic progress to date. Preference is given to students who have had an IBM internship or have closely collaborated with technical or services people from IBM.

Financial data Fellowships pay tuition, fees, and a stipend of $17,500 per year.

Duration 1 year; may be renewed up to 2 additional years, provided the recipient is renominated, interacts with IBM's technical community, and demonstrates continued progress and achievement.

Additional information Recipients are offered an internship at 1 of the IBM Research Division laboratories and are given an IBM computer.

Number awarded Varies each year; recently, 57 of these scholarships were awarded.

Deadline October of each year.

[936]
IDA B. WELLS GRADUATE STUDENT FELLOWSHIP

Coordinating Council for Women in History
c/o Sandra Dawson, Executive Director
Northern Illinois University
Department of History and Women's Studies
715 Zulauf Hall
DeKalb, IL 60115
(815) 895-2624   E-mail: execdir@theccwh.org
Web: theccwh.org/awards.htm

Summary To provide funding to women graduate students for completion of their doctoral dissertations on an historical topic.

Eligibility This program is open to women graduate students in history departments at U.S. institutions who are members of the Coordinating Council for Women in History (CCWH). Applicants must have passed to A.B.D. status. They may be specializing in any field, but they must be working on an historical project. Preference is given to applicants working on a project involving issues of race.

Financial data The grant is $1,000.

Duration 1 year.

Additional information This program, established in 1999, is administered by the CCWH and the Berkshire Conference of Women Historians. The award is presented at the CCWH luncheon at the annual meeting of the American Historical Association, although the recipient does not need to be present to accept the award.

Number awarded 1 each year.

Deadline September of each year.

[937]
IDA FOREMAN FLEISHER SCHOLARSHIP

Jewish Federation of Greater Philadelphia
Attn: Endowments Department
2100 Arch Street, Sixth Floor
Philadelphia, PA 19103
(215) 832-0514   Fax: (215) 832-0503
E-mail: pquarles@jfgp.org
Web: www.jewishphilly.org/page.aspx?id=124638

Summary To provide financial assistance for graduate school to women from any state, especially Jewish women.

Eligibility This program is open to women residents of any state who are interested in obtaining a graduate professional education. Preference is given to Jewish women. Applicants

must submit a personal statement describing their background and career goals. Financial need is considered in the selection process.

Financial data Stipends range from $2,000 to $8,000. Funds are paid directly to the recipient's school.

Duration 1 year.

Additional information This scholarship is administered by the Jewish Federation of Greater Philadelphia and the PNC Private Bank in Philadelphia.

Number awarded 1 or more each year.

Deadline May of each year.

[938]
IDA M. POPE MEMORIAL SCHOLARSHIPS

Hawai'i Community Foundation
Attn: Scholarship Department
827 Fort Street Mall
Honolulu, HI 96813
(808) 537-6333   Toll Free: (888) 731-3863
Fax: (808) 521-6286
E-mail: scholarships@hcf-hawaii.org
Web: www.hawaiicommunityfoundation.org/scholarships

Summary To provide financial assistance to Native Hawaiian women who are interested in working on an undergraduate or graduate degree in designated fields at a school in any state.

Eligibility This program is open to female residents of Hawaii who are Native Hawaiian, defined as a descendant of the aboriginal inhabitants of the Hawaiian islands prior to 1778. Applicants must be enrolled at a school in any state in an accredited associate, bachelor's, or graduate degree program and working on a degree in health, science, or education (including counseling and social work). They must be able to demonstrate academic achievement (GPA of 3.5 or higher), good moral character, and financial need. Along with their application, they must submit a short statement indicating their reasons for attending college, their planned course of study, their career goals, and what community service means to them.

Financial data The amounts of the awards depend on the availability of funds and the need of the recipient. Recently, the average value of each of the scholarships awarded by the foundation was more than $2,000.

Duration 1 year; may be renewed.

Number awarded Varies each year; recently, 61 of these scholarships were awarded.

Deadline February of each year.

[939]
IMMIGRANT WOMEN PROGRAM INTERNSHIPS AT LEGAL MOMENTUM

Legal Momentum
Attn: Immigrant Women Program
1101 14th Street, N.W., Suite 300
Washington, DC 20005
(202) 326-0040   Fax: (202) 589-0511
E-mail: dcinternships@legalmomentum.org
Web: www.legalmomentum.org

Summary To provide work experience to students and recent graduates who are interested in working on the Legal Momentus's immigrant women program in Washington, D.C.

Eligibility The internship is open to undergraduates, graduate students, and recent graduates interested in an immigrant women internship at Legal Momentum. Applicants must be interested in working on a range of tasks, including researching and analyzing legislation; drafting letters, fact sheets, and articles; attending briefings and coalition meetings; answering requests for technical assistance; assisting with administrative tasks as needed; and coordinating the work of coalitions dealing with violence against women, welfare reform, child care, and immigrant women's rights. They should have a strong interest in women's legal rights. A love of feminist issues, politics, and hard work is useful and a working knowledge of the American political process is recommended. Women and men of all ethnic, cultural, economic, and sexual orientations who support feminist concerns are eligible. Bilingual individuals are especially encouraged to apply.

Financial data These are paid internships (stipend not specified).

Duration Interns are asked to work from 15 to 35 hours per week for 10 to 12 weeks. Positions are available in the fall, spring, or summer.

Additional information Legal Momentum was formerly known as the NOW Legal Defense and Education Fund.

Number awarded Varies each year.

Deadline Applications may be submitted at any time.

[940]
INDUSTRY/GOVERNMENT GRADUATE FELLOWSHIPS

American Meteorological Society
Attn: Fellowship/Scholarship Coordinator
45 Beacon Street
Boston, MA 02108-3693
(617) 227-2426, ext. 246   Fax: (617) 742-8718
E-mail: scholar@ametsoc.org
Web: www.ametsoc.org

Summary To encourage students (particularly women, minorities, and students with disabilities) who are entering their first year of graduate school to work on an advanced degree in the atmospheric and related oceanic and hydrologic sciences.

Eligibility This program is open to students entering their first year of graduate study who wish to pursue advanced degrees in the atmospheric or related oceanic or hydrologic sciences. Applicants must be U.S. citizens or permanent residents and have a GPA of 3.25 or higher. Along with their application, they must submit 200-word essays on 1) their most important achievements that qualify them for this scholarship, and 2) their career goals in the atmospheric or related sciences. Selection is based on academic record as an undergraduate. The sponsor specifically encourages applications from women, minorities, and students with disabilities who are traditionally underrepresented in the atmospheric and related oceanic sciences.

Financial data The stipend is $24,000 per academic year.

Duration 9 months.

Additional information This program was initiated in 1991. It is funded by high-technology firms and government agencies.

Number awarded Varies each year; recently, 13 of these scholarships were awarded.

Deadline February of each year.

[941]
INGEBORG HASELTINE SCHOLARSHIP FUND FOR WOMEN

Unitarian Universalist Association
Attn: Ministerial Credentialing Office
25 Beacon Street
Boston, MA 02108-2800
(617) 948-6403   Fax: (617) 742-2875
E-mail: mco@uua.org
Web: www.uua.org

Summary To provide financial assistance to women preparing for the Unitarian Universalist (UU) ministry.

Eligibility This program is open to women currently enrolled or planning to enroll full time in a UU ministerial training program with aspirant or candidate status. Financial need is considered in the selection process.

Financial data The stipend ranges from $1,000 to $11,000 per year.

Duration 1 year.

Number awarded Varies each year; recently, 5 of these scholarships were awarded.

Deadline April of each year.

[942]
INSTITUTE FOR SUPPLY MANAGEMENT DOCTORAL DISSERTATION GRANT PROGRAM

Institute for Supply Management
Attn: Vice President, Education
2055 East Centennial Circle
P.O. Box 22160
Tempe, AZ 85285-2160
(480) 752-6276, ext. 3105
Toll Free: (800) 888-6276, ext. 3105
Fax: (480) 752-7890   E-mail: ssturzl@ism.ws
Web: www.ism.ws

Summary To provide financial support to women, minority, and other doctoral candidates who are conducting dissertation research in purchasing or related fields.

Eligibility This program is open to doctoral candidates who are working on a Ph.D. or D.B.A. in supply management, supply chain management, business, management, logistics, economics, industrial engineering, or a related field at an accredited university in the United States. International applicants are accepted. Examples of research projects that could be funded include: purchasing and supply management models, methodologies, measurement, supply networks, operations and logistics integration, produce/service innovation, supply relationships, supply's role in corporate success, or strategic development of supply. The research proposal (up to 25 pages) must discuss hypotheses, significance of the study, research methodology, and value of the research to the field of purchasing. The program encourages applications from a diverse population, regardless of gender, race, creed, age, ethnic or national origin, sexual orientation, or disability.

Financial data Grants range up to $12,000.

Duration 1 year.

Additional information The sponsoring organization was previously known as the National Association of Purchasing Management.
Number awarded Up to 4 each year.
Deadline January of each year.

[943]
INTEL SCHOLARSHIP

Society of Women Engineers
Attn: Scholarship Selection Committee
120 South LaSalle Street, Suite 1515
Chicago, IL 60603-3572
(312) 596-5223   Toll Free: (877) SWE-INFO
Fax: (312) 644-8557
E-mail: scholarshipapplication@swe.org
Web: societyofwomenengineers.swe.org

Summary To provide financial assistance to women working on a graduate degree in computer science or specified fields of engineering.
Eligibility This program is open to women working on a graduate degree in computer science or chemical, computer, electrical, industrial, manufacturing, materials, or mechanical engineering. Applicants must have a GPA of 3.5 or higher. Selection is based on merit and financial need. Preference is given to members of groups underrepresented in computer science and engineering.
Financial data The stipend is $1,000.
Duration 1 year.
Additional information This program is sponsored by Intel Corporation.
Number awarded 3 each year.
Deadline February of each year.

[944]
INTELLECTUAL PROPERTY LAW SECTION WOMEN AND MINORITY SCHOLARSHIP

State Bar of Texas
Attn: Intellectual Property Law Section
c/o Bhaveeni D. Parmar, Scholarship Selection
  Committee
Klemchuk Kubasta LLP
Campbell Centre II
9150 North Central Expressway, Suite 1150
Dallas, TX 75206
(214) 367-6000   E-mail: bhaveeni@kk-llp.com
Web: www.texasbariplaw.org/index.htm

Summary To provide financial assistance to female and minority students at law schools in Texas who plan to practice intellectual property law.
Eligibility This program is open to women and members of minority groups (African Americans, Hispanics, Asian Americans, and Native Americans) from any state who are currently enrolled at an ABA-accredited law school in Texas. Applicants must be planning to practice intellectual property law in Texas. Along with their application, they must submit a 2-page essay explaining why they plan to prepare for a career in intellectual property law in Texas, any qualifications they believe are relevant for their consideration for this scholarship, and (optionally) any issues of financial need they wish to have considered.
Financial data The stipend is $2,500.

Duration 1 year.
Number awarded 2 each year: 1 to a women and 1 to a minority.
Deadline April of each year.

[945]
INTERMOUNTAIN SECTION AWWA DIVERSITY SCHOLARSHIP

American Water Works Association-Intermountain
  Section
3430 East Danish Road
Sandy, UT 94093
(801) 712-1619   Fax: (801) 487-6699
E-mail: nicoleb@ims-awwa.org
Web: www.ims-awwa.org

Summary To provide financial assistance to female and minority undergraduate and graduate students working on a degree in the field of water quality, supply, and treatment at a university in Idaho or Utah.
Eligibility This program is open to women and students who identify as Hispanic or Latino, Black or African American, Native Hawaiian or other Pacific Islander, Asian, or American Indian or Alaska Native. Applicants must be entering or enrolled in an undergraduate or graduate program at a college or university in Idaho or Utah that relates to water quality, supply, or treatment. Along with their application, they must submit a 2-page essay on their academic interests and career goals and how those relate to water quality, supply, or treatment. Selection is based on that essay, letters of recommendation, and potential to contribute to the field of water quality, supply, and treatment in the Intermountain West.
Financial data The stipend is $1,000. The winner also receives a 1-year student membership in the Intermountain Section of the American Water Works Association (AWWA) and a 1-year subscription to *Journal AWWA*.
Duration 1 year; nonrenewable.
Number awarded 1 each year.
Deadline October of each year.

[946]
INTERNATIONAL COMMUNICATIONS INDUSTRIES FOUNDATION AV SCHOLARSHIPS

InfoComm International
International Communications Industries Foundation
11242 Waples Mill Road, Suite 200
Fairfax, VA 22030
(703) 273-7200   Toll Free: (800) 659-7469
Fax: (703) 278-8082   E-mail: srieger@infocomm.org
Web: www.infocomm.org

Summary To provide financial assistance to high school seniors and college students (especially women and minorities) who are interested in preparing for a career in the audio-visual (AV) industry.
Eligibility This program is open to high school seniors, undergraduates, and graduate students already enrolled in college. Applicants must have a GPA of 2.75 or higher and be majoring or planning to major in audiovisual subjects or related fields, including audio, video, electronics, telecommunications, technical aspects of the theater, data networking, software development, or information technology. Students in other programs, such as journalism, may be eligible if they

can demonstrate a relationship to career goals in the AV industry. Along with their application, they must submit 1) an essay of 150 to 200 words on the career path they plan to pursue in the audiovisual industry in the next 5 years, and 2) an essay of 250 to 300 words on the experience or person influencing them the most in selecting the audiovisual industry as their career of choice. Minority and women candidates are especially encouraged to apply. Selection is based on the essays, presentation of the application, GPA, AV-related experience, work experience, and letters of recommendation.

Financial data The stipend is $1,200 per year. Funds are sent directly to the school.

Duration 1 year; recipients may reapply.

Additional information InfoComm International, formerly the International Communications Industries Association, established the International Communications Industries Foundation (ICIF) to manage its charitable and educational activities.

Number awarded Varies each year; recently, 29 of these scholarships were awarded.

Deadline May of each year.

[947]
IOTA SIGMA PI MEMBERS-AT-LARGE REENTRY AWARD

Iota Sigma Pi
c/o Karen Knaus, MAL National Coordinator
University of Colorado at Denver, Department of Chemistry
1201 Fifth Street
Campus Box 194
Denver, CO 80204
(303) 352-3628   E-mail: karen.knaus@ucdenver.edu
Web: www.iotasigmapi.info

Summary To provide financial assistance to women who are reentering college to work on an undergraduate or graduate degree in chemistry.

Eligibility This program is open to women who have returned to academic studies after an absence of 3 or more years and have completed at least 1 academic year of college chemistry since returning. Students must be working on an undergraduate or graduate degree in chemistry or a related field at a 4-year college or university. They must be nominated by a member of Iota Sigma Pi or by a member of the faculty at their institution. Nominees must submit a short essay describing their goals, pertinent experiences that influenced their choice of major, any interests or talents that will assist them in succeeding in their professional career, and how the scholarship will benefit them in meeting their goals. Financial need is not considered in the selection process.

Financial data The winner receives a stipend of $1,500, a certificate, and a 1-year waiver of Iota Sigma Pi dues.

Duration 1 year.

Additional information This award was first presented in 1991.

Number awarded 1 each year.

Deadline March of each year.

[948]
IRENE AND DAISY MACGREGOR MEMORIAL SCHOLARSHIP

Daughters of the American Revolution-National Society
Attn: Committee Services Office, Scholarships
1776 D Street, N.W.
Washington, DC 20006-5303
(202) 628-1776
Web: www.dar.org/natsociety/edout_scholar.cfm

Summary To provide financial assistance to graduate students (preference given to women) who are working on a degree in medicine or psychiatric nursing.

Eligibility This program is open to students who have been accepted into or are enrolled in an approved program of graduate psychiatric nursing or medicine. Applicants must be U.S. citizens and attend an accredited medical school, college, or university in the United States. They must obtain a letter of sponsorship from a local Daughters of the American Revolution (DAR) chapter. Preference is given to women applicants, provided they are "equally qualified." Selection is based on academic excellence, commitment to the field of study, and financial need.

Financial data The stipend is $5,000 per year.

Duration 1 year; may be renewed for up to 3 additional years.

Number awarded 1 or more each year.

Deadline April of each year.

[949]
IRENE DRINKALL FRANKE/MARY SEELEY KNUDSTRUP SCHOLARSHIP

Women of the Evangelical Lutheran Church in America
Attn: Scholarships
8765 West Higgins Road
Chicago, IL 60631-4101
(773) 380-2736   Toll Free: (800) 638-3522, ext. 2736
Fax: (773) 380-2419   E-mail: Women.elca@elca.org
Web: www.elca.org

Summary To provide financial assistance to lay women who are members of Evangelical Lutheran Church of America (ELCA) congregations and who wish to pursue graduate studies.

Eligibility This program is open to ELCA lay women who are at least 21 years of age and have experienced an interruption of at least 2 years in their education since high school. Applicants must have been admitted to a graduate program at an academic institution to prepare for a career of Christian service but not in the ordained ministry. U.S. citizenship is required.

Financial data The maximum stipend is $1,000.

Duration Up to 2 years.

Number awarded 1 or more each year.

Deadline February of each year.

[950]
ISAAC J. "IKE" CRUMBLY MINORITIES IN ENERGY GRANT

American Association of Petroleum Geologists
 Foundation
Attn: Grants-in-Aid Program
1444 South Boulder Avenue
P.O. Box 979
Tulsa, OK 74101-0979
(918) 560-2644   Toll Free: (888) 945-2274, ext. 644
Fax: (918) 560-2642   E-mail: tcampbell@aapg.org
Web: foundation.aapg.org/gia/crumbly.cfm

Summary To provide funding to female and minority graduate students who are interested in conducting research related to earth science aspects of the petroleum industry.

Eligibility This program is open to women and ethnic minorities (Black, Hispanic, Asian, or Native American, including American Indian, Eskimo, Hawaiian, or Samoan) who are working on a master's or doctoral degree. Applicants must be interested in conducting research related to the search for and development of petroleum and energy-minerals resources and to related environmental geology issues. Selection is based on merit and, in part, on financial need. Factors weighed in selecting the successful applicants include: the applicant's past academic performance, originality and imagination of the proposed project, departmental support, and significance of the project to petroleum, energy minerals, and related environmental geology.

Financial data Grants range from $500 to $3,000. Funds are to be applied to research-related expenses (e.g., a summer of field work). They may not be used to purchase capital equipment or to pay salaries, tuition, room, or board.

Duration 1 year. Doctoral candidates may receive a 1-year renewal.

Number awarded 1 each year.

Deadline January of each year.

[951]
ITT SCHOLARSHIPS

Society of Women Engineers
Attn: Scholarship Selection Committee
120 South LaSalle Street, Suite 1515
Chicago, IL 60603-3572
(312) 596-5223   Toll Free: (877) SWE-INFO
Fax: (312) 644-8557
E-mail: scholarshipapplication@swe.org
Web: societyofwomenengineers.swe.org

Summary To provide financial assistance to women working on an undergraduate or graduate degree in specified fields of engineering or computer science.

Eligibility This program is open to women who will be juniors, seniors, or graduate students at ABET-accredited colleges and universities. Applicants must be working on a degree in computer science or aeronautical, chemical, civil, electrical, environmental, industrial, manufacturing, or mechanical engineering and have a GPA of 3.5 or higher. Preference is given to applicants attending specified schools. Selection is based on merit.

Financial data The stipend is $2,500.

Duration 1 year.

Additional information For a list of the specified schools, contact SWE.

Number awarded 2 each year.

Deadline February of each year.

[952]
J. FRANCES ALLEN SCHOLARSHIP AWARD

American Fisheries Society
Attn: Scholarship Committee
5410 Grosvenor Lane, Suite 110
Bethesda, MD 20814-2199
(301) 897-8616   Fax: (301) 897-8096
E-mail: main@fisheries.org
Web: www.fisheries.org/afs/awards/awards_call

Summary To provide financial assistance for doctoral studies to female members of the American Fisheries Society (AFS).

Eligibility This program is open to women Ph.D. students who are AFS members. Applicants must be studying a branch of fisheries science, including but not limited to aquatic biology, engineering, fish culture, limnology, oceanography, or sociology. Selection is based on research promise, scientific merit, and academic achievement.

Financial data The stipend is $2,500, paid directly to the student. Funds may be used for any aspect of doctoral education, including tuition, textbooks, equipment, travel, or living expenses.

Duration 1 year; nonrenewable.

Additional information This program was established in 1986.

Number awarded 1 each year.

Deadline March of each year.

[953]
JANE M. KLAUSMAN WOMEN IN BUSINESS SCHOLARSHIPS

Zonta International
Attn: Foundation
1211 West 22nd Street, Suite 900
Oak Brook, IL 60523-3384
(630) 928-1400   Fax: (630) 928-1559
E-mail: programs@zonta.org
Web: www.zonta.org

Summary To provide financial assistance to women working on an undergraduate or master's degree in business at a school in any country.

Eligibility This program is open to women who are working on a business-related degree at a college or university anywhere in the world at the level of the second year of an undergraduate program through the final year of a master's degree program. Applicants first compete at the club level, and then advance to district and international levels. Along with their application, they must submit a 500-word essay that describes their academic and professional goals, the relevance of their program to the business field, and how this scholarship will assist them in reaching their goals. Selection is based on that essay, academic record, demonstrated intent to complete a program in business, achievement in business-related subjects, and 2 letters of recommendation.

Financial data District winners receive a $1,000 scholarship; the international winners receive a $5,000 scholarship.

Duration 1 year.

Additional information This program was established in 1998.

Number awarded The number of district winners varies each year; recently, 12 international winners (including 6 from the United States) were selected. Since this program was established, it has awarded nearly 200 of these scholarships to women from 34 countries.

Deadline Clubs set their own deadlines but must submit their winners to the district governor by May of each year.

[954]
JANE WALKER SCHOLARSHIP

United Methodist Church-Alabama-West Florida
  Conference
Attn: Commission on the Status and Role of Women
100 Interstate Park Drive, Suite 120
Montgomery, AL 36109
(334) 356-8014   Toll Free: (888) 873-3127
Fax: (334) 356-8029   E-mail: awfcrc@awfumc.org
Web: www.awfumc.org

Summary To provide financial assistance to female residents of the Alabama-West Florida Conference of the United Methodist Church (UMC) who are undergraduate or seminary students preparing for a church-related career.

Eligibility This program is open to women who are residents of the Alabama-West Florida Conference of the UMW and who affirm, represent, and advocate women's leadership in the church. Applicants must be accepted or enrolled at an approved UMC seminary or working on an undergraduate degree in Christian education at an approved UMC institution in any state. They must be a candidate for ministry or preparing for a UMC church-related career. Along with their application, they must submit a 500-word essay on why they are preparing for full-time Christian ministry and how they can promote the cause of women through this ministry. Financial need is considered in the selection process.

Financial data The stipend is $1,000.

Duration 1 year.

Number awarded 1 each year.

Deadline May of each year.

[955]
JANICE E. ARNETT CONTINUING EDUCATION SCHOLARSHIP

Kappa Delta Sorority
Attn: Foundation Manager
3205 Players Lane
Memphis, TN 38125
(901) 748-1897   Toll Free: (800) 536-1897
Fax: (901) 748-0949 E-mail: kappadelta@kappadelta.org
Web: www.kappadelta.org/scholarships

Summary To provide financial assistance to members of Kappa Delta Sorority who are interested in returning to school to continue their education at the graduate level.

Eligibility This program is open to graduate members of Kappa Delta Sorority who have been out of school for at least 5 years and are returning to further their education at the graduate level. Applicants must submit a personal statement giving their reasons for applying for this scholarship, official undergraduate and graduate transcripts, and 2 letters of rec-

ommendation. Selection is based on academic excellence; service to the chapter, alumnae association, or national Kappa Delta; service to the campus and community; personal objectives and goals; potential; recommendations; and financial need.

Financial data The stipend is $2,000 per year. Funds may be used only for tuition, fees, and books, not for room and board.

Duration 1 year; may be renewed.

Additional information This program was established in 2009.

Number awarded 1 each year.

Deadline January of each year.

[956]
JANICE E. ARNETT SCHOLARSHIP FOR LEADERSHIP AND VOLUNTEERISM

Kappa Delta Sorority
Attn: Foundation Manager
3205 Players Lane
Memphis, TN 38125
(901) 748-1897   Toll Free: (800) 536-1897
Fax: (901) 748-0949 E-mail: kappadelta@kappadelta.org
Web: www.kappadelta.org/scholarships

Summary To provide financial assistance to members of Kappa Delta Sorority who are interested in continuing their education at the graduate level and have an outstanding record of leadership and volunteerism.

Eligibility This program is open to graduate members of Kappa Delta Sorority. Applicants must submit a personal statement giving their reasons for applying for this scholarship, official undergraduate and graduate transcripts, and 2 letters of recommendation. Selection is based primarily on community leadership and volunteerism, although academic excellence, service to the sorority, service to the campus and community, personal objectives and goals, potential, recommendations, and financial need.

Financial data The stipend is $1,500 per year. Funds may be used only for tuition, fees, and books, not for room and board.

Duration 1 year; may be renewed.

Additional information This program was established in 2009.

Number awarded 1 each year.

Deadline January of each year.

[957]
JAZZ PERFORMANCE AWARDS

Sigma Alpha Iota Philanthropies, Inc.
One Tunnel Road
Asheville, NC 28805
(828) 251-0606   Fax: (828) 251-0644
E-mail: nh@sai-national.org
Web: www.sigmaalphaiota.org

Summary To provide financial assistance to members of Sigma Alpha Iota (an organization of women musicians) who are interested in working on an undergraduate or graduate degree in jazz performance.

Eligibility This program is open to members of the organization who are enrolled in an undergraduate or graduate degree program in jazz performance or studies. Applicants must be younger than 32 years of age. Along with their application, they must submit a CD recording of a performance "set" of 30 to 45 minutes.

Financial data Stipends are $2,000 for the winner or $1,500 for the runner-up.

Duration 1 year.

Additional information These awards were first presented in 2006.

Number awarded 2 every 3 years.

Deadline March of the year of the awards (2012, 2015, etc.).

[958]
JEANNE ROSS MILLER SCHOLARSHIP

Kappa Alpha Theta Foundation
Attn: Scholarships
8740 Founders Road
Indianapolis, IN 46268-1337
(317) 876-1870   Toll Free: (800) KAO-1870
Fax: (317) 876-1925
E-mail: FDNmail@kappaalphatheta.org
Web: www.kappaalphathetafoundation.org

Summary To provide financial assistance to alumnae members of Kappa Alpha Theta who are enrolled in medical school.

Eligibility This program is open to members of Kappa Alpha Theta who are currently enrolled full time at a medical school in Canada or the United States. Along with their application, they must submit an official transcript, personal essays on assigned topics related to their involvement in Kappa Alpha Theta, and 2 letters of reference. Financial need is not considered in the selection process.

Financial data The stipend is $3,625.

Duration 1 year.

Number awarded 1 each year.

Deadline January of each year.

[959]
JESSIE FANYO PAYNE SCHOLARSHIP

Alpha Chi Omega Foundation
Attn: Foundation Programs Coordinator
5939 Castle Creek Parkway North Drive
Indianapolis, IN 46250-4343
(317) 579-5050, ext. 262   Fax: (317) 579-5051
E-mail: foundation@alphachiomega.org
Web: www.alphachiomega.org/index.aspx?id=1030

Summary To provide financial assistance to undergraduate or alumnae members of Alpha Chi Omega who are interested in working on a degree in communications.

Eligibility This program is open to junior, senior, and graduate members of Alpha Chi Omega who are full-time students in the field of communications with an emphasis on journalism and public relations. Selection is based on academic achievement, chapter involvement, campus and community involvement, and financial need.

Financial data A stipend is awarded (amount not specified).

Duration 1 year.

Number awarded 1 each year.

Deadline March of each year.

[960]
JILL S. TIETJEN P.E. SCHOLARSHIP

Society of Women Engineers
Attn: Scholarship Selection Committee
120 South LaSalle Street, Suite 1515
Chicago, IL 60603-3572
(312) 596-5223   Toll Free: (877) SWE-INFO
Fax: (312) 644-8557
E-mail: scholarshipapplication@swe.org
Web: societyofwomenengineers.swe.org

Summary To provide financial assistance to women working on an undergraduate or graduate degree in engineering or computer science.

Eligibility This program is open to women who will be sophomores, juniors, seniors, or graduate students at ABET-accredited colleges and universities. Applicants must be U.S. citizens majoring in computer science or engineering and have a GPA of 3.0 or higher. Selection is based on merit.

Financial data The stipend is $1,500.

Duration 1 year.

Number awarded 1 each year.

Deadline February of each year.

[961]
JIM MCKAY SCHOLARSHIP PROGRAM

National Collegiate Athletic Association
Attn: Jim McKay Scholarship Program Staff Liaison
1802 Alonzo Watford Sr. Drive
P.O. Box 6222
Indianapolis, IN 46206-6222
(317) 917-6222   Fax: (317) 917-6888
E-mail: lthomas@ncaa.org
Web: www.ncaa.org

Summary To provide financial assistance to student-athletes who are interested in attending graduate school to prepare for a career in sports communications (females and males are judged separately).

Eligibility This program is open to college seniors planning to enroll full time in a graduate degree program and to students already enrolled full time in graduate study at an institution that is a member of the National Collegiate Athletic Association (NCAA). Applicants must have competed in intercollegiate athletics as a member of a varsity team at an NCAA member institution and have an overall undergraduate cumulative GPA of 3.5 or higher. They must be preparing for a career in the sports communications industry. Women and minorities are especially encouraged to apply. Neither financial need nor U.S. citizenship are required. Nominations must be submitted by the faculty athletics representative or chief academic officer at the institution in which the student is or was an undergraduate.

Financial data The stipend is $10,000.

Duration 1 year; nonrenewable.

Additional information This program was established in 2008.

Number awarded 2 each year: 1 female and 1 male.

Deadline January of each year.

[962]
JOHN AND MURIEL LANDIS SCHOLARSHIPS

American Nuclear Society
Attn: Scholarship Coordinator
555 North Kensington Avenue
La Grange Park, IL 60526-5592
(708) 352-6611   Toll Free: (800) 323-3044
Fax: (708) 352-0499   E-mail: outreach@ans.org
Web: www.ans.org/honors/scholarships

Summary To provide financial assistance to undergraduate or graduate students (especially women and minorities) who are interested in preparing for a career in nuclear-related fields.

Eligibility This program is open to undergraduate and graduate students at colleges or universities located in the United States who are preparing for, or planning to prepare for, a career in nuclear science, nuclear engineering, or a nuclear-related field. Qualified high school seniors are also eligible. Applicants must have greater than average financial need and have experienced circumstances that render them disadvantaged. They must be sponsored by an organization (e.g., plant branch, local section, student section) within the American Nuclear Society (ANS). Along with their application, they must submit an essay on their academic and professional goals, experiences that have affected those goals, etc. Selection is based on that essay, academic achievement, letters of recommendation, and financial need. Women and members of minority groups are especially urged to apply. U.S. citizenship is not required.

Financial data The stipend is $5,000, to be used to cover tuition, books, fees, room, and board.

Duration 1 year; nonrenewable.

Number awarded Up to 8 each year.

Deadline January of each year.

[963]
JOHN RAINER GRADUATE FELLOWSHIP

American Indian Graduate Center
Attn: Executive Director
4520 Montgomery Boulevard, N.E., Suite 1-B
Albuquerque, NM 87109-1291
(505) 881-4584   Toll Free: (800) 628-1920
Fax: (505) 884-0427   E-mail: aigc@aigc.com
Web: www.aigc.com/02scholarships/rainer.htm

Summary To provide financial assistance to female and male Native American students (judged separately) who are interested in working on a graduate degree in any field.

Eligibility This program is open to enrolled members of federally-recognized American Indian tribes and Alaska Native groups and students who can document one-fourth degree federally-recognized Indian blood. Applicants must be enrolled full time at a graduate school in the United States. Along with their application, they must submit a 500-word essay on their extracurricular activities as they relate to American Indian programs at their institution, volunteer and community work as related to American Indian communities, tribal and community involvement, and plans to make positive changes in the American Indian community with their college education. Financial need is also considered in the selection process. Males and females are considered separately.

Financial data The stipend is $1,000, of which $500 may be applied to the cost of education and $500 must be used to support participation in volunteer activities that afford an opportunity to develop leadership skills.

Duration 1 year; nonrenewable.

Additional information The application fee is $15. Since this a supplemental program, students must apply in a timely manner for federal financial aid and campus-based aid at the college they are attending to be considered for this program. Failure to apply will disqualify an applicant.

Number awarded 2 each year: 1 to a male and 1 to a female.

Deadline May of each year.

[964]
JOSEPH B. GITTLER AWARD

American Psychological Foundation
750 First Street, N.E.
Washington, DC 20002-4242
(202) 336-5843   Fax: (202) 336-5812
E-mail: foundation@apa.org
Web: www.apa.org/apf/funding/gittler.aspx

Summary To recognize and reward scholars and graduate students in psychology (particularly women and members of other diverse groups) who have made outstanding contributions to the philosophical foundations of the discipline.

Eligibility This award is available to scholars and graduate students whose body of work or whose individual work has transformed the philosophical foundations of psychological knowledge. Self-nominations are welcome. Selection is based on conformance with stated program goals and magnitude of contributions The sponsor encourages nominations of individuals who represent diversity in race, ethnicity, gender, age, disability, and sexual orientation.

Financial data The award is $10,000.

Duration The award is presented annually.

Additional information This award was first presented in 2008.

Number awarded 1 each year.

Deadline Nominations must be submitted by May of each year.

[965]
JOSEPH L. FISHER DOCTORAL DISSERTATION FELLOWSHIPS

Resources for the Future
Attn: Coordinator for Academic Programs
1616 P Street, N.W., Suite 600
Washington, DC 20036-1400
(202) 328-5008   Fax: (202) 939-3460
E-mail: fisher-award@rff.org
Web: www.rff.org/About_RFF/Pages/default.aspx

Summary To provide funding to women, minority, and other doctoral candidates in economics who are interested in conducting dissertation research on issues related to the environment, natural resources, or energy.

Eligibility This program is open to graduate students in their final year of research on a dissertation related to the environment, natural resources, or energy. Applicants must submit a brief letter of application and a curriculum vitae, a graduate transcript, a 1-page abstract of the dissertation, a technical summary of the dissertation (up to 2,500 words), a letter from the student's department chair, and 2 letters of recommendation from faculty members on the student's dissertation committee. The technical summary should describe clearly the aim of the dissertation, its significance in relation to the existing literature, and the research methods to be used. Women and minority candidates are strongly encouraged to apply.

Financial data The stipend is $18,000.

Duration 1 academic year.

Additional information It is expected that recipients will not hold other employment during the fellowship period. Recipients must notify Resources for the Future of any financial assistance they receive from any other source for support of doctoral work.

Number awarded 2 or 3 each year.

Deadline February of each year.

[966]
JOSEPHINE AND BENJAMIN WEBBER TRUST SCHOLARSHIPS

Arizona Association of Family and Consumer Sciences
Attn: Webber Educational Grant Committee
Kathryn L. Hatch
4843 North Via Sonrisa
Tucson, AZ 85718-5724
(502) 577-6109   E-mail: klhatch@u.arizona.edu
Web: ag.arizona.edu/webbertrusts

Summary To provide financial assistance to Hispanic women from mining towns in Arizona who are interested in working on an undergraduate or graduate degree in a field related to family and consumer sciences at a school in the state.

Eligibility This program is open to Hispanic women who reside in the following Arizona mining towns: Ajo, Arizona City, Bisbee, Clifton, Douglas, Duncan, Globe, Green Valley, Hayden, Kingman, Kearny, Mammoth, Morenci, Prescott, Safford, Sahuarita, San Manuel, Seligman, Superior, or Winkelman. If too few female Hispanic residents of those towns apply, the program may be open to 1) non-Hispanic women who live in those towns, and/or 2) Hispanic women who currently live elsewhere in Arizona and whose parents or grandparents had lived or continue to live in those communities. Applicants must be enrolled or planning to enroll at a college or university in Arizona to work on an undergraduate or graduate degree. Eligible fields of study include those in the following categories: foods, nutrition, and/or dietetics; restaurant and food service management; culinary arts; family studies; interior design; family and consumer science education; dietetic education; early childhood education; or apparel and clothing. Along with their application, they must submit a 4-page essay that includes information on 1) why they have chosen to work on a degree in family and consumer sciences; 2) what they think will be the major obstacles to the successful completion of their first year as a Webber scholar; and 3) what they think their personal and professional life will be like following completion of their postsecondary education. Financial need is also considered in the selection process.

Financial data Funding at public colleges and universities provides for payment of tuition and fees, books, educational supplies, housing, food, and transportation to and from cam-

pus. At private institutions, stipend amounts are equivalent to those at public schools.

Duration 1 year; may be renewed for a total of 8 semesters and 2 summers of undergraduate study or 4 semesters and 2 summers of graduate study.

Additional information This program was established in 1980.

Number awarded Varies each year; recently, 5 of these scholarships were awarded.

Deadline March of each year.

[967]
JOSEPHINE CARROLL NORWOOD MEMORIAL SCHOLARSHIPS

Baptist Convention of Maryland/Delaware
Attn: United Baptist Women of Maryland, Inc.
10255 Old Columbia Road
Columbia, MD 21046
(410) 290-5290   Toll Free: (800) 466-5290
E-mail: gparker@bcmd.org
Web: bcmd.org/wmu

Summary To provide financial assistance to women who are members of Baptist churches associated with an affiliate of United Baptist Women of Maryland and interested in attending seminary or graduate school in any state to prepare for a Christian vocation.

Eligibility This program is open to women who are enrolled or planning to enroll full time at a seminary or graduate school in any state to prepare for a Christian vocation. Applicants must be a member in good standing of a Baptist church associated with an affiliate of United Baptist Women of Maryland. They must have a grade average of "C" or higher and be able to demonstrate financial need. Along with their application, they must submit brief statements on their Christian experience, school activities, church and community activities, and career goals.

Financial data A stipend is awarded (amount not specified).

Duration 1 year.

Number awarded Varies each year.

Deadline June of each year.

[968]
JUDITH MCMANUS PRICE SCHOLARSHIPS

American Planning Association
Attn: Leadership Affairs Associate
205 North Michigan Avenue, Suite 1200
Chicago, IL 60601
(312) 431-9100   Fax: (312) 786-6700
E-mail: fellowship@planning.org
Web: www.planning.org/scholarships/apa

Summary To provide financial assistance to women and underrepresented minority students enrolled in undergraduate or graduate degree programs at recognized planning schools.

Eligibility This program is open to undergraduate and graduate students in urban and regional planning who are women or members of the following minority groups: African American, Hispanic American, or Native American. Applicants must be citizens of the United States and able to document financial need. They must intend to work as practicing planners in the public sector. Along with their application, they must submit a 2-page personal and background statement describing how their education will be applied to career goals and why they chose planning as a career path. Selection is based (in order of importance), on: 1) commitment to planning as reflected in their personal statement and on their resume; 2) academic achievement and/or improvement during the past 2 years; 3) letters of recommendation; 4) financial need; and 5) professional presentation.

Financial data Stipends range from $2,000 to $4,000 per year. The money may be applied to tuition and living expenses only. Payment is made to the recipient's university and divided by terms in the school year.

Duration 1 year; recipients may reapply.

Additional information This program was established in 2002.

Number awarded Varies each year; recently, 3 of these scholarships were awarded.

Deadline April of each year.

[969]
JUDY CORMAN MEMORIAL SCHOLARSHIP AND INTERNSHIP

New York Women in Communications, Inc.
Attn: NYWICI Foundation
355 Lexington Avenue, 15th Floor
New York, NY 10017-6603
(212) 297-2133   Fax: (212) 370-9047
E-mail: nywicipr@nywici.org
Web: www.nywici.org/foundation/scholarships

Summary To provide financial assistance and work experience to female residents of designated eastern states who are interested in preparing for a career in public relations at a college or graduate school in any state.

Eligibility This program is open to women who are seniors graduating from high schools in New York, New Jersey, Connecticut, or Pennsylvania or undergraduate or graduate students who are permanent residents of those states; they must be attending or planning to attend a college or university in any state. Graduate students must be members of New York Women in Communications, Inc. (NYWICI). Also eligible are women who reside outside the 4 states but are currently enrolled at a college or university within 1 of the 5 boroughs of New York City. Applicants must be preparing for a career in public relations and be interested in a summer internship with Scholastic. They must have a GPA of 3.2 or higher. Along with their application, they must submit a 2-page resume that includes school and extracurricular activities, significant achievements, academic honors and awards, and community service work; a personal essay of 300 to 500 words on their choice of an assigned topic that changes annually; 2 letters of recommendation; and an official transcript. Selection is based on academic record, need, demonstrated leadership, participation in school and community activities, honors, work experience, goals and aspirations, and unusual personal and/or family circumstances. U.S. citizenship is required.

Financial data The scholarship stipend ranges up to $10,000; the internship is salaried (amount not specified).

Duration 1 year.

Additional information This program is sponsored by Scholastic, Inc.

Number awarded 1 each year.
Deadline January of each year.

[970]
JULIA BUMRY JONES SCHOLARSHIP PROGRAM

Delta Sigma Theta Sorority, Inc.
Attn: Scholarship and Standards Committee Chair
1707 New Hampshire Avenue, N.W.
Washington, DC 20009
(202) 986-2400   Fax: (202) 986-2513
E-mail: dstemail@deltasigmatheta.org
Web: www.deltasigmatheta.org

Summary To provide financial assistance to members of Delta Sigma Theta who are interested in working on a graduate degree in journalism or another area of communications.

Eligibility This program is open to graduating college seniors and graduate students who are interested in preparing for a career in journalism or another area of communications. Applicants must be active, dues-paying members of Delta Sigma Theta. Selection is based on meritorious achievement.

Financial data The stipends range from $1,000 to $2,000. The funds may be used to cover tuition, fees, and living expenses.

Duration 1 year; may be renewed for 1 additional year.

Additional information This sponsor is a traditionally-African American social sorority. The application fee is $20.

Deadline April of each year.

[971]
JULIETTE DERRICOTTE SCHOLARSHIP

Delta Sigma Theta Sorority, Inc.
Attn: Scholarship and Standards Committee Chair
1707 New Hampshire Avenue, N.W.
Washington, DC 20009
(202) 986-2400   Fax: (202) 986-2513
E-mail: dstemail@deltasigmatheta.org
Web: www.deltasigmatheta.org

Summary To provide financial assistance to members of Delta Sigma Theta who are interested in preparing for a career in social work.

Eligibility This program is open to graduating college seniors or graduate students who are interested in preparing for a career in social work. Applicants must be active, dues-paying members of Delta Sigma Theta. Selection is based on meritorious achievement.

Financial data The stipends range from $1,000 to $2,000 per year. The funds may be used to cover tuition, school, and living expenses.

Duration 1 year; may be renewed for 1 additional year.

Additional information This sponsor is a traditionally-African American social sorority. The application fee is $20.

Deadline April of each year.

[972]
JUSTICE JANIE L. SHORES SCHOLARSHIP
Alabama Law Foundation
415 Dexter Avenue
P.O. Box 671
Montgomery, AL 36101
(334) 269-1515   Fax: (334) 261-6310
E-mail: info@alfinc.org
Web: www.alfinc.org/janieShores.cfm

Summary To provide financial assistance to female residents of Alabama who are attending law school in the state.

Eligibility This program is open to female residents of Alabama who are enrolled at a law school in the state. Applicants must submit documentation of financial need and an essay on their career plans.

Financial data A stipend is awarded (amount not specified).

Duration 1 year.

Additional information This program was established in 2006.

Number awarded 1 or more each year.

Deadline March of each year.

[973]
KAILASH, MONA, AND ANILA JAIN SCHOLARSHIP
Kappa Delta Sorority
Attn: Foundation Manager
3205 Players Lane
Memphis, TN 38125
(901) 748-1897   Toll Free: (800) 536-1897
Fax: (901) 748-0949 E-mail: kappadelta@kappadelta.org
Web: www.kappadelta.org/scholarships

Summary To provide financial assistance to members of Kappa Delta Sorority who are working on a graduate degree in health care.

Eligibility This program is open to graduate members of Kappa Delta Sorority. Applicants must submit a personal statement giving their reasons for applying for this scholarship, official undergraduate and graduate transcripts, and 2 letters of recommendation. They must be working on a graduate degree in a field related to health care. Selection is based on academic excellence; service to the chapter, alumnae association, or national Kappa Delta; service to the campus and community; personal objectives and goals; potential; recommendations; and financial need.

Financial data The stipend is $2,000 per year. Funds may be used only for tuition, fees, and books, not for room and board.

Duration 1 year; may be renewed.

Additional information This program was established in 2001.

Number awarded 1 each year.

Deadline January of each year.

[974]
KAPPA ALPHA THETA ALUMNAE SCHOLARSHIPS
Kappa Alpha Theta Foundation
Attn: Scholarships
8740 Founders Road
Indianapolis, IN 46268-1337
(317) 876-1870   Toll Free: (800) KAO-1870
Fax: (317) 876-1925
E-mail: FDNmail@kappaalphatheta.org
Web: www.kappaalphathetafoundation.org

Summary To provide financial assistance to members of Kappa Alpha Theta (the first Greek letter fraternity for women) who are working on advanced degrees in North America or abroad.

Eligibility This program is open to members of Kappa Alpha Theta who are enrolled as graduate students at a university in Canada or the United States. Along with their application, they must submit an official transcript, personal essays on assigned topics related to their involvement in Kappa Alpha Theta, and 2 letters of reference. Financial need is not considered in the selection process.

Financial data Stipends range from $1,000 to $10,000. Recently, the average was $4,760.

Duration 1 year. Recipients may reapply, but they may not receive a maximum lifetime amount of more than $20,000 from the foundation.

Additional information Recipients may study abroad, provided they do so as part of a program leading to a degree from an institution in the United States or Canada.

Number awarded Varies each year; recently, the organization awarded more than 200 undergraduate and graduate scholarships, with a total value of more than $500,000.

Deadline January of each year.

[975]
KAPPA DELTA SORORITY GRADUATE SCHOLARSHIPS
Kappa Delta Sorority
Attn: Foundation Manager
3205 Players Lane
Memphis, TN 38125
(901) 748-1897   Toll Free: (800) 536-1897
Fax: (901) 748-0949 E-mail: kappadelta@kappadelta.org
Web: www.kappadelta.org/scholarships

Summary To provide financial assistance to members of Kappa Delta Sorority who are interested in continuing their education at the graduate level.

Eligibility This program is open to graduate members of Kappa Delta Sorority. Applicants must submit a personal statement giving their reasons for applying for this scholarship, official undergraduate and graduate transcripts, and 2 letters of recommendation. Most scholarships are available to all graduate members, but some have additional restrictions. Selection is based on academic excellence; service to the chapter, alumnae association, or national Kappa Delta; service to the campus and community; personal objectives and goals; potential; recommendations; and financial need.

Financial data Stipends range from $1,000 to $5,000 per year. Funds may be used only for tuition, fees, and books, not for room and board.

Duration 1 year; may be renewed.

Additional information This program includes the following named scholarships that have no additional restrictions: the Dorothea B. Cavin Scholarship, the Helen A. Snyder Scholarship, the Minnie Mae Prescott Scholarship, the Muriel Johnstone Scholarship, the Herff Jones Graduate Fellowship, the Janice E. Arnett Graduate Scholarship and the Alumna Grant for Continuing Education.

Number awarded Varies each year; recently, the sorority awarded a total of 23 graduate scholarships: 1 at $5,000, 7 at $2,000, 1 at $1,500, and 14 at $1,000.

Deadline January of each year.

[976]
KAPPA KAPPA GAMMA GRADUATE FELLOWSHIP AWARDS

Kappa Kappa Gamma Fraternity
Attn: Foundation Administrator
530 East Town Street
P.O. Box 38
Columbus, OH 43216-0038
(614) 228-6515   Toll Free: (866) KKG-1870
Fax: (614) 228-7809   E-mail: kkghq@kappa.org
Web: www.kappakappagamma.org

Summary To provide financial assistance for graduate school to members of Kappa Kappa Gamma.

Eligibility This program is open to members of Kappa Kappa Gamma who are full-time graduate students with a GPA of 3.0 or higher. Applicants must be initiated members who were in good standing as undergraduates. Along with their application, they must submit a personal essay or letter describing their educational and career goals and financial need. Selection is based on merit, academic achievement, participation in sorority activities, and financial need.

Financial data A stipend is awarded (amount not specified).

Duration 1 year; nonrenewable.

Number awarded Varies each year; recently, the foundation awarded a total of 152 undergraduate and graduate scholarships with a value of $466,812.

Deadline January of each year.

[977]
KATE GLEASON SCHOLARSHIP

ASME International
Attn: Centers Administrator
Three Park Avenue, 22nd Floor
New York, NY 10016-5990
(212) 591-8131   Toll Free: (800) THE-ASME
Fax: (212) 591-7143   E-mail: LefeverB@asme.org
Web: www.asme.org

Summary To provide financial assistance to female undergraduate and graduate students from any country who are working on a degree in mechanical engineering.

Eligibility This program is open to women who are enrolled in an ABET-accredited or equivalent mechanical engineering, mechanical engineering technology, or related undergraduate or graduate program. Applicants must submit a nomination from their department head, a recommendation from a faculty member, and an official transcript. Only 1 nomination may be submitted per department. There are no citi-

zenship requirements, but study must be conducted in the United States. Selection is based on academic ability and potential contribution to the mechanical engineering profession.

Financial data The stipend is $3,000.

Duration 1 year.

Number awarded 1 each year.

Deadline February of each year.

[978]
KATHARINE C. BRYAN GRADUATE SCHOLARSHIP

Tennessee Baptist Convention
Attn: WMU Scholarships
5001 Maryland Way
P.O. Box 728
Brentwood, TN 37024-9728
(615) 373-2255   Toll Free: (800) 558-2090, ext. 2038
Fax: (615) 371-2014   E-mail: jferguson@tnbaptist.org
Web: www.tnbaptist.org/page.asp?page=92

Summary To provide financial assistance to female members of Baptist churches in Tennessee who are interested in attending graduate school in any state.

Eligibility This program is open to women who are members of Tennessee Baptist churches or have Tennessee Baptist ties. Applicants must be active in missions and ministries of their local church. They must be enrolled in full-time graduate study and have a GPA of 2.6 or higher.

Financial data A stipend is awarded (amount not specified).

Duration 1 year; may be renewed if the recipient maintains a GPA of 3.5 or higher.

Number awarded 1 or more each year.

Deadline January of each year.

[979]
KATHERINE J. SCHUTZE MEMORIAL SCHOLARSHIP

Christian Church (Disciples of Christ)
Attn: Disciples Home Missions
130 East Washington Street
P.O. Box 1986
Indianapolis, IN 46206-1986
(317) 713-2652   Toll Free: (888) DHM-2631
Fax: (317) 635-4426   E-mail: mail@dhm.disciples.org
Web: www.discipleshomemissions.org

Summary To provide financial assistance to female seminary students affiliated with the Christian Church (Disciples of Christ).

Eligibility This program is open to female seminary students who are members of a Christian Church (Disciples of Christ) congregation in the United States or Canada. Applicants must plan to prepare for the ordained ministry, be working on an M.Div. or equivalent degree, provide evidence of financial need, be enrolled full time in an accredited school or seminary, provide a transcript of academic work, and be under the care of a regional Commission on the Ministry or in the process of coming under care.

Financial data A stipend is awarded (amount not specified).

Duration 1 year; recipients may reapply.

Number awarded 1 or more each year.

Deadline March of each year.

[980]
KATHERN F. GRUBER SCHOLARSHIPS

Blinded Veterans Association
477 H Street, N.W.
Washington, DC 20001-2694
(202) 371-8880 Toll Free: (800) 669-7079
Fax: (202) 371-8258 E-mail: bva@bva.org
Web: www.bva.org/services.html

Summary To provide financial assistance for undergraduate or graduate study to spouses and children of blinded veterans.

Eligibility This program is open to dependent children and spouses of blinded veterans of the U.S. armed forces. The veteran need not be a member of the Blinded Veterans Association. The veteran's blindness may be either service connected or nonservice connected, but it must meet the following definition: central visual acuity of 20/200 or less in the better eye with corrective glasses, or central visual acuity of more than 20/200 if there is a field defect in which the peripheral field has contracted to such an extent that the widest diameter of visual field subtends an angular distance no greater than 20 degrees in the better eye. Applicants must have been accepted or be currently enrolled as a full-time student in an undergraduate or graduate program at an accredited institution of higher learning. Along with their application, they must submit a 300-word essay on their career goals and aspirations. Financial need is not considered in the selection process.

Financial data The stipend is $2,000; funds are intended to be used to cover the student's expenses, including tuition, other academic fees, books, dormitory fees, and cafeteria fees. Funds are paid directly to the recipient's school.

Duration 1 year; recipients may reapply.

Additional information Scholarships may be used for only 1 degree (vocational, bachelor's, or graduate) or non-graduate certificate (e.g., nursing, secretarial).

Number awarded 6 each year.

Deadline April of each year.

[981]
KATHY LOUDAT MUSIC SCHOLARSHIP

New Mexico Baptist Foundation
5325 Wyoming Boulevard, N.E.
P.O. Box 16560
Albuquerque, NM 87191-6560
(505) 332-3777 Toll Free: (877) 841-3777
Fax: (505) 332-2777 E-mail: foundation@nmbf.com
Web: www.bcnm.com

Summary To provide financial assistance to female members of Southern Baptist churches in New Mexico who are attending college in any state to prepare for a career in church music.

Eligibility This program is open to full-time female college, university, and seminary students who are preparing for a career in church music. Applicants must have a GPA of 3.0 or higher and be able to demonstrate financial need. They must be members of Southern Baptist churches in New Mexico or

former members in good standing with the Southern Baptist Convention.

Financial data A stipend is awarded (amount not specified).

Duration 1 year.

Number awarded 1 or more each year.

Deadline April of each year.

[982]
KENNEDY CENTER INTERNSHIP

Sigma Alpha Iota Philanthropies, Inc.
One Tunnel Road
Asheville, NC 28805
(828) 251-0606 Fax: (828) 251-0644
E-mail: nh@sai-national.org
Web: www.sigmaalphaiota.org

Summary To provide summer internships at the Kennedy Center to members of Sigma Alpha Iota (an organization of women musicians).

Eligibility This program is open to student members of the organization who are interested in a summer internship at the Institute for Arts Management at the John F. Kennedy Center for the Performing Arts in Washington, D.C. Applicants must be juniors, seniors, graduate students, or graduates out of school for less than 2 years.

Financial data The stipend is $800 per month.

Duration 3 months during the summer.

Additional information Assignments are full time, with possible college credit available.

Number awarded 1 or more each year.

Deadline January of each year.

[983]
KITTY STONE GRADUATE SCHOLARSHIP

Alabama Federation of Women's Clubs
Attn: Scholarship Chair
2728 Niazuma Avenue
Birmingham, AL 35205
(205) 323-2392 Fax: (205) 323-8443
Web: www.gfwc-alabama.org/Scholarships.html

Summary To provide financial assistance to women who are residents of Alabama and interested in working on a graduate degree at a public university in the state.

Eligibility This program is open to female residents of Alabama who are attending or planning to attend a public university in the state. Applicants must be interested in working on a graduate degree in any field. Along with their application, they must submit a personal letter on their educational goals, 3 letters of recommendation, and transcripts. Financial need is not considered in the selection process.

Financial data The stipend is $1,500.

Duration 1 year.

Number awarded 1 each year.

Deadline Deadline not specified.

[984]
LAURELS FUND SCHOLARSHIPS
Educational Foundation for Women in Accounting
Attn: Foundation Administrator
136 South Keowee Street
Dayton, OH 45402
(937) 424-3391   Fax: (937) 222-5749
E-mail: info@efwa.org
Web: www.efwa.org/scholarships_laurels_fund.php

Summary To provide financial support to women working on a doctoral degree in accounting.

Eligibility This program is open to women who are working on a Ph.D. degree in accounting and have completed their comprehensive examinations. Applicants must submit a statement of personal and career goals and objectives. Selection is based on 1) scholarship, including academic achievements in course work and research activities; 2) service, including volunteer work to which the applicant has made significant or long-term commitments; and 3) financial need. U.S. citizenship is required.

Financial data The stipend ranges from $1,000 to $5,000.

Duration 1 year; nonrenewable.

Additional information This program was established in 1978.

Number awarded Varies each year.

Deadline May of each year.

[985]
LEAH J. DICKSTEIN, M.D. AWARD
Association of Women Psychiatrists
Attn: Executive Director
P.O. Box 570218
Dallas, TX 75357-0218
(972) 613-0985   E-mail: womenpsych@aol.com
Web: www.womenpsych.org/Dickstein/default.html

Summary To recognize and reward outstanding female medical students.

Eligibility This award is available to female medical students who demonstrate superior academic achievement, creativity, and leadership. Activities that may be recognized include service or clinical aspects of medicine, science research, or excellence in art, music, or literature.

Financial data The award consists of $1,000 and a plaque.

Duration The award is presented annually.

Additional information The awardee is invited to join the award committee for the following year.

Number awarded 1 each year.

Deadline March of each year.

[986]
LEGISLATIVE POLICY INTERNSHIPS AT LEGAL MOMENTUM
Legal Momentum
Attn: Legal Department
1101 14th Street, N.W., Suite 300
Washington, DC 20005
(202) 326-0040   Fax: (202) 589-0511
E-mail: dcinternships@legalmomentum.org
Web: www.legalmomentum.org

Summary To provide work experience to students and recent graduates (particularly women) who are interested in working on legislative policy issues at Legal Momentum in Washington, D.C.

Eligibility The internship is open to undergraduates, graduate students, and recent graduates interested in working on legislative policy issues at Legal Momentum. Issues covered include poverty and welfare reform, immigrant women (including immigration law reform and cultural diversity issues), violence against women, and child care. Applicants must be interested in working on a range of tasks, including researching and analyzing legislation; drafting letters, fact sheets, and articles; attending briefings and coalition meetings; answering requests for technical assistance; assisting with administrative tasks as needed; and coordinating the work of coalitions dealing with issues of concern to the office. They should have a strong interest in women's legal rights. A love of feminist issues, politics, and hard work is useful and a working knowledge of the American political process is recommended. Women and men of all ethnic, cultural, economic, and sexual orientations who support feminist concerns are eligible. Bilingual individuals are especially encouraged to apply.

Financial data These are paid internships (stipend not specified).

Duration Interns are encouraged to work from 15 to 35 hours per week for 10 to 12 weeks. Positions are available in the fall, spring, or summer.

Additional information Legal Momentum was formerly known as the NOW Legal Defense and Education Fund.

Number awarded Varies each year.

Deadline Applications may be submitted at any time.

[987]
LESLIE S. PARKER MEMORIAL SCHOLARSHIP
Order of the Eastern Star-Grand Chapter of Oregon
c/o Candice Hampton, Scholarship Committee Chair
P.O. Box 66
Lyons, OR 97358
Web: www.oregonoes.org/scholarships/index.html

Summary To provide financial assistance to women who are residents of Oregon and attending college or graduate school in the state.

Eligibility This program is open to female residents of Oregon who have completed at least 2 years of undergraduate or graduate study at an accredited non-sectarian college or university in the state. Applicants must be able to demonstrate financial need.

Financial data Stipends are approximately $1,000. Funds are sent directly to the recipient's college or university to be used for books, tuition, room and board, clothing, or medical aid.

Duration 1 year.

Number awarded 1 or more each year.

Deadline April of each year.

[988]
LIBRARY OF CONGRESS JUNIOR FELLOWS PROGRAM

Library of Congress
Library Services
Attn: Junior Fellows Program Coordinator
101 Independence Avenue, S.E., Room LM-642
Washington, DC 20540-4600
(202) 707-0901   Fax: (202) 707-6269
E-mail: jrfell@loc.gov
Web: www.loc.gov/hr/jrfellows/index.html

Summary To provide summer work experience at the Library of Congress (LC) to upper-division students, graduate students, and recent graduates, particularly women, minorities, and persons with disabilities.

Eligibility This program is open to U.S. citizens with subject expertise in the following areas: American history, including veterans and military history; American popular culture; area studies (African, Asian, European, Hispanic, Middle Eastern); bibliographic description and access; film, television, and radio; folklife; geography and maps; history of photography; history of popular and applied graphic arts, architecture, and design; manuscript collections processing; music; preservation and conservation; rare books and manuscripts; science, technology, and business; serials and government publications and newspapers; or sound recordings. Applicants must 1) be juniors or seniors at an accredited college or university, 2) be graduate students, or 3) have completed their degree in the past year. Applications from women, minorities, and persons with disabilities are particularly encouraged. Selection is based on academic achievement, letters of recommendation, and an interview.

Financial data Fellows are paid a taxable stipend of $300 per week.

Duration 3 months, beginning in either May or June. Fellows work a 40-hour week.

Additional information Fellows work with primary source materials and assist selected divisions at LC in the organization and documentation of archival collections, production of finding aids and bibliographic records, preparation of materials for preservation and service, completion of bibliographical research, and digitization of LC's historical collections.

Number awarded Varies each year; recently, 6 of these internships were awarded.

Deadline March of each year.

[989]
LINDA J. MURPHY SCHOLARSHIPS

Women Lawyers' Association of Greater St. Louis
c/o Jamie Boyer, Scholarship Committee Chair
Stinson Morrison Hecker LLP
168 North Meramec, Suite 400
St. Louis, MO 63105
(314) 863-0800   Fax: (314) 863-9388
E-mail: jboyer@stinson.com
Web: www.wlastl.org/scholarship.html

Summary To provide financial assistance to women from any state who are attending law school in Missouri.

Eligibility This program is open to women attending law school in Missouri on a part-time or full-time basis. Applicants must submit a 2-page personal statement on events, deci-

sions, or individuals that have helped to shape their life; short-term and long-term career goals; and/or contributions they would like to make to society in general, their community, women, or the legal profession. Selection is based on commitment to causes that are consistent with the mission of the sponsoring association (advancing the quality of life and stature in our society of women through community service or otherwise), academic achievement, and financial need.

Financial data Stipends range from $1,000 to $6,000.

Duration 1 year.

Additional information This program started in 1996.

Number awarded Varies each year; recently, 3 of these scholarships were awarded.

Deadline March of each year.

[990]
LIZETTE PETERSON-HOMER INJURY PREVENTION RESEARCH GRANT

American Psychological Foundation
750 First Street, N.E.
Washington, DC 20002-4242
(202) 336-5843   Fax: (202) 336-5812
E-mail: foundation@apa.org
Web: www.apa.org/apf/funding/peterson-homer.aspx

Summary To provide funding to women and other graduate students and faculty from diverse groups who are interested in conducting research related to the prevention of injuries in children.

Eligibility This program is open to graduate students and faculty interested in conducting research that focuses on the prevention of physical injury in children and young adults through accidents, violence, abuse, or suicide. Applicants must submit a 100-word abstract, description of the project, detailed budget, curriculum vitae, and letter from the supporting faculty supervisor (if the applicant is a student). Selection is based on conformance with stated program goals, magnitude of incremental contribution, quality of proposed work, and applicant's demonstrated scholarship and research competence. The sponsor encourages applications from individuals who represent diversity in race, ethnicity, gender, age, disability, and sexual orientation.

Financial data Grants up to $5,000 are available.

Additional information This program was established in 1999 as the Rebecca Routh Coon Injury Research Award. The current name was adopted in 2003. It is supported by Division 54 (Society of Pediatric Psychology) of the American Psychological Association and the American Psychological Foundation.

Number awarded 1 each year.

Deadline September of each year.

[991]
LOUISIANA WMU SCHOLARSHIP FOR WOMEN SEMINARY STUDENTS

Louisiana Baptist Convention
Attn: Woman's Missionary Union
P.O. Box 311
Alexandria, LA 71309
(318) 448-3402   Toll Free: (800) 622-6549
E-mail: wmu@lbc.org
Web: www.lbc.org

Summary This provide financial assistance to women from Louisiana who are working on a master's degree at a Southern Baptist seminary.

Eligibility This program is open to women who are active members of a Southern Baptist church in Louisiana. Applicants must be enrolled full time at 1 of the 6 Southern Baptist seminaries, have a GPA of 2.5 or higher, and be working on a master's degree. They must participate in activities of the Woman's Missionary Union (WMU) and be actively involved in missions education of the church or on campus. Along with their application, they must submit a brief summary of their Christian walk in their life, including what they believe the Lord has called them to do in a church-related vocation.

Financial data The stipend is $1,600 per year.

Duration Up to 3 years.

Additional information The eligible seminaries are Southeastern Baptist Theological Seminary (Wake Forest, North Carolina); Southern Baptist Theological Seminary (Louisville, Kentucky); Southwestern Baptist Theological Seminary (Fort Worth, Texas); New Orleans Baptist Theological Seminary (New Orleans, Louisiana); Midwestern Baptist Theological Seminary (Kansas City, Missouri); or Golden Gate Baptist Theological Seminary (Mill Valley, California).

Number awarded 1 or more each year.

Deadline June of each year.

[992]
LUCY KASPARIAN AHARONIAN SCHOLARSHIPS

Armenian International Women's Association
65 Main Street, Room 3A
Watertown, MA 02472
(617) 926-0171   E-mail: aiwainc@aol.com
Web: www.aiwa-net.org/scholarshipinfo.html

Summary To provide financial assistance to Armenian women who are upper-division or graduate students working on a degree in specified fields.

Eligibility This program is open to full-time women students of Armenian descent attending an accredited college or university. Applicants must be full-time juniors, seniors, or graduate students with a GPA of 3.2 or higher. They must be working on a degree in architecture, computer science, engineering, mathematics, science, or technology. Selection is based on financial need and merit.

Financial data Stipends range from $2,000 to $10,000.

Duration 1 year.

Additional information This program, established in 2008, is offered in conjunction with the Boston Section of the Society of Women Engineers.

Number awarded 2 each year.

Deadline April of each year.

[993]
LYDIA I. PICKUP MEMORIAL SCHOLARSHIP

Society of Women Engineers
Attn: Scholarship Selection Committee
120 South LaSalle Street, Suite 1515
Chicago, IL 60603-3572
(312) 596-5223   Toll Free: (877) SWE-INFO
Fax: (312) 644-8557
E-mail: scholarshipapplication@swe.org
Web: societyofwomenengineers.swe.org

Summary To provide financial assistance to women working on an undergraduate or graduate degree in engineering or computer science.

Eligibility This program is open to women who will be sophomores, juniors, seniors, or graduate students at ABET-accredited colleges and universities. Applicants must be majoring in computer science or engineering and have a GPA of 3.0 or higher. Preference is given to graduate students. Selection is based on merit.

Financial data The stipend is $3,000.

Duration 1 year.

Additional information This program was established in 2001.

Number awarded 1 each year.

Deadline February of each year.

[994]
LYDIA SCHOLARSHIP

Network of Presbyterian Women in Leadership
Scholarship Coordinator
8134 New LaGrange Road, Suite 227
Louisville, KY 40222-4679
(502) 425-4630   E-mail: npwl@pfrenewal.org
Web: www.npwl.org/Lydia-scholarship

Summary To provide financial assistance to women who are interested in preparing for a career in the Presbyterian Church (USA) ordained pastoral ministry.

Eligibility This program is open to women who are interested in preparing for ordained pastoral ministry in the Presbyterian Church. Applicants must be working on an M.Div. degree and ordination and be involved in the candidate process (or have specified plans to be involved shortly). Along with their application, they must submit essays on their faith story, personal theology, and call to ministry. Those essays should demonstrate their commitment to work for spiritual renewal within the PCUSA, including a willingness to cooperate with the Network of Presbyterian Women in Leadership and Presbyterians for Renewal (its umbrella organization). Financial need is considered in the selection process.

Financial data The stipend is $2,500 per year.

Duration 2 years; may be renewed for 1 additional year.

Number awarded 1 each year.

Deadline February of each year.

[995]
M.A. CARTLAND SHACKFORD MEDICAL FELLOWSHIP

Wellesley College
Center for Work and Service
Attn: Extramural Graduate Fellowships and Scholarships
106 Central Street
Wellesley, MA 02181-8203
(781) 283-3525   Fax: (781) 283-3674
E-mail: cws-fellowships@wellesley.edu
Web: www.wellesley.edu/CWS/students/wellfs.html

Summary To provide financial assistance to women for graduate study in the medical fields.

Eligibility This program is open to women who have graduated from an American academic institution and are interested in general medical practice (but not psychiatry).

Financial data The fellowship of at least $11,000 is tenable at any institution of the recipient's choice.

Duration 1 year.

Additional information The recipient must pursue full-time graduate study.

Number awarded 1 each year.

Deadline January of each year.

[996]
MABEL BIEVER MUSIC EDUCATION SCHOLARSHIP FOR GRADUATE STUDENTS

Sigma Alpha Iota Philanthropies, Inc.
One Tunnel Road
Asheville, NC 28805
(828) 251-0606 Fax: (828) 251-0644
E-mail: nh@sai-national.org
Web: www.sigmaalphaiota.org

Summary To provide financial assistance for graduate study in music education to members of Sigma Alpha Iota (an organization of women musicians).

Eligibility This program is open to alumnae members of the organization who have completed an undergraduate degree in music education and are currently enrolled in a program leading to a graduate degree in that field. Candidates should have had at least 1 year of teaching experience or equivalent. Applications must include a taped performance audition or a videotape demonstrating effectiveness as a teacher.

Financial data The stipend is $1,500.

Duration 1 year.

Additional information This program is sponsored by the Oak Park Alumnae Chapter of Sigma Alpha Iota.

Number awarded 1 each year.

Deadline March of each year.

[997]
MABEL HEIL SCHOLARSHIP

United Methodist Church-Wisconsin Conference
Attn: Board of Higher Education and Campus Ministry
750 Windsor Street
P.O. Box 620
Sun Prairie, WI 53590-0620
(608) 837-7328 Toll Free: (888) 240-7328
Fax: (608) 837-8547
Web: www.wisconsinumc.org

Summary To provide financial assistance to United Methodist women from Wisconsin who are interested in attending college or graduate school in any state.

Eligibility This program is open to women who are members of congregations affiliated with the Wisconsin Conference of the United Methodist Church and attending or planning to attend college or graduate school in any state. Applicants must submit an essay on why they consider themselves a worthy student and a letter of recommendation from their pastor or the president of the local United Methodist Women. Preference is given to women who are responsible for others and are returning to the employment field.

Financial data A stipend is awarded (amount not specified).

Duration 1 semester; recipients may reapply.

Number awarded 1 or more each year.

Deadline April of each year for the first semester; September of each year for the second semester.

[998]
MAINE VETERANS DEPENDENTS EDUCATIONAL BENEFITS

Bureau of Veterans' Services
117 State House Station
Augusta, ME 04333-0117
(207) 626-4464 Toll Free: (800) 345-0116 (within ME)
Fax: (207) 626-4471 E-mail: mainebvs@maine.gov
Web: www.maine.gov/dvem/bvs/educational_benefits.htm

Summary To provide financial assistance for undergraduate or graduate education to spouses and children of disabled and other Maine veterans.

Eligibility Applicants for these benefits must be children (high school seniors or graduates under 22 years of age), non-divorced spouses, or unremarried widow(er)s of veterans who meet 1 or more of the following requirements: 1) living and determined to have a total permanent disability resulting from a service-connected cause; 2) killed in action; 3) died from a service-connected disability; 4) died while totally and permanently disabled due to a service-connected disability but whose death was not related to the service-connected disability; or 5) a member of the armed forces on active duty who has been listed for more than 90 days as missing in action, captured, forcibly detained, or interned in the line of duty by a foreign government or power. The veteran parent must have been a resident of Maine at the time of entry into service or a resident of Maine for 5 years preceding application for these benefits. Children may be working on an associate or bachelor's degree. Spouses, widows, and widowers may work on an associate, bachelor's, or master's degree.

Financial data Recipients are entitled to free tuition at institutions of higher education supported by the state of Maine.

Duration Children may receive up to 8 semesters of support; they have 6 years from the date of first entrance to complete those 8 semesters. Continuation in the program is based on their earning a GPA of 2.0 or higher each semester. Spouses are entitled to receive up to 120 credit hours of educational benefits and have 10 years from the date of first entrance to complete their program.

Additional information College preparatory schooling and correspondence courses are not supported under this program.

Number awarded Varies each year.

Deadline Deadline not specified.

[999]
MANAHAN-BOHAN AWARD

Philanthrofund Foundation
Attn: Scholarship Committee
1409 Willow Street, Suite 210
Minneapolis, MN 55403-3251
(612) 870-1806 Toll Free: (800) 435-1402
Fax: (612) 871-6587 E-mail: info@PfundOnline.org
Web: www.pfundonline.org/scholarships.html

Summary To provide financial assistance to lesbian students from rural Minnesota.

Eligibility This program is open to residents of Madelia, Minnesota; if no resident of Madelia applies, the award is available to residents of any rural area in Minnesota. Applicants must be self-identified as lesbian. They may be attending or planning to attend trade school, technical college, college, or university in any state (as an undergraduate or graduate student). Selection is based on the applicant's 1) affirmation of lesbian identity or commitment to lesbian communities; 2) evidence of experience and skills in service and leadership; and 3) evidence of service and leadership in lesbian communities, including serving as a role model, mentor, and/or adviser.

Financial data The stipend is $1,000. Funds must be used for tuition, books, fees, or dissertation expenses.

Duration 1 year.

Number awarded 1 each year.

Deadline January of each year.

[1000]
MARGARET MORSE NICE FUND

American Ornithologists' Union
c/o Executive Officer
5405 Villa View Drive
Farmington, NM 87402
(505) 326-1579   E-mail: aou@aou.org
Web: www.aou.org/awards/research

Summary To provide funding to female graduate students and scholars who are members of the American Ornithologists' Union (AOU) and interested in conducting research related to ornithology.

Eligibility This program is open to female AOU members who are graduate students, postdoctorates, or other researchers without access to major funding agencies. Applicants must be interested in conducting research related to ornithology. They should send a cover letter (about 5 pages) describing their proposed project, a budget, and 1 letter of reference. Selection is based on significance and originality of the research question, clarity of the objectives, feasibility of the plan of research, appropriateness of the budget, and the letter of recommendation.

Financial data The maximum award is $2,500 per year.

Duration 1 year; recipients may reapply for 1 additional award.

Number awarded The sponsor awards a total of 28 to 30 grants each year.

Deadline January of each year.

[1001]
MARGARET YARDLEY FELLOWSHIP

New Jersey State Federation of Women's Clubs
Attn: Fellowship Chair
55 Labor Center Way
New Brunswick, NJ 08901-1593
(732) 249-5474   Toll Free: (800) 465-7392
E-mail: njsfwc@njsfwc.org
Web: www.njsfwc.org/index.php/article/sub/9

Summary To provide financial assistance to women from New Jersey interested in graduate studies.

Eligibility Female graduate students from New Jersey are eligible to apply if they are enrolled full time in a master's or doctoral program at a college or university in the United States. Selection is based upon scholastic achievement, potential for career service, and financial need.

Financial data The stipend is $1,000.

Duration 1 year.

Additional information This program was established in 1930. Award recipients must give written assurance of an uninterrupted year of study at an American college of their choice.

Number awarded 6 to 8 each year.

Deadline February of each year.

[1002]
MARIAM K. CHAMBERLAIN FELLOWSHIP

Institute for Women's Policy Research
Attn: Fellowship Coordinator
1200 18th Street, N.W., Suite 301
Washington, DC 20036
(202) 785-5100   Fax: (202) 833-4362
E-mail: iwpr@iwpr.org
Web: www.iwpr.org/about/fellowships

Summary To provide work experience at the Institute for Women's Policy Research (IWPR) to college graduates and graduate students who are interested in economic justice for women.

Eligibility Applicants for this internship should have at least a bachelor's degree in social science, statistics, or women's studies. Graduate work is desirable but not required. They should have strong quantitative and library research skills and knowledge of women's issues. Familiarity with Microsoft Word and Excel is required; knowledge of STATA, SPSS, SAS, and graphics software is a plus.

Financial data The stipend is $23,088 and includes health insurance and a public transportation stipend.

Duration 9 months, beginning in September.

Additional information The institute is a nonprofit, scientific research organization that works primarily on issues related to equal opportunity and economic and social justice for women. Recent research topics for the fellows included women's wages, political participation, access to health care, and other indicators of the status of women on a state-by-state basis; the work and welfare experiences of low-income women on the state and national levels; reforming such income support policies for women as unemployment insurance, family leave, and Social Security; strategies for improving child care access, affordability, and quality; older women's economic issues; and women's values and activism, including new strategies for engaging a diverse range of organizations, including those with a religious affiliation, in women's issue activism.

Number awarded 1 each year.

Deadline February of each year.

[1003]
MARIE MORISAWA RESEARCH AWARD

Geological Society of America-Quaternary Geology and
Geomorphology Division
c/o Jim O'Connor, Second Vice Chair
U.S. Geological Survey
2130 S.W. Fifth Avenue
Portland, OR 97201
(503) 251-3222   Fax: (503) 251-3470
E-mail: oconnor@usgs.gov
Web: rock.geosociety.org/qgg

Summary To provide support to female graduate student members of the Geological Society of America (GSA) interested in conducting research on quaternary geology or geomorphology.

Eligibility This program is open to women who are GSA members working on a master's or doctoral degree at a university in any state. Applicants must be interested in conducting research on quaternary geology or geomorphology. Selection is based on quality of the proposed research.

Financial data The grant is $1,000.

Duration 1 year.

Additional information This program, established in 2008, is sponsored by the Geological Society of America's Quaternary Geology and Geomorphology Division.

Number awarded 1 each year.

Deadline January of each year.

[1004]
MARILYNNE GRABOYS WOOL SCHOLARSHIP

Rhode Island Foundation
Attn: Funds Administrator
One Union Station
Providence, RI 02903
(401) 427-4017   Fax: (401) 331-8085
E-mail: lmonahan@rifoundation.org
Web: www.rifoundation.org

Summary To provide financial assistance to women who are residents of Rhode Island and interested in studying law at a school in any state.

Eligibility This program is open to female residents of Rhode Island who are planning to enroll or are registered in an accredited law school in any state. Applicants must be able to demonstrate financial need. Along with their application, they must submit an essay (up to 300 words) on the impact they would like to have on the legal field.

Financial data The stipend is $2,000.

Duration 1 year; nonrenewable.

Number awarded 1 each year.

Deadline May of each year.

[1005]
MARK T. BANNER SCHOLARSHIP FOR LAW STUDENTS

Richard Linn American Inn of Court
c/o Cynthia M. Ho, Programs Chair
Loyola University School of Law
25 East Pearson Street, Room 1324
Chicago, IL 60611
(312) 915-7148
Web: www.linninn.org/marktbanner.htm

Summary To provide financial assistance to women and other law students who are members of a group historically underrepresented in intellectual property law.

Eligibility This program is open to students at ABA-accredited law schools in the United States who are members of groups historically underrepresented (by race, sex, ethnicity, sexual orientation, or disability) in intellectual property law. Applicants must submit a 1-page statement on how they have focused on ethics, civility, and professionalism and how diversity has impacted them; transcripts; a writing sample; and contact information for 3 references. Selection is based on academic merit, written and oral communication skills (determined in part through a telephone interview), leadership qualities, community involvement, and commitment to the pursuit of a career in intellectual property law.

Financial data The stipend is $5,000.

Duration 1 year.

Number awarded 1 each year.

Deadline November of each year.

[1006]
MARY BALL CARRERA SCHOLARSHIP

National Medical Fellowships, Inc.
Attn: Scholarship Program
347 Fifth Avenue, Suite 510
New York, NY 10016
(212) 483-8880   Toll Free: (877) NMF-1DOC
Fax: (212) 483-8897   E-mail: info@nmfonline.org
Web: www.nmfonline.org

Summary To provide financial assistance to Native American women who are attending medical school.

Eligibility This program is open to Native American women who are enrolled in the first or second year of an accredited medical school in the United States. Applicants must be able to demonstrate academic achievement, leadership, and community service, but selection is based primarily on financial need.

Financial data The stipend is $2,500.

Duration 1 year; nonrenewable.

Number awarded 1 or more each year.

Deadline August of each year.

[1007]
MARY CONNOLLY LIVINGSTON EDUCATIONAL GRANT

Lambda Kappa Sigma Pharmacy Fraternity
Attn: Executive Director
S77 W16906 Casey Drive
P.O. Box 570
Muskego, WI 53150-0570
Toll Free: (800) LKS-1913   Fax: (262) 679-4558
E-mail: lks@lks.org
Web: www.lks.org

Summary To provide financial assistance to members of Lambda Kappa Sigma who are interested in working on a Pharm.D. degree.

Eligibility This program is open to collegiate or alumnae members of Lambda Kappa Sigma who are enrolled in a licensure-eligible pharmacy degree program. (In the United States, the Pharm.D. degree is the only qualifying program at schools or colleges of pharmacy recognized by the Accreditation Council on Pharmacy Education.) Applicants must rank in the top half of their class and be able to demonstrate financial need.

Financial data The stipend is $1,000.

Duration 1 year.

Additional information This program was established in 1986. Lambda Kappa Sigma was founded in 1913 to promote the profession of pharmacy among women.

Number awarded 1 each year.

Deadline October of each year.

[1008]
MARY ISABEL SIBLEY FELLOWSHIP FOR FRENCH STUDIES

Phi Beta Kappa Society
Attn: Director of Society Affairs
1606 New Hampshire Avenue, N.W.
Washington, DC 20009
(202) 745-3235   Fax: (202) 986-1601
E-mail: awards@pbk.org
Web: www.pbk.org/infoview/PBK_InfoView.aspx?t=&id=5

Summary To provide funding to women involved in dissertation or advanced research or writing projects dealing with French studies.

Eligibility This program is open to unmarried women between 25 and 35 years of age who have demonstrated their ability to conduct original research. Applicants must be planning to conduct a research project dealing with French language or literature. They must hold the doctorate or have fulfilled all the requirements for the doctorate except the dissertation, and they must be planning to devote full time to their research during the fellowship year. Along with their application, they must submit a statement that includes a description of the project, the present state of the project, where the study would be carried out, and expectations regarding publication of the results of the study. Eligibility is not restricted to members of Phi Beta Kappa or to U.S. citizens.

Financial data The stipend is $20,000.

Duration 1 year (the fellowship is offered in even-numbered years only).

Additional information Periodic progress reports are not required, but they are welcomed. It is the hope of the committee that the results of the year of research will be made available in some form, although no pressure for publication will be put on the recipient.

Number awarded 1 every other year.

Deadline January of even-numbered years.

[1009]
MARY ISABEL SIBLEY FELLOWSHIP FOR GREEK STUDIES

Phi Beta Kappa Society
Attn: Director of Society Affairs
1606 New Hampshire Avenue, N.W.
Washington, DC 20009
(202) 745-3235   Fax: (202) 986-1601
E-mail: awards@pbk.org
Web: www.pbk.org/infoview/PBK_InfoView.aspx?t=&id=5

Summary To provide funding to women involved in dissertation or advanced research or writing projects dealing with Greek studies.

Eligibility This program is open to unmarried women between 25 and 35 years of age who have demonstrated their ability to conduct original research. Applicants must be planning to conduct a research project dealing with Greek language, literature, history, or archaeology. They must hold the doctorate or have fulfilled all the requirements for the doctorate except the dissertation, and they must be planning to devote full time to their research during the fellowship year. Along with their application, they must submit a statement that includes a description of the project, the present state of the project, where the study would be carried out, and expectations regarding publication of the results of the study. Eligibility is not restricted to members of Phi Beta Kappa or to U.S. citizens.

Financial data The stipend is $20,000.

Duration 1 year (the fellowship is offered in odd-numbered years only).

Additional information Periodic progress reports are not required, but they are welcomed. It is the hope of the committee that the results of the year of research will be made available in some form, although no pressure for publication will be put on the recipient.

Number awarded 1 every other year.

Deadline January of odd-numbered years.

[1010]
MARY LILY RESEARCH GRANTS

Duke University
Rare Book, Manuscript, and Special Collections Library
Attn: Sallie Bingham Center for Women's History and Culture
P.O. Box 90185
Durham, NC 27708-0185
(919) 660-5828   Fax: (919) 660-5934
E-mail: cwhc@duke.edu
Web: library.duke.edu

Summary To provide funding to scholars at all levels who wish to use the resources of the Sallie Bingham Center for Women's History and Culture in the Special Collections Library at Duke University.

Eligibility This program is open to undergraduates, graduate students, faculty members, and independent scholars in any academic field who wish to use the resources of the center for their research in women's studies. Applicants must reside outside a 50-mile radius of Durham, North Carolina. Undergraduate and graduate students must be currently enrolled, be working on a degree, and enclose a letter of recommendation from their adviser or thesis director. Faculty members must be working on a research project and enclose a curriculum vitae. Independent scholars must be working on a nonprofit project and enclose a curriculum vitae.

Financial data Grants up to $1,000 are available; funds may be used for travel, costs of copying pertinent resources, and living expenses while conducting the research.

Additional information The library's collections are especially strong in the history of feminist activism and theory, prescriptive literature, girls' literature, artists' books by women, lay and ordained church women, gender expression, women's sexuality, and the history and culture of women in the South. A number of prominent women writers have placed their personal and professional papers in the collections.

Number awarded Varies each year; recently, 8 of these grants were awarded.

Deadline January of each year.

[1011]
MARY LOVE COLLINS MEMORIAL SCHOLARSHIP

Chi Omega Fraternity
Attn: Chi Omega Foundation
3395 Players Club Parkway
Memphis, TN 38125
(901) 748-8600 Fax: (901) 748-8686
E-mail: foundation@chiomega.com
Web: www.chiomega.com/students/default.aspx

Summary To provide financial assistance to women who are members of Chi Omega Fraternity entering graduate school.

Eligibility This program is open to women who are members of Chi Omega Fraternity planning to enter graduate school as a full-time student. Applicants must submit an essay, from 200 to 500 words in length, on 1) why they want to pursue graduate study; 2) what they hope to gain from it; and 3) why they feel they are particularly qualified for a scholarship designed to honor Mary Love Collins. Selection is based on the essay; academic achievement; aptitude; contributions and service to Chi Omega, the university, and the community; and professional and personal goals.

Financial data The stipend is $1,700.

Duration 1 year.

Additional information This program was established in 1972.

Number awarded 5 each year.

Deadline March of each year.

[1012]
MARY MCEWEN SCHIMKE SCHOLARSHIP

Wellesley College
Center for Work and Service
Attn: Extramural Graduate Fellowships and Scholarships
106 Central Street
Wellesley, MA 02181-8203
(781) 283-3525 Fax: (781) 283-3674
E-mail: cws-fellowships@wellesley.edu
Web: www.wellesley.edu/CWS/students/wellfs.html

Summary To provide financial assistance to women working on a graduate degree who need relief from household or child care responsibilities.

Eligibility Women who have graduated from an American academic institution, are over 30 years of age, are currently engaged in graduate study in literature and/or history (preference is given to American studies), and need relief from household or child care responsibilities while pursuing graduate studies may apply. The award is made on the basis of scholarly ability and financial need.

Financial data The fellowship awards range up to $1,500 and are tenable at the institution of the recipient's choice.

Deadline January of each year.

[1013]
MARY MORGAN WOMEN'S FELLOWSHIP

Pride Law Fund
Attn: Fellowship Program
P.O. Box 2602
San Francisco, CA 94126-2602
E-mail: info@pridelawfund.org
Web: www.pridelawfund.org

Summary To provide funding to law students who are interested in a summer internship project dealing with legal issues of concern to lesbians and bisexual women.

Eligibility This program is open to students at law schools in the United States. Applicants must be interested in gaining work experience in the area of legal issues of concern to lesbians and bisexual women. They must be proposing to conduct a project on which they will work under the supervision of a sponsoring attorney at a tax-exempt nonprofit organization or a government agency in the United States. Preference is given to applicants who have shown a commitment to the lesbian, gay, bisexual, and transgender community (through leadership positions, volunteer activities, etc.) and to those with a demonstrated financial need.

Financial data The maximum grant is $5,000. Funds can be used to supplement other summer fellowships or income, as long as total funding does not exceed $5,000.

Duration The fellowship must be no shorter than 8 weeks during the summer. Preference is given to projects that are at least 10 weeks.

Additional information Since this program was established in 1984, fellowships have funded students to work in the areas of sexual orientation discrimination, individual rights litigation, direct legal services for people with HIV/AIDS, and other legal concerns of the lesbian, gay, bisexual, and transgender community. The program is funded in part through the support of Bay Area Lawyers for Individual Freedom. Fellows must agree to maintain contact with the sponsor, mention the sponsor in any publication produced during the project, draft a short summary for the sponsor's newsletter, and attend sponsor events.

Number awarded 1 or more each year.

Deadline March of each year.

[1014]
MARY PAOLOZZI MEMBER'S SCHOLARSHIP

Navy Wives Clubs of America
P.O. Box 54022
Millington, TN 38053-6022
Toll Free: (866) 511-NWCA
E-mail: nwca@navywivesclubsofamerica.org
Web: www.navywivesclubsofamerica.org/scholarinfo.htm

Summary To provide financial assistance for undergraduate or graduate study to members of the Navy Wives Clubs of America (NWCA).

Eligibility This program is open to NWCA members who can demonstrate financial need. Applicants must be 1) a high school graduate or senior planning to attend college full time next year; 2) currently enrolled in an undergraduate program and planning to continue as a full-time undergraduate; 3) a college graduate or senior planning to be a full-time graduate student next year; or 4) a high school graduate or GED recipient planning to attend vocational or business school next year. Along with their application, they must submit a brief statement on why they feel they should be awarded this scholarship and any special circumstances (financial or other) they wish to have considered. Financial need is also considered in the selection process.

Financial data Stipends range from $500 to $1,000 each year (depending upon the donations from the NWCA chapters).

Duration 1 year.

Additional information Membership in the NWCA is open to spouses of enlisted personnel serving in the Navy, Marine Corps, Coast Guard, and the active Reserve units of those services; spouses of enlisted personnel who have been honorably discharged, retired, or transferred to the Fleet Reserve on completion of duty; and widows of enlisted personnel in those services.

Number awarded 1 or more each year.

Deadline May of each year.

[1015]
MARY R. NORTON MEMORIAL SCHOLARSHIP AWARD

ASTM International
100 Barr Harbor Drive
P.O. Box C700
West Conshohocken, PA 19428-2959
(610) 832-9500
Web: www.astm.org/studentmember/Student_Awards.html

Summary To provide financial assistance to female undergraduate and graduate students working on a degree related to physical metallurgy.

Eligibility This program is open to women entering their senior year of college or first year of graduate study. Applicants must be working on a degree in physical metallurgy or materials science, with an emphasis on relationship of microstructure and properties.

Financial data The stipend is $1,000.

Duration 1 year.

Additional information This program, established in 1975, is administered by ASTM Committee CO4 on Metallography. ASTM International was formerly the American Society for Testing and Materials.

Number awarded 1 or more each year.

Deadline Deadline not specified.

[1016]
MARYLAND CAPITAL CHAPTER ABWA EDUCATION GRANTS

American Business Women's Association-Maryland
  Capital Chapter
Attn: Ann Broduer, Vice President
P.O. Box 1955
Edgewater, MD 21037
E-mail: abrodeur@verizon.net
Web: www.abwamdcap.org/mc/page.do?sitePageID=45248

Summary To provide financial assistance to female residents of Maryland who are working on an undergraduate or graduate degree at a college or university in any state.

Eligibility This program is open to women who are residents of Maryland and enrolled as juniors, seniors, or graduate students at a college or university in any state. Applicants must be U.S. citizens and have a GPA of 2.5 or higher. Along with their application, they must submit a 1-page biographical essay that includes the degree they plan to earn, how they are currently contributing to the community, the kind of salaried work they currently do (if any), their entrepreneurial plan for applying the knowledge and skills gained through their degree, and why they need financial support to continue their education.

Financial data The stipend ranges from $1,500 to $2,000.

Duration 1 year; nonrenewable.

Number awarded 1 or more each year.

Deadline April of each year.

[1017]
MCCONNEL FAMILY SCHOLARSHIP

Epsilon Sigma Alpha International
Attn: ESA Foundation
363 West Drake Road
Fort Collins, CO 80526
(970) 223-2824　　　　　　Fax: (970) 223-4456
E-mail: esainfo@epsilonsigmaalpha.org
Web: www.epsilonsigmaalpha.org

Summary To provide financial assistance to women interested in studying veterinary medicine.

Eligibility This program is open to female residents of any state who are interested in studying veterinary medicine. Applicants may be attending school in any state. Selection is based on character (10%), leadership (20%), service (10%), financial need (30%), and scholastic ability (30%).

Financial data The stipend is $2,500.

Duration 1 year; may be renewed.

Additional information Epsilon Sigma Alpha (ESA) is a women's service organization. These scholarships were first awarded in 2002. Completed applications must be submitted to the ESA state counselor who then verifies the information before forwarding them to the scholarship director. A $5 processing fee is required.

Number awarded 2 each year.
Deadline January of each year.

[1018]
MEDTRONIC SWENET SCHOLARSHIP

Society of Women Engineers-Minnesota Section
Attn: Scholarship Committee
P.O. Box 582813
Minneapolis, MN 55458-2813
E-mail: scholarships@swe-mn.org
Web: swe-mn.org/scholarships.html

Summary To provide financial assistance to women from any state working on an undergraduate or graduate degree in specified fields of engineering at colleges and universities in Minnesota, North Dakota, and South Dakota.

Eligibility This program is open to female undergraduate and graduate students at ABET-accredited engineering programs in Minnesota, North Dakota, or South Dakota. Applicants must be working full time on a degree in biomedical, chemical, electrical, or mechanical engineering. Along with their application, they must submit a short paragraph describing how they plan to utilize their engineering skills after they graduate. Selection is based on potential to succeed as an engineer (20 points), communication skills (10 points), extra-curricular or community involvement and leadership skills (10 points), demonstrated successful work experience (10 points), and academic success (5 points).

Financial data The stipend is $1,000.

Duration 1 year.

Additional information This program is sponsored by Medtronic, Inc.

Number awarded 2 each year.

Deadline March of each year.

[1019]
MEMORIAL EDUCATION FUND FELLOWSHIPS

General Federation of Women's Clubs of Massachusetts
Attn: Scholarship Chair
245 Dutton Road
P.O. Box 679
Sudbury, MA 01776-0679
(781) 443-4569   Fax: (781) 443-1617
E-mail: Jwilchynski@aol.com
Web: www.gfwcma.org/scholarships.html

Summary To provide financial assistance to Massachusetts women interested in working on a graduate degree in designated fields at a school in any state.

Eligibility This program is open to women college graduates who have resided in Massachusetts for at least 5 years. Applicants must be planning to work on a graduate degree in a designated field of study that changes annually. Along with their application, they must submit college and graduate school transcripts, a letter of reference from college department chair or recent employer, and a personal statement of no more than 500 words addressing their professional goals and financial need. An interview is required.

Financial data The stipend is $3,000. Funds are paid directly to the recipient's college or university for tuition only.

Duration 1 year; nonrenewable.

Number awarded 2 each year.

Deadline February of each year.

[1020]
MICHELLE JACKSON SCHOLARSHIP FUND

Christian Church (Disciples of Christ)
Attn: Disciples Home Missions
130 East Washington Street
P.O. Box 1986
Indianapolis, IN 46206-1986
(317) 713-2652   Toll Free: (888) DHM-2631
Fax: (317) 635-4426   E-mail: mail@dhm.disciples.org
Web: www.discipleshomemissions.org

Summary To provide financial assistance to African American women interested in preparing for a career in the ministry of the Christian Church (Disciples of Christ).

Eligibility This program is open to female African American ministerial students who are members of a Christian Church (Disciples of Christ) congregation in the United States or Canada. Applicants must plan to prepare for the ordained ministry, be working on an M.Div. or equivalent degree, provide evidence of financial need, be enrolled full time in an accredited school or seminary, provide a transcript of academic work, and be under the care of a regional Commission on the Ministry or in the process of coming under care.

Financial data A stipend is awarded (amount not specified).

Duration 1 year; recipients may reapply.

Number awarded 1 each year.

Deadline March of each year.

[1021]
MICKEY LELAND ENERGY FELLOWSHIPS

Department of Energy
Attn: Office of Fossil Energy
19901 Germantown Road, FE-6
Germantown, MD 20874
(301) 903-4293   E-mail: MLEF@hq.doe.gov
Web: fossil.energy.gov

Summary To provide summer work experience at fossil energy sites of the Department of Energy (DOE) to women and underrepresented minority students.

Eligibility This program is open to U.S. citizens currently enrolled full time at an accredited college or university. Applicants must be undergraduate, graduate, or postdoctoral students in mathematics, physical sciences, technology, or engineering and have a GPA of 3.0 or higher. They must be interested in a summer work experience at a DOE fossil energy research facility. Along with their application, they must submit a 100-word statement on why they want to participate in this program. A goal of the program is to recruit women and underrepresented minorities into careers related to fossil energy.

Financial data Weekly stipends are $500 for undergraduates, $650 for master's degree students, or $750 for doctoral and postdoctoral students. Travel costs for a round trip to and from the site and for a trip to a designated place for technical presentations are also paid.

Duration 10 weeks during the summer.

Additional information This program began as 3 separate activities: the Historically Black Colleges and Universities Internship Program established in 1995, the Hispanic Internship Program established in 1998, and the Tribal Colleges and Universities Internship Program, established in 2000.

Those 3 programs were merged into the Fossil Energy Minority Education Initiative, renamed the Mickey Leland Energy Fellowship Program in 2000. Sites to which interns may be assigned include the Albany Research Center (Albany, Oregon), the National Energy Technology Laboratory (Morgantown, West Virginia and Pittsburgh, Pennsylvania), Pacific Northwest National Laboratory (Richland, Washington), Rocky Mountain Oilfield Testing Center (Casper, Wyoming), Strategic Petroleum Reserve Project Management Office (New Orleans, Louisiana), or U.S. Department of Energy Headquarters (Washington, D.C.).

Number awarded Varies each year; recently, 30 students participated in this program.

Deadline January of each year.

[1022]
MID-HUDSON SECTION SCHOLARSHIP

Society of Women Engineers
Attn: Scholarship Selection Committee
120 South LaSalle Street, Suite 1515
Chicago, IL 60603-3572
(312) 596-5223   Toll Free: (877) SWE-INFO
Fax: (312) 644-8557
E-mail: scholarshipapplication@swe.org
Web: societyofwomenengineers.swe.org

Summary To provide financial assistance to women, especially those from New York, who are working on an undergraduate or graduate degree in engineering or computer science.

Eligibility This program is open to women who will be sophomores, juniors, seniors, or graduate students at ABET-accredited colleges and universities. Applicants must be working on a degree in computer science or engineering and have a GPA of 3.0 or higher. Selection is based on merit. Preference is given to applicants who reside and attend school in New York.

Financial data The stipend is $1,000.

Duration 1 year.

Number awarded 2 each year.

Deadline February of each year.

[1023]
MIKE EIDSON SCHOLARSHIP

American Association for Justice
Attn: Women Trial Lawyers Caucus
777 Sixth Street, N.W., Suite 200
Washington, DC 20001
(202) 965-3500, ext. 8302
Toll Free: (800) 424-2725, ext. 8302
Fax: (202) 965-0355
E-mail: brandon.grubesky@justice.org
Web: www.justice.org/cps/rde/xchg/justice/hs.xsl/8514.htm

Summary To provide financial assistance to female law students who are interested in a career as a trial lawyer.

Eligibility This program is open to women entering their third year of law school (or fourth year in a night program). Applicants must submit a brief letter explaining their interest in a career as a trial lawyer, dedication to upholding the principles of the Constitution, and commitment to the concept of a fair trial, the adversary system, and a just result for the injured, the accused, and those whose rights are jeopardized.

Financial data A stipend is awarded (amount not specified).

Duration 1 year.

Additional information This program was established in 2008. The American Association for Justice was formerly the Association of Trial Lawyers of America.

Number awarded 1 each year.

Deadline May of each year.

[1024]
MIKE SHINN DISTINGUISHED MEMBER OF THE YEAR AWARDS

National Society of Black Engineers
Attn: Programs Department
205 Daingerfield Road
Alexandria, VA 22314
(703) 549-2207   Fax: (703) 683-5312
E-mail: scholarships@nsbe.org
Web: www.nsbe.org

Summary To provide financial assistance to members of the National Society of Black Engineers (NSBE) who are working on a degree in engineering (females and males are judged separately).

Eligibility This program is open to members of the society who are undergraduate or graduate engineering students. Applicants must have a GPA of 3.2 or higher. Selection is based on an essay; NSBE and university academic achievement; professional development; service to the society at the chapter, regional, and/or national level; and campus and community activities. The male and female applicants for the NSBE Fellows Scholarship Program who are judged most outstanding receive these awards.

Financial data The stipend is $7,500. Travel, hotel accommodations, and registration to the national convention are also provided.

Duration 1 year.

Number awarded 2 each year: 1 male and 1 female.

Deadline November of each year.

[1025]
MILDRED CATER BRADHAM SOCIAL WORK FELLOWSHIP

Zeta Phi Beta Sorority, Inc.
Attn: National Education Foundation
1734 New Hampshire Avenue, N.W.
Washington, DC 20009
(202) 387-3103   Fax: (202) 232-4593
E-mail: scholarship@ZPhiBNEF.org
Web: www.zphib1920.org/nef

Summary To provide financial assistance to members of Zeta Phi Beta Sorority who are interested in studying social work on the graduate level.

Eligibility This program is open to members of Zeta Phi Beta who are interested in working full time on a graduate or professional degree in social work. Applicants must have shown scholarly distinction or unusual ability in their chosen field. Along with their application, they must submit a 150-word essay on their educational goals and professional aspirations, how this award will help them to achieve those goals, and why they should receive the award. Financial need is not considered in the selection process.

Financial data The stipend ranges from $500 to $1,000 per year; funds are paid directly to the college or university.

Duration 1 academic year; may be renewed.

Number awarded 1 each year.

Deadline January of each year.

[1026]
MILDRED RICHARDS TAYLOR MEMORIAL SCHOLARSHIP

United Daughters of the Confederacy
Attn: Education Director
328 North Boulevard
Richmond, VA 23220-4057
(804) 355-1636   Fax: (804) 353-1396
E-mail: hqudc@rcn.com
Web: www.hqudc.org/scholarships/scholarships.html

Summary To provide financial assistance for graduate education in business to female lineal descendants of Confederate veterans.

Eligibility Eligible to apply for these scholarships are female lineal descendants of worthy Confederates or collateral descendants who are members of the Children of the Confederacy or the United Daughters of the Confederacy. Applicants must intend to study business or a business-related field at the graduate level and must submit certified proof of the Confederate record of 1 ancestor, with the company and regiment in which he served. They must have a GPA of 3.0 or higher.

Financial data The amount of this scholarship depends on the availability of funds.

Duration 1 year; may be renewed up to 2 additional years.

Additional information Members of the same family may not hold scholarships simultaneously, and only 1 application per family will be accepted within any 1 year. All requests for applications must be accompanied by a self-addressed stamped envelope.

Number awarded 1 each year.

Deadline April of each year.

[1027]
MINDY SOPHER SCHOLARSHIP

Kappa Delta Sorority
Attn: Foundation Manager
3205 Players Lane
Memphis, TN 38125
(901) 748-1897   Toll Free: (800) 536-1897
Fax: (901) 748-0949 E-mail: kappadelta@kappadelta.org
Web: www.kappadelta.org/scholarships

Summary To provide financial assistance to members of Kappa Delta Sorority who are working on a graduate degree in higher education or student personnel.

Eligibility This program is open to graduate members of Kappa Delta Sorority. Applicants must submit a personal statement giving their reasons for applying for this scholarship, official undergraduate and graduate transcripts, and 2 letters of recommendation. They must be working on a graduate degree in higher education or student personnel. Selection is based on academic excellence; service to the chapter, alumnae association, or national Kappa Delta; service to the campus and community; personal objectives and goals; potential; recommendations; and financial need.

Financial data The stipend is $1,000 per year. Funds may be used only for tuition, fees, and books, not for room and board.

Duration 1 year; may be renewed.

Number awarded 1 each year.

Deadline January of each year.

[1028]
MINNESOTA CHAPTER WTS SCHOLARSHIPS

Women's Transportation Seminar-Minnesota Chapter
c/o Nikki Farrington, Scholarship and Recognitions
  Director
CH2M Hill
1295 Northland Drive, Suite 200
Mendota Heights, MN 55120
(651) 365-8536   Fax: (651) 688-8844
E-mail: nfarring@ch2m.com
Web: www.wtsinternational.org/Chapters.aspx?ID=6964

Summary To provide financial assistance to women working on an undergraduate or graduate degree in a transportation-related field at colleges and universities in Minnesota.

Eligibility This program is open to women currently enrolled in an undergraduate or graduate degree program at a college or university in Minnesota. Applicants must be preparing for a career in transportation or a transportation-related field and be majoring in such fields as transportation engineering, planning, finance, or logistics. They must have a GPA of 3.0 or higher. Along with their application, they must submit a 750-word statement on their career goals after graduation and why they think they should receive this award. Selection is based on transportation goals, academic record, and transportation-related activities or job skills. Minority candidates are encouraged to apply.

Financial data The stipend is $2,000 or $500.

Duration 1 year.

Additional information Winners are also nominated for scholarships offered by the national organization of the Women's Transportation Seminar.

Number awarded 3 each year: 2 undergraduates and 1 graduate student.

Deadline November of each year.

[1029]
MINNESOTA NATIONAL GUARD SURVIVOR ENTITLEMENT TUITION REIMBURSEMENT PROGRAM

Department of Military Affairs
Attn: Education Services Officer
JFMN-J1-ARED
20 West 12th Street
St. Paul, MN 55155-2098
(651) 282-4125   Toll Free: (800) 657-3848
Fax: (651) 282-4694 E-mail: education@mn.ngb.army.mil
Web: www.minnesotanationalguard.org

Summary To provide financial assistance for college or graduate school to widows and children of members of the Minnesota National Guard who were killed on active duty.

Eligibility This program is open to surviving spouses and children of members of the Minnesota Army or Air National Guard who were killed while performing military duty. Spouses remain eligible unless they remarry; dependent children are eligible until their 24th birthday. The Guard member's death must have occurred within the scope of assigned duties while in a federal duty status or on state active service. Applicants must be enrolled as undergraduate or graduate students at colleges or universities in Minnesota. Reimbursement is provided only for undergraduate courses completed with a grade of "C" or better or for graduate courses completed with a grade of "B" or better.

Financial data The maximum reimbursement rate is 100% of the undergraduate tuition rate at the University of Minnesota Twin Cities campus (currently, $326.92 per credit to a maximum of $4,250 per term).

Duration 1 academic term, to a maximum of 18 credits per term; may be renewed for a total of 144 semester credits or 208 quarter credits.

Number awarded Varies each year.

Deadline Participants must request reimbursement within 60 days of the last official day of the term.

[1030]
MINNESOTA SWE LOCKHEED MARTIN SCHOLARSHIPS

Society of Women Engineers-Minnesota Section
Attn: Scholarship Committee
P.O. Box 582813
Minneapolis, MN 55458-2813
E-mail: scholarships@swe-mn.org
Web: swe-mn.org/scholarships.html

Summary To provide financial assistance to women from any state working on an undergraduate or graduate degree in electrical, systems, or mechanical engineering at colleges and universities in Minnesota, North Dakota, and South Dakota.

Eligibility This program is open to female undergraduate and graduate students at ABET-accredited engineering programs in Minnesota, North Dakota, or South Dakota. Applicants must be working full time on a degree in electrical, systems, or mechanical engineering. Along with their application, they must submit a short paragraph describing how they plan to utilize their engineering skills after they graduate. Selection is based on potential to succeed as an engineer (20 points), communication skills (10 points), extracurricular or community involvement and leadership skills (10 points), demonstrated successful work experience (10 points), and academic success (5 points).

Financial data The stipend is $1,500 for electrical or systems engineering or $1,000 for mechanical engineering.

Duration 1 year.

Additional information This program is sponsored by Lockheed Martin Corporation.

Number awarded 2 each year: 1 for electrical or systems engineering and 1 for mechanical engineering.

Deadline March of each year.

[1031]
MINNIE L. MAFFETT FELLOWSHIPS

Texas Business Women
Attn: Texas Business and Professional Women's
    Foundation
P.O. Box 70
Round Rock, TX 78680-0070
(806) 922-7090   Toll Free: (877) 225-4TBW
E-mail: info@texasbusinesswomen.org
Web: www.texasbpwfoundation.org/scholarships.php

Summary To provide financial assistance to women in Texas interested in studying or conducting research in a medical field.

Eligibility This program is open to 1) female graduates of Texas medical schools interested in postgraduate or research work; 2) women who have been awarded a Ph.D. degree from a Texas university and are doing research in a medical field; 3) women who need financial aid for the first year in establishing a family practice in a rural area of Texas with a population of less than 5,000; and 4) fourth-year female medical students who are completing an M.D. or D.O. degree at an accredited medical school in Texas.

Financial data The stipend recently was $1,500.

Duration 1 year; nonrenewable.

Additional information This program was established in 1948 when Texas Business Women was named Texas Federation of Business and Professional Women's Clubs.

Number awarded Varies each year; recently, 3 of these fellowships were awarded.

Deadline December of each year.

[1032]
MISSOURI WARTIME VETERAN'S SURVIVOR GRANT PROGRAM

Missouri Department of Higher Education
Attn: Student Financial Assistance
3515 Amazonas Drive
Jefferson City, MO 65109-5717
(573) 751-2361   Toll Free: (800) 473-6757
Fax: (573) 751-6635   E-mail: info@dhe.mo.gov
Web: www.dhe.mo.gov/wartimevetsurvivor.html

Summary To provide financial assistance to the spouses and children of deceased or disabled Missouri post-September 11, 2001 veterans who plan to attend college or graduate school in the state.

Eligibility This program is open to spouses and children of veterans whose deaths or injuries were a result of combat action or were attributed to an illness that was contracted while serving in combat action, or who became 80% disabled as a result of injuries or accidents sustained in combat action since September 11, 2001. The veteran must have been a Missouri resident when first entering military service or at the time of death or injury. The spouse or child must be a U.S. citizen or permanent resident or otherwise lawfully present in the United States; children of veterans must be younger than 25 years of age. All applicants must be enrolled or accepted for enrollment at least half time at an approved public college or university in Missouri and working on an associate, baccalaureate, master's, or doctoral degree.

Financial data The maximum annual grant is the lesser of 1) the actual tuition charged at the school where the recipient is enrolled, or 2) the amount of tuition charged to a Missouri resident enrolled in the same number of hours at the University of Missouri Columbia. Additional allowances provide up to $2,000 per semester for room and board and the lesser of the actual cost for books or $500.

Duration 1 year. May be renewed, provided the recipient maintains a GPA of 2.5 or higher and makes satisfactory academic progress; children of veterans are eligible until they turn 25 years of age or receive their first bachelor's degree, whichever occurs first.

Number awarded Up to 25 each year.

Deadline There is no application deadline, but early submission of the completed application is encouraged.

[1033]
MORGAN STANLEY MBA FELLOWSHIP

Morgan Stanley
Attn: Diversity Recruiting
1585 Broadway
New York, NY 10036
(212) 762-0211   Fax: (212) 507-4972
E-mail: mbafellowship@morganstanley.com
Web: www.morganstanley.com

Summary To provide financial assistance and work experience to women and members of other underrepresented groups who are working on an M.B.A. degree.

Eligibility This program is open to full-time M.B.A. students who are women, African Americans, Hispanics, Native Americans, or lesbian/gay/bisexual/transgender. Selection is based on assigned essays, academic achievement, recommendations, extracurricular activities, leadership qualities, and on-site interviews.

Financial data The program provides full payment of tuition and fees and a paid summer internship.

Duration 1 year; may be renewed for a second year, providing the student remains enrolled full time in good academic standing and completes the summer internship following the first year.

Additional information The paid summer internship is offered within Morgan Stanley institutional securities (equity research, fixed income, institutional equity, investment banking), investment management, or private wealth management. This program was established in 1999.

Number awarded 1 or more each year.

Deadline December of each year.

[1034]
MOSS ADAMS FOUNDATION SCHOLARSHIP

Educational Foundation for Women in Accounting
Attn: Foundation Administrator
136 South Keowee Street
Dayton, OH 45402
(937) 424-3391   Fax: (937) 222-5749
E-mail: info@efwa.org
Web: www.efwa.org/scholarships_MossAdams.php

Summary To provide financial support to women, including minority women, who are working on an accounting degree.

Eligibility This program is open to women who are enrolled in an accounting degree program at an accredited college or university. Applicants must meet 1 of the following criteria: 1) women pursuing a fifth-year requirement either

through general studies or within a graduate program; 2) women returning to school as current or reentry juniors or seniors; or 3) minority women. Selection is based on aptitude for accounting and business, commitment to the goal of working on a degree in accounting (including evidence of continued commitment after receiving this award), clear evidence that the candidate has established goals and a plan for achieving those goals (both personal and professional), financial need, and a demonstration of how the scholarship will impact her life. U.S. citizenship is required.

Financial data The stipend is $1,000.

Duration 1 year.

Additional information This program was established by Rowling, Dold & Associates LLP, a woman-owned C.P.A. firm based in San Diego. It was renamed when that firm merged with Moss Adams LLP.

Number awarded 1 each year.

Deadline April of each year.

[1035]
MTS SYSTEMS CORPORATION SCHOLARSHIP

Society of Women Engineers-Minnesota Section
Attn: Scholarship Committee
P.O. Box 582813
Minneapolis, MN 55458-2813
E-mail: scholarships@swe-mn.org
Web: swe-mn.org/scholarships.html

Summary To provide financial assistance to women from any state working on an undergraduate or graduate degree in software or mechanical engineering at colleges and universities in Minnesota, North Dakota, and South Dakota.

Eligibility This program is open to female undergraduate and graduate students at ABET-accredited engineering programs in Minnesota, North Dakota, or South Dakota. Applicants must be working full time on a degree in software or mechanical engineering. Along with their application, they must submit a short paragraph describing how they plan to utilize their engineering skills after they graduate. Selection is based on potential to succeed as an engineer (20 points), communication skills (10 points), extracurricular or community involvement and leadership skills (10 points), demonstrated successful work experience (10 points), and academic success (5 points).

Financial data The stipend is $1,500.

Duration 1 year.

Additional information This program is sponsored by MTS Systems Corporation.

Number awarded 1 each year.

Deadline March of each year.

[1036]
MURIEL ANDERSON STEED SCHOLARSHIP

Kappa Alpha Theta Foundation
Attn: Scholarships
8740 Founders Road
Indianapolis, IN 46268-1337
(317) 876-1870   Toll Free: (800) KAO-1870
Fax: (317) 876-1925
E-mail: FDNmail@kappaalphatheta.org
Web: www.kappaalphathetafoundation.org

Summary To provide financial assistance to undergraduate and graduate members of Kappa Alpha Theta who are preparing for a career as a teacher.

Eligibility This program is open to members of Kappa Alpha Theta who are full-time undergraduate or graduate students at a college or university in Canada or the United States. Applicants must be preparing for a career as a teacher. Along with their application, they must submit an official transcript, personal essays on assigned topics related to their involvement in Kappa Alpha Theta, and 2 letters of reference. Financial need is not considered in the selection process.

Financial data The stipend is $1,550.

Duration 1 year.

Number awarded 1 each year.

Deadline January of each year.

[1037]
MUSIC THERAPY SCHOLARSHIP

Sigma Alpha Iota Philanthropies, Inc.
One Tunnel Road
Asheville, NC 28805
(828) 251-0606   Fax: (828) 251-0644
E-mail: nh@sai-national.org
Web: www.sigmaalphaiota.org

Summary To provide financial assistance to members of Sigma Alpha Iota (an organization of women musicians) who are working on an undergraduate or graduate degree in music therapy.

Eligibility This program is open to members of the organization who have completed at least 2 years of study for an undergraduate or graduate degree in music therapy. Applicants must submit an essay that includes their personal definition of music therapy, their career plans and professional goals as a music therapist, and why they feel they are deserving of this scholarship. Selection is based on music therapy skills, musicianship, fraternity service, community service, leadership, self-reliance, and dedication to the field of music therapy as a career.

Financial data The stipend is $1,500.

Duration 1 year.

Number awarded 1 each year.

Deadline March of each year.

[1038]
MUSICIANS WITH SPECIAL NEEDS SCHOLARSHIP

Sigma Alpha Iota Philanthropies, Inc.
One Tunnel Road
Asheville, NC 28805
(828) 251-0606   Fax: (828) 251-0644
E-mail: nh@sai-national.org
Web: www.sigmaalphaiota.org

Summary To provide financial assistance for college or graduate school to members of Sigma Alpha Iota (an organization of women musicians) who have a disability and are working on a degree in music.

Eligibility This program is open to members of the organization who either 1) have a sensory or physical impairment and are enrolled in a graduate or undergraduate degree program in music, or 2) are preparing to become a music teacher

or therapist for people with disabilities. Performance majors must submit a 15-minute DVD of their work; non-performance majors must submit evidence of work in their area of specialization, such as composition, musicology, or research.

Financial data The stipend is $1,500.

Duration 1 year.

Number awarded 1 each year.

Deadline March of each year.

[1039]
MYRA DAVIS HEMMINGS SCHOLARSHIP

Delta Sigma Theta Sorority, Inc.
Attn: Scholarship and Standards Committee Chair
1707 New Hampshire Avenue, N.W.
Washington, DC 20009
(202) 986-2400   Fax: (202) 986-2513
E-mail: dstemail@deltasigmatheta.org
Web: www.deltasigmatheta.org

Summary To provide financial assistance to members of Delta Sigma Theta who are interested in working on a graduate degree in the performing or creative arts.

Eligibility This program is open to graduating college seniors and graduate students who are interested in preparing for a career in the performing or creative arts. Applicants must be active, dues-paying members of Delta Sigma Theta. Selection is based on meritorious achievement.

Financial data The stipends range from $1,000 to $2,000 per year. The funds may be used to cover tuition and living expenses.

Duration 1 year; may be renewed for 1 additional year.

Additional information This sponsor is a traditionally-African American social sorority. The application fee is $20.

Number awarded 1 each year.

Deadline April of each year.

[1040]
MYRNA F. BERNATH FELLOWSHIP AWARD

Society for Historians of American Foreign Relations
c/o Ohio State University
Department of History
106 Dulles Hall
230 West 17th Avenue
Columbus, OH 43210
(614) 292-1951   Fax: (614) 292-2282
E-mail: shafr@osu.edu
Web: www.shafr.org/members/fellowships-grants

Summary To provide funding to women who are members of the Society for Historians of American Foreign Relations (SHAFR) and interested in conducting research on the history of U.S. foreign relations.

Eligibility This program is open to women at U.S. universities who wish to conduct historically-based research in the United States or abroad and to women from other countries who wish to conduct research in the United States. The proposed study should focus on U.S. foreign relations, transnational history, international history, peace studies, cultural interchange, or defense or strategic studies. Preference is given to applications from graduate students and those who completed their Ph.D. within the past 5 years. Applicants must submit a curriculum vitae, a letter of intent, and a detailed research proposal that discusses the sources to be consulted and their value, the funds needed, and the plan for spending those funds.

Financial data The grant is $5,000.

Duration The grant is presented biennially, in odd-numbered years.

Additional information This grant was first presented in 1992.

Number awarded 1 each odd-numbered year.

Deadline September of each even-numbered year.

[1041]
NABA 20 PEARLS SCHOLARSHIP

National Association of Black Accountants
Attn: National Scholarship Program
7474 Greenway Center Drive, Suite 1120
Greenbelt, MD 20770
(301) 474-NABA, ext. 114   Fax: (301) 474-3114
E-mail: customerservice@nabainc.org
Web: www.nabainc.org

Summary To provide financial assistance to student members of the National Association of Black Accountants (NABA) who are also members of Alpha Kappa Alpha sorority and working on an undergraduate or graduate degree in a field related to accounting.

Eligibility This program is open to NABA members who are also Alpha Kappa Alpha members and enrolled full time as 1) an undergraduate freshman, sophomore, junior, or first-semester senior majoring in accounting, business, or finance at a 4-year college or university; or 2) a graduate student working on a master's degree in accounting. High school seniors are not eligible. Applicants must have a GPA of 3.5 or higher in their major and 3.3 or higher overall. Selection is based on grades, financial need, and a 500-word autobiography that discusses career objectives, leadership abilities, community activities, and involvement in NABA.

Financial data The stipend is $1,500.

Duration 1 year.

Number awarded 1 each year.

Deadline January of each year.

[1042]
NANCY B. WOOLRIDGE MCGEE GRADUATE FELLOWSHIP

Zeta Phi Beta Sorority, Inc.
Attn: National Education Foundation
1734 New Hampshire Avenue, N.W.
Washington, DC 20009
(202) 387-3103   Fax: (202) 232-4593
E-mail: scholarship@ZPhiBNEF.org
Web: www.zphib1920.org/nef

Summary To provide financial assistance for graduate school to members of Zeta Phi Beta Sorority.

Eligibility This program is open to members of Zeta Phi Beta Sorority who are working on or are interested in working full time on a graduate or professional degree. Applicants must have shown scholarly distinction or unusual ability in their chosen profession. Along with their application, they must submit a 150-word essay on their educational goals and professional aspirations, how this award will help them to achieve those goals, and why they should receive the award. Financial need is not considered in the selection process.

Financial data The stipend ranges from $500 to $1,000 per year; funds are paid to the college or university.

Duration 1 academic year; may be renewed.

Number awarded 1 each year.

Deadline January of each year.

[1043]
NASA GRADUATE STUDENT RESEARCHERS PROGRAM

National Aeronautics and Space Administration
Attn: Acting National GSRP Project Manager
Jet Propulsion Laboratory
4800 Oak Grove Drive
Pasadena, CA 91109-8099
(818) 354-3274   Fax: (818) 393-4977
E-mail: Linda.L.Rodgers@jpl.nasa.gov
Web: fellowships.nasaprs.com/gsrp/nav

Summary To provide funding to graduate students (especially women, minorities, and individuals with disabilities) who are interested in conducting research in fields of interest to the U.S. National Aeronautics and Space Administration (NASA).

Eligibility This program is open to full-time students enrolled or planning to enroll in an accredited graduate program at a U.S. college or university. Applicants must be citizens of the United States, sponsored by a faculty adviser or department chair, and interested in conducting research in a field of science, mathematics, or engineering related to NASA research and development. Students who are interested in becoming teaching or education administrators are also eligible. Selection is based on academic qualifications, quality of the proposed research and its relevance to NASA's program, proposed utilization of center research facilities (except for NASA headquarters), and ability of the student to accomplish the defined research. Individuals from underrepresented groups in science, technology, engineering, or mathematics (STEM) fields (African Americans, Native Americans, Alaskan Natives, Mexican Americans, Puerto Ricans, Native Pacific Islanders, women, and persons with disabilities) are strongly urged to apply.

Financial data The program provides a $20,000 student stipend, a $6,000 student travel allowance, up to $1,000 for health insurance, and a $3,000 university allowance. The student stipend may cover tuition, room and board, books, software, meal plans, school and laboratory supplies, and other related expenses. The student travel allowance may be used for national and international conferences and data collection. The university allowance is a discretionary award that typically goes to the research adviser. If the student already has health insurance, that $1,000 grant may be added to the student stipend or student travel allowance. <UR>1 year; may be renewed for up to 1 additional year for master's degree students or 2 additional years for doctoral students.

Additional information This program was established in 1980. Students are required to participate in a 10-week research experience at NASA headquarters in Washington, D.C. or at 1 of 10 NASA centers.

Number awarded This program supports approximately 180 graduate students each year.

Deadline February of each year.

[1044]
NATIONAL DEFENSE SCIENCE AND ENGINEERING GRADUATE FELLOWSHIP PROGRAM

American Society for Engineering Education
Attn: NDSEG Fellowship Program
1818 N Street, N.W., Suite 600
Washington, DC 20036-2479
(202) 331-3516   Fax: (202) 265-8504
E-mail: ndseg@asee.org
Web: ndseg.asee.org

Summary   To provide financial assistance to doctoral students (particularly women, minorities, and individuals with disabilities) in areas of science and engineering that are of military importance.

Eligibility   This program is open to U.S. citizens and nationals entering or enrolled in the early stages of a doctoral program in aeronautical and astronautical engineering; biosciences, including toxicology; chemical engineering; chemistry; civil engineering; cognitive, neural, and behavioral sciences; computer and computational sciences; electrical engineering; geosciences, including terrain, water, and air; materials science and engineering; mathematics; mechanical engineering; naval architecture and ocean engineering; oceanography; or physics, including optics. Applications are particularly encouraged from women, members of ethnic minority groups (American Indians, African Americans, Hispanics or Latinos, Native Hawaiians, Alaska Natives, Asians, and Pacific Islanders), and persons with disabilities. Selection is based on all available evidence of ability, including academic records, letters of recommendation, and GRE scores.

Financial data   The annual stipend is $30,500 for the first year, $31,000 for the second year; and $31,500 for the third year; the program also pays the recipient's institution full tuition and required fees (not to include room and board). Medical insurance is covered up to $1,000 per year. An additional allowance may be considered for a student with a disability.

Duration   3 years, as long as satisfactory academic progress is maintained.

Additional information   This program is sponsored by the Army Research Office, the Air Force Office of Scientific Research, and the Office of Naval Research. Recipients do not incur any military or other service obligation. They must attend school on a full-time basis.

Number awarded   Approximately 200 each year.

Deadline   January of each year.

[1045]
NATIONAL HISPANIC BUSINESS WOMEN ASSOCIATION EDUCATIONAL SCHOLARSHIPS

National Hispanic Business Women Association
2024 North Broadway, Suite 100
Santa Ana, CA 92706
(714) 836-4042
Web: nationalhbwa.com

Summary   To provide financial assistance to women in California who are working on an undergraduate or graduate degree at a school in any state and submit an essay related to Latinas in education.

Eligibility   This program is open to female residents of California who are currently enrolled as undergraduate or graduate students at a school in any state. Applicants must have a GPA of 3.0 or higher and be able to demonstrate financial need. They must also have a record of participation in some form of community service. Along with their application, they must submit 2 essays of 2 pages each on 1) their academic and professional goals; and 2) their choice of the importance or value of obtaining a higher education, the potential impacts or influences of a growing Latino population in relation to their field of interest, or the specific challenges faced by Latinas in pursuit of higher education.

Financial data   Stipends range from $500 to $1,000.

Duration   1 year.

Number awarded   Varies each year; recently, 12 of these scholarships were awarded.

Deadline   March of each year.

[1046]
NATIONAL KOREAN PRESBYTERIAN WOMEN GRANTS

National Korean Presbyterian Women
c/o Kyo Mo Chung, Moderator
2309 Misty Haven Lane
Plano, TX 75093
(214) 821-8776   E-mail: jungbang@gmail.com
Web: www.pcusa.org/korean/org-nkpw.htm

Summary   To provide financial assistance to Korean American women preparing for ministry in the Presbyterian Church.

Eligibility   This program is open to second-generation Korean American women who are entering their third semester of full-time study at a Presbyterian seminary. Selection is based on academic ability and leadership skills.

Financial data   The stipend is $1,000.

Duration   1 year.

Deadline   May of each year.

[1047]
NATIONAL ORGANIZATION OF ITALIAN AMERICAN WOMEN SCHOLARSHIPS

National Organization of Italian American Women
25 West 43rd Street, Suite 1005
New York, NY 10036
(212) 642-2003   Fax: (212) 642-2006
E-mail: noiaw@noiaw.org
Web: www.noiaw.org

Summary   To provide financial assistance for college or graduate school to women of Italian descent.

Eligibility   This program is open to women who have at least 1 parent of Italian American descent and are working on an associate, bachelor's, or master's degree. Applicants must be enrolled full time and have a GPA of 3.5 or higher. Along with their application, they must submit a 2-page essay on how being an Italian American has impacted them personally and professionally. Financial need is considered in the selection process.

Financial data   The stipend is $2,000.

Duration   1 year; nonrenewable.

Number awarded 4 each year, including 1 reserved for an undergraduate or graduate student at the City University of New York system.

Deadline April of each year.

[1048]
NATIONAL PATHFINDER SCHOLARSHIPS

National Federation of Republican Women
Attn: Scholarships and Internships
124 North Alfred Street
Alexandria, VA 22314-3011
(703) 548-9688   Fax: (703) 548-9836
E-mail: mail@nfrw.org
Web: www.nfrw.org/programs/scholarships.htm

Summary To provide financial assistance for college or graduate school to Republican women.

Eligibility This program is open to women currently enrolled as college sophomores, juniors, seniors, or master's degree students. Recent high school graduates and first-year college women are not eligible. Applicants must submit 3 letters of recommendation, an official transcript, a 1-page essay on why they should be considered for the scholarship, and a 1-page essay on career goals. Applications must be submitted to the Republican federation president in the applicant's state. Each president chooses 1 application from her state to submit for scholarship consideration. Financial need is not a factor in the selection process. U.S. citizenship is required.

Financial data The stipend is $2,500.

Duration 1 year; nonrenewable.

Additional information This program, previously named the Nancy Reagan Pathfinder Scholarships, was established in 1985.

Number awarded 3 each year.

Deadline Applications must be submitted to the state federation president by May of each year.

[1049]
NATIONAL PHYSICAL SCIENCE CONSORTIUM GRADUATE FELLOWSHIPS

National Physical Science Consortium
c/o University of Southern California
3716 South Hope Street, Suite 348
Los Angeles, CA 90007-4344
(213) 743-2409   Toll Free: (800) 854-NPSC
Fax: (213) 743-2407   E-mail: npschq@npsc.org
Web: www.npsc.org/students/info.html

Summary To provide financial assistance and summer work experience to women and underrepresented minorities who are interested in working on a Ph.D. in designated science and engineering fields.

Eligibility This program is open to U.S. citizens who are seniors graduating from college with a GPA of 3.0 or higher, enrolled in the first year of a doctoral program, completing a terminal master's degree, or returning from the workforce and holding no more than a master's degree. Students currently in the third or subsequent year of a Ph.D. program or who already have a doctoral degree in any field (Ph.D., M.D., J.D., Ed.D.) are ineligible. Applicants must be interested in working on a Ph.D. in the physical sciences or related fields of science or engineering. The program welcomes applications from all qualified students and continues to emphasize the recruit-

ment of underrepresented minority (African American, Hispanic, Native American Indian, Eskimo, Aleut, and Pacific Islander) and women physical science and engineering students. Fellowships are provided to students at the 119 universities that are members of the consortium. Selection is based on academic standing (GPA), course work taken in preparation for graduate school, university and/or industry research experience, letters of recommendation, and GRE scores.

Financial data The fellowship pays tuition and fees plus an annual stipend of $20,000. It also provides on-site paid summer employment to enhance technical experience. The exact value of the fellowship depends on academic standing, summer employment, and graduate school attended; the total amount generally exceeds $200,000.

Duration Support is initially provided for 2 or 3 years, depending on the employer-sponsor. If the fellow makes satisfactory progress and continues to meet the conditions of the award, support may continue for a total of up to 6 years or completion of the Ph.D., whichever comes first.

Additional information This program began in 1989. Tuition and fees are provided by the participating universities. Stipends and summer internships are provided by sponsoring organizations. Students must submit separate applications for internships, which may have additional eligibility requirements. Internships are currently available at Lawrence Livermore National Laboratory in Livermore, California (astronomy, chemistry, computer science, geology, materials science, mathematics, and physics); National Security Agency in Fort Meade, Maryland (astronomy, chemistry, computer science, geology, materials science, mathematics, and physics); Sandia National Laboratory in Livermore, California (biology, chemistry, computer science, environmental science, geology, materials science, mathematics, and physics); and Sandia National Laboratory in Albuquerque, New Mexico (chemical engineering, chemistry, computer science, materials science, mathematics, mechanical engineering, and physics). Fellows must submit a separate application for dissertation support in the year prior to the beginning of their dissertation research program, but not until they can describe their intended research in general terms.

Number awarded Varies each year; recently, 11 of these fellowships were awarded.

Deadline November of each year.

[1050]
NATIONAL SPACE GRANT COLLEGE AND FELLOWSHIP PROGRAM

National Aeronautics and Space Administration
Attn: Office of Education
300 E Street, S.W.
Mail Suite 6M35
Washington, DC 20546-0001
(202) 358-1069   Fax: (202) 358-7097
E-mail: Diane.D.DeTroye@nasa.gov
Web: www.nasa.gov

Summary To provide financial assistance to undergraduate and graduate students (especially women and members of other underrepresented groups) who are interested in preparing for a career in a space-related field.

Eligibility This program is open to undergraduate and graduate students at colleges and universities that participate in the National Space Grant program of the U.S. National

Aeronautics and Space Administration (NASA) through their state consortium. Applicants must be interested in a program of study and/or research in a field of science, technology, engineering, or mathematics (STEM) related to space. A specific goal of the program is to increase preparation by members of underrepresented groups (minorities, women, and persons with disabilities) for STEM space-related careers. Financial need is not considered in the selection process.

Financial data Each consortium establishes the terms of the fellowship program in its state.

Additional information NASA established the Space Grant program in 1989. It operates through 52 consortia in each state, the District of Columbia, and Puerto Rico. Each consortium includes selected colleges and universities in that state as well as other affiliates from industry, museums, science centers, and state and local agencies.

Number awarded Varies each year.

Deadline Each consortium sets its own deadlines.

[1051]
NATIVE AMERICAN PROJECT GRANTS

Delta Kappa Gamma Society International-Mu State
  Organization
c/o Beverly Staff, Native American Project
7407 Lillie Lane
Pensacola, FL 32526
(850) 944-3302   E-mail: leannjax@yahoo.com
Web: www.orgsites.com/fl/mustatedeltakappagamma

Summary To provide financial assistance to female Native Americans from Florida who are working on a degree in education or conducting research into the history of Native Americans at a college or university in the state.

Eligibility This program is open to women who are members of a recognized Native American tribe in Florida. Applicants must be enrolled at an accredited college or university in the state and either working on a degree in education or conducting research into the history of Native Americans in Florida. Along with their application, they must submit a brief statement with details of the purpose of the grant, a letter of recommendation from a tribal official, and a copy of high school or college transcripts.

Financial data The stipend is $1,000.

Duration 1 year.

Number awarded 6 each year: 1 in each of the districts of the sponsoring organization in Florida.

Deadline May of each year.

[1052]
NATIVE AMERICAN WOMEN'S HEALTH EDUCATION RESOURCE CENTER INTERNSHIPS

Native American Women's Health Education Resource
  Center
Attn: Internship Coordinator
P.O. Box 572
Lake Andes, SD 57356-0572
(605) 487-7072   Fax: (605) 487-7964
E-mail: charon@charles-mix.com
Web: www.nativeshop.org

Summary To provide work experience to students and recent graduates interested in working at the Native Ameri-

can Women's Health Education Resource Center and its Domestic Violence Shelter.

Eligibility This program is open to college students, graduate students, and recent graduates. Applicants must have a background of work in Native American rights and health issues to promote civil rights, women's rights, and a healthy environment. They must be interested in working at the Native American Women's Health Education Resource Center and its Domestic Violence Shelter.

Financial data Interns receive a stipend of $500 per month, free room at the shelter, and partial board from the resource center's food pantry.

Duration 3 months to 1 year; priority is given for internships of 6 months or longer.

Additional information The Native American Women's Health Education Resource Center is a project of the Native American Community Board. It is located in Lake Andes, South Dakota in a rural area of the Yankton Sioux Reservation. The Domestic Violence Shelter is 4 blocks away. Past intern projects have included domestic violence advocacy at the shelter, counseling on the youth crisis hotline, environmental activism, Native women's reproductive health and rights, indigenous people's rights projects, web site development, organizing the annual community health fair, producing a Dakota language CD-ROM, and AIDS education.

Number awarded Varies each year.

Deadline Deadline not specified.

[1053]
NAVAL HELICOPTER ASSOCIATION GRADUATE SCHOLARSHIPS

Naval Helicopter Association
Attn: Scholarship Fund
P.O. Box 180578
Coronado, CA 92178-0578
(619) 435-7139   Fax: (619) 435-7354
E-mail: info@nhascholarship.org
Web: www.nhascholarship.org

Summary To provide financial assistance for graduate school to spouses and other students who have an affiliation with the rotary wing activities of the sea services.

Eligibility This program is open to graduate students who are 1) children, grandchildren, or spouses of current or former Navy, Marine Corps, or Coast Guard rotary wing aviators or aircrewmen; 2) individuals who are serving or have served in maintenance or support billets in rotary wing squadrons or wings and their spouses and children. Applicants must provide information on their rotary wing affiliation and a personal statement on their educational plans and future goals. Selection is based on that statement, academic proficiency, scholastic achievements and awards, extracurricular activities, employment history, and letters of recommendation.

Financial data The stipend is $3,000.

Duration 1 year.

Number awarded 1 each year.

Deadline January of each year.

[1054]
NAVY/MARINE CORPS/COAST GUARD ENLISTED DEPENDENT SPOUSE SCHOLARSHIP

Navy Wives Clubs of America
P.O. Box 54022
Millington, TN 38053-6022
Toll Free: (866) 511-NWCA
E-mail: nwca@navywivesclubsofamerica.org
Web: www.navywivesclubsofamerica.org/scholarinfo.htm

Summary To provide financial assistance for undergraduate or graduate study to spouses of naval personnel.

Eligibility This program is open to the spouses of active-duty Navy, Marine Corps, or Coast Guard members who can demonstrate financial need. Applicants must be 1) a high school graduate or senior planning to attend college full time next year; 2) currently enrolled in an undergraduate program and planning to continue as a full-time undergraduate; 3) a college graduate or senior planning to be a full-time graduate student next year; or 4) a high school graduate or GED recipient planning to attend vocational or business school next year. Along with their application, they must submit a brief statement on why they feel they should be awarded this scholarship and any special circumstances (financial or other) they wish to have considered. Financial need is also considered in the selection process.

Financial data The stipends range from $500 to $1,000 each year (depending upon the donations from chapters of the Navy Wives Clubs of America).

Duration 1 year.

Number awarded 1 or more each year.

Deadline May of each year.

[1055]
NCAA POSTGRADUATE SCHOLARSHIP PROGRAM

National Collegiate Athletic Association
Attn: Postgraduate Scholarship Program
1802 Alonzo Watford Sr. Drive
P.O. Box 6222
Indianapolis, IN 46206-6222
(317) 917-6650   Fax: (317) 917-6888
E-mail: lthomas@ncaa.org
Web: www.ncaa.org

Summary To provide financial support for graduate education in any field to student-athletes (females and males are judged separately).

Eligibility Eligible are student-athletes who have excelled academically and athletically and who are in their final year of intercollegiate athletics competition at member schools of the National Collegiate Athletic Association (NCAA). Candidates must be nominated by the faculty athletic representative or director of athletics and must have a GPA of 3.2 or higher. Nominees must be planning full- or part-time graduate study. Foreign student-athletes are eligible. For the fall term, scholarships are presented to athletes who participated in men's and women's cross country, men's football, men's and women's soccer, men's water polo, women's volleyball, women's field hockey, women's equestrian, and women's rugby. For the winter term, scholarships are presented to athletes who participated in men's and women's basketball, men's and women's fencing, men's and women's gymnastics, men's and women's ice hockey, men's and women's rifle,

men's and women's skiing, men's and women's swimming and diving, men's and women's indoor track and field, men's wrestling, women's bowling, and women's squash. For the spring term, scholarships are presented to athletes who participated in men's baseball, men's and women's golf, men's and women's lacrosse, women's rowing, women's softball, men's and women's tennis, men's volleyball, men's and women's outdoor track and field, women's water polo, and women's sand volleyball. Financial need is not considered in the selection process.

Financial data The stipend is $7,500.

Duration These are 1-time, nonrenewable awards.

Number awarded 174 each year: 87 for women and 87 for men. Each term, 29 scholarships are awarded to men and 29 to women.

Deadline January of each year for fall sports; March of each year for winter sports; May of each year for spring sports.

[1056]
NELL I. MONDY FELLOWSHIP

Sigma Delta Epsilon-Graduate Women in Science, Inc.
c/o Julie Gros-Louis, Fellowships Coordinator
University of Iowa-Department of Psychology
11 Seashore Hall E
Iowa City, IA 52242-1407
(319) 384-1816   Fax: (319) 335-0191
E-mail: Julie-gros-louis@uiowa.edu
Web: www.gwis.org/programs.htm

Summary To provide funding to women interested in conducting research anywhere in the world in the natural sciences, especially in food science or nutrition.

Eligibility This program is open to women from any country currently enrolled as a graduate student, engaged in postdoctoral research, or holding a junior faculty position. Applicants must be interested in conducting research anywhere in the world in the natural sciences; preference is given to those working in the areas of food science or nutrition. Along with their application, they must submit 2-paragraph essays on 1) how the proposed research relates to their degree program and/or career development; 2) initiatives in which they are participating to promote the careers of scientists, particularly women, within their institution, program, or peer group; and 3) relevant personal factors, including financial need, that should be considered in evaluating their proposal. Appointments are made without regard to race, religion, nationality, creed, national origin, sexual orientation, or age. Membership in Sigma Delta Epsilon-Graduate Women in Science is required.

Financial data The grant currently is $4,333. Funds may be used for such research expenses as expendable supplies, small equipment, publication of research findings, travel and subsistence while performing field studies, or travel to another laboratory for collaborative research. They may not be used for tuition, child care, travel to professional meetings or to begin a new appointment, administrative overhead or indirect costs, personal computers, living allowances, or equipment for general use.

Duration 1 year.

Additional information This fellowship was first awarded in 2002. An application processing fee of $30 is required.

Number awarded   Varies each year; recently, 3 of these grants were awarded.

Deadline   January of each year.

[1057]
NELLIE YEOH WHETTEN AWARD

AVS-Science and Technology of Materials, Interfaces, and Processing
Attn: Scholarship Committee
125 Maiden Lane, 15th Floor
New York, NY 10038
(212) 248-0200, ext. 221   Fax: (212) 248-0245
E-mail: angela@avs.org
Web: avs.org/inside.awards.aspx

Summary   To provide financial assistance to women interested in studying vacuum science and technology on the graduate school level.

Eligibility   This program is open to women of any nationality who are accepted at or enrolled in a graduate school in North America and studying vacuum science and technology. Applicants are normally expected not to graduate before the award selection. They must submit a description of their current research, including its goals and objectives, the scientific and/or technological reasons that motivate the work, their approach for achieving the goals, progress (if any), program plans, and impact the results might have in the advancement of the area of research. Selection is based on research and academic excellence.

Financial data   The stipend is $1,500; the winner also receives reimbursement of travel costs to attend the society's international symposium.

Duration   1 year.

Additional information   This award was established in 1989. AVS-Science and Technology of Materials, Interfaces, and Processing was formerly the American Vacuum Society.

Number awarded   1 each year.

Deadline   April of each year.

[1058]
NETWORK OF EXECUTIVE WOMEN SCHOLARSHIP

Network of Executive Women
c/o Nathalia Granger, Director of Operations
Accenture
161 North Clark Street, 37th Floor
Chicago, IL 60601
(312) 693-6855   Fax: (312) 726-4704
E-mail: ngranger@newonline.org
Web: www.newonline.org/?page=scholarships

Summary   To provide financial assistance to upper-division and graduate student women preparing for a career in the consumer products and retail industry.

Eligibility   This program is open to women enrolled full time as juniors, seniors, or graduate students in a retail, food, or consumer packaged goods-related program at a U.S. college or university. Applicants must have a GPA of 3.0 or higher. Along with their application, they must submit a 1-page essay explaining why they merit this scholarship and outlining their food, retail, or consumer packaged goods industry interests. Selection is based on that essay, a current resume, a tran-

script, and 2 letters of recommendation; financial need is not considered. U.S. citizenship is required.

Financial data   A stipend is awarded (amount not specified).

Duration   1 year.

Number awarded   1 or more each year.

Deadline   April of each year.

[1059]
NEW MEXICO MINORITY DOCTORAL LOAN-FOR-SERVICE PROGRAM

New Mexico Higher Education Department
Attn: Financial Aid Division
2048 Galisteo Street
Santa Fe, NM 87505-2100
(505) 476-8411   Toll Free: (800) 279-9777
Fax: (505) 476-8454   E-mail: Theresa.acker@state.nm.us
Web: hed.state.nm.us

Summary   To provide funding to women and underrepresented minorities who reside in New Mexico and are interested in working on a doctoral degree in selected fields.

Eligibility   This program is open to ethnic minorities and women who are residents of New Mexico and have received a baccalaureate degree from a public 4-year college or university in the state in mathematics, engineering, the physical or life sciences, or any other academic discipline in which ethnic minorities and women are demonstrably underrepresented in New Mexico academic institutions. Applicants must have been admitted as a full-time doctoral student at an approved university in any state. They must be sponsored by a New Mexico institution of higher education which has agreed to employ them in a tenure-track faculty position after they obtain their degree. U.S. citizenship is required.

Financial data   Loans range up to $25,000 per year but average $15,000. This is a loan-for-service program; for every year of service as a college faculty member in New Mexico, a portion of the loan is forgiven. If the entire service agreement is fulfilled, 100% of the loan is eligible for forgiveness. Penalties may be assessed if the service agreement is not satisfied.

Duration   1 year; may be renewed up to 3 additional years.

Number awarded   Up to 12 each year.

Deadline   March of each year.

[1060]
NINETY-NINES, INC. AMELIA EARHART MEMORIAL SCHOLARSHIPS

Ninety-Nines, Inc.
4300 Amelia Earhart Road
Oklahoma City, OK 73159
(405) 685-7969   Toll Free: (800) 994-1929
Fax: (405) 685-7985   E-mail: AEChair@ninety-nines.org
Web: www.ninety-nines.org/index.cfm/scholarships.htm

Summary   To provide funding to members of the Ninety-Nines (an organization of women pilots) who are interested in advanced flight training or academic study related to aviation.

Eligibility   This program is open to women who have been members of the organization for at least 1 year. Applicants must be interested in 1 of the following 4 types of scholarships: 1) flight training, to complete an additional pilot certificate or rating or pilot training course; 2) jet type rating, to complete type rating certification in any jet; 3) technical certification, to complete an aviation or aerospace technical training or certification course; or 4) academic, to work on an associate, bachelor's, master's, or doctoral degree in such fields as aerospace engineering, aviation technology, aviation business management, air traffic management, or professional pilot. They must submit their application to their Ninety-Nines scholarship chair, who forwards it to the appropriate Amelia Earhart Scholarship Trustee. Applicants for flight training scholarships must be a current pilot with the appropriate medical certification and approaching the flight time requirement for the rating or certificate. Applicants for jet type rating scholarships must be a current airline transport pilot with a first-class medical certificate and at least 100 hours of multi-engine flight time or combined multi-engine and turbine time. Applicants for academic scholarships must be currently enrolled; associate or bachelor's degree students must have a GPA of 3.0 or higher. Financial need is considered in the selection process.

Financial data Flight training, jet type rating, and technical certification scholarships provide payment of all costs to complete the appropriate rating or certificate. Academic scholarships provide a stipend of up to $5,000 per year.

Duration Support is provided until completion of the rating, certificate, or degree.

Additional information This program was established in 1941. It includes the following endowed scholarships: the Jane Zieber Kelley Memorial Scholarship of the Aeons (established in 1979), the Gerda Ruhnke Memorial Flight Instructor Scholarship (established in 1988), the Geraldine Mickelsen Memorial Scholarship (established in 1993), the Alice Hammond Memorial Scholarship (established in 1995), the Lydiellen M. Hagan Memorial Scholarship (established in 1997), the Katherine A. Menges Brick Scholarship (established in 1998), the Betty DeWitt Witmer Scholarship (established in 1999), the Virginia S. Richardson Memorial Scholarship (established in 2000), the Darlene Sanders Memorial Scholarship (established in 2000), the Milton and Bonnie Seymour Memorial Scholarship (established in 2000), the Marion Barnick Memorial Scholarship (established in 2001), the Evelyn Bryan Johnson Memorial Scholarship (established in 2002), and the Mary Kelley Memorial Scholarship (established in 2003).

Number awarded Varies each year; recently, 14 of these scholarships were awarded.

Deadline Applications must be submitted to the chapter scholarship chair by November of each year; they must forward the applications from their chapter to the designated trustee by December of each year.

[1061]
NORMA CHIPMAN WELLS LOYALTY GRANT

Lambda Kappa Sigma Pharmacy Fraternity
Attn: Executive Director
S77 W16906 Casey Drive
P.O. Box 570
Muskego, WI 53150-0570
Toll Free: (800) LKS-1913   Fax: (262) 679-4558
E-mail: lks@lks.org
Web: www.lks.org

Summary To provide financial assistance to members of Lambda Kappa Sigma who are interested in working on a Pharm.D. degree and can demonstrate loyalty.

Eligibility This program is open to collegiate or alumnae members of Lambda Kappa Sigma who are enrolled in a licensure-eligible pharmacy degree program. (In the United States, the Pharm.D. degree is the only qualifying program at schools or colleges of pharmacy recognized by the Accreditation Council on Pharmacy Education.) Applicants must rank in the top half of their class and be able to demonstrate financial need. Along with their application, they must submit a brief essay on their personal loyalty qualities and the importance of loyalty.

Financial data The stipend is $1,000.

Duration 1 year.

Additional information This program was established in 1994. Lambda Kappa Sigma was founded in 1913 to promote the profession of pharmacy among women.

Number awarded 1 each year.

Deadline October of each year.

[1062]
NORTH CAROLINA BUSINESS AND PROFESSIONAL WOMEN'S FOUNDATION SCHOLARSHIPS

North Carolina Federation of Business and Professional Women's Club, Inc.
Attn: BPW/NC Foundation
P.O. Box 276
Carrboro, NC 27510
Web: www.bpw-nc.org/Default.aspx?pageId=837230

Summary To provide financial assistance to women attending North Carolina colleges, community colleges, or graduate schools.

Eligibility This program is open to women who are currently enrolled in a community college, 4-year college, or graduate school in North Carolina. Applicants must be endorsed by a local BPW unit. Along with their application, they must submit a 1-page statement that summarizes their career goals, previous honors, or community activities and justifies their need for this scholarship. U.S. citizenship is required.

Financial data The stipend is $1,000. Funds are paid directly to the recipient's school.

Duration 1 year; recipients may reapply.

Additional information This program was established in 1996.

Number awarded 2 each year.

Deadline April of each year.

[1063]
NORTHWESTERN REGION FELLOWSHIP AWARD

Soroptimist International of the Americas-Northwestern Region
c/o Kathy A. King
22330 Drazil Road
Malin, OR 97632-9722
E-mail: info@soroptimistnwr.org
Web: soroptimistnwr.org/what-we-do/fellowship-award

Summary   To provide financial assistance for graduate study in any state to women who reside in the Northwestern Region of Soroptimist International of the Americas.

Eligibility   This program is open to women who reside in the Northwestern Region of Soroptimist International of the Americas. Applicants must be established in business or a profession and have a bachelor's or master's degree from an accredited university. They must present a plan of graduate study at an accredited college or university in any state that leads to an advanced degree or enhanced standing or competence in their business or profession.

Financial data   The stipend is $4,000.

Duration   1 year.

Additional information   The Northwestern Region includes Alaska, designated counties in Idaho (Benewah, Bonner, Boundary, Clearwater, Idaho, Kootenai, Latah, Lewis, Nez Perce, and Shoshone), Montana, Oregon (except Malheur County), and Washington.

Number awarded   1 each year.

Deadline   The application must be submitted to the sponsoring Soroptimist Club by January of each year.

[1064]
NWSA GRADUATE SCHOLARSHIP AWARD

National Women's Studies Association
7100 Baltimore Avenue, Suite 203
College Park, MD 20740
(301) 403-0407   Fax: (301) 403-4137
E-mail: nwsaoffice@nwsa.org
Web: www.nwsa.org

Summary   To provide funding to members of the National Women's Studies Association (NWSA) working on a graduate thesis in women's studies.

Eligibility   This program is open to association members engaged in the research or writing stages of a master's thesis or Ph.D. dissertation in the interdisciplinary field of women's studies. The research project must focus on women and must enhance the NWSA mission. Applicants must submit brief statements on their financial need, feminist or community activities, and relevance of research to NWSA goals.

Financial data   The grant is $1,000.

Duration   1 year.

Number awarded   1 each year.

Deadline   May of each year.

[1065]
NYWICI FOUNDATION SCHOLARSHIPS

New York Women in Communications, Inc.
Attn: NYWICI Foundation
355 Lexington Avenue, 15th Floor
New York, NY 10017-6603
(212) 297-2133   Fax: (212) 370-9047
E-mail: nywicipr@nywici.org
Web: www.nywici.org/foundation/scholarships

Summary   To provide financial assistance to female residents of designated eastern states who are interested in preparing for a career in communications at a college or graduate school in any state.

Eligibility   This program is open to women who are seniors graduating from high schools in New York, New Jersey, Connecticut, or Pennsylvania or undergraduate or graduate students who are permanent residents of those states; they must be attending or planning to attend a college or university in any state. Graduate students must be members of New York Women in Communications, Inc. (NYWICI). Also eligible are women who reside outside the 4 states but are currently enrolled at a college or university within 1 of the 5 boroughs of New York City. All applicants must be working on a degree in a communications-related field (e.g., advertising, broadcasting, communications, English, film, journalism, marketing, new media, public relations) and have a GPA of 3.2 or higher. Along with their application, they must submit a 2-page resume that includes school and extracurricular activities, significant achievements, academic honors and awards, and community service work; a personal essay of 300 to 500 words on their choice of an assigned topic that changes annually; 2 letters of recommendation; and an official transcript. Selection is based on academic record, need, demonstrated leadership, participation in school and community activities, honors, work experience, goals and aspirations, and unusual personal and/or family circumstances. U.S. citizenship is required.

Financial data   The maximum stipend is $10,000.

Duration   1 year; recipients may reapply.

Number awarded   Varies each year; recently, 19 of these scholarships, with a total value of $103,000, were awarded.

Deadline   January of each year.

[1066]
OKLAHOMA BW FOUNDATION SCHOLARSHIPS

Oklahoma Federation of Business Women, Inc.
Attn: Oklahoma Business Women's Foundation
P.O. Box 160
Maud, OK 74854-0160
(405) 374-2866   Fax: (405) 374-2316
E-mail: askkathy@oklahomabusinesswomen.org
Web: www.oklahomabusinesswomen/obw_foundation.htm

Summary   To provide financial assistance to women from any state who are working on an undergraduate or graduate degree in any field at a school in Oklahoma.

Eligibility   This program is open to women from any state who are working on an undergraduate or graduate degree at a college, university, or technical school in Oklahoma. Applicants must submit a 500-word essay on their career goals and how receiving this scholarship will help them to accomplish those goals and make a difference in their professional career. Selection is based on that essay, academic record, employment and volunteer record, and financial need.

Financial data   Stipends are $1,000, $750, or $500.

Duration   1 year.

Additional information   This program includes the following named scholarships: the Jewell Russell Mann Scholarship, the Dorothy Dickerson Scholarship, the Ann Garrison/Delores Schofield Scholarship, and the Dr. Ann Marie Benson Scholarship.

Number awarded   Varies each year; recently, 9 of these scholarships were awarded.

Deadline   February of each year.

[1067]
OLIVE LYNN SALEMBIER MEMORIAL REENTRY SCHOLARSHIP

Society of Women Engineers
Attn: Scholarship Selection Committee
120 South LaSalle Street, Suite 1515
Chicago, IL 60603-3572
(312) 596-5223   Toll Free: (877) SWE-INFO
Fax: (312) 644-8557
E-mail: scholarshipapplication@swe.org
Web: societyofwomenengineers.swe.org

Summary   To provide financial assistance to women interested in returning to college or graduate school to study engineering or computer science.

Eligibility   This program is open to women who are planning to enroll at an ABET-accredited 4-year college or university. Applicants must have been out of the engineering workforce and school for at least 2 years and must be planning to return as an undergraduate or graduate student to major in computer science or engineering. Selection is based on merit.

Financial data   The award is $1,500.

Duration   1 year; may be renewed up to 3 additional years.

Additional information   This program was established in 1979.

Number awarded   1 each year.

Deadline   February of each year.

[1068]
ON THE ROAD TO MATRIX SCHOLARSHIP

New York Women in Communications, Inc.
Attn: NYWICI Foundation
355 Lexington Avenue, 15th Floor
New York, NY 10017-6603
(212) 297-2133   Fax: (212) 370-9047
E-mail: nywicipr@nywici.org
Web: www.nywici.org/foundation/scholarships

Summary   To provide financial assistance to upper-division and graduate student members of New York Women in Communications, Inc. (NYWICI) who reside in designated eastern states and are interested in preparing for a career in communications at a college or graduate school in any state.

Eligibility   This program is open to residents of New York, New Jersey, Connecticut, or Pennsylvania who are members of NYWICI and attending a college or university in any state. Also eligible are women who reside outside the 4 states but are currently enrolled at a college or university within 1 of the 5 boroughs of New York City. Applicants must be college juniors, seniors, or graduate students and working on a degree in a communications-related field (e.g., advertising, broadcasting, communications, English, film, journalism, marketing, new media, public relations). They must have a GPA of 3.2 or higher. Along with their application, they must submit a 2-page resume that includes school and extracurricular activities, significant achievements, academic honors and awards, and community service work; a personal essay of 300 to 500 words on their choice of an assigned topic that changes annually; 2 letters of recommendation; and an official transcript. Selection is based on academic record, need, demonstrated leadership, participation in school and community activities, honors, work experience, goals and aspira-

tions, and unusual personal and/or family circumstances. U.S. citizenship is required.

Financial data   The stipend ranges up to $10,000.

Duration   1 year.

Additional information   This program is sponsored by the Matrix Hall of Fame, an organization of women who have received special recognition from NYWICI.

Number awarded   1 each year.

Deadline   January of each year.

[1069]
ORGANIC CHEMISTRY GRADUATE STUDENT FELLOWSHIPS

American Chemical Society
Division of Organic Chemistry
1155 16th Street, N.W.
Washington, DC 20036
(202) 872-4401   Toll Free: (800) 227-5558, ext. 4401
E-mail: division@acs.org
Web: www.organicdivision.org/?nd=graduate_fellowship

Summary   To provide funding for research to female, minority, and other members of the Division of Organic Chemistry of the American Chemical Society (ACS) who are working on a doctoral degree in organic chemistry.

Eligibility   This program is open to members of the division who are entering the third or fourth year of a Ph.D. program in organic chemistry. Applicants must submit 3 letters of recommendation, a resume, and a short essay on a research area of their choice. U.S. citizenship or permanent resident status is required. Selection is based primarily on evidence of research accomplishment. Applications from women and minorities are especially encouraged.

Financial data   The stipend is $26,000; that includes $750 for travel support to present a poster of their work at the National Organic Symposium.

Duration   1 year.

Additional information   This program was established in 1982. It includes the Emmanuil Troyansky Fellowship. Current corporate sponsors include Eli Lilly, Pfizer, Roche, GlaxoSmithKline, Genentech, Organic Reactions, Organic Syntheses, Boehringer Ingelheim, and Amgen.

Number awarded   Varies each year; recently, 10 of these fellowships were awarded.

Deadline   May of each year.

[1070]
OUTPUTLINKS WOMAN OF DISTINCTION AWARD

Electronic Document Systems Foundation
Attn: EDSF Scholarship Awards
1845 Precinct Line Road, Suite 212
Hurst, TX 76054
(817) 849-1145   Fax: (817) 849-1185
E-mail: info@edsf.org
Web: www.edsf.org/what_we_do/scholarships/index.html

Summary   To provide financial assistance to female undergraduate and graduate students from any country interested in preparing for a career in document management and graphic communications.

Eligibility   This program is open to full-time female undergraduate and graduate students from any country who demonstrate a strong interest in preparing for a career in the document management and graphic communications industry, including computer science and engineering (e.g., web design, webmaster, software development, materials engineer, applications specialist, information technology designer, systems analyst); graphic and media communications (e.g., graphic designer, illustrator, color scientist, print production, prepress imaging specialist, workflow specialist, document preparation, production and/or document distribution, content management, e-commerce, imaging science, printing, web authoring, electronic publishing, archiving, security); or business (e.g., sales, marketing, trade shows, customer service, project or product development, management). Preference is given to graduate students and upper-division undergraduates, but freshmen and sophomores who can show interest, experience, and/or commitment to the document management and graphic communication industry are encouraged to apply. Applicants must have a GPA of 3.0 or higher. Along with their application, they must submit 2 essays on assigned topics that change annually but relate to the document management and graphic communication industries. Selection is based on the essays, academic excellence, participation in school activities, community service, honors and organizational affiliations, education goals, and recommendations; financial need is not considered.

Financial data   The stipend is $5,000.

Duration   1 year.

Additional information   This program is sponsored by OutputLinks.

Number awarded   1 each year.

Deadline   April of each year.

[1071]
PACIFIC FELLOWSHIPS

American Association of University Women-Honolulu
  Branch
Attn: Scholarship Committee
1802 Ke'eaumoku Street
Honolulu, HI 96822
(808) 537-4702   Fax: (808) 537-4702
E-mail: Edu@aauw-honolulu.org
Web: aauw.xodev01.com

Summary   To provide financial assistance to women who are working on a graduate degree in a field related to the Pacific Islands or Pacific Rim at a university in Hawaii.

Eligibility   This program is open to female graduate students who are currently enrolled at a college or university in Hawaii. Applicants must have been residents of Hawaii for at least 5 years. They must be interested in 1) a program of graduate study and/or research in or on the Pacific Islands or the Pacific Rim countries, or 2) participating in a seminar or conference appropriate to advanced study and/or research relating to the Pacific Islands or to the Pacific Rim countries, defined as islands in the Pacific Ocean and those countries (except the mainland United States), territories, or continents bordering on the Pacific Ocean. Along with their application, they must submit a record of academic and research capabilities; a 500-word statement on their proposed study or research, its relationship to their present academic program, its significance, and its approval by their department chair or academic adviser; and documentation of financial need.

Financial data   Stipends range from $1,500 to $5,000; funds must be used for study or research expenses.

Additional information   The award will not be granted if a visa is denied by the country in which the study or research is to be pursued.

Number awarded   Varies each year; recently, 6 of these fellowships were awarded: 3 at $4,000, 1 at $3,000, and 2 at $1,000.

Deadline   May of each year.

[1072]
PATSY TAKEMOTO MINK EDUCATION FOUNDATION EDUCATION SUPPORT AWARD

Patsy Takemoto Mink Education Foundation for Low-
  Income Women and Children
P.O. Box 479
Honolulu, HI 96809
E-mail: admin@ptmfoundation.net
Web: www.patsyminkfoundation.org/edsupport.html

Summary   To provide financial assistance for college or graduate school to low-income women.

Eligibility   This program is open to women who are at least 17 years of age and are from a low-income family (less than $17,500 annually for a family of 2, $22,000 for a family of 3, or $26,500 for a family of 4). Applicants must be mothers with minor children. They must be 1) enrolled in a skills training, ESL, or GED program; or 2) working on an associate, bachelor's, master's, professional, or doctoral degree. Along with their application, they must submit brief essays on what this award will help them accomplish, the program in which they are or will be enrolled, how they decided on that educational pursuit, their educational goals, their educational experience, and their personal and educational history.

Financial data   The stipend is $2,000.

Duration   1 year.

Additional information   This foundation was established in 2003.

Number awarded   5 each year.

Deadline   July of each year.

[1073]
P.E.O. SCHOLAR AWARDS

P.E.O. Sisterhood
Attn: Scholar Awards Office
3700 Grand Avenue
Des Moines, IA 50312-2899
(515) 255-3153   Fax: (515) 255-3820
E-mail: psa@peodsm.org
Web: www.peointernational.org/peo-projectsphilanthropies

Summary   To provide funding for doctoral study or postdoctoral research in any field to women in the United States or Canada.

Eligibility   This program is open to women who are either working full time on a doctoral degree or conducting postdoctoral research at universities in the United States or Canada. Applicants must be within 2 years of achieving their educational goal but have at least 1 full academic year remaining. They must be sponsored by a local P.E.O. chapter. Selection is based on academic record, academic awards and honors, scholarly activities, and recommendations; financial need is not considered. U.S. or Canadian citizenship is required.

Financial data A significant stipend is awarded (amount not specified).
Duration 1 year; nonrenewable.
Additional information This program was established in 1991 by the Women's Philanthropic Educational Organization (P.E.O.).
Number awarded Varies each year.
Deadline November of each year.

[1074]
PETER B. WAGNER MEMORIAL AWARD FOR WOMEN IN ATMOSPHERIC SCIENCES
Desert Research Institute
Attn: Selection Committee, Wagner Award
2215 Raggio Parkway
Reno, NV 89512-1095
(702) 673-7300   Fax: (702) 673-7397
E-mail: Gannet.Hallar@dri.edu
Web: www.dri.edu/awards-and-honors

Summary To recognize and reward outstanding research papers written by women graduate students on atmospheric sciences.

Eligibility Women working on a master's or doctoral degree in atmospheric sciences or a related field are invited to submit a research paper for consideration. The applicants may be enrolled at a university anywhere in the United States. They must submit a paper, up to 15 pages in length, based on original research directly related to the identification, clarification, and/or resolution of an atmospheric/climatic problem. Selection is based on the originality of ideas expressed, presentation of concept, how well the subject matter relates to real-world atmospheric/climatic problems or their resolution, and how well the research is defined by the introduction, methods, results, and conclusions of the manuscript.

Financial data The award is $1,500.
Duration The award is presented annually.
Additional information This award was first presented in 1998.
Number awarded 1 each year.
Deadline April of each year.

[1075]
PHIPPS MEMORIAL SCHOLARSHIP
General Federation of Women's Clubs of Connecticut
c/o JoAnn Calnen, President
74 Spruceland Road
Enfield, CT 06082-2359
E-mail: gfwcct@yahoo.com
Web: www.gfwcct.org

Summary To provide financial assistance to women in Connecticut who are working on an undergraduate or graduate degree.

Eligibility This program is open to female residents of Connecticut who have completed at least 2 years of college. Applicants must have a GPA of 3.0 or higher and be working on a bachelor's or master's degree. Selection is based on academic ability, future promise, and financial need.

Financial data The stipend is $1,000.
Duration 1 year.

Number awarded 1 each year.
Deadline February of each year.

[1076]
PHYLLIS V. ROBERTS SCHOLARSHIP
General Federation of Women's Clubs of Virginia
Attn: Scholarship Committee
513 Forest Avenue
P.O. Box 8750
Richmond, VA 23226
(804) 288-3724   Toll Free: (800) 699-8392
Fax: (804) 288-0341
E-mail: headquarters@gfwcvirginia.org
Web: www.gfwcvirginia.org/forms/scholarships.htm

Summary To provide financial assistance to women residents of Virginia who are working on a graduate degree in a designated field.

Eligibility This program is open to women residents of Virginia who are working on a graduate degree at a college or university in the state. The field of study varies each year. Applicants must have an undergraduate GPA of 3.0 or higher. Along with their application, they must submit 1) a short statement of their reason for choosing a graduate degree in the designated field; and 2) a resume that includes educational and employment history, community service, and awards received.

Financial data The stipend is $1,000. Funds are paid directly to the recipient's college or university.
Duration 1 year.
Number awarded 3 each year.
Deadline March of each year.

[1077]
PI BETA PHI ALUMNAE CONTINUING EDUCATION SCHOLARSHIPS
Pi Beta Phi
Attn: Pi Beta Phi Foundation
1154 Town and Country Commons Drive
Town and Country, MO 63017
(636) 256-1357   Fax: (636) 256-8124
E-mail: fndn@pibetaphi.org
Web: www.pibetaphifoundation.org/scholarship-program

Summary To provide financial assistance for graduate school or continuing education to alumnae of Pi Beta Phi.

Eligibility This program is open to women who are members of Pi Beta Phi in good standing and have paid their alumnae dues for the current year. Applicants must have been out of undergraduate school for at least 2 years and have a GPA of 3.0 or higher for all undergraduate and graduate study. Advanced work at a college or university is encouraged, but advanced study at a career, vocational, or technical school will also be considered. Along with their application, they must submit documentation of financial need, an employment history, a record of volunteer service, a description of the proposed program of study, transcripts, and recommendations. Selection is based on financial need, academic record, alumnae service, community service, and how the proposed course of study relates to future career development.

Financial data Stipends range from $1,200 to $1,800.
Duration 1 year.

Additional information   This program was established in 1982.

Number awarded   Varies each year; recently, 4 of these scholarships were awarded.

Deadline   February of each year.

[1078]
PI BETA PHI GRADUATE FELLOWSHIPS

Pi Beta Phi
Attn: Pi Beta Phi Foundation
1154 Town and Country Commons Drive
Town and Country, MO 63017
(636) 256-1357   Fax: (636) 256-8124
E-mail: fndn@pibetaphi.org
Web: www.pibetaphifoundation.org/scholarship-program

Summary   To provide financial assistance for graduate school to members of Pi Beta Phi.

Eligibility   This program is open to women who are dues-paying members in good standing of Pi Beta Phi (as a graduating senior or alumna) and graduated no more than 4 years previously. Applicants must be planning full-time graduate work at an accredited college, university, or technical professional school. They must have a GPA of 3.0 or higher for all undergraduate and graduate study. Selection is based on financial need, academic record, and service to the sorority, campus, and community.

Financial data   Stipends range from $2,000 to $6,500.

Duration   1 year.

Additional information   This program was established in 1909. It includes the Past Grand Presidents Memorial Graduate Fellowship, the Corrine Hammond Gray Graduate Fellowship, the Joanie Arnold Graduate Fellowship, and Friendship Fund Fellowships.

Number awarded   Varies each year; recently, 5 of these fellowships were awarded.

Deadline   February of each year.

[1079]
PI STATE NATIVE AMERICAN GRANTS-IN-AID

Delta Kappa Gamma Society International-Pi State
   Organization
c/o Harlene Gilbert
5338 East Lake Road
Romulus, NY 14541
(315) 585-6691   E-mail: hgilbert@happiness.org
Web: www.deltakappagamma.org/NY/ASaGiA.html

Summary   To provide funding to Native American women from New York who plan to work in education or another service field.

Eligibility   This program is open to Native American women from New York who are attending a 2- or 4-year college in the state. Applicants must be planning to work in education or another service field, but preference is given to those majoring in education. Both undergraduate and graduate students are eligible.

Financial data   The grant is $500 per semester ($1,000 per year). Funds may be used for any career-related purpose, including purchase of textbooks.

Duration   1 semester; may be renewed for a total of 5 years and a total of $5,000 over a recipient's lifetime.

Number awarded   Up to 5 each year.

Deadline   July or December of each year.

[1080]
PORTLAND CHAPTER WOMEN'S TRANSPORTATION SEMINAR LEADERSHIP SCHOLARSHIP

Women's Transportation Seminar-Portland Chapter
c/o Lisa Diercksen, Scholarship Chair
DKS Associates
1400 S.W. Fifth Avenue, Suite 500
Portland, OR 97201-5502
(503) 243-3500
E-mail: wts_portland-chapter@yahoo.com
Web: www.wtsinternational.org/Chapters.aspx?ID=7080

Summary   To provide financial assistance to women from Oregon and southwestern Washington who have demonstrated leadership and are working on an undergraduate or graduate degree in a transportation-related field at a school in any state.

Eligibility   This program is open to women who are residents of Oregon or southwestern Washington and currently enrolled as an undergraduate or graduate student at a college or university in any state. Applicants must be preparing for a career in a transportation-related field and be working on a degree in transportation engineering, planning, finance, logistics, or a related field. They must have a GPA of 3.0 or higher and be able to demonstrate leadership qualities. Along with their application, they must submit a 500-word personal statement about their career goals after graduation, how they demonstrate leadership in the transportation industry, and why they think they should receive this scholarship. Minority candidates are encouraged to apply. Selection is based on transportation goals, academic record, and transportation-related activities or job skills.

Financial data   The stipend is $5,000.

Duration   1 year.

Number awarded   1 each year.

Deadline   March of each year.

[1081]
PORTLAND CHAPTER WOMEN'S TRANSPORTATION SEMINAR SCHOLARSHIPS

Women's Transportation Seminar-Portland Chapter
c/o Lisa Diercksen, Scholarship Chair
DKS Associates
1400 S.W. Fifth Avenue, Suite 500
Portland, OR 97201-5502
(503) 243-3500
E-mail: wts_portland-chapter@yahoo.com
Web: www.wtsinternational.org/Chapters.aspx?ID=7080

Summary   To provide financial assistance to women from Oregon and southwestern Washington who are working on an undergraduate or graduate degree in a transportation-related field at a school in any state.

Eligibility   This program is open to women who are residents of Oregon or southwestern Washington and currently enrolled as an undergraduate or graduate student at a college or university in any state. Applicants must be preparing for a career in a transportation-related field and be working on a degree in transportation engineering, planning, finance, logistics, or a related field. They must have a GPA of 3.0 or higher. Along with their application, they must submit a 500-word personal statement about their career goals after graduation and why they think they should receive this scholarship. Minority candidates are encouraged to apply. Selection is based on transportation goals, academic record, and transportation-related activities or job skills.

Financial data The stipend is $3,500.

Duration 1 year.

Number awarded 3 each year.

Deadline March of each year.

[1082]
PREDOCTORAL RESEARCH TRAINING FELLOWSHIPS IN EPILEPSY

Epilepsy Foundation
Attn: Research Department
8301 Professional Place
Landover, MD 20785-2237
(301) 459-3700   Toll Free: (800) EFA-1000
Fax: (301) 577-2684   TDD: (800) 332-2070
E-mail: grants@efa.org
Web: www.epilepsyfoundation.org

Summary To provide funding to doctoral candidates (particularly women, minorities, and individuals with disabilities) who are conducting dissertation research on a topic related to epilepsy.

Eligibility This program is open to full-time graduate students working on a Ph.D. in biochemistry, genetics, neuroscience, nursing, pharmacology, pharmacy, physiology, or psychology. Applicants must be conducting dissertation research on a topic relevant to epilepsy under the guidance of a mentor with expertise in the area of epilepsy investigation. Applications from women, members of minority groups, and people with disabilities are especially encouraged. U.S. citizenship is not required, but the project must be conducted in the United States. Selection is based on the relevance of the proposed work to epilepsy, the applicant's qualifications, the mentor's qualifications, the scientific quality of the proposed dissertation research, the quality of the training environment for research related to epilepsy, and the adequacy of the facility.

Financial data The grant is $20,000, consisting of $19,000 for a stipend and $1,000 to support travel to attend the annual meeting of the American Epilepsy Society.

Duration 1 year.

Additional information Support for this program, which began in 1998, is provided by many individuals, families, and corporations, especially the American Epilepsy Society, Abbott Laboratories, Ortho-McNeil Pharmaceutical, and Pfizer Inc.

Number awarded Varies each year.

Deadline August of each year.

[1083]
PROJECT RED FLAG ACADEMIC SCHOLARSHIP FOR WOMEN WITH BLEEDING DISORDERS

National Hemophilia Foundation
Attn: Manager of Education
P.O. Box 971483
Ypsilanti, MI 48197
(734) 890-2504   E-mail: pflax@hemophilia.org
Web: www.projectredflag.org/scholarship.htm

Summary To provide financial assistance for college or graduate school to women who have a bleeding disorder.

Eligibility This program is open to women who are entering or already enrolled in an undergraduate or graduate program at a university, college, or accredited vocational school. Applicants must have von Willebrand Disease, hemophilia or other clotting factor deficiency, or carrier status. Along with their application, they must submit a 250-word essay that describes how their education and future career plans will benefit others in the bleeding disorders community. Financial need is not considered in the selection process.

Financial data The stipend is $2,500.

Duration 1 year.

Additional information The program was established in 2005 in partnership with the Centers for Disease Control and Prevention (CDC) and with support from CSL Behring.

Number awarded 2 each year.

Deadline May of each year.

[1084]
PUGET SOUND BUSINESS JOURNAL'S WOMEN OF INFLUENCE-LYTLE ENTERPRISES SCHOLARSHIP

Seattle Foundation
Attn: Scholarship Administrator
1200 Fifth Avenue, Suite 1300
Seattle, WA 98101-3151
(206) 622-2294   Fax: (206) 622-7673
E-mail: scholarships@seattlefoundation.org
Web: www.seattlefoundation.org

Summary To provide financial assistance to women from any state working on a graduate business degree at a university in Washington.

Eligibility This program is open to women from any state who are working on a master's degree in business at an accredited college or university in Washington. Applicants must be able to demonstrate financial need. Along with their application, they must submit a 250-word essay about themselves, their educational and career achievements, and their goals. Nontraditional students, including returning students and older adults, are strongly encouraged to apply.

Financial data The stipend is $5,000.

Duration 1 year; nonrenewable.

Additional information This program is supported by the Puget Sound Business Journal and by Chuck and Karen Lytel. The recipient must attend the annual "Women of Influence" event in November.

Number awarded 1 or more each year.

Deadline February of each year.

[1085]
PUGET SOUND CHAPTER HELENE M. OVERLY MEMORIAL SCHOLARSHIP

Women's Transportation Seminar-Puget Sound Chapter
c/o Jennifer Barnes, Scholarship C0-Chair
Heffron Transportation, Inc.
6544 N.E. 61st Street
Seattle, WA 98115
(206) 523-3939   Fax: (206) 523-4949
E-mail: jennifer@hefftrans.com
Web: www.wtsinternational.org/Chapters.aspx?ID=7166

Summary   To provide financial assistance to women from Washington working on a graduate degree related to transportation.

Eligibility   This program is open to women who are residents of Washington, studying at a college in the state, or working as an intern in the state. Applicants must be currently enrolled in a graduate degree program in a transportation-related field, such as engineering, planning, finance, or logistics. They must have a GPA of 3.0 or higher and plans to prepare for a career in a transportation-related field. Minority women are especially encouraged to apply. Along with their application, they must submit a 750-word statement about their career goals after graduation and why they think they should receive this scholarship award. Selection is based on that statement, academic record, and transportation-related activities or job skills. Financial need is not considered.

Financial data   The stipend is $4,000.

Duration   1 year.

Additional information   The winner is also nominated for scholarships offered by the national organization of the Women's Transportation Seminar.

Number awarded   1 each year.

Deadline   November of each year.

[1086]
RACHEL ROYSTON PERMANENT SCHOLARSHIP

Delta Kappa Gamma Society International-Alpha Sigma
    State Organization
c/o Jennee Osburn
6022 25th Avenue N.W.
Seattle, WA 98115-7104
E-mail: roystonscholarship@yahoo.com
Web: www.deltakappagamma.org/WA/rachel.html

Summary   To provide financial assistance to women in Washington who are interested in working on a graduate degree in education at a university in any state.

Eligibility   This program is open to women who are Washington residents doing graduate work in education at an approved institution of higher learning in any state, working on either a master's or doctoral degree or in a field of special interest. Applicants must submit 300-word essays on 1) their long-term professional goal and its significance to the field of education; 2) the steps toward their goal they will complete during the scholarship time period; and 3) anything else they wish the committee to know. Selection is based on scholarship, professional service, potential for future service in education, and promise of distinction. A personal interview is required of all finalists.

Financial data   The amount of each award is set at the discretion of the foundation's board of trustees. Awards generally range from $500 to $2,000.

Duration   Awards may be made for 1 quarter, semester, or academic year. A recipient may, upon fulfilling certain conditions, reapply for a second award.

Additional information   This program became operational in 1967.

Number awarded   Varies each year; recently, 6 of these scholarships, with a value of $10,000, were awarded. Since the program began, 285 scholarships worth $534,640 have been awarded.

Deadline   November of each year.

[1087]
RALPH W. SHRADER DIVERSITY SCHOLARSHIPS

Armed Forces Communications and Electronics
    Association
Attn: AFCEA Educational Foundation
4400 Fair Lakes Court
Fairfax, VA 22033-3899
(703) 631-6149   Toll Free: (800) 336-4583, ext. 6149
Fax: (703) 631-4693   E-mail: scholarship@afcea.org
Web: www.afcea.org

Summary   To provide financial assistance to master's degree students (especially women and minorities) in fields related to communications and electronics.

Eligibility   This program is open to U.S. citizens working on a master's degree at an accredited college or university in the United States. Applicants must be enrolled full time and studying computer science, computer technology, engineering (chemical, electrical, electronic, communications, or systems), mathematics, physics, management information systems, or a field directly related to the support of U.S. national security or intelligence enterprises. At least 1 of these scholarships is set aside for a woman or a minority. Selection is based primarily on academic excellence.

Financial data   The stipend is $3,000. Funds are paid directly to the recipient.

Duration   1 year.

Additional information   This program is sponsored by Booz Allen Hamilton.

Number awarded   Up to 5 each year, at least 1 of which is for a woman or minority candidate.

Deadline   February of each year.

[1088]
RANDY GERSON MEMORIAL GRANT

American Psychological Foundation
750 First Street, N.E.
Washington, DC 20002-4242
(202) 336-5843   Fax: (202) 336-5812
E-mail: foundation@apa.org
Web: www.apa.org/apf/funding/gerson.aspx

Summary   To provide funding to graduate students (particularly women, minorities, and individuals with disabilities) who are interested in conducting research in the psychology of couple and/or family dynamics and/or multi-generational processes.

Eligibility This program is open to full-time graduate students in psychology. Applicants must be proposing a project that advances the systemic understanding of couple and/or family dynamics and/or multi-generational processes. Work that advances theory, assessment, or clinical practice in those areas is eligible. Preference is given to projects that use or contribute to the development of Bowen family systems. Selection is based on conformance with stated program goals, magnitude of incremental contribution, quality of proposed work, and applicant's demonstrated scholarship and research competence. The sponsor encourages applications from individuals who represent diversity in race, ethnicity, gender, age, disability, and sexual orientation.

Financial data The grant is $6,000.

Duration The grant is presented annually.

Additional information This grant was first awarded in 1998.

Number awarded 1 each year.

Deadline January of each year.

[1089]
RED RIVER VALLEY FIGHTER PILOTS ASSOCIATION SCHOLARSHIP GRANT PROGRAM

Red River Valley Association Foundation
Attn: Executive Director
P.O. Box 1553
Front Royal, VA 22630-0033
(540) 639-9798   Toll Free: (866) 401-7287
Fax: (540) 636-9776
E-mail: ExecutiveOffice@river-rats.org
Web: www.river-rats.org/about_us/scholarship.php

Summary To provide financial assistance for college or graduate school to the spouses and children of selected service personnel and members of the Red River Valley Fighter Pilots Association.

Eligibility This program is open to the spouses and children of 1) servicemembers missing in action (MIA) or killed in action (KIA) in combat situations involving U.S. military forces from August 1964 through the present; 2) U.S. military aircrew members killed in a non-combat aircraft accident in which they were performing aircrew duties; and 3) current members of the association and deceased members who were in good standing at the time of their death. Scholarships are also available to students in fields related to aviation and space, even if they have no kinship relationship to a deceased aviator or member of the association. Applicants must be interested in attending an accredited college or university to work on an undergraduate or graduate degree. Selection is based on demonstrated academic achievement, college entrance examination scores, financial need, and accomplishments in school, church, civic, and social activities.

Financial data The amount awarded varies, depending upon the need of the recipient. Recently, undergraduate stipends have ranged from $500 to $3,500 and averaged $1,725; graduate stipends have ranged from $500 to $2,000 and averaged $1,670. Funds are paid directly to the recipient's institution and are to be used for tuition, fees, books, and room and board for full-time students.

Duration 1 year; may be renewed if the recipient maintains a GPA of 2.0 or higher.

Additional information This program was established in 1970, out of concern for the families of aircrews (known as "River Rats") who were killed or missing in action in the Red River Valley of North Vietnam.

Number awarded Varies each year; since this program was established, it has awarded more than 1,000 scholarships worth more than $1,700,000.

Deadline May of each year.

[1090]
REGION F SCHOLARSHIP

Society of Women Engineers
Attn: Scholarship Selection Committee
120 South LaSalle Street, Suite 1515
Chicago, IL 60603-3572
(312) 596-5223   Toll Free: (877) SWE-INFO
Fax: (312) 644-8557
E-mail: scholarshipapplication@swe.org
Web: societyofwomenengineers.swe.org

Summary To provide financial assistance to members of the Society of Women Engineers (SWE) working on an undergraduate or graduate degree in engineering or computer science at a school in its Region F (New England and eastern New York).

Eligibility This program is open to members of the society who will be sophomores, juniors, seniors, or graduate students at ABET-accredited colleges and universities in the New England states or eastern New York. Applicants must be majoring in computer science or engineering and have a GPA of 3.0 or higher. Financial need is considered in the selection process. U.S. citizenship is required.

Financial data The stipend is $1,000.

Duration 1 year.

Number awarded 1 each year.

Deadline February of each year.

[1091]
REGION H SCHOLARSHIP

Society of Women Engineers
Attn: Scholarship Selection Committee
120 South LaSalle Street, Suite 1515
Chicago, IL 60603-3572
(312) 596-5223   Toll Free: (877) SWE-INFO
Fax: (312) 644-8557
E-mail: scholarshipapplication@swe.org
Web: societyofwomenengineers.swe.org

Summary To provide financial assistance to members of the Society of Women Engineers (SWE) working on an undergraduate or graduate degree in engineering or computer science at a school in the upper Midwest (Region H).

Eligibility This program is open to members of the society who will be sophomores, juniors, seniors, or graduate students at ABET-accredited colleges and universities in Illinois, Indiana, Iowa, Michigan, Minnesota, North Dakota, South Dakota, or Wisconsin. Applicants must be majoring in computer science or engineering and have a GPA of 3.0 or higher. Selection is based on merit and participation in SWE activities.

Financial data The stipend is $1,000.

Duration 1 year.

Number awarded 1 each year.
Deadline February of each year.

[1092]
REGIONAL SUMMER MUSIC SCHOLARSHIPS

Sigma Alpha Iota Philanthropies, Inc.
One Tunnel Road
Asheville, NC 28805
(828) 251-0606   Fax: (828) 251-0644
E-mail: nh@sai-national.org
Web: www.sigmaalphaiota.org

Summary To provide financial assistance for summer study in music, in the United States or abroad, to members of Sigma Alpha Iota (an organization of women musicians).
Eligibility This program is open to undergraduate and graduate student members of the organization who are planning to study at a summer music program in the United States or abroad. Applicants must submit a complete resume (including musical studies and activities, academic GPA, community service record, and record of participation in Sigma Alpha Iota), supporting materials (recital and concert programs, reviews, repertoire list, etc.), a statement of why they chose this program and how it will aid their musical growth, a full brochure of information on the program (including cost and payment due dates), a copy of the completed summer school application and acceptance letter (when available), and a letter of recommendation from their major teacher.
Financial data The stipend is $1,000.
Duration Summer months.
Number awarded 10 each year: 2 from each region of Sigma Alpha Iota.
Deadline March of each year.

[1093]
RESOURCES FOR THE FUTURE SUMMER INTERNSHIPS

Resources for the Future
Attn: Internship Coordinator
1616 P Street, N.W., Suite 600
Washington, DC 20036-1400
(202) 328-5008   Fax: (202) 939-3460
E-mail: IC@rff.org
Web: www.rff.org

Summary To provide internships to undergraduate and graduate students (especially women and minorities) who are interested in working on research projects in public policy during the summer.
Eligibility This program is open to undergraduate and graduate students (with priority to graduate students) interested in an internship at Resources for the Future (RFF). Applicants must be working on a degree in the social and natural sciences and have training in economics and quantitative methods or an interest in public policy. They should display strong writing skills and a desire to analyze complex environmental policy problems amenable to interdisciplinary methods. The ability to work without supervision in a careful and conscientious manner is essential. Women and minority candidates are strongly encouraged to apply. Both U.S. and non-U.S. citizens are eligible, if the latter have proper work and residency documentation.

Financial data The stipend is $375 per week for graduate students or $350 per week for undergraduates. Housing assistance is not provided.
Duration 10 weeks during the summer; beginning and ending dates can be adjusted to meet particular student needs.
Deadline March of each year.

[1094]
REV. MARTHA SINGLETARY SCHOLARSHIP FUND

United Methodist Church-New Mexico Conference
Attn: Board of Ordained Ministry
11816 Lomas Boulevard, N.E.
Albuquerque, NM 87112
(505) 255-8786, ext. 101   Toll Free: (800) 678-8786
Fax: (505) 265-6184 E-mail: mridgeway@nmconfum.com
Web: www.nmconfum.com

Summary To provide financial assistance to female Methodists from New Mexico who are interested in attending seminary in any state to prepare for a career in ordained ministry.
Eligibility This program is open to women who are enrolled or planning to enroll at a seminary in any state and who have an affiliation with a congregation of the New Mexico Conference of the United Methodist Church (UMC). Applicants must be preparing for a career in ordained ministry to local churches in the New Mexico Conference. Along with their application, they must submit brief essays on their current financial situation, how their sense of calling to ministry has changed or grown during the past year, the areas of ministry in which they are currently interested, what they believe to be their greatest spiritual gifts, and how they believe God is calling them to use those gifts in the local church.
Financial data A stipend is awarded (amount not specified).
Duration 1 year.
Number awarded 1 or more each year.
Deadline April of each year.

[1095]
RHODA D. HOOD MEMORIAL SCHOLARSHIP

Northwest Baptist Convention
Attn: Woman's Missionary Union
3200 N.E. 109th Avenue
Vancouver, WA 98682
(360) 882-2100   Fax: (360) 882-2295
Web: www.nwbaptist.org

Summary To provide financial assistance to women from the Northwest who are attending college or seminary in any state to prepare for a career in vocational ministry, preferably with a Southern Baptist Convention church.
Eligibility This program is open to women who have been active members of a church affiliated with the Northwest Baptist Convention and a member of the Woman's Missionary Union within their church. Special consideration is given to children of ministers from the Northwest. Applicants must be attending or planning to attend an accredited college, university, or Southern Baptist seminary in any state with the intention of serving in a vocational ministry position through a church or denomination; priority is given to applicants going into a mission vocation affiliated with the Southern Baptist

Convention. Along with their application, they must submit 1) a written account of their conversion experience and their call to vocational ministry; and 2) a written endorsement from their church.

Financial data A stipend is awarded (amount not specified).

Duration 1 year; may be renewed if the recipient maintains a GPA of 2.5 or higher.

Additional information The Northwest Baptist Convention serves Oregon, Washington, and northern Idaho.

Number awarded 1 or more each year.

Deadline May of each year for fall term; October of each year for spring term.

[1096]
RITA MAE KELLY ENDOWMENT FELLOWSHIP

American Political Science Association
Attn: Centennial Center Visiting Scholars Program
1527 New Hampshire Avenue, N.W.
Washington, DC 20036-1206
(202) 483-2512   Fax: (202) 483-2657
E-mail: center@apsanet.org
Web: www.apsanet.org/content_3436.cfm

Summary To provide funding to women, minority, and other members of the American Political Science Association (APSA) who are interested in conducting research on the intersection of gender, race, ethnicity, and political power at the Centennial Center for Political Science and Public Affairs.

Eligibility This program is open to members of the association who are interested in conducting research on the intersection of gender, race, ethnicity, and political power while in residence at the center. Support is available to pre-dissertation graduate students as well as for an award or public presentation. Nonresident scholars may also be eligible.

Financial data Grants provide supplemental financial support to resident scholars.

Duration 2 weeks to 12 months.

Additional information The APSA launched its Centennial Center for Political Science and Public Affairs in 2003 to commemorate the centennial year of the association. This program was established in affiliation with the Women's Caucus for Political Science, the Latina Caucus for Political Science, the Committee for the Status of Latino/Latinas in the Profession, the Women and Politics Research Organized Section, and the Race, Ethnicity and Politics Organized Section.

Number awarded 1 or more each year.

Deadline February, June, or October of each year.

[1097]
ROBIN ROBERTS/WBCA BROADCASTING SCHOLARSHIP

Women's Basketball Coaches Association
Attn: Manager of Events and Awards
4646 Lawrenceville Highway
Lilburn, GA 30047-3620
(770) 279-8027, ext. 105   Fax: (770) 279-8473
E-mail: dtrujillo@wbca.org
Web: www.wbca.org/robertsaward.asp

Summary To provide financial assistance for graduate study in sports communications to women's basketball players.

Eligibility This program is open to women's college basketball players who are seniors planning to work on a graduate degree in sports communication and journalism. Applicants must be nominated by a member of the Women's Basketball Coaches Association (WBCA). Selection is based on a letter of recommendation, academic major and GPA, basketball statistics for all 4 years of college, and campus activities.

Financial data The stipend is $4,000.

Duration 1 year.

Additional information This program began in 2001.

Number awarded 1 each year.

Deadline Deadline not specified.

[1098]
ROCKY MOUNTAIN SECTION COLLEGE SCHOLARSHIPS

Society of Women Engineers-Rocky Mountain Section
Attn: Collegiate Scholarship Committee Chair
P.O. Box 260692
Lakewood, CO 80226-0692
(303) 751-0741   Fax: (303) 751-2581
E-mail: Christina.wisleder@merrick.copm
Web: www.societyofwomenengineers.org

Summary To provide financial assistance to women from any state who are working on an undergraduate or graduate degree in engineering at colleges and universities in Colorado and Wyoming.

Eligibility This program is open to women from any state who are enrolled as an undergraduate or graduate engineering student in an ABET-accredited engineering or computer science program in Colorado or Wyoming (excluding zip codes 80800-81599). Applicants must have a GPA of 3.0 or higher. Along with their application, they must submit an essay on why they have chosen an engineering major, what they will accomplish or how they believe they will make a difference as an engineer, and who or what influenced them to study engineering. Selection is based on merit.

Financial data The stipend is $1,250.

Duration 1 year.

Additional information This program includes the following named scholarships: the Dorolyn Lines Scholarship, the Lottye Miner Scholarship, and the Rocky Mountain Section Pioneer Scholarship.

Number awarded 3 each year.

Deadline January of each year.

[1099]
ROY SCRIVNER MEMORIAL RESEARCH GRANTS

American Psychological Foundation
750 First Street, N.E.
Washington, DC 20002-4242
(202) 336-5843   Fax: (202) 336-5812
E-mail: foundation@apa.org
Web: www.apa.org/apf/funding/scrivner.aspx

Summary To provide funding to graduate students interested in conducting dissertation research on lesbian, gay, bisexual, and transgender (LGBT) family psychology and therapy.

Eligibility   This program is open to doctoral candidates who are interested in conducting empirical research in all fields of the behavioral and social sciences that focus on LGBT family psychology and LGBT family therapy. Proposals are especially encouraged for empirical studies that address the following: problems faced by LGBT families such as those associated with cultural, racial, socioeconomic, and family structure diversity; successful coping mechanisms such as sources of support and resilience for family members; and clinical issues and interventions in the domain of LGBT. Selection is based on conformance with stated program goals, magnitude of incremental contribution, quality of proposed work, and applicant's demonstrated scholarship and research competence. The sponsor encourages applications from individuals who represent diversity in race, ethnicity, gender, age, disability, and sexual orientation.

Financial data   The grant is $12,000.

Duration   1 year.

Number awarded   1 each year.

Deadline   October of each year.

[1100]
RUKMINI AND JOYCE VASUDEVAN SCHOLARSHIP

Wisconsin Medical Society
Attn: Executive Director, Wisconsin Medical Society
  Foundation
330 East Lakeside Street
P.O. Box 1109
Madison, WI 53701-1109
(608) 442-3722   Toll Free: (866) 442-3800, ext. 3722
Fax: (608) 442-3851   E-mail: eileen.wilson@wismed.org
Web: www.wisconsinmedicalsociety.org

Summary   To provide financial assistance to female students enrolled at medical schools in Wisconsin.

Eligibility   This program is open to women who are entering their third or fourth year of full-time study at a medical school in Wisconsin. Applicants must submit a personal statement of 1 to 2 pages on their family background, achievements, current higher educational status, career goals, and financial need; their statement should include examples of their compassion, caring, and courage or hard work despite adversity or obstacles in life. Preference is given to residents of Wisconsin, those close to completing their degree, and those who demonstrate ties to their community and a desire to practice in Wisconsin. U.S. citizenship is required. Selection is based on financial need, academic achievement, personal qualities and strengths, and letters of recommendation.

Financial data   A stipend is awarded (amount not specified).

Duration   1 year.

Number awarded   1 each year.

Deadline   January of each year.

[1101]
RUTH AND LINCOLN EKSTROM FELLOWSHIP

Brown University
Attn: John Carter Brown Library
P.O. Box 1894
Providence, RI 02912
(401) 863-2725   Fax: (401) 863-3477
E-mail: JCBL_Fellowships@Brown.edu
Web: www.brown.edu

Summary   To support scholars and graduate students interested in conducting research on the history of women at the John Carter Brown Library, which is renowned for its collection of historical sources pertaining to the Americas prior to 1830.

Eligibility   This fellowship is open to U.S-based and foreign graduate students, scholars, and independent researchers. Graduate students must have passed their preliminary or general examinations. Applicants must be proposing to conduct research on the history of women and the family in the Americas prior to 1825, including the question of cultural influences on gender formation. Selection is based on the applicant's scholarly qualifications, the merits and significance of the project, and the particular need that the holdings of the John Carter Brown Library will fill in the development of the project.

Financial data   The stipend is $2,100 per month.

Duration   From 2 to 4 months.

Additional information   Fellows are expected to be in regular residence at the library and to participate in the intellectual life of Brown University for the duration of the program.

Number awarded   1 or more each year.

Deadline   December of each year.

[1102]
RUTH BILLOW MEMORIAL EDUCATION FUND

Delta Gamma Foundation
Attn: Director, Service for Sight
3250 Riverside Drive
P.O. Box 21397
Columbus, OH 43221-0397
(614) 481-8169   Toll Free: (800) 644-5414
Fax: (614) 481-0133   E-mail: fngrants@deltagamma.org
Web: www.deltagamma.org

Summary   To provide financial assistance to undergraduate or graduate members of Delta Gamma sorority who are visually impaired or preparing for a career in working with the visually impaired.

Eligibility   This program is open to undergraduate and graduate members of the sorority who are either 1) blind or visually impaired; or 2) pursuing professional training in areas related to working with persons who are blind or visually impaired or in sight preservation. Applicants must be pursuing a program of postsecondary education in the United States or Canada.

Financial data   The stipend is $1,000 for undergraduates or $2,500 for graduate students.

Duration   1 year or more.

Number awarded   2 each year: 1 to an undergraduate and 1 to a graduate student.

Deadline   Applications may be submitted at any time.

[1103]
RUTH G. WHITE P.E.O. SCHOLARSHIP

P.E.O. Foundation-California State Chapter
c/o Carol Born, Scholarship Committee Chair
718 Via La Paloma
Riverside, CA 92507-6403
(951) 686-2728
Web: www.peocalifornia.org/rgw.html

Summary To provide financial assistance to women from California who are interested in working on a medical-related degree at a graduate school in any state.

Eligibility This program is open to female residents of California who have completed their first year of graduate work in the field of medicine. Applicants may be studying in any state. They must submit a personal narrative that describes their background, interests, scholastic achievements, extracurricular activities, service, talents, and goals. Selection is based on character, integrity, academic excellence, and financial need.

Financial data Stipends recently averaged $4,320.

Duration 1 year; recipients may reapply.

Additional information This fund was established in 1957.

Number awarded Varies each year; recently, 12 of these scholarships were awarded.

Deadline January of each year.

[1104]
RUTH H. BUFTON SCHOLARSHIP

American Business Women's Association
Attn: Stephen Bufton Memorial Educational Fund
11050 Roe Avenue, Suite 200
Overland Park, KS 66211
Toll Free: (800) 228-0007
Web: www.sbmef.org/Opportunities.cfm

Summary To provide financial assistance to female graduate students who are working on a degree in a specified field (the field changes each year).

Eligibility This program is open to women who are working on a graduate degree and have a cumulative GPA of 3.0 or higher. Applicants are not required to be members of the American Business Women's Association. Along with their application, they must submit a 250-word biographical sketch that includes information about their background, activities, honors, work experience, and long-term educational and professional goals. Financial need is not considered in the selection process. Annually, the trustees designate an academic discipline for which the scholarship will be presented that year. U.S. citizenship is required.

Financial data The stipend is $10,000 (paid over a 2-year period). Funds are paid directly to the recipient's institution to be used only for tuition, books, and fees.

Duration 2 years.

Additional information This program was created in 1986 as part of ABWA's Stephen Bufton Memorial Education Fund. The ABWA does not provide the names and addresses of local chapters; it recommends that applicants check with their local Chamber of Commerce, library, or university to see if any chapter has registered a contact's name and number.

Number awarded 1 each odd-numbered year.

Deadline May of each odd-numbered year.

[1105]
RUTH R. AND ALYSON R. MILLER FELLOWSHIPS

Massachusetts Historical Society
Attn: Short-Term Fellowships
1154 Boylston Street
Boston, MA 02215-3695
(617) 646-0568   Fax: (617) 859-0074
E-mail: fellowships@masshist.org
Web: www.masshist.org/fellowships/short_term.cfm

Summary To fund research visits to the Massachusetts Historical Society for graduate students and other scholars interested in women's history.

Eligibility This program is open to advanced graduate students, postdoctorates, and independent scholars who are conducting research in women's history and need to use the resources of the Massachusetts Historical Society. Applicants must be U.S. citizens or foreign nationals holding appropriate U.S. government documents. Along with their application, they must submit a curriculum vitae and a proposal describing the project and indicating collections at the society to be consulted. Graduate students must also arrange for a letter of recommendation from a faculty member familiar with their work and with the project being proposed. Preference is given to candidates who live 50 or more miles from Boston.

Financial data The grant is $2,000.

Duration 4 weeks.

Additional information This fellowship was first awarded in 1998.

Number awarded 1 or more each year.

Deadline February of each year.

[1106]
RUTH WHITNEY SCHOLARSHIP

New York Women in Communications, Inc.
Attn: NYWICI Foundation
355 Lexington Avenue, 15th Floor
New York, NY 10017-6603
(212) 297-2133   Fax: (212) 370-9047
E-mail: nywicipr@nywici.org
Web: www.nywici.org/foundation/scholarships

Summary To provide financial assistance to female residents of designated eastern states who are interested in preparing for a career in magazine journalism or publishing at a college or graduate school in any state.

Eligibility This program is open to women who are residents of New York, New Jersey, Connecticut, or Pennsylvania and enrolled as undergraduate or graduate students at a college or university in any state. Graduate students must be members of New York Women in Communications, Inc. (NYWICI). Also eligible are women who reside outside the 4 states but are currently enrolled at a college or university within 1 of the 5 boroughs of New York City. Applicants must have some experience in writing, reporting, or design and be preparing for a career in magazine journalism or publishing. Along with their application, they must submit a 2-page resume that includes school and extracurricular activities, significant achievements, academic honors and awards, and community service work; a personal essay of 300 to 500 words on their choice of an assigned topic that changes annually; 2 letters of recommendation; and an official transcript. Selection is based on academic record, need, demonstrated leadership, participation in school and community activities, honors, work experience, goals and aspirations, and unusual personal and/or family circumstances. U.S. citizenship is required.

Financial data The stipend ranges up to $10,000.

Duration 1 year.

Additional information This program is sponsored by *Glamour* magazine, which invites the recipient to visit its offices and spend a week with its editorial team.

Number awarded 1 each year.

Deadline January of each year.

[1107]
S. EVELYN LEWIS MEMORIAL SCHOLARSHIP IN MEDICAL HEALTH SCIENCES

Zeta Phi Beta Sorority, Inc.
Attn: National Education Foundation
1734 New Hampshire Avenue, N.W.
Washington, DC 20009
(202) 387-3103   Fax: (202) 232-4593
E-mail: scholarship@ZPhiBNEF.org
Web: www.zphib1920.org/nef

Summary To provide financial assistance to women interested in studying medicine or health sciences on the undergraduate or graduate school level.

Eligibility This program is open to women enrolled full time in a program on the undergraduate or graduate school level leading to a degree in medicine or health sciences. Proof of enrollment is required. Applicants need not be members of Zeta Phi Beta Sorority. Along with their application, they must submit a 150-word essay on their educational goals and professional aspirations, how this award will help them to achieve those goals, and why they should receive the award. Financial need is not considered in the selection process.

Financial data The stipend ranges from $500 to $1,000. Funds are paid directly to the college or university.

Duration 1 academic year.

Number awarded 1 or more each year.

Deadline January of each year.

[1108]
SADIE T.M. ALEXANDER SCHOLARSHIP

Delta Sigma Theta Sorority, Inc.
Attn: Scholarship and Standards Committee Chair
1707 New Hampshire Avenue, N.W.
Washington, DC 20009
(202) 986-2400   Fax: (202) 986-2513
E-mail: dstemail@deltasigmatheta.org
Web: www.deltasigmatheta.org

Summary To provide financial assistance to members of Delta Sigma Theta who are interested in preparing for a career in law.

Eligibility This program is open to graduating college seniors and students who are currently enrolled in law school. Applicants must be active, dues-paying members of Delta Sigma Theta. Selection is based on meritorious achievement.

Financial data The stipends range from $1,000 to $2,000 per year. The funds may be used to cover tuition and living expenses.

Duration 1 year; may be renewed for 1 additional year.

Additional information This sponsor is a traditionally African American social sorority. The application fee is $20.

Deadline April of each year.

[1109]
SARA OWEN ETHERIDGE STUDENT SCHOLARSHIP

Baptist Women in Ministry of Georgia
c/o Julie Whidden Long, Scholarship Committee Chair
First Baptist Church of Christ
511 High Street
Macon, GA 31210
(478) 742-6485   E-mail: bwimga@gmail.com
Web: www.bwimga.org/scholarship-info.asp

Summary To provide financial assistance to Baptist women from Georgia who are working on a graduate degree in theology at a seminary in any state.

Eligibility This program is open to women who are, or have been, residents of Georgia. Applicants must be Baptists who have completed at least 30 hours of study for a master's or doctoral degree at a seminary in any state. Along with their application, they must submit a brief narrative that includes a summary of their call to ministry, plans for carrying out their ministry, an autobiography, and a description of any ministry experience that illustrate their gifts for ministry.

Financial data The stipend is $1,500.

Duration 1 year.

Number awarded 1 each year.

Deadline March of each year.

[1110]
SARAH BRADLEY TYSON MEMORIAL FELLOWSHIP

Woman's National Farm and Garden Association, Inc.
P.O. Box 1175
Midland, MI 48641-1175
E-mail: SBTfellowship@aol.com
Web: www.wnfga.org/fellowships.htm

Summary To provide funding to women college graduates with several years of experience who are interested in advanced study in agriculture, horticulture, and allied subjects.

Eligibility The fellowship is open to women interested in working on an advanced degree in the fields of agriculture, horticulture, or allied subjects at educational institutions of recognized standing within the United States. Applicants must have several years of experience. There are no application forms. Interested women should send a letter of application that contains an account of their educational training, a plan of study, references, samples of publishable papers, and a health certificate.

Financial data The fellowship award is $1,000 and is tenable at an American institution of higher learning chosen by the candidate with the approval of the fellowship committee.

Duration 1 year.

Additional information This program was established in 1928. Students who accept the fellowships must agree to devote themselves to the study outlined in their application and to submit any proposed change in their plan to the committee for approval. They must send the committee at least 2 reports on their work, 1 at the end of the first semester and another upon completion of the year's work.

Number awarded Varies each year.

Deadline April of each year.

[1111]
SARASOTA COUNTY BAR ASSOCIATION DIVERSITY SCHOLARSHIP

Community Foundation of Sarasota County
Attn: Scholarship Manager
2635 Fruitville Road
P.O. Box 49587
Sarasota, FL 34230-6587
(941) 556-7156   Fax: (941) 556-7157
E-mail: mimi@cfsarasota.org
Web: www.cfsarasota.org/Default.aspx?tabid=363

Summary To provide financial assistance to students from any state who are attending law school in any state, are interested in practicing in Sarasota County, Florida after graduation, and are women or have other characteristics that will contribute to diversity in the legal profession.

Eligibility This program is open to students currently enrolled in the first through third year of study at a law school in any state. Applicants must come from an underrepresented background, based on race, color, religion, national origin, ethnicity, age, gender, sexual orientation, physical disability, or socioeconomic status. They must first apply for and obtain a summer associateship with a private law firm or governmental agency in Sarasota County, Florida as an indication of their interest in eventually practicing law in the county. Upon completion of their summer employment, they receive this funding. Along with their application, they must submit a 250-word essay describing how their particular background would help the Sarasota County Bar Association in achieving its goal of making the local legal community more diverse. Financial need is considered in the selection process.

Financial data The stipend is at least $2,000. Funds are paid directly to the student's law school.

Duration 1 year.

Additional information This program is sponsored by the Sarasota County Bar Association and administered by the Community Foundation of Sarasota County. During their summer employment, participants are assigned an attorney mentor from the bar association Diversity Committee.

Number awarded 1 or more each year.

Deadline January of each year.

[1112]
SBE DOCTORAL DISSERTATION RESEARCH IMPROVEMENT GRANTS

National Science Foundation
Attn: Directorate for Social, Behavioral, and Economic Sciences
4201 Wilson Boulevard, Room 905N
Arlington, VA 22230
(703) 292-8700   Fax: (703) 292-9083
TDD: (800) 281-8749
Web: www.nsf.gov/funding/pgm_summ.jsp?pims_id=13453

Summary To provide partial support to doctoral candidates (especially women, minorities, and individuals with disabilities) who are conducting dissertation research in areas of interest to the Directorate for Social, Behavioral, and Economic Sciences (SBE) of the National Science Foundation (NSF).

Eligibility Applications may be submitted through regular university channels by dissertation advisers on behalf of graduate students who have advanced to candidacy and have begun or are about to begin dissertation research. Students must be enrolled at U.S. institutions, but they need not be U.S. citizens. The proposed research must relate to SBE's Division of Behavioral and Cognitive Sciences (archaeology, cultural anthropology, geography and spatial sciences, linguistics, or physical anthropology); Division of Social and Economic Sciences (decision, risk, and management science; economics; law and social science; methodology, measurement, and statistics; political science; sociology; or science, technology, and society); Division of Science Resources Statistics (science and technology surveys and statistics); or Office of Multidisciplinary Activities (science and innovation policy). Women, minorities, and persons with disabilities are strongly encouraged to apply.

Financial data Grants have the limited purpose of providing funds to enhance the quality of dissertation research. They are to be used exclusively for necessary expenses incurred in the actual conduct of the dissertation research, including (but not limited to) conducting field research in settings away from campus that would not otherwise be possible, data collection and sample survey costs, payments to subjects or informants, specialized research equipment, analysis and services not otherwise available, supplies, travel to archives, travel to specialized facilities or field research locations, and partial living expenses for conducting necessary research away from the student's U.S. academic institution. Funding is not provided for stipends, tuition, textbooks, journals, allowances for dependents, travel to scientific meetings, publication costs, dissertation preparation or reproduction, or indirect costs.

Duration Up to 2 years.

Number awarded 200 to 300 each year. Approximately $2.5 million is available for this program annually.

Deadline Deadline dates for the submission of dissertation improvement grant proposals differ by program within the divisions of the SBE Directorate; applicants should obtain information regarding target dates for proposals from the relevant program.

[1113]
SCHOLARSHIPS FOR ALL MILITARY SPOUSES

National Military Family Association, Inc.
Attn: Spouse Scholarship Program
2500 North Van Dorn Street, Suite 102
Alexandria, VA 22302-1601
(703) 931-NMFA   Toll Free: (800) 260-0218
Fax: (703) 931-4600
E-mail: scholarships@militaryfamily.org
Web: www.militaryfamily.org

Summary To provide financial assistance for postsecondary study to spouses of active and retired military personnel.

Eligibility This program is open to the spouses of military personnel (active, retired, Reserve, Guard, or survivor). Applicants must be attending or planning to attend an accredited postsecondary institution to work on an undergraduate or graduate degree, professional certification, vocational training, GED or ESL, or other postsecondary training. They may enroll part or full time and in-class or online. Along with their application, they must submit an essay on a question that changes annually; recently, applicants were asked to write about what they like most about the health care they are receiving as a military family member, what they like the least, and what they would recommend to change it. Selection is based on that essay, community involvement, and academic achievement.

Financial data   The stipend is $1,000. Funds are paid directly to the educational institution to be used for tuition, fees, and school room and board. Support is not provided for books, rent, or previous education loans.

Duration   1 year; recipients may reapply.

Additional information   This program, is a component of the Joanne Holbrook Patton Military Spouse Scholarship Program, which began in 2004.

Number awarded   Varies each year; recently, the program awarded a total of 293 scholarships.

Deadline   January of each year.

[1114]
SCHOLARSHIPS FOR SPOUSES OF THE FALLEN

National Military Family Association, Inc.
Attn: Spouse Scholarship Program
2500 North Van Dorn Street, Suite 102
Alexandria, VA 22302-1601
(703) 931-NMFA   Toll Free: (800) 260-0218
Fax: (703) 931-4600
E-mail: scholarships@militaryfamily.org
Web: www.militaryfamily.org

Summary   To provide financial assistance for undergraduate or graduate study to spouses of military personnel who have been killed as a result of service since September 11, 2001.

Eligibility   This program is open to the spouses of military personnel who have been killed as a result of active-duty service since September 11, 2001. Applicants must be able to verify that the death was a result of service in support of the Global War on Terror. They must be attending or planning to attend an accredited postsecondary institution to work on an undergraduate or graduate degree, professional certification, vocational training, GED or ESL, or other postsecondary training. They may enroll part or full time and in-class or online. Along with their application, they must submit an essay on a question that changes annually; recently, applicants were asked to write about what they like most about the health care they are receiving as a military family member, what they like the least, and what they would recommend to change it. Selection is based on that essay, community involvement, and academic achievement.

Financial data   The stipend is $1,000. Funds are paid directly to the educational institution to be used for tuition, fees, and school room and board. Support is not provided for books, rent, or previous education loans.

Duration   1 year; recipients may reapply.

Additional information   This program, is a component of the Joanne Holbrook Patton Military Spouse Scholarship Program, which began in 2004.

Number awarded   Varies each year; recently, the program awarded a total of 293 scholarships.

Deadline   January of each year.

[1115]
SCHOLARSHIPS FOR SPOUSES OF THE WOUNDED

National Military Family Association, Inc.
Attn: Spouse Scholarship Program
2500 North Van Dorn Street, Suite 102
Alexandria, VA 22302-1601
(703) 931-NMFA   Toll Free: (800) 260-0218
Fax: (703) 931-4600
E-mail: scholarships@militaryfamily.org
Web: www.militaryfamily.org

Summary   To provide financial assistance for undergraduate or graduate study to spouses of military personnel who have been wounded as a result of service since September 11, 2001.

Eligibility   This program is open to the spouses of military personnel who have been wounded as a result of active-duty service since September 11, 2001. Applicants must be able to verify that the wound or injury was a result of service in support of the Global War on Terror. They must be attending or planning to attend an accredited postsecondary institution to work on an undergraduate or graduate degree, professional certification, vocational training, GED or ESL, or other postsecondary training. They may enroll part or full time and in-class or online. Along with their application, they must submit an essay on a question that changes annually; recently, applicants were asked to write about what they like most about the health care they are receiving as a military family member, what they like the least, and what they would recommend to change it. Selection is based on that essay, community involvement, and academic achievement.

Financial data   The stipend is $1,000. Funds are paid directly to the educational institution to be used for tuition, fees, and school room and board. Support is not provided for books, rent, or previous education loans.

Duration   1 year; recipients may reapply.

Additional information   This program, is a component of the Joanne Holbrook Patton Military Spouse Scholarship Program, which began in 2004.

Number awarded   Varies each year; recently, the program awarded a total of 293 scholarships.

Deadline   January of each year.

[1116]
SCHOLARSHIPS FOR WOMEN RESIDENTS OF THE STATE OF DELAWARE

American Association of University Women-Wilmington
   Branch
Attn: Scholarship Committee
1800 Fairfax Boulevard
Wilmington, DE 19803-3106
(302) 428-0939   Fax: (775) 890-9043
E-mail: aauwwilm@gmail.com
Web: www.aauwwilmington.org/procedure.html

Summary   To provide financial assistance to female residents of Delaware who plan to attend college or graduate school in any state.

Eligibility This program is open to women who are U.S. citizens and 1) a Delaware resident and a high school graduate; 2) a Delaware resident and a senior at a high school in New Castle County; or 3) a resident of New Castle County, Delaware and a home-schooled student who can meet the admission requirements of the University of Delaware. Applicants must be attending or planning to attend a college or university in any state. Along with their application, they must submit a 150-word essay on what they plan to study and why. High school seniors must also submit a 150-word essay on either 1) what they would do and where they would do it if they had 4 hours to spend any place, either now or in history; or 2) the famous person, past or present, who appeals to them most and why. Selection is based on scholastic standing, contributions to school and community, SAT scores, and financial need. An interview is required.

Financial data A stipend is awarded (amount not specified).

Duration 1 year.

Number awarded Varies each year; recently, 17 of these scholarships, worth $55,000, were awarded.

Deadline February of each year.

[1117]
SCIENCE AND TECHNOLOGY GROUP FELLOWSHIPS

American Association of University Women
Attn: AAUW Educational Foundation
301 ACT Drive, Department 60
P.O. Box 4030
Iowa City, IA 52243-4030
(319) 337-1716, ext. 60   Fax: (319) 337-1204
E-mail: aauw@act.org
Web: www.aauw.org/learn/fellowships_grants/selected.cfm

Summary To aid women who are working on a master's degree in the fields of architecture, computer science, information science, engineering, mathematics, or statistics.

Eligibility This program is open to women who are U.S. citizens or permanent residents and who intend to pursue their professional careers in the United States. Applicants must be working full time on a master's degree in architecture, computer science, information science, engineering, mathematics, or statistics. They must be students in an accredited U.S. institution of higher learning enrolled in any year of study. Special consideration is given to applicants who 1) demonstrate their intent to enter professional practice in disciplines in which women are underrepresented, to serve underserved populations and communities, or to pursue public interest areas; and 2) are nontraditional students. Selection is based on professional promise and personal attributes (50%), academic excellence and related academic success indicators (40%), and financial need (10%).

Financial data Stipends range from $5,000 to $18,000.

Duration 1 academic year, beginning in September.

Additional information The filing fee is $35.

Number awarded Varies each year.

Deadline January of each year.

[1118]
SEATTLE PROFESSIONAL CHAPTER SCHOLARSHIPS

Association for Women in Communications-Seattle
  Professional Chapter
c/o Pam Love, Scholarship Chair
3417 30th Avenue West
Seattle, WA 98199
(425) 280-1968   E-mail: pamlove@grappanetwork.og
Web: www.seattleawc.org/about/student-chapter

Summary To provide financial assistance to female upper-division and graduate students in Washington who are preparing for a career in the communications industry.

Eligibility This program is open to female Washington state residents who are enrolled at a 4-year college or university in the state as a junior, senior, or graduate student (sophomores at 2-year colleges applying to a 4-year institution are also eligible). Applicants must be majoring, or planning to major, in a communications program, including print and broadcast journalism, television and radio production, film, advertising, public relations, marketing, graphic design, multimedia design, photography, or technical communication. Selection is based on demonstrated excellence in communications; contributions made to communications on campus and in the community; scholastic achievement; financial need; and writing samples from journalism, advertising, public relations, or broadcasting.

Financial data The stipend is $1,500. Funds are paid directly to the recipient's school and must be used for tuition and fees.

Duration 1 year.

Number awarded 2 each year.

Deadline April of each year.

[1119]
SECTION OF BUSINESS LAW DIVERSITY CLERKSHIP PROGRAM

American Bar Association
Attn: Section of Business Law
321 North Clark Street
Chicago, IL 60654-7598
(312) 988-5588   Fax: (312) 988-5578
E-mail: businesslaw@abanet.org
Web: www.abanet.org/buslaw/students/clerkship.shtml

Summary To provide summer work experience in business law to student members of the American Bar Association (ABA) and its Section of Business Law who will help the section to fulfill its goal of promoting diversity (particularly those who are female, minority, disabled, or GLBT).

Eligibility This program is open to first- and second-year students at ABA-accredited law schools who are interested in a summer business court clerkship. Applicants must 1) be a member of an underrepresented group (student of color, woman, student with disabilities, gay, lesbian, bisexual, or transgender); or 2) have overcome social or economic disadvantages, such as a physical disability, financial constraints, or cultural impediments to becoming a law student. They must be able to demonstrate financial need. Along with their application, they must submit a 500-word essay that covers why they are interested in this clerkship program, what they would gain from the program, how it would positively influence their future professional goals as a business lawyer, and how they meet the program's criteria. Membership in the ABA and its Section of Business Law are required.

Financial data The stipend is $6,000.

Duration Summer months.

Additional information This program began in 2008. Assignments vary, but have included the Philadelphia Commerce Court, the Prince George's District Court in Upper Marlboro, Maryland, and the Delaware Court of Chancery.

Number awarded 9 each year.

Deadline January of each year.

[1120]
SEMICONDUCTOR RESEARCH CORPORATION MASTER'S SCHOLARSHIP PROGRAM

Semiconductor Research Corporation
Attn: Global Research Collaboration
1101 Slater Road, Suite 120
P.O. Box 12053
Research Triangle Park, NC 27709-2053
(919) 941-9400   Fax: (919) 941-9450
E-mail: apply@src.org
Web: grc.src.org/member/about/aboutmas.asp

Summary To provide financial assistance to women and minorities who are interested in working on a master's degree in a field of microelectronics relevant to the interests of the Semiconductor Research Corporation (SRC).

Eligibility This program is open to women and members of underrepresented minority groups (African Americans, Hispanics, and Native Americans). Applicants must be U.S. citizens or have permanent resident, refugee, or political asylum status in the United States. They must be admitted to an SRC participating university to work on a master's degree in a field relevant to microelectronics under the guidance of an SRC-sponsored faculty member and under an SRC-funded contract. Selection is based on academic achievement.

Financial data The fellowship provides full tuition and fee support, a monthly stipend of $2,186, an annual grant of $2,000 to the university department with which the student recipient is associated, and travel expenses to the Graduate Fellowship Program Annual Conference.

Duration Up to 2 years.

Additional information This program was established in 1997 for underrepresented minorities and expanded to include women in 1999.

Number awarded Up to 30 each year.

Deadline February of each year.

[1121]
SERVICE SCHOLARSHIPS

Zeta Tau Alpha Foundation, Inc.
Attn: Director of Foundation Administration
3450 Founders Road
Indianapolis, IN 46268
(317) 872-0540   Fax: (317) 876-3948
E-mail: zetataualpha@zetataualpha.org
Web: www.zetataualpha.org

Summary To provide financial assistance for graduate study in specified fields to women who are alumnae of Zeta Tau Alpha.

Eligibility This program is open to graduate students who have been members of Zeta Tau Alpha. Applicants must be studying special education, social work, or other health-related professions. Selection is based on academic achievement (GPA of 2.75 or higher), involvement in campus and community activities, recommendations, current class status, and financial need.

Financial data The stipend is at least $1,000.

Duration 1 year; renewable.

Number awarded Varies each year; recently, the foundation awarded a total of more than $600,000 to 235 undergraduate and graduate members for all of its scholarship programs.

Deadline February of each year.

[1122]
SHAWN MARGARET DONNELLEY SCHOLARSHIP

Alpha Chi Omega Foundation
Attn: Foundation Programs Coordinator
5939 Castle Creek Parkway North Drive
Indianapolis, IN 46250-4343
(317) 579-5050, ext. 262   Fax: (317) 579-5051
E-mail: foundation@alphachiomega.org
Web: www.alphachiomega.org/index.aspx?id=1030

Summary To provide financial assistance for college or graduate school to undergraduate or graduate members of Alpha Chi Omega.

Eligibility This program is open to undergraduate and graduate members of Alpha Chi Omega. Preference is given to applicants affiliated with Zeta Psi Chapter (Loyola University of New Orleans). If there are no qualified applicants from that chapter, the grant is then opened to all undergraduate and graduate members of the sorority. Selection is based on academic achievement, chapter involvement, community and campus involvement, and financial need.

Financial data A stipend is awarded (amount not specified).

Duration 1 year.

Number awarded 1 or more each year.

Deadline March of each year.

[1123]
SHAWNA MULHALL MEMORIAL SCHOLARSHIP

Women's Transportation Seminar-Puget Sound Chapter
c/o Jennifer Barnes, Scholarship Co-Chair
Heffron Transportation, Inc.
6544 N.E. 61st Street
Seattle, WA 98115
(206) 523-3939   Fax: (206) 523-4949
E-mail: jennifer@hefftrans.com
Web: www.wtsinternational.org/Chapters.aspx?ID=7166

Summary To provide financial assistance to women undergraduate and graduate students from Washington working on a degree related to transportation.

Eligibility This program is open to women who are residents of Washington, studying at a college in the state, or working as an intern in the state. Applicants must be currently enrolled in an undergraduate or graduate degree program in a transportation-related field, such as engineering, planning, finance, or logistics. They must have a GPA of 3.0 or higher and plans to prepare for a career in a transportation-related field. Minority women are especially encouraged to apply. Along with their application, they must submit a 500-word statement about their career goals after graduation and why they think they should receive this scholarship award. Selection is based on that statement, academic record, financial need, and transportation-related activities or job skills.

Financial data The stipend is $4,000.

Duration 1 year.

Number awarded 1 each year.

Deadline November of each year.

[1124]
SIGMA ALPHA IOTA GRADUATE PERFORMANCE AWARDS

Sigma Alpha Iota Philanthropies, Inc.
One Tunnel Road
Asheville, NC 28805
(828) 251-0606   Fax: (828) 251-0644
E-mail: nh@sai-national.org
Web: www.sigmaalphaiota.org

Summary To recognize and reward outstanding performances in vocal and instrumental categories by graduate student members of Sigma Alpha Iota (an organization of women musicians).

Eligibility This program is open to college and alumna members of the organization who are working on a graduate degree in the field of performance. Competitions are held in 4 categories: voice, piano and percussion, strings, and winds and brass.

Financial data Awards are $2,000 for first place or $1,500 for second place. Funds must be used for graduate study in the field of performance.

Duration The competition is held triennially.

Additional information The awards for piano and percussion and for woodwinds and brass are designated as the Mary Ann Starring Memorial Awards. The awards for strings are designated as the Dorothy E. Morris Memorial Awards. The awards for vocalists are designated the Lucille Marsh Memorial Awards.

Number awarded 8 every 3 years: 1 first place and 1 second place in each of the 4 categories.

Deadline March of the year of the awards (2012, 2015, etc.).

[1125]
SIGMA DELTA EPSILON FELLOWSHIPS

Sigma Delta Epsilon-Graduate Women in Science, Inc.
c/o Julie Gros-Louis, Fellowships Coordinator
University of Iowa-Department of Psychology
11 Seashore Hall E
Iowa City, IA 52242-1407
(319) 384-1816   Fax: (319) 335-0191
E-mail: Julie-gros-louis@uiowa.edu
Web: www.gwis.org/programs.htm

Summary To provide funding to women interested in conducting research anywhere in the world in the natural sciences.

Eligibility This program is open to women from any country currently enrolled as a graduate student, engaged in post-doctoral research, or holding a junior faculty position. Appli-

cants must be interested in conducting research anywhere in the world in the natural sciences (including physical, environmental, mathematical, computer, or life sciences), anthropology, psychology, or statistics. Along with their application, they must submit 2-paragraph essays on 1) how the proposed research relates to their degree program and/or career development; 2) initiatives in which they are participating to promote the careers of scientists, particularly women, within their institution, program, or peer group; and 3) relevant personal factors, including financial need, that should be considered in evaluating their proposal. Appointments are made without regard to race, religion, nationality, creed, national origin, sexual orientation, or age.

Financial data Grants are $3,500 or $2,500. Funds may be used for such research expenses as expendable supplies, small equipment, publication of research findings, travel and subsistence while performing field studies, or travel to another laboratory for collaborative research. They may not be used for tuition, child care, travel to professional meetings or to begin a new appointment, administrative overhead or indirect costs, personal computers, living allowances, or equipment for general use.

Duration 1 year.

Additional information The highest scoring applicant receives the Adele Lewis Fellowship. The second-highest scoring applicant receives the Hartley Corporation Fellowship. An application processing fee of $30 is required.

Number awarded Varies each year; recently, 3 of these grants were awarded: the Adele Lewis Fellowship at $3,500, 1 other fellowship at $3,500, and the Hartley Corporation Fellowship at $2,500.

Deadline January of each year.

[1126]
SIGMA KAPPA ALUMNAE CONTINUING EDUCATION SCHOLARSHIPS

Sigma Kappa Foundation Inc.
Attn: Scholarship Committee
8733 Founders Road
Indianapolis, IN 46268
(317) 381-5531   Fax: (317) 872-0716
E-mail: foundation@sigmakappa.org
Web: www.sigmakappafoundation.org/scholaravail.asp

Summary To provide financial assistance to alumnae members of Sigma Kappa sorority who are working on a graduate degree.

Eligibility This program is open to alumnae members of the sorority who have an undergraduate degree from a 4-year institution and are entering or continuing in a graduate degree program. Applicants must have an undergraduate GPA of 3.0 or higher. Along with their application, they must submit an essay describing themselves, their future career goals after graduation, and why they are qualified for this scholarship. Financial need is considered in the selection process.

Financial data The stipend is $1,000.

Duration 1 year.

Number awarded 4 each year.

Deadline March of each year.

[1127]
**SOCIETY OF PEDIATRIC PSYCHOLOGY
DIVERSITY RESEARCH GRANT**

American Psychological Association
Attn: Division 54 (Society of Pediatric Psychology)
c/o John M. Chaney
Oklahoma State University
Department of Psychology
407 North Murray
Stillwater, OK 74078
(405) 744-5703   E-mail: john.chaney@okstate.edu
Web: www.societyofpediatricpsychology.org

Summary To provide funding to women, minority, and other graduate student and postdoctoral members of the Society of Pediatric Psychology who are interested in conducting research on diversity aspects of pediatric psychology.

Eligibility This program is open to current members of the society who are graduate students, fellows, or early-career (within 3 years of appointment) faculty. Applicants must be interested in conducting pediatric psychology research that features diversity-related variables, such as race or ethnicity, gender, culture, sexual orientation, language differences, socioeconomic status, and/or religiosity. Along with their application, they must submit a 2,000-word description of the project, including its purpose, methodology, predictions, and implications; a detailed budget; a current curriculum vitae, and (for students) a curriculum vitae of the faculty research mentor and a letter of support from that mentor. Selection is based on relevance to diversity in child health (5 points), significance of the study (5 points), study methods and procedures (10 points), and investigator qualifications (10 points).

Financial data Grants up to $1,000 are available. Funds may not be used for convention or meeting travel, indirect costs, stipends of principal investigators, or costs associated with manuscript preparation.

Duration The grant is presented annually.

Additional information The Society of Pediatric Psychology is Division 54 of the American Psychological Association (APA). This grant was first presented in 2008.

Number awarded 1 each year.

Deadline September of each year.

[1128]
**SOCIETY OF WOMEN ENGINEERS/ADA I.
PRESSMAN SCHOLARSHIP**

Society of Women Engineers
Attn: Scholarship Selection Committee
120 South LaSalle Street, Suite 1515
Chicago, IL 60603-3572
(312) 596-5223   Toll Free: (877) SWE-INFO
Fax: (312) 644-8557
E-mail: scholarshipapplication@swe.org
Web: societyofwomenengineers.swe.org

Summary To provide financial assistance to women working on an undergraduate or graduate degree in engineering or computer science.

Eligibility This program is open to women who will be sophomores, juniors, seniors, or graduate students at ABET-accredited colleges and universities. Applicants must be U.S. citizens working on a degree in engineering or computer sci-

ence and have a GPA of 3.0 or higher. Selection is based on merit.

Financial data The stipend is $5,000.

Duration 1 year.

Number awarded 6 each year.

Deadline February of each year.

[1129]
**SOPHIA SCHOLAR AND ELISE LIPSCOMB
FERGUSON SCHOLARSHIP**

Kappa Alpha Theta Foundation
Attn: Scholarships
8740 Founders Road
Indianapolis, IN 46268-1337
(317) 876-1870   Toll Free: (800) KAO-1870
Fax: (317) 876-1925
E-mail: FDNmail@kappaalphatheta.org
Web: www.kappaalphathetafoundation.org

Summary To provide financial assistance to members of Kappa Alpha Theta who are working on an undergraduate or graduate degree in the arts.

Eligibility This program is open to members of Kappa Alpha Theta who are full-time juniors, seniors, or graduate students at a college or university in Canada or the United States. Applicants must be working on a degree in the arts and be able to demonstrate creative ability. Along with their application, they must submit an official transcript, personal essays on assigned topics related to their involvement in Kappa Alpha Theta, and 2 letters of reference. Financial need is not considered in the selection process.

Financial data The stipend is $2,225.

Duration 1 year.

Number awarded 1 each year.

Deadline January of each year.

[1130]
**SPECIAL FUND FOR THE STUDY OF WOMEN
AND POLITICS**

American Political Science Association
Attn: Centennial Center Visiting Scholars Program
1527 New Hampshire Avenue, N.W.
Washington, DC 20036-1206
(202) 483-2512   Fax: (202) 483-2657
E-mail: center@apsanet.org
Web: www.apsanet.org/content_3436.cfm

Summary To provide funding to members of the American Political Science Association (APSA) who are interested in conducting research on women and politics at the Centennial Center for Political Science and Public Affairs.

Eligibility This program is open to members of the association who are interested in conducting research on women and politics while in residence at the center. Junior faculty members, postdoctoral fellows, and advanced graduate students are strongly encouraged to apply, but scholars at all stages of their careers are eligible. International applicants are also welcome if they have demonstrable command of spoken English. Nonresident scholars may also be eligible.

Financial data Grants provide supplemental financial support to resident scholars.

Duration 2 weeks to 12 months.

Additional information The APSA launched its Centennial Center for Political Science and Public Affairs in 2003 to commemorate the centennial year of the association.

Number awarded 1 or more each year.

Deadline February, June, or October of each year.

[1131]
STAR FELLOWSHIPS FOR GRADUATE ENVIRONMENTAL STUDY

Environmental Protection Agency
Attn: National Center for Environmental Research
Ariel Rios Building
1200 Pennsylvania Avenue, N.W.
Washington, DC 20460
(202) 343-9798   Toll Free: (800) 490-9194
E-mail: gentry.james@epa.gov
Web: epa.gov/ncer/rfa

Summary To provide financial support to graduate students (particularly women, minorities, and individuals with disabilities) who are planning to obtain advanced degrees and prepare for a career in environmentally-related fields.

Eligibility Applicants must be U.S. citizens or permanent residents enrolled or accepted for enrollment at an accredited U.S. college or university. They must be interested in working on a master's or doctoral degree, in the United States or abroad, in an environmentally-related field of specialization. Specific fields of interest include innovative investigations for oil spill impacts, social sciences, information science, tribes and American Indian/Alaska Native/Pacific Islander communities, nanotechnology, environmental entrepreneurship, green engineering/building/chemical products and processes/materials development, green energy/natural resources production and use, global change, clean air, drinking water, hydrogeology and surface water, coastal and estuarine processes, public health, risk assessment and risk management, aquatic systems ecology, terrestrial systems soil and plant ecology, terrestrial systems animal ecology, pesticides and toxic substances, and land protection. Students who have been enrolled for more than 2 years in a master's program or 4 years in a doctoral program are not eligible. Women, minorities, and students with disabilities are strongly encouraged to apply.

Financial data The total award is $42,000 per year, including a student stipend of $25,000 (paid at the rate of $2,083 per month for 12 months), an expense allowance of $5,000, and an allowance of up to $12,000 for tuition and fees paid directly to the institution.

Duration Up to 2 years for master's students; up to 3 years for doctoral students, usable over a period of 5 years.

Additional information This program, which began in 1995, is the graduate student component of the Science to Achieve Results (STAR) program of the Environmental Protection Agency. Fellows may conduct research outside the United States, but no additional funding is provided for foreign travel or other expenses.

Number awarded Approximately 105 each year.

Deadline November of each year.

[1132]
STEPHEN BUFTON MEMORIAL EDUCATION FUND OUTRIGHT GRANTS PROGRAM

American Business Women's Association
Attn: Stephen Bufton Memorial Educational Fund
11050 Roe Avenue, Suite 200
Overland Park, KS 66211
Toll Free: (800) 228-0007
Web: www.sbmef.org/Opportunities.cfm

Summary To provide financial assistance to women undergraduate and graduate students in any field who are sponsored by a chapter of the American Business Women's Association (ABWA).

Eligibility This program is open to women who are at least juniors at an accredited college or university. Applicants must be working on an undergraduate or graduate degree and have a GPA of 2.5 or higher. They are not required to be ABWA members, but they must be sponsored by an ABWA chapter that has contributed to the fund in the previous chapter year. U.S. citizenship is required.

Financial data The maximum grant is $1,500. Funds are paid directly to the recipient's institution to be used only for tuition, books, and fees.

Duration 1 year. Grants are not automatically renewed, but recipients may reapply.

Additional information This program was established in 1953. The ABWA does not provide the names and addresses of local chapters; it recommends that applicants check with their local Chamber of Commerce, library, or university to see if any chapter has registered a contact's name and number.

Number awarded Varies each year; since the inception of this program, it has awarded more than $14 million to more than 14,000 students.

Deadline May of each year.

[1133]
SUMMER TRANSPORTATION INTERNSHIP PROGRAM FOR DIVERSE GROUPS

Department of Transportation
Attn: Summer Transportation Internship Program for Diverse Groups
HAHR-40, Room E63-433
1200 New Jersey Avenue, S.E.
Washington, DC 20590
(202) 366-2907   E-mail: lafayette.melton@dot.gov
Web: www.fhwa.dot.gov/education/stipdg.htm

Summary To enable female, minority, and disabled undergraduate, graduate, and law students to gain work experience during the summer at facilities of the U.S. Department of Transportation (DOT).

Eligibility This program is open to all qualified applicants, but it is designed to provide women, persons with disabilities, and members of diverse social and ethnic groups with summer opportunities in transportation. Applicants must be U.S. citizens currently enrolled in a degree-granting program of study at an accredited institution of higher learning at the undergraduate (community or junior college, university, college, or Tribal College or University) or graduate level. Undergraduates must be entering their junior or senior year; students attending a Tribal or community college must have completed their first year of school; law students must be entering their second or third year of school. Students who will graduate during the spring or summer are not eligible unless they have been accepted for enrollment in graduate school. The program accepts applications from students in all majors who are interested in working on transportation-related topics and issues. Preference is given to students with a GPA of 3.0 or higher. Undergraduates must submit a 1-page essay on their transportation interests and how participation in this program will enhance their educational and career plans and goals. Graduate students must submit a writing sample representing their educational and career plans and goals. Law students must submit a legal writing sample.

Financial data The stipend is $4,000 for undergraduates or $5,000 for graduate and law students. The program also provides housing and reimbursement of travel expenses from interns' homes to their assignment location.

Duration 10 weeks during the summer.

Additional information Assignments are at the DOT headquarters in Washington, D.C., a selected modal administration, or selected field offices around the country.

Number awarded 80 to 100 each year.

Deadline January of each year.

[1134]
SURVIVORS' AND DEPENDENTS' EDUCATIONAL ASSISTANCE PROGRAM

Department of Veterans Affairs
Attn: Veterans Benefits Administration
810 Vermont Avenue, N.W.
Washington, DC 20420
(202) 418-4343   Toll Free: (888) GI-BILL1
Web: www.gibill.va.gov/GI_Bill_Info/benefits.htm

Summary To provide financial assistance for undergraduate or graduate study to spouses and children of deceased and disabled veterans, MIAs, and POWs.

Eligibility Eligible for this assistance are spouses and children of 1) veterans who died or are permanently and totally disabled as the result of active service in the armed forces; 2) veterans who died from any cause while rated permanently and totally disabled from a service-connected disability; 3) servicemembers listed as missing in action or captured in the line of duty by a hostile force; 4) servicemembers listed as forcibly detained or interned by a foreign government or power; and 5) servicemembers who are hospitalized or receiving outpatient treatment for a service-connected permanent and total disability and are likely to be discharged for that disability. Children must be between 18 and 26 years of age, although extensions may be granted. Spouses and children over 14 years of age with physical or mental disabilities are also eligible.

Financial data Monthly stipends from this program for study at an academic institution are $925 for full time, $694 for three-quarter time, or $461 for half-time. For farm cooperative work, the monthly stipends are $745 for full-time, $559 for three-quarter time, or $372 for half-time. For an apprenticeship or on-the-job training, the monthly stipend is $674 for the first 6 months, $505 for the second 6 months, $333 for the third 6 months, and $168 for the remainder of the program. For special restorative training by beneficiaries with a physical or mental disability, the monthly stipend for full-time training is $925.

Duration Up to 45 months (or the equivalent in part-time training). Spouses must complete their training within 10 years of the date they are first found eligible. For spouses of servicemembers who died on active duty, benefits end 20 years from the date of death.

Additional information Benefits may be used to work on associate, bachelor, or graduate degrees at colleges and universities, including independent study, cooperative training, and study abroad programs. Courses leading to a certificate or diploma from business, technical, or vocational schools may also be taken. Other eligible programs include apprenticeships, on-the-job training programs, farm cooperative courses, correspondence courses (for spouses only), secondary school programs (for recipients who are not high school graduates), tutorial assistance, remedial deficiency and refresher training, or work-study (for recipients who are enrolled at least three-quarter time). Eligible children who are handicapped by a physical or mental disability that prevents pursuit of an educational program may receive special restorative training that includes language retraining, lip reading, auditory training, Braille reading and writing, and similar programs. Eligible spouses and children over 14 years of age who are handicapped by a physical or mental disability that prevents pursuit of an educational program may receive specialized vocational training that includes specialized courses, alone or in combination with other courses, leading to a vocational objective that is suitable for the person and required by reason of physical or mental handicap. Ineligible courses include bartending; audited courses; non-accredited independent study courses; any course given by radio; self-improvement courses, such as reading, speaking, woodworking, basic seamanship, and English as a second language; audited courses; any course that is avocational or recreational in character; courses not leading to an educational, professional, or vocational objective; courses taken and successfully completed previously; courses taken by a federal government employee and paid for under the Government Employees' Training Act; and courses taken while in receipt of benefits for the same program from the Office of Workers' Compensation Programs.

Number awarded Varies each year.

Deadline Applications may be submitted at any time.

[1135]
SUSAN STEIN SCHOLARSHIP

American College of Nurse-Midwives
Attn: ACNM Foundation, Inc.
8403 Colesville Road, Suite 1550
Silver Spring, MD 20910-6374
(240) 485-1850   Fax: (240) 485-1818
Web: www.midwife.org/foundation_award.cfm

Summary To provide financial assistance for midwifery education to student members of the American College of Nurse-Midwives (ACNM) who have had a personal experience with breast cancer.

Eligibility This program is open to ACNM members who are currently enrolled in an accredited basic midwife education program and have successfully completed 1 academic or clinical semester/quarter or clinical module. Applicants must have had or currently have a personal experience with breast cancer, either their own or a family member's. Along with their application, they must submit a 300-word essay on the effect of breast cancer on their identity as a midwife. Selection is based primarily on the quality of the application, although leadership potential, financial need, academic achievement, and personal goals may also be considered.

Financial data The stipend is $3,000.

Duration 1 year.

Additional information This program was established in 2010.

Number awarded 1 each year.

Deadline May of each year.

[1136]
SWE PAST PRESIDENTS SCHOLARSHIPS

Society of Women Engineers
Attn: Scholarship Selection Committee
120 South LaSalle Street, Suite 1515
Chicago, IL 60603-3572
(312) 596-5223   Toll Free: (877) SWE-INFO
Fax: (312) 644-8557
E-mail: scholarshipapplication@swe.org
Web: societyofwomenengineers.swe.org

Summary To provide financial assistance to women working on an undergraduate or graduate degree in engineering or computer science.

Eligibility This program is open to women who will be sophomores, juniors, seniors, or graduate students at ABET-accredited colleges and universities. Applicants must be U.S. citizens majoring in computer science or engineering and have a GPA of 3.0 or higher. Along with their application, they must submit a 1-page essay on why they want to be an engineer or computer scientist, how they believe they will make a difference as an engineer or computer scientist, and what influenced them to study engineering or computer science. Selection is based on merit.

Financial data The stipend is $1,500.

Duration 1 year.

Additional information This program was established in 1999 by an anonymous donor to honor the commitment and accomplishments of past presidents of the Society of Women Engineers (SWE).

Number awarded 2 each year.

Deadline February of each year.

[1137]
SYLVA ASHWORTH SCHOLARSHIP

Federation of Straight Chiropractors and Organizations
Attn: Scholarships
2276 Wassergass Road
Hellertown, PA 18055
Toll Free: (800) 521-9856   Fax: (610) 838-3031
E-mail: FSCO@juno.com
Web: www.straightchiropractic.org

Summary To provide financial assistance to single mothers currently enrolled at a chiropractic college.

Eligibility This program is open to students currently enrolled at a chiropractic college who are single mothers. Applicants must be able to demonstrate financial need. Along with their application, they must submit a 2-page essay on their future practice of chiropractic as a single mother.

Financial data The stipend is $1,000.

Duration 1 year.

Number awarded 1 each year.

Deadline April of each year.

[1138]
SYLVIA LANE MENTOR RESEARCH FELLOWSHIP

Committee on Women in Agricultural Economics
c/o Cheryl Doss
Yale University
MacMillan Center
P.O. Box 208206
New Haven, CT 06520-8206
(203) 432-9395   E-mail: Cheryl.Doss@yale.edu
Web: www.aaea.org/sections/cwae/lane.htm

Summary To provide funding to young female scholars who are working on food, agricultural, or resource issues and interested in relocating in order to conduct research with an established expert at another university, institution, or firm.

Eligibility These fellowships are awarded to mentee/mentor pairs of individuals. Mentees must have completed at least 1 year in residence in an accredited American graduate degree program in agricultural economics or a closely-related discipline; women with Ph.D. degrees and advanced graduate students are encouraged to apply. Mentors must have a Ph.D. and established expertise in an area of food, agriculture, or natural resources. The goal is to enable female scholars to relocate in order to conduct research with an established expert at another university, institution, or firm, even though they may reside in different parts of the country or the world. Selection is based on the relevance of the research problem, potential for generating output, synergy of the mentor/mentee pairing, and opportunity for advancing the mentee's research skills beyond her graduate studies and current position.

Financial data Awards may be used to cover direct research costs, travel, and temporary relocation expenses for the mentee.

Duration Several weeks.

Additional information This program is sponsored by the American Agricultural Economics Association Foundation and by academic, foundation, and industry donors; it is administered by the Committee on Women in Agricultural Economics.

Number awarded 1 each year.

Deadline September of each year.

[1139]
TARGETED OPPORTUNITY PROGRAM (TOPJOBS)

Wisconsin Office of State Employment Relations
Attn: Division of Affirmative Action Workforce Planning
101 East Wilson Street, Fourth Floor
P.O. Box 7855
Madison, WI 53707-7855
(608) 267-1005   Fax: (608) 267-1020
E-mail: Claire.Dehnert@wisconsin.gov
Web: oser.state.wi.us/category.asp?linkcatid=342

Summary To provide an opportunity for women, minorities, and persons with disabilities to gain summer work experience with agencies of the state of Wisconsin.

Eligibility This program is open to women, ethnic/racial minorities (Black or African American, Asian, Native Hawaiian or other Pacific Islander, American Indian or Alaska Native, or Hispanic or Latino), and persons with disabilities. Applicants must be juniors, seniors, or graduate students at an accredited 4-year college or university or second-year students in the second year of a 2-year technical or vocational school program. They must be 1) Wisconsin residents enrolled full time at a school in Wisconsin or any other state, or 2) residents of other states who are enrolled full time at a school in Wisconsin.

Financial data Most internships provide a competitive stipend.

Duration Summer months.

Additional information This program was established in 1974. Relevant fields of study include, but are not limited to, the liberal arts and sciences (e.g., history, mathematics, library science, political science, philosophy, physics, psychology, social services, social work, sociology, women's studies); agriculture and natural resources (e.g., animal and dairy science, biology, botany, chemistry, geography, entomology, environmental studies, horticulture, landscape architecture, microbiology, plant pathology, soil science, urban planning, water resources management, wildlife ecology); business (e.g., accounting, business management, economics, finance, human resources, marketing, public administration, real estate); criminal justice; education; health care (including nursing); engineering; information systems and computers; journalism and communications; and law.

Number awarded Varies each year. Since the program was established, it has placed more than 2,500 students with more than 30 different agencies and universities throughout the state.

Deadline February of each year.

[1140]
TEXAS YOUNG LAWYERS ASSOCIATION MINORITY SCHOLARSHIP PROGRAM

Texas Young Lawyers Association
Attn: Minority Involvement Committee
1414 Colorado, Suite 502
P.O. Box 12487
Austin, TX 78711-2487
(512) 427-1529   Toll Free: (800) 204-2222, ext. 1529
Fax: (512) 427-4117   E-mail: btrevino@texasbar.com
Web: www.tyla.org

Summary To provide financial assistance to women and minority residents of any state who are attending law school in Texas.

Eligibility This program is open to members of recognized minority groups, including but not limited to women, African Americans, Hispanic Americans, Asian Americans, and Native Americans. Applicants must be attending an ABA-accredited law school in Texas. Along with their application, they must submit a 2-page essay on either 1) the role the minority attorney should play in the community and profession, or 2) how attorneys, specifically minority attorneys, can improve the image of the legal profession. Selection is based on academic performance, merit, participation in extracurricular activities inside and outside law school, and financial need.

Financial data The stipend is $1,000.

Duration 1 year.

Number awarded 9 each year: 1 at each accredited law school in Texas.

Deadline October of each year.

[1141]
THEODORE AND MARY JANE RICH MEMORIAL SCHOLARSHIPS

Slovak Catholic Sokol
Attn: Membership Memorial Scholarship Fund
205 Madison Street
P.O. Box 899
Passaic, NJ 07055-0899
(973) 777-2605   Toll Free: (800) 886-7656
Fax: (973) 779-8245 E-mail: life@slovakcatholicsokol.org
Web: www.slovakcatholicsokol.org

Summary To provide financial assistance to female and male members (judged separately) of the Slovak Catholic Sokol who are working on a medically-related degree at a college or graduate school in any state.

Eligibility This program is open to members of the Slovak Catholic Sokol who have completed at least 1 semester of college and are currently enrolled full time as an undergraduate or graduate student at an accredited college, university, or professional school in any state. Applicants must have been a member for at least 5 years, have at least $3,000 permanent life insurance coverage, and have at least 1 parent who is a member and is of Slovak ancestry. They must be studying a medical program. Males and females compete for scholarships separately.

Financial data The stipend is $2,500 per year.

Duration 1 year; may be renewed 1 additional year.

Additional information Slovak Catholic Sokol was founded as a fraternal benefit society in 1905. It is licensed to operate in the following states: Connecticut, Illinois, Indiana, Massachusetts, Michigan, New Jersey, New York, Ohio, Pennsylvania, and Wisconsin. This program was established in 2003.

Number awarded 2 each year: 1 for a male and 1 for a female.

Deadline March of each year.

[1142]
THOMPSON SCHOLARSHIP FOR WOMEN IN SAFETY

American Society of Safety Engineers
Attn: ASSE Foundation
1800 East Oakton Street
Des Plaines, IL 60018
(847) 768-3435   Fax: (847) 768-3434
E-mail: agabanski@asse.org
Web: www.asse.org

Summary To provide financial assistance to graduate students, especially women, who are working on a degree in safety-related fields.

Eligibility This program is open to students working on a graduate degree in safety engineering, safety management, occupational health nursing, occupational medicine, risk management, ergonomics, industrial hygiene, fire safety, environmental safety, environmental health, or another safety-related field. Priority is given to women. Applicants must be full-time students who have completed at least 9 semester hours with a GPA of 3.5 or higher. Their undergraduate GPA must have been 3.0 or higher. Along with their application, they must submit 2 essays of 300 words or less: 1) why they are seeking a degree in occupational safety and health or a closely-related field, a brief description of their current activities, and how those relate to their career goals and objectives; and 2) why they should be awarded this scholarship (including career goals and financial need). U.S. citizenship is not required.

Financial data The stipend is $1,000 per year.

Duration 1 year; recipients may reapply.

Number awarded 1 each year.

Deadline November of each year.

[1143]
THORNBERG/HAVENS SCHOLARSHIP

Delta Zeta Sorority
Attn: Foundation Coordinator
202 East Church Street
Oxford, OH 45056
(513) 523-7597   Fax: (513) 523-1921
E-mail: DZFoundation@dzshq.com
Web: www.deltazeta.org

Summary To provide financial assistance for continued undergraduate or graduate study to members of Delta Zeta Sorority.

Eligibility This program is open to undergraduate and graduate members of the sorority who have a GPA of 3.0 or higher. Applicants must submit an official transcript, a statement of their career goals, information on their service to the sorority, documentation of campus activities and/or community involvement, a list of academic honors, and an explanation of their financial need.

Financial data The stipend ranges from $500 to $2,500 for undergraduates or from $1,000 to $15,000 for graduate students, depending on the availability of funds.

Duration 1 year; nonrenewable.

Number awarded 1 each year.

Deadline February of each year.

[1144]
TOWNSEND AND TOWNSEND AND CREW DIVERSITY SCHOLARSHIP

Townsend and Townsend and Crew LLP
Attn: Diversity Committee
Two Embarcadero Center, Eighth Floor
San Francisco, CA 94111-3834
(415) 576-0200   Fax: (415) 576-0300
Web: www.townsend.com/Who/Who-Diversity

Summary To provide financial assistance to women and minority students attending law school to prepare for a career in patent law.

Eligibility This program is open to students enrolled at ABA-accredited law schools who are women or members of minority groups that historically have been underrepresented in the field of patent law (American Indians/Alaskan Natives, Blacks/African Americans, Hispanics/Latinos, and Asian Americans/Pacific Islanders). Applicants must have an undergraduate or graduate degree in a field that will help prepare them for a career in patent law (e.g., life sciences, engi-

neering). They must have a demonstrated commitment to preparing for a career in patent law in a city in which the sponsoring law firm has an office. Selection is based on academic performance; work experience related to science, engineering, or patent law; community service; and demonstrated leadership ability.

Financial data The stipend is $2,000 per year.

Duration 1 year; recipients may reapply.

Additional information This program was established in 2005. Townsend and Townsend and Crew has offices in San Francisco, Palo Alto (California), Denver, Walnut Creek (California), San Diego, Seattle, Tokyo, and Washington, D.C.

Number awarded Varies each year; recently, 11 of these scholarships were awarded.

Deadline April of each year.

[1145]
TRAUB-DICKER RAINBOW SCHOLARSHIPS

Stonewall Community Foundation
Attn: Bee's Fund
446 West 33rd Street, Sixth Floor
New York, NY 10001
(212) 367-1155   Fax: (212) 367-1157
E-mail: stonewall@stonewallfoundation.org
Web: stonewallfoundation.org

Summary To provide financial assistance for college or graduate school to lesbians.

Eligibility This program is open to lesbian-identified students who are 1) graduating high school seniors planning to attend a recognized college or university; 2) currently-enrolled undergraduates; and 3) graduate students. Applicants must submit 400-word essays on 1) their personal history, including a significant challenge or achievement in terms of community service, academic excellence, or dynamic leadership; 2) a particularly important experience they have had as a lesbian and how it has affected them; and 3) their plans or goals to give back to or focus on the lesbian, gay, bisexual, and transgender (LGBT) community while in school or after graduating. Selection is based on academic excellence, community service, and commitment to impacting LGBT issues. Financial need is not considered.

Financial data The stipend is $3,000. Funds are paid directly to the recipient's school to help pay for tuition, books, or room and board.

Duration 1 year.

Additional information This program was established in 2004.

Number awarded 3 each year.

Deadline April of each year.

[1146]
UNITED METHODIST WOMEN OF COLOR SCHOLARS PROGRAM

United Methodist Church
Attn: General Board of Higher Education and Ministry
Office of Loans and Scholarships
1001 19th Avenue South
P.O. Box 340007
Nashville, TN 37203-0007
(615) 340-7344   Fax: (615) 340-7367
E-mail: umscholar@gbhem.org
Web: www.gbhem.org/loansandscholarships

Summary To provide financial assistance to Methodist women of color who are working on a doctoral degree to prepare for a career as an educator at a United Methodist seminary.

Eligibility This program is open to women of color (have at least 1 parent who is African American, African, Hispanic, Asian, Native American, Alaska Native, or Pacific Islander) who have an M.Div. degree. Applicants must have been active, full members of a United Methodist Church for at least 3 years prior to applying. They must be enrolled full time in a degree program at the Ph.D. or Th.D. level to prepare for a career teaching at a United Methodist seminary.

Financial data The maximum stipend is $10,000 per year.

Duration 1 year; may be renewed up to 3 additional years.

Number awarded Varies each year; recently, 10 of these scholarships were awarded.

Deadline January of each year.

[1147]
VASHTI TURLEY MURPHY SCHOLARSHIP PROGRAM

Delta Sigma Theta Sorority, Inc.
Attn: Scholarship and Standards Committee Chair
1707 New Hampshire Avenue, N.W.
Washington, DC 20009
(202) 986-2400   Fax: (202) 986-2513
E-mail: dstemail@deltasigmatheta.org
Web: www.deltasigmatheta.org

Summary To provide financial assistance to members of Delta Sigma Theta who are interested in working on a graduate degree to prepare for a career in ministry.

Eligibility This program is open to graduating college seniors and graduate students who are interested in working on a master's or doctoral degree to prepare for a career in ministry. Applicants must be active, dues-paying members of Delta Sigma Theta. Selection is based on meritorious achievement.

Financial data The stipends range from $1,000 to $2,000. The funds may be used to cover tuition, fees, and living expenses.

Duration 1 year; may be renewed for 1 additional year.

Additional information This sponsor is a traditionally-African American social sorority. The application fee is $20.

Deadline April of each year.

[1148]
VERIZON SCHOLARSHIPS OF THE SOCIETY OF WOMEN ENGINEERS

Society of Women Engineers
Attn: Scholarship Selection Committee
120 South LaSalle Street, Suite 1515
Chicago, IL 60603-3572
(312) 596-5223   Toll Free: (877) SWE-INFO
Fax: (312) 644-8557
E-mail: scholarshipapplication@swe.org
Web: societyofwomenengineers.swe.org

Summary To provide financial assistance to women working on an undergraduate or graduate degree in designated engineering specialties.

Eligibility This program is open to women who are enrolling as freshmen, sophomores, juniors, seniors, or graduate students at an ABET-accredited 4-year college or university. Applicants must be majoring in computer science or computer, electrical, industrial, or mechanical engineering and have a GPA of 3.0 or higher. Preference is given to students attending specified colleges and universities. Selection is based on merit.

Financial data The stipend is $3,500.

Duration 1 year.

Additional information This program is sponsored by Verizon. For a list of the specified colleges and universities, contact the Society of Women Engineers.

Number awarded 2 each year.

Deadline February of each year for entering freshmen; May of each year for continuing undergraduate and graduate students.

[1149]
VESSA NOTCHEV FELLOWSHIP

Sigma Delta Epsilon-Graduate Women in Science, Inc.
c/o Julie Gros-Louis, Fellowships Coordinator
University of Iowa-Department of Psychology
11 Seashore Hall E
Iowa City, IA 52242-1407
(319) 384-1816   Fax: (319) 335-0191
E-mail: Julie-gros-louis@uiowa.edu
Web: www.gwis.org/programs.htm

Summary To provide funding to women interested in conducting research anywhere in the world in the natural sciences.

Eligibility This program is open to women from any country currently enrolled as a graduate student, engaged in post-doctoral research, or holding a junior faculty position. Applicants must be interested in conducting research anywhere in the world in the natural sciences (including physical, environmental, mathematical, computer, or life sciences), anthropology, psychology, or statistics. Along with their application, they must submit 2-paragraph essays on 1) how the proposed research relates to their degree program and/or career development; 2) initiatives in which they are participating to promote the careers of scientists, particularly women, within their institution, program, or peer group; and 3) relevant personal factors, including financial need, that should be considered in evaluating their proposal. Appointments are made without regard to race, religion, nationality, creed, national origin, sexual orientation, or age.

Financial data The grant currently is $3,000. Funds may be used for such research expenses as expendable supplies, small equipment, publication of research findings, travel and subsistence while performing field studies, or travel to another laboratory for collaborative research. They may not be used for tuition, child care, travel to professional meetings or to begin a new appointment, administrative overhead or indirect costs, personal computers, living allowances, or equipment for general use.

Duration 1 year.

Additional information This program was established in 1994. An application processing fee of $30 is required.

Number awarded 1 each year.

Deadline January of each year.

[1150]
VICTORIA FISHER MEMORIAL PRIZE ESSAY

University of Leicester
Attn: Faculty of Law
Leicester
LE1 7RH
United Kingdom
44 116 252 2363   Fax: 44 116 252 5023
E-mail: law@leicester.ac.uk
Web: www.le.ac.uk/law/news/fisher.html

Summary To recognize and reward outstanding essays on topics related to women and the law.

Eligibility Entries are encouraged from people regardless of age, experience, qualifications, or place of residence, as long as they have never had work published in a learned journal or as a nonfiction book. Essays may be on any topic relating to women and the law, up to 10,000 words in length, in English.

Financial data The prize is 250 pounds.

Duration The competition is held annually.

Number awarded 1 each year.

Deadline September of each year.

[1151]
VICTORIA NAMAN GRADUATE SCHOOL SCHOLARSHIP

Delta Sigma Theta Sorority, Inc.-Denver Alumnae
  Chapter
Attn: Scholarship Committee
P.O. Box 7330
Denver, CO 80207
(303) 371-7112   E-mail: info@milehighdst.com
Web: www.milehighdst.com/EducationalDevelopment.aspx

Summary To provide financial assistance to female African American residents of Colorado who are interested in attending graduate school in any state.

Eligibility This program is open to African American women who are residents of Colorado and enrolled or planning to enroll at a graduate school in any state. Applicants must have a GPA of 3.0 or higher. They must submit an essay of at least 200 words on their personal goals, academic achievements, and plans for making a difference in their community. Selection is based on the essay, financial need, scholastic record, 2 letters of recommendation, and an interview.

Financial data Stipends range from $1,000 to $3,000.

Duration 1 year.

Number awarded 1 or more each year.

Deadline March of each year.

[1152]
VIOLET AND CYRIL FRANKS SCHOLARSHIP

American Psychological Foundation
750 First Street, N.E.
Washington, DC 20002-4242
(202) 336-5843   Fax: (202) 336-5812
E-mail: foundation@apa.org
Web: www.apa.org/apf/funding/franks.aspx

Summary To provide funding to doctoral students (especially women, minorities, and individuals with disabilities) who are interested in conducting research related to mental illness.

Eligibility This program is open to full-time graduate students who are interested in conducting a research project that uses a psychological perspective to help understand and reduce stigma associated with mental illness. Applicants must identify the project's goal, the prior research that has been conducted in the area, whom the project will serve, the in intended outcomes and how the project will achieve those, and the total cost of the project. Selection is based on conformance with stated program goals and quality of proposed work. The sponsor encourages applications from individuals who represent diversity in race, ethnicity, gender, age, disability, and sexual orientation.

Financial data The grant is $5,000.

Duration 1 year.

Additional information This grant was first awarded in 2007.

Number awarded 1 each year.

Deadline May of each year.

[1153]
VIRGINIA A. POMEROY SCHOLARSHIPS

Association for Women Lawyers
Attn: AWL Foundation
3322 North 92nd Street
Milwaukee, WI 53222
(414) 463-0758   Fax: (414) 463-0759
E-mail: dana@barefoot-marketing.com
Web: www.wisbar.org

Summary To provide financial assistance to women who are attending law school in Wisconsin and have demonstrated an interest in service to the disadvantaged.

Eligibility This program is open to women from any state currently enrolled at law schools in Wisconsin. Applicants must have demonstrated a special interest in service to the vulnerable or disadvantaged, civil rights law, appellate practice, public service, public policy, or public interest law. Selection is based on academic achievement, service to others, unique life experience or circumstance, and financial need.

Financial data The stipend varies; recently, awards averaged $2,500.

Duration 1 year.

Additional information This program was established in 1998.

Number awarded Varies each year; recently, 2 of these scholarships were awarded.

Deadline June of each year.

[1154]
VIRGINIA BURNS BOYNTON SCHOLARSHIP
Kappa Alpha Theta Foundation
Attn: Scholarships
8740 Founders Road
Indianapolis, IN 46268-1337
(317) 876-1870   Toll Free: (800) KAO-1870
Fax: (317) 876-1925
E-mail: FDNmail@kappaalphatheta.org
Web: www.kappaalphathetafoundation.org
Summary To provide financial assistance to alumnae members of Kappa Alpha Theta who are working on a graduate degree in medicine or the sciences.
Eligibility This program is open to members of Kappa Alpha Theta who are currently enrolled full time at a graduate or medical school in Canada or the United States. Applicants must be working on a degree in the sciences, medicine, or medical research. Along with their application, they must submit an official transcript, personal essays on assigned topics related to their involvement in Kappa Alpha Theta, and 2 letters of reference. Financial need is not considered in the selection process.
Financial data The stipend is $2,525.
Duration 1 year.
Number awarded 1 each year.
Deadline January of each year.

[1155]
VIRGINIA M. WAGNER EDUCATIONAL GRANT
Soroptimist International of the Americas-Midwestern
  Region
c/o Alexandra Nicholis
2117 Quayle Drive
Akron, OH 44312-2332
(330) 524-7113   E-mail: soroptimist@simwr.org
Web: simwr.org/id61.html
Summary To provide financial assistance to women working on an undergraduate or graduate degree at a college or university in midwestern states.
Eligibility This program is open to women who reside in Illinois, Indiana, Kentucky, Michigan, Ohio, or Wisconsin and are attending college or graduate school in any state. Applicants must be working on a bachelor's, master's, or doctoral degree in the field of their choice. Awards are first presented at the club level, then in districts, and finally for the entire region. Selection is based on the effort toward education by the applicant and her family, cumulative GPA, extracurricular activities, general impression, and financial need.
Financial data Club level awards vary at the discretion of the club. District finalists receive a $500 award and are then judged at the regional level. The regional winner receives a $3,000 award.
Duration 1 year.
Additional information This program was established in 1972 and given its current name in 2004.
Number awarded 4 district winners are selected each year; 1 of those receives the regional award.
Deadline January of each year.

[1156]
VIRGINIA PEACE MACKEY-ALTHOUSE VOICE AWARD
National Federation of Music Clubs
1646 Smith Valley Road
Greenwood, IN 46142
(317) 882-4003   Fax: (317) 882-4019
E-mail: info@nfmc-music.org
Web: www.nfmc-music.org
Summary To recognize and reward outstanding female student singers who are members of the National Federation of Music Clubs (NFMC).
Eligibility This award is presented to female singers between 19 and 26 years of age. Student membership in the federation and U.S. citizenship are required. Candidates for the NFMC Biennial Student Audition Awards competition are automatically considered for this award; no separate application is necessary.
Financial data The prize is $1,750. Funds must be used for continued study.
Duration The competition is held biennially, in odd-numbered years.
Additional information The entry fee is $30.
Number awarded 1 every other year.
Deadline January of odd-numbered years.

[1157]
WAI/BOEING COMPANY CAREER ENHANCEMENT SCHOLARSHIP
Women in Aviation, International
Attn: Scholarships
Morningstar Airport
3647 State Route 503 South
West Alexandria, OH 45381-9354
(937) 839-4647   Fax: (937) 839-4645
E-mail: scholarships@wai.org
Web: www.wai.org/education/scholarships.cfm
Summary To provide financial assistance to members of Women in Aviation, International (WAI) who are active in aerospace and need financial support to advance their career.
Eligibility This program is open to WAI members who wish to advance their career in the aerospace industry in the fields of engineering, technology development, or management. Applicants may be 1) full-time or part-time employees working in the aerospace industry or a related field, or 2) students working on an aviation-related degree who are at least sophomores and have a GPA of 2.5 or higher. Along with their application, they must submit a 500-word essay on their aviation history and goals, 2 letters of recommendation, a resume, copies of all aviation licenses and medical certificates, and the last 3 pages of their pilot logbook, if applicable. Selection is based on achievements, attitude toward self and others, commitment to success, dedication to career, financial need, motivation, reliability, responsibility, and teamwork.
Financial data The stipend is $2,500.
Duration 1 year.
Additional information WAI is a nonprofit professional organization dedicated to encouraging women to consider an aviation career and to providing educational outreach activi-

ties and networking resources to women active in the industry. This program is sponsored by the Boeing Company.

Number awarded 2 each year.

Deadline November of each year.

[1158]
WALTER BYERS POSTGRADUATE SCHOLARSHIP PROGRAM

National Collegiate Athletic Association
Attn: Walter Byers Scholarship Committee Staff Liaison
1802 Alonzo Watford Sr. Drive
P.O. Box 6222
Indianapolis, IN 46206-6222
(317) 917-6477   Fax: (317) 917-6888
E-mail: lthomas@ncaa.org
Web: www.ncaa.org

Summary To provide financial assistance for graduate education in any field to student-athletes with outstanding academic records (females and males are judged separately).

Eligibility This program is open to student-athletes who are seniors or already enrolled in graduate school while completing their final year of athletics eligibility at a member institution of the National Collegiate Athletic Association (NCAA). Men and women compete for scholarships separately. Applicants must be planning to work full time on a graduate degree or postbaccalaureate professional degree. They must have a GPA of 3.5 or higher, have evidenced superior character and leadership, and have demonstrated that participation in athletics and community service has been a positive influence on their personal and intellectual development. Candidates must be nominated by their institution's faculty athletic representative or chief academic officer. Financial need is not considered in the selection process.

Financial data The stipend is $24,000 per year.

Duration 2 years.

Additional information This program was established in 1988 in honor of the former executive director of the NCAA.

Number awarded 2 each year: 1 is set aside for a female and 1 for a male.

Deadline January of each year.

[1159]
WALTER O. SPOFFORD, JR. MEMORIAL INTERNSHIP

Resources for the Future
Attn: Coordinator for Academic Programs
1616 P Street, N.W., Suite 600
Washington, DC 20036-1400
(202) 328-5008   Fax: (202) 939-3460
E-mail: spofford-award@rff.org
Web: www.rff.org/About_RFF/Pages/default.aspx

Summary To provide summer internships to graduate students (especially women and minorities) who are interested in working on Chinese environmental issues at Resources for the Future (RFF).

Eligibility This program is open to first- or second-year graduate students in the social or natural sciences. Applicants must have a special interest in Chinese environmental issues and outstanding policy analysis and writing skills. They must be interested in an internship in Washington, D.C. at RFF. Women and minority candidates are strongly encour-

aged to apply. Both U.S. and non-U.S. citizens (especially Chinese students) are eligible, if the latter have proper work and residency documentation.

Financial data The stipend is $375 per week. Housing assistance is not provided.

Duration The duration of the internship depends on the intern's situation.

Number awarded 1 each year.

Deadline February of each year.

[1160]
WANDA MUNN SCHOLARSHIP

Society of Women Engineers-Eastern Washington
  Section
Attn: Sandy Brower, Scholarship Committee Chair
P.O. Box 364
Richland, WA 99352
(509) 375-3112   E-mail: embrower@aol.com
Web: www.eastwashingtonswe.org/Scholarships/WM.html

Summary To provide financial assistance to nontraditional women engineering students who live in the northwestern United States and plan to attend school in any state.

Eligibility This program is open to female residents of Alaska, Idaho, Montana, Oregon, and Washington who are nontraditional students attempting to reenter the workforce or enhance career growth and potential. Applicants must have completed at least 2 years of full-time study at an ABET-accredited college or university in any state (do not have to be in an engineering curriculum) and be able to enter an undergraduate or graduate engineering program in the following year. Along with their application, they must submit 2 essays of 100 to 300 words on 1) their short-term and long-term career goals and their plan to reach those goals; and 2) a major obstacle they have encountered in their life, how they responded to it, and how they overcame it. Financial need and academic success are considered in the selection process, but greater weight is given to the applicant's motivation, leadership potential, and ability to follow projects through to completion. All other factors being equal, preference is given to residents of eastern Washington.

Financial data The stipend is $1,000.

Duration 1 year.

Number awarded 1 each year.

Deadline February of each year.

[1161]
WANDA SCHAFER GRADUATE SCHOLARSHIP

Women's Transportation Seminar-Greater Dallas/Fort
  Worth Chapter
c/o Amanda Wilson, Scholarship Chair
North Central Texas COG
616 Six Flags Drive
P.O. Box 5888
Arlington, TX 76005-5888
(817) 695-9284   Fax: (817) 640-3028
E-mail: awilson@nctcog.org
Web: www.wtsinternational.org/Chapters.aspx?ID=6888

Summary To provide financial assistance to women from any state working on a graduate degree in a field related to transportation at specified colleges and universities in Oklahoma or Texas.

Eligibility This program is open to women from any state who are enrolled at a college or university in Oklahoma or Texas that has been selected to participate. Applicants must be working on an graduate degree in a transportation-related field, such as transportation engineering, planning, finance, or logistics and have a GPA of 3.0 or higher. They must be preparing for a career in a transportation-related field. Along with their application, they must submit a 500-word statement about their career goals after graduation and why they think they should receive this scholarship. Selection is based on transportation involvement and goals, job skills, and academic record. Minority women are especially encouraged to apply.

Financial data The stipend is $1,500.

Duration 1 year; nonrenewable.

Additional information This program was established in 2002. The winner is also nominated for scholarships offered by the national organization of the Women's Transportation Seminar. For a list of the eligible Oklahoma and Texas schools, contact the sponsor.

Number awarded 1 each year.

Deadline November of each year.

[1162]
WASHINGTON EPISCOPAL CHURCH WOMEN MEMORIAL SCHOLARSHIP FUND

Episcopal Diocese of Washington
Attn: Episcopal Church Women
Episcopal Church House
Mount St. Alban
Washington, DC 20016-5094
(202) 537-6530   Toll Free: (800) 642-4427
Fax: (202) 364-6605   E-mail: ecw@edow.org
Web: ecw.edow.org/programs.html

Summary To provide financial assistance for graduate school to women who are members of Episcopal churches in Washington, D.C.

Eligibility This program is open to women members of the Episcopal Church who have been a canonical member of the Diocese of Washington for at least 1 year prior to application. Priority is given to members who reside in the Diocese of Washington. Applicants must be enrolled in graduate or professional study and their course of study must be related to church work or activity in preparation for some pertinent field of Christian endeavor. Along with their application, they must submit a statement of purpose for working on a graduate degree and how they plan to use it, letters of recommendation (including 1 from their vicar or rector), financial information, and (if seeking ordination) a letter from their parish intern committee.

Financial data A stipend is awarded (amount not specified); funds are sent directly to the recipient's school.

Duration 1 year; may be renewed.

Additional information This program was established in 1925. The Episcopal Diocese of Washington serves the District of Columbia and the Maryland counties of Charles, St. Mary's, Prince George's, and Montgomery.

Number awarded 1 or more each year.

Deadline May of each year.

[1163]
WATSON MIDWIVES OF COLOR SCHOLARSHIP

American College of Nurse-Midwives
Attn: ACNM Foundation, Inc.
8403 Colesville Road, Suite 1550
Silver Spring, MD 20910-6374
(240) 485-1850   Fax: (240) 485-1818
Web: www.midwife.org/foundation_award.cfm

Summary To provide financial assistance for midwifery education to students of color who belong to the American College of Nurse-Midwives (ACNM).

Eligibility This program is open to ACNM members of color who are currently enrolled in an accredited basic midwife education program and have successfully completed 1 academic or clinical semester/quarter or clinical module. Applicants must submit a 150-word essay on their 5-year midwifery career plans and a 100-word essay on their intended future participation in the local, regional, and/or national activities of the ACNM. Selection is based on leadership potential, financial need, academic history, and potential for future professional contribution to the organization.

Financial data The stipend is $3,000.

Duration 1 year.

Number awarded Varies each year; recently, 3 of these scholarships were awarded.

Deadline March of each year.

[1164]
WAWH FOUNDERS DISSERTATION FELLOWSHIP

Western Association of Women Historians
c/o Amy Essington, Executive Director
3242 Petaluma Avenue
Long Beach, CA 90808-4249
E-mail: amyessington@wawh.org
Web: wawh.org/awards/currentinfo.html

Summary To provide dissertation funding to graduate students who are members of the Western Association of Women Historians (WAWH).

Eligibility This program is open to graduate students who are members of WAWH, have advanced to candidacy, are writing their dissertation at the time of application, and are expecting to receive their Ph.D. no earlier than December of the calendar year in which the award is made. Selection is based on scholarly potential of the student, significance of the dissertation project for historical scholarship, and progress already made towards completing the necessary research.

Financial data The grant is $1,000. Funds may be used for any expenses related to the dissertation.

Duration 1 year.

Additional information This fellowship was first awarded in 1986.

Number awarded 1 each year.

Deadline January of each year.

[1165]
WAYNE F. PLACEK GRANTS

American Psychological Foundation
750 First Street, N.E.
Washington, DC 20002-4242
(202) 336-5843   Fax: (202) 336-5812
E-mail: foundation@apa.org
Web: www.apa.org/apf/funding/placek.aspx

Summary To provide funding to pre- and postdoctoral scholars (particularly women, minorities, and individuals with disabilities) who are interested in conducting research that will increase the general public's understanding of homosexuality and alleviate the stress experienced by lesbians and gay men.

Eligibility This program is open to scholars who have a doctoral degree (e.g., Ph.D., Psy.D., M.D.), and to graduate students in all fields of the behavioral and social sciences. Applicants must be interested in conducting empirical studies that address the following topics: prejudice, discrimination, and violence based on sexual orientation, including heterosexuals' attitudes and behaviors toward lesbian, gay, bisexual, and transgender (LGBT) people; family and workplace issues relevant to LGBT people; and subgroups of the LGBT population that have been historically underrepresented in scientific research. Selection is based on conformance with stated program goals, magnitude of incremental contribution, quality of proposed work, and applicant's demonstrated scholarship and research competence. The sponsor encourages applications from individuals who represent diversity in race, ethnicity, gender, age, disability, and sexual orientation.

Financial data The grant is $15,000.

Duration 1 year.

Additional information This program began in 1995.

Number awarded 2 each year.

Deadline February of each year.

[1166]
WBF SCHOLARSHIP AWARDS

Women's Bar Association of Illinois
Attn: Women's Bar Foundation
321 South Plymouth Court, Suite 4S
P.O. Box 641068
Chicago, IL 60664-1068
(312) 341-8530   E-mail: illinoiswbf@aol.com
Web: www.illinoiswbf.org/?page_id=19

Summary To provide financial assistance to women from any state attending law school in Illinois.

Eligibility This program is open to female residents of any state enrolled at accredited law schools in Illinois.

Financial data The stipend is $10,000.

Duration 1 year.

Additional information This program was established in 1966. It includes the Chief Justice Mary Ann G. McMorrow Scholarship, first presented in 2004, and the Esther Rothstein Scholarship, first awarded in 2002.

Number awarded Varies each year; recently, 5 of these scholarships were awarded. Since the program was established, it has awarded more than 260 scholarships worth more than $1.1 million.

Deadline Deadline not specified.

[1167]
WILLIAM RUCKER GREENWOOD SCHOLARSHIP

Association for Women Geoscientists
Attn: AWG Foundation
12000 North Washington Street, Suite 285
Thornton, CO 80241
(303) 412-6219   Fax: (303) 253-9220
E-mail: office@awg.org
Web: www.awg.org/EAS/scholarships.html

Summary To provide financial assistance to minority women from any state working on an undergraduate or graduate degree in the geosciences at a college in the Potomac Bay region.

Eligibility This program is open to minority women who are residents of any state and currently enrolled as full-time undergraduate or graduate geoscience majors at an accredited, degree-granting college or university in Delaware, the District of Columbia, Maryland, Virginia, or West Virginia. Selection is based on the applicant's 1) participation in geoscience or earth science educational activities, and 2) potential for leadership as a future geoscience professional.

Financial data The stipend is $1,000. The recipient also is granted a 1-year membership in the Association for Women Geoscientists (AWG).

Duration 1 year.

Additional information This program is sponsored by the AWG Potomac Area Chapter.

Number awarded 1 each year.

Deadline April of each year.

[1168]
WINIFRED HILL BOYD GRADUATE SCHOLARSHIP

Kappa Delta Sorority
Attn: Foundation Manager
3205 Players Lane
Memphis, TN 38125
(901) 748-1897   Toll Free: (800) 536-1897
Fax: (901) 748-0949 E-mail: kappadelta@kappadelta.org
Web: www.kappadelta.org/scholarships

Summary To provide financial assistance to members of Kappa Delta Sorority who are working on a graduate degree in science or mathematics.

Eligibility This program is open to graduate members of Kappa Delta Sorority. Applicants must submit a personal statement giving their reasons for applying for this scholarship, official undergraduate and graduate transcripts, and 2 letters of recommendation. They must be working on a graduate degree in science or mathematics. Selection is based on academic excellence; service to the chapter, alumnae association, or national Kappa Delta; service to the campus and community; personal objectives and goals; potential; recommendations; and financial need.

Financial data The stipend is $5,000 per year. Funds may be used only for tuition, fees, and books, not for room and board.

Duration 1 year; may be renewed.

Additional information This program was established in 2002.

Number awarded 1 each year.

Deadline January of each year.

[1169]
WISCONSIN JOB RETRAINING GRANTS

Wisconsin Department of Veterans Affairs
30 West Mifflin Street
P.O. Box 7843
Madison, WI 53707-7843
(608) 266-1311   Toll Free: (800) WIS-VETS
Fax: (608) 267-0403   E-mail: WDVAInfo@dva.state.wi.us
Web: www.dva.state.wi.us/Ben_retraininggrants.asp

Summary To provide funds to recently unemployed Wisconsin veterans or their spouses and children who need financial assistance while being retrained for employment.

Eligibility This program is open to current residents of Wisconsin who 1) were residents of the state when they entered or reentered active duty in the U.S. armed forces, or 2) have moved to the state and have been residents for any consecutive 12-month period after entry or reentry into service. Applicants must have served on active duty for at least 2 continuous years or for at least 90 days during specified wartime periods. Unremarried spouses and minor or dependent children of deceased veterans who would have been eligible for the grant if they were living today may also be eligible. The applicant must, within the year prior to the date of application, have become unemployed (involuntarily laid off or discharged, not due to willful misconduct) or underemployed (experienced an involuntary reduction of income). Underemployed applicants must have current annual income from employment that does not exceed federal poverty guidelines. All applicants must be retraining at accredited schools in Wisconsin or in a structured on-the-job program. Course work toward a college degree does not qualify. Training does not have to be full time, but the program must be completed within 2 years and must reasonably be expected to lead to employment.

Financial data The maximum grant is $3,000 per year; the actual amount varies, depending upon the amount of the applicant's unmet need. In addition to books, fees, and tuition, the funds may be used for living expenses.

Duration 1 year; may be renewed 1 additional year.

Number awarded Varies each year.

Deadline Applications may be submitted at any time.

[1170]
WISCONSIN LEGION AUXILIARY CHILD WELFARE SCHOLARSHIP

American Legion Auxiliary
Department of Wisconsin
Attn: Education Chair
2930 American Legion Drive
P.O. Box 140
Portage, WI 53901-0140
(608) 745-0124   Toll Free: (866) 664-3863
Fax: (608) 745-1947   E-mail: alawi@amlegionauxwi.org
Web: www.amlegionauxwi.org/Scholarships.htm

Summary To provide financial assistance for graduate training in special education at a school in any state to wives, widows, and descendants of veterans in Wisconsin.

Eligibility This program is open to the children, wives, and widows of veterans who are college graduates and have a GPA of 3.5 or higher. Grandchildren and great-grandchildren of members of the American Legion Auxiliary are also eligible. Applicants must be residents of Wisconsin and interested in working on a graduate degree in special education at a school in any state. Along with their application, they must submit a 300-word essay on "Education-An Investment in the Future." Financial need is considered in the selection process.

Financial data The stipend is $1,000.

Duration 1 year; nonrenewable.

Number awarded 1 each year.

Deadline March of each year.

[1171]
WLAM FOUNDATION SCHOLARS

Women Lawyers Association of Michigan Foundation
3300 Penobscot Building
645 Griswold
Detroit, MI 48226
(313) 256-9833   E-mail: dvanhoek@sado.org
Web: www.wlamfoundation.org/where.html

Summary To provide financial assistance to women from any state enrolled at law schools in Michigan.

Eligibility This program is open to women from any state enrolled full or part time and in good academic standing at accredited law schools in Michigan. Applicants must be able to demonstrate leadership capabilities in advancing the position of women in society, including service in such areas as social justice, equality, family law, child advocacy, domestic violence, or work on behalf of underserved areas of populations. Along with their application, they must submit law school transcripts, a detailed letter of interest explaining how they meet the award criteria, a resume, and up to 3 letters of recommendation.

Financial data The stipend is $2,500.

Duration 1 year.

Additional information The accredited law schools are the University of Michigan Law School, Wayne State University Law School, University of Detroit Mercy School of Law, Thomas M. Cooley Law School, and Michigan State University-Detroit College of Law. This program includes the Kimberly M. Cahill Scholarship (for a student at the University of Michigan Law School) and the Dickinson Wright Women's Network Scholarship (for a student at Wayne State University Law School).

Number awarded 10 each year: 2 at each participating law school.

Deadline October of each year.

[1172]
WMACCA CORPORATE SCHOLARS PROGRAM

Washington Metropolitan Area Corporate Counsel
  Association, Inc.
Attn: Executive Director
P.O. Box 2147
Rockville, MD 20847-2147
(301) 881-3018   E-mail: Ilene.Reid@wmacca.com
Web: www.wmacca.org

Summary To provide an opportunity for summer work experience in the metropolitan Washington, D.C. area to women and other students at law schools in the area who will contribute to the diversity of the profession.

Eligibility This program is open to students entering their second or third year of part- or full-time study at law schools in the Washington, D.C. metropolitan area (including suburban Maryland and all of Virginia). Applicants must be able to demonstrate how they contribute to diversity in the legal profession, based not only on ideas about gender, race, and ethnicity, but also concepts of socioeconomic background and their individual educational and career path. They must be interested in working during the summer at a sponsoring private corporation and nonprofit organizations in the Washington, D.C. area. Along with their application, they must submit a personal statement of 250 to 500 words explaining why they qualify for this program, a writing sample, their law school transcript, and a resume.

Financial data The stipend is at least $9,000.

Duration 10 weeks during the summer.

Additional information The Washington Metropolitan Area Corporate Counsel Association (WMACCA) is the local chapter of the Association of Corporate Counsel (ACC). It established this program in 2004 with support from the Minority Corporate Counsel Association (MCCA).

Number awarded Varies each year; recently, 11 of these internships were awarded.

Deadline January of each year.

[1173]
WOMEN CHEFS & RESTAURATEURS SCHOLARSHIP PROGRAM

Women Chefs & Restaurateurs
Attn: Scholarship Program Coordinator
P.O. Box 1875
Madison, AL 35758
(256) 975-1346   Toll Free: (877) 927-7787
E-mail: Admin@womenchefs.org
Web: www.womenchefs.org

Summary To provide financial assistance to members of Women Chefs & Restaurateurs (WCR) who are interested in preparing for a culinary or related career.

Eligibility This program is open to women who are members of WCR, interested in attending a culinary or related school, and at least 18 years of age (21 for the wine scholarships). Recently, support was offered for the bachelor of science degree in culinary arts, culinary nutrition, or baking and pastry arts at Johnson & Wales University (Charlotte, North Carolina; Denver, Colorado; North Miami, Florida; and Providence, Rhode Island); the mastering wine program and the ProChef Certification program at the Culinary Institute of America at Greystone (St. Helena, California) and at Hyde Park, New York); the pastry arts career evening program and the culinary arts career evening program at the French Culinary Institute (New York, New York); the Le Cordon Bleu culinary management program at Le Cordon Bleu (Secaucus, New Jersey); and the pastry and baking diploma program and the culinary management diploma program at the Institute of Culinary Education (New York, New York). Applicants must submit a 1-page essay about their food service career, their culinary interests, what inspires them professionally, and how the scholarship will contribute to their career.

Financial data In general, scholarships provide payment of full or partial tuition, or stipends of $5,000 or $7,500 per year.

Duration Program lengths vary; scholarships must be used during the calendar year in which they are awarded.

Additional information Students may apply for only 1 program on a single application; the fee is $25 for the first application and (if they wish to apply for more than 1 program) $15 for each additional application.

Number awarded Varies each year; recently, 18 of these scholarships were awarded.

Deadline April of each year.

[1174]
WOMEN CHEMISTS COMMITTEE/ELI LILLY TRAVEL AWARDS

American Chemical Society
Attn: Department of Diversity Programs
1155 16th Street, N.W.
Washington, DC 20036
(202) 872-6334   Toll Free: (800) 227-5558, ext. 6334
Fax: (202) 776-8003   E-mail: diversity@acs.org
Web: womenchemists.sites.acs.org/attracting.htm

Summary To provide funding to women chemists or chemistry students who are interested in traveling to scientific meetings.

Eligibility This program is open to undergraduate, graduate, and postdoctoral women chemists who wish to travel to scientific meetings to present the results of their research. Only U.S. citizens and permanent residents are eligible. Preference is given to those who have not made a previous presentation at a national or major meeting. Women who have received a prior award under this program are ineligible.

Financial data Awards apply to registration, travel, and accommodations only.

Additional information Funding for this program is provided by Eli Lilly and Company. Grants are restricted to travel within the United States.

Number awarded Varies each year.

Deadline September of each year for meetings between January and June; February of each year for meetings between July and December.

[1175]
WOMEN IN ENGINEERING AND COMPUTER AND INFORMATION SCIENCE AWARDS

National Science Foundation
Directorate for Education and Human Resources
Attn: Division of Graduate Education
4201 Wilson Boulevard, Room 907N
Arlington, VA 22230
(703) 292-8545   Toll Free: (866) NSF-GRFP
Fax: (703) 292-9048   E-mail: help@nsfgrfp.org
Web: www.nsf.gov/funding/pgm_summ.jsp?pims_id=6201

Summary To provide financial assistance to women interested in working on a graduate degree in engineering, computer sciences, or information science in the United States or abroad.

Eligibility This program is open to women who are at or near the beginning of graduate study; normally, they should apply during the senior year of college or in the first year of graduate school. Applicants must be intending to work on a research-based master's or doctoral degree in engineering or computer and information science. They must be U.S. citizens, nationals, or permanent residents.

Financial data   The stipend is $30,000 per year; an additional $10,500 cost-of-education allowance is provided to the recipient's institution. If a fellow affiliates with a foreign institution, tuition and fees are reimbursed to the fellow up to a maximum of $10,500 per tenure year and an additional international research travel allowance of $1,000 is provided.

Duration   Up to 3 years, usable over a 5-year period.

Additional information   This program is part of the National Science Foundation (NSF) Graduate Fellowship Program, but it is open only to women studying engineering or computer and information science and engineering. Additional funding is provided by the NSF Directorate for Computer and Information Science and the Directorate for Engineering. Recipients may use their fellowship at appropriate institutions in the United States or abroad.

Number awarded   As part of the more than 1,600 NSF Graduate Fellowship awards made each year, approximately 90 are set aside specifically for the Women in Engineering and Computer and Information Science component.

Deadline   November of each year.

[1176]
WOMEN IN FEDERAL LAW ENFORCEMENT MEMBERS-ONLY SCHOLARSHIP

Women in Federal Law Enforcement
Attn: Scholarship Coordinator
2200 Wilson Boulevard, Suite 102
PMB 204
Arlington, VA 22201-3324
(703) 548-9211   Toll Free: (866) 399-4353
Fax: (410) 451-7373   E-mail: WIFLE@comcast.net
Web: www.wifle.com/scholarshipprogram.htm

Summary   To provide financial assistance for college or graduate school to women who are interested in preparing for a career in law enforcement and are members of Women in Federal Law Enforcement (WIFLE) or sponsored by a member.

Eligibility   This program is open to women who are members of WIFLE or sponsored by a member and have completed at least 1 academic year of full-time study at an accredited 4-year college or university (or at a community college with the intention of transferring to a 4-year school). Applicants must be majoring in criminal justice or a related field (e.g., social sciences, public administration, computer science, finance, linguistic arts, chemistry, physics). They must have a GPA of 3.0 or higher. Students in graduate and postgraduate programs are also eligible, but those working on an associate degree are not. Along with their application, they must submit a letter demonstrating their financial need and describing their career objectives. U.S. citizenship is required.

Financial data   The stipend is $1,500.

Duration   1 year; may be renewed automatically for 1 additional year.

Number awarded   1 each year.

Deadline   April of each year.

[1177]
WOMEN IN FEDERAL LAW ENFORCEMENT SCHOLARSHIP

Women in Federal Law Enforcement
Attn: Scholarship Coordinator
2200 Wilson Boulevard, Suite 102
PMB 204
Arlington, VA 22201-3324
(703) 548-9211   Toll Free: (866) 399-4353
Fax: (410) 451-7373   E-mail: WIFLE@comcast.net
Web: www.wifle.com/scholarshipprogram.htm

Summary   To provide financial assistance for college or graduate school to women interested in preparing for a career in law enforcement.

Eligibility   This program is open to women who have completed at least 1 academic year of full-time study at an accredited 4-year college or university (or at a community college with the intention of transferring to a 4-year school). Applicants must be majoring in criminal justice or a related field (e.g., social sciences, public administration, computer science, finance, linguistic arts, chemistry, physics). They must have a GPA of 3.0 or higher. Students in graduate and postgraduate programs are also eligible, but those working on an associate degree are not. Along with their application, they must submit a 500-word essay describing a community project in which they have been involved and the results or impact to the community. Selection is based on academic potential, achievement, and commitment to serving communities in the field of law enforcement. U.S. citizenship is required.

Financial data   The stipend is $2,500.

Duration   1 year; may be renewed.

Number awarded   Several each year.

Deadline   April of each year.

[1178]
WOMEN IN TOXICOLOGY SPECIAL INTEREST GROUP VERA W. HUDSON AND ELIZABETH K. WEISBURGER SCHOLARSHIP FUND

Society of Toxicology
Attn: Women in Toxicology Special Interest Group
1821 Michael Faraday Drive, Suite 300
Reston, VA 20190-5348
(703) 438-3115   Fax: (703) 438-3113
E-mail: sothq@toxicology.org
Web: www.toxicology.org/ai/af/awards.aspx

Summary   To provide funding to members of the Society of Toxicology (SOT), especially its Women in Toxicology Special Interest Group (WIT), who are conducting doctoral research in the field.

Eligibility   This program is open to full-time graduate student members of the society who have been advanced to candidacy for a Ph.D. in toxicology. Students who are not WIT members are strongly encouraged to join. Along with their application, they must submit a narrative of 1 to 2 pages describing their graduate research hypothesis, background, and significance. Selection is based on relevance of the research to toxicology, scholastic achievement, demonstrated leadership (professionally and/or in the community), and letters of recommendation.

Financial data   The grant is $2,000. Funds are paid to the recipient's university to be used for a tuition payment and/or other education and research-related expenses, including travel.

Duration 1 year.

Number awarded 1 each year.

Deadline December of each year.

[1179]
WOMEN OF ALPFA DELOITTE STUDENT ESSAY COMPETITION

Association of Latino Professionals in Finance and
  Accounting
Attn: Student Essay Contest
801 South Grand Avenue, Suite 650
Los Angeles, CA 90017
(213) 243-0004   Fax: (213) 243-0006
Web: alpfa.org

Summary To recognize and reward, with scholarships for further study, female members of the Association of Latino Professionals in Finance and Accounting (ALPFA) who submit outstanding essays on topics related to business.

Eligibility This competition is open to women who are members of ALPFA and working full time on an undergraduate or master's degree in accounting, business, finance, or a related field at a college or university in the United States or Puerto Rico. Applicants must have a GPA of 3.0 or higher. They must submit an essay, approximately 800 words in length, in response to an assigned problem related to professional development in business-related fields. Their essay should include descriptions and explanations of their ability to demonstrate leadership, strategize and problem solve effectively, overcome team doubt, and show strength derived from their culture. U.S. citizenship or permanent resident status is required.

Financial data The award is a $1,250 scholarship. The winner also receives complimentary registration, airfare, and accommodations for the ALPFA annual convention.

Duration The competition is held annually.

Additional information This competition is sponsored by Deloitte & Touche LLP.

Number awarded 1 each year.

Deadline May of each year.

[1180]
WOMEN OF THE ELCA SCHOLARSHIP PROGRAM

Women of the Evangelical Lutheran Church in America
Attn: Scholarships
8765 West Higgins Road
Chicago, IL 60631-4101
(773) 380-2736   Toll Free: (800) 638-3522, ext. 2736
Fax: (773) 380-2419   E-mail: Women.elca@elca.org
Web: www.elca.org

Summary To provide financial assistance to lay women who are members of Evangelical Lutheran Church of America (ELCA) congregations and who wish to take classes on the undergraduate, graduate, professional, or vocational school level.

Eligibility This program is open to ELCA lay women who are at least 21 years of age and have experienced an interruption of at least 2 years in their education since high school. Applicants must have been admitted to an educational institu-

tion to prepare for a career in other than the ordained ministry. They may be working on an undergraduate, graduate, professional, or vocational school degree. U.S. citizenship is required.

Financial data The maximum stipend is $1,000.

Duration Up to 2 years.

Additional information These scholarships are supported by several endowment funds: the Cronk Memorial Fund, the First Triennial Board Scholarship Fund, the General Scholarship Fund, the Mehring Fund, the Paepke Scholarship Fund, the Piero/Wade/Wade Fund, and the Edwin/Edna Robeck Scholarship.

Number awarded Varies each year; recently, 15 of these scholarships were awarded.

Deadline February of each year.

[1181]
WOMEN'S BUSINESS ALLIANCE SCHOLARSHIP PROGRAM

Choice Hotels International
Attn: Women's Business Alliance
4225 East Windrose Drive
Phoenix, AZ 85032
(602) 953-4478
Web: www.choicehotels.com/en/about-choice/wba

Summary To provide financial assistance to women interested in preparing for a career in the hospitality industry.

Eligibility This program is open to female high school seniors, undergraduates, and graduate students. Applicants must be U.S. citizens or permanent residents interested in preparing for a career in the hospitality industry. They must submit an essay of 500 words or less on why they are interested in a career in the hospitality industry, the area of the industry that appeals to them the most, and some of their major accomplishments and/or personal characteristics that will benefit their work in the hospitality industry. Selection is based on that essay, academic record, and 2 letters of recommendation.

Financial data The stipend is $2,000.

Duration 1 year; recipients may reapply.

Additional information This program was established in 2004.

Number awarded 2 or more each year.

Deadline January of each year.

[1182]
WOMEN'S ENHANCEMENT POSTGRADUATE SCHOLARSHIP PROGRAM

National Collegiate Athletic Association
Attn: Office for Diversity and Inclusion
1802 Alonzo Watford Sr. Drive
P.O. Box 6222
Indianapolis, IN 46206-6222
(317) 917-6222   Fax: (317) 917-6888
E-mail: tstrum@ncaa.org
Web: www.ncaa.org

Summary To provide funding to women who are interested in working on a graduate degree in athletics.

Eligibility This program is open to women who have been accepted into a program at a National Collegiate Athletic Association (NCAA) member institution that will prepare them for a career in intercollegiate athletics (athletics administrator, coach, athletic trainer, or other career that provides a direct service to intercollegiate athletics). Applicants must be U.S. citizens, have performed with distinction as a student body member at their respective undergraduate institution, and be entering the first semester or term of full-time postgraduate study. Selection is based on the applicant's involvement in extracurricular activities, course work, commitment to preparing for a career in intercollegiate athletics, and promise for success in that career. Financial need is not considered.

Financial data   The stipend is $6,000; funds are paid to the college or university of the recipient's choice.

Duration   1 year; nonrenewable.

Number awarded   13 each year.

Deadline   November of each year.

[1183]
WOMEN'S ENVIRONMENTAL COUNCIL SCHOLARSHIPS

Women's Environmental Council
Attn: Scholarship Chair
P.O. Box 36
Solano Beach, CA 92075
E-mail: sarah.anunsen@gmail.com
Web: www.wecweb.org/Scholarships/scholarships.html

Summary   To provide financial assistance to women from any state working on an undergraduate or graduate degree in an environmental field at colleges and universities in southern California.

Eligibility   This program is open to female undergraduate and graduate students from any state who are enrolled at colleges and universities in Los Angeles, Orange, and San Diego counties in California. Applicants must be studying such environmental fields as architecture, biology, chemistry, environmental science, ecology, environmental engineering, forestry, geography, geology/hydrology, marine studies, or urban planning. They must have a GPA of 3.0 or higher. Along with their application, they must submit a personal statement that includes a description of their academic professional, and environmental achievements and goals; how they became interested in preparing for a career in the environmental field; and how this scholarship will help them achieve their professional and personal goals. Selection is based on that statement (50%); personal incentive, volunteerism, and extracurricular activities (20%); grades and course work (10%); a letter of references (15%); and thoroughness and presentation of the application packet (5%).

Financial data   The stipend is $1,000. Recipients are also given a 1-year membership in the Women's Environmental Council (WEC).

Duration   1 year.

Additional information   The WEC, founded in 1993, currently has chapters in Los Angeles, Orange County, and San Diego. Recipients are expected to attend the WEC annual meeting in the spring to receive their awards.

Number awarded   Varies each year; recently, 6 of these scholarships were awarded.

Deadline   December of each year.

[1184]
WOMEN'S INDEPENDENCE SCHOLARSHIP PROGRAM

Women's Independence Scholarship Program, Inc.
Attn: WISP Program
4900 Randall Parkway, Suite H
Wilmington, NC 28403
(910) 397-7742   Toll Free: (866) 255-7742
Fax: (910) 397-0023   E-mail: nancy@wispinc.org
Web: www.wispinc.org

Summary   To provide financial assistance for college or graduate school to women who are victims of partner abuse.

Eligibility   This program is open to women who are victims of partner abuse and have worked for at least 6 months with a nonprofit domestic violence victim services provider that is willing to sponsor them. Applicants must be interested in attending a vocational school, community college, 4-year college or university, or (in exceptional circumstances) graduate school as a full- or part-time student. They should have left an abusive partner at least 1 year previously; women who have been parted from their batterer for more than 5 years are also eligible but funding for such applicants may be limited. Preference is given to single mothers with young children. Special consideration is given to applicants who plan to use their education to further the rights of, and options for, women and girls. Selection is based primarily on financial need. U.S. citizenship or permanent resident status is required.

Financial data   Stipends depend on the need of the recipient, but they are at least $250 and average $2,000 per academic term. First priority is given to funding for direct educational expenses (tuition, books, and fees), which is paid directly to the educational institution. Second priority is for assistance in reducing indirect financial barriers to education (e.g., child care, transportation), which is paid directly to the sponsoring agency.

Duration   1 year; may be renewed if the recipient maintains a GPA of 2.75 or higher.

Additional information   This program was established in 1999 when the sponsor was known as the Sunshine Lady Foundation.

Number awarded   Varies each year.

Deadline   Applications may be submitted at any time, but they must be received at least 2 months before the start of the intended program.

[1185]
WOMEN'S MUSIC COMMISSION

Broadcast Music Inc.
Attn: BMI Foundation, Inc.
7 World Trade Center
250 Greenwich Street
New York, NY 10007-0030
(212) 220-3000   E-mail: info@bmifoundation.org
Web: www.bmifoundation.org

Summary   To recognize and reward, with a commission for production of a new work, outstanding young female composers.

Eligibility   This competition is open to women between 20 and 30 years of age who are citizens or permanent residents of the United States. Applicants must submit samples of their original compositions.

Financial data The winner receives a $5,000 commission to create a new work.

Duration The competition is held annually.

Additional information This program began in 2006. Each year, the sponsor partners with a different world-class performer, ensemble, or presenter to present the premier performance.

Number awarded 1 each year.

Deadline May of each year.

[1186]
WOMEN'S TRANSPORTATION SEMINAR CHAPTER OF COLORADO ANNUAL SCHOLARSHIPS

Women's Transportation Seminar-Colorado Chapter
c/o Nyssa Beach, Scholarship Chair
Jacobs Engineering Group Inc.
707 17th Street, Suite 2300
Denver, CO 80202-5131
(303) 820-5240   Fax: (303) 820-2402
E-mail: nyssa.beach@jacobs.com
Web: www.wtsinternational.org/Chapters.aspx?ID=6842

Summary To provide financial assistance to female undergraduate and graduate students in Colorado and Wyoming preparing for a career in transportation.

Eligibility This program is open to women at colleges and universities in Colorado and Wyoming who are working on a bachelor's or graduate degree in a field related to transportation. Those fields may include transportation or civil engineering, urban planning, finance, architecture, or logistics. Applicants must submit an essay on their career goals after graduation and why they should receive this scholarship. They must have a GPA of 3.0 or higher. Minority women are especially encouraged to apply.

Financial data Undergraduate stipends are $2,000 or $1,000. Graduate stipends are $3,000.

Duration 1 year.

Additional information Winners are also nominated for scholarships offered by the national organization of the Women's Transportation Seminar.

Number awarded 4 each year: 2 to undergraduates and 2 to graduate students.

Deadline November of each year.

[1187]
WORKSHOPS FOR WOMEN GRADUATE STUDENTS AND RECENT PH.D.S

Association for Women in Mathematics
11240 Waples Mill Road, Suite 200
Fairfax, VA 22030
(703) 934-0163   Fax: (703) 359-7562
E-mail: awm@awm-math.org
Web: sites.google.com/site/awmmath/programs/workshops

Summary To enable women graduate students and recent Ph.D.s in mathematics to participate in workshops in conjunction with major meetings.

Eligibility Eligible for funding are women graduate students who have begun work on a thesis problem in mathematics and women mathematicians who received their Ph.D.s within the preceding 5 years. Applicants must wish to participate in workshops held in conjunction with major mathemat-

ics meetings at which each participating graduate student presents a poster on her thesis problem and each postdoctorate presents a talk on her research.

Financial data Funding covers travel and subsistence.

Duration Funding for 2 days is provided.

Additional information Participants have the opportunity to present and discuss their research and to meet with other women mathematicians at all stages of their careers. The workshop also includes a panel discussion on issues of career development and a luncheon. This program is supported by the Office of Naval Research, the Department of Energy, and the National Security Agency.

Number awarded Up to 20 at each of 2 workshops each year.

Deadline October of each year for a workshop in July in conjunction with the International Congress on Industrial and Applied Mathematics; August of each year for a workshop in January in conjunction with the Joint Mathematics Meetings of the American Mathematical Society and the Mathematical Association of America.

[1188]
WTS PRESIDENT'S LEGACY SCHOLARSHIP

Women's Transportation Seminar
Attn: WTS Foundation
1701 K Street, N.W., Suite 800
Washington, DC 20006
(202) 955-5085   Fax: (202) 955-5088
E-mail: wts@wtsinternational.org
Web: www.wtsinternational.org

Summary To provide financial assistance to graduate women interested in a career in transportation.

Eligibility This program is open to women who are working on a graduate degree in transportation or a transportation-related field (e.g., transportation engineering, planning, business management, finance, or logistics). Applicants must have a GPA of 3.0 or higher and be interested in a career in transportation. Along with their application, they must submit a 1,000-word statement about their vision of how their education will give them the tools to better serve their community's needs and transportation issues. Applications must be submitted first to a local chapter; the chapters forward selected applications for consideration on the national level. Minority women are especially encouraged to apply. Selection is based on transportation involvement and goals, job skills, and academic record; financial need is not considered.

Financial data The stipend is $3,000.

Duration 1 year.

Additional information This scholarship was first awarded in 2008. Each year, it uses the name of the currently serving president of the Women's Transportation Seminar (WTS).

Number awarded 1 each year.

Deadline Applications must be submitted by November to a local WTS chapter.

[1189]
YOUNG LADIES' RADIO LEAGUE SCHOLARSHIP

Foundation for Amateur Radio, Inc.
Attn: Scholarship Committee
P.O. Box 911
Columbia, MD 21044-0911
(410) 552-2652   Fax: (410) 981-5146
E-mail: dave.prestel@gmail.com
Web: www.farweb.org/scholarships

Summary To provide funding to licensed radio amateurs (especially women) who are interested in earning a bachelor's or graduate degree in the United States.

Eligibility This program is open to radio amateurs who have at least an FCC Technician Class license or equivalent foreign authorization. Applicants must intend to work full time on a bachelor's or graduate degree at a college or university in the United States. There are no restrictions on the course of study or residency location. Non-U.S. amateurs are eligible. Preference is given to female applicants and to those studying communications, electronics, or related arts and sciences. Financial need is considered in the selection process.

Financial data The stipend is $1,500.

Duration 1 year.

Additional information This program is sponsored by the Young Ladies' Radio League. It includes the following named scholarships: the Ethel Smith-K4LMB Memorial Scholarship and the Mary Lou Brown-NM7N Memorial Scholarship.

Number awarded 2 each year.

Deadline March of each year.

[1190]
YOUNG WOMEN'S ALLIANCE HIGHER EDUCATION SCHOLARSHIPS

Young Women's Alliance
Attn: Foundation
P.O. Box 1503
Austin, TX 78767
(512) 553-6176
E-mail: foundationpresident@youngwomensalliance.org
Web: www.youngwomensalliance.org/scholarships

Summary To provide financial assistance to women from any state enrolled as upper-division or graduate students at a college or university in Texas.

Eligibility This program is open to women from any state who are younger than 40 years of age. Applicants must have completed at least 60 undergraduate semester hours or be working on a graduate degree at an accredited institution of higher learning in central Texas. They must have devoted at least 40 hours of work on a Community Impact Project during the current semester. Along with their application, they must submit a description of their Community Impact Project and a personal statement about why they should be chosen to receive this scholarship. Selection is based on academic achievement, demonstrated leadership, commitment to both past community service and the Community Impact Project, and financial need.

Financial data The stipend is $2,500.

Duration 1 year.

Additional information This foundation was established in 1997.

Number awarded 1 or more each year.

Deadline March of each year.

[1191]
ZETA PHI BETA GENERAL GRADUATE FELLOWSHIPS

Zeta Phi Beta Sorority, Inc.
Attn: National Education Foundation
1734 New Hampshire Avenue, N.W.
Washington, DC 20009
(202) 387-3103   Fax: (202) 232-4593
E-mail: scholarship@ZPhiBNEF.org
Web: www.zphib1920.org/nef

Summary To provide financial assistance to women who are working on a professional degree, master's degree, doctorate, or postdoctorate.

Eligibility Women graduate or postdoctoral students are eligible to apply if they have achieved distinction or shown promise of distinction in their chosen fields. Applicants need not be members of Zeta Phi Beta. They must be enrolled full time in a professional, graduate, or postdoctoral program. Along with their application, they must submit a 150-word essay on their educational goals and professional aspirations, how this award will help them to achieve those goals, and why they should receive the award. Financial need is not considered in the selection process.

Financial data The stipend ranges up to $2,500, paid directly to the recipient.

Duration 1 academic year; may be renewed.

Deadline January of each year.

[1192]
ZETA TAU ALPHA FOUNDERS GRANTS

Zeta Tau Alpha Foundation, Inc.
Attn: Director of Foundation Administration
3450 Founders Road
Indianapolis, IN 46268
(317) 872-0540   Fax: (317) 876-3948
E-mail: zetataualpha@zetataualpha.org
Web: www.zetataualpha.org

Summary To provide financial assistance to graduate women who are alumnae of Zeta Tau Alpha.

Eligibility This program is open to graduate students who have been members of Zeta Tau Alpha. Applicants must be able to demonstrate leadership abilities, academic achievement, and financial need. Selection is based on academic achievement (GPA of 2.75 or higher), involvement in campus and community activities, recommendations, current class status, and financial need.

Financial data The stipend is $9,000.

Duration 1 year; renewable.

Number awarded 9 each year.

Deadline February of each year.

Professionals/ Postdoctorates

Listed alphabetically by program title and described in detail here are 297 grants, awards, educational support programs, residencies, and other sources of "free money" available to women who are professionals and post-doctorates. This funding can be used to support research, creative activities, formal academic classes, training courses, and/or residencies in the United States.

[1193]
ACM-W ATHENA LECTURER AWARD

Association for Computing Machinery
Attn: Awards Committee Liaison
2 Penn Plaza, Suite 701
New York, NY 10121-0701
(212) 626-0561   Toll Free: (800) 342-6626
Fax: (212) 944-1318   E-mail: mcguinness@acm.org
Web: awards.acm.org/homepage.cfm?awd=166

Summary To recognize and reward women researchers who have made outstanding contributions to computer science.

Eligibility This award is presented to women who have made outstanding contributions to research on computer science. Nominees must be available to deliver a lecture at the Symposium on the Theory of Computing sponsored by the Special Interest Group on Algorithms and Computation Theory (SIGACT) of the Association for Computing Machinery (ACM).

Financial data The award is $10,000.

Duration The award is presented annually.

Additional information This award was established in 2006 by the ACM-W Council, originally known as the Committee on Women in Computing of ACM. Financial support is provided by Google, Inc.

Number awarded 1 each year.

Deadline November of each year.

[1194]
AERA-ETS FELLOWSHIP PROGRAM IN MEASUREMENT

American Educational Research Association
1430 K Street, N.W., Suite 1200
Washington, DC 20005
(202) 238-3200   Fax: (202) 238-3250
E-mail: fellowships@aera.net
Web: www.aera.net

Summary To provide an opportunity for junior scholars (particularly women and minorities) in the field of education to engage in a program of research and advanced training while in residence at Educational Testing Service (ETS) in Princeton, New Jersey.

Eligibility This program is open to junior scholars and early career research scientists in fields and disciplines related to education research. Applicants must have completed their Ph.D. or Ed.D. degree within the past 3 years. They must be proposing a program of intensive research and training at the ETS campus in Princeton, New Jersey in such areas as educational measurement, assessment design, psychometrics, statistical analyses, large-scale evaluations, and other studies directed to explaining student progress and achievement. A particular goal of the program is to increase the involvement of women and underrepresented minority professionals in measurement, psychometrics, assessment, and related fields. U.S. citizenship or permanent resident status is required.

Financial data The stipend is $50,000 per year. Fellows also receive relocation expenses and ETS employee benefits.

Duration Up to 2 years.

Additional information This program is jointly sponsored by the American Educational Research Association (AERA) and ETS.

Number awarded Up to 2 each year.

Deadline December of each year.

[1195]
AGNES MORRIS EDUCATION SCHOLARSHIP

Louisiana Federation of Business and Professional Women's Clubs, Inc.
c/o Linda Burns
1424 Evangeline Road
Glenmora, LA 71433
(318) 748-7603   E-mail: amesfchair@bpwlouisiana.org
Web: lafbpw.wildapricot.org/Default.aspx?pageId=880660

Summary To provide financial assistance to members of the Louisiana Federation of Business and Professional Women's Clubs (BPW/LA) who are interested in pursuing college or professional advancement in any state.

Eligibility This program is open to women who are 25 years of age or older and members of the BPW/LA and a BPW local organization in Louisiana. Applicants must be enrolled at or entering an accredited university, college, technical school, or program for licensing or career advancement in any state. Along with their application, they must submit transcripts from their high school and any institution of higher education they have attended, entrance examination scores, 3 letters of recommendation, and a 250-word statement on why they want this scholarship and their plans for using it. Financial need is not considered in the selection process.

Financial data The stipend is $1,000 per year.

Duration 2 years, provided the recipient completes at least 6 hours per semester and maintains a GPA of 2.5 or higher.

Additional information This program originated as the Agnes Morris Educational Loan Fund.

Number awarded 1 or more each year.

Deadline January of each year.

[1196]
ALEXANDER GRALNICK RESEARCH INVESTIGATOR PRIZE

American Psychological Foundation
750 First Street, N.E.
Washington, DC 20002-4242
(202) 336-5843   Fax: (202) 336-5812
E-mail: foundation@apa.org
Web: www.apa.org/apf/funding/gralnick.aspx

Summary To recognize and reward psychologists (especially women and minorities) who are conducting exceptional research on serious mental illness.

Eligibility This program is open to psychologists who have a doctoral degree, have a record of significant research productivity, and are able to demonstrate evidence on continuing creativity in the area of research on serious mental illness (including, but not limited to, schizophrenia, bipolar disorder, and paranoia). Nominees must also have significant involvement in training and development of younger investigators. They must have an affiliation with an accredited college, university, or other treatment or research institution. The sponsor encourages nominations of individuals who represent diversity in race, ethnicity, gender, age, disability, and sexual orientation.

Financial data The award is $20,000.

Duration The award is presented biennially, in even-numbered years.

Additional information This award was first presented in 2002.

Number awarded 1 each even-numbered. year.

Deadline April of each even-numbered year.

[1197]
ALEXANDRA AND MARTIN SYMONDS FOUNDATION FELLOWSHIPS

Association of Women Psychiatrists
Attn: Executive Director
P.O. Box 570218
Dallas, TX 75357-0218
(972) 613-0985   Fax: (972) 613-5532
E-mail: womenpsych@aol.com
Web: www.womenpsych.org/Fellowships/default.html

Summary To recognize and reward outstanding women psychiatry residents.

Eligibility This award is available to women currently enrolled in a psychiatry residency program who are nominated by their training director. Nominees must be members of the Association of Women Psychiatrists. Selection is based on demonstrated leadership potential, accomplishment in and commitment to women's health, and academic excellence (with an emphasis on interest and experience in psychoanalytic theory and practice).

Financial data The grant is $1,500. Funds are to be used to attend the annual meeting of the association.

Duration The grants are presented annually.

Number awarded 2 each year.

Deadline March of each year.

[1198]
ALFRED P. SLOAN FOUNDATION RESEARCH FELLOWSHIPS

Alfred P. Sloan Foundation
630 Fifth Avenue, Suite 2550
New York, NY 10111-0242
(212) 649-1649   Fax: (212) 757-5117
E-mail: researchfellows@sloan.org
Web: www.sloan.org/fellowships

Summary To provide funding for research in selected fields of science to recent doctorates, particularly women and minorities.

Eligibility This program is open to scholars who are no more than 6 years from completion of the most recent Ph.D. or equivalent in computational and evolutionary molecular biology, chemistry, physics, mathematics, computer science, economics, neuroscience, or a related interdisciplinary field. Direct applications are not accepted; candidates must be nominated by department heads or other senior scholars. Although fellows must be at an early stage of their research careers, they should give strong evidence of independent research accomplishments and creativity. The sponsor strongly encourages the participation of women and members of underrepresented minority groups.

Financial data The stipend is $25,000 per year. Funds are paid directly to the fellow's institution to be used by the fellow for equipment, technical assistance, professional travel, trainee support, or any other research-related expense; they may not be used to augment an existing full-time salary.

Duration 2 years; may be extended if unexpended funds still remain.

Additional information This program began in 1955, when it awarded $235,000 to 22 chemists, physicists, and pure mathematicians. Neuroscience was added in 1972, economics and applied mathematics in 1980, computer science in 1993, and computational and evolutionary molecular biology in 2002. Currently, the program awards $5.22 million in grants annually.

Number awarded 118 each year: 23 in chemistry, 12 in computational and evolutionary molecular biology, 16 in computer science, 8 in economics, 20 in mathematics, 16 in neuroscience, and 23 in physics.

Deadline September of each year.

[1199]
AMELIA EARHART RESEARCH SCHOLAR GRANT

Ninety-Nines, Inc.
Attn: Chair, Research Scholar Grants
4300 Amelia Earhart Road
Oklahoma City, OK 73159
(405) 685-7969   Toll Free: (800) 994-1929
Fax: (405) 685-7985   E-mail: AEChair@ninety-nines.org
Web: www.ninety-nines.org/index.cfm/scholarships.htm

Summary To provide funding to scholars interested in expanding knowledge about women in aviation and space.

Eligibility This program is open to scholars who are conducting research on the role of women in aviation and space. Disciplines may include, but are not limited to, biology, business administration, economics, ergonomics, history, human engineering, psychology, and sociology. Applicants may be seeking funding to be used in conjunction with other research activities, such as completion of requirements for an advanced degree or matching funds with other grants to support a program larger than either grant could sponsor independently.

Financial data The amount awarded varies; generally, the grant is at least $1,000.

Duration The grant is awarded periodically.

Number awarded 1 each granting period.

Deadline Deadline not specified.

[1200]
AMERICAN ACADEMY OF CHILD AND ADOLESCENT PSYCHIATRY-NATIONAL INSTITUTE ON DRUG ABUSE CAREER DEVELOPMENT AWARD

American Academy of Child and Adolescent Psychiatry
Attn: Department of Research, Training, and Education
3615 Wisconsin Avenue, N.W.
Washington, DC 20016-3007
(202) 966-7300   Fax: (202) 966-2891
E-mail: research@aacap.org
Web: www.aacap.org/cs/awards

Summary To provide funding to child and adolescent psychiatrists (especially women and minorities) who are interested in a program of mentored training in addiction-related research focused on children and adolescents.

Eligibility This program is open to qualified child and adolescent psychiatrists who intend to established careers as independent investigators in mental health and addiction research. Applicants must design a career development and research training program in collaboration with a research mentor. The program may include prevention; early intervention or treatment research; epidemiology; etiology; genetics, gene-environment interactions, or pharmacogenetics; developmental risk factors; psychiatric comorbidity; medical comorbidity including HIV, Hepatitis C, and STD risk reduction; pathophysiology; services research; special populations (minorities, pregnancy, juvenile justice); health disparities; or imaging studies. U.S. citizenship, nationality, or permanent resident status is required. Women and minority candidates are especially encouraged to apply.

Financial data Grants provide salary support for 75% of the recipient's salary (up to $90,000 plus fringe benefits) and $50,000 per year to cover research and training costs.

Duration Up to 5 years.

Additional information This program is co-sponsored by the American Academy of Child and Adolescent Psychiatry (AACAP) and the National Institute on Drug Abuse (NIDA) as a K12 program of the National Institutes of Health (NIH).

Number awarded 1 or more each year.

Deadline Letters of intent must be submitted in early January of each year; completed applications are due the following March.

[1201]
AMERICAN ASSOCIATION OF OBSTETRICIANS AND GYNECOLOGISTS FOUNDATION SCHOLARSHIPS

American Gynecological and Obstetrical Society
Attn: American Association of Obstetricians and
  Gynecologists Foundation
409 12th Street, S.W.
Washington, DC 20024-2188
(202) 863-1649   Fax: (202) 554-0453
E-mail: clarkins@acog.org
Web: www.agosonline.org/aaogf/index.asp

Summary To provide funding to physicians (particularly women and minorities) who are interested in a program of research training in obstetrics and gynecology.

Eligibility Applicants must have an M.D. degree and be eligible for the certification process of the American Board of Obstetrics and Gynecology (ABOG). They must be interested in participating in research training conducted by 1 or more faculty mentors at an academic department of obstetrics and gynecology in the United States or Canada. The research training may be either laboratory-based or clinical, and should focus on fundamental biology, disease mechanisms, interventions or diagnostics, epidemiology, or translational research. There is no formal application form, but departments must supply a description of the candidate's qualifications, including a curriculum vitae, bibliography, prior training, past research experience, and evidence of completion of residency training in obstetrics and gynecology; a comprehensive description of the proposed training program; a descrip-

tion of departmental resources appropriate to the training; a detailed mentoring plan; a list of other research grants, training grants, or scholarships previously or currently held by the applicant; and a budget. Applicants for the scholarship co-sponsored by the Society for Maternal-Fetal Medicine (SMFM) must also be members or associate members of the SMFM. Women and minority candidates are strongly encouraged to apply. Selection is based on the scholarly, clinical, and research qualifications of the candidate; evidence of the candidate's commitment to an investigative career in academic obstetrics and gynecology in the United States or Canada; qualifications of the sponsoring department and mentor; overall quality of the mentoring plan; and quality of the research project. Preference may be given to applications from candidates training in areas currently underrepresented in academic obstetrics and gynecology (e.g., urogynecology, family planning).

Financial data The grant is $100,000 per year, of which at least $5,000 but not more than $15,000 must be used for employee benefits. In addition, sufficient funds to support travel to the annual fellows' retreat must be set aside. The balance of the funds may be used for salary, technical support, and supplies. The grant co-sponsored by the SMFM must be matched by an institutional commitment of at least $30,000 per year.

Duration 1 year; may be renewed for 2 additional years, based on satisfactory progress of the scholar.

Additional information Scholars must devote at least 75% of their effort to the program of research training.

Number awarded 2 each year: 1 co-sponsored by ABOG and 1 co-sponsored by SMFM.

Deadline June of each year.

[1202]
AMERICAN ASSOCIATION OF UNIVERSITY WOMEN POSTDOCTORAL RESEARCH LEAVE FELLOWSHIPS

American Association of University Women
Attn: AAUW Educational Foundation
301 ACT Drive, Department 60
P.O. Box 4030
Iowa City, IA 52243-4030
(319) 337-1716, ext. 60   Fax: (319) 337-1204
E-mail: aauw@act.org
Web: www.aauw.org/learn/fellowships_grants/american.cfm

Summary To enable American women scholars who have achieved distinction or promise of distinction in their fields of scholarly work to engage in additional research.

Eligibility This program is open to women who have a research doctorate (e.g., Ph.D., Ed.D., D.B.A., D.M.) or an M.F.A. degree as of the application deadline. Applicants must be interested in conducting independent research; preference is given to projects that are not simply a revision of a doctoral dissertation. Fields of study include the arts and humanities, social sciences, and natural sciences. Selection is based on scholarly excellence, quality of project design, originality of project, scholarly significance of project to discipline, feasibility of project and proposed schedule, qualifications of applicant, potential of applicant to make a significant contribution to field, applicant's commitment to women's issues in profession and community, applicant's teaching experience, and applicant's mentoring of other women. U.S. citizenship or permanent resident status is required.

Financial data   The stipend is $30,000. Funding is not provided for laboratory supplies and equipment, research assistants, publication costs, travel to professional meetings or seminars, tuition for additional course work, repayment of loans or other personal obligations, or tuition for a dependent's education.

Duration   1 year, beginning in July.

Additional information   The filing fee is $45.

Number awarded   Varies each year; recently, 10 of these fellowships were awarded.

Deadline   November of each year.

[1203]
AMERICAN ASSOCIATION OF UNIVERSITY WOMEN SUMMER/SHORT-TERM RESEARCH PUBLICATION GRANTS

American Association of University Women
Attn: AAUW Educational Foundation
301 ACT Drive, Department 60
P.O. Box 4030
Iowa City, IA 52243-4030
(319) 337-1716, ext. 60   Fax: (319) 337-1204
E-mail: aauw@act.org
Web: www.aauw.org/learn/fellowships_grants/american.cfm

Summary   To provide summer or short-term fellowships to women scholars interested in conducting postdoctoral research.

Eligibility   This program is open to women who are interested in preparing research manuscripts for publication (but not to undertake new research). Applicants may be tenure-track, part-time, or temporary faculty or may be independent scholars or researchers, either new or established. They must have completed a doctoral or M.F.A. degree. U.S. citizenship or permanent resident status is required. Scholars with strong publishing records are discouraged from applying. Selection is based on scholarly excellence, quality of project design, originality of project, scholarly significance of project to discipline, feasibility of project and proposed schedule, qualifications of applicant, potential of applicant to make a significant contribution to field, applicant's commitment to women's issues in profession and community, applicant's teaching experience, and applicant's mentoring of other women.

Financial data   The grant is $6,000. Funds may be used for stipends for recipient, clerical and technical support, research assistance related to verification (not basic research), supplies, and expenses. Grants do not cover travel, purchase of equipment, indirect costs, salary increase, or doctoral dissertation research or writing.

Duration   8 weeks; most recipients, especially full-time faculty, use the awards during the summer, but the research may be conducted at any time during the year.

Additional information   The filing fee is $40.

Number awarded   Varies each year; recently, 14 of these grants were awarded.

Deadline   November of each year.

[1204]
AMERICAN COLLEGE OF NURSE-MIDWIVES FOUNDATION FELLOWSHIP FOR GRADUATE EDUCATION

American College of Nurse-Midwives
Attn: ACNM Foundation, Inc.
8403 Colesville Road, Suite 1550
Silver Spring, MD 20910-6374
(240) 485-1850   Fax: (240) 485-1818
Web: www.midwife.org/foundation_award.cfm

Summary   To provide financial assistance for midwifery education to graduate student members of the American College of Nurse-Midwives (ACNM).

Eligibility   This program is open to ACNM members who are currently enrolled in a doctoral or postdoctoral midwife education program. Applicants must be a certified nurse midwife (CNM) or a certified midwife (CM). Along with their application, they must submit a curriculum vitae; a sample of up to 30 pages of scholarly work; and brief essays on their 5-year academic career plans, intended use of the fellowship money, and intended future participation in the local, regional, and/or national activities of ACNM or other activities that contribute to midwifery research, education, or practice.

Financial data   A stipend is awarded (amount not specified).

Duration   1 year.

Additional information   This program was established in 1997.

Number awarded   1 each year.

Deadline   March of each year.

[1205]
AMERICAN COUNCIL OF LEARNED SOCIETIES COLLABORATIVE RESEARCH FELLOWSHIPS

American Council of Learned Societies
Attn: Office of Fellowships and Grants
633 Third Avenue
New York, NY 10017-6795
(212) 697-1505   Fax: (212) 949-8058
E-mail: fellowships@acls.org
Web: www.acls.org

Summary   To provide funding for collaborative research to scholars (particularly women and minorities) who are specializing in the humanities and the humanities-related social sciences.

Eligibility   This program is open to teams of 2 or more scholars interested in collaborating on a single, substantive project. The project coordinator must have an appointment at a U.S.-based institution of higher education; other project members may be at institutions outside the United States or may be independent scholars. Appropriate fields of specialization include, but are not limited to, American studies; anthropology; archaeology; art and architectural history; classics; economics; film; geography; history; languages and literatures; legal studies; linguistics; musicology; philosophy; political science; psychology; religious studies; rhetoric, communication, and media studies; sociology; and theater, dance, and performance studies. Proposals in those fields of the social sciences are eligible only if they employ predominantly humanistic approaches (e.g., economic history, law and literature, political philosophy). Proposals in interdisciplinary and cross-disciplinary studies are welcome, as are proposals focused on a geographic region or on a cultural or linguistic group. Applications are particularly invited from women and members of minority groups.

Financial data The amount of the grant depends on the number of collaborators, their academic rank, and the duration of research leaves. Funding for salaries is provided at the rate of $60,000 for full professors, $40,000 for associate professors, or $35,000 for assistant professors. An additional $20,000 may be provided for collaboration funds (e.g., travel, materials, research assistance). The maximum amount for any single project is $140,000.

Duration Up to 24 months.

Additional information This program, established in 2008, is supported by funding from the Andrew W. Mellon Foundation.

Number awarded Up to 7 each year.

Deadline September of each year.

[1206]
AMERICAN COUNCIL OF LEARNED SOCIETIES FELLOWSHIPS

American Council of Learned Societies
Attn: Office of Fellowships and Grants
633 Third Avenue
New York, NY 10017-6795
(212) 697-1505   Fax: (212) 949-8058
E-mail: fellowships@acls.org
Web: www.acls.org/programs/acls

Summary To provide research funding to women, minority, and other scholars in all disciplines of the humanities and the humanities-related social sciences.

Eligibility This program is open to scholars at all stages of their careers who received a Ph.D. degree at least 2 years previously. Established scholars who can demonstrate the equivalent of the Ph.D. in publications and professional experience may also qualify. Applicants must be U.S. citizens or permanent residents who have not had supported leave time for at least 2 years prior to the start of the proposed research. Appropriate fields of specialization include, but are not limited to, American studies; anthropology; archaeology; art and architectural history; classics; economics; film; geography; history; languages and literatures; legal studies; linguistics; musicology; philosophy; political science; psychology; religious studies; rhetoric, communication, and media studies; sociology; and theater, dance, and performance studies. Proposals in those fields of the social sciences are eligible only if they employ predominantly humanistic approaches (e.g., economic history, law and literature, political philosophy). Proposals in interdisciplinary and cross-disciplinary studies are welcome, as are proposals focused on a geographic region or on a cultural or linguistic group. Awards are available at 3 academic levels: full professor, associate professor, and assistant professor. Applications are particularly invited from women and members of minority groups.

Financial data The maximum grant is $60,000 for full professors and equivalent, $40,000 for associate professors and equivalent, or $35,000 for assistant professors and equivalent. Normally, fellowships are intended as salary replacement and may be held concurrently with other fellowships, grants, and sabbatical pay, up to an amount equal to the candidate's current academic year salary.

Duration 6 to 12 months.

Additional information This program is supported in part by funding from the Ford Foundation, the Andrew W. Mellon Foundation, the National Endowment for the Humanities, the William and Flora Hewlett Foundation, and the Rockefeller Foundation.

Number awarded Approximately 57 each year: 17 at the full professor level, 18 at the association professor level, and 22 at the assistant professor level.

Deadline September of each year.

[1207]
AMERICAN GASTROENTEROLOGICAL ASSOCIATION RESEARCH SCHOLAR AWARDS

American Gastroenterological Association
Attn: AGA Research Foundation
Research Awards Manager
4930 Del Ray Avenue
Bethesda, MD 20814-2512
(301) 222-4012   Fax: (301) 654-5920
E-mail: awards@gastro.org
Web: www.gastro.org/aga-foundation/grants

Summary To provide research funding to women, minorities, and other young investigators who are developing an independent career in an area of gastroenterology, hepatology, or related fields.

Eligibility Applicants must hold full-time faculty positions at North American universities or professional institutes at the time of application. They should be early in their careers (fellows and established investigators are not appropriate candidates). Candidates with an M.D. degree must have completed clinical training within the past 5 years and those with a Ph.D. must have completed their degree within the past 5 years. Membership in the American Gastroenterological Association (AGA) is required. Selection is based on significance, investigator, innovation, approach, environment, relevance to AGA mission, and evidence of institutional commitment. Women, minorities, and physician/scientist investigators are strongly encouraged to apply.

Financial data The grant is $60,000 per year. Funds are to be used for project costs, including salary, supplies, and equipment but excluding travel. Indirect costs are not allowed.

Duration 2 years; a third year of support may be available, contingent upon availability of funds and a competitive review.

Additional information At least 70% of the recipient's research effort should relate to the gastrointestinal tract or liver.

Number awarded 1 or more each year.

Deadline September of each year.

[1208]
AMERICAN LEGION AUXILIARY EMERGENCY FUND

American Legion Auxiliary
8945 North Meridian Street
Indianapolis, IN 46260
(317) 569-4500   Fax: (317) 569-4502
E-mail: alahq@legion-aux.org
Web: www.legion-aux.org

Summary To provide funding to members of the American Legion Auxiliary who are facing temporary emergency needs or need educational training.

Eligibility This program is open to members of the American Legion Auxiliary who have maintained their membership for the immediate past 2 consecutive years and have paid their dues for the current year. Applicants must need emergency assistance for the following purposes: 1) food, shelter, and utilities during a time of financial crisis; 2) food and shelter because of weather-related emergencies and natural disasters; or 3) educational training because of the death of a spouse, divorce, separation, or the need to become the main source of support for their family. They must have exhausted all other sources of financial assistance, including funds and/or services available through the local Post and/or Unit, appropriate community welfare agencies, or state and federal financial aid for education. Grants are not available to settle already existing or accumulated debts, handle catastrophic illness, resettle disaster victims, or other similar problems.

Financial data The maximum grant is $2,400. Payments may be made directly to the member or to the mortgage company or utility. Educational grants may be paid directly to the educational institution.

Duration Grants are expended over no more than 3 months.

Additional information This program was established in 1969. In 1981, it was expanded to include the Displaced Homemaker Fund (although that title is no longer used).

Number awarded Varies each year.

Deadline Applications may be submitted at any time.

[1209]
AMERICAN SOCIETY OF TRANSPLANTATION CLINICAL SCIENCE FELLOWSHIP GRANTS

American Society of Transplantation
Attn: Chair, Awards and Grants Committee
15000 Commerce Parkway, Suite C
Mt. Laurel, NJ 08054
(856) 439-9986   Fax: (856) 439-9982
E-mail: info@a-s-t.org
Web: www.a-s-t.org/research-funding/research-funding

Summary To provide funding to women, minority, and other recent postdoctorates interested in a program of research training related to transplantation clinical science under the mentorship of a member of the American Society of Transplantation (AST).

Eligibility This program is open to scientists who have an M.D., D.O., Ph.D., D.V.M. or equivalent graduate degree and have spent 2 years or less performing research in clinical transplantation science since obtaining their last degree. Applicants must be sponsored by an AST member at a North American institution who will serve as their mentor. They must be citizens, permanent residents, or lawfully-admitted foreign nationals with appropriate visas in Canada, Mexico, or the United States. Their proposed training must relate to clinical trials, clinical outcomes, or translational research that involves materials from human patients. Topics that involve underrepresented areas (minorities, women, and pediatrics) are strongly encouraged. The AST also encourages applications from women and underrepresented minority investigators. Selection is based on the quality of the applicant, scientific project, sponsor, and institution, with an emphasis on pre-

paring the applicant for a career as an independent investigator.

Financial data The grant is $40,000 per year. Funds are to support salary of the fellow and cannot be used for indirect costs.

Duration 2 years.

Number awarded 1 or more each year.

Deadline December of each year.

[1210]
ANDREW W. MELLON FOUNDATION/ACLS RECENT DOCTORAL RECIPIENTS FELLOWSHIPS

American Council of Learned Societies
Attn: Office of Fellowships and Grants
633 Third Avenue
New York, NY 10017-6795
(212) 697-1505   Fax: (212) 949-8058
E-mail: fellowships@acls.org
Web: www.acls.org/programs/rdr

Summary To provide funding to women, minority, and other recent recipients of doctoral degrees in all disciplines of the humanities and the humanities-related social sciences who need funding to advance their scholarly career.

Eligibility This program is open to recent recipients of a doctoral degree in a humanities or humanities-related social science discipline. Applicants must have been 1) a recipient of an Andrew W. Mellon Foundation/ACLS Dissertation Completion Fellowship in the previous year; 2) designated as an alternate in that fellowship program; or 3) a recipient of a dissertation completion fellowship in another program of national stature (e.g., Whiting, AAUW, Newcombe). They must be seeking funding to position themselves for further scholarly advancement, whether or not they hold academic positions. Appropriate fields of specialization include, but are not limited to, American studies; anthropology; archaeology; art and architectural history; classics; economics; film; geography; history; languages and literatures; legal studies; linguistics; musicology; philosophy; political science; psychology; religious studies; rhetoric, communication, and media studies; sociology; and theater, dance, and performance studies. Proposals in those fields of the social sciences are eligible only if they employ predominantly humanistic approaches (e.g., economic history, law and literature, political philosophy). Proposals in interdisciplinary and cross-disciplinary studies are welcome, as are proposals focused on any geographic region or on any cultural or linguistic group. Applications are particularly invited from women and members of minority groups.

Financial data The stipend is $30,000.

Duration 1 academic year. Grantees may accept this fellowship during the 2 years following the date of the award.

Additional information This program, which began in 2007, is supported by funding from the Andrew W. Mellon Foundation and administered by the American Council of Learned Societies (ACLS). Fellows may not teach during the tenure of the fellowship. If they have a faculty position, they may use the fellowship to take research leave. Fellows who do not have a full-time position may choose to affiliate with a humanities research center or conduct research independently.

Number awarded 25 each year.
Deadline November of each year.

[1211]
ANN E. KAMMER MEMORIAL FELLOWSHIP FUND

Woods Hole Marine Biological Laboratory
Attn: Research Award Coordinator
7 MBL Street
Woods Hole, MA 02543-1015
(508) 289-7173   Fax: (508) 457-1924
E-mail: researchawards@mbl.edu
Web: www.mbl.edu/research/summer/awards_general.html

Summary To provide funding to women who have faculty positions and wish to conduct summer research at the Woods Hole Marine Biological Laboratory (MBL).

Eligibility This program is open to female faculty members who are interested in conducting summer research at the MBL. Applicants must submit a statement of the potential impact of this award on their career development. Preference is given to investigators working in the neurosciences.

Financial data The grant provides funds for summer research at the MBL. Recently, grants averaged approximately $1,500.

Duration At least 6 weeks during the summer.

Number awarded 1 each year.

Deadline December of each year.

[1212]
ANNE BRIDGE BADDOUR AVIATION SCHOLARSHIP

Women in Aviation, International
Attn: Scholarships
Morningstar Airport
3647 State Route 503 South
West Alexandria, OH 45381-9354
(937) 839-4647   Fax: (937) 839-4645
E-mail: scholarships@wai.org
Web: www.wai.org/education/scholarships.cfm

Summary To provide funding to members of Women in Aviation, International (WAI) who are interested in working on an Airline Transport Pilot (ATP) certificate.

Eligibility This program is open to women who are WAI members and have at least a private pilot certificate with 150 hours of flying time. Applicants must be able to demonstrate "a burning desire to become a professional pilot" and be on track towards the ATP. They must submit 2 letters of recommendation, a 500-word essay on their aviation history and goals, a resume, copies of all aviation licenses and medical certificates, and the last 3 pages of their pilot logbook (if applicable). Selection is based on achievements, attitude toward self and others, commitment to success, dedication to career, financial need, motivation, reliability, responsibility, and teamwork.

Financial data The stipend is $2,000.

Duration Training must be completed within 1 year.

Additional information WAI is a nonprofit professional organization dedicated to encouraging women to consider an aviation career and to providing educational outreach activities and networking resources to women active in the industry.

Number awarded 1 each year.
Deadline November of each year.

[1213]
ANNIE JUMP CANNON AWARD IN ASTRONOMY

American Astronomical Society
Attn: Secretary
2000 Florida Avenue, N.W., Suite 400
Washington, DC 20009-1231
(202) 328-2010   Fax: (202) 234-2560
E-mail: aassec@aas.org
Web: aas.org/prizes/cannon

Summary To recognize and reward female postdoctoral scholars for significant research in astronomy.

Eligibility This award is available to North American female astronomers who completed their Ph.D. within the past 5 years. Self nominations are allowed. Selection is based on completed research and promise for future research.

Financial data The award is $1,500.

Duration The award is presented annually.

Additional information This award was established in 1934 by the American Astronomical Society (AAS). From 1974 through 2004, it was awarded by the American Association of University Women (AAUW) Educational Foundation with the advice of the AAS. Effective in 2005, the AAS resumed administration of the award.

Number awarded 1 each year.

Deadline June of each year.

[1214]
APF VISIONARY GRANTS

American Psychological Foundation
750 First Street, N.E.
Washington, DC 20002-4242
(202) 336-5843   Fax: (202) 336-5812
E-mail: foundation@apa.org
Web: www.apa.org/apf/funding/vision-weiss.aspx

Summary To provide funding to professionals (especially women, minorities, and individuals with disabilities) who are interested in conducting projects that use psychology to solve social problems related to the priorities of the American Psychological Foundation (APF).

Eligibility This program is open to professionals at nonprofit organizations engaged in research, education, and intervention projects and programs. Applicants must be interested in conducting an activity that uses psychology to solve social problems in the following priority areas: understanding and fostering the connection between mental and physical health; reducing stigma and prejudice; understanding and preventing all forms of violence; or addressing the long-term psychological needs of individuals and communities in the aftermath of disaster. Selection is based on the criticality of the proposed funding for the proposed work; conformance with stated program goals and requirements; innovative and potential impact qualities; quality, viability, and promise of proposed work, and competence and capability of project leaders. The sponsor encourages applications from individuals who represent diversity in race, ethnicity, gender, age, disability, and sexual orientation.

Financial data Grants range from $5,000 to $20,000.

Duration 1 year; nonrenewable.

Additional information This program was established in 2003.

Number awarded 1 or more each year.

Deadline March of each year.

[1215]
ART MEETS ACTIVISM GRANT PROGRAM

Kentucky Foundation for Women
Heyburn Building
332 West Broadway, Suite 1215-A
Louisville, KY 40202-2184
(502) 562-0045   Toll Free: (866) 654-7564
Fax: (502) 561-0420   E-mail: info@kfw.org
Web: www.kfw.org/artact.html

Summary To support women and organizations in Kentucky wishing to conduct artistic activities that will benefit women and girls in the state.

Eligibility This program is open to women artists who have resided in Kentucky for at least 1 year and whose work is feminist in nature and is intentionally focused on social change outcomes. Nonprofit organizations are also eligible if their proposed project is artist driven. Applicants may be seeking funding for a range of artistic activities, including arts education programs focused on women or girls, community participation in the creation of new art forms, community based projects involving new partnerships between artists and activists, and arts-based community projects with social change themes or contents. In the selection process, the following criteria are considered: artwork in the sample is strong, highly original, and reflects feminism and social change; the proposed activities will directly benefit women and girls in Kentucky; application and work sample demonstrate applicant's understanding and practice of feminism; application and work sample demonstrate a clear understanding of the relationship between art and social change; work plan, timeline, and budget are clear, detailed, and realistic; and applicant's ability to complete the proposed activities in clearly shown. If applications are of equal artistic merit, priority is given to first-time applicants, women from rural and inner-city areas, women of color (especially African American women), lesbians, low-income women, women who did not complete high school, and women with disabilities.

Financial data Grants may range from $1,000 to $7,500, but most average between $3,000 and $5,000.

Duration Up to 1 year.

Additional information The foundation was established in 1985. Funding is not provided for general operating costs for organizations or for-profit organizations; tuition costs or living expenses while working toward a degree; endowment or capital campaigns; activities that do not focus on changing the lives of women in Kentucky; the promotion of religious doctrines; non-art related expenses, such as overdue bills or taxes; or work conducted by artists or organizations that have not resided in Kentucky for at least 1 year.

Number awarded Varies each year; recently, 33 of these grants were awarded. A total of $100,000 is available annually.

Deadline February of each year.

[1216]
ART-IN-EDUCATION RESIDENCY GRANTS

Women's Studio Workshop
722 Binnewater Lane
P.O. Box 489
Rosendale, NY 12472
(845) 658-9133   Fax: (845) 658-9031
E-mail: info@wsworkshop.org
Web: www.wsworkshop.org/_art_opp/artopp_grant_aie.htm

Summary To provide a residency and financial support to women interested in producing a limited edition artist's book and working with young people.

Eligibility This program is open to emerging artists who come from different regions of the country and/or diverse cultural backgrounds. Applicants must be interested in spending half their time involved with the design and production of a limited edition artist's book, and the other half working with young people in an arts-in-education program. Along with their application, they must submit a 1-page description of the proposed project; a 1-page history of their relevant experience working with youth; a structural dummy of the project; a materials budget; and a resume.

Financial data The program provides a stipend of $400 per week, a $750 materials grant, travel costs (within the continental United States), and housing while in residence.

Duration Up to 10 weeks (March and April with fifth-grade students or September and October with high school students).

Number awarded 2 each year.

Deadline November of each year.

[1217]
ARTIST-IN-RESIDENCE PROGRAM

Brandeis University
Hadassah-Brandeis Institute
Attn: Program Manager
515 South Street
Mailstop 079
Waltham, MA 02454-9110
(781) 736-2064   Fax: (781) 736-2078
E-mail: hbi@brandeis.edu
Web: www.brandeis.edu/hbi/grants/grants.html

Summary To provide an opportunity for artists to work on a significant project in the field of Jewish women's studies while in residence at the Hadassah-Brandeis Institute (HBI) of Brandeis University.

Eligibility This program is open to artists who are working in the area of Jewish women's and gender studies. Applicants must be interested in working on a significant artistic project while in residence at the institute and in producing an exhibit for the Kniznick Gallery at the Brandeis University Women's Studies Research Center (WSRC). Preference is given to artists who create a site-specific exhibit that 1) is visually and artistically impressive and original; 2) is related to fresh ways of thinking about Jews and gender; 3) is international in nature; 4) asks important questions and provokes dialogue; 5) is related to research being produced and promoted by the HBI; 6) provides a context for education; 7) is appropriate in scale for the Kniznick Gallery; and 8) includes new work produced during the residency. Applications (in English) from outside the United States are welcome.

Financial data Artists receive a stipend of $3,000 ($750 per week), a materials subsidy of $250, and studio space at the WSRC.

Duration 3 to 4 weeks, in March.

Additional information The Hadassah-Brandeis Institute was formerly the Hadassah International Research Institute on Jewish Women at Brandeis University.

Number awarded 1 or more each year.

Deadline September of each year.

[1218]
ASA S. BUSHNELL INTERNSHIP PROGRAM

Eastern College Athletic Conference
Attn: Director of Business Service
1311 Craigville Beach Road
Centerville, MA 02632
(508) 771-5060   Fax: (508) 778-4935
Web: www.ecac.org/about/bushnell/Bushnell_internship

Summary To provide work experience to recent college graduates (especially women and minorities) who are interested in college sports.

Eligibility This program is open to recent graduates of a member institution of the Eastern College Athletic Conference (ECAC). Applicants must submit the following: a cover letter describing their experience in athletics administration, public relations, sports information or sports writing, event management, marketing, fundraising, and computer literacy; a current resume detailing academic achievement, intercollegiate athletics participation, extracurricular activities and honors, and employment history; 2 writing samples or publications, if available; and 2 written recommendations and 1 additional reference. They must have demonstrated an interest in preparing for a career in athletics administration and should have proficient working knowledge of Microsoft Office, Microsoft Outlook, Facebook, and Adobe Creative Suite. Women and minorities are especially encouraged to apply.

Financial data This is a paid internship. Recently, the stipend was $1,125 per month, if the intern elected to accept medical, dental, and long-term disability insurance, or $1,575 per month if they chose to forego those benefits.

Duration 9 months, from September through May.

Additional information The ECAC is comprised of more than 300 colleges and universities located in New England and the Middle Atlantic states. Most schools hold dual membership with the Ivy, Northeast, or Patriot Leagues or the America East, Atlantic 10, Big East, Colonial Athletic, or Metro Atlantic conferences. Interns work at the ECAC offices in Centerville, Massachusetts. Recently, the internship concentrations included communications, championships, sport administration, and marketing/new media.

Number awarded Varies each year; recently, 4 of these interns were appointed.

Deadline March of each year.

[1219]
ASECS WOMEN'S CAUCUS EDITING AND TRANSLATION FELLOWSHIP

American Society for Eighteenth-Century Studies
c/o Wake Forest University
P.O. Box 7867
Winston-Salem, NC 27109
(336) 727-4694   Fax: (336) 727-4697
E-mail: asecs@wfu.edu
Web: asecs.press.jhu.edu/awards.html

Summary To provide funding to postdoctoral scholars working on or editing or translating project that deals with women's issues in the 18th century.

Eligibility This program is open to members of the American Society for Eighteenth-Century Studies (ASECS) who are working on an editing or translating project. Applicants must have a Ph.D. or be an emeritae/i faculty who does not already have professional support for the project. The project must translate and/or edit works by 18th century women writers or works that significantly advance understanding of women's experiences in the 18th century or offer a feminist analysis of an aspect of 18th-century culture and/or society.

Financial data The grant is $1,000.

Duration The grant is offered annually.

Additional information This award, offered by the Women's Caucus of the ASECS, was first presented in 2004. The recipient is asked to submit a brief written report on the progress of the project 1 year after receiving the award and, wherever possible, will serve on the award committee in the following year.

Number awarded 1 each year.

Deadline January of each year.

[1220]
ASM CAREER DEVELOPMENT GRANTS FOR POSTDOCTORAL WOMEN

American Society for Microbiology
Attn: Membership Services
1752 N Street, N.W.
Washington, DC 20036-2904
(202) 942-9253   Fax: (202) 942-9346
E-mail: lkent@asmusa.org
Web: www.asm.org

Summary To provide funding for career development activities to female postdoctorates who are members of the American Society for Microbiology (ASM).

Eligibility This program is open to women who have a doctoral degree, are currently performing postdoctoral work in microbiology at an institution in the United States, have no more than 5 years of relevant research experience since completing their doctorate, and are ASM members. Applicants must be seeking funding to travel to a meeting, visit another laboratory, take a course in a geographically distant place, or other purpose to advance their career. Along with their application, they must submit a statement that describes their academic accomplishments, career goals, and intended use of the grant to aid their career.

Financial data The grant is $1,200.

Duration Grants are awarded annually.

Number awarded 3 each year.

Deadline January of each year.

[1221]
ASSOCIATION FOR WOMEN IN MATHEMATICS TRAVEL GRANTS FOR WOMEN RESEARCHERS

Association for Women in Mathematics
11240 Waples Mill Road, Suite 200
Fairfax, VA 22030
(703) 934-0163   Fax: (703) 359-7562
E-mail: awm@awm-math.org
Web: sites.google.com

Summary To enable women mathematicians to attend research conferences in their fields.

Eligibility This program is open to women who wish to attend a research conference on a topic sponsored by the Division of Mathematical Sciences (DMS) of the National Science Foundation (NSF). The proposed research conference must be in an area supported by the DMS. That includes certain areas of statistics but excludes most mathematics education and the history of mathematics. Applicants must be women holding a doctorate (or equivalent) and with a work address in the United States (or home address, in the case of unemployed mathematicians). Women who have been awarded this grant in the past 2 years or who have other sources of external funding (e.g., a regular NSF grant) are ineligible. Partial institutional support does not, however, make the applicant ineligible. Interested applicants must use an online registration system that will call for 1) a description of their current research and how the proposed travel would benefit their research program; 2) their curriculum vitae; 3) a budget for the proposed travel; and 4) information about all other sources of travel funding available to the applicant.

Financial data These grants provide full or partial support for travel and subsistence for a meeting or conference in the applicant's field of specialization. A maximum of $1,500 for domestic travel and of $2,000 for foreign travel may be awarded.

Duration There are 3 award periods each year.

Additional information Funding for this program is provided by the Division of Mathematical Sciences of the National Science Foundation. For foreign travel, U.S. carriers must be used whenever possible.

Number awarded Varies each year; recently, 36 of these grants were awarded.

Deadline January, April, or September of each year.

[1222]
ASSOCIATION FOR WOMEN IN SPORTS MEDIA MEMBER TRAINING GRANTS

Association for Women in Sports Media
Attn: President
3899 North Front Street
Harrisburg, PA 17110
(717) 703-3086   E-mail: amy.moritz@awsmonline.org
Web: awsmonline.org/midcareertraining-grant

Summary To provide funding to members of the Association for Women in Sports Media (AWSM) who are interested in mid-career training.

Eligibility This program is open to AWSM members who are interested in obtaining additional training, as through on online journalism seminar or video production class. Applicants must submit a resume that includes their professional experience, formal education, professional development

seminars or workshops, or other relevant training experiences; a 500-word statement on how this grant would help them; and a description of how the grant would be used.

Financial data Grants range from $500 to $1,500.

Duration These are 1-time grants.

Additional information This program was established in 2008 with funding from the Ethics and Excellence in Journalism Foundation.

Number awarded Up to 5 each year.

Deadline November of each year.

[1223]
ASSOCIATION OF WOMEN PSYCHIATRISTS FELLOWSHIP

Association of Women Psychiatrists
Attn: Executive Director
P.O. Box 570218
Dallas, TX 75357-0218
(972) 613-0985   Fax: (972) 613-5532
E-mail: womenpsych@aol.com
Web: www.womenpsych.org/Fellowships/default.html

Summary To recognize and reward outstanding women psychiatry residents.

Eligibility This award is available to women currently enrolled in a psychiatry residency program who are nominated by their training director. Nominees must be members of the Association of Women Psychiatrists. Selection is based on demonstrated leadership potential, interest in and commitment to women's health, community mental health service, and academic excellence.

Financial data The grant is $1,500.

Duration The grants are presented annually.

Number awarded 1 each year.

Deadline March of each year.

[1224]
AST BASIC SCIENCE FELLOWSHIP GRANT

American Society of Transplantation
Attn: Chair, Awards and Grants Committee
15000 Commerce Parkway, Suite C
Mt. Laurel, NJ 08054
(856) 439-9986   Fax: (856) 439-9982
E-mail: info@a-s-t.org
Web: www.a-s-t.org/research-funding/research-funding

Summary To provide funding to recent postdoctorates (especially women and underrepresented minorities) who are interested in a program of research training related to the basic science of transplantation under the mentorship of a member of the American Society of Transplantation (AST).

Eligibility This program is open to scientists who have an M.D., D.O., Ph.D., D.V.M. or equivalent graduate degree and have spent 2 years or less performing research in basic transplantation science since obtaining their last degree. Applicants must be sponsored by an AST member at a North American institution who will serve as their mentor. They must be citizens, permanent residents, or lawfully-admitted foreign nationals with appropriate visas in Canada, Mexico, or the United States. Their proposed research training must involve support work in transplantation biology, ranging from pertinent basic immunology to animal studies; all types of organ, tissue, and cell transplants are considered. Research topics that involve underrepresented areas (minorities, women, and pediatrics) are strongly encouraged. The AST also encourages applications from women and underrepresented minority investigators. Selection is based on the quality of the applicant, scientific project, sponsor, and institution, with an emphasis on preparing the applicant for a career as an independent investigator.

Financial data The grant is $40,000 per year. Funds are to support the fellow's salary and cannot be used for indirect costs.

Duration 2 years.

Number awarded 1 or more each year.

Deadline December of each year.

[1225]
ASTRAEA VISUAL ARTS FUND

Astraea Lesbian Foundation for Justice
Attn: Program Director
116 East 16th Street, Seventh Floor
New York, NY 10003
(212) 529-8021   Fax: (212) 982-3321
E-mail: grants@astraeafoundation.org
Web: www.astraeafoundation.org

Summary To recognize and reward the work of lesbian artists.

Eligibility This program is open to U.S. residents who agree to be acknowledged publicly as lesbian artists in the following categories: sculpture, painting in any medium, prints, drawing, work on paper, and mixed media (traditional or nontraditional materials). Students currently enrolled in an arts degree-granting program or its equivalent are not eligible. Applicants must submit slides of their original works of art, a current resume, and a 250-word statement responding to the goal of the fund.

Financial data The award is $2,500.

Duration The awards are presented annually.

Additional information This program was established in 2002. An application fee of $5 must be included.

Number awarded 3 each year.

Deadline October of each year.

[1226]
AWHONN NOVICE RESEARCHER AWARD

Association of Women's Health, Obstetric and Neonatal Nurses
Attn: Research Grants Program
2000 L Street, N.W., Suite 740
Washington, DC 20036
(202) 261-2431   Toll Free: (800) 673-8499, ext. 2431
Fax: (202) 728-0575
E-mail: ResearchPrograms@awhonn.org
Web: www.awhonn.org

Summary To provide funding for small research projects to members of the Association of Women's Health, Obstetric and Neonatal Nurses (AWHONN) who qualify as novice researchers.

Eligibility This program is open to members of the association who have at least a master's degree or are currently enrolled in a master's program and completing a thesis or clinical research project. Applicants must be interested in beginning areas of study, investigating clinical issues, and/or

launching a pilot study. They must identify a senior researcher who has agreed to serve as mentor and who submits a letter of support describing the role he or she will be implementing.

Financial data The grant is $5,000. Funds may not be used for indirect costs, tuition, computer hardware or printers, conference attendance, or salary for the principal investigator or other investigators.

Duration 1 year.

Number awarded 1 each year.

Deadline November of each year.

[1227]
AWM MATHEMATICS EDUCATION RESEARCH TRAVEL GRANTS FOR WOMEN RESEARCHERS

Association for Women in Mathematics
11240 Waples Mill Road, Suite 200
Fairfax, VA 22030
(703) 934-0163   Fax: (703) 359-7562
E-mail: awm@awm-math.org
Web: sites.google.com

Summary To enable women mathematicians to attend research conferences related to education.

Eligibility This program is open to women who wish to attend a research conference on mathematics or mathematics education. They may be mathematicians attending a mathematics education research conference or mathematics education researchers attending a mathematics conference. Applicants must be women holding a doctorate (or equivalent) and with a work address in the United States (or home address, in the case of unemployed mathematicians). Women who have been awarded this grant in the past 2 years or who have other sources of external funding (e.g., a regular NSF grant) are ineligible. Partial institutional support does not, however, make the applicant ineligible. Interested applicants must use an online registration system that will call for 1) a description of their current research and how the proposed travel would benefit their research program; 2) their curriculum vitae; 3) a budget for the proposed travel; and 4) information about all other sources of travel funding available to the applicant.

Financial data These grants provide full or partial support for travel and subsistence for a meeting or conference in the applicant's field of specialization. A maximum of $1,500 for domestic travel and of $2,000 for foreign travel may be awarded.

Duration There are 3 award periods each year.

Additional information Funding for this program, established in 2006, is provided by the Division of Mathematical Sciences of the National Science Foundation. For foreign travel, U.S. carriers must be used whenever possible.

Number awarded Varies each year.

Deadline January, April, or September of each year.

[1228]
B. JUNE WEST RECRUITMENT GRANT

Delta Kappa Gamma Society International-Theta State
　Organization
c/o Megan Savage, Committee on Professional Affairs
　Chair
1101 West Third Street
Roswell, NM 88201-3031
E-mail: meganandjames@cableone.net
Web: deltakappagamma.org/NM

Summary To provide financial assistance to women in New Mexico who are interested in preparing for a career as a teacher.

Eligibility This program is open to women residents of New Mexico who are 1) graduating high school seniors planning to go into education; 2) college students majoring in education; or 3) teachers needing educational assistance. Applicants must submit a list of activities in which they are involved, 3 letters of recommendation, a list of achievements and awards, and a statement of their educational goal and how this grant would be of assistance to them. Financial need is not considered in the selection process.

Financial data A stipend is awarded (amount not specified).

Duration 1 year.

Number awarded 1 or more each year.

Deadline February of each year.

[1229]
BARNARD WOMEN POETS PRIZE

Barnard College
Attn: Department of English
417 Barnard Hall
3009 Broadway
New York, NY 10027-6598
(212) 854-2116　　　　　　　　Fax: (212) 854-9498
E-mail: english@barnard.edu
Web: english.barnard.edu/women-poets/contest

Summary To recognize and reward outstanding unpublished poetry written by American women.

Eligibility This program is open to women writers who have already published 1 book of poetry (in an edition of 500 copies or more) and are seeking a publisher for a second collection. Manuscripts that are under option to another publisher are not eligible. Applicants should submit 3 copies of a book-length manuscript (the page limit is not specified).

Financial data The prize is $1,500 and publication of the manuscript.

Duration The prize is awarded biennially.

Additional information This prize was first awarded in 2003. Winning submissions are published by W.W. Norton & Co. The entry fee is $20.

Number awarded 1 each odd-numbered year.

Deadline October of each even-numbered year.

[1230]
BASIC SCIENCE FACULTY DEVELOPMENT GRANT

American Society of Transplantation
Attn: Chair, Awards and Grants Committee
15000 Commerce Parkway, Suite C
Mt. Laurel, NJ 08054
(856) 439-9986　　　　　　　　Fax: (856) 439-9982
E-mail: info@a-s-t.org
Web: www.a-s-t.org/research-funding/research-funding

Summary To provide funding to women, minority, and other junior members of the American Society of Transplantation (AST) who are interested in conducting basic research.

Eligibility This program is open to AST members who have an M.D., D.O., Ph.D., D.V.M. or equivalent graduate degree and have completed postgraduate training. Applicants must have an academic appointment at an accredited institution of higher education and be within 5 years of their initial faculty appointment. They must be citizens, permanent residents, or lawfully-admitted foreign nationals with appropriate visas in Canada, Mexico, or the United States. Their proposed research project must involve support work in transplantation biology, ranging from pertinent basic immunology to animal studies; all types of organ, tissue, and cell transplants are considered. Research topics that involve underrepresented areas (minorities, women, and pediatrics) are strongly encouraged. The AST also encourages applications from women and underrepresented minority investigators.

Financial data The grant is $40,000 per year. No indirect costs are permitted.

Duration 2 years.

Number awarded 1 or more each year.

Deadline December of each year.

[1231]
BEHAVIORAL SCIENCES POSTDOCTORAL FELLOWSHIPS IN EPILEPSY

Epilepsy Foundation
Attn: Research Department
8301 Professional Place
Landover, MD 20785-2237
(301) 459-3700　　　　　　　　Toll Free: (800) EFA-1000
Fax: (301) 577-2684　　　　　　TDD: (800) 332-2070
E-mail: grants@efa.org
Web: www.epilepsyfoundation.org

Summary To provide funding to postdoctorates in the behavioral sciences (particularly women, minorities, and individuals with disabilities) who wish to pursue research training in an area related to epilepsy.

Eligibility Applicants must have received a Ph.D. or equivalent degree in a field of social science, including (but not limited to) sociology, social work, anthropology, nursing, or economics. They must be interested in receiving additional research training to prepare for a career in clinical behavioral aspects of epilepsy. Academic faculty holding the rank of instructor or above are not eligible, nor are graduate or medical students, medical residents, permanent government employees, or employees in private industry. Because these fellowships are designed as training opportunities, the quality of the training plans and environment are considered in the selection process. Other selection criteria include the scientific quality of the proposed research, a statement regarding the relevance of the research to epilepsy, the applicant's qualifications, the preceptor's qualifications, adequacy of the facility, and related epilepsy programs at the institution. Applications from women, members of minority groups, and people with disabilities are especially encouraged. U.S. citizenship is not required, but the research must be conducted in the United States.

Financial data Grants up to $40,000 are available.

Duration 1 year.

Number awarded Varies each year.

Deadline March of each year.

[1232]
BERKSHIRE CONFERENCE FIRST BOOK PRIZE

Berkshire Conference of Women Historians
c/o Serena Zabin
Carleton College
History Department, Leighton Hall 210
1 North College Street
Northfield, MN 55057
(507) 222-7160   E-mail: szabin@carleton.edu
Web: berksconference.org/prizes-awards

Summary To recognize and reward women who have written outstanding first books in history.

Eligibility This prize is awarded for the best first book on any historical subject written by a woman normally resident in North America during the preceding year. Books need not focus on women's history. Textbooks, juveniles, fiction, poetry, collections of essays, and documentary collections are not eligible.

Financial data The prize $1,000.

Duration The prize is awarded annually.

Number awarded 1 each year.

Deadline January of each year.

[1233]
BILL WHITEHEAD AWARD FOR LIFETIME ACHIEVEMENT

Publishing Triangle
332 Bleecker Street, D36
New York, NY 10014
E-mail: awards@publishingtriangle.org
Web: www.publishingtriangle.org/awards.asp

Summary To recognize and reward female and male writers (judged separately) who have dealt openly with gay or lesbian issues.

Eligibility This is a lifetime achievement award. It is presented to writers whose body of work makes a significant contribution to gay and lesbian literature. The award alternates between women (in even-numbered years) and men (in odd-numbered years). Only members of the Publishing Triangle may nominate candidates for the award.

Financial data The award is $3,000.

Duration The award is presented annually.

Additional information The Publishing Triangle is an association of lesbians and gay men in publishing. This award was first presented in 1989.

Number awarded 1 each year.

Deadline November of each year.

[1234]
B.K. KRENZER MEMORIAL REENTRY SCHOLARSHIP

Society of Women Engineers
Attn: Scholarship Selection Committee
120 South LaSalle Street, Suite 1515
Chicago, IL 60603-3572
(312) 596-5223   Toll Free: (877) SWE-INFO
Fax: (312) 644-8557
E-mail: scholarshipapplication@swe.org
Web: societyofwomenengineers.swe.org

Summary To provide financial assistance to women (particularly women engineers) who are interested in returning to college or graduate school to continue their study of engineering or computer science.

Eligibility This program is open to women who are planning to enroll at an ABET-accredited 4-year college or university. Applicants must have been out of the engineering workforce and school for at least 2 years and must be planning to return as an undergraduate or graduate student to work on a degree in computer science or engineering. They must have a GPA of 3.0 or higher. Selection is based on merit. Preference is given to engineers who already have a degree and are planning to reenter the engineering workforce after a period of temporary retirement.

Financial data The stipend is $2,000.

Duration 1 year.

Additional information This program was established in 1996.

Number awarded 1 each year.

Deadline February of each year.

[1235]
BOOK ARTISTS' RESIDENCY GRANTS

Women's Studio Workshop
722 Binnewater Lane
P.O. Box 489
Rosendale, NY 12472
(845) 658-9133   Fax: (845) 658-9031
E-mail: info@wsworkshop.org
Web: www.wsworkshop.org/_art_opp/artopp_grant_abr.htm

Summary To provide financial assistance and a residency at the Women's Studio Workshop (WSW) to women book artists.

Eligibility This program is open to female artists who are interested in producing new books that will have a press run of 50 to 100 copies. Applicants must submit a 1-page description of the proposed project, a description of the media/studios they will need to print the book, a structural dummy, a materials budget, a resume, and 10 images of recent work.

Financial data The program provides a stipend of $2,000 to $3,000, a $750 materials grant, travel costs (within the continental United States), and housing while in residence.

Duration 6 to 8 weeks.

Additional information This program provides an opportunity for book artists to come and work in residency at WSW in Rosendale, New York. Selected artists are involved in all aspects of the design and production of their new books. The studio provides technical advice and, when possible, help with editing. Assistance with marketing is also available. The contract requires that 10% of the published books go to the sponsor for archives, exhibition, and display copies; 10% to the artist; and 80% for general marketing.

Number awarded Varies each year.

Deadline November of each year.

[1236]
BRANCH-OUT GRANTS

American Society of Transplantation
Attn: Chair, Awards and Grants Committee
15000 Commerce Parkway, Suite C
Mt. Laurel, NJ 08054
(856) 439-9986   Fax: (856) 439-9982
E-mail: info@a-s-t.org
Web: www.a-s-t.org/research-funding/research-funding

Summary To provide funding for research to women, minority, and other junior members of the American Society of Transplantation (AST) who are interested in conducting research in collaboration with a senior colleague.

Eligibility This program is open to AST members who have an M.D., D.O., Ph.D., D.V.M. or equivalent graduate degree and have completed postgraduate training. Applicants must have an academic appointment at an accredited institution of higher education and be within 5 years of their initial faculty appointment. They must be citizens, permanent residents, or lawfully-admitted foreign nationals with appropriate visas in Canada, Mexico, or the United States. Their proposed research project must involve collaboration with a mid-level basic science investigator who is neither an AST member nor a transplant researcher. Both applicants must be independent investigators. Research topics that involve underrepresented areas (minorities, women, and pediatrics) are strongly encouraged. The AST also encourages applications from women and underrepresented minority investigators. Selection is based on scientific merit, feasibility, relevance to transplantation research, and novelty of the proposed study.

Financial data The grant is $40,000 ($20,000 per investigator). No indirect costs are permitted.

Duration 1 year.

Number awarded 1 or more each year.

Deadline December of each year.

[1237]
BUTCHER SCHOLAR AWARD

Autry National Center
Attn: Women of the West Chair
4700 Western Heritage Way
Los Angeles, CA 90027-1462
(323) 667-2000   Fax: (323) 660-5721
Web: theautry.org/research/prizes

Summary To provide funding to scholars interested in conducting research on the history of women in the West at the Autry Museum of Western Heritage.

Eligibility This program is open to scholars interested in conducting research projects that explore the relationships between the experiences, stories, and memories of women in the American West. Preference is given to projects that promise to deepen understanding of the history of diverse women in the historical and contemporary West.

Financial data The maximum grant is $5,000.

Duration 1 year.

Additional information This program was established in 2001 by the Women of the West Museum, which has since merged with the Autry National Center. The museum works with the scholar to create and implement a community outreach component that enhances its public impact. In addition, the scholar is asked to make a presentation at the Autry Museum History Workshop.

Number awarded 1 each year.

Deadline March of each year.

[1238]
BYRD FELLOWSHIP PROGRAM

Ohio State University
Byrd Polar Research Center
Attn: Fellowship Committee
Scott Hall Room 108
1090 Carmack Road
Columbus, OH 43210-1002
(614) 292-6531   Fax: (614) 292-4697
Web: bprc.osu.edu/byrdfellow

Summary To provide funding to postdoctorates (particularly women, minorities, and individuals with disabilities) who are interested in conducting research on the Arctic or Antarctic areas at Ohio State University.

Eligibility This program is open to postdoctorates of superior academic background who are interested in conducting advanced research on either Arctic or Antarctic problems at the Byrd Polar Research Center at Ohio State University. Applicants must have received their doctorates within the past 5 years. Each application should include a statement of general research interest, a description of the specific research to be conducted during the fellowship, and a curriculum vitae. Women, minorities, Vietnam-era veterans, disabled veterans, and individuals with disabilities are particularly encouraged to apply.

Financial data The stipend is $40,000 per year; an allowance of $3,000 for research and travel is also provided.

Duration 18 months.

Additional information This program was established by a major gift from the Byrd Foundation in memory of Rear Admiral Richard Evelyn Byrd and Marie Ames Byrd, his wife. Except for field work or other research activities requiring absence from campus, fellows are expected to be in residence at the university for the duration of the program.

Deadline October of each year.

[1239]
CAREER AWARDS FOR MEDICAL SCIENTISTS

Burroughs Wellcome Fund
21 T.W. Alexander Drive, Suite 100
P.O. Box 13901
Research Triangle Park, NC 27709-3901
(919) 991-5100   Fax: (919) 991-5160
E-mail: info@bwfund.org
Web: www.bwfund.org

Summary To provide funding to biomedical scientists in the United States and Canada (priority given to women and minorities) who require assistance to make the transition from postdoctoral training to faculty appointment.

Eligibility This program is open to citizens and permanent residents of the United States and Canada who have an M.D.,

D.D.S., D.V.M., Pharm.D., or equivalent clinical degree. Applicants must be interested in a program of research training in the area of basic biomedical, disease-oriented, translational, or molecular, genetic, or pharmacological epidemiology research. Training must take place at a degree-granting medical school, graduate school, hospital, or research institute in the United States or Canada. Each U.S. and Canadian institution may nominate up to 5 candidates. The sponsor encourages institutions to nominate women and underrepresented minorities (African Americans, Hispanics, or Native Americans); if a woman or underrepresented minority is among the initial 5 candidates, the institution may nominate a sixth candidate who is a woman or underrepresented minority. Following their postdoctoral training, awardees may accept a faculty position at a U.S. or Canadian institution.

Financial data For each year of postdoctoral support, the stipend is $65,000, the research allowance is $20,500, and the administrative fee is $9,500. For each year of faculty support, the stipend is $150,000, the research allowance is $3,000, and the administrative fee is $17,000. The maximum portion of the award that can be used during the postdoctoral period is $190,000 or $95,000 per year. The faculty portion of the award is $700,000 minus the portion used during the postdoctoral years.

Duration The awards provide up to 2 years of postdoctoral support and up to 3 years of support during the faculty appointment.

Additional information This program began in 1995 as Career Awards in the Biomedical Sciences (CABS). It was revised to its current format in 2006 as a result of the NIH K99/R00 Pathway to Independence program. As the CABS, the program provided more than $100 million in support to 241 U.S. and Canadian scientists. Awardees are required to devote at least 75% of their time to research-related activities.

Number awarded Varies each year: recently, 5 of these awards were granted.

Deadline September of each year.

[1240]
CAREER DEVELOPMENT AWARDS IN DIABETES RESEARCH

Juvenile Diabetes Research Foundation International
Attn: Grant Administrator
26 Broadway, 14th Floor
New York, NY 10004
(212) 479-7572   Toll Free: (800) 533-CURE
Fax: (212) 785-9595   E-mail: info@jdrf.org
Web: www.jdrf.org/index.cfm?page_id=111715

Summary To assist young scientists (especially women and minorities) to develop into independent investigators in diabetes-related research.

Eligibility This program is open to postdoctorates early in their faculty careers who show promise as diabetes researchers. Applicants must have received their first doctoral (M.D., Ph.D., D.M.D., D.V.M., or equivalent) degree at least 3 but not more than 7 years previously. They may not have an academic position at the associate professor, professor, or equivalent level, but they must be a faculty member (instructor or assistant professor) at a university, health science center, or comparable institution with strong, well-established research and training programs. The proposed research must relate to Type 1 diabetes, but it may be basic or clinical. There are no

citizenship requirements. Applications are encouraged from women, members of minority groups underrepresented in the sciences, and people with disabilities. The proposed research may be conducted at foreign or domestic, for-profit or nonprofit, or public or private institutions, including universities, colleges, hospitals, laboratories, units of state or local government, or eligible agencies of the federal government. Selection is based on the applicant's perceived ability and potential for a career in Type 1 diabetes research, the caliber of the proposed research, and the quality and commitment of the host institution.

Financial data The total award may be up to $150,000 each year. Indirect costs cannot exceed 10%.

Duration Up to 5 years.

Additional information Fellows must spend up to 75% of their time in research.

Deadline January or July of each year.

[1241]
CAREER DEVELOPMENT GRANTS

American Association of University Women
Attn: AAUW Educational Foundation
301 ACT Drive, Department 60
P.O. Box 4030
Iowa City, IA 52243-4030
(319) 337-1716, ext. 60   Fax: (319) 337-1204
E-mail: aauw@act.org
Web: www.aauw.org

Summary To provide financial assistance to women who are seeking career advancement, career change, or reentry into the workforce.

Eligibility This program is open to women who are U.S. citizens or permanent residents, have earned a bachelor's degree, received their most recent degree more than 4 years ago, and are making career changes, seeking to advance in current careers, or reentering the work force. Applicants must be interested in working toward a master's degree, second bachelor's or associate degree, professional degree (e.g., M.D., J.D.), certification program, or technical school certificate. They must be planning to undertake course work at an accredited 2- or 4-year college or university (or a technical school that is licensed, accredited, or approved by the U.S. Department of Education). Special consideration is given to women of color and women pursuing credentials in nontraditional fields. Support is not provided for prerequisite course work or for Ph.D. course work or dissertations. Selection is based on demonstrated commitment to education and equity for women and girls, reason for seeking higher education or technical training, degree to which study plan is consistent with career objectives, potential for success in chosen field, documentation of opportunities in chosen field, feasibility of study plans and proposed time schedule, validity of proposed budget and budget narrative (including sufficient outside support), and quality of written proposal.

Financial data Grants range from $2,000 to $12,000. Funds may be used for tuition, fees, books, supplies, local transportation, dependent child care, or purchase of a computer required for the study program.

Duration 1 year, beginning in July; nonrenewable.

Additional information The filing fee is $35.

Number awarded Varies each year; recently, 47 of these grants, with a value of $500,000, were awarded.
Deadline December of each year.

[1242]
CAROL TYLER AWARD

International Precious Metals Institute
5101 North 12th Avenue, Suite C
Pensacola, FL 32504
(850) 476-1156   Fax: (850) 476-1548
E-mail: mail@ipmi.org
Web: www.ipmi.org/awards/index.cfm

Summary To recognize and reward women who have made outstanding contributions to the field of precious metals.

Eligibility This award is available to women who are graduate students or currently employed in industry or academia. Nominees must have made outstanding theoretical and experimental contributions to the science and technology of precious metals. They may be residents of any country.

Financial data The award is $5,000 and a certificate.

Duration The award is presented annually.

Additional information This award was first presented in 2011.

Number awarded 1 each year.

Deadline January of each year.

[1243]
CARRIE CHAPMAN CATT PRIZE FOR RESEARCH ON WOMEN AND POLITICS

Iowa State University
Attn: Carrie Chapman Catt Center for Women and Politics
309 Carrie Chapman Catt Hall
Ames, IA 50011-1305
(515) 294-3181   Fax: (515) 294-3741
E-mail: cattcntr@iastate.edu
Web: www.iastate.edu/CattCenter/cattprize.shtml

Summary To recognize and reward outstanding research in the area of women and politics.

Eligibility This competition is open to scholars at all levels, including graduate students and junior faculty, who are planning to conduct research in the area of women and politics. Applicants must submit a detailed description of their research project, including 1) its purpose and content; 2) a discussion of relevant theory, contributions to literature in the field, and methodology; 3) a statement on how this prize will contribute to the research project; and 4) a timetable for completion of the project. They also must submit a 1-page biographical statement, highlighting their research interests, significant publications and/or presentations, and professional interests and experiences. Research projects can address the annual conference theme or any other topic related to women and politics.

Financial data Prizes are $1,000 for winners or $500 for honorable mention. All prize-winners may also receive travel expenses to Des Moines, Iowa where awards are presented at the annual conference of the Carrie Chapman Catt Center for Women and Politics.

Duration The prizes are awarded annually.

Number awarded Up to 2 winners and up to 2 honorable mentions are selected each year.
Deadline November of each year.

[1244]
CATHERINE PRELINGER AWARD

Coordinating Council for Women in History
c/o Sandra Dawson, Executive Director
Northern Illinois University
Department of History and Women's Studies
715 Zulauf Hall
DeKalb, IL 60115
(815) 895-2624   E-mail: execdir@theccwh.org
Web: theccwh.org/awards.htm

Summary To provide funding to members of the Coordinating Council for Women in History (CCWH) for a project that focuses on women's roles in history.

Eligibility This program is open to members of CCWH whose academic path has not followed the traditional pattern of uninterrupted study. Applicants must hold either A.B.D. status or a Ph.D. and be engaged in scholarship that is historical in nature, although their degree may be in related fields. They must submit a description of a project they propose to undertake with this award, including the work they intend to complete, the schedule they have developed, the sources they intend to use, and the contribution the work will make to women in history. Independent and non-academic scholars are encouraged to apply.

Financial data The grant is $20,000.

Duration 1 year.

Additional information This program was established in 1998.

Number awarded 1 each year.

Deadline September of each year.

[1245]
CENTER FOR ADVANCED STUDY IN THE BEHAVIORAL SCIENCES RESIDENTIAL POSTDOCTORAL FELLOWSHIPS

Center for Advanced Study in the Behavioral Sciences
Attn: Secretary and Program Coordinator
75 Alta Road
Stanford, CA 94305-8090
(650) 321-2052   Fax: (650) 321-1192
E-mail: secretary@casbs.org
Web: www.casbs.org

Summary To provide funding to women, minority, and other behavioral scientists who are interested in conducting research at the Center for Advanced Study in the Behavioral Sciences in Stanford, California.

Eligibility Eligible to be nominated for this fellowship are scientists and scholars from this country or abroad who show exceptional accomplishment or promise in the core social and behavioral disciplines: anthropology, economics, political science, psychology, or sociology; applications are also accepted from scholars in a wide range of humanistic disciplines, education, linguistics, and the biological sciences. Selection is based on standing in the field rather than on the merit of a particular project under way at a given time. A special effort is made to promote diversity among the scholars by encouraging participation from groups that often have been overlooked in academia: younger scholars, women, minorities, international scholars, and scholars whose home universities are not research-oriented.

Financial data The stipend is based on the fellow's regular salary for the preceding year, with a cap of $60,000. In most cases, the fellow contributes to the cost of the stipend with support from sabbatical or other funding source.

Duration From 9 to 11 months.

Additional information Fellows must be in residence in a community within 10 miles of the center for the duration of the program (that requirement excludes San Francisco, Berkeley, and San Jose, for example).

Number awarded Approximately 45 each year.

Deadline February of each year.

[1246]
CENTER FOR THE EDUCATION OF WOMEN VISITING SCHOLAR PROGRAM

University of Michigan
Attn: Center for the Education of Women
330 East Liberty Street
Ann Arbor, MI 48104-2289
(734) 764-6005   Fax: (734) 998-6203
E-mail: contactcew@umich.edu
Web: www.cew.umich.edu/research/vs

Summary To provide funding to scholars from any country interested in conducting research on women at the University of Michigan's Center for the Education of Women.

Eligibility This program is open to scholars from the United States and abroad who have a Ph.D. or equivalent degree. Applicants must be interested in utilizing the resources of the center to explore the following or related issues: women in nontraditional fields, leadership, women and work, gender and poverty, women in higher education, women of color in the academy, or gender equity in education and employment.

Financial data Scholars receive office space, full access to University of Michigan facilities and programs (including library and computing resources), and stipends up to $7,500. An additional $1,000 is paid upon receipt of the scholar's paper.

Duration From 2 to 12 months.

Additional information Visiting scholars must be in residence at the center for the duration of the program. They are expected to prepare a working paper on the basis of their research.

Number awarded Varies each year.

Deadline February of each year.

[1247]
CHANCELLOR'S POSTDOCTORAL FELLOWSHIPS FOR ACADEMIC DIVERSITY

University of California at Berkeley
Attn: Office for Faculty Equity
200 California Hall
Berkeley, CA 94720-1500
(510) 642-1935   E-mail: admin.ofe@berkeley.edu
Web: vcei.berkeley.edu/ChancPostdocFellowship

Summary To provide an opportunity for women and other recent postdoctorates who will increase diversity at the University of California at Berkeley and are interested in conducting research on the campus.

Eligibility This program is open to U.S. citizens and permanent residents who received a doctorate within 3 years of the start of the fellowship. The program particularly solicits applications from individuals who are members of groups that are underrepresented in American universities (e.g., women, ethnic minorities, religious minorities, differently-abled, lesbian/gay/bisexual/transgender). Special consideration is given to applicants committed to careers in university research and teaching and whose life experience, research, or employment background will contribute significantly to academic diversity and excellence at the Berkeley campus.

Financial data The stipend is $41,496 per year (11 months, plus 1 month vacation). The award also includes health insurance, vision and dental benefits, and up to $4,000 for research-related and program travel expenses.

Duration 1 year; may be renewed 1 additional year.

Additional information Research opportunities, mentoring, and guidance are provided as part of the program.

Number awarded Varies each year; recently, 5 of these fellowships were awarded.

Deadline November of each year.

[1248]
CHARLES A. RYSKAMP RESEARCH FELLOWSHIPS

American Council of Learned Societies
Attn: Office of Fellowships and Grants
633 Third Avenue
New York, NY 10017-6795
(212) 697-1505   Fax: (212) 949-8058
E-mail: fellowships@acls.org
Web: www.acls.org/programs/ryskamp

Summary To provide research funding to women, minority, and other advanced assistant professors in all disciplines of the humanities and the humanities-related social sciences.

Eligibility This program is open to advanced assistant and untenured associate professors in the humanities and related social sciences. Applicants must have successfully completed their institution's last reappointment review before tenure review. They must have a Ph.D. or equivalent degree and be employed at an academic institution in the United States. Appropriate fields of specialization include, but are not limited to, American studies; anthropology; archaeology; art and architectural history; classics; economics; film; geography; history; languages and literatures; legal studies; linguistics; musicology; philosophy; political science; psychology; religious studies; rhetoric, communication, and media studies; sociology; and theater, dance, and performance studies. Proposals in those fields of the social sciences are eligible only if they employ predominantly humanistic approaches (e.g., economic history, law and literature, political philosophy). Proposals in interdisciplinary and cross-disciplinary studies are welcome, as are proposals focused on any geographic region or on any cultural or linguistic group. Applicants are encouraged to spend substantial periods of their leaves in residential interdisciplinary centers, research libraries, or other scholarly archives in the United States or abroad. Applications are particularly invited from women and members of minority groups.

Financial data Fellows receive a stipend of $64,000, a grant of $2,500 for research and travel, and the possibility of an additional summer's support, if justified by a persuasive case.

Duration   1 academic year (9 months) plus an additional summer's research (2 months) if justified.

Additional information   This program, first available for the 2002-03 academic year, is supported by funding from the Andrew W. Mellon Foundation.

Number awarded   Up to 12 each year.

Deadline   September of each year.

[1249]
CHARLES L. BREWER DISTINGUISHED TEACHING OF PSYCHOLOGY AWARD

American Psychological Foundation
750 First Street, N.E.
Washington, DC 20002-4242
(202) 336-5843   Fax: (202) 336-5812
E-mail: foundation@apa.org
Web: www.apa.org/apf/funding/brewer.aspx

Summary   To recognize and reward distinguished career contributions to the teaching of psychology by women, minorities, and others.

Eligibility   This award is available to psychologists who demonstrate outstanding teaching. Selection is based on evidence of influence as a teacher of students who become psychologists, research on teaching, development of effective teaching methods and/or materials, development of innovation curricula and courses, performance as a classroom teacher, demonstrated training of teachers of psychology, teaching of advanced research methods and practice in psychology, and/or administrative facilitation of teaching. Nominators must complete an application form, write a letter of support, and submit the nominee's current vitae and bibliography. The sponsor encourages nominations of individuals who represent diversity in race, ethnicity, gender, age, disability, and sexual orientation.

Financial data   Awardees receive a plaque, a $2,000 honorarium, and an all-expense paid trip to the annual convention where the award is presented.

Duration   The award is presented annually.

Additional information   This award, originally named the Distinguished Teaching in Psychology Award, was first presented in 1970.

Number awarded   1 each year.

Deadline   Nominations must be submitted by November of each year.

[1250]
CHURCH TRAINING AND DEACONESS HOUSE SCHOLARSHIP

Episcopal Diocese of Pennsylvania
Attn: Church Training and Deaconess House Scholarship Fund
240 South Fourth Street
Philadelphia, PA 19106
(215) 627-6434, ext. 101   Fax: (215) 627-7550
E-mail: diopa@libertynet.org
Web: www.diopa.org/leadership/transition/deaconess

Summary   To provide financial assistance for graduate school to women preparing for a career in religious or benevolent work for the Episcopal Church.

Eligibility   This program is open to women at the graduate level who are training for religious and benevolent work for the Episcopal Church. Preference is given to women in the Diocese of Pennsylvania. Applicants must have an earned bachelor's degree and acceptance into 1) a seminary; 2) an accredited college or university advanced degree program in education, religion, social work, medicine, or allied fields; or 3) a degree credit program of continuing education in their present field of work. Along with their application, they must submit a 250-word essay on how they expect to use this graduate educational training to advance their ordained or lay ministry within the Episcopal Church or the church at large. Selection is based on the quality of the essay, academic record, and financial need.

Financial data   Stipends range from $2,000 to $3,000.

Duration   1 year; may be renewed up to 2 additional years.

Number awarded   1 or more each year.

Deadline   March of each year.

[1251]
CLINICAL SCIENCE FACULTY DEVELOPMENT GRANT

American Society of Transplantation
Attn: Chair, Awards and Grants Committee
15000 Commerce Parkway, Suite C
Mt. Laurel, NJ 08054
(856) 439-9986   Fax: (856) 439-9982
E-mail: info@a-s-t.org
Web: www.a-s-t.org/research-funding/research-funding

Summary   To provide funding for research to women, minority, and other junior members of the American Society of Transplantation (AST) who are interested in conducting clinical research.

Eligibility   This program is open to AST members who have an M.D., D.O., Ph.D., D.V.M. or equivalent graduate degree and have completed postgraduate training. Applicants must have an academic appointment at an accredited institution of higher education and be within 5 years of their initial faculty appointment. They must be citizens, permanent residents, or lawfully-admitted foreign nationals with appropriate visas in Canada, Mexico, or the United States. Their proposed research project must involve clinical outcomes or observational studies to better define the causes and/or consequences of pathological or biological processes in transplantation. Research topics that involve underrepresented areas (minorities, women, and pediatrics) are strongly encouraged. The AST also encourages applications from women and underrepresented minority investigators.

Financial data   The grant is $40,000 per year. No more indirect costs are permitted.

Duration   2 years.

Number awarded   1 or more each year.

Deadline   December of each year.

[1252]
COMMUNITY ACTION GRANTS

American Association of University Women
Attn: AAUW Educational Foundation
301 ACT Drive, Department 60
P.O. Box 4030
Iowa City, IA 52243-4030
(319) 337-1716, ext. 60   Fax: (319) 337-1204
E-mail: aauw@act.org
Web: www.aauw.org

Summary To provide seed money to branches or divisions of the American Association of University Women (AAUW) or to individual women for projects or nondegree research that promote education and equity for women and girls.

Eligibility This program is open to individual women who are U.S. citizens or permanent residents, AAUW branches, AAUW state organizations, and local community-based nonprofit organizations. Applicants must be proposing projects that have direct public impact, are nonpartisan, and take place within the United States or its territories. Grants for 1 year provide seed money for new projects; topic areas are unrestricted but should include a clearly defined activity that promotes education and equity for women and girls. Grants for 2 years provide start-up funds for longer-term programs that address the particular needs of the community and develop girls' sense of efficacy through leadership or advocacy opportunities; funds support planning activities, coalition building, implementation, and evaluation. Special consideration is given to 1) AAUW branch and state projects that seek community partners (e.g., local schools or school districts, businesses, other community-based organizations); and 2) projects focused on K-14 girls' achievement in mathematics, science, and/or technology. Selection is based on relevance of the proposed project to education and equity for women and girls, strength of the project rationale, clarity and creativity of the project design, feasibility of the project, strength of the evaluation plan, strength of the dissemination plan, impact of the project, overall quality of the proposal, and potential for and/or commitment of additional funds and involvement from community organizations and/or businesses.

Financial data Grants for 1 year range from $2,000 to $7,000. Grants for 2 years range from $5,000 to $10,000. Funds are to be used for such project-related expenses as office supplies, mailing, photocopying, honoraria, and transportation. Funds cannot cover salaries for project directors or regular, ongoing overhead costs for any organization.

Duration 1 or 2 years.

Additional information The filing fee is $35.

Number awarded Varies each year; recently, 16 1-year grants and 17 2-year grants, with a total value of $260,000, were awarded.

Deadline January of each year.

[1253]
CONGRESSIONAL FELLOWSHIPS ON WOMEN AND PUBLIC POLICY

Women's Research and Education Institute
Attn: Education and Training Programs
714 G Street, S.E., Suite 200
Washington, DC 20003
(202) 280-2720   E-mail: wrei@wrei.org
Web: www.wrei.org

Summary To provide graduate students and young professionals with an opportunity to work as a Congressional aide on policy issues affecting women.

Eligibility This program is open to women and men who are currently enrolled in a master's or doctoral program at an accredited institution in the United States or who have completed such a program within the past 18 months. Applicants should have completed at least 9 hours of graduate course work or the equivalent and have a demonstrated interest in research or political activity relating to women's social and political status. They may be of any age, gender, race, religion, sexual orientation, experience, or academic field, but they must be articulate and adaptable and have strong writing skills. Selection is based on academic competence and demonstrated interest in the public policy process. Interviews are required of semifinalists.

Financial data Fellows receive a stipend of $1,450 per month, $500 for health insurance, and up to $1,500 for reimbursement of 3 hours of tuition at their home institutions.

Duration 8 months, from January through August; nonrenewable.

Additional information This program began in 1977. Fellows are assigned to Congressional or committee offices to work for at least 30 hours per week as a legislative assistant monitoring, researching, and providing information on policy issues affecting women.

Number awarded At least 5 each year; since the program began, 277 fellows (all women) have been appointed to these positions.

Deadline June of each year.

[1254]
COUNSELING PSYCHOLOGY GRANTS

American Psychological Foundation
750 First Street, N.E.
Washington, DC 20002-4242
(202) 336-5843   Fax: (202) 336-5812
E-mail: foundation@apa.org
Web: www.apa.org/apf/funding/counseling.aspx

Summary To provide funding to psychologists (especially women, minorities, and individuals with disabilities) who wish to conduct a project related to counseling psychology.

Eligibility This program is open to psychologists who wish to conduct a project to enhance the science and practice of counseling psychology, including basic and applied research, literary, and educational activities. Applicants must be members of Division 17 (Society of Counseling Psychotherapy) of the American Psychological Association, members of an educational institution or nonprofit organization, or affiliate of an educational institution or nonprofit organization. Selection is based on conformance with stated program goals, magnitude of incremental contribution in specified activity area, quality of proposed work, and applicant's demonstrated competence and capability to execute the proposed work. The sponsor encourages applications from individuals who represent diversity in race, ethnicity, gender, age, disability, and sexual orientation.

Financial data   Grants range up to $5,000.

Duration   1 year.

Additional information   These grants were first awarded in 2007.

Number awarded   Varies each year; recently, 4 of these grants were awarded.

Deadline   March of each year.

[1255]
DANIEL H. EFRON RESEARCH AWARD

American College of Neuropsychopharmacology
Attn: Executive Office
5034-A Thoroughbred Lane
Brentwood, TN 37027
(615) 324-2360   Fax: (615) 523-1715
E-mail: acnp@acnp.org
Web: www.acnp.org/programs/awards.aspx

Summary   To recognize and reward young scientists (priority is given to women and minorities) who have conducted outstanding basic or translational research to neuropsychopharmacology.

Eligibility   This award is available to scientists who are younger than 50 years of age. Nominees must have made an outstanding basic or translational contribution to neuropsychopharmacology. The contribution may be preclinical or work that emphasizes the relationship between basic and clinical research. Selection is based on the quality of the contribution and its impact on advancing neuropsychopharmacology. Membership in the American College of Neuropsychopharmacology (ACNP) is not required. Nomination of women and minorities is highly encouraged.

Financial data   The award consists of an expense-paid trip to the ACNP annual meeting, a monetary honorarium, and a plaque.

Duration   The award is presented annually.

Additional information   This award was first presented in 1974.

Number awarded   1 each year.

Deadline   Nominations must be submitted by June of each year.

[1256]
DARE TO DREAM SCHOLARSHIP

Women in Aviation, International
Attn: Scholarships
Morningstar Airport
3647 State Route 503 South
West Alexandria, OH 45381-9354
(937) 839-4647   Fax: (937) 839-4645
E-mail: scholarships@wai.org
Web: www.wai.org/education/scholarships.cfm

Summary   To provide funding to members of Women in Aviation, International (WAI) who are interested in obtaining an additional rating or certificate.

Eligibility   This program is open to women who are WAI members and interested in furthering their career in aviation.

Applicants must be interested in working on an instrument or multiengine rating, a commercial license, or certified flight instructor (CFI) certificate. They must submit 2 letters of recommendation (including 1 from a pilot who has flown with them), a 500-word essay on their aviation history and goals, a resume, copies of all aviation licenses and medical certificates, and the last 3 pages of their pilot logbook (if applicable). Selection is based on achievements, attitude toward self and others, commitment to success, dedication to career, financial need, motivation, reliability, responsibility, and teamwork.

Financial data   The stipend is $3,000. Funds are paid directly to the flight school.

Duration   Training must be completed within 1 year.

Additional information   WAI is a nonprofit professional organization dedicated to encouraging women to consider an aviation career and to providing educational outreach activities and networking resources to women active in the industry.

Number awarded   1 each year.

Deadline   November of each year.

[1257]
DARLENE CLARK HINE AWARD

Organization of American Historians
Attn: Award and Committee Coordinator
112 North Bryan Street
Bloomington, IN 47408-4141
(812) 855-7311   Fax: (812) 855-0696
E-mail: khamm@oah.org
Web: www.oah.org/awards/awards.hine.index.html

Summary   To recognize and reward authors of outstanding books dealing with African American women's and gender history.

Eligibility   This award is presented to the author of the outstanding book in African American women's and gender history. Entries must have been published during the current calendar year.

Financial data   The award is $1,000.

Duration   The award is presented annually.

Additional information   This award was first presented in 2010.

Number awarded   1 each year.

Deadline   September of each year.

[1258]
DEPARTMENT OF HOMELAND SECURITY SMALL BUSINESS INNOVATION RESEARCH GRANTS

Department of Homeland Security
Homeland Security Advanced Research Projects Agency
Attn: SBIR Program Manager
Washington, DC 20528
(202) 254-6768   Toll Free: (800) 754-3043
Fax: (202) 254-7170   E-mail: elissa.sobolewski@dhs.gov
Web: www.dhs.gov/files/grants/gc_1247254058883.shtm

Summary   To support small businesses (especially those owned by women, minorities, and disabled veterans) that have the technological expertise to contribute to the research and development mission of the Department of Homeland Security (DHS).

Eligibility For the purposes of this program, a "small business" is defined as a firm that is organized for profit with a location in the United States; is in the legal form of an individual proprietorship, partnership, limited liability company, corporation, joint venture, association, trust, or cooperative; is at least 51% owned and controlled by 1 or more individuals who are citizens or permanent residents of the United States; and has (including its affiliates) fewer than 500 employees. The primary employment of the principal investigator must be with the firm at the time of award and during the conduct of the proposed project. Preference is given to women-owned small business concerns, service-disabled veteran small business concerns, veteran small business concerns, and socially and economically disadvantaged small business concerns. Women-owned small business concerns are those that are at least 51% owned by a woman or women who also control and operate them. Service-disabled veteran small business concerns are those that are at least 51% owned by a service-disabled veteran and controlled by such a veteran or (for veterans with permanent and severe disability) the spouse or permanent caregiver of such a veteran. Veteran small business concerns are those that are at least 51% owned by a veteran or veterans who also control and manage them. Socially and economically disadvantaged small business concerns are at least 51% owned by an Indian tribe, a Native Hawaiian organization, a Community Development Corporation, or 1 or more socially and economically disadvantaged individuals (African Americans, Hispanic Americans, Native Americans, Asian Pacific Americans, or subcontinent Asian Americans). The project must be performed in the United States. Currently, DHS has 7 research priorities: explosives; border and maritime security; command, control, and interoperability; human factors; infrastructure and geophysical; chemical and biological; and domestic nuclear detection. Selection is based on the soundness, technical merit, and innovation of the proposed approach and its incremental progress toward topic or subtopic solution; the qualifications of the proposed principal investigators, supporting staff, and consultants; and the potential for commercial application and the benefits expected to accrue from this commercialization.

Financial data Grants are offered in 2 phases. In phase 1, awards normally range up to $100,000 (or $150,000 for domestic nuclear detection); in phase 2, awards normally range up to $750,000 (or $1,000,000 for domestic nuclear detection).

Duration Phase 1 awards may extend up to 6 months; phase 2 awards may extend up to 2 years.

Number awarded Varies each year; recently, 61 Phase 1 awards were granted.

Deadline February of each year.

[1259]
DEPARTMENT OF TRANSPORTATION SMALL BUSINESS INNOVATION RESEARCH GRANTS

Department of Transportation
Attn: Research and Innovative Technology Administration
John A. Volpe National Transportation Systems Center
55 Broadway, Kendall Square
Cambridge, MA 02142-1093
(617) 494-2051   Fax: (617) 494-2370
E-mail: leisa.moniz@dot.gov
Web: www.volpe.dot.gov/sbir/index.html

Summary To support small businesses (especially those owned by women, minorities, and veterans) that have the technological expertise to contribute to the research and development mission of the Department of Transportation.

Eligibility For the purposes of this program, a "small business" is defined as a firm that is organized for profit with a location in the United States; is in the legal form of an individual proprietorship, partnership, limited liability company, corporation, joint venture, association, trust, or cooperative; is at least 51% owned and controlled by 1 or more individuals who are citizens or permanent residents of the United States; and has (including its affiliates) fewer than 500 employees. The primary employment of the principal investigator must be with the firm at the time of award and during the conduct of the proposed project. Preference is given to 1) women-owned small business concerns; 2) veteran-owned small businesses; and 3) socially and economically disadvantaged small business concerns. Women-owned small business concerns are those that are at least 51% owned by a woman or women who also control and operate them. Veteran-owned small businesses are those that are at least 51% owned and controlled by 1 or more veterans. Socially and economically disadvantaged small business concerns are at least 51% owned by an Indian tribe, a Native Hawaiian organization, or 1 or more socially and economically disadvantaged individuals (African Americans, Hispanic Americans, Native Americans, Asian Pacific Americans, or subcontinent Asian Americans). The project must be performed in the United States. Selection is based on scientific and technical merit, the feasibility of the proposal's commercial potential, the adequacy of the work plan, qualifications of the principal investigator, and adequacy of supporting staff and facilities, equipment, and data.

Financial data Support is offered in 2 phases. In phase 1, awards normally do not exceed $100,000 (for both direct and indirect costs); in phase 2, awards normally do not exceed $750,000 (including both direct and indirect costs).

Duration Phase 1 awards may extend up to 6 months; phase 2 awards may extend up to 2 years.

Number awarded Varies each year; recently, DOT planned to award 16 of these grants: 1 to the Federal Aviation Administration, 3 to the Federal Highway Administration, 1 to the Pipeline and Hazardous Materials Safety Administration, 2 to the National Highway and Traffic Safety Administration, 3 to the Federal Transit Administration, and 6 to the Federal Railroad Administration.

Deadline November of each year.

[1260]
DESERT JET CORPORATE AVIATION MANAGEMENT SCHOLARSHIP

Women in Aviation, International
Attn: Scholarships
Morningstar Airport
3647 State Route 503 South
West Alexandria, OH 45381-9354
(937) 839-4647   Fax: (937) 839-4645
E-mail: scholarships@wai.org
Web: www.wai.org/education/scholarships.cfm

Summary To provide financial assistance to members of Women in Aviation, International (WAI) who are business aviation pilots interested in preparing for a career in aviation management.

Eligibility This program is open to WAI members who are business aviation pilots. Applicants must be interested in preparing for a career in aviation management or starting their own aviation-related business. They must desire to participate in activities that include, but are not limited to, certification in the National Business Aviation Association (NBAA) aviation manager program, aviation safety officer training, course work towards the University of Southern California aviation safety and security certificate, attendance at NBAA's leadership conference, enrollment in Darden Graduate School of Business corporate aviation function programs, NBAA professional development program courses, or Embry-Riddle Aeronautical University corporate aviation management certificate program. Along with their application, they must submit 2 letters of recommendation, a 500-word essay on their aviation history and goals (including how this scholarship will help them achieve their goals, a resume, copies of all aviation licenses and medical certificates, and the last 3 pages of their pilot logbook (if applicable). Selection is based on achievements, attitude toward self and others, commitment to success, dedication to career, financial need, motivation, reliability, responsibility, and teamwork.

Financial data The stipend is $1,000.

Duration Funds must be used within 1 year.

Additional information WAI is a nonprofit professional organization dedicated to encouraging women to consider an aviation career and to providing educational outreach activities and networking resources to women active in the industry. This program is sponsored by Desert Jet, an aircraft charter and management company based in the Palm Springs area of California.

Number awarded 1 each year.

Deadline November of each year.

[1261]
DIFFUSION OF RESEARCH-BASED INNOVATIONS GRANTS OF THE RESEARCH ON GENDER IN SCIENCE AND ENGINEERING PROGRAM

National Science Foundation
Directorate for Education and Human Resources
Attn: Division of Human Resource Development
4201 Wilson Boulevard, Room 815N
Arlington, VA 22230
(703) 292-7303   Fax: (703) 292-9018
TDD: (800) 281-8749   E-mail: jjesse@nsf.gov
Web: www.nsf.gov/funding/pgm_summ.jsp?pims_id=5475

Summary To provide funding to scholars interested in conducting activities designed to engage a wider audience of practitioners with research findings and strategies for changing educational practice relative to the underrepresentation of girls and women in science, technology, engineering, or mathematics (STEM) education.

Eligibility This program is open to scholars interested in engaging in activities designed to engage a wider audience of practitioners (e.g., teachers, faculty, guidance counselors, parents, policy makers) with research findings and strategies for changing educational practice to address gender-related issues. Applicants may be interested in conducting 1) pilot projects, to provide funds for small-scale development of

materials and/or piloting of promising practices; 2) scale up projects, to reach broader regional or national audiences one proof of concept is established; or 3) dissemination of outcomes projects, to communicate the findings from currently- or previously-funded research of this program. Priority is given to proposals that are collaborative in nature and that focus on populations underrepresented across STEM fields (especially underrepresented minority, first-generation, or disability communities). Proposals that involve partnerships with minority-serving institutions, community colleges, or K-12 school districts are encouraged.

Financial data Pilot projects may request $125,000 per year; scale up projects may request $200,000 per year; and dissemination of outcomes projects may request $125,000 per year.

Duration Support for pilot projects is available for 1 to 3 years, for scale up projects for 3 to 5 years, or for dissemination of outcomes projects for 1 to 3 years.

Additional information The National Science Foundation (NSF) established the Research on Gender in Science and Engineering (GSE) program in 1993 under the name "Program for Women and Girls." That was replaced with the "Program for Gender Equity in Science, Mathematics, Engineering and Technology," and then in the 2003 fiscal year by "Gender Diversity in STEM Education." The current title became effective in the 2007 fiscal year.

Number awarded 7 to 10 each year. The GSE program plans to award 15 to 22 grants per year for all of its activities. A total of $5,000,000 is available for the program annually.

Deadline October of each year.

[1262]
DIGITAL INNOVATION FELLOWSHIPS

American Council of Learned Societies
Attn: Office of Fellowships and Grants
633 Third Avenue
New York, NY 10017-6795
(212) 697-1505   Fax: (212) 949-8058
E-mail: fellowships@acls.org
Web: www.acls.org/programs/digital

Summary To provide funding to scholars (particularly women and minority scholars) who are interested in conducting digitally-based research in the humanities and the humanities-related social sciences.

Eligibility This program is open to scholars who have a Ph.D. in any field of the humanities or the humanistic social sciences. Applicants must be interested in conducting research projects that utilize digital technologies intensively and innovatively. Projects might include, but are not limited to, new digital tools that further humanistic research (such as digital research archives or innovative databases), research that depends on or is greatly enhanced by the use of such tools, the representation of research that depends on or is greatly enhanced by the use of such tools, or some combination of those features. The program does not support creative works (e.g., novels or films), textbooks, straightforward translations, or purely pedagogical projects. U.S. citizenship or permanent resident status is required. Applications are particularly invited from women and members of minority groups. Selection is based on scholarly excellence (the project's intellectual ambitions and technological underpinnings), the project's likely contribution as a digital scholarly work to humanistic study, satisfaction of technical requirements for completing a successful research project, degree and significance of preliminary work already completed, extent to which the proposed project would promote teamwork and collaboration, and the project's articulation with local infrastructure.

Financial data Fellows receive a stipend of $60,000 and up to $25,000 for project costs.

Duration 1 academic year.

Additional information This program, first available for the 2006-07 academic year, is supported by funding from the Andrew W. Mellon Foundation.

Number awarded Up to 6 each year.

Deadline September of each year.

[1263]
DIRECTING WORKSHOP FOR WOMEN

American Film Institute
Attn: Directing Workshop for Women
2021 North Western Avenue
Los Angeles, CA 90027-1657
(323) 856-7628   Fax: (323) 467-4578
E-mail: DWWinfo@afi.com
Web: www.afi.com/dww

Summary To provide funding to women who have no professional credits as a narrative director but are interested in developing a movie or television project.

Eligibility This program is open to women who have at least 5 years' experience in the arts but no professional credits as a narrative director. Applicants must submit a narrative script of 15 pages or less for a movie or television project they propose to develop; the script may have been written by anyone. They must be U.S. citizens or permanent residents and must reside and work in the United States during the grant period.

Financial data A board and room allowance of $6,300 is provided to each participant. They are required to raise $5,000 in support of their production, available by the first day of the workshop. Those who reside in Los Angeles are encouraged to raise an additional $20,000 to cover living expenses; those who live outside the area should raise an additional $25,000. The institute provides production equipment and editing facilities.

Duration The program includes a 3-week training workshop, followed by 5 weeks for pre-production activity, a 5-day production shoot, and 30 days for editing.

Additional information Sponsors of this program, which began in 1974, include the Academy of Motion Picture Arts and Sciences, Sony Corporation of America, and the National Endowment for the Arts. The application fee is $100.

Number awarded 8 participants are chosen each year.

Deadline January of each year.

[1264]
DIVISION 29 EARLY CAREER AWARD

American Psychological Foundation
750 First Street, N.E.
Washington, DC 20002-4242
(202) 336-5843   Fax: (202) 336-5812
E-mail: foundation@apa.org
Web: www.apa.org/apf/funding/div-29.aspx

Summary To recognize and reward women, minority, and other young psychologists who have made outstanding contributions to psychotherapy.

Eligibility This award is available to psychologists who are no more than 7 years past completion of their doctoral degree. Nominees must have demonstrated promising professional achievement related to psychotherapy theory, practice, research, or training. They must be members of Division 29 (Psychotherapy) of the American Psychological Association. Self-nominations are not accepted. Selection is based on conformance with stated program goals and qualifications and applicant's demonstrated accomplishments and promise. The sponsor encourages nominations of individuals who represent diversity in race, ethnicity, gender, age, disability, and sexual orientation.

Financial data The award is $2,500.

Duration The award is presented annually.

Additional information This award was established in 1981 and named the Jack D. Krasner Memorial Award. It was renamed in 2007.

Number awarded 1 each year.

Deadline Nominations must be submitted by December of each year.

[1265]
DOROTHEA M. LANG PIONEER AWARD

American College of Nurse-Midwives
Attn: ACNM Foundation, Inc.
8403 Colesville Road, Suite 1550
Silver Spring, MD 20910-6374
(240) 485-1850   Fax: (240) 485-1818
Web: www.midwife.org/foundation_award.cfm

Summary To recognize and reward members of the American College of Nurse-Midwives (ACNM) who have made outstanding contributions to the profession of midwifery.

Eligibility Nominees for this award must have been ACNM members for at least 10 years. They must have demonstrated vision and leadership in 1 of the following categories: pioneering midwives who, after 1958, demonstrated what midwifery care could and should be on the health team; pioneering efforts to integrate midwives and midwifery into the health care system of the United States or internationally; unsung heroes who initiated, rescued, enhanced, or saved midwifery services or educational programs or are working to accomplish those goals; visionaries who encouraged or created open-minded pathways in education for professional midwives or are working to accomplish that goal; energetic anticipants who have furthered or are furthering the legislative agenda for certified midwives; or have contributed other pioneering activities.

Financial data The award includes a cash honorarium and a necklace.

Duration The award is presented annually.

Additional information This program was established in 2002.

Number awarded Varies each year; recently, 3 of these awards were presented.

Deadline April of each year.

[1266]
DR. BESSIE ELIZABETH DELANEY FELLOWSHIP

National Dental Association
Attn: National Dental Association Foundation, Inc.
3517 16th Street, N.W.
Washington, DC 20010
(202) 588-1697   Fax: (202) 588-1244
E-mail: admin@ndaonline.org
Web: www.ndaonline.org

Summary To provide financial assistance to female dental postdoctoral students who are members of underrepresented minority groups.

Eligibility This program is open to female members of underrepresented minority groups who are working on a postdoctoral degree in subspecialty areas of dentistry, public health, administration, research, or law. Students working on a master's degree beyond their residency may be considered. Applicants must be members of the National Dental Association (NDA) and U.S. citizens or permanent residents. Along with their application, they must submit a letter explaining why they should be considered for this scholarship, 2 letters of recommendation, a curriculum vitae, a description of the program, nomination by their program director, and documentation of financial need.

Financial data The stipend is $10,000.

Duration 1 year.

Additional information This program, established in 1990, is supported by the Colgate-Palmolive Company.

Number awarded 1 each year.

Deadline May of each year.

[1267]
DRS. ROSALEE G. AND RAYMOND A. WEISS RESEARCH AND PROGRAM INNOVATION GRANT

American Psychological Foundation
750 First Street, N.E.
Washington, DC 20002-4242
(202) 336-5843   Fax: (202) 336-5812
E-mail: foundation@apa.org
Web: www.apa.org/apf/funding/vision-weiss.aspx

Summary To provide funding to professionals (particularly women, minorities, and individuals with disabilities) who are interested in conducting projects that use psychology to solve social problems related to the priorities of the American Psychological Foundation (APF).

Eligibility This program is open to professionals at non-profit organizations engaged in research, education, and intervention projects and programs. Applicants must be interested in conducting an activity that uses psychology to solve social problems in the following priority areas: understanding and fostering the connection between mental and physical health; reducing stigma and prejudice; understanding and preventing all forms of violence; or addressing the long-term psychological needs of individuals and communities in the aftermath of disaster. Selection is based on the criticality of the proposed funding for the proposed work; conformance with stated program goals and requirements; innovative and potential impact qualities; quality, viability, and promise of proposed work, and competence and capability of project leaders. The sponsor encourages applications from individuals

who represent diversity in race, ethnicity, gender, age, disability, and sexual orientation.

Financial data The grant is $10,000.

Duration 1 year; nonrenewable.

Additional information This program was established in 2003.

Number awarded 1 each year.

Deadline March of each year.

[1268]
DUPONT MINORITIES IN ENGINEERING AWARD

American Society for Engineering Education
Attn: Manager, Administrative Services
1818 N Street, N.W., Suite 600
Washington, DC 20036-2479
(202) 331-3500   Fax: (202) 265-8504
Web: www.asee.org/activities/awards/special.cfm

Summary To recognize and reward outstanding achievements by engineering educators to increase diversity by gender or ethnicity in science, engineering, and technology.

Eligibility Eligible for nomination are engineering or engineering technology educators who, as part of their educational activity, either assume or are charged with the responsibility of motivating underrepresented students to enter and continue in engineering or engineering technology curricula at the college or university level, graduate or undergraduate. Nominees must demonstrate leadership in the conception, organization, and operation of pre-college and college activities designed to increase participation by underrepresented students in engineering and engineering technology.

Financial data The award consists of $1,500, a certificate, and a grant of $500 for travel expenses to the ASEE annual conference.

Duration The award is granted annually.

Additional information Funding for this award is provided by DuPont. It was originally established in 1956 as the Vincent Bendix Minorities in Engineering Award.

Number awarded 1 each year.

Deadline January of each year.

[1269]
EARLY CAREER PATIENT-ORIENTED DIABETES RESEARCH AWARD

Juvenile Diabetes Research Foundation International
Attn: Grant Administrator
26 Broadway, 14th Floor
New York, NY 10004
(212) 479-7572   Toll Free: (800) 533-CURE
Fax: (212) 785-9595   E-mail: info@jdrf.org
Web: www.jdrf.org/index.cfm?page_id=111715

Summary To provide funding to physician scientists (particularly women, minorities, and persons with disabilities) who are interested in pursuing a program of clinical diabetes-related research training.

Eligibility This program is open to investigators in diabetes-related research who have an M.D. or M.D./Ph.D. degree and a faculty appointment at the late training or assistant professor level. Applicants must be sponsored by an investigator who is affiliated full time with an accredited institution, who pursues patient-oriented clinical research, and who agrees to supervise the applicant's training. There are no citizenship requirements. Applications are encouraged from women, members of minority groups underrepresented in the sciences, and people with disabilities. Areas of relevant research can include: mechanisms of human disease, therapeutic interventions, clinical trials, and the development of new technologies. The proposed research may be conducted at foreign or domestic, for-profit or nonprofit, or public or private institutions, including universities, colleges, hospitals, laboratories, units of state or local government, or eligible agencies of the federal government.

Financial data The total award may be up to $150,000 each year, up to $75,000 of which may be requested for research (including a technician, supplies, equipment, and travel). The salary request must be consistent with the established salary structure of the applicant's institution. Equipment purchases in years other than the first must be strongly justified. Indirect costs may not exceed 10%.

Duration The award is for 5 years.

Deadline January or July of each year.

[1270]
EARLY CAREER POSTDOCTORAL FELLOWSHIPS IN EAST EUROPEAN STUDIES

American Council of Learned Societies
Attn: Office of Fellowships and Grants
633 Third Avenue
New York, NY 10017-6795
(212) 697-1505　　　　　Fax: (212) 949-8058
E-mail: fellowships@acls.org
Web: www.acls.org/grants/Default.aspx?id=534

Summary To provide funding to women, minority, and other postdoctorates who are interested in conducting original research in the social sciences and humanities relating to eastern Europe.

Eligibility This program is open to U.S. citizens and permanent residents who hold a Ph.D. degree or equivalent as demonstrated by professional experience and publications. Priority is given to scholars in the early part of their careers; tenured faculty are not eligible. Applicants must be interested in conducting research in the social sciences or humanities relating to Albania, Bosnia and Herzegovina, Bulgaria, Croatia, Czech Republic, Estonia, Hungary, Former Yugoslav Republic of Macedonia, Kosovo, Latvia, Lithuania, Montenegro, Poland, Romania, Serbia, Slovakia, or Slovenia. Projects comparing more than 1 country in eastern Europe or relating eastern European societies to those of other parts of the world are also supported. Selection is based on the scholarly merit of the proposal, its importance to the development of eastern European studies, and the scholarly potential and accomplishments of the applicant. Applications are particularly invited from women and members of minority groups.

Financial data Up to $25,000 is provided as a stipend. Funds are intended primarily as salary replacement, but they may be used to supplement sabbatical salaries or awards from other sources.

Duration 6 to 12 consecutive months.

Additional information This program is sponsored jointly by the American Council of Learned Societies, (ACLS) and the Social Science Research Council, funded by the U.S. Department of State under the Research and Training for Eastern Europe and the Independent States of the Former

Soviet Union Act of 1983 (Title VIII), and administered by ACLS. Funds may not be used in western Europe.

Number awarded Varies each year; recently, 3 of these fellowships were awarded.

Deadline November of each year.

[1271]
EAST EUROPEAN LANGUAGE GRANTS TO INDIVIDUALS FOR SUMMER STUDY

American Council of Learned Societies
Attn: Office of Fellowships and Grants
633 Third Avenue
New York, NY 10017-6795
(212) 697-1505　　　　　Fax: (212) 949-8058
E-mail: fellowships@acls.org
Web: www.acls.org/grants/Default.aspx?id=540

Summary To provide financial support to graduate students, professionals, and postdoctorates (particularly women and minorities) who are interested in studying eastern European languages during the summer.

Eligibility Applicants must have completed at least a 4-year college degree. They must be interested in a program of training in the languages of eastern Europe, including Albanian, Bosnian-Croatian-Serbian, Bulgarian, Czech, Estonian, Hungarian, Latvian, Lithuanian, Macedonian, Polish, Romanian, Slovak, or Slovene. The language course may be at the beginning, intermediate, or advanced level. Normally, requests for beginning and intermediate level training should be for attendance at intensive courses offered by institutions in the United States; proposals for study at the advanced level are ordinarily for courses in eastern Europe. Applications are particularly encouraged from women and members of minority groups.

Financial data Grants up to $2,500 are available.

Duration Summer months.

Additional information This program, reinstituted in 2002, is supported by the U.S. Department of State under the Research and Training for Eastern Europe and the Independent States of the Former Soviet Union Act of 1983 (Title VIII).

Number awarded Approximately 15 each year.

Deadline January of each year.

[1272]
EDUCATOR'S AWARD

Delta Kappa Gamma Society International
Attn: Information Services
416 West 12th Street
P.O. Box 1589
Austin, TX 78767-1589
(512) 478-5748　　　　　Toll Free: (888) 762-4685
Fax: (512) 478-3961　　　　E-mail: soceditr@dkg.org
Web: www.dkg.org

Summary To recognize women's contributions to education that may influence future directions in the profession; these contributions may be in research, philosophy, or any other area of learning that is stimulating and creative.

Eligibility Any published book in research, philosophy, or another area of learning that stimulates the intellect and imagination may be submitted for consideration if it is written by 1 or 2 women in Canada, Costa Rica, El Salvador, Finland,

Germany, Guatemala, Iceland, Mexico, the Netherlands, Norway, Puerto Rico, Sweden, the United Kingdom, or the United States and copyrighted (in its first edition or the first English translation) during the preceding calendar year. Contributions should possess excellence in style, be well-edited and attractive in format, and be of more than local interest. Ineligible are methods books, skill books, textbooks, and unpublished manuscripts.

Financial data   The award is $1,500. In the case of dual authorship, the prize is divided in the same manner as royalties are divided by the awardees' publisher.

Duration   The award is granted annually.

Additional information   This award was first presented in 1946.

Number awarded   1 each year.

Deadline   February of each year.

[1273]
EINSTEIN POSTDOCTORAL FELLOWSHIP PROGRAM

Smithsonian Astrophysical Observatory
Attn: Chandra X-Ray Center
Einstein Fellowship Program Office
60 Garden Street, MS4
Cambridge, MA 02138
(617) 496-7941   Fax: (617) 495-7356
E-mail: fellows@head.cfa.harvard.edu
Web: cxc.harvard.edu/fellows

Summary   To provide funding to recent postdoctoral scientists (particularly women and minorities) who are interested in conducting research related to high energy astrophysics missions of the National Aeronautics and Space Administration (NASA).

Eligibility   This program is open to postdoctoral scientists who completed their Ph.D., Sc.D., or equivalent doctoral degree within the past 3 years in astronomy, physics, or related disciplines. Applicants must be interested in conducting research related to NASA Physics of the Cosmos program missions: Chandra, Fermi, XMM-Newton and International X-Ray Observatory, cosmological investigations relevant to the Planck and JDEM missions, and gravitational astrophysics relevant to the LISA mission. They must be citizens of the United States or English-speaking citizens of other countries who have valid visas. Women and minorities are strongly encouraged to apply.

Financial data   Stipends are approximately $64,500 per year. Fellows may also receive health insurance, relocation costs, and moderate support (up to $16,000 per year) for research-related travel, computing services, publications, and other direct costs.

Duration   3 years (depending on a review of scientific activity).

Additional information   This program, which began in 2009 with funding from NASA, incorporates the former Chandra and GLAST Fellowship programs.

Number awarded   Up to 10 each year.

Deadline   November of each year.

[1274]
ELEANOR ROOSEVELT FUND AWARD

American Association of University Women
Attn: AAUW Educational Foundation
1111 16th Street, N.W.
Washington, DC 20036-4873
(202) 785-7624   Toll Free: (800) 326-AAUW
Fax: (202) 872-1425   TDD: (202) 785-7777
E-mail: fellowships@aauw.org
Web: www.aauw.org/learn/awards/erfund.cfm

Summary   To recognize and reward individuals, organizations, institutions, or projects that provide an equitable school environment for women and girls.

Eligibility   Nominations for this award are not solicited from the general public. The goals of the Eleanor Roosevelt Fund are to 1) remove barriers to women's and girls' participation in education; 2) promote the value of diversity and cross-cultural communication; and 3) develop greater understanding of the ways women learn, think, work, and play. Individuals, organizations, institutions, or projects that work for those goals are eligible to be nominated for this award. Their activities may include classroom teaching, educational and research contributions, or legal and legislative work that contributes to equity for women and girls. Although the award focuses on education, the nominee need not be an educator.

Financial data   The award is $5,000.

Duration   The award is presented biennially.

Additional information   This award was established in 1989.

Number awarded   1 each odd-numbered year.

Deadline   Nominations must be submitted by October of even-numbered years.

[1275]
ELOISE GERRY FELLOWSHIPS

Sigma Delta Epsilon-Graduate Women in Science, Inc.
c/o Julie Gros-Louis, Fellowships Coordinator
University of Iowa-Department of Psychology
11 Seashore Hall E
Iowa City, IA 52242-1407
(319) 384-1816   Fax: (319) 335-0191
E-mail: Julie-gros-louis@uiowa.edu
Web: www.gwis.org/programs.htm

Summary   To provide funding to women interested in conducting research in the natural sciences anywhere in the world.

Eligibility   This program is open to women from any country currently enrolled as a graduate student, engaged in postdoctoral research, or holding a junior faculty position. Applicants must be interested in conducting research anywhere in the world in the natural sciences (including physical, environmental, mathematical, computer, or life sciences), anthropology, psychology, or statistics. Along with their application, they must submit 2-paragraph essays on 1) how the proposed research relates to their degree program and/or career development; 2) initiatives in which they are participating to promote the careers of scientists, particularly women, within their institution, program, or peer group; and 3) relevant personal factors, including financial need, that should be considered in evaluating their proposal. Appointments are made without regard to race, religion, nationality, creed, national origin, sexual orientation, or age.

Financial data The grant currently is $2,500. Funds may be used for such research expenses as expendable supplies, small equipment, publication of research findings, travel and subsistence while performing field studies, or travel to another laboratory for collaborative research. They may not be used for tuition, child care, travel to professional meetings or to begin a new appointment, administrative overhead or indirect costs, personal computers, living allowances, or equipment for general use.

Duration 1 year.

Additional information This fellowship was first awarded in 1975. An application processing fee of $30 is required.

Number awarded Varies each year; recently, 2 of these grants were awarded.

Deadline January of each year.

[1276]
ELSEVIER PILOT RESEARCH AWARDS

American Gastroenterological Association
Attn: AGA Research Foundation
Research Awards Manager
4930 Del Ray Avenue
Bethesda, MD 20814-2512
(301) 222-4012   Fax: (301) 654-5920
E-mail: awards@gastro.org
Web: www.gastro.org/aga-foundation/grants

Summary To provide funding to new or established investigators (particularly women and minorities) for pilot research projects in areas related to gastroenterology or hepatology.

Eligibility Applicants must have an M.D., Ph.D., or equivalent degree and a full-time faculty position at an accredited North American institution. They may not hold grants for projects on a similar topic from other agencies. Individual membership in the American Gastroenterology Association (AGA) is required. The proposal must involve obtaining new data that can ultimately provide the basis for subsequent grant applications for more substantial funding and duration in gastroenterology- or hepatology-related areas. Women and minority investigators are strongly encouraged to apply. Selection is based on novelty, importance, feasibility, environment, commitment of the institution, and overall likelihood that the project will lead to more substantial grant applications.

Financial data The grant is $25,000 per year. Funds may be used for salary, supplies, or equipment. Indirect costs are not allowed.

Duration 1 year.

Additional information This award is sponsored by Elsevier Science.

Number awarded 1 each year.

Deadline January of each year.

[1277]
EMILY SCHOENBAUM RESEARCH AND COMMUNITY DEVELOPMENT GRANTS

Tulane University
Newcomb College Center for Research on Women
Attn: Executive Director
200 Caroline Richardson Hall
New Orleans, LA 70118
(504) 865-5238   Fax: (504) 862-8948
E-mail: nccrow@tulane.edu
Web: tulane.edu/nccrow/programs/schoenbaum-grant.cfm

Summary To provide funding to scholars and students in Louisiana interested in conducting research or other projects related to women and girls.

Eligibility This program is open to students, faculty, and staff of primary and secondary schools, colleges, and universities in Louisiana, as well as community scholars and activists. Applicants must be interested in conducting a project with potential to bring about change in women's lives or effect public policy so as to improve the well-being of women and girls, particularly those in the New Orleans area.

Financial data The grant is $1,500.

Duration 1 year.

Additional information This program was established in 1999.

Number awarded 1 each year.

Deadline March of each year.

[1278]
EMMA HARPER TURNER FUND

Pi Beta Phi
Attn: Pi Beta Phi Foundation
1154 Town and Country Commons Drive
Town and Country, MO 63017
(636) 256-1357   Fax: (636) 256-8124
E-mail: fndn@pibetaphi.org
Web: www.pibetaphifoundation.org/emma-harper-turner

Summary To provide assistance to members or alumnae of Pi Beta Phi Sorority who are in extreme financial need.

Eligibility Any member of Pi Beta Phi needing financial assistance is eligible to be considered for this funding. Each potential recipient must be sponsored by 3 Pi Beta Phi alumnae who are aware of the candidate's need and are personally acquainted with her. Applicants must submit a confidential financial information form to validate their need. The program includes 3 types of grants: collegian (for college students who have experienced a life change that jeopardizes their ability to stay in school), alumna (for college graduates who are experiencing financial difficulties), and immediate needs (for alumnae who are victims of a natural disaster).

Financial data Small monthly gifts are awarded.

Duration Awards are provided for 1 year; the recipient's application is then reviewed to determine if the "gifts of love" should continue.

Additional information This fund was established in 1946.

Number awarded Varies each year.

Deadline Applications may be submitted at any time.

[1279]
ENID A. NEIDLE SCHOLAR-IN-RESIDENCE PROGRAM FOR WOMEN

American Dental Education Association
Attn: Awards Program Coordinator
1400 K Street, N.W., Suite 1100
Washington, DC 20005
(202) 289-7201, ext. 166   Fax: (202) 289-7204
E-mail: sinkfordj@adea.org
Web: www.adea.org

Summary To provide funding to women dental faculty members who are interested in a residency at the American Dental Education Association (ADEA) in Washington, D.C.

Eligibility This program is open to full-time female faculty with primary teaching appointments in predoctoral and advanced dental education programs at ADEA-member institutions; female junior dental and dental hygiene faculty members are particularly encouraged to apply. Candidates must belong to ADEA. They must be interested in concentrating on issues that affect women faculty during a 3 month residency at ADEA in Washington, D.C. Interested faculty members should submit the following: a completed application form, a personal statement on their general interests and expectations for the residency, a letter of recommendation from their dean or chief administrative officer, a current curriculum vitae, and a formal letter of support from a colleague or mentor.

Financial data Scholars receive a $6,000 stipend to cover travel and living expenses while at the residency in Washington, D.C. It is a requirement of the program that the fellow's institution continue to provide salary support and fringe benefits for the duration of the experience.

Duration At least 3-months.

Additional information This program, established in 1994, is sponsored by the ADEA and Johnson & Johnson Healthcare Products. While in Washington, D.C., it is expected that the scholar will gain perspectives on issues facing women faculty, including promotion, advancement, and tenure policies; entry and reentry into the workforce; child care and elder care; women's health; work patterns; advanced education and research opportunities; and other gender-related issues. The scholar is assigned to a senior ADEA staff member and will have the opportunity to be involved in a range of activities there, in addition to her own project.

Number awarded 1 each year.

Deadline January of each year.

[1280]
EPILEPSY FOUNDATION RESEARCH GRANTS PROGRAM

Epilepsy Foundation
Attn: Research Department
8301 Professional Place
Landover, MD 20785-2237
(301) 459-3700   Toll Free: (800) EFA-1000
Fax: (301) 577-2684   TDD: (800) 332-2070
E-mail: grants@efa.org
Web: www.epilepsyfoundation.org

Summary To provide funding to junior investigators (especially women, minorities, and individuals with disabilities) who are interested in conducting research that will advance the understanding, treatment, and prevention of epilepsy.

Eligibility Applicants must have a doctoral degree and an academic appointment at the level of assistant professor in a university or medical school (or equivalent standing at a research institution or medical center). They must be interested in conducting basic or clinical research in the biological, behavioral, or social sciences related to the causes of epilepsy. Faculty with appointments at the level of associate professor or higher are not eligible. Applications from women, members of minority groups, and people with disabilities are especially encouraged. U.S. citizenship is not required, but the research must be conducted in the United States. Selection is based on the scientific quality of the research plan, the relevance of the proposed research to epilepsy, the applicant's qualifications, and the adequacy of the institution and facility where research will be conducted.

Financial data The grant is $50,000 per year.

Duration 1 year; recipients may reapply for 1 additional year of funding.

Additional information Support for this program is provided by many individuals, families, and corporations, especially the American Epilepsy Society, Abbott Laboratories, Ortho-McNeil Pharmaceutical, and Pfizer Inc.

Number awarded Varies each year.

Deadline August of each year.

[1281]
EPILEPSY RESEARCH RECOGNITION AWARDS PROGRAM

American Epilepsy Society
342 North Main Street
West Hartford, CT 06117-2507
(860) 586-7505   Fax: (860) 586-7550
E-mail: ctubby@aesnet.org
Web: www.aesnet.org/research/research-awards

Summary To provide funding to women, minority, and other investigators who are interested in conducting research related to epilepsy.

Eligibility This program is open to active scientists and clinicians working in any aspect of epilepsy. Candidates must be nominated by their home institution and be at the level of associate professor or professor. There are no geographic restrictions; nominations from outside the United States and North America are welcome. Nominations of women and members of minority groups are especially encouraged. Selection is based on pioneering research, originality of research, quality of publications, research productivity, relationship of the candidate's work to problems in epilepsy, training activities, other contributions in epilepsy, and productivity over the next decade; all criteria are weighted equally.

Financial data The grant is $10,000. No institutional overhead is allowed.

Additional information This program was established in 1991.

Number awarded 2 each year.

Deadline August of each year.

[1282]
ERIC AND BARBARA DOBKIN NATIVE ARTIST FELLOWSHIP FOR WOMEN

School for Advanced Research
Attn: Indian Arts Research Center
660 Garcia Street
P.O. Box 2188
Santa Fe, NM 87504-2188
(505) 954-7205   Fax: (505) 954-7207
E-mail: iarc@sarsf.org
Web: sarweb.org/index.php?artists

Summary To provide an opportunity for Native American women artists to improve their skills through a spring residency at the Indian Arts Research Center in Santa Fe, New Mexico.

Eligibility This program is open to Native American women who excel in the arts, including sculpture, performance, basketry, painting, printmaking, digital art, mixed media, photography, pottery, writing, and filmmaking. Applicants should be attempting to explore new avenues of creativity, grapple with new ideas to advance their work, and strengthen existing talents. Along with their application, they must submit a current resume, examples of their current work, and a 2-page statement that explains why they are applying for this fellowship, how it will help them realize their professional and/or personal goals as an artist, and the scope of the project they plan to complete during the residency.

Financial data The fellowship provides a stipend of $3,000 per month, housing, studio space, supplies allowance, and travel reimbursement to and from the center.

Duration 3 months, beginning in March.

Additional information Fellows work with the staff and research curators at the Indian Arts Research Center, an academic division of the School of American Research that is devoted solely to Native American art scholarship. The center has a significant collection of Pueblo pottery, Navajo and Pueblo Indian textiles, and early 20th-century Indian paintings, as well as holdings of jewelry and silverwork, basketry, clothing, and other ethnological materials. This fellowship was established in 2001.

Number awarded 1 each year.

Deadline January of each year.

[1283]
ETHEL K. ALLEN FELLOWSHIP

Sigma Delta Epsilon-Graduate Women in Science, Inc.
c/o Julie Gros-Louis, Fellowships Coordinator
University of Iowa-Department of Psychology
11 Seashore Hall E
Iowa City, IA 52242-1407
(319) 384-1816   Fax: (319) 335-0191
E-mail: Julie-gros-louis@uiowa.edu
Web: www.gwis.org/programs.htm

Summary To provide funding to women interested in conducting research anywhere in the world in the natural sciences.

Eligibility This program is open to women from any country currently enrolled as a graduate student, engaged in postdoctoral research, or holding a junior faculty position. Applicants must be interested in conducting research anywhere in the world in the natural sciences (including physical, environ-

mental, mathematical, computer, or life sciences), anthropology, psychology, or statistics. Along with their application, they must submit 2-paragraph essays on 1) how the proposed research relates to their degree program and/or career development; 2) initiatives in which they are participating to promote the careers of scientists, particularly women, within their institution, program, or peer group; and 3) relevant personal factors, including financial need, that should be considered in evaluating their proposal. Appointments are made without regard to race, religion, nationality, creed, national origin, sexual orientation, or age.

Financial data The grant currently is $3,000. Funds may be used for such research expenses as expendable supplies, small equipment, publication of research findings, travel and subsistence while performing field studies, or travel to another laboratory for collaborative research. They may not be used for tuition, child care, travel to professional meetings or to begin a new appointment, administrative overhead or indirect costs, personal computers, living allowances, or equipment for general use.

Duration 1 year.

Additional information This program was established in 1994. An application processing fee of $30 is required.

Number awarded 1 each year.

Deadline January of each year.

[1284]
EUDORA WELTY PRIZE

Mississippi University for Women
Attn: Department of Languages, Literature, and
   Philosophy
Painter Hall, Room 111
W-Box 1634
Columbus, MS 39701
(662) 329-7386   Fax: (662) 329-7387
E-mail: info@humanities.muw.edu
Web: www.muw.edu/welty

Summary To recognize and reward original works of interpretive scholarship from disciplines within the humanities and related to women's studies, Southern studies, or modern letters.

Eligibility Eligible to be submitted are unpublished book-length manuscripts (80,000 to 100,000 words) complete at the time of submission and not under consideration by any other press. Submissions must be original works of interpretive scholarship and from disciplines within the humanities related to women's studies, Southern studies, or modern literature. Collections of essays, bibliographies, translations, and unrevised theses or dissertations are not eligible.

Financial data The prize consists of a cash award of $1,500 and publication of the winning manuscript by the University Press of Mississippi.

Duration The prize is presented annually.

Additional information This prize, established in 1989, is jointly sponsored by Mississippi University for Women and the University Press of Mississippi.

Number awarded 1 each year.

Deadline April of each year.

[1285]
EVA LOIS EVANS MATHEMATICS AND SCIENCE FELLOWSHIPS

Alpha Kappa Alpha Sorority, Inc.
Attn: Educational Advancement Foundation
5656 South Stony Island Avenue
Chicago, IL 60637
(773) 947-0026   Toll Free: (800) 653-6528
Fax: (773) 947-0277   E-mail: akaeaf@akaeaf.net
Web: www.akaeaf.org/fellowships_endowments.htm

Summary To provide funding to pre- and postdoctoral scholars (especially African American women) who are engaged in research in mathematics, science, or technology.

Eligibility This program is open to graduate students and more advanced scholars who are interested in conducting research in the area of mathematics, science, or technology. Applicants must submit 1) a list of honors, awards, and scholarships received; 2) a list of organizations in which they have memberships, especially minority organizations; 3) a description of the project or research on which they are currently working, or (if they are not involved in a project or research) the aspects of their field that interest them; and 4) a statement of their personal and career goals, including how this scholarship will enhance their ability to attain those goals. The sponsor is a traditionally African American women's sorority.

Financial data A stipend is awarded (amount not specified).

Duration These fellowships are awarded biennially, in even-numbered years.

Number awarded Varies each biennium; recently, 2 of these fellowships were awarded.

Deadline April of even-numbered years.

[1286]
EXTENSION SERVICES GRANTS OF THE RESEARCH ON GENDER IN SCIENCE AND ENGINEERING PROGRAM

National Science Foundation
Directorate for Education and Human Resources
Attn: Division of Human Resource Development
4201 Wilson Boulevard, Room 815N
Arlington, VA 22230
(703) 292-7303   Fax: (703) 292-9018
TDD: (800) 281-8749   E-mail: jjesse@nsf.gov
Web: www.nsf.gov/funding/pgm_summ.jsp?pims_id=5475

Summary To provide funding to professionals interested in providing consulting services to educators and institutions, to enable them to adopt policies and programs related to the underrepresentation of girls and women in science, technology, engineering, or mathematics (STEM) education.

Eligibility This program is open to anyone with professional skills that will enable them to 1) integrate various findings about gender in science and engineering into a comprehensive program of change or to facilitate the interpretation of research knowledge into practice; 2) show educators how to adapt exemplary projects, research-based learning tools, pedagogical approaches, and service or support programs; 3) communicate to researchers the problems that practicing educators find most urgent or troublesome in adopting the new methods or tools; or 4) provide training and consulting services that will develop a cadre of extension service agents that will reach significant practitioner communities in a train-the-trainer model. The target community may be a mix of teachers, counselors, parents, community leaders, administrators, faculty, and others.

Financial data Grants up to $500,000 per year are available.

Duration Up to 5 years; support in years 4 and 5 depends upon performance.

Additional information The National Science Foundation (NSF) established the Research on Gender in Science and Engineering (GSE) program in 1993 under the name "Program for Women and Girls." That was replaced with the "Program for Gender Equity in Science, Mathematics, Engineering and Technology," and then in the 2003 fiscal year by "Gender Diversity in STEM Education." The current title became effective in the 2007 fiscal year.

Number awarded 1 to 2 each year. The GSE program plans to award 15 to 22 grants per year for research, outreach and communication, and extension service activities. A total of $5,000,000 is available for the program annually.

Deadline Letters of intent must be submitted in September of each year; full proposals are due in October.

[1287]
FACULTY EARLY CAREER DEVELOPMENT PROGRAM

National Science Foundation
Directorate for Education and Human Resources
Senior Staff Associate for Cross Directorate Programs
4201 Wilson Boulevard, Room 805
Arlington, VA 22230
(703) 292-8600   TDD: (800) 281-8749
Web: www.nsf.gov

Summary To provide funding to outstanding new faculty (especially women, minorities, and individuals with disabilities) who are working in science and engineering fields of interest to the National Science Foundation (NSF) and intend to develop academic careers involving both research and education.

Eligibility This program, identified as the CAREER program, is open to faculty members who meet all of the following requirements: 1) be employed in a tenure-track (or equivalent) position at an institution in the United States, its territories or possessions, or the Commonwealth of Puerto Rico that awards degrees in a field supported by NSF or that is a nonprofit, non-degree granting organization, such as a museum, observatory, or research laboratory; 2) have a doctoral degree in a field of science or engineering supported by NSF: 3) not have competed more than 3 times in this program; 4) be untenured; and 5) not be a current or former recipient of a Presidential Early Career Award for Scientists and Engineers (PECASE) or CAREER award. Applicants are not required to be U.S. citizens or permanent residents. They must submit a career development plan that indicates a description of the proposed research project, including preliminary supporting data (if appropriate), specific objectives, methods, procedures to be used, and expected significance of the results; a description of the proposed educational activities, including plans to evaluate their impact; a description of how the research and educational activities are integrated with each other; and results of prior NSF support (if applicable). Proposals from women, underrepresented minorities, and persons with disabilities are especially encouraged.

Financial data The grant is at least $80,000 per year (or $100,000 per year for the Directorate of Biological Sciences), including indirect costs or overhead.

Duration 5 years.

Additional information This program is operated by various disciplinary divisions within the NSF; for a list of the participating divisions and their telephone numbers, contact the sponsor. Outstanding recipients of these grants are nominated for the NSF component of the PECASE awards, which are awarded to 20 recipients of these grants as an honorary award.

Number awarded Approximately 425 each year.

Deadline July of each year.

[1288]
FASEB EXCELLENCE IN SCIENCE AWARD

Federation of American Societies for Experimental Biology
Attn: Excellence in Science Award
9650 Rockville Pike
Bethesda, MD 20814-3998
(301) 634-7092   Fax: (301) 634-7049
E-mail: lstricker@faseb.org
Web: www.faseb.org

Summary To recognize and reward women whose research in experimental biology has contributed significantly to our understanding of their discipline.

Eligibility Nominations for this award may be submitted by members of the component societies of the Federation of American Societies for Experimental Biology (FASEB). Nominees must be women who are also members of 1 or more of the 24 societies of FASEB. Letters of nomination should identify the nominee's contributions to the field that represents her outstanding achievement in science, leadership and mentorship, evidence of national recognition, honors and awards, and a selected bibliography. Self-nominations are not accepted.

Financial data The award consists of a $10,000 unrestricted research grant, travel expenses to the annual meeting, complimentary registration at the meeting, and a plaque.

Duration This award is presented annually.

Additional information This award was first presented in 1989. Member societies of FASEB include the American Physiological Society (APS), American Society for Biochemistry and Molecular Biology (ASBMB), American Society for Pharmacology and Experimental Therapeutics (ASPET), American Society for Investigative Pathology (ASIP), American Society for Nutrition (ASN), American Association of Immunologists (AAI), American Association of Anatomists (AAA), The Protein Society, American Society for Bone and Mineral Research (ASBMR), American Society for Clinical Investigation (ASCI), The Endocrine Society, American Society of Human Genetics (ASHG), Society for Developmental Biology (SDB), American Peptide Society (APEPS), Association of Biomolecular Resource Facilities (ABRF), Society for the Study of Reproduction (SSR), Teratology Society, Environmental Mutagen Society (EMS), International Society for Computational Biology (ISCB), American College of Sports Medicine (ACSM), Biomedical Engineering Society (BMES), Genetics Society of America, American Federation for Medi-

cal Research (AFMR), and The Histochemical Society (HCS).

Number awarded 1 each year.

Deadline Nominations must be submitted by February of each year.

[1289]
FELLOWSHIP TO FACULTY TRANSITION AWARDS

American Gastroenterological Association
Attn: AGA Research Foundation
Research Awards Manager
4930 Del Ray Avenue
Bethesda, MD 20814-2512
(301) 222-4012   Fax: (301) 654-5920
E-mail: awards@gastro.org
Web: www.gastro.org/aga-foundation/grants

Summary To provide funding to women, minority, and other physicians for research training in an area of gastrointestinal, liver function, or related diseases.

Eligibility This program is open to trainee members of the American Gastroenterological Association (AGA) who have an M.D. or equivalent degree and a gastroenterology-related fellowship at an accredited institution. Applicants must be committed to an academic career; have completed at least 1 year of research training at their current institution; have a commitment from their home institution for a full-time faculty position; and have a preceptor who will supervise their research activities and serve as a mentor. Women and minority investigators are strongly encouraged to apply. Selection is based on the candidate's promise for future success, feasibility and significance of the proposal, attributes of the candidate, record and commitment of the sponsors, and institutional and laboratory environment.

Financial data The grant is $40,000 per year. Funds are to be used as salary support for the recipient. Indirect costs are not allowed.

Duration 2 years.

Additional information Fellows must devote 70% effort to research related to the gastrointestinal tract or liver.

Number awarded 2 each year.

Deadline August of each year.

[1290]
FELLOWSHIPS IN SCIENCE AND INTERNATIONAL AFFAIRS

Harvard University
John F. Kennedy School of Government
Belfer Center for Science and International Affairs
Attn: Fellowship Coordinator
79 John F. Kennedy Street
Cambridge, MA 02138
(617) 495-8806   Fax: (617) 495-8963
E-mail: bcsia_fellowships@ksg.harvard.edu
Web: belfercenter.ksg.harvard.edu/fellowships

Summary To provide funding to professionals, postdoctorates, and doctoral students (particularly women and minorities) who are interested in conducting research in areas of concern to the Belfer Center for Science and International Affairs at Harvard University in Cambridge, Massachusetts.

Eligibility The postdoctoral fellowship is open to recent recipients of the Ph.D. or equivalent degree, university faculty members, and employees of government, military, international, humanitarian, and private research institutions who have appropriate professional experience. Applicants for predoctoral fellowships must have passed their general examinations. Lawyers, economists, political scientists, those in the natural sciences, and others of diverse disciplinary backgrounds are also welcome to apply. The program especially encourages applications from women, minorities, and citizens of all countries. All applicants must be interested in conducting research in 1 of the 3 major program areas of the center: 1) the International Security Program (ISP), including Religion in International Affairs; 2) the Science, Technology, and Public Policy Program (STPP), including information and communications technology, energy and water policy, managing the atom project, and the energy technology innovation policy research group; 3) and the Dubai initiative.

Financial data The stipend is $34,000 for postdoctoral research fellows or $20,000 for predoctoral research fellows. Health insurance is also provided.

Duration 10 months.

Number awarded A limited number each year.

Deadline January of each year.

[1291]
FEMINIST ACTIVISM AWARD

Sociologists for Women in Society
Attn: Executive Officer
University of Rhode Island
Department of Sociology
10 Chafee Road
Kingston, RI 02881
(401) 874-9510   Fax: (401) 874-2588
E-mail: swseo@socwomen.org
Web: www.socwomen.org/web/awards.html

Summary To recognize and reward members of Sociologists for Women in Society (SWS) who have used sociology to improve conditions for women in society.

Eligibility This program is open to SWS members who have notably and consistently used sociology to improve conditions for women in society. The award honors outstanding feminist advocacy efforts that embody the goal of service to women and that have identifiably improved women's lives. Selection is based on activist contributions, rather than occupational and academic achievements.

Financial data The award includes an honorarium of $1,000 and a travel budget of $1,500 for presentations (lectures, workshops, or training sessions) related to the recipient's field of activism at 2 selected campus sites.

Duration The award is presented annually.

Additional information This award was first presented in 1995.

Number awarded 1 each year.

Deadline Nominations must be submitted by March of each year.

[1292]
FICHTER RESEARCH GRANT COMPETITION

Association for the Sociology of Religion
Attn: Executive Officer
618 S.W. Second Avenue
Galva, IL 61434-1912
(309) 932-2727   Fax: (309) 932-2282
Web: www.sociologyofreligion.com

Summary To provide funding to scholars interested in conducting research on women and religion.

Eligibility This program is open to scholars involved in research on women and religion, gender issues, and feminist perspectives on religion. Scholars at the beginning of their careers are particularly encouraged to apply; dissertation research qualifies for funding. Applicants must be members of the association at the time the application is submitted. The proposal must not be more than 5 double-spaced pages and should outline the rationale and plan of the research, previous research, methodology proposed, timeline, and budget; a curriculum vitae should also be included. Simultaneous submissions to other grant competitions are permissible if the applicant is explicit about which budget items in the Fichter grant proposal do not overlap items in other submitted proposals.

Financial data Each year, a total of $24,000 is available to be awarded.

Duration 1 year.

Number awarded Varies each year; recently, 6 of these grants were awarded.

Deadline April of each year.

[1293]
FILM FINISHING FUND GRANTS

Women in Film/Los Angeles
Attn: Film Finishing Fund
6100 Wilshire Boulevard, Suite 710
Los Angeles, CA 90048
(323) 935-2211   Fax: (323) 935-2212
E-mail: foundation@wif.org
Web: www.wif.org/film-finishing-fund

Summary To provide funding to women from any country for the completion of films of any length or genre.

Eligibility This program is open to female filmmakers who have completed principal photography and can submit a complete rough cut of an edited film (narrative feature length films are accepted if at least 90% of the film is complete). Projects in all genres (narrative, documentary, educational, animated, and experimental) and all lengths are eligible. No student projects, including thesis projects and films initiated while the applicant was a student, are considered. Applicants do not need to be members of Women in Film, although they are encouraged to join. Applications are accepted from filmmakers worldwide, but projects must be accessible to English-speaking audiences or at least have English subtitles. Selection is based on a demonstration that this grant will make a critical contribution to the completion of the film, the number of women involved in key creative personnel, and the film's positive statement about women and/or the way in which it deals with issues relevant to women.

Financial data Grants provide cash (up to $15,000) and in-kind services.

Additional information This program, which began in 1985, currently receives support from Netflix. A $75 processing fee is charged.

Number awarded Varies each year; recently, 7 of these grants were awarded. Since the program began, it has awarded more than $2 million in cash and in-kind services to 170 films.

Deadline May of each year.

[1294]
F.J. MCGUIGAN EARLY CAREER INVESTIGATOR RESEARCH PRIZE

American Psychological Foundation
750 First Street, N.E.
Washington, DC 20002-4242
(202) 336-5843   Fax: (202) 336-5812
E-mail: foundation@apa.org
Web: www.apa.org/apf/funding/mcguigan-prize.aspx

Summary To provide funding to young psychologists (especially women, minorities, and individuals with disabilities) who are interested in conducting research related to the human mind.

Eligibility This program is open to investigators who have earned a doctoral degree in psychology or in a related field within the past 9 years. Nominees must have an affiliation with an accredited college, university, or other research institution. They must be engaged in research that seeks to explicate the concept of the human mind. The approach must be materialistic and should be primarily psychophysiological, but physiological and behavioral research may also qualify. Self-nominations are not accepted; candidates must be nominated by a senior colleague. The sponsor encourages nominations of individuals who represent diversity in race, ethnicity, gender, age, disability, and sexual orientation.

Financial data The grant is $25,000.

Duration These grants are awarded biennially, in even-numbered years.

Additional information The first grant under this program was awarded in 2002. Information is also available from the APA Science Directorate, E-mail: science@apa.org.

Number awarded 1 every other year.

Deadline February of even-numbered years.

[1295]
FLORENCE NIGHTINGALE DAVID AWARD

Committee of Presidents of Statistical Societies
c/o Alice S. Whittemore, David Award Committee Chair
Stanford University School of Medicine
Department of Health Research and Policy
Redwood Building, Room T204
259 Campus Drive
Stanford, CA 94305-5405
(650) 723-5460   Fax: (650) 725-6951
E-mail: alicesw@stanford.edu
Web: nisla05.niss.org/copss/committees.htm

Summary To recognize and reward female statisticians who have made notable contributions to the field.

Eligibility This program is open to women who have demonstrated excellence as a role model to women in statistical research, leadership of multidisciplinary collaborative groups, statistics education, or service to the statistics profession.

Nominees may be of any age, race, sexual orientation, nationality, or citizenship, but they must be living at the time of their nomination.

Financial data The award consists of a plaque and a cash honorarium of $1,000.

Duration The award is presented biennially, in odd-numbered years.

Additional information The award was established in 2001.

Number awarded 1 every other year.

Deadline January of odd-numbered years.

[1296]
FOUNDATION FOR THE HISTORY OF WOMEN IN MEDICINE FELLOWSHIPS

Foundation for the History of Women in Medicine
P.O. Box 543
Pottstown, PA 19464
(610) 970-9143   Fax: (610) 970-7520
Web: www.fhwim.org/programs/fellowships.php

Summary To provide funding to students and scholars interested in short-term use of resources in the Boston area to conduct research on the history of women and medicine.

Eligibility This program is open to doctoral candidates and other advanced scholars interested in using the Archives for Women in Medicine at the Countway Library's Center for the History of Medicine in Boston. Applicants must be interested in conducting research on the history of women in medicine. Preference is given to projects that deal specifically with women as physicians or other health workers, but proposals dealing with the history of women's health issues are also considered. Preference is given to applicants who live beyond commuting distance of the Countway.

Financial data The grant is $5,000.

Duration Recipients may conduct research on a flexible schedule during 1 academic year.

Additional information The Francis A. Countway Library of Medicine, the largest academic medical library in the United States, was established in 1960 as the result of an alliance between the Boston Medical Library and the Harvard Medical School Library. Information is available from the Countway Library, Center for the History of Medicine, Archives for Women in Medicine, 10 Shattuck Street, Boston, MA 02115, (617) 432-6206, Fax: (617) 432-4737, E-mail: arm@hms.harvard.edu.

Number awarded 1 each year.

Deadline February of each year.

[1297]
FRAN SARGENT SCHOLARSHIP

Ninety-Nines, Inc.-Florida Goldcoast Chapter
c/o Kimberley Lowe
100 Edgewater Drive, Unit 342
Coral Gables, FL 33133-6980
(305) 984-0561   E-mail: flynlowe@comcast.net
Web: www.flgoldcoast99s.org/scholarships.html

Summary To provide financial assistance to female pilots in Florida who are interested in an aviation training program at a college or flight school in the state.

Eligibility This program is open to women who are either 1) residents of Florida and have a private pilot's certificate; or

2) private pilots currently enrolled in an aviation training program in the state. Applicants must be interested in acquiring an additional rating or certificate, attending a college program, or engaging in another aviation endeavor. Along with their application, they must submit a statement describing their education, aviation training and experience, aviation organizations, and employment history; another statement covering their educational purpose and/or aviation goals, their goals, why they chose aviation, and the pilot certificate or rating, college degree, or other goal they plan to attain using this scholarship; and 2 letters of reference. Selection is based on financial need, desire to prepare for a career in aviation, ability to represent women in aviation, likelihood of success in reaching goals, and neatness and completeness of application package.

Financial data The stipend is $2,000.

Duration 1 year.

Number awarded 1 or more each year.

Deadline September of each year.

[1298]
FRANCIS P. GARVAN-JOHN M. OLIN MEDAL

American Chemical Society
Attn: Office of the National Awards Program
1155 16th Street, N.W.
Washington, DC 20036-4800
(202) 872-4575   Toll Free: (800) 227-5558, ext. 4575
Fax: (202) 776-8008   E-mail: awards@acs.org
Web: portal.acs.org

Summary To recognize and reward distinguished service to chemistry by women chemists.

Eligibility Nominees must be female citizens of the United States who have performed distinguished service to the field of chemistry.

Financial data The award consists of $5,000, a medallion with a presentation box, a certificate, and reimbursement of up to $2,500 for travel expenses to the meeting at which the award is presented.

Duration The award is presented annually.

Additional information This award was established in 1936 through a donation from Francis P. Garvan and has been supported by a fund set up at that time. The Olin Corporation currently sponsors the award.

Number awarded 1 each year.

Deadline Nominations must be submitted by the end of October of each year.

[1299]
FRANK NELSON DOUBLEDAY MEMORIAL AWARD

Wyoming Arts Council
2320 Capitol Avenue
Cheyenne, WY 82002
(307) 777-7742   Fax: (307) 777-5499
TDD: (307) 777-5964
Web: wyoarts.state.wy.us/Artists/Literature.aspx

Summary To recognize and reward outstanding female writers (in any genre) who live in Wyoming.

Eligibility This program is open to female writers who live in Wyoming for at least 10 months of the year, are older than 18 years of age, and are not full-time students or faculty members. Writers are eligible if they have never published a book; if they have published only 1 full-length book of fiction, poetry, or nonfiction; of if they have published no more than 1 book of poetry, 1 of fiction, and 1 of nonfiction. They are invited to submit manuscripts of poetry (up to 10 printed pages with no more than 1 poem per page), fiction or creative nonfiction (up to 25 pages), or drama and screenplays (up to 25 pages).

Financial data The award is $1,000.

Duration The award is presented annually.

Number awarded 1 each year.

Deadline October of each year.

[1300]
FREDERICK BURKHARDT RESIDENTIAL FELLOWSHIPS FOR RECENTLY TENURED SCHOLARS

American Council of Learned Societies
Attn: Office of Fellowships and Grants
633 Third Avenue
New York, NY 10017-6795
(212) 697-1505   Fax: (212) 949-8058
E-mail: fellowships@acls.org
Web: www.acls.org/programs/burkhardt

Summary To provide funding to women, minority, and other scholars in all disciplines of the humanities and the humanities-related social sciences who are interested in conducting research at designated residential centers.

Eligibility This program is open to citizens and permanent residents of the United States who achieved tenure in a humanities or humanities-related social science discipline at a U.S. institution within the past 4 years. Applicants must be interested in conducting research at 1 of 12 participating residential centers in the United States or abroad. Appropriate fields of specialization include, but are not limited to, American studies; anthropology; archaeology; art and architectural history; classics; economics; film; geography; history; languages and literatures; legal studies; linguistics; musicology; philosophy; political science; psychology; religious studies; rhetoric, communication, and media studies; sociology; and theater, dance, and performance studies. Proposals in those fields of the social sciences are eligible only if they employ predominantly humanistic approaches (e.g., economic history, law and literature, political philosophy). Proposals in interdisciplinary and cross-disciplinary studies are welcome, as are proposals focused on a geographic region or on a cultural or linguistic group. Applications are particularly invited from women and members of minority groups.

Financial data The stipend is $75,000. If that stipend exceeds the fellow's normal academic year salary, the excess is available for research and travel expenses.

Duration 1 academic year.

Additional information This program, which began in 1999, is supported by funding from the Andrew W. Mellon Foundation. The participating residential research centers are the National Humanities Center (Research Triangle Park, North Carolina), the Center for Advanced Study in the Behavioral Sciences (Stanford, California), the Institute for Advanced Study, Schools of Historical Studies and Social Science (Princeton, New Jersey), the Radcliffe Institute for Advanced Study at Harvard University (Cambridge, Massachusetts), the American Antiquarian Society (Worcester,

Massachusetts), the John W. Kluge Center at the Library of Congress (Washington, D.C.), the Folger Shakespeare Library (Washington, D.C.), the Newberry Library (Chicago, Illinois), the Huntington Library, Art Collections, and Botanical Gardens (San Marino, California), the American Academy in Rome, Collegium Budapest, and Villa I Tatti (Florence, Italy).

Number awarded Up to 9 each year.

Deadline September of each year.

[1301]
FUTURAMA FOUNDATION CAREER ADVANCEMENT SCHOLARSHIP

Maine Federation of Business and Professional Women's Clubs
Attn: BPW/Maine Futurama Foundation
c/o Susan Tardie, Co-President
25 Hall Street
Fort Kent, ME 04743
E-mail: susan.tardie@maine.edu
Web: www.bpwmefoundation.org/files/index.php?id=10

Summary To provide financial assistance to women in Maine who are over 30 years of age and continuing a program of higher education or retraining.

Eligibility This program is open to women who are older than 30 years of age and residents of Maine. Applicants must be continuing in, or returning to, an accredited program of higher education or job-related training, either full or part time. They must have a definite plan to use the desired training in a practical and immediate way to improve chances for advancement, train for a new career field, or enter or reenter the job market. Along with their application, they must submit a statement describing their educational, personal, and career goals, including financial need, expectations of training, and future plans for using this educational program. Preference is given to members of Maine Federation of Business and Professional Women's Clubs.

Financial data The stipend is $1,200. Funds are paid directly to the school.

Duration 1 year.

Number awarded 1 or more each year.

Deadline April of each year.

[1302]
GAIUS CHARLES BOLIN DISSERTATION AND POST-MFA FELLOWSHIPS

Williams College
Attn: Dean of the Faculty
Hopkins Hall, Third Floor
P.O. Box 141
Williamstown, MA 01267
(413) 597-4351   Fax: (413) 597-3553
E-mail: gburda@williams.edu
Web: dean-faculty.williams.edu/graduate-fellowships

Summary To provide financial assistance to women and members of other underrepresented groups who are interested in teaching courses at Williams College while working on their doctoral dissertation or building their post-M.F.A. professional portfolio.

Eligibility This program is open to members of underrepresented groups, including ethnic minorities, first-generation college students, women in predominantly male fields, and scholars with disabilities. Applicants must be 1) doctoral candidates in any field who have completed all work for a Ph.D. except for the dissertation; or 2) artists who completed an M.F.A. degree within the past 2 years and are building their professional portfolio. They must be willing to teach a course at Williams College. Along with their application, they must submit a full curriculum vitae, a graduate school transcript, 3 letters of recommendation, a copy of their dissertation prospectus or samples of their artistic work, and a description of their teaching interests within a department or program at Williams College. U.S. citizenship or permanent resident status is required.

Financial data Fellows receive $33,000 for the academic year, plus housing assistance, office space, computer and library privileges, and a research allowance of up to $4,000.

Duration 2 years.

Additional information Bolin fellows are assigned a faculty adviser in the appropriate department. This program was established in 1985. Fellows are expected to teach a 1-semester course each year. They must be in residence at Williams College for the duration of the fellowship.

Number awarded 3 each year.

Deadline November of each year.

[1303]
GEOPHYSICAL FLUID DYNAMICS FELLOWSHIPS

Woods Hole Oceanographic Institution
Attn: Academic Programs Office
Clark Laboratory, MS 31
266 Woods Hole Road
Woods Hole, MA 02543-1541
(508) 289-2950   Fax: (508) 457-2188
E-mail: gfd@whoi.edu
Web: www.whoi.edu/gfd

Summary To provide summer research and study opportunities at Woods Hole Oceanographic Institution (WHOI) to pre- and postdoctoral scholars (particularly women and minorities) who are interested in geophysical fluid dynamics.

Eligibility This program is open to pre- and postdoctorates who are interested in pursuing research or study opportunities in a field that involves nonlinear dynamics of rotating, stratified fluids. Fields of specialization include classical fluid dynamics, physical oceanography, meteorology, geophysical fluid dynamics, astrophysics, planetary atmospheres, hydromagnetics, physics, and applied mathematics. Applications from women and members of underrepresented groups are particularly encouraged.

Financial data Participants receive a stipend of $5,400 and an allowance for travel expenses within the United States.

Duration 10 weeks during the summer.

Additional information Each summer, the program at WHOI revolves around a central theme. A recent theme related to shear turbulence. The main components of the summer program are a series of principal lectures, a set of supplementary research seminars, and research projects conducted by the student fellows with the active support of the staff. Funding for this program, which began in 1959, is provided by the National Science Foundation and Office of Naval Research.

Number awarded Up to 10 graduate students are supported each year.

Deadline February of each year.

[1304]
GEORGIA HARKNESS SCHOLARSHIP AWARDS

United Methodist Church
Attn: General Board of Higher Education and Ministry
Division of Ordained Ministry
1001 19th Avenue South
P.O. Box 340007
Nashville, TN 37203-0007
(615) 340-7409   Fax: (615) 340-7367
E-mail: gharkness@gbhem.org
Web: www.gbhem.org/loansandscholarships

Summary To provide financial assistance to women over 35 years of age who are preparing for a second career in ordained ministry as an elder in the United Methodist Church.

Eligibility This program is open to women over 35 years of age who have a bachelor's degree. Applicants must be enrolled full time in a school of theology approved by the University Senate of the United Methodist Church and working on an M.Div. degree. They must be currently certified as candidates for ordained ministry as an elder in the United Methodist Church. The award is not available for undergraduate, D.Min., or Ph.D. work. Selection is based on financial need, academic scholarship, spiritual leadership, and commitment to social justice.

Financial data The stipend is $5,000.

Duration 1 year; recipients may reapply.

Number awarded Varies each year.

Deadline February of each year.

[1305]
GERTRUDE AND MAURICE GOLDHABER DISTINGUISHED FELLOWSHIPS

Brookhaven National Laboratory
Attn: Dr. Kathleen Barkigia
Building 460
P.O. Box 5000
Upton, NY 11973-5000
(631) 344-4467   E-mail: Barkigia@bnl.gov
Web: www.bnl.gov/hr/goldhaber.asp

Summary To provide funding to women, minorities, and other postdoctoral scientists interested in conducting research at Brookhaven National Laboratory (BNL).

Eligibility This program is open to scholars who are no more than 3 years past receipt of the Ph.D. and are interested in working at BNL. Candidates must be interested in working in close collaboration with a member of the BNL scientific staff and qualifying for a scientific staff position at BNL upon completion of the appointment. The sponsoring scientist must have an opening and be able to support the candidate at the standard starting salary for postdoctoral research associates. The program especially encourages applications from minorities and women.

Financial data The program provides additional funds to bring the salary to $75,000 per year.

Duration 3 years.

Additional information This program is funded by Battelle Memorial Institute and the State University of New York at Stony Brook.

Number awarded Up to 8 each year.

Deadline August of each year.

[1306]
GILBERT F. WHITE POSTDOCTORAL FELLOWSHIP PROGRAM

Resources for the Future
Attn: Coordinator for Academic Programs
1616 P Street, N.W., Suite 600
Washington, DC 20036-1400
(202) 328-5008   Fax: (202) 939-3460
E-mail: white-award@rff.org
Web: www.rff.org/About_RFF/Pages/default.aspx

Summary To provide funding to women, minorities, and other postdoctoral researchers who wish to devote a year to scholarly work at Resources for the Future (RFF) in Washington, D.C.

Eligibility This program is open to individuals in any discipline who have completed their doctoral requirements and are interested in conducting scholarly research at RFF in social or policy science areas that relate to natural resources, energy, or the environment. Teaching and/or research experience at the postdoctoral level is preferred but not essential. Individuals holding positions in government as well as at academic institutions are eligible. Women and minority candidates are strongly encouraged to apply.

Financial data Fellows receive an annual stipend (based on their academic salary) plus research support, office facilities at RFF, and an allowance of up to $1,000 for moving or living expenses. Fellowships do not provide medical insurance or other RFF fringe benefits.

Duration 11 months.

Additional information Fellows are assigned to an RFF research division: the Energy and Natural Resources division, the Quality of the Environment division, or the Center for Risk, Resource, and Environmental Management. Fellows are expected to be in residence at Resources for the Future for the duration of the program.

Number awarded 1 each year.

Deadline February of each year.

[1307]
GITA CHUADHURI PRIZE

Western Association of Women Historians
c/o Amy Essington, Executive Director
3242 Petaluma Avenue
Long Beach, CA 90808-4249
E-mail: amyessington@wawh.org
Web: wawh.org/awards/currentinfo.html

Summary To recognize and reward outstanding books on rural women published by members of the Western Association of Women Historians (WAWH).

Eligibility Members of the WAWH are eligible to submit their books for consideration if they were published any time during the preceding 3 years. The entry must be a single-authored monograph based on original research that relates to rural women, from any era and any place in the world.

Anthologies and edited works are not eligible for consideration.

Financial data The award is $1,000.

Duration The award is presented annually.

Additional information This award was first presented in 2009.

Number awarded 1 each year.

Deadline January of each year.

[1308]
GLORIA E. ANZALDUA BOOK PRIZE

National Women's Studies Association
Attn: Book Prizes
7100 Baltimore Avenue, Suite 203
College Park, MD 20740
(301) 403-0407   Fax: (301) 403-4137
E-mail: nwsaoffice@nwsa.org
Web: www.nwsa.org/awards/index.php

Summary To recognize and reward members of the National Women's Studies Association (NWSA) who have written outstanding books on women of color and transnational issues.

Eligibility This award is available to NWSA members who submit a book that was published during the preceding year. Entries must present groundbreaking scholarship in women's studies and make a significant multicultural feminist contribution to women of color and/or transnational studies.

Financial data The award provides an honorarium of $1,000 and lifetime membership in NWSA.

Duration The award is presented annually.

Additional information This award was first presented in 2008.

Number awarded 1 each year.

Deadline April of each year.

[1309]
GLORIA HOEGH MEMORIAL SCHOLARSHIP FOR THE EDUCATION OF RURAL LIBRARIANS

Wisconsin Library Association
Attn: Scholarship Committee
5250 East Terrace Drive, Suite A1
Madison, WI 53718-8345
(608) 245-3640   Fax: (608) 245-3646
E-mail: wla@scls.lib.wi.us
Web: www.wla.lib.wi.us/scholarships/rural.htm

Summary To provide funding to librarians (especially women, minorities, and individuals with disabilities) in rural areas of Wisconsin who are interested in attending a continuing education program.

Eligibility This program is open to librarians who are currently employed in a Wisconsin community with a population of 5,000 or less or who work with library employees in those communities. Applicants must be planning to attend a workshop, conference, or continuing education program in any state. Along with their application, they must submit a 500-word essay describing their professional work experience and performance, the knowledge or information they will gain from the proposed conference or other continuing education program, and how the program will benefit them and their library. Selection is based on need and desire for the scholarship, experience and background in library work, and potential to contribute to rural librarianship. Racial and ethnic minorities, women, and persons with disabilities are specifically encouraged to apply and may identify themselves as such.

Financial data The stipend is $1,050.

Duration The award is presented annually.

Number awarded 1 each year.

Deadline September of each year.

[1310]
HADASSAH-BRANDEIS INSTITUTE RESEARCH AWARDS

Brandeis University
Hadassah-Brandeis Institute
Attn: Program Manager
515 South Street
Mailstop 079
Waltham, MA 02454-9110
(781) 736-2064   Fax: (781) 736-2078
E-mail: hbi@brandeis.edu
Web: www.brandeis.edu/hbi/grants/res_awards.html

Summary To provide funding to scholars, graduate students, writers, activists, and artists conducting research in the field of Jewish women's studies.

Eligibility This program offers senior grants (for established scholars and professionals) and junior grants (for graduate students and scholars within 3 years of receiving a Ph.D.). All applicants must be interested in conducting interdisciplinary research on Jewish women and gender issues, although there are no gender or religious limitations. Graduate students in recognized master's and Ph.D. programs are encouraged to apply. Applications from outside the United States are welcome. Grants are awarded in 10 categories: history; the Yishuv and Israel; Diaspora studies; families, children, and the Holocaust; gender, culture, religion, and the law; women's health; Judaism; biography; the arts (performance arts, visual arts, creative writing); and film and video. Applications must specify the category and may be for only 1 category. Selection is based on excellence.

Financial data Senior grants are $5,000 and junior grants are $2,000.

Duration 1 year.

Additional information The Hadassah-Brandeis Institute was formerly the Hadassah International Research Institute on Jewish Women at Brandeis University.

Number awarded Between 20 and 30 each year.

Deadline September of each year.

[1311]
HADASSAH-BRANDEIS INSTITUTE SCHOLAR-IN-RESIDENCE PROGRAM

Brandeis University
Hadassah-Brandeis Institute
Attn: Program Manager
515 South Street
Mailstop 079
Waltham, MA 02454-9110
(781) 736-2064   Fax: (781) 736-2078
E-mail: hbi@brandeis.edu
Web: www.brandeis.edu/hbi/grants/grants.html

Summary To provide an opportunity for scholars, artists, writers, and communal professionals to conduct research in the field of Jewish women's studies while in residence at the Hadassah-Brandeis Institute of Brandeis University.

Eligibility This program is open to scholars, artists, writers, and communal professionals who are working in the area of Jewish women's and gender studies. Applicants must be interested in taking time from their regular institutional duties to work at the institute. Scholars outside the United States and those with an international research focus are especially encouraged to apply.

Financial data Scholars receive a stipend of $3,000 per month and office space at the Brandeis University Women's Studies Research Center.

Duration 1 month to 1 semester.

Additional information The Hadassah-Brandeis Institute was formerly the Hadassah International Research Institute on Jewish Women at Brandeis University.

Number awarded Varies each year; recently, 12 of these residencies were awarded.

Deadline January of each year.

[1312]
HARRY AND MIRIAM LEVINSON AWARD FOR EXCEPTIONAL CONTRIBUTIONS TO CONSULTING ORGANIZATIONAL PSYCHOLOGY

American Psychological Association
Attn: Office of Division Services
750 First Street, N.E.
Washington, DC 20002-4242
(202) 336-6022   E-mail: divisions@apa.org
Web: www.apa.org/about/awards/div-13-levinson.aspx

Summary To recognize and reward outstanding consulting psychologists, particularly women, minorities, and individuals with disabilities.

Eligibility This award is presented to a member of the American Psychological Association (APA) who is a consulting psychologist. Nominees must have shown evidence of ability to convert psychological theory and concepts into applications through which managers and leaders can create effective, healthy, and humane organizations. The sponsor encourages nominations of individuals who represent diversity in race, ethnicity, gender, age, disability, and sexual orientation.

Financial data The award is $5,000.

Duration The award is presented annually.

Additional information This award, first presented in 1992, is sponsored by Division 13 (Consulting Psychology) in conjunction with Division 12 (Society of Clinical Psychology), Division 14 (Industrial/Organizational Psychology), and Division 39 (Psychoanalysis) of the APA.

Number awarded 1 each year.

Deadline Nominations must be submitted by March of each year.

[1313]
HATTIE HEMSCHEMEYER AWARD

American College of Nurse-Midwives
Attn: Associate Director
8403 Colesville Road, Suite 1550
Silver Spring, MD 20910-6374
(240) 485-1800   Fax: (240) 485-1818
Web: www.midwife.org/awards.cfm

Summary To recognize and reward long-time members of the American College of Nurse-Midwives (ACNM) who have made outstanding contributions to midwifery.

Eligibility Nominees for this award must be ACNM members who have been certified nurse midwives (CNMs) or certified midwives (CMs) for at least 10 years. They must have demonstrated 1) continuous outstanding contributions or distinguished service to midwifery and/or MCH, or 2) contributions of historical significance to the development and advancement of midwifery, ACNM, or MCH.

Financial data A monetary award is presented.

Duration The award is presented annually.

Additional information This award was first presented in 1977.

Number awarded 1 each year.

Deadline January of each year.

[1314]
HEALTH AND AGING POLICY FELLOWSHIPS

Columbia University College of Physicians and Surgeons
Attn: Department of Psychiatry
Deputy Director, Health and Aging Policy Fellows
1051 Riverside Drive, Unit 9
New York, NY 10032
(212) 543-6213   Fax: (212) 543-6021
E-mail: healthandagingpolicy@columbia.edu
Web: www.healthandagingpolicy.org

Summary To provide an opportunity for women, minority, and other health professionals with an interest in aging and policy issues to work as legislative assistants in Congress or at other sites.

Eligibility This program is open to physicians, nurses, and social workers who have a demonstrated commitment to health and aging issues and a desire to be involved in health policy at the federal, state, or local levels. Other professionals with clinical backgrounds (e.g., pharmacists, dentists, clinical psychologists) working in the field of health and aging are also eligible. Preference is given to professionals early or midway through their careers. Applicants must be interested serving as residential fellows by participating in the policy-making process on either the federal or state level as legislative assistants in Congress or as professional staff members in executive agencies or policy organizations. A non-residential track is also available to applicants who wish to work on a policy project throughout the year at relevant sites. The program seeks to achieve racial, ethnic, gender, and discipline diversity; members of groups that historically have been underrepresented are strongly encouraged to apply. Selection is based on commitment to health and aging issues and improving the health and well-being of older Americans, potential for leadership in health policy, professional qualifications and achievements, impact of the fellowship experience on the applicant's career, and interpersonal and communication skills. U.S. citizenship or permanent resident status is required.

Financial data For residential fellows, the stipend depends on their current base salary, to a maximum of $120,000 per year; other benefits include a travel allowance for pre-fellowship arrangements and to fellowship-related meetings, a relocation grant of up to $3,500, and up to $400 per month for health insurance. For non-residential fellows, grants provide up to $30,000 to cover related fellowship and travel costs.

Duration 9 to 12 months; fellows may apply for a second year of participation.

Additional information This program, which began in 2009, operates in collaboration with the American Political Science Association Congressional Fellowship Program. Funding is provided by The Atlantic Philanthropies. The John Heinz Senate Fellowship Program, an activity of the Teresa and H. John Heinz III Foundation, supports 1 fellow to work in the Senate. In addition, the Centers for Disease Control and Prevention Health Aging Program sponsors 1 non-residential fellow to work with its staff in Atlanta, Georgia.

Number awarded Varies each year; recently, 4 residential and 5 non-residential fellowships were awarded.

Deadline May of each year.

[1315]
HEALTH AND SOCIETY SCHOLARS PROGRAM

Robert Wood Johnson Foundation
c/o New York Academy of Medicine
1216 Fifth Avenue
New York, NY 10029-5202
(212) 419-3566   Toll Free: (212) 419-3569
E-mail: hss@nyam.org
Web: www.healthandsocietyscholars.org

Summary To provide support to scholars (especially women and minorities) from a variety of disciplines who wish to engage in a program of training and research aimed at helping them become leaders in health policy.

Eligibility This program is open to scholars who have a doctoral degree in fields that include (but are not limited to) behavioral and social sciences, biological and natural sciences, health professions, public policy, public health, history, demography, environmental sciences, urban planning, engineering, and ethics. Applicants must be U.S. citizens or permanent residents who have significant research experience. They must be interested in participating in a program at 1 of 6 universities that includes intensive seminars, mentored research, and focused training in the skills necessary for effective leadership, program implementation, and policy change. The sponsor is committed to a program that embraces diversity and inclusion across multiple dimensions of race, ethnicity, gender, age, socioeconomic background, and academic discipline; it encourages applications from candidates who will help it include diverse perspectives and experiences.

Financial data The stipend is $80,000 per year. Additional support is available for research-related expenses, training workshops, and travel to professional meetings.

Duration 2 years.

Additional information Fellows train at 1 of 6 nationally prominent universities: University of California at Berkeley (in collaboration with the University of California at San Fran-

cisco), Harvard University, University of Michigan, Columbia University, University of Pennsylvania, or University of Wisconsin at Madison.

Number awarded Up to 12 each year.

Deadline September of each year.

[1316]
HEATHER WESTPHAL MEMORIAL SCHOLARSHIP AWARD

International Association of Fire Chiefs
Attn: IAFC Foundation
4025 Fair Ridge Drive
Fairfax, VA 22033-2868
(703) 273-0911   Fax: (703) 273-9363
E-mail: foundation@iafc.org
Web: www.iafcf.org./Scholarship.htm

Summary To provide financial assistance to female fire fighters who wish to further their academic education.

Eligibility This program is open to women who are active members of state, county, provincial, municipal, community, industrial, or federal fire departments in the United States or Canada and have demonstrated proficiency as members for at least 2 years of paid or 3 years of volunteer service. Dependents of members are not eligible. Applicants must be planning to attend a recognized institution of higher education. Along with their application, they must submit a 250-word essay that includes a brief description of the course work, how the course work will benefit their fire service career and department and improve the fire service, and their financial need. Preference is given to members of the International Association of Fire Chiefs (IAFC).

Financial data A stipend is awarded (amount not specified).

Additional information This program was established in 2009.

Number awarded 1 each year.

Deadline May of each year.

[1317]
HELICOPTER ADD-ON FLIGHT TRAINING SCHOLARSHIP

Whirly-Girls International
c/o Britta Penca, Scholarship Director
P.O. Box 222
Oracle, AZ 85623
(520) 840-0951
E-mail: WGScholarshipdirector2@whirlygirls.org
Web: www.whirlygirls.org

Summary To provide financial assistance to women pilots interested in obtaining an additional helicopter rating.

Eligibility This program is open to certificated female pilots who do not currently have a helicopter rating but desire to add that on to their certificate. Along with their application, they must submit information on honors or awards they have received, organizations with which they are affiliated, activities or hobbies they pursue, involvement in aviation-related activities, achievements and contributions in aviation, what originally sparked their interest in the helicopter industry, how they have helped other women become interested in aviation, their flying experience, how they intend to utilize this scholarship, how they intend to provide additional funding to cover the total cost of the flight training, their career goals in the helicopter industry and how this scholarship will help achieve those, and their financial need. Selection is based on evidence of intent to work in the helicopter industry.

Financial data   The stipend is $6,000.

Duration   The stipend is offered annually.

Additional information   Completed applications must include $40 to cover the cost of processing and mailing.

Number awarded   1 each year.

Deadline   September of each year.

[1318]
HENRY DAVID RESEARCH GRANT IN HUMAN REPRODUCTIVE BEHAVIOR AND POPULATION STUDIES

American Psychological Foundation
750 First Street, N.E.
Washington, DC 20002-4242
(202) 336-5843   Fax: (202) 336-5812
E-mail: foundation@apa.org
Web: www.apa.org/apf/funding/david.aspx

Summary   To provide funding to young psychologists (particularly women, minorities, and individuals with disabilities) who are interested in conducting research on reproductive behavior.

Eligibility   This program is open to doctoral students in psychology working on a dissertation and young psychologists who have no more than 7 years of postgraduate experience. Applicants must be interested in conducting research on human reproductive behavior or an area related to population concerns. Along with their application, they must submit a current curriculum vitae, 2 letters of recommendation, and an essay of 1 to 2 pages on their interest in human reproductive behavior or in population studies. The sponsor encourages applications from individuals who represent diversity in race, ethnicity, gender, age, disability, and sexual orientation.

Financial data   The grant is $1,500.

Duration   The grant is presented annually.

Number awarded   1 each year.

Deadline   February of each year.

[1319]
HERBERT AND BETTY CARNES FUND

American Ornithologists' Union
c/o Executive Officer
5405 Villa View Drive
Farmington, NM 87402
(505) 326-1579   E-mail: aou@aou.org
Web: www.aou.org/awards/research

Summary   To provide funding to female graduate students and scholars who are members of the American Ornithologists' Union (AOU) and interested in conducting research on avian biology.

Eligibility   This program is open to female AOU members who are graduate students, postdoctorates, or other researchers without access to major funding agencies. Applicants must be interested in conducting research on avian biology. They must be nonsmokers (have not smoked in at least the previous 6 months). Along with their application, they should send a cover letter (about 5 pages) describing their proposed project, a budget, and 1 letter of reference.

Selection is based on significance and originality of the research question, clarity of the objectives, feasibility of the plan of research, and appropriateness of the budget.

Financial data   The maximum award is $2,500 per year.

Duration   1 year; recipients may reapply for 1 additional award.

Number awarded   The sponsor awards a total of 28 to 30 grants each year.

Deadline   January of each year.

[1320]
HERBERT W. AND CORRINE CHILSTROM SCHOLARSHIP

Women of the Evangelical Lutheran Church in America
Attn: Scholarships
8765 West Higgins Road
Chicago, IL 60631-4101
(773) 380-2736   Toll Free: (800) 638-3522, ext. 2736
Fax: (773) 380-2419   E-mail: Women.elca@elca.org
Web: www.elca.org

Summary   To provide financial assistance to mature women who are studying for a second career in the ordained ministry in the Evangelical Lutheran Church of America (ELCA).

Eligibility   Applicants for this scholarship must be women who have experienced an interruption of at least 5 years in their education since college graduation and are currently entering the final year of an M.Div. program at an ELCA seminary. They must have been endorsed by the Synodical Candidacy Committee. Selection is based on academic achievement, personal commitment and determination to serve as a pastor in the ELCA, and financial need. U.S. citizenship is required.

Financial data   The maximum stipend is $2,000.

Duration   1 year.

Additional information   This scholarship was established in 1995 to honor Rev. Herbert W. Chilstrom and Rev. Corrine Chilstrom during the 25th anniversary year of the ordination of women in the predecessor bodies of the ELCA. Recipients must agree to serve for at least 3 years as an ELCA pastor after graduation from seminary.

Number awarded   1 each year.

Deadline   February of each year.

[1321]
HIGH PRIORITY, SHORT-TERM BRIDGE AWARDS IN DIABETES RESEARCH

Juvenile Diabetes Research Foundation International
Attn: Grant Administrator
26 Broadway, 14th Floor
New York, NY 10004
(212) 479-7572   Toll Free: (800) 533-CURE
Fax: (212) 785-9595   E-mail: info@jdrf.org
Web: www.jdrf.org/index.cfm?page_id=111715

Summary   To provide funding to scientists (especially women, minorities, and individuals with disabilities) who are interested in conducting diabetes-related research but have not yet received any support.

Eligibility   Applicants must have an M.D., D.M.D., D.V.M., Ph.D., or equivalent degree and have a full-time faculty position or equivalent at a college, university, medical school, or other research facility. They must have applied for grants previously and scored within 10% of the funding payline of a research funding agency but failed to receive support. Awards must be used to obtain new data to support the feasibility or validity of the research, address reviewers' concerns, or revise approaches to the research. There are no citizenship requirements. Applications are encouraged from women, members of minority groups underrepresented in the sciences, and people with disabilities. The proposed research may be conducted at foreign or domestic, for-profit or non-profit, or public or private institutions, including universities, colleges, hospitals, laboratories, units of state or local government, or eligible agencies of the federal government.

Financial data Awards are limited to $50,000 plus 10% indirect costs.

Duration 1 year; may be renewed 1 additional year.

Deadline February, June, or November of each year.

[1322]
HILL-ROM, CELESTE PHILLIPS FAMILY-CENTERED MATERNITY CARE AWARD

Association of Women's Health, Obstetric and Neonatal Nurses
Attn: Research Grants Program
2000 L Street, N.W., Suite 740
Washington, DC 20036
(202) 261-2431   Toll Free: (800) 673-8499, ext. 2431
Fax: (202) 728-0575
E-mail: ResearchPrograms@awhonn.org
Web: www.awhonn.org

Summary To provide funding for small research projects to members of the Association of Women's Health, Obstetric and Neonatal Nurses (AWHONN).

Eligibility This program is open to members of the association who are interested in conducting research related to women's health, obstetric, or neonatal nursing. Researchers who are currently principal investigators on a federally-funded grant, or who have already received an AWHONN-funded research grant within the past 5 years, are not eligible.

Financial data The grant is $10,000. Funds may not be used for indirect costs, tuition, computer hardware or printers, conference attendance, or salary for the principal investigator or other investigators.

Duration 1 year.

Additional information This program is funded by Hill-Rom.

Number awarded 1 each year.

Deadline November of each year.

[1323]
HORIZONS FOUNDATION SCHOLARSHIP PROGRAM

Women in Defense
c/o National Defense Industrial Association
2111 Wilson Boulevard, Suite 400
Arlington, VA 22201-3061
(703) 247-2552   Fax: (703) 522-1885
E-mail: wid@ndia.org
Web: wid.ndia.org/horizons/Pages/default.aspx

Summary To provide financial assistance to women (including those already working in national security fields)

who are upper-division or graduate students working on a degree related to the national security interests of the United States.

Eligibility This program is open to women who are already working in national security fields as well as women planning such careers. Applicants must 1) be currently enrolled at an accredited college or university, either full time or part time, as graduate students or upper-division undergraduates; 2) demonstrate financial need; 3) be U.S. citizens; 4) have a GPA of 3.25 or higher; and 5) demonstrate interest in preparing for a career related to national security. The preferred fields of study include business (as it relates to national security or defense), computer science, economics, engineering, government relations, international relations, law (as it relates to national security or defense), mathematics, military history, political science, physics, and security studies; others are considered if the applicant can demonstrate relevance to a career in national security or defense. Selection is based on academic achievement, participation in defense and national security activities, field of study, work experience, statements of objectives, recommendations, and financial need.

Financial data The stipend ranges up to $12,000.

Duration 1 year; renewable.

Additional information This program was established in 1988.

Number awarded Varies each year; recently, 3 of these scholarships were awarded: 1 at $12,000, 1 at $10,000, and 1 at $3,000. Since the program was established, 104 women have received more than $119,000 in support.

Deadline June of each year.

[1324]
HUBBLE FELLOWSHIPS

Space Telescope Science Institute
Attn: Hubble Fellowship Program Office
3700 San Martin Drive
Baltimore, MD 21218
(410) 338-4574   Fax: (410) 338-4211
E-mail: rjallen@stsci.edu
Web: www.stsci.edu

Summary To provide funding to women, minority, and other recent postdoctoral scientists who are interested in conducting research related to the Hubble Space Telescope or related missions of the National Aeronautics and Space Administration (NASA).

Eligibility This program is open to postdoctoral scientists who completed their doctoral degree within the past 3 years in astronomy, physics, or related disciplines. Applicants must be interested in conducting research related to NASA Cosmic Origins missions: the Hubble Space Telescope, Herschel Space Observatory, James Webb Space Telescope, Stratospheric Observatory for Infrared Astronomy, or the Spitzer Space Telescope. They may be of any nationality, provided that all research is conducted at U.S. institutions and that non-U.S. nationals have valid visas. Research may be theoretical, observational, or instrumental. Women and members of minority groups are strongly encouraged to apply.

Financial data Stipends are $58,500 for the first year, $59,500 for the second year, and $60,500 for the third year. Other benefits may include health insurance, relocation costs, and support for travel, equipment, and other direct costs of research.

Duration 3 years: an initial 1-year appointment and 2 annual renewals, contingent on satisfactory performance and availability of funds.

Additional information This program, funded by NASA, began in 1990 and was limited to work with the Hubble Space Telescope. A parallel program, called the Spitzer Fellowship, began in 2002 and was limited to work with the Spitzer Space Telescope. In 2009, those programs were combined into this single program, which was also broadened to include the other NASA Cosmic Origins missions. Fellows are required to be in residence at their host institution engaged in full-time research for the duration of the grant.

Number awarded Varies each year; recently, 17 of these fellowships were awarded.

Deadline June of each year.

[1325]
IMMIGRANT WOMEN PROGRAM INTERNSHIPS AT LEGAL MOMENTUM

Legal Momentum
Attn: Immigrant Women Program
1101 14th Street, N.W., Suite 300
Washington, DC 20005
(202) 326-0040   Fax: (202) 589-0511
E-mail: dcinternships@legalmomentum.org
Web: www.legalmomentum.org

Summary To provide work experience to students and recent graduates who are interested in working on the Legal Momentus's immigrant women program in Washington, D.C.

Eligibility The internship is open to undergraduates, graduate students, and recent graduates interested in an immigrant women internship at Legal Momentum. Applicants must be interested in working on a range of tasks, including researching and analyzing legislation; drafting letters, fact sheets, and articles; attending briefings and coalition meetings; answering requests for technical assistance; assisting with administrative tasks as needed; and coordinating the work of coalitions dealing with violence against women, welfare reform, child care, and immigrant women's rights. They should have a strong interest in women's legal rights. A love of feminist issues, politics, and hard work is useful and a working knowledge of the American political process is recommended. Women and men of all ethnic, cultural, economic, and sexual orientations who support feminist concerns are eligible. Bilingual individuals are especially encouraged to apply.

Financial data These are paid internships (stipend not specified).

Duration Interns are asked to work from 15 to 35 hours per week for 10 to 12 weeks. Positions are available in the fall, spring, or summer.

Additional information Legal Momentum was formerly known as the NOW Legal Defense and Education Fund.

Number awarded Varies each year.

Deadline Applications may be submitted at any time.

[1326]
INITIAL HELICOPTER SCHOLARSHIP

Women in Aviation, International
Attn: Scholarships
Morningstar Airport
3647 State Route 503 South
West Alexandria, OH 45381-9354
(937) 839-4647   Fax: (937) 839-4645
E-mail: scholarships@wai.org
Web: www.wai.org/education/scholarships.cfm

Summary To provide financial assistance to members of Women in Aviation, International (WAI) who are interested in completing a private helicopter rating.

Eligibility This program is open to women who are WAI members and interested in obtaining a private helicopter rating. Preference is given to applicants who have completed at least 5 hours logged in a helicopter. Along with their application, they must submit 2 letters of recommendation, a 500-word essay on their aviation history and goals, a resume, copies of all aviation licenses and medical certificates, and the last 3 pages of their pilot logbook (if applicable). Selection is based on achievements, attitude toward self and others, commitment to success, dedication to career, financial need, motivation, reliability, responsibility, and teamwork.

Financial data The stipend is $1,000.

Duration Training must be completed within 18 months.

Additional information WAI is a nonprofit professional organization dedicated to encouraging women to consider an aviation career and to providing educational outreach activities and networking resources to women active in the industry.

Number awarded 1 each year.

Deadline November of each year.

[1327]
INNOVATIONS IN CLINICAL RESEARCH AWARDS

Doris Duke Charitable Foundation
Attn: Grantmaking Programs
650 Fifth Avenue, 19th Floor
New York, NY 10019
(212) 974-7000   Fax: (212) 974-7590
E-mail: ddcf@aibs.org
Web: www.ddcf.org

Summary To provide funding to women, minority, and other investigators interested in conducting clinical research that may develop innovations in specified disease areas.

Eligibility This program is open to investigators who have received an M.D., Ph.D., M.D./Ph.D., or foreign equivalent and have a faculty appointment at a U.S. degree-granting institution (although U.S. citizenship is not required). Applicants must be interested in conducting innovative clinical research on a topic that changes annually but recently was limited to sickle cell disease; in other years, research was restricted to cardiovascular disease, stroke, blood disorders, or the development of diagnostics and therapeutic monitoring of AIDS in resource-poor countries. Preference is given to applicants who 1) work in other research areas, in an effort to bring new thinking to the field of sickle cell disease research; 2) are women or underrepresented minorities in medicine (Blacks or African Americans, Hispanics or Latinos, American Indians, Alaska Natives or Native Hawaiians); or 3) propose the following types of sickle cell disease research: drug discovery, genetic and genomic approaches to study variability in the severity of sickle cell disease, early phase corrective approaches such as gene therapy and transplantation of blood-forming cells, identification of new risks for disease complication, or development of new treatments drawing from innovations in other fields such as cancer research. Selection is based on originality and inventiveness of the concept and approach, relevance of the question posed to the field of sickle cell disease, potential for clinical application, and evidence of the investigator's potential to drive innovation in sickle cell disease clinical research.

Financial data Grants provide $150,000 per year for direct costs and $12,000 per year for indirect costs.

Duration 3 years.

Additional information This program began in 2000.

Number awarded Up to 9 each year. Since this program was established, it has awarded 49 grants worth approximately $12 million.

Deadline Letters of intent must be submitted by June of each year.

[1328]
INSTITUTE FOR SUPPLY MANAGEMENT DISTINGUISHED LEADERSHIP GRANTS

Institute for Supply Management
Attn: Vice President, Education
2055 East Centennial Circle
P.O. Box 22160
Tempe, AZ 85285-2160
(480) 752-6276, ext. 3105
Toll Free: (800) 888-6276, ext. 3105
Fax: (480) 752-7890   E-mail: ssturzl@ism.ws
Web: www.ism.ws

Summary To provide funding to distinguished scholars (especially women and members of other diverse groups) who are interested in conducting research in purchasing and materials management.

Eligibility This program is open to full-time faculty members who wish to conduct research that can be applied to the advancement of purchasing and materials management. Applicants should normally be senior full professors and have 16 to 25 years of teaching and research experience. They should also have a distinguished record of publication and leadership experience. The area of study for applicants may be purchasing, business, management, logistics, economics, industrial engineering, or a related field. Selection is based on teaching and research record, evidence of extensive academic and other professional leadership activities, evidence of significant contribution to the profession of supply management, service to other organizations such as editorial boards or academic organizations, evidence that the proposal will help the sponsoring organization over the longer term, and willingness to teach and/or speak for the organization as reasonably requested. The program encourages applications from a diverse population, regardless of gender, race, creed, age, ethnic or national origin, sexual orientation, or disability.

Financial data The grant is $25,000 per year.

Duration Both 1-year and multi-year projects are considered.

Additional information The sponsoring organization was previously known as the National Association of Purchasing Management.

Number awarded 1 or more each year.

Deadline January of each year.

[1329]
INSTITUTE FOR SUPPLY MANAGEMENT PROFESSIONAL RESEARCH AND COLLABORATION GRANTS

Institute for Supply Management
Attn: Vice President, Education
2055 East Centennial Circle
P.O. Box 22160
Tempe, AZ 85285-2160
(480) 752-6276, ext. 3105
Toll Free: (800) 888-6276, ext. 3105
Fax: (480) 752-7890   E-mail: ssturzl@ism.ws
Web: www.ism.ws

Summary To provide funding to established scholars (especially women and minorities) who are interested in conducting research in purchasing and materials management.

Eligibility This program is open to full-time faculty members who wish to conduct research that can be applied to the advancement of purchasing and materials management. Applicants should normally be at the associate or beginning full professor level and have 9 to 18 years of teaching and research experience. They should also have recognition for extensive publications. The area of study for applicants may be purchasing, business, management, logistics, economics, industrial engineering, or a related field. Selection is based on teaching and research record, evidence of significant academic leadership, evidence of significant contribution to the profession of supply management, previous involvement with the sponsoring organization at local or national levels, evidence that the proposal will help the organization over the longer term, and willingness to teach and/or speak for the organization as reasonably requested. The program encourages applications from a diverse population, regardless of gender, race, creed, age, ethnic or national origin, sexual orientation, or disability.

Financial data The grant is $15,000 for 1-year projects or up to $12,000 per year for longer projects.

Duration Both 1-year and multi-year (up to 3 year) projects are considered.

Additional information The sponsoring organization was previously known as the National Association of Purchasing Management.

Number awarded 1 or more each year.

Deadline January of each year.

[1330]
INSTITUTE FOR SUPPLY MANAGEMENT PROFESSIONAL RESEARCH DEVELOPMENT GRANTS

Institute for Supply Management
Attn: Vice President, Education
2055 East Centennial Circle
P.O. Box 22160
Tempe, AZ 85285-2160
(480) 752-6276, ext. 3105
Toll Free: (800) 888-6276, ext. 3105
Fax: (480) 752-7890   E-mail: ssturzl@ism.ws
Web: www.ism.ws

Summary To provide funding to women, minority, and other emerging scholars who are interested in conducting research in purchasing and materials management.

Eligibility This program is open to full-time faculty members who wish to conduct research that can be applied to the advancement of purchasing and materials management. Applicants should normally be at the assistant or beginning associate professor level and have 2 to 8 years of teaching and research experience. They should also have publication experience beyond the doctoral degree. The area of study for applicants may be purchasing, business, management, logistics, economics, industrial engineering, or a related field. Selection is based less on what the applicants intend to do with the project and more on what they can contribute to the profession over time; factors considered include the project proposal, research and teaching record, potential impact on the near-term needs of the profession, and potential impact on the field in the next 5 to 10 years. The program encourages applications from a diverse population, regardless of gender, race, creed, age, ethnic or national origin, sexual orientation, or disability.

Financial data The grant is $10,000.

Duration 1 year; a second year of support may be considered.

Additional information The sponsoring organization was previously known as the National Association of Purchasing Management.

Number awarded 2 each year.

Deadline January of each year.

[1331]
INTERNATIONAL AND AREA STUDIES FELLOWSHIPS

American Council of Learned Societies
Attn: Office of Fellowships and Grants
633 Third Avenue
New York, NY 10017-6795
(212) 697-1505   Fax: (212) 949-8058
E-mail: fellowships@acls.org
Web: www.acls.org/programs/acls

Summary To provide funding to women, minority, and other postdoctoral scholars interested in conducting humanities-related research on the societies and cultures of Asia, Africa, the Middle East, Latin America and the Caribbean, eastern Europe, and the former Soviet Union.

Eligibility This program is open to U.S. citizens and residents who have lived in the United States for at least 3 years. Applicants must have a Ph.D. degree and not have received

supported research leave time for at least 3 years prior to the start of the proposed research. They must be interested in conducting humanities and humanities-related social science research on the societies and cultures of Asia, Africa, the Middle East, Latin America and the Caribbean, eastern Europe, or the former Soviet Union. Selection is based on the intellectual merit of the proposed research and the likelihood that it will produce significant and innovative scholarship. Applications are particularly invited from women and members of minority groups.

Financial data The maximum grant is $60,000 for full professors and equivalent, $40,000 for associate professors and equivalent, or $35,000 for assistant professors and equivalent. These fellowships may not be held concurrently with another major fellowship.

Duration 6 to 12 months.

Additional information This program is jointly supported by the American Council of Learned Societies (ACLS) and the Social Science Research Council (SSRC), with funding provided by the National Endowment for the Humanities (NEH).

Number awarded Up to 10 each year.

Deadline September of each year.

[1332]
INVESTIGATORS IN PATHOGENESIS OF INFECTIOUS DISEASE

Burroughs Wellcome Fund
21 T.W. Alexander Drive, Suite 100
P.O. Box 13901
Research Triangle Park, NC 27709-3901
(919) 991-5100   Fax: (919) 991-5160
E-mail: info@bwfund.org
Web: www.bwfund.org

Summary To provide funding to women, minority, and other physician/scientists in the United States and Canada who wish to conduct research on pathogenesis, with a focus on the intersection of human and pathogen biology.

Eligibility This program is open to established physicians and scientists who are citizens or permanent residents of the United States or Canada and affiliated with accredited degree-granting U.S. or Canadian medical schools. Applicants must be interested in conducting research projects that hold potential for advancing significantly the biochemical, pharmacological, immunological, and molecular biological understanding of how infectious agents and the human body interact. Although work on AIDS, malaria, and tuberculosis is not excluded, preference is given to research shedding new light on unexplored pathogenesis. Research on understudied infectious diseases, including pathogenic fungi, protozoan and metazoan diseases, and emerging infections, is of especial interest. Candidates must have an M.D., D.V.M., or Ph.D. degree and be tenure-track investigators as an assistant professor or equivalent at a degree-granting institution. Each institution (including its medical school, graduate schools, and all affiliated hospitals and research institutes) may nominate up to 2 candidates. Institutions that nominate a researcher who has a D.V.M. are allowed 3 nominations. The sponsor also encourages institutions to nominate underrepresented minorities and women. Selection is based on qualifications of the candidate and potential to conduct innovative research; demonstration of an established record of independent research; and quality and originality of the proposed research and its potential to advance understanding of fundamental issues of how infectious agents and human hosts interact.

Financial data The grant provides $100,000 per year.

Duration 5 years.

Additional information This program was established in 2001 as a replacement for several former programs: New Investigator and Scholar Awards in Molecular Pathogenic Mycology, New Investigator and Scholar Awards in Molecular Parasitology, and New Initiatives in Malaria Awards. Awardees are required to devote at least 75% of their time to research-related activities.

Number awarded Varies each year; recently, 6 of these grants were awarded.

Deadline October of each year.

[1333]
IOTA SIGMA PI NATIONAL HONORARY MEMBER

Iota Sigma Pi
c/o Dr. Sara Paisner, National Director for Professional
  Awards
Lord Corporation
110 Lord Drive
Cary, NC 27511
(919) 469-2500, ext. 2490   Fax: (919) 469-9688
E-mail: sara.paisner@lord.com
Web: www.iotasigmapi.info

Summary To recognize exceptional and significant achievement by women working in chemistry or allied fields.

Eligibility Nominees for the award must be outstanding women chemists. They may be from any country and need not be members of Iota Sigma Pi. Each active chapter is entitled to make only 1 nomination, but individual members, individual chemists, or groups of chemists may make independent nominations if properly documented. The nomination dossier must contain the candidate's name and address, educational and professional background, membership in professional societies, area of specialization or research, honors, awards, citations, publications, and letters of recommendation.

Financial data The award consists of $1,500, a certificate, and a lifetime waiver of Iota Sigma Pi dues.

Duration The award is granted triennially (2014, 2017, etc.).

Additional information This award was first presented in 1921.

Number awarded 1 every 3 years.

Deadline Nominations must be submitted by February of the year of award.

[1334]
J. CORDELL BREED AWARD FOR WOMEN LEADERS

Society of Automotive Engineers
Attn: Award Program Staff
400 Commonwealth Drive
Warrendale, PA 15096-0001
(724) 776-4970   Toll Free: (877) 606-7323
Fax: (724) 776-0790   E-mail: awards@sae.org
Web: www.sae.org/news/awards/list/wec

Summary To recognize and reward female members of the Society of Automotive Engineering (SAE) who have been active in the mobility industry.

Eligibility This award is presented to women who participate in and are involved in SAE activities. Nominees must 1) exhibit outstanding service to their company and community; 2) demonstrate excellent leadership as a supervisor, manager, or member in a team environment; 3) display innovation and uniqueness in achieving corporate and personal goals; 4) provide important engineering or technical contributions to the mobility industry; 5) demonstrate strong interpersonal skills; and 6) have overcome adversity.

Financial data The award consists of an engraved plaque and an honorarium of $2,000.

Duration The award is presented annually.

Additional information This award was established in 1999 by the SAE Women Engineers Committee (WEC).

Number awarded 1 each year.

Deadline Nominations must be submitted by July of each year.

[1335]
JAMES H. DUNN, JR. MEMORIAL FELLOWSHIP PROGRAM

Office of the Governor
Attn: Department of Central Management Services
503 William G. Stratton Building
Springfield, IL 62706
(217) 524-1381   Fax: (217) 558-4497
TDD: (217) 785-3979
Web: www.ilga.gov/commission/lru/internships.html

Summary To provide an opportunity for recent college graduates (especially women, minorities, and individuals with disabilities) to intern at the Illinois Governor's office.

Eligibility This program in open to residents of any state who have completed a bachelor's degree and are interested in working in the Illinois Governor's office or in various agencies under the Governor's jurisdiction. Applicants may have majored in any field, but they must be able to demonstrate a substantial commitment to excellence as evidenced by academic honors, leadership ability, extracurricular activities, and involvement in community or public service. Along with their application, they must submit 1) a 500-word personal statement on the qualities or attributes they will bring to the program, their career goals or plans, how their selection for this program would assist them in achieving those goals, and what they expect to gain from the program; and 2) a 1,000-word essay in which they identify and analyze a public issue that they feel has great impact on state government. A particular goal of the program is to achieve affirmative action through the nomination of qualified minorities, women, and persons with disabilities.

Financial data The stipend is $2,611 per month.

Duration 1 year, beginning in August.

Additional information Assignments are in Springfield and, to a limited extent, in Chicago or Washington, D.C.

Number awarded Varies each year.

Deadline February of each year.

[1336]
JAN JONES MEMORIAL SCHOLARSHIP

International Council of Air Shows
Attn: ICAS Foundation, Inc.
751 Miller Drive, S.E., Suite F-4
Leesburg, VA 20175
(703) 779-8510   Fax: (703) 779-8511
E-mail: scholarships@icasfoundation.org
Web: www.icasfoundation.org/scholarships_jones.htm

Summary   To provide financial assistance to female pilots interested in obtaining aerobatic flight training.

Eligibility   This program is open to women who have a private pilot certificate and are interested in acquiring aerobatic flight training. Applicants must submit a 1-page essay on why they want to receive this scholarship, how the funds will be used, their goals, and why they wish to learn aerobatics.

Financial data   The stipend is $2,000.

Duration   1 year.

Number awarded   1 each year.

Deadline   December of each year.

[1337]
JDRF ADVANCED POSTDOCTORAL FELLOWSHIPS IN DIABETES RESEARCH

Juvenile Diabetes Research Foundation International
Attn: Grant Administrator
26 Broadway, 14th Floor
New York, NY 10004
(212) 479-7572   Toll Free: (800) 533-CURE
Fax: (212) 785-9595   E-mail: info@jdrf.org
Web: www.jdrf.org/index.cfm?page_id=111715

Summary   To provide advanced research training to women, minority, and other scientists who are beginning their professional careers and are interested in conducting research on the causes, treatment, prevention, or cure of diabetes or its complications.

Eligibility   This program is open to postdoctorates who show extraordinary promise for a career in diabetes research. Applicants must have received their first doctoral degree (M.D., Ph.D., D.M.D., or D.V.M.) within the past 5 years and should have completed 1 to 3 years of postdoctoral training. They may not have a faculty appointment. There are no citizenship requirements. Applications are encouraged from women, members of minority groups underrepresented in the sciences, and people with disabilities. The proposed research training may be conducted at foreign or domestic, for-profit or nonprofit, or public or private institutions, including universities, colleges, hospitals, laboratories, units of state or local government, or eligible agencies of the federal government. Selection is based on the applicant's previous experience and academic record; the caliber of the proposed research; the quality of the mentor, training program, and environment; and the applicant's potential to obtain an independent research position in the future. Fellows who obtain a faculty position at any time during the term of the fellowship may apply for a transition award for support during their first year as a faculty member.

Financial data   The total award is $90,000 per year, including salary that depends on number of years of experience, ranging from $37,740 for zero up to $52,068 for 7 or more years of experience. In the first year only, funds in excess of the grant may be used for travel to scientific meetings (up to $2,000), journal subscriptions, books, training courses, laboratory supplies, equipment, or purchase of a personal computer (up to $2,000). Indirect costs are not allowed. Fellows who receive a faculty position are granted a transition award of up to $110,000 for 1 year, including up to 10% in indirect costs.

Duration   Up to 3 years.

Deadline   January or July of each year.

[1338]
JDRF SCHOLAR AWARDS

Juvenile Diabetes Research Foundation International
Attn: Grant Administrator
26 Broadway, 14th Floor
New York, NY 10004
(212) 479-7572   Toll Free: (800) 533-CURE
Fax: (212) 785-9595   E-mail: info@jdrf.org
Web: www.jdrf.org/index.cfm?page_id=111715

Summary   To provide funding to established independent physician scientists (particularly women, minorities, and individuals with disabilities) who are interested in conducting basic or clinical diabetes-related research.

Eligibility   This program is open to established investigators in diabetes-related research who have an M.D., D.M.D., D.O., Ph.D., D.V.M., or equivalent degree and an independent investigator position at a university, health science center, or comparable institution. Normally, applicants should have at least 7 years of relevant experience since receiving their doctoral degree. They must be willing to take risks and attempt new approaches to accelerate Type 1 diabetes research. This program is not intended to expand the funding of scientists already well supported for exploring this concept. There are no citizenship requirements. Applications are encouraged from women, members of minority groups underrepresented in the sciences, and people with disabilities. The proposed research may be conducted at foreign or domestic, for-profit or nonprofit, or public or private institutions, including universities, colleges, hospitals, laboratories, units of state or local government, or eligible agencies of the federal government. Selection is based on relevance of the research to and impact on the mission of the Juvenile Diabetes Research Foundation (JDRF); innovation, creativity, and the potential for future innovation relative to the applicant's career stage; and the applicant's motivation, enthusiasm, and intellectual energy to pursue a challenging problem.

Financial data   The total award may be up to $250,000 each year, including indirect costs.

Duration   Up to 5 years.

Number awarded   Up to 4 each year.

Deadline   An intent to submit must be received by August of each year. Completed applications are due in September.

[1339]
JOAN KELLY MEMORIAL PRIZE IN WOMEN'S HISTORY

American Historical Association
Attn: Book Prize Administrator
400 A Street, S.E.
Washington, DC 20003-3889
(202) 544-2422   Fax: (202) 544-8307
E-mail: info@historians.org
Web: www.historians.org

Summary To recognize and reward outstanding works in women's history and/or feminist theory that were published during the previous year.

Eligibility The prize is open to works in any chronological period, any geographical location, or any area of feminist theory that incorporate an historical perspective. Preference is given to books that demonstrate originality of research, creativity of insight, graceful stylistic presentation, analytical skills, and recognition of the important role of sex and gender in the historical process.

Financial data The prize is $1,000.

Duration The award is granted annually.

Additional information This prize was established in 1984 by the Coordinating Committee on Women in the Historical Profession and the Conference Group on Women's History (now the Coordinating Council for Women in History) and is administered by the American Historical Association.

Number awarded 1 each year.

Deadline May of each year.

[1340]
JOEL ELKES RESEARCH AWARD

American College of Neuropsychopharmacology
Attn: Executive Office
5034-A Thoroughbred Lane
Brentwood, TN 37027
(615) 324-2360   Fax: (615) 523-1715
E-mail: acnp@acnp.org
Web: www.acnp.org/programs/awards.aspx

Summary To recognize and reward women, minority, and other young scientists who have contributed outstanding clinical or translational research to neuropsychopharmacology.

Eligibility This award is available to scientists who are younger than 50 years of age. Nominees must have made an outstanding clinical or translational contribution to neuropsychopharmacology. The contribution may be based on a single discovery or a cumulative body of work. Emphasis is placed on contributions that further understanding of self-regulatory processes as they affect mental function and behavior in disease and well-being. Membership in the American College of Neuropsychopharmacology (ACNP) is not required. Nomination of women and minorities is highly encouraged.

Financial data The award consists of an expense-paid trip to the ACNP annual meeting, a monetary honorarium, and a plaque.

Duration The award is presented annually.

Additional information This award was first presented in 1986.

Number awarded 1 each year.

Deadline Nominations must be submitted by June of each year.

[1341]
JOHN V. KRUTILLA RESEARCH STIPEND

Resources for the Future
Attn: Coordinator for Academic Programs
1616 P Street, N.W., Suite 600
Washington, DC 20036-1400
(202) 328-5088   Fax: (202) 939-3460
E-mail: krutilla-award@rff.org
Web: www.rff.org/About_RFF/Pages/default.aspx

Summary To provide funding for research related to environmental and resource economics to young scholars (particularly women and minorities).

Eligibility This program is open to scholars who received their doctoral degree within the past 5 years. Applicants must be interested in conducting research related to environmental and resource economics. They must submit a short description of the proposed research, a curriculum vitae, and a letter of recommendation. Women and minority candidates are strongly encouraged to apply.

Financial data The grant is $9,000.

Duration 1 year.

Additional information This award was first presented in 2006.

Number awarded 1 each year.

Deadline February of each year.

[1342]
JOSEPH B. GITTLER AWARD

American Psychological Foundation
750 First Street, N.E.
Washington, DC 20002-4242
(202) 336-5843   Fax: (202) 336-5812
E-mail: foundation@apa.org
Web: www.apa.org/apf/funding/gittler.aspx

Summary To recognize and reward scholars and graduate students in psychology (particularly women and members of other diverse groups) who have made outstanding contributions to the philosophical foundations of the discipline.

Eligibility This award is available to scholars and graduate students whose body of work or whose individual work has transformed the philosophical foundations of psychological knowledge. Self-nominations are welcome. Selection is based on conformance with stated program goals and magnitude of contributions The sponsor encourages nominations of individuals who represent diversity in race, ethnicity, gender, age, disability, and sexual orientation.

Financial data The award is $10,000.

Duration The award is presented annually.

Additional information This award was first presented in 2008.

Number awarded 1 each year.

Deadline Nominations must be submitted by May of each year.

[1343]
JUDY GRAHN AWARD FOR LESBIAN NONFICTION

Publishing Triangle
332 Bleecker Street, D36
New York, NY 10014
E-mail: awards@publishingtriangle.org
Web: www.publishingtriangle.org/awards.asp

Summary To recognize and reward outstanding lesbian nonfiction writers or writings.

Eligibility This award is presented to authors of books that have had significant influence on lesbians. For the purposes of this award, "lesbian nonfiction" is defined as nonfiction affecting lesbian lives. The book may be written by a lesbian, or about lesbians or lesbian culture, or both. It must have been published in the United States or Canada.

Financial data The award is $1,000.

Duration The award is presented annually.

Additional information The Publishing Triangle is an association of lesbians and gay men in publishing. This award was first presented in 1997. Current members of the Publishing Triangle may nominate authors for free; all others must pay a $35 fee.

Number awarded 1 each year.

Deadline November of each year.

[1344]
JULIUS AXELROD MENTORSHIP AWARD

American College of Neuropsychopharmacology
Attn: Executive Office
5034-A Thoroughbred Lane
Brentwood, TN 37027
(615) 324-2360　　　　　　　　　Fax: (615) 523-1715
E-mail: acnp@acnp.org
Web: www.acnp.org/programs/awards.aspx

Summary To recognize and reward women, minority, and other members of the American College of Neuropsychopharmacology (ACNP) who have demonstrated outstanding mentoring of young scientists.

Eligibility This award is available to ACNP members who have made an outstanding contribution to neuropsychopharmacology by mentoring and developing young scientists into leaders in the field. Nominations must be accompanied by letters of support from up to 3 people who have been mentored by the candidate. Nomination of women and minorities is highly encouraged.

Financial data The award consists of a monetary honorarium and a plaque.

Duration The award is presented annually.

Additional information This award was first presented in 2004.

Number awarded 1 each year.

Deadline Nominations must be submitted by June of each year.

[1345]
JUVENILE DIABETES RESEARCH FOUNDATION INNOVATIVE GRANTS

Juvenile Diabetes Research Foundation International
Attn: Grant Administrator
26 Broadway, 14th Floor
New York, NY 10004
(212) 479-7572　　　　　　　Toll Free: (800) 533-CURE
Fax: (212) 785-9595　　　　　　E-mail: info@jdrf.org
Web: www.jdrf.org/index.cfm?page_id=111715

Summary To provide funding to scientists (especially women, minorities, and individuals with disabilities) who are interested in conducting innovative diabetes-related research.

Eligibility Applicants must have an M.D., D.M.D., D.V.M., Ph.D., or equivalent degree and have a full-time faculty position or equivalent at a college, university, medical school, or other research facility. They must be seeking "seed" money for investigative work based on a sound hypothesis for which preliminary data are insufficient for a regular research grant but that are likely to lead to important results for the treatment of diabetes and its complications. Applicants must specifically explain how the proposal is innovative. Selection is based on whether 1) the proposed research is innovative; 2) the underlying premise, goal, or hypothesis is plausible; 3) the proposed research can be completed in 1 year; and 4) the proposed research is relevant to the mission of the Juvenile Diabetes Research Foundation and its potential impact. There are no citizenship requirements. Applications are encouraged from women, members of minority groups underrepresented in the sciences, and people with disabilities. The proposed research may be conducted at foreign or domestic, for-profit or nonprofit, or public or private institutions, including universities, colleges, hospitals, laboratories, units of state or local government, or eligible agencies of the federal government.

Financial data Awards are limited to $100,000 plus 10% indirect costs.

Duration 1 year; nonrenewable.

Deadline January or July of each year.

[1346]
KATHERINE E. WEIMER AWARD

American Physical Society
Attn: Division of Plasma Physics
One Physics Ellipse
College Park, MD 20740-3844
(301) 209-3200　　　　　　　Fax: (301) 209-0865
Web: www.apsdpp.org

Summary To recognize and reward women who have made outstanding contributions to plasma science research.

Eligibility This award is available to female plasma scientists who received their Ph.D. within the previous 10 years. Nominees must have made outstanding achievements in plasma science research.

Financial data The award consists of $2,000, a certificate citing the contributions of the recipient, and an allowance for travel to the meeting of the American Physical Society (APS) at which the award is presented.

Duration The award is presented triennially (2014, 2017, etc.).

Additional information This prize was established in 2001.

Number awarded 1 every 3 years.

Deadline March of the year of the award.

[1347]
KENNEDY CENTER INTERNSHIP

Sigma Alpha Iota Philanthropies, Inc.
One Tunnel Road
Asheville, NC 28805
(828) 251-0606   Fax: (828) 251-0644
E-mail: nh@sai-national.org
Web: www.sigmaalphaiota.org

Summary To provide summer internships at the Kennedy Center to members of Sigma Alpha Iota (an organization of women musicians).

Eligibility This program is open to student members of the organization who are interested in a summer internship at the Institute for Arts Management at the John F. Kennedy Center for the Performing Arts in Washington, D.C. Applicants must be juniors, seniors, graduate students, or graduates out of school for less than 2 years.

Financial data The stipend is $800 per month.

Duration 3 months during the summer.

Additional information Assignments are full time, with possible college credit available.

Number awarded 1 or more each year.

Deadline January of each year.

[1348]
KFW ARTIST ENRICHMENT GRANT PROGRAM

Kentucky Foundation for Women
Heyburn Building
332 West Broadway, Suite 1215-A
Louisville, KY 40202-2184
(502) 562-0045   Toll Free: (866) 654-7564
Fax: (502) 561-0420   E-mail: info@kfw.org
Web: www.kfw.org/artenr.html

Summary To support women in Kentucky who wish to promote positive social change through feminist expression in the arts.

Eligibility This program is open to women who have resided in Kentucky for at least 1 year and are artists at any stage in their career able to demonstrate potential in terms of quality of work and an understanding of the power of art for social change. Applicants must be seeking funding for a range of activities, including artistic development, artist residencies, the exploration of new areas or techniques, or bu9ilding a body of work. In the selection process, the following criteria are considered: artwork in the sample is strong, highly original, and reflects feminism and social change; the proposed activities will further the applicant's development as a feminist social change artist; application and work sample demonstrate applicant's understanding and practice of feminism; application and work sample demonstrate a clear understanding of the relationship between art and social change; work plan, timeline, and budget are clear, detailed, and realistic; and applicant's ability to complete the proposed activities in clearly shown. If applications are of equal artistic merit, priority is given to first-time applicants, women from rural and inner-city areas, women of color (especially African

American women), lesbians, low-income women, women who did not complete high school, and women with disabilities.

Financial data Grants may range from $1,000 to $7,500, but most average between $2,000 and $4,000.

Duration Up to 1 year.

Additional information The foundation was established in 1985. Funding is not provided for general operating costs for organizations; for-profit organizations; tuition costs or living expenses while working toward a degree; endowment or capital campaigns; projects that do not focus on changing the lives of women in Kentucky; the promotion of religious doctrines; non-art related expenses, such as overdue bills or taxes; or work conducted by artists or organizations that have not resided in Kentucky for at least 1 year.

Number awarded Varies each year; recently, 45 of these grants were awarded. A total of $100,000 is available annually.

Deadline August of each year.

[1349]
KITTY ERNST AWARD

American College of Nurse-Midwives
Attn: Associate Director
8403 Colesville Road, Suite 1550
Silver Spring, MD 20910-6374
(240) 485-1800   Fax: (240) 485-1818
Web: www.midwife.org/awards.cfm

Summary To recognize and reward recent members of the American College of Nurse-Midwives (ACNM) who have made outstanding contributions to midwifery.

Eligibility Nominees for this award must be ACNM members who have been certified nurse midwives (CNMs) or certified midwives (CMs) for less than 10 years. They must have demonstrated innovative, creative endeavors in midwifery and/or women's health clinical practice, education, administration, or research.

Financial data A monetary award is presented.

Duration The award is presented annually.

Additional information This award was first presented in 1998.

Number awarded 1 each year.

Deadline January of each year.

[1350]
KPMG OUTSTANDING DISSERTATION AWARD GENDER SECTION

American Accounting Association
Attn: Gender Issues and Worklife Balance Section
5717 Bessie Drive
Sarasota, FL 34233-2399
(941) 921-7747   Fax: (941) 923-4093
E-mail: info@aaahq.org
Web: aaahq.org/awards/GenderIssuesAwards.htm

Summary To recognize and reward outstanding dissertations on gender issues in accounting.

Eligibility This competition is open to authors of dissertations completed in the prior calendar year. Manuscripts need not be focused solely on gender issues and worklife balance, but they must include some consideration of those topics.

Financial data The award is $1,000.

Duration The award is presented annually.

Additional information This award is supported by the KPMG Foundation.

Number awarded 1 each year.

Deadline February of each year.

[1351]
KPMG OUTSTANDING PUBLISHED MANUSCRIPT AWARD GENDER SECTION

American Accounting Association
Attn: Gender Issues and Worklife Balance Section
5717 Bessie Drive
Sarasota, FL 34233-2399
(941) 921-7747   Fax: (941) 923-4093
E-mail: info@aaahq.org
Web: aaahq.org/awards/GenderIssuesAwards.htm

Summary To recognize and reward outstanding research publications on gender issues in accounting.

Eligibility This competition is open to authors of articles published in the prior calendar year. Manuscripts need not be focused solely on gender issues and worklife balance, but they must include some consideration of those topics. At least 1 of the authors must be a member of the Gender Issues and Worklife Balance section of the American Accounting Association.

Financial data The award is $1,000.

Duration The award is presented annually.

Additional information This award is supported by the KPMG Foundation.

Number awarded 1 each year.

Deadline February of each year.

[1352]
LAWRENCE FELLOWS IN THE LIBERAL ARTS AND SCIENCES

Lawrence University
Office of the Provost
711 East Bold Way
Appleton, WI 54911-5626
(920) 832-6528   Fax: (920) 832-6978
E-mail: david.burrows@lawrence.edu
Web: www.lawrence.edu/dept/fellows

Summary To provide an opportunity for recent postdoctorates (particularly women and minorities) to teach and conduct research at Lawrence University in Appleton, Wisconsin.

Eligibility This program is open to scholars in the liberal arts and sciences who completed a Ph.D. (or M.Mus. or M.F.A.) within the past 5 years. Applicants must be interested in teaching and conducting research at Lawrence University. They should submit a letter of interest (including teaching and research statements), curriculum vitae, and 3 letters of recommendation. Applications from women and individuals of diverse backgrounds are especially encouraged.

Financial data The stipend is $36,000 per year; benefits are included and an additional $2,500 is provided for research, travel, and other initiatives.

Duration 2 years.

Additional information This program began in 2005. Fellows teach 3 courses in the first year and 4 in the second

year. They participate in a faculty development program and are encouraged to engage in tutorials and research projects with undergraduates as well as teaching and research collaborations with faculty.

Number awarded Normally, 8 each year.

Deadline Applications are accepted beginning in May of each year and are received until all positions are filled.

[1353]
LEGISLATIVE POLICY INTERNSHIPS AT LEGAL MOMENTUM

Legal Momentum
Attn: Legal Department
1101 14th Street, N.W., Suite 300
Washington, DC 20005
(202) 326-0040   Fax: (202) 589-0511
E-mail: dcinternships@legalmomentum.org
Web: www.legalmomentum.org

Summary To provide work experience to students and recent graduates (particularly women) who are interested in working on legislative policy issues at Legal Momentum in Washington, D.C.

Eligibility The internship is open to undergraduates, graduate students, and recent graduates interested in working on legislative policy issues at Legal Momentum. Issues covered include poverty and welfare reform, immigrant women (including immigration law reform and cultural diversity issues), violence against women, and child care. Applicants must be interested in working on a range of tasks, including researching and analyzing legislation; drafting letters, fact sheets, and articles; attending briefings and coalition meetings; answering requests for technical assistance; assisting with administrative tasks as needed; and coordinating the work of coalitions dealing with issues of concern to the office. They should have a strong interest in women's legal rights. A love of feminist issues, politics, and hard work is useful and a working knowledge of the American political process is recommended. Women and men of all ethnic, cultural, economic, and sexual orientations who support feminist concerns are eligible. Bilingual individuals are especially encouraged to apply.

Financial data These are paid internships (stipend not specified).

Duration Interns are encouraged to work from 15 to 35 hours per week for 10 to 12 weeks. Positions are available in the fall, spring, or summer.

Additional information Legal Momentum was formerly known as the NOW Legal Defense and Education Fund.

Number awarded Varies each year.

Deadline Applications may be submitted at any time.

[1354]
LESBIAN WRITERS FUND AWARDS

Astraea Lesbian Foundation for Justice
Attn: Program Director
116 East 16th Street, Seventh Floor
New York, NY 10003
(212) 529-8021   Fax: (212) 982-3321
E-mail: grants@astraeafoundation.org
Web: www.astraeafoundation.org

Summary To recognize and reward lesbian writers.

Eligibility These awards are presented to emerging lesbian writers of poetry and fiction who reside in the United States. Applicants must have published at least 1 piece of their writing (in any genre) in a newspaper, magazine, journal, or anthology, but no more than 1 book. Their work must include some lesbian content. Submissions may consist of up to 20 pages of fiction (a novel or collection of short stories) or at least 10 but no more than 15 pages of poetry.

Financial data Awards are either $10,000 or $1,500; honorable mentions are $100.

Additional information This fund was established in 1991. It includes the *Claire of the Moon* Award for Fiction, the Loving Lesbians Award for Fiction, and the Loving Lesbians Award for Poetry. Requests for applications must be accompanied by a self-addressed stamped envelope.

Number awarded Varies each year; recently, 12 of these grants were awarded: 2 at $10,000 (1 for fiction and 1 for poetry), 4 at $1,500 (2 for fiction and 2 for poetry), and 6 honorable mentions (3 for fiction and 3 for poetry).

Deadline February of each year.

[1355]
LIBRARY OF CONGRESS JUNIOR FELLOWS PROGRAM

Library of Congress
Library Services
Attn: Junior Fellows Program Coordinator
101 Independence Avenue, S.E., Room LM-642
Washington, DC 20540-4600
(202) 707-0901   Fax: (202) 707-6269
E-mail: jrfell@loc.gov
Web: www.loc.gov/hr/jrfellows/index.html

Summary To provide summer work experience at the Library of Congress (LC) to upper-division students, graduate students, and recent graduates, particularly women, minorities, and persons with disabilities.

Eligibility This program is open to U.S. citizens with subject expertise in the following areas: American history, including veterans and military history; American popular culture; area studies (African, Asian, European, Hispanic, Middle Eastern); bibliographic description and access; film, television, and radio; folklife; geography and maps; history of photography; history of popular and applied graphic arts, architecture, and design; manuscript collections processing; music; preservation and conservation; rare books and manuscripts; science, technology, and business; serials and government publications and newspapers; or sound recordings. Applicants must 1) be juniors or seniors at an accredited college or university, 2) be graduate students, or 3) have completed their degree in the past year. Applications from women, minorities, and persons with disabilities are particularly encouraged. Selection is based on academic achievement, letters of recommendation, and an interview.

Financial data Fellows are paid a taxable stipend of $300 per week.

Duration 3 months, beginning in either May or June. Fellows work a 40-hour week.

Additional information Fellows work with primary source materials and assist selected divisions at LC in the organization and documentation of archival collections, production of finding aids and bibliographic records, preparation of materials for preservation and service, completion of bibliographical research, and digitization of LC's historical collections.

Number awarded Varies each year; recently, 6 of these internships were awarded.

Deadline March of each year.

[1356]
LINDA FENNER YOUNG WOMEN'S SCHOLARSHIP

Allied Jewish Federation of Colorado
Attn: Donor Relationship Manager
300 South Dahlia Street, Suite 300
Denver, CO 80246-8118
(303) 321-3399   Fax: (303) 322-8328
E-mail: federation@AJFcolorado.org
Web: www.jewishcolorado.org/page.aspx?id=240413

Summary To provide funding for professional development activities to young Jewish women in Colorado.

Eligibility This program is open to female residents of Colorado between 21 and 45 years of age. Applicants must have been identified as a leader or someone with leadership potential in the Jewish community. They must be interested in attending educational conferences, missions to Israel, or other young adult program that will develop their leadership skills in order to better the Jewish community.

Financial data The grant is $2,500.

Duration These are 1-time grants.

Additional information This program is supported by the Jewish Community Foundation, (303) 316-6469.

Number awarded 1 or more each year.

Deadline April of each year.

[1357]
LIZETTE PETERSON-HOMER INJURY PREVENTION RESEARCH GRANT

American Psychological Foundation
750 First Street, N.E.
Washington, DC 20002-4242
(202) 336-5843   Fax: (202) 336-5812
E-mail: foundation@apa.org
Web: www.apa.org/apf/funding/peterson-homer.aspx

Summary To provide funding to women and other graduate students and faculty from diverse groups who are interested in conducting research related to the prevention of injuries in children.

Eligibility This program is open to graduate students and faculty interested in conducting research that focuses on the prevention of physical injury in children and young adults through accidents, violence, abuse, or suicide. Applicants must submit a 100-word abstract, description of the project, detailed budget, curriculum vitae, and letter from the supporting faculty supervisor (if the applicant is a student). Selection is based on conformance with stated program goals, magnitude of incremental contribution, quality of proposed work, and applicant's demonstrated scholarship and research competence. The sponsor encourages applications from individuals who represent diversity in race, ethnicity, gender, age, disability, and sexual orientation.

Financial data Grants up to $5,000 are available.

Additional information This program was established in 1999 as the Rebecca Routh Coon Injury Research Award.

The current name was adopted in 2003. It is supported by Division 54 (Society of Pediatric Psychology) of the American Psychological Association and the American Psychological Foundation.

Number awarded   1 each year.

Deadline   September of each year.

[1358]
LONE STAR RISING CAREER SCHOLARSHIP

Association for Women Geoscientists
Attn: AWG Foundation
12000 North Washington Street, Suite 285
Thornton, CO 80241
(303) 412-6219   Fax: (303) 253-9220
E-mail: chrysalis@awg.org
Web: www.awg.org/EAS/scholarships.html

Summary   To provide assistance to female geoscientists who have been out of the workforce and need funding to resume their career.

Eligibility   This program is open to women in the geoscience profession who wish to resume their career after having been out of the workforce. Applicants must be seeking funding for such professional development costs as enrollment in geoscience training courses or workshops, fees for certifications and licensing, professional membership fees, or any other costs to help them reenter the workforce. Along with their application, they must submit a 1-page personal statement describing their academic qualifications, professional work history, and any recent volunteer or home activities relevant to their area of expertise.

Financial data   A total of $1,000 is available for this program each year.

Duration   1 year.

Additional information   This program is sponsored by the Lone Star Chapter of the Association for Women Geoscientists (AWG), but neither Texas residency nor AWG membership are required.

Number awarded   1 or more each year.

Deadline   December of each year.

[1359]
L'OREAL USA FELLOWSHIPS FOR WOMEN IN SCIENCE

L'Oréal USA
c/o American Association for the Advancement of Science
1200 New York Avenue, Sixth Floor
Washington, DC 20005
(202) 326-6677   E-mail: lorealusafellowships@aaas.org
Web: www.lorealusa.com/forwomeninscience

Summary   To provide research funding to postdoctoral women scientists.

Eligibility   This program is open to women who have a Ph.D., Sc.D., or D.P.H. in the life sciences, physical or material sciences, engineering, technology, computer science, or mathematics, as well as immunology, all areas of chemistry, earth science, and medical research. Women who have an M.D. or whose work is in psychology, science education, or social science are not eligible. Applicants must be planning to conduct a research project in their field of specialization. They must be U.S. citizens, plan to become citizens by the time the awards are announced, or permanent residents.

Financial data   The grant is $60,000.

Duration   1 year.

Additional information   This program, established in 2003, is sponsored by L'Oréal USA.

Number awarded   5 each year.

Deadline   December of each year.

[1360]
LOREEN ARBUS DISABILITY AWARENESS GRANTS

New York Women in Film & Television
6 East 39th Street, 12th Floor
New York, NY 10016-0870
(212) 679-0870   Fax: (212) 679-0899
E-mail: info@nywift.org
Web: www.nywift.org/article.aspx?id=LAS

Summary   To provide funding to women filmmakers who are interested in making a film on disability issues.

Eligibility   This program is open to women who are interested in making a film of any length or genre that is already in progress. Applicants must either have a disability or be proposing to make a film about disability issues. They must submit a 2- to 4-page description of the project, a budget indicating amount raised to date, a list of key creative personnel with 1-paragraph bios, and a DVD or a link to an upload of the work-in-progress.

Financial data   The grant is $7,500. Funds may be used only completion work.

Duration   These grants are provided annually.

Number awarded   1 or more each year.

Deadline   September of each year.

[1361]
LOUISE EISENHARDT RESIDENT TRAVEL SCHOLARSHIP

American Association of Neurological Surgeons
Attn: Grants Coordinator
5550 Meadowbrook Drive
Rolling Meadows, IL 60008-3852
(847) 378-0500   Toll Free: (888) 566-AANS
Fax: (847) 378-0600   E-mail: cap@aans.org
Web: www.neurosurgerywins.org/resident/index.html

Summary   To recognize and reward female neurosurgical residents who submit outstanding abstracts for presentation at the annual meeting of the American Association of Neurological Surgeons (AANS).

Eligibility   This program is open to female neurosurgical residents who submit outstanding pioneering clinical or laboratory research abstracts for presentation at the AANS annual meeting.

Financial data   The award consists of $2,000.

Duration   The award is presented annually.

Additional information   This award, first presented in 2000, is sponsored by Women in Neurosurgery.

Number awarded   1 each year.

Deadline   Deadline not specified.

[1362]
M. CAREY THOMAS AWARD

Alumnae Association of Bryn Mawr College
Wyndham Alumnae House
101 North Merion Avenue
Bryn Mawr, PA 19010-2899
(610) 526-5227   Toll Free: (800) BMC-ALUM
Fax: (610) 526-5228   E-mail: bmcalum@brynmawr.edu
Web: www.brynmawr.edu/alumnae

Summary To recognize and reward unusual achievement on the part of distinguished American women.

Eligibility Applications are not accepted. Recipients are chosen by a special committee that is formed several months prior to the presentation of the award. Selection is based on eminent and outstanding achievement. Recipients may be affiliated with Bryn Mawr College.

Financial data The award is $10,000.

Duration The award is granted every 5 years (2017, 2022).

Additional information Past recipients have included Martha Graham and Georgia O'Keefe.

Deadline Deadline not specified.

[1363]
M. HILDRED BLEWETT SCHOLARSHIP

American Physical Society
Attn: Committee on the Status of Women in Physics
One Physics Ellipse, Fourth Floor
College Park, MD 20740-3844
(301) 209-3231   Fax: (301) 209-0865
E-mail: blewett@aps.org
Web: www.aps.org

Summary To provide funding to early-career women interested in returning to physics research after interrupting their career for family reasons.

Eligibility This program is open to women who have completed work toward a Ph.D. in physics and currently have an affiliation with a research-active educational institution or national laboratory in Canada or the United States. Applicants must be interested in conducting a research project after interrupting their career for family reasons. They must currently reside in the United States or Canada and be citizens or legal residents of those countries. No matching contribution from the institution is required, but institutional support is considered as evidence of support for the applicant.

Financial data The grant is $45,000. Funds may be used for dependent care (limited to 50% of the award), salary, travel, equipment, and tuition and fees.

Duration 1 year.

Additional information This program was established in 2005.

Number awarded 1 each year.

Deadline May of each year.

[1364]
MANAGEMENT SCHOLARSHIP

Women in Aviation, International
Attn: Scholarships
Morningstar Airport
3647 State Route 503 South
West Alexandria, OH 45381-9354
(937) 839-4647   Fax: (937) 839-4645
E-mail: scholarships@wai.org
Web: www.wai.org/education/scholarships.cfm

Summary To provide financial assistance to members of Women in Aviation, International (WAI) who are in an aviation management field and interested in attending leadership-related courses or seminars.

Eligibility This program is open to WAI members in an aviation management field who have exemplified the traits of leadership, community spirit, and volunteerism. They must be interested in attending a leadership-related course or seminar or participating in some other means of advancing their managerial position. Along with their application, they must submit 2 letters of recommendation, a 500-word essay on their aviation history and goals, a resume, copies of all aviation licenses and medical certificates, and the last 3 pages of their pilot logbook (if applicable). Selection is based on achievements, attitude toward self and others, commitment to success, dedication to career, financial need, motivation, reliability, responsibility, and teamwork.

Financial data The stipend is $1,250.

Additional information WAI is a nonprofit professional organization dedicated to encouraging women to consider an aviation career and to providing educational outreach activities and networking resources to women active in the industry.

Number awarded 1 each year.

Deadline November of each year.

[1365]
MARA CRAWFORD PERSONAL DEVELOPMENT SCHOLARSHIP

Kansas Federation of Business & Professional Women's
    Clubs, Inc.
Attn: Kansas BPW Educational Foundation, Inc.
c/o Kathy Niehoff, Executive Secretary
605 East 15th
Ottawa, KS 66067
(785) 242-9319   Fax: (785) 242-1047
E-mail: kathyniehoff@sbcglobal.net
Web: kansasbpw.memberlodge.org

Summary To provide financial assistance to women in Kansas who are already in the workforce but are interested in pursuing additional education.

Eligibility This program is open to women residents of Kansas who graduated from high school more than 5 years previously and are already in the workforce. Applicants may be seeking a degree in any field of study and may be attending a 2-year, 4-year, vocational, or technological program. They must submit a 3-page personal biography in which they express their career goals, the direction they want to take in the future, their proposed field of study, their reason for selecting that field, the institutions they plan to attend and why, their circumstances for reentering school (if a factor), and what makes them uniquely qualified for this scholarship.

Preference is given to applicants who demonstrate they have serious family responsibilities and obligations. Applications must be submitted through a local unit of the sponsor.

Financial data A stipend is awarded (amount not specified).

Duration 1 year.

Number awarded 1 or more each year.

Deadline December of each year.

[1366]
MARCH OF DIMES "SAVING BABIES, TOGETHER" AWARD

Association of Women's Health, Obstetric and Neonatal Nurses
Attn: Research Grants Program
2000 L Street, N.W., Suite 740
Washington, DC 20036
(202) 261-2431   Toll Free: (800) 673-8499, ext. 2431
Fax: (202) 728-0575
E-mail: ResearchPrograms@awhonn.org
Web: www.awhonn.org

Summary To provide funding for small research projects to members of the Association of Women's Health, Obstetric and Neonatal Nurses (AWHONN).

Eligibility This program is open to members of the association who are interested in conducting research related to women's health, obstetric, or neonatal nursing. Researchers who are currently principal investigators on a federally-funded grant, or who have already received an AWHONN-funded research grant within the past 5 years, are not eligible.

Financial data The grant is $9,000. Funds may not be used for indirect costs, tuition, computer hardware or printers, conference attendance, or salary for the principal investigator or other investigators.

Duration 1 year.

Additional information This program is funded by the March of Dimes.

Number awarded 1 each year.

Deadline November of each year.

[1367]
MARCIA FEINBERG AWARD

Association of Jewish Women Publishers
3160 Wedgewood Court
Reno, NV 89509-7103

Summary To recognize and reward Jewish women who have made outstanding contributions to careers in library science and publishing.

Eligibility This award is presented to Jewish women who received a library science doctoral degree from a university in the upper Midwest (Montana, South Dakota, North Dakota, or Minnesota). Nominees must have spent a portion of their career working as a librarian, and then changed careers to enter the field of publishing. They may currently reside in any state except Nebraska or Rhode Island. Selection is based on service to the library profession, awards received for librarianship, innovativeness, and loyalty to colleagues.

Financial data The award includes an honorarium of $10,000 and a gold engraved plaque.

Duration The award is presented annually.

Additional information This award, named in honor of a well-known 19th-century Jewish woman librarian and publisher, has been presented annually since 1923. Self-nominations are not accepted. Only professional colleagues may nominate a candidate.

Number awarded 1 each year.

Deadline August of each year.

[1368]
MARGARET MORSE NICE FUND

American Ornithologists' Union
c/o Executive Officer
5405 Villa View Drive
Farmington, NM 87402
(505) 326-1579   E-mail: aou@aou.org
Web: www.aou.org/awards/research

Summary To provide funding to female graduate students and scholars who are members of the American Ornithologists' Union (AOU) and interested in conducting research related to ornithology.

Eligibility This program is open to female AOU members who are graduate students, postdoctorates, or other researchers without access to major funding agencies. Applicants must be interested in conducting research related to ornithology. They should send a cover letter (about 5 pages) describing their proposed project, a budget, and 1 letter of reference. Selection is based on significance and originality of the research question, clarity of the objectives, feasibility of the plan of research, appropriateness of the budget, and the letter of recommendation.

Financial data The maximum award is $2,500 per year.

Duration 1 year; recipients may reapply for 1 additional award.

Number awarded The sponsor awards a total of 28 to 30 grants each year.

Deadline January of each year.

[1369]
MARGARET OAKLEY DAYHOFF AWARD

Biophysical Society
Attn: Awards Committee
11400 Rockville Pike, Suite 800
Rockville, MD 20852
(240) 290-5600   Fax: (240) 290-5555
E-mail: society@biophysics.org
Web: www.biophysics.org

Summary To recognize and reward outstanding junior women scientists in fields of interest to the Biophysical Society.

Eligibility This program is open to junior women scientists whose writings have made substantial contributions to scientific fields within the range of interest of the society but who have not yet attained university tenure. Candidates who have a Ph.D. or equivalent degree remain eligible until they have completed 10 years of full-time work following the degree. Candidates with a baccalaureate degree but without a Ph.D. have 12 years of eligibility. Time taken off for child rearing is not counted. Candidates who work in non-academic environments are eligible if their work is published and meets academic standards, and if they do not have tenure equivalency. Membership is the society is required. Nominations may be submitted by any member of the society in good standing, but self-nominations are not accepted.

Financial data The award is $2,000.

Duration The award is presented annually.

Additional information This award was established in 1984.

Number awarded 1 each year.

Deadline April of each year.

[1370]
MARGARET W. ROSSITER HISTORY OF WOMEN IN SCIENCE PRIZE

History of Science Society
Attn: Nominations
University of Notre Dame
440 Geddes Hall
Notre Dame, IN 46556
(574) 631-1194   Fax: (574) 631-1533
E-mail: prizes@hssonline.org
Web: www.hssonline.org/about/society_awards.html

Summary To recognize and reward scholars who publish outstanding work in the specialty field of women in the history of science.

Eligibility Books and articles published during the last 4 years are eligible for consideration, provided they deal with a topic related to women in science, including discussions of women's activities in science, analyses of past scientific practices that deal explicitly with gender, and investigations regarding women as viewed by scientists. Entries may take a biographical, institutional, theoretical, or other approach to the topic. They may relate to medicine, technology, and the social sciences as well as the natural sciences.

Financial data The prize is $1,000.

Duration This is an annual award, presented in alternate years to the most outstanding article (even-numbered years) and the most outstanding book (odd-numbered years).

Additional information This award was established in 1987 and given its current name in 2004.

Number awarded 1 each year.

Deadline March of each year.

[1371]
MARIA GOEPPERT-MAYER AWARD

American Physical Society
Attn: Honors Program
One Physics Ellipse
College Park, MD 20740-3844
(301) 209-3268   Fax: (301) 209-0865
E-mail: honors@aps.org
Web: www.aps.org

Summary To recognize the achievements of outstanding women physicists and to offer them an opportunity to share these achievements by delivering public lectures.

Eligibility This award is available to female U.S. citizens and permanent residents who are working in a field of physics and are in the early stages of their careers. They must have received their doctorates no more than 10 years ago.

Financial data The award is $2,500 plus a $4,000 travel allowance to cover the costs of providing lectures at 4 institutions of the recipient's choice.

Duration The lectures must be given within 2 years after the award is presented.

Additional information The lectures may be given at 4 institutions of the recipient's choice within the United States or its possessions, and at the meeting of the American Physical Society at which the award is presented. The award was established by the General Electric Foundation (now the GE Fund) in 1985.

Number awarded 1 each year.

Deadline June of each year.

[1372]
MARIAM K. CHAMBERLAIN FELLOWSHIP

Institute for Women's Policy Research
Attn: Fellowship Coordinator
1200 18th Street, N.W., Suite 301
Washington, DC 20036
(202) 785-5100   Fax: (202) 833-4362
E-mail: iwpr@iwpr.org
Web: www.iwpr.org/about/fellowships

Summary To provide work experience at the Institute for Women's Policy Research (IWPR) to college graduates and graduate students who are interested in economic justice for women.

Eligibility Applicants for this internship should have at least a bachelor's degree in social science, statistics, or women's studies. Graduate work is desirable but not required. They should have strong quantitative and library research skills and knowledge of women's issues. Familiarity with Microsoft Word and Excel is required; knowledge of STATA, SPSS, SAS, and graphics software is a plus.

Financial data The stipend is $23,088 and includes health insurance and a public transportation stipend.

Duration 9 months, beginning in September.

Additional information The institute is a nonprofit, scientific research organization that works primarily on issues related to equal opportunity and economic and social justice for women. Recent research topics for the fellows included women's wages, political participation, access to health care, and other indicators of the status of women on a state-by-state basis; the work and welfare experiences of low-income women on the state and national levels; reforming such income support policies for women as unemployment insurance, family leave, and Social Security; strategies for improving child care access, affordability, and quality; older women's economic issues; and women's values and activism, including new strategies for engaging a diverse range of organizations, including those with a religious affiliation, in women's issue activism.

Number awarded 1 each year.

Deadline February of each year.

[1373]
MARIAN NORBY SCHOLARSHIP

Society for Technical Communication
9401 Lee Highway, Suite 300
Fairfax, VA 22031
(703) 522-4114   Fax: (703) 522-2075
E-mail: stc@stc.org
Web: www.stc.org/edu/scholarships.asp

Summary   To provide financial assistance to female employees of the federal government who are interested in training or academic study related to technical communications.

Eligibility   This program is open to women who working full or part time for the federal government as a secretary or administrative assistant. Applicants must be interested in enrolling in a training or academic class related to technical communication, including technical writing, editing, graphical design, interface design, or web design. Along with their application, they must submit a 1- to 3-page description of their career goals and significant achievements to date. Financial need is not considered in the selection process.

Financial data   The stipend is $2,500.

Duration   1 academic year.

Number awarded   1 each year.

Deadline   May of each year.

[1374]
MARY ISABEL SIBLEY FELLOWSHIP FOR FRENCH STUDIES

Phi Beta Kappa Society
Attn: Director of Society Affairs
1606 New Hampshire Avenue, N.W.
Washington, DC 20009
(202) 745-3235   Fax: (202) 986-1601
E-mail: awards@pbk.org
Web: www.pbk.org/infoview/PBK_InfoView.aspx?t=&id=5

Summary   To provide funding to women involved in dissertation or advanced research or writing projects dealing with French studies.

Eligibility   This program is open to unmarried women between 25 and 35 years of age who have demonstrated their ability to conduct original research. Applicants must be planning to conduct a research project dealing with French language or literature. They must hold the doctorate or have fulfilled all the requirements for the doctorate except the dissertation, and they must be planning to devote full time to their research during the fellowship year. Along with their application, they must submit a statement that includes a description of the project, the present state of the project, where the study would be carried out, and expectations regarding publication of the results of the study. Eligibility is not restricted to members of Phi Beta Kappa or to U.S. citizens.

Financial data   The stipend is $20,000.

Duration   1 year (the fellowship is offered in even-numbered years only).

Additional information   Periodic progress reports are not required, but they are welcomed. It is the hope of the committee that the results of the year of research will be made available in some form, although no pressure for publication will be put on the recipient.

Number awarded   1 every other year.

Deadline   January of even-numbered years.

[1375]
MARY ISABEL SIBLEY FELLOWSHIP FOR GREEK STUDIES

Phi Beta Kappa Society
Attn: Director of Society Affairs
1606 New Hampshire Avenue, N.W.
Washington, DC 20009
(202) 745-3235   Fax: (202) 986-1601
E-mail: awards@pbk.org
Web: www.pbk.org/infoview/PBK_InfoView.aspx?t=&id=5

Summary   To provide funding to women involved in dissertation or advanced research or writing projects dealing with Greek studies.

Eligibility   This program is open to unmarried women between 25 and 35 years of age who have demonstrated their ability to conduct original research. Applicants must be planning to conduct a research project dealing with Greek language, literature, history, or archaeology. They must hold the doctorate or have fulfilled all the requirements for the doctorate except the dissertation, and they must be planning to devote full time to their research during the fellowship year. Along with their application, they must submit a statement that includes a description of the project, the present state of the project, where the study would be carried out, and expectations regarding publication of the results of the study. Eligibility is not restricted to members of Phi Beta Kappa or to U.S. citizens.

Financial data   The stipend is $20,000.

Duration   1 year (the fellowship is offered in odd-numbered years only).

Additional information   Periodic progress reports are not required, but they are welcomed. It is the hope of the committee that the results of the year of research will be made available in some form, although no pressure for publication will be put on the recipient.

Number awarded   1 every other year.

Deadline   January of odd-numbered years.

[1376]
MARY JANE OESTMANN PROFESSIONAL WOMEN'S ACHIEVEMENT AWARD

American Nuclear Society
Attn: Honors and Awards
555 North Kensington Avenue
La Grange Park, IL 60526-5592
(708) 352-6611   Toll Free: (800) 323-3044
Fax: (708) 579-8295   E-mail: honors@ans.org
Web: www.ans.org/honors/va-oestmann

Summary   To recognize and reward women who have made outstanding contributions to the field of nuclear science.

Eligibility   This award is presented to women who have contributed outstanding personal dedication and technical achievement in the fields of nuclear science, engineering, research, or education. Nominees need not be a member of the American Nuclear Society (ANS), but they should be affiliated with the nuclear community in some manner. The award may be given for lifetime achievement or for a singular outstanding contribution to the technical community.

Financial data   The award consists of a monetary honorarium and an engraved plaque.

Duration The award is presented annually.
Additional information This award was first presented in 1991.
Number awarded 1 each year.
Deadline June of each year.

[1377]
MARY LILY RESEARCH GRANTS

Duke University
Rare Book, Manuscript, and Special Collections Library
Attn: Sallie Bingham Center for Women's History and
  Culture
P.O. Box 90185
Durham, NC 27708-0185
(919) 660-5828   Fax: (919) 660-5934
E-mail: cwhc@duke.edu
Web: library.duke.edu

Summary To provide funding to scholars at all levels who wish to use the resources of the Sallie Bingham Center for Women's History and Culture in the Special Collections Library at Duke University.

Eligibility This program is open to undergraduates, graduate students, faculty members, and independent scholars in any academic field who wish to use the resources of the center for their research in women's studies. Applicants must reside outside a 50-mile radius of Durham, North Carolina. Undergraduate and graduate students must be currently enrolled, be working on a degree, and enclose a letter of recommendation from their adviser or thesis director. Faculty members must be working on a research project and enclose a curriculum vitae. Independent scholars must be working on a nonprofit project and enclose a curriculum vitae.

Financial data Grants up to $1,000 are available; funds may be used for travel, costs of copying pertinent resources, and living expenses while conducting the research.

Additional information The library's collections are especially strong in the history of feminist activism and theory, prescriptive literature, girls' literature, artists' books by women, lay and ordained church women, gender expression, women's sexuality, and the history and culture of women in the South. A number of prominent women writers have placed their personal and professional papers in the collections.

Number awarded Varies each year; recently, 8 of these grants were awarded.

Deadline January of each year.

[1378]
MATHEMATICS EDUCATION RESEARCH MENTORING TRAVEL GRANTS FOR WOMEN

Association for Women in Mathematics
11240 Waples Mill Road, Suite 200
Fairfax, VA 22030
(703) 934-0163   Fax: (703) 359-7562
E-mail: awm@awm-math.org
Web: sites.google.com

Summary To provide funding to female postdoctorates in mathematics who wish to travel to develop a long-term working and mentoring relationship with an educational researcher.

Eligibility This program is open to women holding a doctorate or with equivalent experience and with a work address in the United States (or home address if unemployed). The applicant's research may be in any field that is funded by the Division of Mathematical Sciences (DMS) of the National Science Foundation (NSF). The proposed travel must be to collaborate with a mentor who holds a doctorate in mathematics education or in a related field, such as psychology or curriculum and instruction.

Financial data These grants provide full or partial support for travel, subsistence, and other required expenses, to a maximum of $5,000.

Duration The proposed visit may last up to 1 month.

Additional information Funding for this program is provided by the DMS of the NSF. For foreign travel, U.S. carriers must be used whenever possible.

Number awarded Up to 7 each year.

Deadline January of each year.

[1379]
MATHEMATICS MENTORING TRAVEL GRANTS FOR WOMEN

Association for Women in Mathematics
11240 Waples Mill Road, Suite 200
Fairfax, VA 22030
(703) 934-0163   Fax: (703) 359-7562
E-mail: awm@awm-math.org
Web: sites.google.com

Summary To provide funding to junior female postdoctorates in mathematics who wish to travel to develop a long-term working and mentoring relationship with a senior mathematician.

Eligibility This program is open to women holding a doctorate or with equivalent experience and with a work address in the United States. They must be untenured. The applicant's research may be in any field that is funded by the Division of Mathematical Sciences (DMS) of the National Science Foundation (NSF). The proposed travel must be to an institute or a department (in the United States or abroad) to do research with a senior mathematician so the applicant can establish her research program and eventually receive tenure.

Financial data These grants provide full or partial support for travel, subsistence, and other required expenses, to a maximum of $5,000.

Duration The proposed visit may last up to 1 month.

Additional information Funding for this program is provided by the DMS of the NSF. For foreign travel, U.S. carriers must be used whenever possible.

Number awarded Up to 7 each year.

Deadline January of each year.

[1380]
MEDTRONIC PRIZE FOR SCIENTIFIC CONTRIBUTIONS TO WOMEN'S HEALTH

Society for Women's Health Research
1025 Connecticut Avenue, N.W., Suite 701
Washington, DC 20036
(202) 223-8224   Fax: (202) 833-3472
E-mail: communications@swhr.org
Web: www.womenshealthresearch.org

Summary To recognize and reward women scientists and engineers who have made outstanding contributions to women's health.

Eligibility This award is available to women scientists and engineers in midcareer whose work has led or will lead directly to the improvement of women's health. Nominees should have devoted a significant part of their careers to the area of women's health, especially to work on sex differences. They must be U.S. citizens who completed their first graduate degree within the past 15 years. Priority is given to nominees whose commitment to women's health has been passed on to their collaborators and students, both as a role model and as a mentor.

Financial data The award is $75,000.

Duration The award is presented annually.

Additional information This award, first presented in 2006, is sponsored by Medtronic.

Number awarded 1 each year.

Deadline January of each year.

[1381]
MEERSBURGER DROSTE-PREIS

Kulturamt der Stadt Meersburg
Postfach 1140
D-88701 Meersburg
Germany
49 7532 440 260   Fax: 49 7532 440 264
E-mail: kulturamt@meersburg.de

Summary To recognize and reward women poets writing in the German language.

Eligibility The competition is open to women poets of any nationality writing in German. Self-nominations are not accepted.

Financial data The prize is 6,000 Euros.

Duration The competition is held every 3 years (2015, 2018, etc.).

Additional information This prize was first awarded in 1957.

Number awarded 1 every 3 years.

Deadline Deadline not specified.

[1382]
MERLE MONTGOMERY OPERA AWARDS

National Federation of Music Clubs
1646 Smith Valley Road
Greenwood, IN 46142
(317) 882-4003   Fax: (317) 882-4019
E-mail: info@nfmc-music.org
Web: www.nfmc-music.org

Summary To recognize and reward outstanding female and male opera singers (judged separately) who participate in the Biennial Young Artist Awards competition of the National Federation of Music Clubs (NFMC).

Eligibility Opera voice entrants must be between 25 and 36 years of age. Separate competitions are held for men and women. Membership in the federation and U.S. citizenship are required. Candidates for the NFMC Biennial Young Artist Awards competition are automatically considered for this award; no separate application is necessary.

Financial data Each award is $2,500.

Duration The competition is held biennially, in odd-numbered years.

Additional information There is a $50 entry fee.

Number awarded 2 every other year: 1 for a man and 1 for a woman.

Deadline January of odd-numbered years.

[1383]
MICKEY LELAND ENERGY FELLOWSHIPS

Department of Energy
Attn: Office of Fossil Energy
19901 Germantown Road, FE-6
Germantown, MD 20874
(301) 903-4293   E-mail: MLEF@hq.doe.gov
Web: fossil.energy.gov

Summary To provide summer work experience at fossil energy sites of the Department of Energy (DOE) to women and underrepresented minority students.

Eligibility This program is open to U.S. citizens currently enrolled full time at an accredited college or university. Applicants must be undergraduate, graduate, or postdoctoral students in mathematics, physical sciences, technology, or engineering and have a GPA of 3.0 or higher. They must be interested in a summer work experience at a DOE fossil energy research facility. Along with their application, they must submit a 100-word statement on why they want to participate in this program. A goal of the program is to recruit women and underrepresented minorities into careers related to fossil energy.

Financial data Weekly stipends are $500 for undergraduates, $650 for master's degree students, or $750 for doctoral and postdoctoral students. Travel costs for a round trip to and from the site and for a trip to a designated place for technical presentations are also paid.

Duration 10 weeks during the summer.

Additional information This program began as 3 separate activities: the Historically Black Colleges and Universities Internship Program established in 1995, the Hispanic Internship Program established in 1998, and the Tribal Colleges and Universities Internship Program, established in 2000. Those 3 programs were merged into the Fossil Energy Minority Education Initiative, renamed the Mickey Leland Energy Fellowship Program in 2000. Sites to which interns may be assigned include the Albany Research Center (Albany, Oregon), the National Energy Technology Laboratory (Morgantown, West Virginia and Pittsburgh, Pennsylvania), Pacific Northwest National Laboratory (Richland, Washington), Rocky Mountain Oilfield Testing Center (Casper, Wyoming), Strategic Petroleum Reserve Project Management Office (New Orleans, Louisiana), or U.S. Department of Energy Headquarters (Washington, D.C.).

Number awarded Varies each year; recently, 30 students participated in this program.

Deadline January of each year.

[1384]
MID KOLSTAD SCHOLARSHIP

Women Soaring Pilots Association
c/o Phyllis Wells
1938 15th Street
Penrose, CO 81240
(719) 372-0410 E-mail: pwells1634@aol.com
Web: www.womensoaring.org/?p=info

Summary To provide financial assistance to mature women from any country interested in obtaining their private glider license.

Eligibility This program is open to women over 25 years of age who are student glider pilots or licensed airplane pilots. Applicants must be members of the Women Soaring Pilots Association (WSPA) and the Soaring Society of America (SSA) or equivalent organization if they live outside the United States. They must be interested in a program of training for a private glider certificate or add-on rating. Along with their application, they must submit a 500-word essay explaining their goals and previous experiences as they relate to gliders and how this scholarship will help them meet their goals.

Financial data The stipend is $1,500.

Duration 1 year.

Number awarded 1 or more each year.

Deadline May of each year.

[1385]
MINNIE L. MAFFETT FELLOWSHIPS

Texas Business Women
Attn: Texas Business and Professional Women's
  Foundation
P.O. Box 70
Round Rock, TX 78680-0070
(806) 922-7090 Toll Free: (877) 225-4TBW
E-mail: info@texasbusinesswomen.org
Web: www.texasbpwfoundation.org/scholarships.php

Summary To provide financial assistance to women in Texas interested in studying or conducting research in a medical field.

Eligibility This program is open to 1) female graduates of Texas medical schools interested in postgraduate or research work; 2) women who have been awarded a Ph.D. degree from a Texas university and are doing research in a medical field; 3) women who need financial aid for the first year in establishing a family practice in a rural area of Texas with a population of less than 5,000; and 4) fourth-year female medical students who are completing an M.D. or D.O. degree at an accredited medical school in Texas.

Financial data The stipend recently was $1,500.

Duration 1 year; nonrenewable.

Additional information This program was established in 1948 when Texas Business Women was named Texas Federation of Business and Professional Women's Clubs.

Number awarded Varies each year; recently, 3 of these fellowships were awarded.

Deadline December of each year.

[1386]
MOTHERWELL PRIZE

Fence Books
Attn: Motherwell Prize
University at Albany
Science Library 320
1400 Washington Avenue
Albany, NY 12222-0100
E-mail: fence@albany.edu
Web: fence.fenceportal.org/contest/motherwell.html

Summary To recognize and reward outstanding unpublished first or second books of poetry by American women.

Eligibility Interested women poets are invited to submit an unpublished manuscript (48 to 80 pages). They may not have published more than 1 book of poetry previously. Unpublished poets are also eligible. Translations are not accepted.

Financial data The prize is $5,000 and publication of the winning manuscript by Fence Books.

Duration The competition is held annually.

Additional information This prize was formerly known as the Alberta Prize. There is a $25 entry fee.

Number awarded 1 each year.

Deadline November of each year.

[1387]
MYRNA F. BERNATH BOOK AWARD

Society for Historians of American Foreign Relations
c/o Ohio State University
Department of History
106 Dulles Hall
230 West 17th Avenue
Columbus, OH 43210
(614) 292-1951 Fax: (614) 292-2282
E-mail: shafr@osu.edu
Web: www.shafr.org/members/prizes

Summary To recognize and reward outstanding books written by women on U.S. foreign relations.

Eligibility Eligible to be considered for this award are books written by women on U.S. foreign relations, transnational history, international history, peace studies, cultural interchange, and defense or strategic studies that were published during the previous 2 years. Authors or publishers should submit 5 copies of books that meet these requirements. Selection is based on the book's contribution to scholarship.

Financial data The award is $2,500.

Duration The award is offered biennially.

Additional information This award was first presented in 1991.

Number awarded 1 each even-numbered year.

Deadline November of each odd-numbered year.

[1388]
MYRNA F. BERNATH FELLOWSHIP AWARD

Society for Historians of American Foreign Relations
c/o Ohio State University
Department of History
106 Dulles Hall
230 West 17th Avenue
Columbus, OH 43210
(614) 292-1951   Fax: (614) 292-2282
E-mail: shafr@osu.edu
Web: www.shafr.org/members/fellowships-grants

Summary   To provide funding to women who are members of the Society for Historians of American Foreign Relations (SHAFR) and interested in conducting research on the history of U.S. foreign relations.

Eligibility   This program is open to women at U.S. universities who wish to conduct historically-based research in the United States or abroad and to women from other countries who wish to conduct research in the United States. The proposed study should focus on U.S. foreign relations, transnational history, international history, peace studies, cultural interchange, or defense or strategic studies. Preference is given to applications from graduate students and those who completed their Ph.D. within the past 5 years. Applicants must submit a curriculum vitae, a letter of intent, and a detailed research proposal that discusses the sources to be consulted and their value, the funds needed, and the plan for spending those funds.

Financial data   The grant is $5,000.

Duration   The grant is presented biennially, in odd-numbered years.

Additional information   This grant was first presented in 1992.

Number awarded   1 each odd-numbered year.

Deadline   September of each even-numbered year.

[1389]
NATIVE AMERICAN WOMEN'S HEALTH EDUCATION RESOURCE CENTER INTERNSHIPS

Native American Women's Health Education Resource
   Center
Attn: Internship Coordinator
P.O. Box 572
Lake Andes, SD 57356-0572
(605) 487-7072   Fax: (605) 487-7964
E-mail: charon@charles-mix.com
Web: www.nativeshop.org

Summary   To provide work experience to students and recent graduates interested in working at the Native American Women's Health Education Resource Center and its Domestic Violence Shelter.

Eligibility   This program is open to college students, graduate students, and recent graduates. Applicants must have a background of work in Native American rights and health issues to promote civil rights, women's rights, and a healthy environment. They must be interested in working at the Native American Women's Health Education Resource Center and its Domestic Violence Shelter.

Financial data   Interns receive a stipend of $500 per month, free room at the shelter, and partial board from the resource center's food pantry.

Duration   3 months to 1 year; priority is given for internships of 6 months or longer.

Additional information   The Native American Women's Health Education Resource Center is a project of the Native American Community Board. It is located in Lake Andes, South Dakota in a rural area of the Yankton Sioux Reservation. The Domestic Violence Shelter is 4 blocks away. Past intern projects have included domestic violence advocacy at the shelter, counseling on the youth crisis hotline, environmental activism, Native women's reproductive health and rights, indigenous people's rights projects, web site development, organizing the annual community health fair, producing a Dakota language CD-ROM, and AIDS education.

Number awarded   Varies each year.

Deadline   Deadline not specified.

[1390]
NAVAL RESEARCH LABORATORY BROAD AGENCY ANNOUNCEMENT

Naval Research Laboratory
Attn: Contracting Division
4555 Overlook Avenue, S.W.
Washington, DC 20375-5320
(202) 767-5227   Fax: (202) 767-0494
Web: heron.nrl.navy.mil/contracts/home.htm

Summary   To provide funding to women and other investigators from underrepresented groups who are interested in conducting scientific research of interest to the U.S. Navy.

Eligibility   This program is open to investigators qualified to perform research in designated scientific and technical areas. Topics cover a wide range of technical and scientific areas; recent programs included radar technology, information technology, optical sciences, tactical electronic warfare, materials science and component technology, chemistry, computational physics and fluid dynamics, plasma physics, electronics science and technology, biomolecular science and engineering, ocean and atmospheric science and technology, acoustics, remote sensing, oceanography, marine geosciences, marine meteorology, and space science. Proposals may be submitted by any non-governmental entity, including commercial firms, institutions of higher education with degree-granting programs in science or engineering, or by consortia led by such concerns. The Naval Research Laboratory (NRL) encourages participation by small businesses, small disadvantaged business concerns, women-owned small businesses, veteran-owned small businesses, service-disabled veteran-owned small businesses, HUBZone small businesses, Historically Black Colleges and Universities, and Minority Institutions. Selection is based on the degree to which new and creative solutions to technical issues important to NRL programs are proposed and the feasibility of the proposed approach and technical objectives; the offeror's ability to implement the proposed approach; the degree to which technical data and/or computer software developed under the proposed contract are to be delivered to the NRL with rights compatible with NRL research and development objectives; and proposed cost and cost realism.

Financial data   The typical range of funding is from $100,000 to $2,000,000.

Duration   1 year.

Additional information   The Naval Research Laboratory conducts most of its research in its own facilities in Washington, D.C., Stennis Space Center, Mississippi, and Monterey, California, but it also funds some related research.

Number awarded Varies each year.

Deadline Each program establishes its own application deadline; for a complete list of all the programs, including their deadlines, contact the NRL.

[1391]
NELL I. MONDY FELLOWSHIP

Sigma Delta Epsilon-Graduate Women in Science, Inc.
c/o Julie Gros-Louis, Fellowships Coordinator
University of Iowa-Department of Psychology
11 Seashore Hall E
Iowa City, IA 52242-1407
(319) 384-1816   Fax: (319) 335-0191
E-mail: Julie-gros-louis@uiowa.edu
Web: www.gwis.org/programs.htm

Summary To provide funding to women interested in conducting research anywhere in the world in the natural sciences, especially in food science or nutrition.

Eligibility This program is open to women from any country currently enrolled as a graduate student, engaged in postdoctoral research, or holding a junior faculty position. Applicants must be interested in conducting research anywhere in the world in the natural sciences; preference is given to those working in the areas of food science or nutrition. Along with their application, they must submit 2-paragraph essays on 1) how the proposed research relates to their degree program and/or career development; 2) initiatives in which they are participating to promote the careers of scientists, particularly women, within their institution, program, or peer group; and 3) relevant personal factors, including financial need, that should be considered in evaluating their proposal. Appointments are made without regard to race, religion, nationality, creed, national origin, sexual orientation, or age. Membership in Sigma Delta Epsilon-Graduate Women in Science is required.

Financial data The grant currently is $4,333. Funds may be used for such research expenses as expendable supplies, small equipment, publication of research findings, travel and subsistence while performing field studies, or travel to another laboratory for collaborative research. They may not be used for tuition, child care, travel to professional meetings or to begin a new appointment, administrative overhead or indirect costs, personal computers, living allowances, or equipment for general use.

Duration 1 year.

Additional information This fellowship was first awarded in 2002. An application processing fee of $30 is required.

Number awarded Varies each year; recently, 3 of these grants were awarded.

Deadline January of each year.

[1392]
NEW PILOT AWARDS

Ninety-Nines, Inc.
4300 Amelia Earhart Road
Oklahoma City, OK 73159
(405) 685-7969   Toll Free: (800) 994-1929
Fax: (405) 685-7985   E-mail: AEChair@ninety-nines.org
Web: www.ninety-nines.org/index.cfm/scholarships.htm

Summary To provide financial support to Future Woman Pilot members of the Ninety-Nines (an organization of women pilots) who are interested in earning a private pilot certificate.

Eligibility This program is open to women who are Future Woman Pilot members of the organization, have a current medical certificate, have log book entries showing at least 20 hours of flight time, have soloed, have passed the private pilot written test, meet all requirements specific to the country where training will occur, and are able to demonstrate financial need. Applicants must be interested in taking flight training for a private pilot certificate. They must be nominated by their chapter. Each chapter is allowed 1 applicant and an alternate.

Financial data The maximum stipend is $1,500 per year.

Duration The training must be completed within 1 year.

Additional information Recipients must agree to become a full member of the Ninety-Nines upon earning their private pilot certificate.

Number awarded Varies each year; recently, 5 of these scholarships were awarded.

Deadline Applications must be submitted to the chapter scholarship chair by November of each year.

[1393]
NEW YORK PUBLIC LIBRARY FELLOWSHIPS

American Council of Learned Societies
Attn: Office of Fellowships and Grants
633 Third Avenue
New York, NY 10017-6795
(212) 697-1505   Fax: (212) 949-8058
E-mail: fellowships@acls.org
Web: www.acls.org/programs/acls

Summary To provide funding to postdoctorates (particularly women and minorities) who dare interested in conducting research at the Dorothy and Lewis B. Cullman Center for Scholars and Writers of the New York Public Library.

Eligibility This program is open to scholars at all stages of their careers who received a Ph.D. degree at least 2 years previously. Established scholars who can demonstrate the equivalent of the Ph.D. in publications and professional experience may also qualify. Applicants must be U.S. citizens or permanent residents who have not had supported leave time for at least 2 years prior to the start of the proposed research. Appropriate fields of specialization include, but are not limited to, American studies; anthropology; archaeology; art and architectural history; classics; economics; film; geography; history; languages and literatures; legal studies; linguistics; musicology; philosophy; political science; psychology; religious studies; rhetoric, communication, and media studies; sociology; and theater, dance, and performance studies. Proposals in the social sciences are eligible only if they employ predominantly humanistic approaches (e.g., economic history, law and literature, political philosophy). Proposals in interdisciplinary and cross-disciplinary studies are welcome, as are proposals focused on any geographic region or on any cultural or linguistic group. Applicants must be interested in conducting research at the New York Public Library's Dorothy and Lewis B. Cullman Center for Scholars and Writers. Women and members of minority groups are particularly invited to apply.

Financial data The stipend is $60,000.

Duration 9 months, beginning in September.

Additional information This program was first offered for 1999-2000, the inaugural year of the center. Candidates must also submit a separate application that is available from the New York Public Library, Humanities and Social Sciences Library, Dorothy and Lewis B. Cullman Center for Scholars and Writers, Fifth Avenue and 42nd Street, New York, NY 10018-2788, E-mail: csw@nypl.org. Fellows are required to be in continuous residence at the center and participate actively in its activities and programs.

Number awarded Up to 5 each year.

Deadline September of each year.

[1394]
NFMC BIENNIAL YOUNG ARTIST AWARDS

National Federation of Music Clubs
1646 Smith Valley Road
Greenwood, IN 46142
(317) 882-4003		Fax: (317) 882-4019
E-mail: info@nfmc-music.org
Web: www.nfmc-music.org

Summary To recognize and reward outstanding young musicians (including a separate competition for women singers) who are members of the National Federation of Music Clubs (NFMC).

Eligibility Vocalists must be between 25 and 36 years of age; instrumentalists must be between 18 and 29. Competitions are held in 4 categories: women's voice, men's voice, piano, and strings. Membership in the federation and U.S. citizenship are required.

Financial data Awards are $10,000 for first place and $1,250 for second place in each category.

Duration The competition is held biennially, in odd-numbered years.

Additional information Musicians who enter this competition are also automatically considered for a number of supplemental awards. There is a $50 entry fee for each category.

Number awarded 8 every other year: 2 in each of the 4 categories.

Deadline January of odd-numbered years.

[1395]
NINETY-NINES, INC. AMELIA EARHART MEMORIAL SCHOLARSHIPS

Ninety-Nines, Inc.
4300 Amelia Earhart Road
Oklahoma City, OK 73159
(405) 685-7969		Toll Free: (800) 994-1929
Fax: (405) 685-7985	E-mail: AEChair@ninety-nines.org
Web: www.ninety-nines.org/index.cfm/scholarships.htm

Summary To provide funding to members of the Ninety-Nines (an organization of women pilots) who are interested in advanced flight training or academic study related to aviation.

Eligibility This program is open to women who have been members of the organization for at least 1 year. Applicants must be interested in 1 of the following 4 types of scholarships: 1) flight training, to complete an additional pilot certificate or rating or pilot training course; 2) jet type rating, to complete type rating certification in any jet; 3) technical certification, to complete an aviation or aerospace technical training or certification course; or 4) academic, to work on an associate, bachelor's, master's, or doctoral degree in such

fields as aerospace engineering, aviation technology, aviation business management, air traffic management, or professional pilot. They must submit their application to their Ninety-Nines scholarship chair, who forwards it to the appropriate Amelia Earhart Scholarship Trustee. Applicants for flight training scholarships must be a current pilot with the appropriate medical certification and approaching the flight time requirement for the rating or certificate. Applicants for jet type rating scholarships must be a current airline transport pilot with a first-class medical certificate and at least 100 hours of multi-engine flight time or combined multi-engine and turbine time. Applicants for academic scholarships must be currently enrolled; associate or bachelor's degree students must have a GPA of 3.0 or higher. Financial need is considered in the selection process.

Financial data Flight training, jet type rating, and technical certification scholarships provide payment of all costs to complete the appropriate rating or certificate. Academic scholarships provide a stipend of up to $5,000 per year.

Duration Support is provided until completion of the rating, certificate, or degree.

Additional information This program was established in 1941. It includes the following endowed scholarships: the Jane Zieber Kelley Memorial Scholarship of the Aeons (established in 1979), the Gerda Ruhnke Memorial Flight Instructor Scholarship (established in 1988), the Geraldine Mickelsen Memorial Scholarship (established in 1993), the Alice Hammond Memorial Scholarship (established in 1995), the Lydiellen M. Hagan Memorial Scholarship (established in 1997), the Katherine A. Menges Brick Scholarship (established in 1998), the Betty DeWitt Witmer Scholarship (established in 1999), the Virginia S. Richardson Memorial Scholarship (established in 2000), the Darlene Sanders Memorial Scholarship (established in 2000), the Milton and Bonnie Seymour Memorial Scholarship (established in 2000), the Marion Barnick Memorial Scholarship (established in 2001), the Evelyn Bryan Johnson Memorial Scholarship (established in 2002), and the Mary Kelley Memorial Scholarship (established in 2003).

Number awarded Varies each year; recently, 14 of these scholarships were awarded.

Deadline Applications must be submitted to the chapter scholarship chair by November of each year; they must forward the applications from their chapter to the designated trustee by December of each year.

[1396]
NUPUR CHAUDHURI FIRST ARTICLE PRIZE

Coordinating Council for Women in History
c/o Sandra Dawson, Executive Director
Northern Illinois University
Department of History and Women's Studies
715 Zulauf Hall
DeKalb, IL 60115
(815) 895-2624		E-mail: execdir@theccwh.org
Web: theccwh.org/awards.htm

Summary To recognize and reward members of the Coordinating Council for Women in History (CCWH) who have published outstanding first articles in an historical journal.

Eligibility This award is available to CCWH members who have published an article in a refereed journal during the preceding 2 years. The article must be the first published by the candidate and must have full scholarly apparatus. All fields of history are eligible.

Financial data The award is $1,000.

Duration The award is presented annually.

Additional information This award was established in 2010.

Number awarded 1 each year.

Deadline September of each year.

[1397]
ONLINE BIBLIOGRAPHIC SERVICES/ TECHNICAL SERVICES JOINT RESEARCH GRANT

American Association of Law Libraries
Attn: Online Bibliographic Services Special Interest
  Section
105 West Adams Street, Suite 3300
Chicago, IL 60603
(312) 939-4764   Fax: (312) 431-1097
E-mail: aallhq@aall.org
Web: www.aallnet.org/sis/obssis/research/funding.htm

Summary To provide funding to members of the American Association of Law Libraries (AALL), particularly women and minorities, who are interested in conducting a research project related to technical services.

Eligibility This program is open to AALL members who are technical services law librarians. Preference is given to members of the Online Bibliographic Services and Technical Services Special Interest Sections, although members of other special interest sections are eligible if their work relates to technical services law librarianship. Applicants must be interested in conducting research that will enhance law librarianship. Women and minorities are especially encouraged to apply. Preference is given to projects that can be completed in the United States or Canada, although foreign research projects are given consideration.

Financial data Grants range up to $1,000.

Duration 1 year.

Number awarded 1 or more each year.

Deadline June of each year.

[1398]
ORANGE BROADBAND PRIZE FOR FICTION

Booktrust
45 East Hill
London SW18 2QZ
England
44 20 8516 2977   Fax: 44 20 8516 2978
E-mail: Claire.Shanahan@booktrust.org.uk
Web: www.orangeprize.co.uk

Summary To recognize and reward the most outstanding novels by women from any country that are written in English and published in the United Kingdom.

Eligibility Eligible to be considered for this prize are novels written by women (of any nationality) in English and published in the United Kingdom during the 12 months prior to March 31 of the year of the award. Submissions may also have been published in other countries, including the United States, as long as its first U.K. publication was within the prescribed time period. Ineligible works include books of short stories, novel-

las (stories between 12,000 and 30,000 words), and translations of books originally written in other languages.

Financial data The prize is 30,000 pounds and a bronze figurine known as the "Bessie."

Duration The prize is awarded annually.

Additional information This prize, first awarded in 1996, is the United Kingdom's largest annual literary award for a single novel. It is administered by Booktrust and sponsored by Orange Personal Communications Services Limited, the national digital wireless telephone service.

Number awarded 1 each year.

Deadline Deadline not specified.

[1399]
OREGON LITERARY FELLOWSHIPS TO WOMEN WRITERS

Literary Arts, Inc.
Attn: Oregon Book Awards and Fellowships Program
  Coordinator
224 N.W. 13th Avenue, Suite 306
Portland, OR 97209
(503) 227-2583   Fax: (503) 243-1167
E-mail: susan@literary-arts.org
Web: www.literary-arts.org/fellowships

Summary To provide funding to women writers in Oregon interested in working on a literary project.

Eligibility This program is open to women who are residents of Oregon and interested in initiating, developing, or completing a literary project in the areas of poetry, fiction, literary nonfiction, drama, or young readers' literature. Priority is given to women whose writing explores race, ethnicity, class, physical disability, and/or sexual orientation. Writers in the early stages of their careers are especially encouraged to apply. Selection is based primarily on literary merit.

Financial data Grants are at least $2,500.

Duration The grants are presented annually.

Additional information Funding for this program is provided by the Ralph L. Smith Foundation.

Number awarded 1 each year.

Deadline June of each year.

[1400]
OSHKOSH CHAPTER SPIRIT OF FLIGHT SCHOLARSHIP

Women in Aviation, International
Attn: Scholarships
Morningstar Airport
3647 State Route 503 South
West Alexandria, OH 45381-9354
(937) 839-4647   Fax: (937) 839-4645
E-mail: scholarships@wai.org
Web: www.wai.org/education/scholarships.cfm

Summary To provide funding to members of Women in Aviation, International (WAI) who are interested in working on an additional license or certificate.

Eligibility This program is open to women of any age who are WAI members and have already soloed. Applicants must be working on 1) a recreational, sport pilot, private pilot, or commercial certificate; 2) instrument or multiengine rating; or 3) certified flight instructor (CFI) license. They must submit 2 letters of recommendation, a 500-word essay on their aviation history and goals, a resume, copies of all aviation licenses and medical certificates, and the last 3 pages of their pilot logbook (if applicable). Preference is given to Wisconsin residents, but all who qualify are encouraged to apply. Selection is based on achievements, attitude toward self and others, commitment to success, dedication to career, financial need, motivation, reliability, responsibility, and teamwork.

Financial data   The stipend is $1,000. Funds are paid directly to the flight school.

Duration   Training must be completed within 1 year.

Additional information   WAI is a nonprofit professional organization dedicated to encouraging women to consider an aviation career and to providing educational outreach activities and networking resources to women active in the industry.

Number awarded   1 each year.

Deadline   November of each year.

[1401]
PAUL HOCH DISTINGUISHED SERVICE AWARD

American College of Neuropsychopharmacology
Attn: Executive Office
5034-A Thoroughbred Lane
Brentwood, TN 37027
(615) 324-2360   Fax: (615) 523-1715
E-mail: acnp@acnp.org
Web: www.acnp.org/programs/awards.aspx

Summary   To recognize and reward female, minority, and other members of the American College of Neuropsychopharmacology (ACNP) who have contributed outstanding service to the organization.

Eligibility   This award is available to ACNP members who have made unusually significant contributions to the College. The emphasis of the award is on service to the organization, not on teaching, clinical, or research accomplishments. Any member or fellow of ACNP may nominate another member. Nomination of women and minorities is highly encouraged.

Financial data   The award consists of an expense-paid trip to the ACNP annual meeting, a monetary honorarium, and a plaque.

Duration   The award is presented annually.

Additional information   This award was first presented in 1965.

Number awarded   1 each year.

Deadline   Nominations must be submitted by June of each year.

[1402]
PAULA DE MERIEUX RHEUMATOLOGY FELLOWSHIP AWARD

American College of Rheumatology
Attn: Research and Education Foundation
2200 Lake Boulevard N.E.
Atlanta, GA 30319
(404) 633-3777   Fax: (404) 633-1870
E-mail: ref@rheumatology.org
Web: www.rheumatology.org/ref/awards/index.asp

Summary   To provide funding to women and underrepresented minorities interested in a program of training for a career providing clinical care to people affected by rheumatic diseases.

Eligibility   This program is open to trainees at ACGME-accredited institutions. Applications must be submitted by the training program director at the institution who is responsible for selection and appointment of trainees. The program must train and prepare fellows to provide clinical care to those affected by rheumatic diseases. Trainees must be women or members of underrepresented minority groups, defined as Black Americans, Hispanics, and Native Americans (Native Hawaiians, Alaska Natives, and American Indians). They must be U.S. citizens, nationals, or permanent residents. Selection is based on the institution's pass rate of rheumatology fellows, publication history of staff and previous fellows, current positions of previous fellows, and status of clinical faculty.

Financial data   The grant is $25,000 per year, to be used as salary for the trainee. Other trainee costs (e.g., fees, health insurance, travel, attendance at scientific meetings) are to be incurred by the recipient's institutional program. Supplemental or additional support to offset the cost of living may be provided by the grantee institution.

Duration   Up to 1 year.

Additional information   This fellowship was first awarded in 2005.

Number awarded   1 each year.

Deadline   July of each year.

[1403]
PEARSON EARLY CAREER GRANT

American Psychological Foundation
750 First Street, N.E.
Washington, DC 20002-4242
(202) 336-5843   Fax: (202) 336-5812
E-mail: foundation@apa.org
Web: www.apa.org/apf/funding/pearson.aspx

Summary   To provide funding to early career psychologists (especially women, minorities, and individuals with disabilities) who are interested in conducting a project in an area of critical society need.

Eligibility   This program is open to psychologists who have an Ed.D., Psy.D., or Ph.D. from an accredited experience and no more than 7 years of postdoctoral experience. Applicants must be interested in conducting a project to improve areas of critical need in society, including (but not limited to) innovative scientifically-based clinical work with serious mental illness, serious emotional disturbance, incarcerated or homeless individuals, children with serious emotional disturbance (SED), or adults with serious mental illness (SMI). The sponsor encourages applications from individuals who represent diversity in race, ethnicity, gender, age, disability, and sexual orientation.

Financial data   The grant is $12,000.

Duration   1 year.

Additional information   This grant was first awarded in 2010.

Number awarded   1 each year.

Deadline   December of each year.

[1404]
PEGGY VATTER MEMORIAL SCHOLARSHIPS

Washington Science Teachers Association
c/o Patricia MacGowan, Washington MESA
University of Washington
P.O. Box 352181
Seattle, WA 98195-2181
(206) 543-0562   Fax: (206) 685-0666
E-mail: macgowan@engr.washington.edu
Web: www.wsta.net

Summary To provide financial assistance to upper-division students and teachers in Washington (preference given to women and minorities) who are interested in training in science education.

Eligibility This program is open to 1) juniors and seniors at colleges and universities in Washington who are working on certification in science education or in elementary education with an emphasis on science; and 2) certified teachers in Washington interested in improving their skills in providing equitable science education through professional development. In the student category, preference is given to African Americans, Hispanics, Native Americans, and women. Applicants must submit a 1-page essay on why they are applying for this scholarship.

Financial data The stipend is $1,500.

Duration 1 year; nonrenewable.

Additional information This program was established in 2003.

Number awarded 1 or more each year.

Deadline April of each year.

[1405]
PEMBROKE CENTER POSTDOCTORAL FELLOWSHIPS

Brown University
Attn: Pembroke Center for Teaching and Research on
  Women
172 Meeting Street
Box 1958
Providence, RI 02912
(401) 863-2643   Fax: (401) 863-1298
E-mail: Pembroke_Center@brown.edu
Web: www.pembrokecenter.org/research/postdoc.html

Summary To provide funding to postdoctoral scholars interested in conducting research at Brown University's Pembroke Center for Teaching and Research on Women on the cross-cultural study of gender.

Eligibility Fellowships are open to scholars in the humanities, social sciences, or life sciences who have completed their Ph.D. but do not have a tenured position at an American college or university. Applicants must be willing to spend a year in residence at the Pembroke Center for Teaching and Research on Women and participate in a research project related to gender. The project focuses on a theme that changes annually (recently: "Economics of Perception"). The center encourages underrepresented minority scholars to apply.

Financial data The stipend is $50,000. Health insurance is also provided.

Duration 1 academic year.

Additional information Postdoctoral fellows in residence participate in weekly seminars and present at least 2 public papers during the year, as well as conduct an individual research project. Supplementary funds are available for assistance with travel expenses from abroad. This program includes the following named fellowships: the Nancy L. Buc Postdoctoral Fellowship, the Artemis A.W. and Martha Joukowsky Postdoctoral Fellowship, and the Carol G. Lederer Postdoctoral Fellowship.

Number awarded 3 or 4 each year.

Deadline December of each year.

[1406]
P.E.O. SCHOLAR AWARDS

P.E.O. Sisterhood
Attn: Scholar Awards Office
3700 Grand Avenue
Des Moines, IA 50312-2899
(515) 255-3153   Fax: (515) 255-3820
E-mail: psa@peodsm.org
Web: www.peointernational.org/peo-projectsphilanthropies

Summary To provide funding for doctoral study or postdoctoral research in any field to women in the United States or Canada.

Eligibility This program is open to women who are either working full time on a doctoral degree or conducting postdoctoral research at universities in the United States or Canada. Applicants must be within 2 years of achieving their educational goal but have at least 1 full academic year remaining. They must be sponsored by a local P.E.O. chapter. Selection is based on academic record, academic awards and honors, scholarly activities, and recommendations; financial need is not considered. U.S. or Canadian citizenship is required.

Financial data A significant stipend is awarded (amount not specified).

Duration 1 year; nonrenewable.

Additional information This program was established in 1991 by the Women's Philanthropic Educational Organization (P.E.O.).

Number awarded Varies each year.

Deadline November of each year.

[1407]
PI BETA PHI ALUMNAE CONTINUING EDUCATION SCHOLARSHIPS

Pi Beta Phi
Attn: Pi Beta Phi Foundation
1154 Town and Country Commons Drive
Town and Country, MO 63017
(636) 256-1357   Fax: (636) 256-8124
E-mail: fndn@pibetaphi.org
Web: www.pibetaphifoundation.org/scholarship-program

Summary To provide financial assistance for graduate school or continuing education to alumnae of Pi Beta Phi.

Eligibility This program is open to women who are members of Pi Beta Phi in good standing and have paid their alumnae dues for the current year. Applicants must have been out of undergraduate school for at least 2 years and have a GPA of 3.0 or higher for all undergraduate and graduate study. Advanced work at a college or university is encouraged, but advanced study at a career, vocational, or technical school will also be considered. Along with their application, they must submit documentation of financial need, an employment history, a record of volunteer service, a description of the proposed program of study, transcripts, and recommendations. Selection is based on financial need, academic record, alumnae service, community service, and how the proposed course of study relates to future career development.

Financial data   Stipends range from $1,200 to $1,800.

Duration   1 year.

Additional information   This program was established in 1982.

Number awarded   Varies each year; recently, 4 of these scholarships were awarded.

Deadline   February of each year.

[1408]
PILOTMALL.COM AVIATION SUPERSTORE CFI SCHOLARSHIP

Women in Aviation, International
Attn: Scholarships
Morningstar Airport
3647 State Route 503 South
West Alexandria, OH 45381-9354
(937) 839-4647   Fax: (937) 839-4645
E-mail: scholarships@wai.org
Web: www.wai.org/education/scholarships.cfm

Summary   To provide financial assistance to members of Women in Aviation, International (WAI) who are interested in attending college or flight school to become a Certified Flight Instructor (CFI).

Eligibility   This program is open to WAI members who are enrolled at a flight school, college, or university to earn certification as a CFI. Applicants should have their Instrument Rating and Commercial Certificate and hold a second class medical. Along with their application, they must submit 2 letters of recommendation, a 500-word essay on their aviation history and goals, a resume, copies of all aviation licenses and medical certificates, and the last 3 pages of their pilot logbook (if applicable). Selection is based on achievements, attitude toward self and others, commitment to success, dedication to career, financial need, motivation, reliability, responsibility, and teamwork.

Financial data   The stipend is $1,250. Funds are paid directly to the flight school, college, or university.

Duration   Funds must be used within 1 year.

Additional information   WAI is a nonprofit professional organization dedicated to encouraging women to consider an aviation career and to providing educational outreach activities and networking resources to women active in the industry. This program was established in 2011 by PilotMall.com Aviation Superstore.

Number awarded   1 each year.

Deadline   November of each year.

[1409]
POSTDOCTORAL FELLOWSHIP IN THE HISTORY OF MODERN SCIENCE AND TECHNOLOGY IN EAST ASIA

Harvard University
Attn: Department of East Asian Languages and
   Civilizations
2 Divinity Avenue
Cambridge, MA 02138
(617) 495-2754   Fax: (617) 496-6040
E-mail: ealc@fas.harvard.edu
Web: harvardealc.org/postdoc.html

Summary   To provide funding to postdoctoral scholars (particularly women and minorities) who wish to conduct research at Harvard University on a topic related to the history of science and technology in east Asia.

Eligibility   This program is open to junior scholars who completed a Ph.D. within the past 5 years. Applicants must be interested in conducting research in residence at Harvard University to revise their dissertation and prepare it for publication. Preference is given to research projects exploring the understudied histories of modern science and technology in Korea and Japan, but all proposals concerning the development of science and technology in post-19th century east Asia are eligible. Applicants from women and minority candidates are strongly encouraged.

Financial data   The stipend is $43,000.

Duration   1 academic year.

Additional information   Fellows are provided with office space and access to the libraries and resources of Harvard University. They are invited to participate in the academic life of the Departments of East Asian Languages and Civilizations and the History of Science. Fellows are expected to reside in the Cambridge/Boston area during the term of the fellowship; work on revising their dissertation for publication; teach or collaborate on a course related to the history of modern science and/or technology in east Asia; and give at least 1 presentation of research to faculty and graduate students in East Asian Languages and Civilizations and the History of Science.

Number awarded   1 each year.

Deadline   February of each year.

[1410]
POSTDOCTORAL FELLOWSHIPS IN DIABETES RESEARCH

Juvenile Diabetes Research Foundation International
Attn: Grant Administrator
26 Broadway, 14th Floor
New York, NY 10004
(212) 479-7572   Toll Free: (800) 533-CURE
Fax: (212) 785-9595   E-mail: info@jdrf.org
Web: www.jdrf.org/index.cfm?page_id=111715

Summary   To provide research training to scientists (especially women, minorities, and individuals with disabilities) who are beginning their professional careers and are interested in participating in research training on the causes, treatment, prevention, or cure of diabetes or its complications.

Eligibility   This program is open to postdoctorates who are interested in a career in Type 1 diabetes-relevant research. Applicants must have received their first doctoral degree

(M.D., Ph.D., D.M.D., or D.V.M.) within the past 5 years and may not have a faculty appointment. There are no citizenship requirements. Applications are encouraged from women, members of minority groups underrepresented in the sciences, and people with disabilities. The proposed research training may be conducted at foreign or domestic, for-profit or nonprofit, or public or private institutions, including universities, colleges, hospitals, laboratories, units of state or local government, or eligible agencies of the federal government. Applicants must be sponsored by an investigator who is affiliated full time with an accredited institution and who agrees to supervise the applicant's training. Selection is based on the applicant's previous experience and academic record; the caliber of the proposed research; and the quality of the mentor, training program, and environment.

Financial data Stipends range from $37,740 to $47,940 (depending upon years of experience). In any case, the award may not exceed the salary the recipient is currently earning. Fellows also receive a research allowance of $5,500 per year.

Duration 1 year; may be renewed for up to 1 additional year.

Additional information Fellows must devote at least 80% of their effort to the fellowship project.

Deadline January or July of each year.

[1411]
POSTDOCTORAL RESEARCH TRAINING FELLOWSHIPS IN EPILEPSY

Epilepsy Foundation
Attn: Research Department
8301 Professional Place
Landover, MD 20785-2237
(301) 459-3700   Toll Free: (800) EFA-1000
Fax: (301) 577-2684   TDD: (800) 332-2070
E-mail: grants@efa.org
Web: www.epilepsyfoundation.org

Summary To provide funding for a program of postdoctoral training to academic physicians and scientists (particularly women, minorities, and individuals with disabilities) who are committed to epilepsy research.

Eligibility Applicants must have a doctoral degree (M.D., Sc.D., Ph.D., or equivalent) and be a clinical or postdoctoral fellow at a university, medical school, research institution, or medical center. They must be interested in participating in a training experience and research project that has potential significance for understanding the causes, treatment, or consequences of epilepsy. The program is geared toward applicants who will be trained in research in epilepsy rather than those who use epilepsy as a tool for research in other fields. Equal consideration is given to applicants interested in acquiring experience either in basic laboratory research or in the conduct of human clinical studies. Academic faculty holding the rank of instructor or higher are not eligible, nor are graduate or medical students, medical residents, permanent government employees, or employees of private industry. Applications from women, members of minority groups, and people with disabilities are especially encouraged. U.S. citizenship is not required, but the project must be conducted in the United States. Selection is based on scientific quality of the proposed research, a statement regarding its relevance to epilepsy, the applicant's qualifications, the preceptor's qualifi-

cations, and the adequacy of facility and related epilepsy programs at the institution.

Financial data The grant is $45,000. No indirect costs are covered.

Duration 1 year.

Additional information Support for this program is provided by many individuals, families, and corporations, especially the American Epilepsy Society, Abbott Laboratories, Ortho-McNeil Pharmaceutical, and Pfizer Inc. The fellowship must be carried out at a facility in the United States where there is an ongoing epilepsy research program.

Number awarded Varies each year.

Deadline August of each year.

[1412]
PRESIDENTIAL EARLY CAREER AWARDS FOR SCIENTISTS AND ENGINEERS

National Science and Technology Council
Executive Office of the President
Attn: Office of Science and Technology Policy
725 17th Street, Room 5228
Washington, DC 20502
(202) 456-7116   Fax: (202) 456-6021
Web: www.ostp.gov

Summary To recognize and reward the nation's most outstanding young science and engineering faculty members (particularly women, minorities, and individuals with disabilities) by providing them with additional research funding.

Eligibility Eligible for these awards are U.S. citizens, nationals, and permanent residents who have been selected to receive research grants from other departments of the U.S. government. Recipients of designated research grant programs are automatically considered for these Presidential Early Career Awards for Scientists and Engineers (PECASE). Most of the participating programs encourage applications from racial/ethnic minority individuals, women, and persons with disabilities.

Financial data Awards carry a grant of at least $80,000 per year.

Duration 5 years.

Additional information The departments with research programs that nominate candidates for the PECASE program are: 1) the National Aeronautics and Space Administration, which selects recipients of Early Career Awards based on exceptionally meritorious proposals funded through the traditional research grant process or the unsolicited proposal process; 2) the Department of Veterans Affairs, which nominates the most meritorious recipients of Veterans Health Administration Research Awards in the categories in medical research, rehabilitation research, and health services research; 3) the National Institutes of Health, which nominates the most meritorious investigators funded through its First Independent Research Support and Transition (FIRST) Awards and NIH Individual Research Project Grants (R01) programs; 4) the Department of Energy, which nominates staff members of the national laboratories and the most meritorious recipients of the DOE–Energy Research Young Scientist Awards and DOE–Defense Programs Early Career Scientist and Engineer Awards; 5) the Department of Defense, which nominates outstanding recipients of the Office of Naval Research Young Investigator Program, the Air Force Office of

Scientific Research Broad Agency Program, and the Army Research Office Young Investigator Program; 6) the Department of Agriculture, which nominates staff scientists from the Agricultural Research Service, the most meritorious investigators funded through the National Research Initiative Competitive Grants Program (NRICGP) New Investigator Awards, and staff scientists of the Forest Service; 7) the Department of Commerce, which nominates outstanding staff members of the National Oceanic and Atmospheric Administration and the National Institute of Standards and Technology; 8) the Department of Transportation, which nominates the most qualified and innovative researchers in its University Transportation Centers and University Research Institutes programs; and 9) the National Science Foundation, which selects its nominees from the most meritorious investigators funded through the Faculty Early Career Development (CAREER) Program. For a list of the names, addresses, and telephone numbers of contact persons at each of the participating agencies, contact the Office of Science and Technology Policy.

Number awarded Varies each year; recently, 85 of these awards were granted.

Deadline Deadline not specified.

[1413]
PRIORITY RESEARCH GRANTS

Juvenile Diabetes Research Foundation International
Attn: Grant Administrator
26 Broadway, 14th Floor
New York, NY 10004
(212) 479-7572   Toll Free: (800) 533-CURE
Fax: (212) 785-9595   E-mail: info@jdrf.org
Web: www.jdrf.org/index.cfm?page_id=111715

Summary To provide funding to scientists (particularly women, minorities, and individuals with disabilities) who are interested in conducting research on diabetes and its related complications.

Eligibility Applicants must have an M.D., D.M.D., D.V.M., Ph.D., or equivalent degree and have a full-time faculty position or equivalent at a college, university, medical school, or other research facility. They must be interested in conducting research related to the priorities of the Juvenile Diabetes Research Foundation (JDRF), which currently include 1) restoration and maintenance of normal glucose regulation in Type 1 diabetes, including restoration of beta cell function, immunoregulation, and metabolic control; 2) prevention and treatment of complications of diabetes; 3) improvements in glucose control; and 4) prevention of Type 1 diabetes. There are no citizenship requirements. Applications are encouraged from women, members of minority groups underrepresented in the sciences, and people with disabilities. The proposed research may be conducted at foreign or domestic, for-profit or nonprofit, or public or private institutions, including universities, colleges, hospitals, laboratories, units of state or local government, or eligible agencies of the federal government. Selection is based on potential to generate new approaches to unsolved scientific problems related to Type 1 diabetes; relevance to the objectives of JDRF: scientific, technical, or medical significance of the research proposal; innovativeness; appropriateness and adequacy of the experimental approach and methodology; qualifications and research experience of the principal investigator and collaborators;

availability of resources and facilities necessary for the project; and appropriateness of the proposed budget in relation to the proposed research.

Financial data Grants up to $165,000 (plus 10% for indirect costs) per year are available.

Duration 3 years.

Deadline Letters of intent must be submitted by November of each year.

[1414]
PROFESSIONAL ASSOCIATES PROGRAM FOR WOMEN AND MINORITIES AT BROOKHAVEN NATIONAL LABORATORY

Brookhaven National Laboratory
Attn: Diversity Office, Human Resources Division
Building 400B
P.O. Box 5000
Upton, New York 11973-5000
(631) 344-2703   Fax: (631) 344-5305
E-mail: palmore@bnl.gov
Web: www.bnl.gov/diversity/programs.asp

Summary To provide professional experience in scientific areas at Brookhaven National Laboratory (BNL) to women and members of other underrepresented groups.

Eligibility This program is open to underrepresented minorities (African Americans, Hispanics, or Native Americans), people with disabilities, and women. Applicants must have earned at least a bachelor's degree and be seeking professional experience in such fields as biology, chemistry, computer science, engineering, health physics, medical research, or physics. They must plan to attend a graduate or professional school and express an interest in long-term employment at BNL. U.S. citizenship or permanent resident status is required.

Financial data Participants receive a competitive salary.

Duration 1 year.

Additional information Interns work in a goal-oriented on-the-job training program under the supervision of employees who are experienced in their areas of interest.

Number awarded Varies each year.

Deadline Applications may be submitted at any time.

[1415]
R. ROBERT & SALLY D. FUNDERBURG RESEARCH AWARD IN GASTRIC CANCER

American Gastroenterological Association
Attn: AGA Research Foundation
Research Awards Manager
4930 Del Ray Avenue
Bethesda, MD 20814-2512
(301) 222-4012   Fax: (301) 654-5920
E-mail: awards@gastro.org
Web: www.gastro.org/aga-foundation/grants

Summary To provide funding to established investigators (especially women and minorities) who are working on research that enhances fundamental understanding of gastric cancer pathobiology.

Eligibility This program is open to faculty at accredited North American institutions who have established themselves as independent investigators in the field of gastric biology, pursuing novel approaches to gastric mucosal cell biology, including the fields of gastric mucosal cell biology, regeneration and regulation of cell growth, inflammation as precancerous lesions, genetics of gastric carcinoma, oncogenes in gastric epithelial malignancies, epidemiology of gastric cancer, etiology of gastric epithelial malignancies, or clinical research in diagnosis or treatment of gastric carcinoma. Applicants must be individual members of the American Gastroenterological Association (AGA). Women and minority investigators are strongly encouraged to apply. Selection is based on the novelty, feasibility, and significance of the proposal. Preference is given to novel approaches.

Financial data The grant is $50,000 per year. Funds are to be used for the salary of the investigator. Indirect costs are not allowed.

Duration 2 years.

Number awarded 1 each year.

Deadline September of each year.

[1416]
RESEARCH AND TRAINING FELLOWSHIPS IN EPILEPSY FOR CLINICIANS

Epilepsy Foundation
Attn: Research Department
8301 Professional Place
Landover, MD 20785-2237
(301) 459-3700   Toll Free: (800) EFA-1000
Fax: (301) 577-2684   TDD: (800) 332-2070
E-mail: clinical_postdocs@efa.org
Web: www.epilepsyfoundation.org

Summary To provide funding to clinically-trained professionals (especially women, minorities, and individuals with disabilities) who are interested in gaining additional training in order to develop an epilepsy research program.

Eligibility Applicants must have an M.D., D.O., Ph.D., D.S., or equivalent degree and be a clinical or postdoctoral fellow at a university, medical school, or other appropriate research institution. Holders of other doctoral-level degrees (e.g., Pharm.D., D.S.N.) may also be eligible. Candidates must be interested in a program of research training that may include mechanisms of epilepsy, novel therapeutic approaches, clinical trials, development of new technologies, or behavioral and psychosocial impact of epilepsy. The training program may consist of both didactic training and a supervised research experience that is designed to develop the necessary knowledge and skills in the chosen area of research and foster the career goals of the candidate. Academic faculty holding the rank of instructor or higher are not eligible, nor are graduate or medical students, medical residents, permanent government employees, or employees of private industry. Applications from women, members of minority groups, and people with disabilities are especially encouraged. U.S. citizenship is not required, but the project must be conducted in the United States. Selection is based on the quality of the proposed research training program, the applicant's qualifications, the preceptor's qualifications, and the adequacy of clinical training, research facilities, and other epilepsy-related programs at the institution.

Financial data The grant is $50,000 per year. No indirect costs are provided.

Duration Up to 2 years.

Additional information Support for this program is provided by many individuals, families, and corporations, espe-

cially the American Epilepsy Society, Abbott Laboratories, Ortho-McNeil Pharmaceutical, and Pfizer Inc. Grantees are expected to dedicate at least 50% of their time to research training and conducting research.

Number awarded Varies each year.

Deadline September of each year.

[1417]
RESEARCH GRANTS OF THE RESEARCH ON GENDER IN SCIENCE AND ENGINEERING PROGRAM

National Science Foundation
Directorate for Education and Human Resources
Attn: Division of Human Resource Development
4201 Wilson Boulevard, Room 815N
Arlington, VA 22230
(703) 292-7303   Fax: (703) 292-9018
TDD: (800) 281-8749   E-mail: jjesse@nsf.gov
Web: www.nsf.gov/funding/pgm_summ.jsp?pims_id=5475

Summary To provide funding to investigators interested in conducting research related to the underrepresentation of girls and women in science, technology, engineering, or mathematics (STEM) education.

Eligibility This program is open to investigators interested in conducting research designed to 1) discover and describe gender-based differences and preferences in learning STEM at the K-16 levels and factors that affect interest, performance, and choice of STEM study and careers in fields where there are significant gender gaps; 2) discover and describe how experiences and interactions in informal and formal educational settings inhibit or encourage interest and performance of students based on gender; 3) increase the knowledge about organizational models that lead to more equitable and inviting STEM educational environments at the K-16 levels; or 4) increase knowledge of the process of institutional change required to achieve more equitable and inviting STEM educational environments at the K-16 levels. Behavioral, cognitive, affective, learning, and social differences may be investigated, using methods of sociology, psychology, anthropology, economics, statistics or other social and behavioral science and education disciplines. Gender should be the major variable in the analysis.

Financial data Grants up to a total of $525,000 are available.

Duration Up to 3 years.

Additional information The National Science Foundation (NSF) established the Research on Gender in Science and Engineering (GSE) program in 1993 under the name "Program for Women and Girls." That was replaced with the "Program for Gender Equity in Science, Mathematics, Engineering and Technology," and then in the 2003 fiscal year by "Gender Diversity in STEM Education." The current title became effective in the 2007 fiscal year.

Number awarded 7 to 10 each year. The GSE program plans to award 15 to 22 grants per year for research, outreach and communication, and extension service activities. A total of $5,000,000 is available for the program annually.

Deadline Letters of intent must be submitted in February of each year; full proposals are due in March.

[1418]
RITA MAE KELLY ENDOWMENT FELLOWSHIP

American Political Science Association
Attn: Centennial Center Visiting Scholars Program
1527 New Hampshire Avenue, N.W.
Washington, DC 20036-1206
(202) 483-2512   Fax: (202) 483-2657
E-mail: center@apsanet.org
Web: www.apsanet.org/content_3436.cfm

Summary To provide funding to women, minority, and other members of the American Political Science Association (APSA) who are interested in conducting research on the intersection of gender, race, ethnicity, and political power at the Centennial Center for Political Science and Public Affairs.

Eligibility This program is open to members of the association who are interested in conducting research on the intersection of gender, race, ethnicity, and political power while in residence at the center. Support is available to pre-dissertation graduate students as well as for an award or public presentation. Nonresident scholars may also be eligible.

Financial data Grants provide supplemental financial support to resident scholars.

Duration 2 weeks to 12 months.

Additional information The APSA launched its Centennial Center for Political Science and Public Affairs in 2003 to commemorate the centennial year of the association. This program was established in affiliation with the Women's Caucus for Political Science, the Latina Caucus for Political Science, the Committee for the Status of Latino/Latinas in the Profession, the Women and Politics Research Organized Section, and the Race, Ethnicity and Politics Organized Section.

Number awarded 1 or more each year.

Deadline February, June, or October of each year.

[1419]
RJOS/OREF/DEPUY RESEARCH GRANT IN WOMEN'S MUSCULOSKELETAL HEALTH

Orthopaedic Research and Education Foundation
Attn: Vice President, Grants
6300 North River Road, Suite 700
Rosemont, IL 60018-4261
(847) 698-9980   Fax: (847) 698-7806
E-mail: communications@oref.org
Web: www.oref.org

Summary To provide funding to female orthopedic surgeons who are interested in a program of research training in women's musculoskeletal health.

Eligibility This program is open to female orthopedic surgeons who are members of the Ruth Jackson Orthopaedic Society (RJOS). Applicants must be interested in participating in a program of training to enhance their understanding of gender and diversity differences in the outcomes of orthopedic procedures.

Financial data The grant is $45,000.

Duration 1 year.

Number awarded 1 each year.

Deadline September of each year.

[1420]
ROBERT L. FANTZ MEMORIAL AWARD

American Psychological Foundation
750 First Street, N.E.
Washington, DC 20002-4242
(202) 336-5843   Fax: (202) 336-5812
E-mail: foundation@apa.org
Web: www.apa.org/apf/funding/fantz.aspx

Summary To provide funding to promising young investigators in psychology, particularly women, minorities, and individuals with disabilities.

Eligibility This program is open to young investigators in psychology or related disciplines. Candidates must show 1) evidence of basic scientific research or scholarly writing in perceptual-cognitive development and the development of selection attention; and 2) research and writing on the development of individuality, creativity, and free-choice of behavior. The sponsor encourages applications from individuals who represent diversity in race, ethnicity, gender, age, disability, and sexual orientation.

Financial data The award is $2,000. Funds are paid directly to the recipient's institution for equipment purchases, travel, computer resources, or other expenses related to the work recognized by the award.

Duration The award is presented annually.

Additional information This award was first presented in 1992.

Number awarded 1 each year.

Deadline Deadline not specified.

[1421]
RONA JAFFE FOUNDATION FELLOWSHIP

Vermont Studio Center
80 Pearl Street
P.O. Box 613
Johnson, VT 05656
(802) 635-2727   Fax: (802) 635-2730
E-mail: info@vermontstudiocenter.org
Web: www.vermontstudiocenter.org

Summary To provide funding to emerging women writers who are interested in a residency at the Vermont Studio Center in Johnson, Vermont.

Eligibility This program is open to women writers of fiction, poetry, or creative nonfiction who are unpublished, or have begun publishing in literary journals, or are just completing their first book. Applicants must be interested in a first-time residency at the center in Johnson, Vermont. Poets must submit up to 10 pages or their work and other writers must submit 10 to 15 pages. Selection is based on artistic merit. U.S. citizenship or permanent resident status is required.

Financial data The award pays $3,750, which covers all residency fees. An additional stipend of $1,250 is designed to help cover expenses associated with taking the residency, including (but not limited to) travel, rent, child care, or the replacement of lost income.

Duration 4 weeks.

Additional information This award is sponsored by the Rona Jaffe Foundation. The application fee is $25.

Number awarded 1 each year.

Deadline September of each year.

[1422]
ROSE MARY CRAWSHAY PRIZES

British Academy
Attn: Chief Executive and Secretary
10-11 Carlton House Terrace
London SW1Y 5AH
England
44 20 7969 5255   Fax: 44 20 7969 5300
E-mail: chiefexec@britac.ac.uk
Web: www.britac.ac.uk/about/medals/crawshay.cfm

Summary To recognize and reward women who have written or published outstanding historical or critical works on any subject connected with English literature.

Eligibility Women of any nationality are eligible to be nominated if within the preceding 3 years they have written an historical or critical work on any subject connected with English literature. Preference is given to works on Byron, Shelley, or Keats. Submissions are invited from publishing houses only.

Financial data The prize is 500 pounds.

Duration The prize is awarded each year.

Additional information The prize was established by Rose Mary Crawshay in 1888.

Number awarded 2 each year.

Deadline December of each year.

[1423]
RUTH AND LINCOLN EKSTROM FELLOWSHIP

Brown University
Attn: John Carter Brown Library
P.O. Box 1894
Providence, RI 02912
(401) 863-2725   Fax: (401) 863-3477
E-mail: JCBL_Fellowships@Brown.edu
Web: www.brown.edu

Summary To support scholars and graduate students interested in conducting research on the history of women at the John Carter Brown Library, which is renowned for its collection of historical sources pertaining to the Americas prior to 1830.

Eligibility This fellowship is open to U.S.-based and foreign graduate students, scholars, and independent researchers. Graduate students must have passed their preliminary or general examinations. Applicants must be proposing to conduct research on the history of women and the family in the Americas prior to 1825, including the question of cultural influences on gender formation. Selection is based on the applicant's scholarly qualifications, the merits and significance of the project, and the particular need that the holdings of the John Carter Brown Library will fill in the development of the project.

Financial data The stipend is $2,100 per month.

Duration From 2 to 4 months.

Additional information Fellows are expected to be in regular residence at the library and to participate in the intellectual life of Brown University for the duration of the program.

Number awarded 1 or more each year.

Deadline December of each year.

[1424]
RUTH ANDERSON PRIZE

International Alliance for Women in Music
c/o Pamela Marshall, Search for New Music Competition
  Coordinator
38 Dexter Road
Lexington, MA 02420
E-mail: snm@iawm.org
Web: www.iawm.org/oppsComp_snm.htm

Summary To recognize and reward members of the International Alliance for Women (IAWM) who are commissioned to compose a new sound installation for electro-acoustic music.

Eligibility This award is presented to an IAWM member who is commissioned to compose a new sound installation for electro-acoustic music. Applicants must submit a detailed proposal of the sound installation. The location of the installation may be, but is not restricted to, an IAWM annual concert or congress.

Financial data The prize is $1,000. The prize is presented to the recipient after submitting a report to IAWM following the public showing of the completed installation.

Duration The project must be completed within 12 months.

Number awarded 1 each year.

Deadline March of each year.

[1425]
RUTH I. MICHLER MEMORIAL PRIZE

Association for Women in Mathematics
11240 Waples Mill Road, Suite 200
Fairfax, VA 22030
(703) 934-0163   Fax: (703) 359-7562
E-mail: michlerprize@awm-math.org
Web: sites.google.com

Summary To recognize and reward, with a fellowship at Cornell University, outstanding women mathematicians.

Eligibility This prize is available to women recently promoted to associate professor or equivalent position in the mathematical sciences at an institution of higher learning other than Cornell University. Applicants may be of any nationality and hold a position in any country. They must submit a proposal describing a research or book project to be undertaken during the fellowship period and explaining how the semester in the mathematics department at Cornell University will enhance their project or research career. Selection is based on the excellence of the applicant's research and the potential benefit to her of a semester in the mathematics department at Cornell.

Financial data The prize is $46,000. A supplemental housing and subsistence award of $3,000 is also provided.

Duration The prize is presented annually. The recipient may spend a semester of her choice in residence at Cornell.

Additional information This prize was first presented in 2007.

Number awarded 1 each year.

Deadline October of each year.

[1426]
RUTH JACKSON ORTHOPAEDIC SOCIETY PRACTICE ENRICHMENT TRAVELING FELLOWSHIP

Ruth Jackson Orthopaedic Society
6300 North River Road, Suite 727
Rosemont, IL 60018-4226
(847) 698-1626   Fax: (847) 823-0536
E-mail: rjos@aaos.org
Web: www.rjos.org/web/awards/index.htm

Summary To provide funding to female orthopedic surgeons who are interested in traveling to enhance their practice.

Eligibility This program is open to women who are members of the Ruth Jackson Orthopaedic Society (RJOS). Applicants must be Board Eligible orthopedic surgeons and citizens of the United States or Canada. They must be interested in a program of travel to learn new techniques or expand their sub-specialty interests.

Financial data Grants up to $6,000 are available.

Additional information Funding for this program is provided by Zimmer, Inc.

Number awarded 1 each year.

Deadline September of each year.

[1427]
RUTH LYTTLE SATTER PRIZE IN MATHEMATICS

American Mathematical Society
Attn: Prizes and Awards
201 Charles Street
Providence, RI 02904-2294
(401) 455-4107   Toll Free: (800) 321-4AMS
Fax: (401) 455-4046
Web: www.ams.org/profession/prizes-awards/prizes

Summary To recognize and reward women who have made outstanding contributions to mathematics.

Eligibility This program is open to female mathematicians who have made outstanding contributions to research in the field. The work must have been completed within the past 6 years.

Financial data The prize is $5,000.

Duration The prize is awarded biennially, in odd-numbered years.

Additional information This prize was first awarded in 1991.

Number awarded 1 every other year.

Deadline June of each even-numbered year.

[1428]
RUTH R. AND ALYSON R. MILLER FELLOWSHIPS

Massachusetts Historical Society
Attn: Short-Term Fellowships
1154 Boylston Street
Boston, MA 02215-3695
(617) 646-0568   Fax: (617) 859-0074
E-mail: fellowships@masshist.org
Web: www.masshist.org/fellowships/short_term.cfm

Summary To fund research visits to the Massachusetts Historical Society for graduate students and other scholars interested in women's history.

Eligibility This program is open to advanced graduate students, postdoctorates, and independent scholars who are conducting research in women's history and need to use the resources of the Massachusetts Historical Society. Applicants must be U.S. citizens or foreign nationals holding appropriate U.S. government documents. Along with their application, they must submit a curriculum vitae and a proposal describing the project and indicating collections at the society to be consulted. Graduate students must also arrange for a letter of recommendation from a faculty member familiar with their work and with the project being proposed. Preference is given to candidates who live 50 or more miles from Boston.

Financial data The grant is $2,000.

Duration 4 weeks.

Additional information This fellowship was first awarded in 1998.

Number awarded 1 or more each year.

Deadline February of each year.

[1429]
SARA WHALEY BOOK PRIZE

National Women's Studies Association
Attn: Book Prizes
7100 Baltimore Avenue, Suite 203
College Park, MD 20740
(301) 403-0407   Fax: (301) 403-4137
E-mail: nwsaoffice@nwsa.org
Web: www.nwsa.org/awards/index.php

Summary To recognize and reward members of the National Women's Studies Association (NWSA) who have written outstanding books on topics related to women and labor.

Eligibility This award is available to NWSA members who submit a book manuscript that relates to women and labor, including migration and women's paid jobs, illegal immigration and women's work, impact of AIDS on women's employment, trafficking of women and women's employment, women and domestic work, or impact of race on women's work. Both senior scholars (who have a record of publication of at least 2 books and published the entry within the past year) and junior scholars (who have a publication contract or a book in production) are eligible. U.S. women of color and women of international origin are encouraged to apply.

Financial data The award is $2,000.

Duration The awards are presented annually.

Additional information This award was first presented in 2008.

Number awarded 2 each year: 1 to a senior scholar and 1 to a junior scholar.

Deadline April of each year.

[1430]
SARAH BRADLEY TYSON MEMORIAL FELLOWSHIP

Woman's National Farm and Garden Association, Inc.
P.O. Box 1175
Midland, MI 48641-1175
E-mail: SBTfellowship@aol.com
Web: www.wnfga.org/fellowships.htm

Summary To provide funding to women college graduates with several years of experience who are interested in advanced study in agriculture, horticulture, and allied subjects.

Eligibility The fellowship is open to women interested in working on an advanced degree in the fields of agriculture, horticulture, or allied subjects at educational institutions of recognized standing within the United States. Applicants must have several years of experience. There are no application forms. Interested women should send a letter of application that contains an account of their educational training, a plan of study, references, samples of publishable papers, and a health certificate.

Financial data The fellowship award is $1,000 and is tenable at an American institution of higher learning chosen by the candidate with the approval of the fellowship committee.

Duration 1 year.

Additional information This program was established in 1928. Students who accept the fellowships must agree to devote themselves to the study outlined in their application and to submit any proposed change in their plan to the committee for approval. They must send the committee at least 2 reports on their work, 1 at the end of the first semester and another upon completion of the year's work.

Number awarded Varies each year.

Deadline April of each year.

[1431]
SCHMIEDER LEADERSHIP SCHOLARSHIP

Women of the Evangelical Lutheran Church in America
Attn: Scholarships
8765 West Higgins Road
Chicago, IL 60631-4101
(773) 380-2736   Toll Free: (800) 638-3522, ext. 2736
Fax: (773) 380-2419   E-mail: Women.elca@elca.org
Web: www.elca.org

Summary To provide financial assistance to female faculty members at Evangelical Lutheran Church of America (ELCA) institutions who want to attend a leadership and management summer training institute.

Eligibility This program is open to female faculty at ELCA colleges, universities, and seminaries. Applicants must be interested in enrolled at a summer institute of their choice, provided that the program includes work in governance, financial management, administration, and professional development. They must be nominated by the president of their institution, which also must agree to provide partial assistance for the program. Preference is given to applicants who have a terminal degree in their discipline and who have at least 3 years of experience in teaching or administration.

Financial data The program provides a grant of $2,000 to $4,000; additional funding must be provided by the recipient's institution.

Duration These are 1-time grants.

Additional information Recipients are expected to submit an evaluation of the institute experience to the sponsor within 3 months of the training and to share learning experiences with colleagues at their home institution and, if requested, at Women of the ELCA events.

Number awarded Varies each year, depending upon the funds available.

Deadline February of each year.

[1432]
SHARON KEILLOR AWARD FOR WOMEN IN ENGINEERING EDUCATION

American Society for Engineering Education
Attn: Manager, Administrative Services
1818 N Street, N.W., Suite 600
Washington, DC 20036-2479
(202) 331-3500   Fax: (202) 265-8504
Web: www.asee.org/activities/awards/special.cfm

Summary To recognize and reward outstanding women engineering educators.

Eligibility This award is presented to a woman engineering educator who has an outstanding record in teaching engineering students and reasonable performance histories of research and service within an engineering school. Nominees must have an earned doctoral degree in an engineering discipline and have at least 5 years of teaching experience in an engineering school.

Financial data The award consists of a $2,000 honorarium and an inscribed plaque.

Duration The award is granted annually.

Number awarded 1 each year.

Deadline January of each year.

[1433]
SHERRY APPLE RESIDENT TRAVEL SCHOLARSHIP

American Association of Neurological Surgeons
Attn: Grants Coordinator
5550 Meadowbrook Drive
Rolling Meadows, IL 60008-3852
(847) 378-0500   Toll Free: (888) 566-AANS
Fax: (847) 378-0600   E-mail: cap@aans.org
Web: www.neurosurgerywins.org/resident/index.html

Summary To recognize and reward female neurosurgical residents who submit outstanding abstracts for presentation at the annual meeting of the Congress of Neurological Surgeons (CNS).

Eligibility This program is open to female neurosurgical residents who submit outstanding pioneering clinical or laboratory research abstracts for presentation at the CNS annual meeting.

Financial data The award consists of $2,000.

Duration The award is presented annually.

Additional information This award, first presented in 2006, is sponsored by Women in Neurosurgery.

Number awarded 1 each year.

Deadline Deadline not specified.

[1434]
SHIRLEY HOLDEN HELBERG ART GRANTS FOR MATURE WOMEN

National League of American Pen Women
1300 17th Street, N.W.
Washington, DC 20036-1973
(202) 785-1997   Fax: (202) 452-8868
E-mail: nlapw1@verizon.net
Web: www.americanpenwomen.org

Summary To recognize and reward, with funding for additional education, mature women artists.

Eligibility Women artists or photographers who are 35 years of age or older are eligible to apply if neither they nor members of their immediate family are members of the league. They must submit 3 color prints (4 by 5 inches or larger) of any media (oil, water color, original works on paper, acrylic, or sculpture) or 3 color or black-and-white prints (4 by 6 inches) of photographic works. U.S. citizenship is required.

Financial data The award is $1,000. Funds are to be used for education.

Duration The award is granted biennially.

Additional information An entry fee of $10 and a self-addressed stamped envelope must accompany each application.

Number awarded 1 each even-numbered year.

Deadline January of even-numbered years.

[1435]
SHIRLEY HOLDEN HELBERG LETTERS GRANTS FOR MATURE WOMEN

National League of American Pen Women
1300 17th Street, N.W.
Washington, DC 20036-1973
(202) 785-1997   Fax: (202) 452-8868
E-mail: nlapw1@verizon.net
Web: www.americanpenwomen.org

Summary To recognize and reward, with funding for additional education, mature women writers.

Eligibility Women writers who are 35 years of age or older are eligible to apply if they (or their immediate family) are not affiliated with the league. They must submit an unpublished manuscript, up to 3,000 words in length, of an article, drama, essay, chapter of a novel, 3 poems, short story, or television script. U.S. citizenship is required.

Financial data The award is $1,000. Funds are to be used for education.

Duration The award is granted biennially.

Additional information An entry fee of $10 and a self-addressed stamped envelope must accompany each application.

Number awarded 1 each even-numbered year.

Deadline January of even-numbered years.

[1436]
SHIRLEY HOLDEN HELBERG MUSIC GRANTS FOR MATURE WOMEN

National League of American Pen Women
1300 17th Street, N.W.
Washington, DC 20036-1973
(202) 785-1997   Fax: (202) 452-8868
E-mail: nlapw1@verizon.net
Web: www.americanpenwomen.org

Summary To recognize and reward, with funding for additional education, mature women composers.

Eligibility Women composers who are 35 years of age or older are eligible to apply if they (or their immediate family) are not affiliated with the sponsor. They must submit 2 compositions with performance times of 3 minutes and a separate composition with a performance time of 5 minutes. U.S. citizenship is required.

Financial data The award is $1,000. Funds are to be used for education.

Duration The award is granted biennially.

Additional information An entry fee of $10 and a self-addressed stamped envelope must accompany each application.

Number awarded 1 each even-numbered year.

Deadline January of even-numbered years.

[1437]
SIGMA DELTA EPSILON FELLOWSHIPS

Sigma Delta Epsilon-Graduate Women in Science, Inc.
c/o Julie Gros-Louis, Fellowships Coordinator
University of Iowa-Department of Psychology
11 Seashore Hall E
Iowa City, IA 52242-1407
(319) 384-1816   Fax: (319) 335-0191
E-mail: Julie-gros-louis@uiowa.edu
Web: www.gwis.org/programs.htm

Summary To provide funding to women interested in conducting research anywhere in the world in the natural sciences.

Eligibility This program is open to women from any country currently enrolled as a graduate student, engaged in post-doctoral research, or holding a junior faculty position. Applicants must be interested in conducting research anywhere in the world in the natural sciences (including physical, environmental, mathematical, computer, or life sciences), anthropology, psychology, or statistics. Along with their application, they must submit 2-paragraph essays on 1) how the proposed research relates to their degree program and/or career development; 2) initiatives in which they are participating to promote the careers of scientists, particularly women, within their institution, program, or peer group; and 3) relevant personal factors, including financial need, that should be considered in evaluating their proposal. Appointments are made without regard to race, religion, nationality, creed, national origin, sexual orientation, or age.

Financial data Grants are $3,500 or $2,500. Funds may be used for such research expenses as expendable supplies, small equipment, publication of research findings, travel and subsistence while performing field studies, or travel to another laboratory for collaborative research. They may not be used for tuition, child care, travel to professional meetings or to begin a new appointment, administrative overhead or indirect costs, personal computers, living allowances, or equipment for general use.

Duration 1 year.

Additional information The highest scoring applicant receives the Adele Lewis Fellowship. The second-highest scoring applicant receives the Hartley Corporation Fellowship. An application processing fee of $30 is required.

Number awarded Varies each year; recently, 3 of these grants were awarded: the Adele Lewis Fellowship at $3,500, 1 other fellowship at $3,500, and the Hartley Corporation Fellowship at $2,500.

Deadline January of each year.

[1438]
SOCIETY OF AVIATION AND FLIGHT EDUCATORS SCHOLARSHIP

Women in Aviation, International
Attn: Scholarships
Morningstar Airport
3647 State Route 503 South
West Alexandria, OH 45381-9354
(937) 839-4647   Fax: (937) 839-4645
E-mail: scholarships@wai.org
Web: www.wai.org/education/scholarships.cfm

Summary To provide financial assistance to members of Women in Aviation, International (WAI) who are aviation educators interested in furthering their credentials, knowledge, or skills.

Eligibility This program is open to WAI members who possess current aviation instructor credentials (such as sport pilot, flight, ground, or maintenance instructor) or have an ongoing history of teaching an aviation technical subject at any level. Applicants must be interested in attending a school or recognized program to further their instructional credentials, knowledge, or skills. Along with their application, they must submit 2 letters of recommendation, a 500-word essay on their aviation history and goals (including a summary of their current involvement in aviation education), a resume, copies of all aviation licenses and medical certificates, a copy of documentation as an aviation educator, and the last 3 pages of their pilot logbook (if applicable). Selection is based on achievements, attitude toward self and others, commitment to success, dedication to career, financial need, motivation, reliability, responsibility, and teamwork.

Financial data The stipend is $1,000. Funds are paid directly to the school.

Duration Funds must be used within 1 year.

Additional information WAI is a nonprofit professional organization dedicated to encouraging women to consider an aviation career and to providing educational outreach activities and networking resources to women active in the industry. This program was established in 2011 by the Society of Aviation and Flight Educators (SAFE).

Number awarded 1 each year.

Deadline November of each year.

[1439]
SOCIETY OF PEDIATRIC PSYCHOLOGY DIVERSITY RESEARCH GRANT

American Psychological Association
Attn: Division 54 (Society of Pediatric Psychology)
c/o John M. Chaney
Oklahoma State University
Department of Psychology
407 North Murray
Stillwater, OK 74078
(405) 744-5703   E-mail: john.chaney@okstate.edu
Web: www.societyofpediatricpsychology.org

Summary To provide funding to women, minority, and other graduate student and postdoctoral members of the Society of Pediatric Psychology who are interested in conducting research on diversity aspects of pediatric psychology.

Eligibility This program is open to current members of the society who are graduate students, fellows, or early-career (within 3 years of appointment) faculty. Applicants must be interested in conducting pediatric psychology research that features diversity-related variables, such as race or ethnicity, gender, culture, sexual orientation, language differences, socioeconomic status, and/or religiosity. Along with their application, they must submit a 2,000-word description of the project, including its purpose, methodology, predictions, and implications; a detailed budget; a current curriculum vitae, and (for students) a curriculum vitae of the faculty research mentor and a letter of support from that mentor. Selection is based on relevance to diversity in child health (5 points), significance of the study (5 points), study methods and procedures (10 points), and investigator qualifications (10 points).

Financial data Grants up to $1,000 are available. Funds may not be used for convention or meeting travel, indirect costs, stipends of principal investigators, or costs associated with manuscript preparation.

Duration The grant is presented annually.

Additional information The Society of Pediatric Psychology is Division 54 of the American Psychological Association (APA). This grant was first presented in 2008.

Number awarded 1 each year.

Deadline September of each year.

[1440]
SONIA KOVALEVSKY HIGH SCHOOL MATHEMATICS DAYS GRANTS

Association for Women in Mathematics
11240 Waples Mill Road, Suite 200
Fairfax, VA 22030
(703) 934-0163   Fax: (703) 359-7562
E-mail: awm@awm-math.org
Web: sites.google.com

Summary To provide funding to women, minority, and other faculty at colleges and universities who wish to conduct Sonia Kovalevsky High School and Middle School Mathematics Days.

Eligibility Faculty and staff at universities and colleges may apply for these grants to support Sonia Kovalevsky High School and Middle School Mathematics Days; staff at Historically Black Colleges and Universities are particularly encouraged to apply. Programs targeted towards inner-city or rural high schools are especially welcomed. The proposed activity should consist of workshops, talks, and problem-solving competitions for female high school or middle school students and their teachers (both women and men).

Financial data The maximum grant is $3,000; most range from $1,500 to $2,200. Funds must be used for direct costs for the activity. Stipends and personnel costs are not permitted for organizers. Reimbursement for indirect costs or fringe benefits is not allowed.

Duration The grants are awarded annually.

Additional information This program is supported by grants from the National Security Agency and Elizabeth City State University.

Number awarded 12 to 20 each year.

Deadline August or February of each year.

[1441]
SPECIAL FUND FOR THE STUDY OF WOMEN AND POLITICS

American Political Science Association
Attn: Centennial Center Visiting Scholars Program
1527 New Hampshire Avenue, N.W.
Washington, DC 20036-1206
(202) 483-2512   Fax: (202) 483-2657
E-mail: center@apsanet.org
Web: www.apsanet.org/content_3436.cfm

Summary   To provide funding to members of the American Political Science Association (APSA) who are interested in conducting research on women and politics at the Centennial Center for Political Science and Public Affairs.

Eligibility   This program is open to members of the association who are interested in conducting research on women and politics while in residence at the center. Junior faculty members, postdoctoral fellows, and advanced graduate students are strongly encouraged to apply, but scholars at all stages of their careers are eligible. International applicants are also welcome if they have demonstrable command of spoken English. Nonresident scholars may also be eligible.

Financial data   Grants provide supplemental financial support to resident scholars.

Duration   2 weeks to 12 months.

Additional information   The APSA launched its Centennial Center for Political Science and Public Affairs in 2003 to commemorate the centennial year of the association.

Number awarded   1 or more each year.

Deadline   February, June, or October of each year.

[1442]
SPORTY'S FOUNDATION FLIGHT TRAINING SCHOLARSHIP

Women in Aviation, International
Attn: Scholarships
Morningstar Airport
3647 State Route 503 South
West Alexandria, OH 45381-9354
(937) 839-4647   Fax: (937) 839-4645
E-mail: scholarships@wai.org
Web: www.wai.org/education/scholarships.cfm

Summary   To provide funding to members of Women in Aviation, International (WAI) who are interested in working on a recreational pilot certificate.

Eligibility   This program is open to women who are WAI members and working on a recreational pilot certificate. Applicants may not be working toward achieving instrument rating, commercial, multiengine, instructor certificate, or another endorsement. They must submit 2 letters of recommendation, a 500-word essay on their aviation history and goals, a resume, copies of all aviation licenses and medical certificates, and the last 3 pages of their pilot logbook (if applicable). Selection is based on achievements, attitude toward self and others, commitment to success, dedication to career, financial need, motivation, reliability, responsibility, and teamwork.

Financial data   The stipend is $5,000. Funds are paid jointly to the recipient and the flight trainer.

Duration   Training must be completed within 1 year.

Additional information   WAI is a nonprofit professional organization dedicated to encouraging women to consider an aviation career and to providing educational outreach activities and networking resources to women active in the industry.

Number awarded   1 each year.

Deadline   November of each year.

[1443]
SSRC ABE FELLOWSHIP PROGRAM

Social Science Research Council
Attn: Japan Program
One Pierrepont Plaza, 15th Floor
Brooklyn, NY 11201
(212) 377-2700   Fax: (212) 377-2727
E-mail: abe@ssrc.org
Web: www.ssrc.org/fellowships/abe-fellowship

Summary   To provide funding to postdoctoral scholars (especially women and minorities) who are interested in conducting research on contemporary policy-relevant affairs in Japan.

Eligibility   This program is open to citizens of the United States and Japan as well as to nationals of other countries (especially women and minorities) who can demonstrate strong and serious long-term affiliations with research communities in Japan or the United States. Applicants must have a Ph.D. or the terminal degree for their field, or have attained an equivalent level of professional experience. They should be interested in conducting multidisciplinary research on topics of pressing global concern. Currently, research must focus on the 3 themes of traditional and nontraditional approaches to security and diplomacy, global and regional economic issues, or the role of civil society. Previous language training is not a prerequisite for this fellowship. Minorities and women are particularly encouraged to apply.

Financial data   The terms of the fellowship include a base award and funds to pay supplementary research and travel expenses as necessary for completion of the research project.

Duration   The program provides support for 3 to 12 months over a 24-month period.

Additional information   Fellows are expected to affiliate with an American or Japanese institution appropriate to their research aims. In addition to receiving fellowship awards, fellows attend annual Abe Fellows Conferences, which promote the development of an international network of scholars concerned with research on contemporary policy issues. Funds are provided by the Japan Foundation's Center for Global Partnership. Fellows should plan to spend at least one-third of their tenure abroad in Japan or the United States.

Deadline   August of each year.

[1444]
SUBARU OUTSTANDING WOMAN IN SCIENCE AWARD

Geological Society of America
Attn: Program Officer-Grants, Awards and Recognition
3300 Penrose Place
P.O. Box 9140
Boulder, CO 80301-9140
(303) 357-1028   Toll Free: (800) 472-1988, ext. 1028
Fax: (303) 357-1070   E-mail: awards@geosociety.org
Web: www.geosociety.org/awards/aboutAwards.htm

Summary To recognize and reward women who have exerted a major impact on the field of geosciences through their Ph.D. research.

Eligibility This program is open to women geoscientists who are within 3 years of completion of their Ph.D. degree. Nominations should include a letter that describes how the Ph.D. research has impacted geosciences in a major way, a short summary of the research, a short resume with a list of publications, and a copy of the dissertation abstract, published abstracts, and/or reprints if available.

Financial data The award is $2,500.

Duration The award is presented annually.

Additional information This award, first presented in 2001, is sponsored by Subaru of America, Inc. It was formerly named the Doris M. Curtis Memorial Fund for Women in Science Award.

Number awarded 1 each year.

Deadline January of each year.

[1445]
SUPPLEMENTS TO PROMOTE REENTRY INTO BIOMEDICAL AND BEHAVIORAL RESEARCH CAREERS

National Institutes of Health
Attn: Office of Research on Women's Health
6707 Democracy Boulevard, Suite 400
Bethesda, MD 20892-5484
(301) 402-1770   Fax: (301) 402-1798
TDD: (301) 451-5936
E-mail: ODORWH-research@mail.nih.gov
Web: grants.nih.gov/grants/guide/index.html

Summary To provide research grants to support individuals with high potential who wish to reenter an active research career after taking time off to care for children or parents or to attend to other family responsibilities.

Eligibility Principal investigators on various research awards from the National Institutes of Health (NIH) may submit a request for an administrative supplement to support an eligible candidate interested in reestablishing a research career. The parent grant must have at least 2 years of support remaining. Candidates must have a doctoral degree (M.D., D.D.S., Ph.D., O.D., D.V.M., or equivalent) and sufficient prior research experience to qualify for a doctoral-level research staff or faculty position. In general, they must have undergone a career interruption for at least 1 but no more than 8 years. Examples of qualifying career interruptions include child rearing; an incapacitating illness or injury of the candidate, spouse, partner, or member of the immediate family; relocation to accommodate a spouse, partner, or other family member; pursuit of non-research endeavors that would permit ear-

lier retirement of debt incurred in obtaining a doctoral degree; and military service. Candidates who have begun the reentry process through a fellowship, traineeship, or similar mechanism are not eligible. The program is not intended to support additional graduate training or career changes from non-research to research careers. Only U.S. citizens, nationals, and permanent residents are eligible.

Financial data The proposed salary and fringe benefits for the candidate must be in accordance with the salary structure of the grantee institution, consistent with the level of effort. Up to $10,000 may be requested for supplies, domestic travel, and publication costs relevant to the proposed research.

Duration Up to 3 years.

Additional information Supplements provided under this program may be for either part-time or full-time support for the candidate; all supported time is to be spent updating and enhancing research skills. Awards under this program are available from all NIH agencies. The names and addresses of staff people at each agency are available from the NIH.

Number awarded Varies each year.

Deadline Applications may be submitted at any time.

[1446]
SUSAN SMITH BLACKBURN PRIZE

Susan Smith Blackburn Prize, Inc.
c/o Emilie S. Kilgore, Chair
3239 Avalon Place
Houston, TX 77019-5917
(713) 522-8529
Web: www.blackburnprize.org

Summary To recognize and reward women who have written works of outstanding quality for the English-speaking theater.

Eligibility This award is available to women who have written a full-length play in English. Playwrights may not submit their work directly. Each year, prominent professionals (directors or literary managers) are asked to nominate plays from the United States, United Kingdom, Ireland, Canada, South Africa, Australia, and New Zealand for consideration. Plays are eligible whether or not they have been produced, but any premier production must have taken place within the preceding 12 months. Each script is read by at least 3 members of a screening committee in order to select 10 finalists. All final nominations are read by all 6 judges.

Financial data The prizes are $20,000 to the winner, $5,000 for special commendation, and $1,000 to each of the other finalists.

Duration The prizes are awarded annually.

Additional information The prizes are administered in Houston, London, and New York by a board of directors who choose 6 judges each year, 3 in the United States and 3 in the United Kingdom. The prize was established in 1978 by the friends and family of Susan Smith Blackburn, the American writer/actress who spent the last 15 years of her life in London.

Number awarded 1 winner, 1 special commendation recipient, and 8 other finalists are chosen each year.

Deadline September of each year.

[1447]
SUSIE PRYOR AWARD IN ARKANSAS WOMEN'S HISTORY

Arkansas Women's History Institute
P.O. Box 7704
Little Rock, AR 72217
Web: www.arkansaswomen.org

Summary To recognize and reward the best unpublished essay or article on topics related to Arkansas women's history.

Eligibility This competition is open to authors at any academic level from any state. Applicants must submit manuscripts, from 20 to 35 pages in length, on a topic related to the history of women in Arkansas. Entries are judged on the basis of 1) contribution to knowledge of women in Arkansas history; 2) use of primary and secondary materials; 3) creative interpretation; 4) originality; and 5) stylistic excellence.

Financial data The prize is $1,000.

Duration The prize is awarded annually.

Additional information The winning paper may be published in the *Arkansas Historical Quarterly*. This prize was first awarded in 1986 as a feature of Arkansas' sesquicentennial celebration. All entries, including illustrations, become the property of the Arkansas Women's History Institute and will not be returned. They will be placed in archival collections that receive contributions from the institute.

Number awarded 1 each year.

Deadline February of each year.

[1448]
SWS FEMINIST LECTURER AWARD

Sociologists for Women in Society
Attn: Executive Officer
University of Rhode Island
Department of Sociology
10 Chafee Road
Kingston, RI 02881
(401) 874-9510   Fax: (401) 874-2588
E-mail: swseo@socwomen.org
Web: www.socwomen.org

Summary To bring major feminist scholars to campuses that might otherwise not be able to afford to do so.

Eligibility Feminists scholars (with advanced degrees or the equivalent experience) are eligible to be nominated. They must be interested in delivering a lecture at 2 college campuses that are rural, isolated, or not located in or near major metropolitan centers.

Financial data The society pays the recipient $1,000 as an honorarium and provides travel funds (up to $750) to visit each site; the host college pays the remainder of the travel expenses and other direct costs.

Duration The award is presented annually.

Additional information This program was established in 1985. The lecture may be published in the association's journal, *Gender and Society*.

Number awarded 1 lecturer is selected each year; 2 institutions are selected to host her.

Deadline Nominations for the lecturer and applications from institutions interested in serving as a host are due by March of each year.

[1449]
SYLVIA LANE MENTOR RESEARCH FELLOWSHIP

Committee on Women in Agricultural Economics
c/o Cheryl Doss
Yale University
MacMillan Center
P.O. Box 208206
New Haven, CT 06520-8206
(203) 432-9395   E-mail: Cheryl.Doss@yale.edu
Web: www.aaea.org/sections/cwae/lane.htm

Summary To provide funding to young female scholars who are working on food, agricultural, or resource issues and interested in relocating in order to conduct research with an established expert at another university, institution, or firm.

Eligibility These fellowships are awarded to mentee/mentor pairs of individuals. Mentees must have completed at least 1 year in residence in an accredited American graduate degree program in agricultural economics or a closely-related discipline; women with Ph.D. degrees and advanced graduate students are encouraged to apply. Mentors must have a Ph.D. and established expertise in an area of food, agriculture, or natural resources. The goal is to enable female scholars to relocate in order to conduct research with an established expert at another university, institution, or firm, even though they may reside in different parts of the country or the world. Selection is based on the relevance of the research problem, potential for generating output, synergy of the mentor/mentee pairing, and opportunity for advancing the mentee's research skills beyond her graduate studies and current position.

Financial data Awards may be used to cover direct research costs, travel, and temporary relocation expenses for the mentee.

Duration Several weeks.

Additional information This program is sponsored by the American Agricultural Economics Association Foundation and by academic, foundation, and industry donors; it is administered by the Committee on Women in Agricultural Economics.

Number awarded 1 each year.

Deadline September of each year.

[1450]
TAKEDA RESEARCH SCHOLAR AWARD IN GASTROESOPHAGEAL REFLUX DISEASE

American Gastroenterological Association
Attn: AGA Research Foundation
Research Awards Manager
4930 Del Ray Avenue
Bethesda, MD 20814-2512
(301) 222-4012   Fax: (301) 654-5920
E-mail: awards@gastro.org
Web: www.gastro.org/aga-foundation/grants

Summary To provide research funding to young investigators (especially women and minorities) who are developing an independent career in an area related to gastroesophageal reflux disease.

Eligibility This program is open to investigators interested in conducting research related to gastroesophageal reflux disease. Applicants must hold full-time faculty positions at

North American universities or professional institutes at the time of application. They should be early in their careers (fellows and established investigators are not appropriate candidates). Candidates with an M.D. degree must have completed clinical training within the past 5 years and those with a Ph.D. must have completed their degree within the past 5 years. Membership in the American Gastroenterological Association (AGA) is required. Selection is based on significance, investigator, innovation, approach, environment, relevance to AGA mission, and evidence of institutional commitment. Women, underrepresented minorities, physician/scientist investigators, and candidates interested in translational research are strongly encouraged to apply.

Financial data The grant is $60,000 per year. Funds are to be used for project costs, including salary, supplies, and equipment but excluding travel. Indirect costs are not allowed.

Duration 2 years.

Additional information This program is supported by Takeda Pharmaceuticals. At least 70% of the recipient's effort should involve research related to the digestive system.

Number awarded 1 each year.

Deadline September of each year.

[1451]
THEODORE BLAU EARLY CAREER AWARD FOR OUTSTANDING CONTRIBUTION TO PROFESSIONAL CLINICAL PSYCHOLOGY

American Psychological Foundation
750 First Street, N.E.
Washington, DC 20002-4242
(202) 336-5843   Fax: (202) 336-5812
E-mail: foundation@apa.org
Web: www.apa.org/apf/funding/blau.aspx

Summary To recognize and reward young clinical psychologists (particularly women, minorities, and individuals with disabilities) who have made outstanding professional accomplishments.

Eligibility This award is available to clinical psychologists who are no more than 7 years past completion of their doctoral degree. Nominees must have a record of accomplishments that may include promoting the practice of clinical psychology through professional service; innovation in service delivery; novel application of applied research methodologies to professional practice; positive impact on health delivery systems; development of creative educational programs for practice; or other novel or creative activities advancing the service of the profession. Self-nominations are accepted. The sponsor encourages nominations of individuals who represent diversity in race, ethnicity, gender, age, disability, and sexual orientation.

Financial data The award is $5,000.

Duration The award is presented annually.

Additional information This award, first presented in 1998, is sponsored by Division 12 (Society of Clinical Psychology) of the American Psychological Association.

Number awarded 1 each year.

Deadline Nominations must be submitted by October of each year.

[1452]
THEODORE MILLON AWARD IN PERSONALITY PSYCHOLOGY

American Psychological Foundation
750 First Street, N.E.
Washington, DC 20002-4242
(202) 336-5843   Fax: (202) 336-5812
E-mail: foundation@apa.org
Web: www.apa.org/apf/funding/millon.aspx

Summary To recognize and reward psychologists (especially women, minorities, and individuals with disabilities) who have made outstanding contributions to the science of personality psychology.

Eligibility This award is available to psychologists engaged in advancing the science of personality psychology, including the areas of personology, personality theory, personality disorders, and personality measurement. Nominees should be between 8 and 20 years past completion of their doctoral degree. The sponsor encourages nominations of individuals who represent diversity in race, ethnicity, gender, age, disability, and sexual orientation.

Financial data The award is $1,000.

Duration The award is presented annually.

Additional information This award, established in 2004, is sponsored by Division 12 (Society of Clinical Psychology) of the American Psychological Association.

Number awarded 1 each year.

Deadline Nominations must be submitted by October of each year.

[1453]
TIMOTHY JEFFREY MEMORIAL AWARD IN CLINICAL HEALTH PSYCHOLOGY

American Psychological Foundation
750 First Street, N.E.
Washington, DC 20002-4242
(202) 336-5843   Fax: (202) 336-5812
E-mail: foundation@apa.org
Web: www.apa.org/apf/funding/jeffrey.aspx

Summary To recognize and reward psychologists (especially women, minorities, and individuals with disabilities) who have made outstanding contributions to clinical health psychology.

Eligibility This award is available to full-time providers of direct clinical services who demonstrate an outstanding commitment to clinical health psychology. Nominees must be members of Division 38 (Health Psychology) of the American Psychological Association. Letters of nomination should be accompanied by a curriculum vitae, at least 1 letter of support from a non-psychologist professional colleague, and another letter of support from a psychologist colleague. The sponsor encourages nominations of individuals who represent diversity in race, ethnicity, gender, age, disability, and sexual orientation.

Financial data The award is $3,000.

Duration The award is presented annually.

Additional information This award is sponsored by Division 38.

Number awarded 1 each year.

Deadline April of each year.

[1454]
TRANSLATION COMPETITION

Brandeis University
Hadassah-Brandeis Institute
Attn: Program Manager
515 South Street
Mailstop 079
Waltham, MA 02454-9110
(781) 736-2064   Fax: (781) 736-2078
E-mail: hbi@brandeis.edu
Web: www.brandeis.edu/hbi/grants/grants.html

Summary To provide funding for the translation of books that deal with Jewish women's studies, generally from another language into English.

Eligibility This program is open to authors of books that deal in a significant way with Jews and gender and to potential translators who have the author's permission to translate the book. The book to be translated must already have been published in another language and may be fiction, academic scholarship, or a trade book with general public interest. Preference is given to books to be translated from another language into English.

Financial data Grant amounts vary, and may be used only for payment of actual translation costs.

Duration Grants are awarded annually.

Additional information The Hadassah-Brandeis Institute was formerly the Hadassah International Research Institute on Jewish Women at Brandeis University.

Number awarded 1 or more each year.

Deadline Applications may be submitted at any time.

[1455]
TWINING HUMBER AWARD FOR LIFETIME ARTISTIC ACHIEVEMENT

Artist Trust
Attn: Director of Grant Programs
1835 12th Avenue
Seattle, WA 98122-2437
(206) 467-8734   Toll Free: (866) 21-TRUST
Fax: (206) 467-9633   E-mail: info@artisttrust.org
Web: artisttrust.org/index.php/for-artists/money

Summary To recognize and reward the artistic achievements of older women artists in Washington.

Eligibility Eligible to be nominated for this award are women visual artists over 60 years of age from Washington state. Nominees must have devoted at least 25 years of their lives to creating art. Selection is based on creative excellence, professional accomplishment, and dedication to the visual arts.

Financial data The award is $10,000.

Duration The award is presented annually.

Number awarded At least 1 each year.

Deadline December of each year.

[1456]
UNIVERSITY OF CALIFORNIA PRESIDENT'S POSTDOCTORAL FELLOWSHIP PROGRAM FOR ACADEMIC DIVERSITY

University of California at Berkeley
Attn: Office of Equity and Inclusion
102 California Hall
Berkeley, CA 94720-1508
(510) 643-6566   E-mail: kadkinson@berkeley.edu
Web: www.ucop.edu/acadadv/ppfp

Summary To provide an opportunity to conduct research at campuses of the University of California to recent postdoctorates (particularly women, minorities, and individuals with disabilities) who are committed to careers in university teaching and research and who will contribute to diversity.

Eligibility This program is open to U.S. citizens or permanent residents who have a Ph.D. from an accredited university. Applicants must be proposing to conduct research at a branch of the university under the mentorship of a faculty or laboratory sponsor. Preference is given to applicants 1) with the potential to bring to their academic careers the critical perspective that comes from their nontraditional educational background or their understanding of the experiences of groups historically underrepresented in higher education; 2) who have the communications skill and cross-cultural abilities to maximize effective collaboration with a diverse cross-section of the academic community; 3) who have demonstrated significant academic achievement by overcoming barriers such as economic, social, or educational disadvantage; and 4) who have the potential to contribute to higher education through their understanding of the barriers facing women, domestic minorities, students with disabilities, and other members of groups underrepresented in higher education careers, as evidenced by life experiences and educational background.

Financial data The stipend ranges from $40,000 to $50,000, depending on the field and level of experience. The program also offers health benefits and up to $4,000 for supplemental and research-related expenses.

Duration Appointments are for 1 academic year, with possible renewal for a second year.

Additional information Research may be conducted at any of the University of California's 10 campuses (Berkeley, Davis, Irvine, Los Angeles, Merced, Riverside, San Diego, San Francisco, Santa Barbara, or Santa Cruz). The program provides mentoring and guidance in preparing for an academic career. This program was established in 1984 to encourage applications from minority and women scholars in fields where they were severely underrepresented; it is now open to all qualified candidates who are committed to university careers in research, teaching, and service that will enhance the diversity of the academic community at the university.

Number awarded 15 to 20 each year.

Deadline November of each year.

[1457]
UNIVERSITY OF HOUSTON AFRICAN AMERICAN STUDIES PROGRAM VISITING SCHOLARS

University of Houston
African American Studies Program
Attn: Visiting Scholars Program
629 Agnes Arnold Hall
Houston, TX 77204-3047
(713) 743-2811   Fax: (713) 743-2818
E-mail: jconyers@uh.edu
Web: www.class.uh.edu/aas

Summary To provide support to junior scholars (especially women, minorities, and individuals with disabilities) who are interested in conducting research on the African American community while affiliated with the University of Houston's African American Studies Program.

Eligibility Applications are sought from junior scholars in social sciences, humanities, or African American studies who completed their Ph.D. within the past 6 years. They must be interested in conducting research on the African American community while affiliated with the University of Houston's African American Studies Program and in assuming a tenured or tenure-track position there after their residency as a Visiting Scholar is completed. They must be available for consultation with students and professional colleagues, make at least 2 formal presentations based on their research project, and contribute generally to the intellectual discourse in the discipline of African Studies/Africology. Along with their application, they must submit a current curriculum vitae, a 2-page description of the proposed research, 3 letters of recommendation, and a syllabus of the undergraduate course to be taught. Minorities, women, veterans, and persons with disabilities are specifically encouraged to apply.

Financial data Visiting Scholars receive a salary appropriate to their rank.

Duration 1 academic year.

Additional information Visiting Scholars are assigned a research assistant, if needed, and are provided administrative support. Recipients must teach 1 class related to African American studies. They are required to be in residence at the university for the entire academic year and must make 2 presentations on their research. In addition, they must acknowledge the sponsor's support in any publication that results from their tenure at the university.

Number awarded At least 2 each year.

Deadline February of each year.

[1458]
VANESSA RUDLOFF SCHOLARSHIP PROGRAM

Texas Women in Law Enforcement
Attn: Scholarship Awards Chair
P.O. Box 542376
Dallas, TX 75354-2376
E-mail: suggestions@twle.net
Web: www.twle.net

Summary To provide financial assistance to members of Texas Women in Law Enforcement (TWLE) and their relatives who are interested in attending college in any state.

Eligibility This program is open to 1) members of TWLE who have been active for the past 2 years, are currently in good standing with their department, are enrolled at an accredited college or university in any state, and submit a 1-page essay stating why they deserve the scholarship; 2) dependents of TWLE members who are entering a college or university in any state; are the spouse, child, brother, sister, niece, nephew, or grandchild of the member; are in the top 25% of their graduating class; have a cumulative high school GPA of 3.0 or higher; submit 2 letters of recommendation; and submit a 500-word essay on an assigned topic that changes annually; and 3) dependents of TWLE members who are already enrolled full time at a college or university in any state, have a college GPA of 3.0 or higher, and submit a 500-word essay on an assigned topic that changes annually. For dependents, the sponsor must have been an active member of TWLE for the past 2 years. Financial need is not considered in the selection process.

Financial data The stipend is $1,000.

Duration 1 year.

Number awarded At least 4 each year.

Deadline March of each year.

[1459]
VERNA ROSS ORNDORFF CAREER PERFORMANCE AWARD

Sigma Alpha Iota Philanthropies, Inc.
One Tunnel Road
Asheville, NC 28805
(828) 251-0606   Fax: (828) 251-0644
E-mail: nh@sai-national.org
Web: www.sigmaalphaiota.org

Summary To provide funding for advanced study, coaching, or other activities directly related to the development of a musical career to members of Sigma Alpha Iota (an organization of women musicians).

Eligibility This program is open to members of the organization who are preparing for a concert career. Singers may not be older than 35 years of age and instrumentalists may not be older than 32. Applicants may not have professional management, but they must have had considerable performing experience outside the academic environment.

Financial data The grant is $5,000; funds must be used for advanced study, coaching, or other purposes directly related to the development of a professional performing career.

Duration 1 year.

Additional information The area supported rotates annually among strings, woodwinds, and brass (2011); piano, harpsichord, organ, and percussion (2012); and voice (2013).

Number awarded 1 each year.

Deadline March of each year.

[1460]
VESSA NOTCHEV FELLOWSHIP

Sigma Delta Epsilon-Graduate Women in Science, Inc.
c/o Julie Gros-Louis, Fellowships Coordinator
University of Iowa-Department of Psychology
11 Seashore Hall E
Iowa City, IA 52242-1407
(319) 384-1816   Fax: (319) 335-0191
E-mail: Julie-gros-louis@uiowa.edu
Web: www.gwis.org/programs.htm

Summary To provide funding to women interested in conducting research anywhere in the world in the natural sciences.

Eligibility This program is open to women from any country currently enrolled as a graduate student, engaged in postdoctoral research, or holding a junior faculty position. Applicants must be interested in conducting research anywhere in the world in the natural sciences (including physical, environmental, mathematical, computer, or life sciences), anthropology, psychology, or statistics. Along with their application, they must submit 2-paragraph essays on 1) how the proposed research relates to their degree program and/or career development; 2) initiatives in which they are participating to promote the careers of scientists, particularly women, within their institution, program, or peer group; and 3) relevant personal factors, including financial need, that should be considered in evaluating their proposal. Appointments are made without regard to race, religion, nationality, creed, national origin, sexual orientation, or age.

Financial data The grant currently is $3,000. Funds may be used for such research expenses as expendable supplies, small equipment, publication of research findings, travel and subsistence while performing field studies, or travel to another laboratory for collaborative research. They may not be used for tuition, child care, travel to professional meetings or to begin a new appointment, administrative overhead or indirect costs, personal computers, living allowances, or equipment for general use.

Duration 1 year.

Additional information This program was established in 1994. An application processing fee of $30 is required.

Number awarded 1 each year.

Deadline January of each year.

[1461]
VICKI CRUSE MEMORIAL SCHOLARSHIP

Women in Aviation, International
Attn: Scholarships
Morningstar Airport
3647 State Route 503 South
West Alexandria, OH 45381-9354
(937) 839-4647   Fax: (937) 839-4645
E-mail: scholarships@wai.org
Web: www.wai.org/education/scholarships.cfm

Summary To provide funding to members of Women in Aviation, International (WAI) who are interested in pursuing aerobatic flight training.

Eligibility This program is open to women who are WAI members and have a private pilot certificate and valid third class medical certificate. Applicants must be interested in undertaking basic aerobatic or unusual attitude flight training (or further training for skills already acquired in that regimen). They must submit 2 letters of recommendation, a 500-word essay on their aviation history and goals, a resume, copies of all aviation licenses and medical certificates, and the last 3 pages of their pilot logbook (if applicable). Selection is based on achievements, attitude toward self and others, commitment to success, dedication to career, financial need, motivation, reliability, responsibility, and teamwork.

Financial data The stipend is $1,000. Funds are paid directly to the flight school.

Duration Training must be completed within 1 year.

Additional information WAI is a nonprofit professional organization dedicated to encouraging women to consider an aviation career and to providing educational outreach activities and networking resources to women active in the industry. This program is sponsored by Aero-News Network (ANN).

Number awarded 2 each year.

Deadline November of each year.

[1462]
VICTORIA FISHER MEMORIAL PRIZE ESSAY

University of Leicester
Attn: Faculty of Law
Leicester
LE1 7RH
United Kingdom
44 116 252 2363   Fax: 44 116 252 5023
E-mail: law@leicester.ac.uk
Web: www.le.ac.uk/law/news/fisher.html

Summary To recognize and reward outstanding essays on topics related to women and the law.

Eligibility Entries are encouraged from people regardless of age, experience, qualifications, or place of residence, as long as they have never had work published in a learned journal or as a nonfiction book. Essays may be on any topic relating to women and the law, up to 10,000 words in length, in English.

Financial data The prize is 250 pounds.

Duration The competition is held annually.

Number awarded 1 each year.

Deadline September of each year.

[1463]
VICTORIA SCHUCK AWARD

American Political Science Association
1527 New Hampshire Avenue, N.W.
Washington, DC 20036-1206
(202) 483-2512   Fax: (202) 483-2657
E-mail: apsa@apsanet.org
Web: www.apsanet.org/content_4129.cfm

Summary To recognize and reward outstanding scholarly books on women and politics.

Eligibility Eligible to be nominated (by publishers or individuals) are scholarly political science books issued the previous year on women and politics.

Financial data The award is $1,000.

Duration The award is presented annually.

Additional information This award was first presented in 1988.

Number awarded 1 each year.

Deadline January of each year for nominations from individuals; February of each year for nominations from publishers.

[1464]
VIOLET DILLER PROFESSIONAL EXCELLENCE AWARD

Iota Sigma Pi
c/o Dr. Sara Paisner, National Director for Professional
  Awards
Lord Corporation
110 Lord Drive
Cary, NC 27511
(919) 469-2500, ext. 2490   Fax: (919) 469-9688
E-mail: sara.paisner@lord.com
Web: www.iotasigmapi.info

Summary To recognize exceptional and significant achievement by women working in chemistry or allied fields.

Eligibility Nominees for the award must be women chemists who have made significant contributions to academic, governmental, or industrial chemistry; in education; in administration; or in a combination of those areas. They may be from any country and need not be members of Iota Sigma Pi. Each active chapter is entitled to make only 1 nomination, but individual members, individual chemists, or groups of chemists may make independent nominations if properly documented. Contributions may include innovation design, development, application, or promotion of a principle or practice that has widespread significance to the scientific community or society on a national level.

Financial data The award consists of $1,000, a certificate, and a lifetime waiver of Iota Sigma Pi dues.

Duration The award is granted triennially (2014, 2017, etc.).

Additional information This award was first presented in 1984.

Number awarded 1 every 3 years.

Deadline Nominations must be submitted by February of the year of award.

[1465]
VITO MARZULLO INTERNSHIP PROGRAM

Office of the Governor
Attn: Department of Central Management Services
503 William G. Stratton Building
Springfield, IL 62706
(217) 524-1381   Fax: (217) 558-4497
TDD: (217) 785-3979
Web: www.ilga.gov/commission/lru/internships.html

Summary To provide an internship to recent college graduates (particularly women, minorities, and persons with disabilities) who are interested in working in the Illinois Governor's office.

Eligibility This program is open to residents of Illinois who have completed a bachelor's degree and are interested in working in the Illinois Governor's office or in various agencies under the Governor's jurisdiction. Applicants may have majored in any field, but they must be able to demonstrate a substantial commitment to excellence as evidenced by academic honors, leadership ability, extracurricular activities, and involvement in community or public service. Along with their application, they must submit 1) a 500-word personal statement on the qualities or attributes they will bring to the program, their career goals or plans, how their selection for this program would assist them in achieving those goals, and

what they expect to gain from the program; and 2) a 1,000-word essay in which they identify and analyze a public issue that they feel has great impact on state government. A particular goal of the program is to achieve affirmative action through the nomination of qualified minorities, women, and persons with disabilities.

Financial data The stipend is $2,611 per month.

Duration 1 year, beginning in August.

Additional information Assignments are in Springfield and, to a limited extent, in Chicago or Washington, D.C.

Number awarded Varies each year.

Deadline February of each year.

[1466]
W. NEWTON LONG AWARD

American College of Nurse-Midwives
Attn: ACNM Foundation, Inc.
8403 Colesville Road, Suite 1550
Silver Spring, MD 20910-6374
(240) 485-1850   Fax: (240) 485-1818
Web: www.midwife.org/foundation_award.cfm

Summary To provide funding to midwives who are interested in conducting a research or other project in the United States or abroad.

Eligibility This program is open to midwives, including certified nurse midwives (CNMs) and certified midwives (CMs). Applicants must be seeking funding for a project that relates to 1 or more of the following areas: advancement of nurse-midwifery clinical skills; advancement of nurse-midwifery through research; dissemination of nurse-midwifery research; promotion of professional nurse-midwifery; presentations by nurse midwives at medical or midwifery conferences; establishment of new nurse-midwifery practice or service; or study of different aspects of nurse-midwifery practice in the United States and abroad.

Financial data The maximum grant is $1,000.

Duration The grants are presented annually.

Number awarded 1 or 2 each year.

Deadline April of each year.

[1467]
WAI/BOEING COMPANY CAREER ENHANCEMENT SCHOLARSHIP

Women in Aviation, International
Attn: Scholarships
Morningstar Airport
3647 State Route 503 South
West Alexandria, OH 45381-9354
(937) 839-4647   Fax: (937) 839-4645
E-mail: scholarships@wai.org
Web: www.wai.org/education/scholarships.cfm

Summary To provide financial assistance to members of Women in Aviation, International (WAI) who are active in aerospace and need financial support to advance their career.

Eligibility This program is open to WAI members who wish to advance their career in the aerospace industry in the fields of engineering, technology development, or management. Applicants may be 1) full-time or part-time employees working in the aerospace industry or a related field, or 2) students working on an aviation-related degree who are at least sophomores and have a GPA of 2.5 or higher. Along with their application, they must submit a 500-word essay on their aviation history and goals, 2 letters of recommendation, a resume, copies of all aviation licenses and medical certificates, and the last 3 pages of their pilot logbook, if applicable. Selection is based on achievements, attitude toward self and others, commitment to success, dedication to career, financial need, motivation, reliability, responsibility, and teamwork.

Financial data　The stipend is $2,500.

Duration　1 year.

Additional information　WAI is a nonprofit professional organization dedicated to encouraging women to consider an aviation career and to providing educational outreach activities and networking resources to women active in the industry. This program is sponsored by the Boeing Company.

Number awarded　2 each year.

Deadline　November of each year.

[1468]
WASHINGTON STATE BUSINESS AND PROFESSIONAL WOMEN'S FOUNDATION MATURE WOMAN EDUCATIONAL SCHOLARSHIP

Washington State Business and Professional Women's
  Foundation
Attn: Virginia Murphy, Scholarship Committee Chair
P.O. Box 631
Chelan, WA 98816-0631
(509) 682-4747　　　　　E-mail: vamurf@nwi.net
Web: www.bpwwa.org/scholarships.htm

Summary　To provide financial assistance to mature women from Washington interested in attending postsecondary school in the state for retraining or continuing education.

Eligibility　This program is open to women over 35 years of age who have been residents of Washington for at least 2 years. Applicants must be planning to enroll at a college or university in the state for a program of retraining or continuing education. Along with their application, they must submit a 500-word essay on their specific short-term goals and how the proposed training will help them accomplish those goals and make a difference in their professional career. Financial need is considered in the selection process. U.S. citizenship is required.

Financial data　The stipend is $1,000.

Duration　1 year.

Number awarded　1 or more each year.

Deadline　March of each year.

[1469]
WAYNE F. PLACEK GRANTS

American Psychological Foundation
750 First Street, N.E.
Washington, DC 20002-4242
(202) 336-5843　　　　　Fax: (202) 336-5812
E-mail: foundation@apa.org
Web: www.apa.org/apf/funding/placek.aspx

Summary　To provide funding to pre- and postdoctoral scholars (particularly women, minorities, and individuals with disabilities) who are interested in conducting research that will increase the general public's understanding of homosexuality and alleviate the stress experienced by lesbians and gay men.

Eligibility　This program is open to scholars who have a doctoral degree (e.g., Ph.D., Psy.D., M.D.), and to graduate students in all fields of the behavioral and social sciences. Applicants must be interested in conducting empirical studies that address the following topics: prejudice, discrimination, and violence based on sexual orientation, including heterosexuals' attitudes and behaviors toward lesbian, gay, bisexual, and transgender (LGBT) people; family and workplace issues relevant to LGBT people; and subgroups of the LGBT population that have been historically underrepresented in scientific research. Selection is based on conformance with stated program goals, magnitude of incremental contribution, quality of proposed work, and applicant's demonstrated scholarship and research competence. The sponsor encourages applications from individuals who represent diversity in race, ethnicity, gender, age, disability, and sexual orientation.

Financial data　The grant is $15,000.

Duration　1 year.

Additional information　This program began in 1995.

Number awarded　2 each year.

Deadline　February of each year.

[1470]
WHIRLY-GIRLS MEMORIAL FLIGHT TRAINING SCHOLARSHIP

Whirly-Girls International
c/o Britta Penca, Scholarship Director
P.O. Box 222
Oracle, AZ 85623
(520) 840-0951
E-mail: WGScholarshipdirector2@whirlygirls.org
Web: www.whirlygirls.org

Summary　To provide financial assistance to members of Whirly-Girls International who are interested in obtaining an additional helicopter rating.

Eligibility　This program is open to women who have been members of Whirly-Girls International for at least 1 year. Applicants must be interested in advanced helicopter flight training to upgrade their current rating (typically, toward commercial, instrument, instructor, ATP, long line or turbine transition training). Along with their application, they must submit information on honors or awards they have received, organizations with which they are affiliated, activities or hobbies they pursue, involvement in aviation-related activities, achievements and contributions in aviation, what originally sparked their interest in the helicopter industry, how they have helped other women become interested in aviation, their flying experience, how they intend to utilize this scholarship, how they intend to provide additional funding to cover the total cost of the flight training, their career goals in the helicopter industry and how this scholarship will help achieve those, and their financial need.

Financial data　The stipend is $6,000.

Duration　The stipend is offered annually.

Additional information　This program combines the former Phelan International Flight Training Scholarship and Doris Mullen Flight Training Scholarship. Completed applications must include $40 to cover the cost of processing and mailing.

Number awarded　1 each year.

Deadline　September of each year.

[1471]
WILLIAM L. FISHER CONGRESSIONAL GEOSCIENCE FELLOWSHIP

American Geological Institute
Attn: Government Affairs Program
4220 King Street
Alexandria, VA 22302-1502
(703) 379-2480, ext. 212   Fax: (703) 379-7563
E-mail: govt@agiweb.org
Web: www.agiweb.org/gap/csf/index.html

Summary   To provide women, minority, and other members of an American Geological Institute (AGI) component society with an opportunity to gain professional experience in the office of a member of Congress or a Congressional committee.

Eligibility   This program is open to members of 1 of AGI's 44 member societies who have a master's degree and at least 3 years of post-degree work experience or a Ph.D. Applicants should have a broad geoscience background and excellent written and oral communications skills. They must be interested in working with Congress. Although prior experience in public policy is not required, a demonstrated interest in applying science to the solution of public problems is desirable. Applications from women and minorities are especially encouraged. U.S. citizenship or permanent resident status is required.

Financial data   Fellows receive a stipend of up to $60,000 plus allowances for health insurance, relocation, and travel.

Duration   12 months, beginning in September.

Additional information   This program is 1 of more than 20 Congressional Science Fellowships operating in affiliation with the American Association for the Advancement of Science (AAAS), which provides a 2-week orientation on Congressional and executive branch operations.

Number awarded   1 each year.

Deadline   January of each year.

[1472]
WOMEN CHEMISTS COMMITTEE/ELI LILLY TRAVEL AWARDS

American Chemical Society
Attn: Department of Diversity Programs
1155 16th Street, N.W.
Washington, DC 20036
(202) 872-6334   Toll Free: (800) 227-5558, ext. 6334
Fax: (202) 776-8003   E-mail: diversity@acs.org
Web: womenchemists.sites.acs.org/attracting.htm

Summary   To provide funding to women chemists or chemistry students who are interested in traveling to scientific meetings.

Eligibility   This program is open to undergraduate, graduate, and postdoctoral women chemists who wish to travel to scientific meetings to present the results of their research. Only U.S. citizens and permanent residents are eligible. Preference is given to those who have not made a previous presentation at a national or major meeting. Women who have received a prior award under this program are ineligible.

Financial data   Awards apply to registration, travel, and accommodations only.

Additional information   Funding for this program is provided by Eli Lilly and Company. Grants are restricted to travel within the United States.

Number awarded   Varies each year.

Deadline   September of each year for meetings between January and June; February of each year for meetings between July and December.

[1473]
WOMEN IN AVIATION, INTERNATIONAL ACHIEVEMENT AWARDS

Women in Aviation, International
Attn: Scholarships
Morningstar Airport
3647 State Route 503 South
West Alexandria, OH 45381-9354
(937) 839-4647   Fax: (937) 839-4645
E-mail: scholarships@wai.org
Web: www.wai.org/education/scholarships.cfm

Summary   To provide financial assistance to members of Women in Aviation, International (WAI) who are working on a college degree or other training in the aviation field.

Eligibility   This program is open to WAI members who are 1) full-time college or university students working on an aviation or aviation-related degree; or 2) non-college students preparing for an aviation or aviation-related career. Applicants must submit 2 letters of recommendation, a 500-word essay on their aviation history and goals, a resume, copies of all aviation licenses and medical certificates, and the last 3 pages of their pilot logbook (if applicable). Selection is based on achievements, attitude toward self and others, commitment to success, dedication to career, financial need, motivation, reliability, responsibility, and teamwork.

Financial data   The stipend is $1,000.

Duration   1 year.

Additional information   WAI is a nonprofit professional organization dedicated to encouraging women to consider an aviation career and to providing educational outreach activities and networking resources to women active in the industry.

Number awarded   2 each year: 1 college scholarship and 1 non-college scholarship.

Deadline   November of each year.

[1474]
WOMEN IN UNITED METHODIST HISTORY RESEARCH GRANT

United Methodist Church
General Commission on Archives and History
Attn: General Secretary
36 Madison Avenue
P.O. Box 127
Madison, NJ 07940
(973) 408-3189   Fax: (973) 408-3909
E-mail: gcah@gcah.org
Web: www.gcah.org

Summary   To support research related to the history of women in the United Methodist Church.

Eligibility   Proposed research projects must deal specifically with the history of women in the United Methodist Church or its antecedents. Proposals on women of color and on history at the grassroots level are especially encouraged. Applicants must submit a description of the project, including its significance, format, timetable, budget, and how the results will be disseminated.

Financial data The grant is at least $1,000. Grant funds are not to be used for equipment, publication costs, or researcher's salary.

Duration These grants are awarded annually.

Number awarded Varies each year. A total of $2,500 is available for this program annually.

Deadline December of each year.

[1475]
WOMEN MILITARY AVIATORS DREAM OF FLIGHT SCHOLARSHIP

Women in Aviation, International
Attn: Scholarships
Morningstar Airport
3647 State Route 503 South
West Alexandria, OH 45381-9354
(937) 839-4647   Fax: (937) 839-4645
E-mail: scholarships@wai.org
Web: www.wai.org/education/scholarships.cfm

Summary To provide financial assistance to members of Women in Aviation, International (WAI) who are interested in flight training or academic study.

Eligibility This program is open to WAI members who are students in high school, an accredited flight program, or an accredited college or university. Applicants must submit 2 letters of recommendation, a 500-word essay on their aviation history and goals, a resume, and copies of all aviation licenses and medical certificates, and the last 3 pages of their pilot logbook (if applicable). Selection is based on the applicant's ambition to further women in aviation, demonstrated persistence and determination, financial need, ability to complete training, and ability to bring honor to the women of Women Military Aviators, Inc. (WMA).

Financial data The stipend is $2,500.

Duration Recipients must be able to complete training within 1 year.

Additional information WAI is a nonprofit professional organization dedicated to encouraging women to consider an aviation career and to providing educational outreach activities and networking resources to women active in the industry. WMA established this program in 2005 to honor the women aviators who are serving or have served in Iraq and Afghanistan.

Number awarded 1 each year.

Deadline November of each year.

[1476]
WOMEN'S ART STUDIO INTERNSHIPS

Women's Studio Workshop
722 Binnewater Lane
P.O. Box 489
Rosendale, NY 12472
(845) 658-9133   Fax: (845) 658-9031
E-mail: info@wsworkshop.org
Web: www.wsworkshop.org/_art_opp/intern_sixmo.htm

Summary To provide internship opportunities in the arts at the Women's Studio Workshop (WSW) in Rosendale, New York.

Eligibility This program is open to young women artists interested in working with the staff at the studio on projects including papermaking, book arts, and arts administration. Applicants should send a resume, 10 to 20 images of recent works, 3 letters of reference, and a letter of interest. They should have studio experience, be hard-working, and have a desire and ability to live in a close-knit community of women artists. Along with their application, they must submit a letter of interest explaining why an internship at WSW is important to them and why type of experiences they would bring to the position, 3 letters of reference, a resume, and a CD with 10 images of recent work.

Financial data Interns receive on-site housing and a stipend of $250 per month.

Duration Approximately 6 months, either as winter-spring interns (beginning in January) or as summer-fall interns (beginning in June). Interns may reapply for a second 6-month assignment.

Additional information Tasks include (but are not limited to) preparing the studios; assisting in the production of artists' books; administrative duties (including data entry and web maintenance); designing, printing, and distributing brochures and posters; assisting in all aspects of the exhibition program; preparing the apartments for visiting artists; setting up evening programs; managing the set up and break down of lunch each day; assisting with preparations for fundraising events; and assisting in the day-to-day running of the studios (including general maintenance and cleaning).

Number awarded 2 to 3 each term (winter-spring or summer-fall).

Deadline October of each year for winter-spring internships; February of each year for summer-fall internships.

[1477]
WOMEN'S BAR FOUNDATION PUBLIC SERVICE STIPEND AWARD

Women's Bar Association of Illinois
Attn: Women's Bar Foundation
321 South Plymouth Court, Suite 4S
P.O. Box 641068
Chicago, IL 60664-1068
(312) 341-8530   E-mail: illinoiswbf@aol.com
Web: www.illinoiswbf.org/?page_id=17

Summary To provide funding for a project to women practicing public interest law in Illinois.

Eligibility This program is open to women who graduated from an Illinois law school and are currently practicing public interest or public service law in the state in the nonprofit or public sector. Applicants must be proposing to conduct a public interest law project. They must be able to demonstrate a strong academic record, present and past extracurricular activities reflecting community involvement, personal qualities that suggest a future leadership role in the legal community, involvement with diversity initiatives within law school or the legal community, and financial need. Along with their application, they must submit a personal statement describing why they believe they should receive this award.

Financial data The grant is $15,000.

Duration 1 year.

Additional information This program was established in 2008.

Number awarded 1 or more each year.

Deadline July of each year.

[1478]
WOMEN'S CAMPAIGN FUND FELLOWSHIP PROGRAM

Women's Campaign Fund
Attn: Political Director
1900 L Street, N.W., Suite 500
Washington, DC 20036
(202) 393-8164   Toll Free: (800) 446-8170
Fax: (202) 393-0649   E-mail: info@wcfonline.org
Web: www.wcfonline.org

Summary To provide an opportunity for professionals to gain work experience at the Women's Campaign Fund, a national political organization committed to protecting women's reproductive choices.

Eligibility This program is open to anyone who has a strong interest in protecting women's reproductive choices and options. Applicants must be interested in working on the Women's Campaign Fund in such areas as donor cultivation and event planning; candidate research, tracking, and support; new media efforts within a nonprofit atmosphere; political database basics and nonprofit infrastructure; and public speaking and presentation. They must have excellent research, writing, and communications skills as well as the ability to work independently and in a small group setting.

Financial data The stipend is $500 per month for full-time fellows or $250 per month for part-time fellows.

Duration 14 weeks during spring or fall; 10 weeks during summer.

Additional information The Women's Campaign Fund is the first national nonpartisan committee founded in America dedicated to the election of pro-choice women to public office.

Number awarded Approximately 3 each term.

Deadline November of each year for spring; April of each year for summer; July of each year for fall.

[1479]
WOMEN'S EDUCATIONAL EQUITY ACT PROGRAM GRANTS

Department of Education
Office of Elementary and Secondary Education
Attn: School Improvement Programs
400 Maryland Avenue, S.W., Room 4W242, LBJ Building
Washington, DC 20202-5950
(202) 205-3145   Fax: (202) 205-5630
E-mail: oii.weea@ed.gov
Web: www2.ed.gov/programs/equity/index.html

Summary To provide funding for women's equity projects.

Eligibility This program is open to nonprofit organizations (including faith-based and community organizations), public agencies, institutions, student groups, and individuals developing programs that promote gender equity. Applications are especially solicited for local implementation of gender-equity policies and practices. Research, development, and dissemination activities may also be funded. Examples of eligible activities include training for teachers and other school personnel to encourage gender equity in the classroom; evaluating exemplary model programs to advance gender equity; school-to-work transition programs; guidance and counseling activities to increase opportunities for women in technologically demanding workplaces; and developing strategies to assist local educational agencies in evaluating, disseminating, and replicating gender-equity programs.

Financial data Recently, these awards ranged from $115,113 to $216,062.

Duration Projects may be funded for up to 4 years.

Number awarded Varies each year; recently, 13 of these grants were awarded.

Deadline February of each year.

[1480]
WOMEN'S FILM PRESERVATION FUND GRANTS

New York Women in Film & Television
6 East 39th Street, 12th Floor
New York, NY 10016-0870
(212) 679-0870   Fax: (212) 679-0899
E-mail: info@nywift.org
Web: www.nywift.org/article.aspx?id=FPF

Summary To provide funding to restore and preserve films in which women have had significant creative roles.

Eligibility Eligible to apply for this funding are individuals and nonprofit organizations who are interested in preserving films in which women had key creative roles, as directors, writers, producers, editors, or performers. Films may be of any length, on any subject matter, and in any film format or base. Selection is based on the artistic, historic, cultural, and/or educational importance of the film, especially in relation to the role of women in film history; significance of the key creative women in the production; evidence of the artistic and technical expertise of those planning and executing the project; urgency of the need to preserve the film; appropriateness of the budget for the proposed work; and realism of the plan for making the film available to professionals, scholars, and interested audiences.

Financial data The maximum grant is $10,000. Funds may be used only for actual costs connected with restoration and preservation, not for salaries or general administrative costs. In addition to cash grants, the fund also awards approximately $25,000 worth of in-kind post-production services for films created by or related to women.

Duration These grants are provided annually.

Number awarded Since 1995, the fund has provided financial support for the preservation of more than 90 women-created films.

Deadline March of each year.

[1481]
WOMEN'S LAW AND PUBLIC POLICY FELLOWSHIP PROGRAM

Georgetown University Law Center
Attn: Women's Law and Public Policy Fellowship Program
600 New Jersey Avenue, N.W., Hotung 5024A
Washington, DC 20001
(202) 662-9650   Fax: (202) 662-9117
E-mail: wlppfp@law.georgetown.edu
Web: www.law.georgetown.edu/wlppfp

Summary To provide an opportunity for recently-graduated lawyers in the Washington D.C. area to work on women's rights issues.
Eligibility This program is open to recent graduates of law schools accredited by the American Bar Association. Applicants must be interested in working on women's rights issues in the Washington, D.C. area (e.g., at the Georgetown University School of Law, the National Partnership for Women and Families, and the National Women's Law Center).

Financial data The stipend is approximately $39,000 per year.

Duration The fellowships at Georgetown Law are 2-year teaching assignments; other fellowships are for 1 year.

Additional information This program includes 2 named fellowships: the Rita Charmatz Davidson Fellowship (to work on issues primarily affecting poor women) and the Harriet R. Burg Fellowship (to work primarily on issues affecting women with disabilities). In addition, the Ford Foundation supports fellowships at organizations focusing on issues concerning women and AIDS/HIV. Fellows are supervised by attorneys at the participating organizations.

Number awarded Varies each year.

Deadline November of each year.

[1482]
WOMEN'S MUSIC COMMISSION

Broadcast Music Inc.
Attn: BMI Foundation, Inc.
7 World Trade Center
250 Greenwich Street
New York, NY 10007-0030
(212) 220-3000   E-mail: info@bmifoundation.org
Web: www.bmifoundation.org

Summary To recognize and reward, with a commission for production of a new work, outstanding young female composers.
Eligibility This competition is open to women between 20 and 30 years of age who are citizens or permanent residents of the United States. Applicants must submit samples of their original compositions.

Financial data The winner receives a $5,000 commission to create a new work.

Duration The competition is held annually.

Additional information This program began in 2006. Each year, the sponsor partners with a different world-class performer, ensemble, or presenter to present the premier performance.

Number awarded 1 each year.

Deadline May of each year.

[1483]
WOMEN'S SPORTS FOUNDATION TRAVEL AND TRAINING FUND

Women's Sports Foundation
Attn: Award and Grant Programs Manager
Eisenhower Park
1899 Hempstead Turnpike, Suite 400
East Meadow, NY 11554-1000
(516) 542-4700   Toll Free: (800) 227-3988
Fax: (516) 542-4716
E-mail: info@womenssportsfoundation.org
Web: www.womenssportsfoundation.org

Summary To provide funding for travel and training activities to women athletes (both individuals and teams).
Eligibility This program is open to women who are amateur athletes and U.S. citizens or legal residents. Applicants must demonstrate the ability, based on competitive record and years in training, to reach and compete at an elite level; they should have competed regionally (outside their state), nationally, or internationally and/or be ranked by a national governing body. Athletes may apply as individuals or as a team consisting of 2 or more women. High school, college, university, and community recreation sports teams are not eligible.

Financial data Grants range from $2,500 to $10,000.

Duration Individuals and teams may receive only 1 grant per calendar year and 3 grants in a lifetime.

Additional information This program, established in 1984, is currently funded by the Gatorade Company.

Number awarded Varies each year; recently, 24 of these grants (19 to individuals and 5 to teams) with a total value of $100,000 were awarded. Since the program was established, it has awarded grants to more than 260 teams and 940 athletes.

Deadline May or September of each year.

[1484]
WOMEN'S STUDIES IN RELIGION PROGRAM

Harvard Divinity School
Attn: Director of Women's Studies in Religion Program
45 Francis Avenue
Cambridge, MA 02138
(617) 495-5705   Fax: (617) 495-8564
E-mail: wsrp@hds.harvard.edu
Web: www.hds.harvard.edu/wsrp

Summary To encourage and support research on the relationship between religion, gender, and culture.
Eligibility This program is open to scholars who have a Ph.D. in the field of religion. Candidates with primary competence in other humanities, social sciences, and public policy fields who have a serious interest in religion and religious professionals with equivalent achievements are also eligible. Applicants should be proposing to conduct research projects at Harvard Divinity School's Women's Studies in Religion Program (WSRP) on topics related to the history and function of gender in religious traditions, the institutionalization of gender roles in religious communities, or the interaction between religion and the personal, social, and cultural situations of women. Appropriate topics include feminist theology, biblical studies, ethics, women's history, and interdisciplinary scholarship on women in world religions. Selection is based on the

quality of the applicant's research prospectus, outlining objectives and methods; its fit with the program's research priorities; the significance of the contribution of the proposed research to the study of religion, gender, and culture, and to its field; and agreement to produce a publishable piece of work by the end of the appointment.

Financial data The stipend is $45,000; health insurance and reimbursement of some expenses are also provided.

Duration 1 academic year, from September to June.

Additional information This program was founded in 1973. Fellows at the WSRP devote the majority of their appointments to individual research projects in preparation for publication, meeting together regularly for discussion of research in process. They also design and teach new courses related to their research projects and offer a series of lectures in the spring. Recipients are required to be in full-time residence at the school while carrying out their research project.

Number awarded 5 each year. The group each year usually includes at least 1 international scholar, 1 scholar working on a non-western tradition, 1 scholar of Judaism, and 1 minority scholar.

Deadline October of each year.

[1485]
WOMEN'S STUDIO WORKSHOP STUDIO RESIDENCIES

Women's Studio Workshop
722 Binnewater Lane
P.O. Box 489
Rosendale, NY 12472
(845) 658-9133   Fax: (845) 658-9031
E-mail: info@wsworkshop.org
Web: www.wsworkshop.org

Summary To provide a residency and financial support at the Women's Studio Workshop (WSW) to women artists.

Eligibility This program is open to artists in all stages of their careers and working in printmaking, papermaking, photography, book arts, or ceramics. Applicants must be interested in creating a new body of work while in residence at the WSW. They must provide a 1-sentence summary of their proposed project, a resume, and a CD with 10 images of their recent work.

Financial data The program provides a stipend of $2,000, a $500 materials grant, a travel stipend, unlimited studio use, and housing while in residence.

Duration 6 to 8 weeks.

Number awarded Varies each year.

Deadline March of each year.

[1486]
WORKSHOPS FOR WOMEN GRADUATE STUDENTS AND RECENT PH.D.S

Association for Women in Mathematics
11240 Waples Mill Road, Suite 200
Fairfax, VA 22030
(703) 934-0163   Fax: (703) 359-7562
E-mail: awm@awm-math.org
Web: sites.google.com/site/awmmath/programs/workshops

Summary To enable women graduate students and recent Ph.D.s in mathematics to participate in workshops in conjunction with major meetings.

Eligibility Eligible for funding are women graduate students who have begun work on a thesis problem in mathematics and women mathematicians who received their Ph.D.s within the preceding 5 years. Applicants must wish to participate in workshops held in conjunction with major mathematics meetings at which each participating graduate student presents a poster on her thesis problem and each postdoctorate presents a talk on her research.

Financial data Funding covers travel and subsistence.

Duration Funding for 2 days is provided.

Additional information Participants have the opportunity to present and discuss their research and to meet with other women mathematicians at all stages of their careers. The workshop also includes a panel discussion on issues of career development and a luncheon. This program is supported by the Office of Naval Research, the Department of Energy, and the National Security Agency.

Number awarded Up to 20 at each of 2 workshops each year.

Deadline October of each year for a workshop in July in conjunction with the International Congress on Industrial and Applied Mathematics; August of each year for a workshop in January in conjunction with the Joint Mathematics Meetings of the American Mathematical Society and the Mathematical Association of America.

[1487]
YOUNG INVESTIGATOR GRANT IN TOTAL JOINT AND TRAUMA SURGERY

Orthopaedic Research and Education Foundation
Attn: Vice President, Grants
6300 North River Road, Suite 700
Rosemont, IL 60018-4261
(847) 698-9980   Fax: (847) 698-7806
E-mail: communications@oref.org
Web: www.oref.org

Summary To provide funding to new orthopedic surgeons (particularly women and minorities) who are interested in conducting research in total joint surgery and/or trauma treatment.

Eligibility This program is open to orthopedic surgeons (particularly women and minorities) who have completed formal training within the past 4 years and have a clinical or scientific interest in total joint surgery and/or trauma treatment. Applicants must be seeking seed or start-up funding for promising research. They must be working at an institution in the United States or Canada. Both laboratory and clinical projects are acceptable, but the clinical relevance must be clearly and explicitly described. Minority and female surgeons are especially encouraged to apply.

Financial data Grants up to $50,000 are awarded.

Duration 1 year.

Additional information Funding for minority surgeons is provided by the J. Robert Gladden Society. Funding for women surgeons is provided by the Ruth Jackson Orthopaedic Society.

Number awarded 8 each year, of which 6 are funded by Zimmer Holdings, Inc. and 2 are reserved for members of the

J. Robert Gladden Society or the Ruth Jackson Orthopaedic Society. Those organizations select their recipients.
Deadline　September of each year.

[1488]
ZETA PHI BETA GENERAL GRADUATE FELLOWSHIPS

Zeta Phi Beta Sorority, Inc.
Attn: National Education Foundation
1734 New Hampshire Avenue, N.W.
Washington, DC 20009
(202) 387-3103　　　　　　Fax: (202) 232-4593
E-mail: scholarship@ZPhiBNEF.org
Web: www.zphib1920.org/nef

Summary　To provide financial assistance to women who are working on a professional degree, master's degree, doctorate, or postdoctorate.

Eligibility　Women graduate or postdoctoral students are eligible to apply if they have achieved distinction or shown promise of distinction in their chosen fields. Applicants need not be members of Zeta Phi Beta. They must be enrolled full time in a professional, graduate, or postdoctoral program. Along with their application, they must submit a 150-word essay on their educational goals and professional aspirations, how this award will help them to achieve those goals, and why they should receive the award. Financial need is not considered in the selection process.

Financial data　The stipend ranges up to $2,500, paid directly to the recipient.

Duration　1 academic year; may be renewed.

Deadline　January of each year.

[1489]
ZIMMER RESEARCH GRANT

Ruth Jackson Orthopaedic Society
6300 North River Road, Suite 727
Rosemont, IL 60018-4226
(847) 698-1626　　　　　　Fax: (847) 823-0536
E-mail: rjos@aaos.org
Web: www.rjos.org/web/awards/index.htm

Summary　To provide funding to women who are members of the Ruth Jackson Orthopaedic Society (RJOS) and interested in conducting pilot research.

Eligibility　This program is open to women who are board certified or board eligible orthopaedic surgeons and RJOS members. Applicants must be seeking seed and start-up funding for promising research projects. Clinical or basic science projects are encouraged. Preference is given to grants with a focus on women's musculoskeletal health.

Financial data　The grant is a $30,000.

Duration　1 year; nonrenewable.

Additional information　Funding for this program is provided by Zimmer, Inc.

Number awarded　2 each year.

Deadline　September of each year.

Indexes

- *Program Title Index* ●
- *Sponsoring Organization Index* ●
- *Residency Index* ●
- *Tenability Index* ●
- *Subject Index* ●
- *Calendar Index* ●

Program Title Index

If you know the name of a particular funding program open to women and want to find out where it is covered in the directory, use the Program Title Index. Here, program titles are arranged alphabetically, word by word. To assist you in your search, every program is listed by all its known names or abbreviations. In addition, we've used an alphabetical code (within parentheses) to help you determine if the program is aimed at you: U = Undergraduates; G = Graduate Students; P = Professionals/Postdoctorates. Here's how the code works: if a program is followed by (U) 241, the program is described in the Undergraduates chapter, in entry 241. If the same program title is followed by another entry number—for example, (P) 1370—the program is also described in the Professionals/Postdoctorates chapter, in entry 1370. Remember: the numbers cited here refer to program entry numbers, not to page numbers in the book.

A

A. Margaret Boyd Scholarship. *See* Delta Kappa Gamma Scholarship Program, entry (G) 821

AARP Women's Scholarship Program, (U) 1

Abe Fellowship Program. *See* SSRC Abe Fellowship Program, entry (P) 1443

Abraham Scholarship. *See* Alpha Epsilon Phi Foundation Scholarships, entries (U) 19, (G) 722

ABWA President's Scholarship, (G) 712

Achievement Scholarships, (U) 2, (G) 713

ACLS Dissertation Completion Fellowships. *See* Andrew W. Mellon Foundation/ACLS Dissertation Completion Fellowships, entry (G) 740

ACLS Dissertation Fellowships in American Art. *See* Henry Luce Foundation/ACLS Dissertation Fellowships in American Art, entry (G) 919

ACLS Recent Doctoral Recipients Fellowships. *See* Andrew W. Mellon Foundation/ACLS Recent Doctoral Recipients Fellowships, entry (P) 1210

ACM-W Athena Lecturer Award, (P) 1193

A.C.N.M. Foundation Memorial Scholarship. *See* Basic Midwifery Student Scholarships, entries (U) 72, (G) 765

ACT Summer Internship Program, (G) 714

Ada I. Pressman Scholarship. *See* Society of Women Engineers/ Ada I. Pressman Scholarship, entries (U) 588, (G) 1128

Adalin Macauley Scholarship. *See* Wisconsin Legion Auxiliary Merit and Memorial Scholarships, entry (U) 665

Adele Lewis Fellowship. *See* Sigma Delta Epsilon Fellowships, entries (G) 1125, (P) 1437

Adele Lobracio Lowe Leadership Grant, (G) 715

Admiral Grace Murray Hopper Memorial Scholarships, (U) 3

Advanced Postdoctoral Fellowships in Diabetes Research. *See* JDRF Advanced Postdoctoral Fellowships in Diabetes Research, entry (P) 1337

AERA-ETS Fellowship Program in Measurement, (P) 1194

African American Studies Program Visiting Scholars. *See* University of Houston African American Studies Program Visiting Scholars, entry (P) 1457

Agenda for Delaware Women Trailblazer Scholarships, (U) 4

Aggesen Grand Bethel Memorial Scholarship. *See* Grand Guardian Council of California Scholarships, entry (U) 262

Agnes C. Allen Memorial Scholarship, (U) 5

Agnes Missirian Scholarship, (U) 6, (G) 716

Agnes Morris Education Scholarship, (U) 7, (P) 1195

Agnes Morris Educational Loan Fund. *See* Agnes Morris Education Scholarship, entries (U) 7, (P) 1195

Aharonian Scholarships. *See* Lucy Kasparian Aharonian Scholarships, entries (U) 382, (G) 992

AHIMA Foundation Diversity Scholarships, (U) 8

Air Force Officers' Wives' Club of Washington, D.C. Continuing Education Scholarships for Non-Military Air Force Spouses, (U) 9, (G) 717

Air Products and Chemicals Scholarship for Diversity in Engineering, (U) 10

Aircraft Spruce Memorial Scholarship. *See* Flo Irwin/Aircraft Spruce Memorial Scholarship, entry (U) 229

AirTran Airways Maintenance Scholarship. *See* WAI/AirTran Airways Maintenance Scholarship, entry (U) 646

Al Neuharth Free Spirit Scholarship and Conference Program, (U) 11

Alabama G.I. Dependents' Scholarship Program, (U) 12, (G) 718

Alabama Golf Association Women's Scholarship Fund, (U) 13

Alaska Free Tuition for Spouse or Dependent of Armed Services Member, (U) 14

Alberta E. Crowe Star of Tomorrow Award, (U) 15

Alberta Prize. *See* Motherwell Prize, entry (P) 1386

Alexander and Geraldine Wanek Fund Award. *See* Geological Society of America Graduate Student Research Grants, entry (G) 896

Alexander Gralnick Research Investigator Prize, (P) 1196

Alexander Memorial Scholarship. *See* Daughters of Penelope Undergraduate Scholarships, entry (U) 144

U–Undergraduates　　　**G–Graduate Students**　　　**P–Professionals/Postdoctorates**

American Legion Auxiliary Spirit of Youth Scholarship for Junior Members. *See* Spirit of Youth Scholarship for Junior Members, entry (U) 596

American Medical Women's Association Scholarships, (G) 738

American Meteorological Society Graduate Fellowship in the History of Science, (G) 739

American Meteorological Society Undergraduate Named Scholarships, (U) 36

American Orchid Society Graduate Fellowship. *See* Furniss Foundation/AOS Graduate Fellowship, entry (G) 891

American Orchid Society/Norman's Orchids Masters Scholarship. *See* AOS/Norman's Orchids Masters Scholarship, entry (G) 747

American Psychological Foundation/Council of Graduate Departments of Psychology Graduate Research Scholarships. *See* APF/COGDOP Graduate Research Scholarships, entry (G) 748

American Psychological Foundation Visionary Grants. *See* APF Visionary Grants, entry (P) 1214

American Society for Eighteenth-Century Studies Women's Caucus Editing and Translation Fellowship. *See* ASECS Women's Caucus Editing and Translation Fellowship, entry (P) 1219

American Society for Microbiology Career Development Grants for Postdoctoral Women. *See* ASM Career Development Grants for Postdoctoral Women, entry (P) 1220

American Society of Transplantation Basic Science Faculty Development Grant. *See* Basic Science Faculty Development Grant, entry (P) 1230

American Society of Transplantation Basic Science Fellowship Grant <CR>Basic Science Fellowship Grant. *See* AST Basic Science Fellowship Grant, entry (P) 1224

American Society of Transplantation Branch-Out Grants. *See* Branch-Out Grants, entry (P) 1236

American Society of Transplantation Clinical Science Fellowship Grants, (P) 1209

American Society of Women Accountants Undergraduate Scholarships, (U) 37

America's Junior Miss Scholarships. *See* Distinguished Young Women Scholarships, entry (U) 170

AMVETS National Ladies Auxiliary Scholarships, (U) 38

Amy Krueger Scholarship. *See* U.S. Army Women's Foundation Legacy Scholarships, entry (U) 632

Anchor Grants, (U) 39

Anderson Memorial Scholarship. *See* Gladys C. Anderson Memorial Scholarship, entries (U) 254, (G) 902

Anderson Prize. *See* Ruth Anderson Prize, entry (P) 1424

Anderson Scholarship. *See* California P.E.O. Selected Scholarships, entries (U) 106, (G) 786, 850

Andrew Mullins Courageous Achievement Award. *See* VHSL-Allstate Achievement Awards, entry (U) 641

Andrew W. Mellon Foundation/ACLS Dissertation Completion Fellowships, (G) 740

Andrew W. Mellon Foundation/ACLS Recent Doctoral Recipients Fellowships, (P) 1210

Andrews Scholarship. *See* Leta Andrews Scholarship, entry (U) 371

Andy Stone Scholarships, (U) 40

Angela Paez Memorial Scholarship. *See* Seattle Chapter AWIS Scholarships, entry (U) 574

Angeline Lewis Scholarships. *See* H.S. and Angeline Lewis Scholarships, entries (U) 289, (G) 933

Angels of Kappa Theta Memorial Scholarship. *See* Alpha Omicron Pi Foundation Named Scholarships, entries (U) 23, (G) 725

Anila Jain Scholarship. *See* Kailash, Mona, and Anila Jain Scholarship, entry (G) 973

Anita Borg Memorial Scholarships, (U) 41, (G) 741

Anita Borg Scholarships for First Years. *See* Google Anita Borg Scholarships for First Years, entry (U) 260

Ann Arbor AWC Scholarship for Women in Computing, (U) 42

Ann Clark Nursing Scholarship, (U) 43, (G) 742

Ann E. Dickerson Scholarships, (G) 743

Ann E. Kammer Memorial Fellowship Fund, (P) 1211

Ann Garrison/Delores Schofield Scholarship. *See* Oklahoma BW Foundation Scholarships, entries (U) 489, (G) 1066

Ann Hershfang/Helene M. Overly Memorial Scholarship, (G) 744

Ann Irwin Leadership Scholarship, (U) 44

Ann Marie Benson Scholarship. *See* Oklahoma BW Foundation Scholarships, entries (U) 489, (G) 1066

Ann Samford Upchurch Scholarship. *See* Alabama Golf Association Women's Scholarship Fund, entry (U) 13

Anna Gear Junior Scholarship, (U) 45

Anna Lind Scholarship, (U) 46

Anne Bridge Baddour Aviation Scholarship, (P) 1212

Anne C. Carter Student Leadership Award, (G) 745

Anne E. Helliwell Sisters Assistance Grants. *See* Alpha Chi Omega Member Assistance Grants, entry (U) 18

Anne Klauber Berson Memorial Scholarship. *See* Alpha Epsilon Phi Foundation Scholarships, entries (U) 19, (G) 722

Anne Maureen Whitney Barrow Memorial Scholarship, (U) 47

Anne Sowles Calhoun Memorial Scholarship, (U) 48

Annette Urso Rickel Dissertation Award for Public Policy, (G) 746

Annie Jump Cannon Award in Astronomy, (P) 1213

Annie Webb Blanton Scholarship. *See* Delta Kappa Gamma Scholarship Program, entry (G) 821

Anzaldúa Book Prize. *See* Gloria E. Anzaldúa Book Prize, entry (P) 1308

AOS Graduate Fellowship. *See* Furniss Foundation/AOS Graduate Fellowship, entry (G) 891

AOS/Norman's Orchids Masters Scholarship, (G) 747

AOWCGWA Scholarship Program, (U) 49

APF/COGDOP Graduate Research Scholarships, (G) 748

APF Visionary Grants, (P) 1214

Apple Resident Travel Scholarship. *See* Sherry Apple Resident Travel Scholarship, entry (P) 1433

Appraisal Institute Minorities and Women Educational Scholarship Program, (U) 50

Arbus Disability Awareness Grants. *See* Loreen Arbus Disability Awareness Grants, entry (P) 1360

AREVA NP Scholarship, (U) 51, (G) 749

ARFORA/Martha Gavrila Scholarship for Women, (G) 750

ARFORA Undergraduate Scholarship for Women, (U) 52

Arizona BPW Foundation Annual Scholarships, (U) 53

Arkansas Military Dependents' Scholarship Program, (U) 54

Arkansas Missing in Action/Killed in Action Dependents' Scholarship Program. *See* Arkansas Military Dependents' Scholarship Program, entry (U) 54

Arlene Davis Scholarship, (U) 55

Arline Andrews Lovejoy Scholarship, (U) 56

Armstrong Foundation Scholarships. *See* ELA Foundation Scholarships, entry (G) 854

Army Emergency Relief Stateside Spouse Education Assistance Program, (U) 57

U–Undergraduates   **G–Graduate Students**   **P–Professionals/Postdoctorates**

Army Judge Advocate General Corps Summer Intern Program, (G) 751

Army Officers' Wives' Club of the Greater Washington Area Scholarship Program. *See* AOWCGWA Scholarship Program, entry (U) 49

Arne Administrative Leadership Scholarship, (G) 752

Arnett Continuing Education Scholarship. *See* Janice E. Arnett Continuing Education Scholarship, entry (G) 955

Arnett Graduate Scholarship. *See* Kappa Delta Sorority Graduate Scholarships, entry (G) 975

Arnett Scholarship for Leadership and Volunteerism. *See* Janice E. Arnett Scholarship for Leadership and Volunteerism, entry (G) 956

Arnold Education Grant Program. *See* General Henry H. Arnold Education Grant Program, entry (U) 247

Arnold Graduate Fellowship. *See* Pi Beta Phi Graduate Fellowships, entry (G) 1078

Art Meets Activism Grant Program, (P) 1215

Artemis A.W. and Martha Joukowsky Postdoctoral Fellowship. *See* Pembroke Center Postdoctoral Fellowships, entry (P) 1405

Art-in-Education Residency Grants, (P) 1216

Artist Enrichment Grant Program. *See* KFW Artist Enrichment Grant Program, entry (P) 1348

Artist-in-Residence Program, (P) 1217

Asa S. Bushnell Internship Program, (P) 1218

ASECS Women's Caucus Editing and Translation Fellowship, (P) 1219

Ashworth Scholarship. *See* Sylva Ashworth Scholarship, entry (G) 1137

ASM Career Development Grants for Postdoctoral Women, (P) 1220

Association for Women Geoscientists Minority Scholarship, (U) 58

Association for Women in Architecture Scholarships, (U) 59

Association for Women in Communications-District of Columbia Scholarship. *See* AWIC-DC Matrix Scholarship, entry (U) 65

Association for Women in Mathematics Education Research Travel Grants for Women Researchers. *See* AWM Mathematics Education Research Travel Grants for Women Researchers, entry (P) 1227

Association for Women in Mathematics Travel Grants for Women Researchers, (P) 1221

Association for Women in Science Internships, (U) 60

Association for Women in Science Seattle Scholarships. *See* Seattle Chapter AWIS Scholarships, entry (U) 574

Association for Women in Sports Media Member Training Grants, (P) 1222

Association for Women in Sports Media Scholarship/Internship Program, (U) 61, (G) 753

Association for Women Journalists Scholarships, (U) 62

Association for Women Lawyers Foundation Scholarships, (G) 754

Association of Romanian Orthodox Ladies Auxiliaries/Martha Gavrila Scholarship for Women. *See* ARFORA/Martha Gavrila Scholarship for Women, entry (G) 750

Association of Romanian Orthodox Ladies Auxiliaries Undergraduate Scholarship for Women. *See* ARFORA Undergraduate Scholarship for Women, entry (U) 52

Association of the United States Navy Education Assistance Program, (U) 63

Association of Women Psychiatrists Fellowship, (P) 1223

AST Basic Science Fellowship Grant, (P) 1224

Astraea Visual Arts Fund, (P) 1225

AT&T Laboratories Fellowship Program, (G) 755

Autry Memorial Scholarship. *See* Association for Women in Sports Media Scholarship/Internship Program, entries (U) 61, (G) 753

Award in Arkansas Women's History. *See* Susie Pryor Award in Arkansas Women's History, entry (P) 1447

Awards for Advanced Placement, (U) 64

AWHONN Novice Researcher Award, (G) 756, (P) 1226

AWIC-DC Matrix Scholarship, (U) 65

AWM Mathematics Education Research Travel Grants for Women Researchers, (P) 1227

Axelrod Mentorship Award. *See* Julius Axelrod Mentorship Award, entry (P) 1344

Ayer Music Scholarship. *See* Waldo and Alice Ayer Music Scholarship, entry (U) 650

B

B. June West Recruitment Grant, (U) 66, (P) 1228

B. Olive Cole Graduate Educational Grant. *See* Dr. B. Olive Cole Graduate Educational Grant, entry (G) 841

Baddour Aviation Scholarship. *See* Anne Bridge Baddour Aviation Scholarship, entry (P) 1212

Bailey Scholarship. *See* Sandra Sebrell Bailey Scholarship, entry (U) 563

Baker Corporation Scholarship Program for Diversity in Engineering. *See* Michael Baker Corporation Scholarship Program for Diversity in Engineering, entry (U) 416

Baker Graduate Fellowship. *See* Claudia Steele Baker Graduate Fellowship, entry (G) 805

Baker Hughes Scholarships, (U) 67, (G) 757

Banks Memorial Undergraduate Scholarship. *See* Sharon D. Banks Memorial Undergraduate Scholarship, entry (U) 578

Banner Diversity Scholarship. *See* Donald W. Banner Diversity Scholarship, entry (G) 831

Banner Engineering Minnesota SWE Scholarship, (U) 68, (G) 758

Banner Scholarship for Law Students. *See* Mark T. Banner Scholarship for Law Students, entry (G) 1005

Baptist Women in Ministry of North Carolina Student Scholarships, (G) 759

Barbara Alice Mower Memorial Scholarship, (U) 69, (G) 760

Barbara Dobkin Native Artist Fellowship for Women. *See* Eric and Barbara Dobkin Native Artist Fellowship for Women, entry (P) 1282

Barbara Edith Quincey Thorndyke Memorial Scholarship. *See* Daughters of Penelope Undergraduate Scholarships, entry (U) 144

Barbara Furse Mackey Scholarship. *See* California P.E.O. Selected Scholarships, entries (U) 106, (G) 786

Barbara Gibson Froemming Scholarship, (G) 761

Barbara Kranig Scholarship. *See* Wisconsin Legion Auxiliary Merit and Memorial Scholarships, entry (U) 665

Barbara McBride Scholarship, (U) 70, (G) 762

Barbara Rosenblum Cancer Dissertation Scholarship, (G) 763

Barnard Women Poets Prize, (P) 1229

Barnick Memorial Scholarship. *See* Ninety-Nines, Inc. Amelia Earhart Memorial Scholarships, entries (U) 478, (G) 1060, (P) 1395

Barnum Festival Foundation/Jenny Lind Competition for Sopranos, (U) 71, (G) 764

Barrett Memorial Scholarship. *See* Claire Barrett Memorial Scholarship, entry (G) 804

Barrow Memorial Foundation Scholarships. *See* Bessie Barrow Memorial Foundation Scholarships, entry (U) 79

U–Undergraduates   G–Graduate Students   P–Professionals/Postdoctorates

U–Undergraduates   G–Graduate Students   P–Professionals/Postdoctorates

Edmundson Scholarship. *See* Basic Midwifery Student Scholarships, entries (U) 72, (G) 765

Educational Foundation for Women in Accounting IMA Undergraduate Scholarship, (U) 195

Educational Foundation for Women in Accounting Masters Scholarship, (G) 851

Educational Foundation for Women in Accounting Seattle Chapter ASWA Scholarship. *See* EFWA Seattle Chapter ASWA Scholarship, entries (U) 197, (G) 852

Educational Testing Service Fellowship Program in Measurement. *See* AERA-ETS Fellowship Program in Measurement, entry (P) 1194

Educator's Award, (P) 1272

Edwards Graduate Scholarship. *See* Esther Edwards Graduate Scholarship, entry (G) 868

Edwin G. and Lauretta M. Michael Scholarship, (U) 196

Efron Research Award. *See* Daniel H. Efron Research Award, entry (P) 1255

EFWA Seattle Chapter ASWA Scholarship, (U) 197, (G) 852

Eidson Scholarship. *See* Mike Eidson Scholarship, entry (G) 1023

Einstein Postdoctoral Fellowship Program, (P) 1273

Eisenhardt Resident Travel Scholarship. *See* Louise Eisenhardt Resident Travel Scholarship, entry (P) 1361

E.K. Wise Loan Program. *See* E.K. Wise Scholarship Fund, entry (G) 853

E.K. Wise Scholarship Fund, (G) 853

Ekdale Memorial Scholarship. *See* Susan Ekdale Memorial Scholarship, entry (U) 602

Ekstrom Fellowship. *See* Ruth and Lincoln Ekstrom Fellowship, entries (G) 1101, (P) 1423

ELA Foundation Scholarships, (G) 854

Elaine Osborne Jacobson Award for Women Working in Health Care Law, (G) 855

Eleanor Roosevelt Fund Award, (P) 1274

Eleanor Smith Scholarship. *See* Wisconsin Legion Auxiliary Merit and Memorial Scholarships, entry (U) 665

Eleanore I. McKinley Scholarship. *See* John L. and Eleanore I. McKinley Scholarship, entry (U) 336

Eleanore Kline Memorial Scholarship, (U) 198, (G) 856

Eleanore MacCurdy Scholarship. *See* Alpha Omicron Pi Foundation Named Scholarships, entries (U) 23, (G) 725

Electronics for Imaging Scholarships, (U) 199, (G) 857

Elise Bonneville Daskam Memorial Scholarship. *See* Grand Guardian Council of California Scholarships, entry (U) 262

Elise Lipscomb Ferguson Scholarship. *See* Sophia Scholar and Elise Lipscomb Ferguson Scholarship, entries (U) 590, (G) 1129

Elizabeth Ahlemeyer Quick/Gamma Phi Beta Scholarship, (U) 200

Elizabeth Banta Mueller Scholarships, (U) 201

Elizabeth Candon Scholarship. *See* Sister Elizabeth Candon Scholarship, entry (U) 586

Elizabeth Furbur Fellowship, (G) 858

Elizabeth K. Weisburger Scholarship Fund. *See* Women in Toxicology Special Interest Group Vera W. Hudson and Elizabeth K. Weisburger Scholarship Fund, entry (G) 1178

Elizabeth Lowell Putnam Prize, (U) 202

Elizabeth M. Gruber Scholarships, (G) 859

Elizabeth McLean Memorial Scholarship, (U) 203

Elizabeth Munsterberg Koppitz Child Psychology Graduate Fellowships, (G) 860

Elkes Research Award. *See* Joel Elkes Research Award, entry (P) 1340

Elks National Foundation "Most Valuable Student" Scholarship Award, (U) 204

Ellen Bowers Hofstead Scholarships, (U) 205

Ellen Cushing Scholarships, (G) 861

Elliott G. Heard Jr. Memorial Scholarship, (G) 862

Elliott Memorial Scholarship. *See* Bernice F. Elliott Memorial Scholarship, entries (U) 75, (G) 769

Ellis Scholarship. *See* Ethel Lee Hoover Ellis Scholarship, entry (U) 213, (G) 821

Elman National Undergraduate Scholarship. *See* Carolyn B. Elman National Undergraduate Scholarship, entry (U) 111

Eloise Campbell Memorial Scholarships, (U) 206

Eloise Gerry Fellowships, (G) 863, (P) 1275

Elsa Ludeke Graduate Scholarships, (G) 864

Elsevier Pilot Research Awards, (P) 1276

Elsie G. Riddick Scholarship, (U) 207, (G) 865

Emerson Scholarship. *See* Gladys Anderson Emerson Scholarship, entry (U) 253

Emily Schoenbaum Research and Community Development Grants, (U) 208, (G) 866, (P) 1277

Emma Giles Scholarship. *See* Delta Kappa Gamma Scholarship Program, entry (G) 821

Emma Harper Turner Fund, (U) 209, (P) 1278

Emma Reinhart Scholarship. *See* Delta Kappa Gamma Scholarship Program, entry (G) 821

Emma Wettstein Scholarship. *See* Scholarships for ELCA Service Abroad, entry (U) 568

Emmanuil Troyansky Fellowship. *See* Organic Chemistry Graduate Student Fellowships, entry (G) 1069

Endicott Scholarships. *See* Priscilla Maxwell Endicott Scholarships, entry (U) 531

Enid A. Neidle Scholar-in-Residence Program for Women, (P) 1279

Environmental Protection Agency Greater Research Opportunities (GRO) Fellowships for Undergraduate Environmental Study. *See* EPA Greater Research Opportunities (GRO) Fellowships for Undergraduate Environmental Study, entry (U) 210

EOD Memorial Scholarships. *See* Explosive Ordnance Disposal (EOD) Memorial Scholarships, entry (U) 222

Eos #1 Mother Lodge Chapter Scholarship. *See* Daughters of Penelope Undergraduate Scholarships, entry (U) 144

EPA Greater Research Opportunities (GRO) Fellowships for Undergraduate Environmental Study, (U) 210

Epilepsy Foundation Research Grants Program, (P) 1280

Epilepsy Research Recognition Awards Program, (P) 1281

Eric and Barbara Dobkin Native Artist Fellowship for Women, (P) 1282

Erma Metz Brown Scholarship, (U) 211

Ernestine L. Newman Scholarship. *See* Kappa Delta Sorority Undergraduate Scholarships, entry (U) 351

Ernst Award. *See* Kitty Ernst Award, entry (P) 1349

Esperanza Scholarship, (U) 212, (G) 867

Esther Edwards Graduate Scholarship, (G) 868

Esther Katz Rosen Fellowships, (G) 869

Esther Ngan-ling Chow and Mareyjoyce Green Scholarship, (G) 870

Esther R. Howard Scholarship. *See* Oliver and Esther R. Howard Scholarship, entry (U) 493

Esther Rothstein Scholarship. *See* WBF Scholarship Awards, entry (G) 1166

Ethel F. Lord Award, (G) 871

U–Undergraduates   G–Graduate Students   P–Professionals/Postdoctorates

History of Women in Science Prize. *See* Margaret W. Rossiter History of Women in Science Prize, entry (P) 1370

Hoch Distinguished Service Award. *See* Paul Hoch Distinguished Service Award, entry (P) 1401

Hodo Scholarship. *See* Alabama Golf Association Women's Scholarship Fund, entry (U) 13

Hoegh Memorial Scholarship for the Education of Rural Librarians. *See* Gloria Hoegh Memorial Scholarship for the Education of Rural Librarians, entry (P) 1309

Hoffman Memorial Award for Voice. *See* Scholarships for Undergraduate Performance, entry (U) 571

Hoffman Scholarships. *See* Dorothy M. and Earl S. Hoffman Scholarships, entry (U) 183

Hofstead Scholarships. *See* Ellen Bowers Hofstead Scholarships, entry (U) 205

Holden Scholarship. *See* Delta Kappa Gamma Scholarship Program, entry (G) 821

Holland & Hart Summer Associates Program Diversity Initiative, (G) 925

Holliman Scholarship. *See* Houston/Nancy Holliman Scholarship, entry (U) 288

Holly A. Cornell Scholarship, (G) 926

Holmes Memorial Scholarship. *See* Susie Holmes Memorial Scholarship, entry (U) 605

Holmgreen Memorial Scholarship. *See* Shirley Holmgreen Memorial Scholarship, entry (U) 582

Hologgitas Ph.D. Scholarship. *See* Daughters of Penelope Undergraduate Scholarships, entry (U) 144

Holt Scholarships. *See* Phyllis Dobbyn Holt Scholarships, entry (U) 519

Hon. Geraldine A. Ferraro Endowed Scholarship, (G) 927

Honeywell International Scholarships, (U) 284

Honorable Harrison W. Ewing Fellowships, (G) 928

Hood Memorial Scholarship. *See* Rhoda D. Hood Memorial Scholarship, entries (U) 548, (G) 1095

Hopewell Agave Chapter 224 Scholarship. *See* Daughters of Penelope Undergraduate Scholarships, entry (U) 144

Hopgood Future Teachers High School Senior Scholarships. *See* Rollie Hopgood Future Teachers High School Senior Scholarships, entry (U) 557

Hopper Memorial Scholarships. *See* Admiral Grace Murray Hopper Memorial Scholarships, entry (U) 3

Horizons Foundation Scholarship Program, (U) 285, (G) 929, (P) 1323

Horizons-Michigan Scholarship, (U) 286, (G) 930

Horn Memorial Softball Scholarship. *See* Jaime Horn Memorial Softball Scholarship, entry (U) 314

Houston Chapter Helene M. Overly Memorial Scholarship, (G) 931

Houston Chapter Sharon D. Banks Memorial Scholarship, (U) 287

Houston/Nancy Holliman Scholarship, (U) 288

Houston Scholarship. *See* Sarah Jane Houston Scholarship, entry (U) 565

Howard Hughes Medical Institute Research Training Fellowships for Medical Students, (G) 932

Howard Medlin Memorial Scholarship. *See* New Mexico Elks Association Charitable and Benevolent Trust Scholarships, entry (U) 476

Howard Scholarship. *See* Oliver and Esther R. Howard Scholarship, entry (U) 493

Howarth Scholarships. *See* Dorothy Lemke Howarth Scholarships, entry (U) 182

Howell Scholarship. *See* Fletcher Mae Howell Scholarship, entry (G) 884

Hricik Memorial Scholarship Award for Females. *See* Thomas M. Hricik Memorial Scholarship Award for Females, entry (U) 623

H.S. and Angeline Lewis Scholarships, (U) 289, (G) 933

Hubble Fellowships, (P) 1324

Hudson and Elizabeth K. Weisburger Scholarship Fund. *See* Women in Toxicology Special Interest Group Vera W. Hudson and Elizabeth K. Weisburger Scholarship Fund, entry (G) 1178

Huenefeld/Denton Scholarship, (U) 290

Hughes Medical Institute Research Training Fellowships for Medical Students. *See* Howard Hughes Medical Institute Research Training Fellowships for Medical Students, entry (G) 932

Humber Award for Lifetime Artistic Achievement. *See* Twining Humber Award for Lifetime Artistic Achievement, entry (P) 1455

Huneycutt Scholarship. *See* Sarah E. Huneycutt Scholarship, entry (U) 564

Hutcheson Education Assistance Fund. *See* Alpha Chi Omega Educational Assistance Grants, entries (U) 17, (G) 720

I

IADES Fellowship Award, (G) 934

IBM Corporation SWE Scholarships, (U) 291

IBM PhD Fellowship Program, (G) 935

Ida B. Wells Graduate Student Fellowship, (G) 936

Ida Foreman Fleisher Scholarship, (G) 937

Ida M. Pope Memorial Scholarships, (U) 292, (G) 938

Ike Crumbly Minorities in Energy Grant. *See* Isaac J. "Ike" Crumbly Minorities in Energy Grant, entry (G) 950

Illinois MIA/POW Scholarship, (U) 293

Illinois Scholarships for Junior Members, (U) 294

Immigrant Women Program Internships at Legal Momentum, (U) 295, (G) 939, (P) 1325

Independent Women's Forum College Essay Contest, (U) 296

Indiana American Legion Gold Award Girl Scout of the Year Scholarship Achievement Award, (U) 297

Indiana BPW Girl Scout Scholarship, (U) 298

Indiana Women in Public Finance Scholarship, (U) 299

Indiana Women in Transition Scholarship, (U) 300

Indiana Working Woman Scholarship, (U) 301

Industry/Government Graduate Fellowships, (G) 940

Ingeborg Haseltine Scholarship Fund for Women, (G) 941

Initial Helicopter Scholarship, (P) 1326

Innovations in Clinical Research Awards, (P) 1327

Institute for Supply Management Distinguished Leadership Grants, (P) 1328

Institute for Supply Management Doctoral Dissertation Grant Program, (G) 942

Institute for Supply Management Professional Research and Collaboration Grants, (P) 1329

Institute for Supply Management Professional Research Development Grants, (P) 1330

Institutional Equity Women's College Fellowship Program, (U) 302

Intel Scholarship, (G) 943

Intellectual Property Law Section Women and Minority Scholarship, (G) 944

Intermountain Section AWWA Diversity Scholarship, (U) 303, (G) 945

International Alumnae of Delta Epsilon Sorority Fellowship Award. *See* IADES Fellowship Award, entry (G) 934

International and Area Studies Fellowships, (P) 1331

U–Undergraduates   **G–Graduate Students**   **P–Professionals/Postdoctorates**

U–Undergraduates   G–Graduate Students   P–Professionals/Postdoctorates

Mabel Biever Music Education Scholarship for Graduate Students, (G) 996

Mabel Heil Scholarship, (U) 386, (G) 997

Macauley Scholarship. *See* Wisconsin Legion Auxiliary Merit and Memorial Scholarships, entry (U) 665

MacCurdy Scholarship. *See* Alpha Omicron Pi Foundation Named Scholarships, entries (U) 23, (G) 725

MacGregor Memorial Scholarship. *See* Irene and Daisy MacGregor Memorial Scholarship, entry (G) 948

Mackey Scholarship. *See* California P.E.O. Selected Scholarships, entries (U) 106, (G) 786

Mackey-Althouse Voice Award. *See* Virginia Peace Mackey-Althouse Voice Award, entries (U) 645, (G) 1156

Maffett Fellowships. *See* Minnie L. Maffett Fellowships, entries (G) 1031, (P) 1385

Mahindra USA Women in Ag Scholarships, (U) 387

Mahr Memorial Scholarship. *See* New Mexico Elks Association Charitable and Benevolent Trust Scholarships, entry (U) 476

Maine BPW Continuing Education Scholarship, (U) 388

Maine Veterans Dependents Educational Benefits, (U) 389, (G) 998

Making a Difference Leader Scholarship, (U) 390

Malina James and Dr. Louis P. James Legacy Scholarship. *See* APF/COGDOP Graduate Research Scholarships, entry (G) 748

Malveaux Scholarship. *See* Dr. Julianne Malveaux Scholarship, entry (U) 188

Mamie Sue Bastian Scholarship. *See* Delta Kappa Gamma Scholarship Program, entry (G) 821

Management Scholarship, (P) 1364

Manahan-Bohan Award, (U) 391, (G) 999

Manfred Meier Scholarship. *See* Benton-Meier Neuropsychology Scholarships, entry (G) 766

Mann Scholarship. *See* Oklahoma BW Foundation Scholarships, entries (U) 489, (G) 1066

Mara Crawford Personal Development Scholarship, (U) 392, (P) 1365

March of Dimes "Saving Babies, Together" Award, (P) 1366

Marcia Feinberg Award, (P) 1367

Mareyjoyce Green Scholarship. *See* Esther Ngan-ling Chow and Mareyjoyce Green Scholarship, entry (G) 870

Margaret Budd Haemer Scholarship. *See* Kappa Delta Sorority Undergraduate Scholarships, entry (U) 351

Margaret Edmundson Scholarship. *See* Basic Midwifery Student Scholarships, entries (U) 72, (G) 765

Margaret M. Prickett Scholarship Fund. *See* Society of Daughters of the United States Army Scholarships, entry (U) 587

Margaret Morse Nice Fund, (G) 1000, (P) 1368

Margaret Oakley Dayhoff Award, (P) 1369

Margaret Stafford Memorial Scholarship. *See* Delta Delta Delta Unrestricted Graduate Scholarships, entry (G) 819

Margaret W. Rossiter History of Women in Science Prize, (P) 1370

Margaret Yardley Fellowship, (G) 1001

Maria Goeppert-Mayer Award, (P) 1371

Mariam K. Chamberlain Fellowship, (G) 1002, (P) 1372

Marian McKee Smith–Rosalie McKinney Jackson Scholarships, (U) 393

Marian Norby Scholarship, (U) 394, (P) 1373

Marie Morisawa Research Award, (G) 1003

Marilyn Mock Scholarship. *See* Kappa Delta Sorority Undergraduate Scholarships, entry (U) 351

Marilynn Smith Scholarship, (U) 395

Marilynne Graboys Wool Scholarship, (G) 1004

Marine Corps/Coast Guard Enlisted Dependent Spouse Scholarship. *See* Navy/Marine Corps/Coast Guard Enlisted Dependent Spouse Scholarship, entries (U) 465, (G) 1054

Marine Corps Counterintelligence Association Scholarships, (U) 396

Marion Barnick Memorial Scholarship. *See* Ninety-Nines, Inc. Amelia Earhart Memorial Scholarships, entries (U) 478, (G) 1060, (P) 1395

Marion Day Mullins Scholarship, (U) 397

Marjorie Jeanne Allen Scholarship. *See* Delta Kappa Gamma Scholarship Program, entry (G) 821

Marjorie M. McDonald P.E.O. Scholarship. *See* California P.E.O. Selected Scholarships, entries (U) 106, (G) 786

Mark T. Banner Scholarship for Law Students, (G) 1005

Marsh Memorial Awards. *See* Sigma Alpha Iota Graduate Performance Awards, entry (G) 1124

Marshall Graduate Scholarship. *See* Delta Delta Delta Unrestricted Graduate Scholarships, entry (G) 819

Marshall Scholarship. *See* Delta Delta Delta Unrestricted Undergraduate Scholarships, entry (U) 158, 402

Marshall-Martha Belle Scholarships. *See* Bernadine Johnson Marshall-Martha Belle Scholarships, entry (G) 768

Martha Belle Scholarships. *See* Bernadine Johnson Marshall-Martha Belle Scholarships, entry (G) 768

Martha C. Johnson Tuition Scholarships, (U) 398

Martha Drouyor Belknap DeCamp Scholarship, (U) 399

Martha Gavrila Scholarship for Women. *See* ARFORA/Martha Gavrila Scholarship for Women, entry (G) 750

Martha Guerra-Arteaga Scholarship, (U) 400

Martha Joukowsky Postdoctoral Fellowship. *See* Pembroke Center Postdoctoral Fellowships, entry (P) 1405

Martha McKinney Wilhoite Scholarship. *See* Alpha Omicron Pi Foundation Named Scholarships, entries (U) 23, (G) 725

Martha Singletary Scholarship Fund. *See* Rev. Martha Singletary Scholarship Fund, entry (G) 1094

Martha Stickland Scholarship, (U) 401

Martin Scholarship. *See* Katie Rose Martin Scholarship, entry (U) 357

Martin Sisters Scholarship. *See* Delta Delta Delta Unrestricted Undergraduate Scholarships, entry (U) 158

Martin Symonds Foundation Fellowships. *See* Alexandra and Martin Symonds Foundation Fellowships, entry (P) 1197

Mary Ann G. McMorrow Scholarship. *See* WBF Scholarship Awards, entry (G) 1166

Mary Ann Starring Memorial Award for Piano or Percussion. *See* Scholarships for Undergraduate Performance, entry (U) 571

Mary Ann Starring Memorial Award for Woodwinds or Brass. *See* Scholarships for Undergraduate Performance, entry (U) 571

Mary Ann Starring Memorial Awards. *See* Sigma Alpha Iota Graduate Performance Awards, entry (G) 1124

Mary Ball Carrera Scholarship, (G) 1006

Mary Barrett Marshall Scholarship, (U) 402

Mary Connolly Livingston Educational Grant, (G) 1007

Mary Ellen Russell Memorial Scholarship, (U) 403

Mary Frances White Scholarship. *See* Delta Kappa Gamma Scholarship Program, entry (G) 821

Mary Frances-Guilbert Mariani-Bigler Continuing Education Grant. *See* Alpha Chi Omega Educational Assistance Grants, entries (U) 17, (G) 720

Mary Isabel Sibley Fellowship for French Studies, (G) 1008, (P) 1374

Mary Isabel Sibley Fellowship for Greek Studies, (G) 1009, (P) 1375

Native American Project Grants, (U) 463, (G) 1051

Native American Women's Health Education Resource Center Internships, (U) 464, (G) 1052, (P) 1389

Nau Scholarship. *See* California P.E.O. Selected Scholarships, entries (U) 106, (G) 786

Naval Helicopter Association Graduate Scholarships, (G) 1053

Naval Research Laboratory Broad Agency Announcement, (P) 1390

Navy/Marine Corps/Coast Guard Enlisted Dependent Spouse Scholarship, (U) 465, (G) 1054

NCAA Postgraduate Scholarship Program, (G) 1055

NCAIAW Scholarship, (U) 466

NCCE Scholarships, (U) 467

Nearly New Scholarship. *See* California P.E.O. Selected Scholarships, entries (U) 106, (G) 786

Nebraska Waiver of Tuition for Veterans' Dependents, (U) 468

Need-Based Scholarships, (U) 469

NEH International and Area Studies Fellowships. *See* International and Area Studies Fellowships, entry (P) 1331

Neidle Scholar-in-Residence Program for Women. *See* Enid A. Neidle Scholar-in-Residence Program for Women, entry (P) 1279

Neil Kinnear Scholarship. *See* Wings Over America Scholarships, entry (U) 662

Nell I. Mondy Fellowship, (G) 1056, (P) 1391

Nellie Yeoh Whetten Award, (G) 1057

Nelson Medical Scholarship. *See* Jessie D. Nelson Medical Scholarship, entry (U) 331

Network of Executive Women Scholarship, (U) 470, (G) 1058

Neuharth Free Spirit Scholarship and Conference Program. *See* Al Neuharth Free Spirit Scholarship and Conference Program, entry (U) 11

New Horizons Leader Scholarship, (U) 471

New Initiatives in Malaria Awards. *See* Investigators in Pathogenesis of Infectious Disease, entry (P) 1332

New Investigator and Scholar Awards in Molecular Parasitology. *See* Investigators in Pathogenesis of Infectious Disease, entry (P) 1332

New Investigator and Scholar Awards in Molecular Pathogenic Mycology. *See* Investigators in Pathogenesis of Infectious Disease, entry (P) 1332

New Jersey Bankers Education Foundation Scholarships, (U) 472

New Jersey State Elks Special Children's Scholarship, (U) 473

New Jersey SWE Scholarship, (U) 474

New Jersey Utilities Association Equal Employment Opportunity Scholarships, (U) 475

New Mexico Elks Association Charitable and Benevolent Trust Scholarships, (U) 476

New Mexico Minority Doctoral Loan-for-Service Program, (G) 1059

New Pilot Awards, (P) 1392

New York Public Library Fellowships, (P) 1393

New York Women in Communications, Inc. Foundation Scholarships. *See* NYWICI Foundation Scholarships, entries (U) 487, (G) 1065

Newman Scholarship. *See* Kappa Delta Sorority Undergraduate Scholarships, entry (U) 351

NFMC Biennial Young Artist Awards, (P) 1394

NFWL/NRA Bill of Rights Essay Contest, (U) 477

Nice Fund. *See* Margaret Morse Nice Fund, entries (G) 1000, (P) 1368

Nies Scholarship. *See* Helen W. Nies Scholarship, entry (G) 915

Ninety-Nines, Inc. Amelia Earhart Memorial Scholarships, (U) 478, (G) 1060, (P) 1395

Nolop Scholarship in Audiology and Allied Fields. *See* Helen Woodruff Nolop Scholarship in Audiology and Allied Fields, entry (G) 916

Nonresident Tuition Waivers for Veterans and Their Dependents Who Move to Texas, (U) 479

Norby Scholarship. *See* Marian Norby Scholarship, entries (U) 394, (P) 1373

Norfleet Scholarship. *See* Nannie W. Norfleet Scholarship, entry (U) 454

Norma Bristow Salter Scholarship. *See* Delta Kappa Gamma Scholarship Program, entry (G) 821

Norma Chipman Wells Loyalty Grant, (G) 1061

Norma Ross Walter Scholarship Program, (U) 480

Norman's Orchids Masters Scholarship. *See* AOS/Norman's Orchids Masters Scholarship, entry (G) 747

North Carolina Association of Intercollegiate Athletics for Women Scholarship. *See* NCAIAW Scholarship, entry (U) 466

North Carolina Business and Professional Women's Foundation Scholarships, (U) 481, (G) 1062

North Dakota Educational Assistance for Dependents of Veterans, (U) 482

North Dakota Women's Opportunity Scholarship Fund, (U) 483

Northrop Grumman Foundation Scholarship, (U) 484

Northwest Women in Educational Administration Scholarship, (U) 485

Northwestern Region Fellowship Award, (G) 1063

Norton Memorial Scholarship Award. *See* Mary R. Norton Memorial Scholarship Award, entries (U) 408, (G) 1015

Norwood Memorial Scholarships. *See* Josephine Carroll Norwood Memorial Scholarships, entry (G) 967

Notchev Fellowship. *See* Vessa Notchev Fellowship, entries (G) 1149, (P) 1460

NRA Bill of Rights Essay Contest. *See* NFWL/NRA Bill of Rights Essay Contest, entry (U) 477

NSPE Auxiliary Legacy Scholarship, (U) 486

NSTI Summer Scholars Program. *See* NASA Science and Technology Institute (NSTI) Summer Scholars Program, entry (U) 457

Nu Iota Scholarship in Memory of Julia V. Nelson and in Honor of Elaine Nelson Mackenzie. *See* Alpha Omicron Pi Foundation Named Scholarships, entries (U) 23, (G) 725

Nupur Chaudhuri First Article Prize, (P) 1396

Nutterville Scholarship. *See* Delta Kappa Gamma Scholarship Program, entry (G) 821

NWSA Graduate Scholarship Award, (G) 1064

NYWICI Foundation Scholarships, (U) 487, (G) 1065

O

Oestmann Professional Women's Achievement Award. *See* Mary Jane Oestmann Professional Women's Achievement Award, entry (P) 1376

Ohio Newspaper Women's Scholarship, (U) 488

Oklahoma BW Foundation Scholarships, (U) 489, (G) 1066

Oklahoma City Chapter Scholarships, (U) 490

Okwu Girl Scout Gold Award Scholarship. *See* Dr. Bea Okwu Girl Scout Gold Award Scholarship, entry (U) 185

Ola B. Hiller Scholarship. *See* Delta Kappa Gamma Scholarship Program, entry (G) 821

Olin Medal. *See* Francis P. Garvan-John M. Olin Medal, entry (P) 1298

Phoenix Section Freshman Scholarships, (U) 518
Phyllis Dobbyn Holt Scholarships, (U) 519
Phyllis G. Meekins Scholarship, (U) 520
Phyllis J. Van Deventer Scholarship. *See* California P.E.O. Selected Scholarships, entries (U) 106, (G) 786
Phyllis Sanders Scholarship, (U) 521
Phyllis V. Roberts Scholarship, (G) 1076
Pi Beta Phi Alumnae Continuing Education Scholarships, (G) 1077, (P) 1407
Pi Beta Phi Graduate Fellowships, (G) 1078
Pi Beta Phi Undergraduate Scholarships, (U) 522
Pi State Native American Grants-in-Aid, (U) 523, (G) 1079
Pickup Memorial Scholarship. *See* Lydia I. Pickup Memorial Scholarship, entries (U) 383-384, (G) 993
Pierce Scholarship. *See* Delta Kappa Gamma Scholarship Program, entry (G) 821
PilotMall.com Aviation Superstore CFI Scholarship, (U) 524, (P) 1408
Pioneers Scholarship, (U) 525
Pistilli Scholarships. *See* P.O. Pistilli Scholarships, entry (U) 526
Placek Grants. *See* Wayne F. Placek Grants, entries (G) 1165, (P) 1469
P.O. Pistilli Scholarships, (U) 526
Polissino Memorial Scholarship. *See* William J. Polissino Memorial Scholarship, entry (U) 660
Polly Thompson Memorial Music Scholarship. *See* California P.E.O. Selected Scholarships, entries (U) 106, (G) 786
Pomeroy Scholarships. *See* Virginia A. Pomeroy Scholarships, entry (G) 1153
Pope Memorial Scholarships. *See* Ida M. Pope Memorial Scholarships, entries (U) 292, (G) 938
Portland Chapter Women's Transportation Seminar Leadership Scholarship, (U) 527, (G) 1080
Portland Chapter Women's Transportation Seminar Scholarships, (U) 528, (G) 1081
Portland Women's Club Scholarship, (U) 529
Postdoctoral Fellowship in the History of Modern Science and Technology in East Asia, (P) 1409
Postdoctoral Fellowships in Diabetes Research, (P) 1410
Postdoctoral Research Training Fellowships in Epilepsy, (P) 1411
Powell Alumnae Assistance Grants. *See* Alpha Chi Omega Member Assistance Grants, entry (U) 18
Predoctoral Research Training Fellowships in Epilepsy, (G) 1082
Prelinger Award. *See* Catherine Prelinger Award, entries (G) 793, (P) 1244
Prentice Gautt Postgraduate Scholarships. *See* Dr. Prentice Gautt Postgraduate Scholarships, entry (G) 845
Prescott Scholarship. *See* Kappa Delta Sorority Graduate Scholarships, entry (G) 975
Presidential Early Career Awards for Scientists and Engineers, (P) 1412
Pressman Scholarship. *See* Society of Women Engineers/Ada I. Pressman Scholarship, entries (U) 588, (G) 1128
Price Scholarships. *See* Judith McManus Price Scholarships, entries (U) 342, (G) 968
Prickett Scholarship Fund. *See* Society of Daughters of the United States Army Scholarships, entry (U) 587
Prime Scholarship. *See* California P.E.O. Selected Scholarships, entries (U) 106, (G) 786
Prince Scholarship. *See* Scholarships for ELCA Service Abroad, entry (U) 568
Priority Research Grants, (P) 1413

Priscilla Carney Jones Scholarship, (U) 530
Priscilla Maxwell Endicott Scholarships, (U) 531
Professional Associates Program for Women and Minorities at Brookhaven National Laboratory, (P) 1414
Professional Golf Management Diversity Scholarship, (U) 532
Project Red Flag Academic Scholarship for Women with Bleeding Disorders, (U) 533, (G) 1083
Providence Alumnae Chapter College Awards, (U) 534
Providence Memoriam Award, (U) 535
Pryor Award in Arkansas Women's History. *See* Susie Pryor Award in Arkansas Women's History, entry (P) 1447
Puget Sound Business Journal's Women of Influence-Lytle Enterprises Scholarship, (G) 1084
Puget Sound Chapter Helene M. Overly Memorial Scholarship, (G) 1085
Puget Sound Chapter Sharon D. Banks Memorial Undergraduate Scholarship, (U) 536
Pulvermacher-Ryan Scholarship. *See* Wisconsin Legion Auxiliary Merit and Memorial Scholarships, entry (U) 665
Putnam Prize. *See* Elizabeth Lowell Putnam Prize, entry (U) 202
Pvt. Francheska Velez Scholarship. *See* U.S. Army Women's Foundation Legacy Scholarships, entry (U) 632

Q
Quality of Life Awards, (U) 537
Queen Scholarship. *See* Alpha Omicron Pi Foundation Named Scholarships, entries (U) 23, (G) 725
Quick/Gamma Phi Beta Scholarship. *See* Elizabeth Ahlemeyer Quick/Gamma Phi Beta Scholarship, entry (U) 200
Quincey Memorial Graduate Scholarship. *See* Daughters of Penelope Graduate Student Scholarships, entry (G) 815

R
R. Robert & Sally D. Funderburg Research Award in Gastric Cancer, (P) 1415
Rachel E. Lemieux Youth Scholarship, (U) 538
Rachel Royston Permanent Scholarship, (G) 1086
Rainer Graduate Fellowship. *See* John Rainer Graduate Fellowship, entry (G) 963
Ralph W. Shrader Diversity Scholarships, (G) 1087
Ramage Scholarship. *See* Kappa Delta Sorority Undergraduate Scholarships, entry (U) 351
Randy Gerson Memorial Grant, (G) 1088
Rankin Award. *See* Jeannette Rankin Award, entry (U) 329
Rayam Prize in Sacred Music. *See* Grady-Rayam Prize in Sacred Music, entry (U) 261
Raymond A. Weiss Research and Program Innovation Grant. *See* Drs. Rosalee G. and Raymond A. Weiss Research and Program Innovation Grant, entry (P) 1267
Reagan Pathfinder Scholarships. *See* National Pathfinder Scholarships, entries (U) 460, (G) 1048
Rebecca Routh Coon Injury Research Award. *See* Lizette Peterson-Homer Injury Prevention Research Grant, entries (G) 990, (P) 1357
Recognition Scholarships, (U) 539
Red River Valley Fighter Pilots Association Scholarship Grant Program, (U) 540, (G) 1089
Red Speigle Award. *See* Virginia Golf Foundation Scholarship Program, entry (U) 643
Redi-Tag Corporation Scholarship, (U) 541
Reed and Gloria Pennington Scholarship, (U) 542

U–Undergraduates　　　　**G–Graduate Students**　　　　**P–Professionals/Postdoctorates**

Shonnette Meyer Kahn Scholarship. *See* Alpha Epsilon Phi Foundation Scholarships, entries (U) 19, (G) 722

Shore Scholarship. *See* Dinah Shore Scholarship, entry (U) 168

Shores Scholarship. *See* Justice Janie L. Shores Scholarship, entry (G) 972

Shoup Scholarship. *See* Delta Kappa Gamma Scholarship Program, entry (G) 821

Shrader Diversity Scholarships. *See* Ralph W. Shrader Diversity Scholarships, entry (G) 1087

Sibley Fellowship for French Studies. *See* Mary Isabel Sibley Fellowship for French Studies, entries (G) 1008, (P) 1374

Sibley Fellowship for Greek Studies. *See* Mary Isabel Sibley Fellowship for Greek Studies, entries (G) 1009, (P) 1375

Sigma Alpha Iota Graduate Performance Awards, (G) 1124

Sigma Alpha Iota Undergraduate Scholarships, (U) 583

Sigma Delta Epsilon Fellowships, (G) 1125, (P) 1437

Sigma Kappa Alumnae Continuing Education Scholarships, (G) 1126

Sigma Kappa Founders' Scholarships, (U) 584

Sign of the Arrow Melissa Scholarship, (U) 585

Silversteen Scholarship. *See* Charlotte Fields Silversteen Scholarship, entry (G) 798

Simpson Scholarship Fund. *See* Society of Daughters of the United States Army Scholarships, entry (U) 587

Singletary Scholarship Fund. *See* Rev. Martha Singletary Scholarship Fund, entry (G) 1094

Sisson Award. *See* Geological Society of America Graduate Student Research Grants, entry (G) 896

Sister Elizabeth Candon Scholarship, (U) 586

Sloan Foundation Research Fellowships. *See* Alfred P. Sloan Foundation Research Fellowships, entry (P) 1198

Small Science and Business Scholarship. *See* D. Anita Small Science and Business Scholarship, entries (U) 140, (G) 812

Smiley Scholarship. *See* Robert Smiley Scholarship, entry (U) 552

Smith Memorial Scholarship. *See* Catheryn Smith Memorial Scholarship, entry (U) 113

Smith Scholarship. *See* Marilynn Smith Scholarship, entry (U) 395, 665

Smith Scholarship Program. *See* Walter Reed Smith Scholarship Program, entry (U) 651

Smith/Sharon D. Banks Memorial Undergraduate Scholarship. *See* Jacquelyn R. Smith/Sharon D. Banks Memorial Undergraduate Scholarship, entry (U) 313

Smith-K4LMB Memorial Scholarship. *See* Young Ladies' Radio League Scholarship, entries (U) 703, (G) 1189

Smith–Rosalie McKinney Jackson Scholarships. *See* Marian McKee Smith–Rosalie McKinney Jackson Scholarships, entry (U) 393

Snavely, Jr. Cascadia Research Fund Award. *See* Geological Society of America Graduate Student Research Grants, entry (G) 896

Snyder Scholarship. *See* Kappa Delta Sorority Graduate Scholarships, entry (G) 975

Social, Behavioral, and Economic Sciences Doctoral Dissertation Research Improvement Grants. *See* SBE Doctoral Dissertation Research Improvement Grants, entry (G) 1112

Social Science Research Council Abe Fellowship Program. *See* SSRC Abe Fellowship Program, entry (P) 1443

Social Science Research Council/NEH International and Area Studies Fellowships. *See* International and Area Studies Fellowships, entry (P) 1331

Society of Aviation and Flight Educators Scholarship, (P) 1438

Society of Daughters of the United States Army Scholarships, (U) 587

Society of Pediatric Psychology Diversity Research Grant, (G) 1127, (P) 1439

Society of Women Engineers/Ada I. Pressman Scholarship, (U) 588, (G) 1128

Society of Women Engineers New Jersey Scholarship. *See* New Jersey SWE Scholarship, entry (U) 474

Society of Women Engineers Past Presidents Scholarships. *See* SWE Past Presidents Scholarships, entries (U) 606, (G) 1136

Society of Women Engineers Phoenix Section Scholarship. *See* Phoenix Section Freshman Scholarships, entry (U) 518

Society of Women Engineers Region F Scholarship. *See* Region H Scholarship, entries (U) 544, (G) 1091

Sociologists for Women in Society Feminist Lecturer Award. *See* SWS Feminist Lecturer Award, entry (P) 1448

Solar Turbines Scholarship, (U) 589

Sonenfeld Scholarship. *See* Daughters of Penelope Undergraduate Scholarships, entry (U) 144

Sonia Kovalevsky High School Mathematics Days Grants, (P) 1440

Sonja Stefanadis Graduate Scholarship. *See* Daughters of Penelope Graduate Student Scholarships, entry (G) 815

Sopher Scholarship. *See* Mindy Sopher Scholarship, entry (G) 1027

Sophia Scholar and Elise Lipscomb Ferguson Scholarship, (U) 590, (G) 1129

South Dakota Job's Daughters Scholarships, (U) 591

South Dakota Reduced Tuition for Dependents of Prisoners of War or Missing in Action, (U) 592

South Eastern Region Fellowship for Life-Long Learning, (U) 593

Southall Scholarship. *See* Delta Kappa Gamma Scholarship Program, entry (G) 821

Southwest Idaho Section SWE Scholarships, (U) 594

Space Coast Section SWE FIRST Freshman Scholarship Program, (U) 595

Special Fund for the Study of Women and Politics, (G) 1130, (P) 1441

Speigle Award. *See* Virginia Golf Foundation Scholarship Program, entry (U) 643

Spencer-Wilkinson Award. *See* Virginia Golf Foundation Scholarship Program, entry (U) 643

Spirit of Youth Scholarship for Junior Members, (U) 596

Spitzer Fellowship. *See* Hubble Fellowships, entry (P) 1324

Spofford, Jr. Memorial Internship. *See* Walter O. Spofford, Jr. Memorial Internship, entry (G) 1159

Sports Illustrated Scholarship, (U) 597

Sporty's Foundation Flight Training Scholarship, (P) 1442

SSRC Abe Fellowship Program, (P) 1443

SSRC/NEH International and Area Studies Fellowships. *See* International and Area Studies Fellowships, entry (P) 1331

Stafford Memorial Scholarship. *See* Delta Delta Delta Unrestricted Graduate Scholarships, entry (G) 819

Staples Scholarship. *See* Pam Barton Staples Scholarship, entry (U) 503

STAR Fellowships for Graduate Environmental Study, (G) 1131

Starring Memorial Award for Piano or Percussion. *See* Scholarships for Undergraduate Performance, entry (U) 571

Starring Memorial Award for Woodwinds or Brass. *See* Scholarships for Undergraduate Performance, entry (U) 571

Starring Memorial Awards. *See* Sigma Alpha Iota Graduate Performance Awards, entry (G) 1124

Tom Crow Memorial Scholarship. *See* CPO Scholarship Fund, entry (U) 138

Tompkins Nursing and Applied Health Sciences Scholarship. *See* Captain Sally Tompkins Nursing and Applied Health Sciences Scholarship, entry (U) 107

TOPjobs Program. *See* Targeted Opportunity Program (TOPjobs), entries (U) 609, (G) 1139

Townsend and Townsend and Crew Diversity Scholarship, (G) 1144

Translation Competition, (P) 1454

Traub-Dicker Rainbow Scholarships, (U) 625, (G) 1145

Trefz Scholarship. *See* Delta Kappa Gamma Scholarship Program, entry (G) 821

TREWA Scholarships, (U) 626

Troyansky Fellowship. *See* Organic Chemistry Graduate Student Fellowships, entry (G) 1069

Tucker Centennial Scholarship. *See* Alpha Omicron Pi Foundation Named Scholarships, entries (U) 23, (G) 725

TUMS Calcium for Life Scholarship. *See* Basic Midwifery Student Scholarships, entries (U) 72, (G) 765

Tuohey Memorial Scholarship. *See* Glorine Tuohey Memorial Scholarship, entry (G) 904

Turner Fund. *See* Emma Harper Turner Fund, entries (U) 209, (P) 1278

Turner Georgia Girls State Scholarship. *See* Betty Turner Georgia Girls State Scholarship, entry (U) 85

Tweet Coleman Aviation Scholarship, (U) 627

Twining Humber Award for Lifetime Artistic Achievement, (P) 1455

TWISTER Scholarship, (U) 628

Tyler Award. *See* Carol Tyler Award, entries (G) 789, (P) 1242

Tyson Memorial Fellowship. *See* Sarah Bradley Tyson Memorial Fellowship, entries (G) 1110, (P) 1430

U

Ullyot Fellows. *See* Zannoni Individual Summer Undergraduate Research Fellowships, entry (U) 706

Undergraduate Leadership Scholarship, (U) 629

United Methodist Women of Color Scholars Program, (G) 1146

United Parcel Service Scholarship for Female Students, (U) 630

United States Bowling Congress Youth Ambassador of the Year Awards. *See* USBC Youth Ambassador of the Year Awards, entry (U) 633

United States Bowling Congress Youth Leader of the Year Awards. *See* USBC Youth Ambassador of the Year Awards, entry (U) 633

United States Department of State Student Intern Program. *See* Department of State Student Intern Program, entries (U) 164, (G) 824

United States Steel Corporation Scholarships, (U) 631

United States Tennis Association/Dwight Mosley Scholarships. *See* USTA/Dwight Mosley Scholarships, entry (U) 636

University of California President's Postdoctoral Fellowship Program for Academic Diversity, (P) 1456

University of Houston African American Studies Program Visiting Scholars, (P) 1457

Upchurch Scholarship. *See* Alabama Golf Association Women's Scholarship Fund, entry (U) 13

U.S. Army Women's Foundation Legacy Scholarships, (U) 632

U.S. Department of State Student Intern Program. *See* Department of State Student Intern Program, entries (U) 164, (G) 824

USBC Youth Ambassador of the Year Awards, (U) 633

USBC Youth Leader of the Year Awards. *See* USBC Youth Ambassador of the Year Awards, entry (U) 633

USO Desert Storm Education Fund, (U) 634

USS Stark Memorial Scholarship Fund, (U) 635

USTA/Dwight Mosley Scholarships, (U) 636

V

Van Deuren Memorial Scholarships. *See* Della Van Deuren Memorial Scholarships, entry (U) 153

Van Deventer Scholarship. *See* California P.E.O. Selected Scholarships, entries (U) 106, (G) 786

Vanessa Rudloff Scholarship Program, (U) 637, (P) 1458

Vanguard Women in Information Technology Scholarship Program, (U) 638

Vashti Turley Murphy Scholarship Program, (G) 1147

Vasudevan Scholarship. *See* Rukmini and Joyce Vasudevan Scholarship, entry (G) 1100

Vatter Memorial Scholarships. *See* Peggy Vatter Memorial Scholarships, entries (U) 507, (P) 1404

Velez Scholarship. *See* U.S. Army Women's Foundation Legacy Scholarships, entry (U) 632

Vera W. Hudson and Elizabeth K. Weisburger Scholarship Fund. *See* Women in Toxicology Special Interest Group Vera W. Hudson and Elizabeth K. Weisburger Scholarship Fund, entry (G) 1178

Verges Scholarship. *See* Daughters of Penelope Undergraduate Scholarships, entry (U) 144

Verizon Scholarships of the Society of Women Engineers, (U) 639, (G) 1148

Vermont Armed Services Scholarships, (U) 640

Verna Ross Orndorff Career Performance Award, (P) 1459

Vessa Notchev Fellowship, (G) 1149, (P) 1460

VHSL-Allstate Achievement Awards, (U) 641

Vickers/Raup Scholarship. *See* Scholarships for ELCA Service Abroad, entry (U) 568

Vicki Cruse Memorial Scholarship, (P) 1461

Victoria Fisher Memorial Prize Essay, (G) 1150, (P) 1462

Victoria Naman Graduate School Scholarship, (G) 1151

Victoria Schuck Award, (P) 1463

Vincent Bendix Minorities in Engineering Award. *See* Dupont Minorities in Engineering Award, entry (P) 1268

Violet and Cyril Franks Scholarship, (G) 1152

Violet Diller Professional Excellence Award, (P) 1464

VIP Women in Technology Scholarships, (U) 642

Virginia A. Pomeroy Scholarships, (G) 1153

Virginia Badger Scholarship. *See* Seattle Chapter AWIS Scholarships, entry (U) 574

Virginia Burns Boynton Scholarship, (G) 1154

Virginia Golf Foundation Scholarship Program, (U) 643

Virginia Hester Special Education Scholarship. *See* Sue and Virginia Hester Special Education Scholarship, entry (U) 599

Virginia M. Wagner Educational Grant, (U) 644, (G) 1155

Virginia Peace Mackey-Althouse Voice Award, (U) 645, (G) 1156

Virginia S. Richardson Memorial Scholarship. *See* Ninety-Nines, Inc. Amelia Earhart Memorial Scholarships, entries (U) 478, (G) 1060, (P) 1395

Visionary Integration Professionals Women in Technology Scholarships. *See* VIP Women in Technology Scholarships, entry (U) 642

Vitelli Memorial Scholarship. *See* Joyce Anne Vitelli Memorial Scholarship, entry (U) 338

Vito Marzullo Internship Program, (P) 1465

U–Undergraduates   **G–Graduate Students**   **P–Professionals/Postdoctorates**

W

W. Newton Long Award, (P) 1466

Wagner Educational Grant. *See* Virginia M. Wagner Educational Grant, entries (U) 644, (G) 1155

Wagner Memorial Award for Women in Atmospheric Sciences. *See* Peter B. Wagner Memorial Award for Women in Atmospheric Sciences, entry (G) 1074

Wagner Memorial Fund. *See* Society of Daughters of the United States Army Scholarships, entry (U) 587

Wagy Memorial Scholarship. *See* Irene and Leeta Wagy Memorial Scholarship, entry (U) 307

WAI/AirTran Airways Maintenance Scholarship, (U) 646

WAI/Boeing Company Career Enhancement Scholarship, (U) 647, (G) 1157, (P) 1467

Waivers of Nonresident Tuition for Dependents of Military Personnel Moving to Texas, (U) 648

Waivers of Nonresident Tuition for Dependents of Military Personnel Who Previously Lived in Texas, (U) 649

Waldo and Alice Ayer Music Scholarship, (U) 650

Walker Scholarship. *See* Jane Walker Scholarship, entries (U) 320, (G) 954

Wall Scholarship. *See* Lillian Wall Scholarship, entry (U) 374

Walter Byers Postgraduate Scholarship Program, (G) 1158

Walter O. Spofford, Jr. Memorial Internship, (G) 1159

Walter Reed Smith Scholarship Program, (U) 651

Walter Scholarship Program. *See* Norma Ross Walter Scholarship Program, entry (U) 480

Wanda Munn Scholarship, (U) 652, (G) 1160

Wanda Schafer Graduate Scholarship, (G) 1161

Wanek Fund Award. *See* Geological Society of America Graduate Student Research Grants, entry (G) 896

Warman Scholarship. *See* U.S. Army Women's Foundation Legacy Scholarships, entry (U) 632

Washington Episcopal Church Women Memorial Scholarship Fund, (G) 1162

Washington Metropolitan Area Corporate Counsel Association Corporate Scholars Program. *See* WMACCA Corporate Scholars Program, entry (G) 1172

Washington State Business and Professional Women's Foundation Mature Woman Educational Scholarship, (U) 653, (P) 1468

Washington State Business and Professional Women's Foundation Single Parent Scholarship, (U) 654

Washington University Amgen Scholars Program, (U) 655

Washington Women in Need Educational Grants, (U) 656

Watson Midwives of Color Scholarship, (U) 657, (G) 1163

WAWH Founders Dissertation Fellowship, (G) 1164

Wayne F. Placek Grants, (G) 1165, (P) 1469

WBCA Sports Communication Scholarship Award. *See* Robin Roberts/WBCA Broadcasting Scholarship, entry (G) 1097

WBF Scholarship Awards, (G) 1166

Weatherford Scholarship Fund. *See* Carolyn Weatherford Scholarship Fund, entry (G) 790

Webber Trust Scholarships. *See* Josephine and Benjamin Webber Trust Scholarships, entries (U) 337, (G) 966

Weese Scholarship. *See* Dean Weese Scholarship, entry (U) 148

Weimer Award. *See* Katherine E. Weimer Award, entry (P) 1346

Weisburger Scholarship Fund. *See* Women in Toxicology Special Interest Group Vera W. Hudson and Elizabeth K. Weisburger Scholarship Fund, entry (G) 1178

Weiss Research and Program Innovation Grant. *See* Drs. Rosalee G. and Raymond A. Weiss Research and Program Innovation Grant, entry (P) 1267

Weller PEO Scholarship. *See* Dorothy L. Weller PEO Scholarship, entries (U) 181, (G) 836

Wells Graduate Student Fellowship. *See* Ida B. Wells Graduate Student Fellowship, entry (G) 936

Wells Loyalty Grant. *See* Norma Chipman Wells Loyalty Grant, entry (G) 1061

Welty Prize. *See* Eudora Welty Prize, entry (P) 1284

West Recruitment Grant. *See* B. June West Recruitment Grant, entries (U) 66, (P) 1228

Western Association of Women Historians Founders Dissertation Fellowship. *See* WAWH Founders Dissertation Fellowship, entry (G) 1164

Westphal Memorial Scholarship Award. *See* Heather Westphal Memorial Scholarship Award, entries (U) 278, (P) 1316

Wettstein Scholarship. *See* Scholarships for ELCA Service Abroad, entry (U) 568

Whaley Book Prize. *See* Sara Whaley Book Prize, entry (P) 1429

Whetten Award. *See* Nellie Yeoh Whetten Award, entry (G) 1057

Whinery Music Business/Technology Scholarship. *See* Dorothy Cooke Whinery Music Business/Technology Scholarship, entry (U) 179

Whirly-Girls Memorial Flight Training Scholarship, (P) 1470

White P.E.O. Scholarship. *See* Ruth G. White P.E.O. Scholarship, entry (G) 1103

White Postdoctoral Fellowship Program. *See* Gilbert F. White Postdoctoral Fellowship Program, entry (P) 1306

White Scholarship. *See* Delta Kappa Gamma Scholarship Program, entry (G) 821

Whitehead Award for Lifetime Achievement. *See* Bill Whitehead Award for Lifetime Achievement, entry (P) 1233

Whitman Memorial Scholarship. *See* Olive Whitman Memorial Scholarship, entry (U) 492

Whitney Scholarship. *See* Ruth Whitney Scholarship, entries (U) 561, (G) 1106

Wilder Educational Fund Scholarship. *See* Fannie Wilder Educational Fund Scholarship, entry (U) 224

Wilhoite Scholarship. *See* Alpha Omicron Pi Foundation Named Scholarships, entries (U) 23, (G) 725

Willa Haverstick Dial Scholarship, (U) 658

Willey Scholarship. *See* Myrt Willey Scholarship, entry (U) 451

William Bridge Scholarship, (U) 659

William F. Cooper Scholarship. *See* Judge William F. Cooper Scholarship, entry (U) 341

William J. Polissino Memorial Scholarship, (U) 660

William L. Fisher Congressional Geoscience Fellowship, (P) 1471

William Rucker Greenwood Scholarship, (U) 661, (G) 1167

Wilson Scholarship. *See* Carol Green Wilson Scholarship, entry (U) 110

Wings Over America Scholarships, (U) 662

Wings to the Future Management Scholarship. *See* GAT Wings to the Future Management Scholarship, entry (U) 244

Winifred Hill Boyd Graduate Scholarship, (G) 1168

Wisconsin Job Retraining Grants, (U) 663, (G) 1169

Wisconsin Legion Auxiliary Child Welfare Scholarship, (G) 1170

Wisconsin Legion Auxiliary Department President's Scholarship, (U) 664

Wisconsin Legion Auxiliary Merit and Memorial Scholarships, (U) 665

Wisconsin Legion Auxiliary Past Presidents Parley Health Career Scholarships, (U) 666

Wisconsin Legion Auxiliary Past Presidents Parley Registered Nurse Scholarships, (U) 667

U–Undergraduates   **G–Graduate Students**   **P–Professionals/Postdoctorates**

Y

Yardley Fellowship. *See* Margaret Yardley Fellowship, entry (G) 1001

Young Investigator Grant in Total Joint and Trauma Surgery, (P) 1487

Young Ladies' Radio League Scholarship, (U) 703, (G) 1189

Young Women in Public Affairs Awards. *See* Zonta International Young Women in Public Affairs Awards, entry (U) 711

Young Women's Alliance Higher Education Scholarships, (U) 704, (G) 1190

Youth Partners in Access to Capital Program, (U) 705

Z

Zannoni Individual Summer Undergraduate Research Fellowships, (U) 706

Zeta Phi Beta General Graduate Fellowships, (G) 1191, (P) 1488

Zeta Tau Alpha Endowed Scholarships, (U) 707

Zeta Tau Alpha Founders Grants, (G) 1192

Zimmer Research Grant, (P) 1489

Zoe Cavalaris Hellenic Athletic Women's Award, (U) 708

Zoe Gore Perrin Scholarship. *See* Delta Delta Delta Unrestricted Undergraduate Scholarships, entry (U) 158

Zonta Club of Bangor Scholarships, (U) 709

Zonta Club of Milwaukee Technical Specialty Scholarship Award, (U) 710

Zonta International Young Women in Public Affairs Awards, (U) 711

Zora Ellis Scholarship. *See* Delta Kappa Gamma Scholarship Program, entry (G) 821

U–Undergraduates   **G–Graduate Students**   **P–Professionals/Postdoctorates**

Sponsoring Organization Index

The Sponsoring Organization Index makes it easy to identify agencies that offer financial aid primarily or exclusively to women. In this index, the sponsoring organizations are listed alphabetically, word by word. In addition, we've used an alphabetical code (within parentheses) to help you identify the intended recipients of the funding offered by the organizations: U = Undergraduates;   G = Graduate Students;   P = Professionals/Postdoctorates. For example, if the name of a sponsoring organization is followed by (U) 241, a program sponsored by that organization is described in the Undergraduates chapter, in entry 241. If that sponsoring organization's name is followed by another entry number—for example, (G) 1370—the same or a different program sponsored by that organization is described in the Professionals/Postdoctorates chapter, in entry 1370. Remember: the numbers cited here refer to program entry numbers, not to page numbers in the book.

U–Undergraduates   **G–Graduate Students**   **P–Professionals/Postdoctorates**

Association for Women Geoscientists, (U) 58, 322, 602, 661, (G) 801, 1167, (P) 1358

Association for Women in Architecture, (U) 59

Association for Women in Communications. Oklahoma City Chapter, (U) 490

Association for Women in Communications. Seattle Professional Chapter, (U) 575, (G) 1118

Association for Women in Communications. Washington DC Chapter, (U) 65

Association for Women in Computing. Ann Arbor Chapter, (U) 42

Association for Women in Mathematics, (U) 16, (G) 1187, (P) 1221, 1227, 1378-1379, 1425, 1440, 1486

Association for Women in Science, (U) 60

Association for Women in Science. Seattle Chapter, (U) 574

Association for Women in Sports Media, (U) 61, (G) 753, (P) 1222

Association for Women Journalists, (U) 62

Association for Women Lawyers, (G) 754, 1153

Association of Black Women Lawyers of New Jersey, Inc., (G) 768

Association of Independent Colleges and Universities of Pennsylvania, (U) 10, 275, 416

Association of Jewish Women Publishers, (P) 1367

Association of Latino Professionals in Finance and Accounting, (U) 683, (G) 1179

Association of Romanian Orthodox Ladies Auxiliaries of North America, (U) 52, 279, (G) 750

Association of the United States Navy, (U) 63

Association of Women Psychiatrists, (G) 985, (P) 1197, 1223

Association of Women's Health, Obstetric and Neonatal Nurses, (G) 756, (P) 1226, 1322, 1366

Association on American Indian Affairs, Inc., (U) 169

ASTM International, (U) 408, (G) 1015

Astraea Lesbian Foundation for Justice, (P) 1225, 1354

The Atlantic Philanthropies, (P) 1314

AT&T Laboratories, (G) 755

Autry National Center, (P) 1237

Aviation Boatswain's Mates Association, (U) 309

AVS-Science and Technology of Materials, Interfaces, and Processing, (G) 1057

B

Babe Ruth League, Inc., (U) 314

Baker Hughes Incorporated, (U) 67, (G) 757

Banner Engineering Corporation, (U) 68, (G) 758

Banner & Witcoff, Ltd., (G) 831

Baptist Convention of Maryland/Delaware, (U) 79, (G) 967

Baptist Convention of New Mexico, (U) 75, (G) 769

Baptist General Convention of Texas, (G) 875

Baptist Women in Ministry of Georgia, (G) 1109

Baptist Women in Ministry of North Carolina, (G) 759

Barbara Alice Mower Memorial Scholarship Committee, (U) 69, (G) 760

Barnard College. Department of English, (P) 1229

Barnum Festival Foundation, (U) 71, (G) 764

Battelle Memorial Institute, (P) 1305

Bay Area Lawyers for Individual Freedom, (G) 1013

Bechtel Group Foundation, (U) 74

Berkshire Conference of Women Historians, (G) 767, 936, (P) 1232

Best Friends Foundation, (U) 80

Big 12 Conference, (G) 845

Biophysical Society, (P) 1369

Black Women in Entertainment Law, (G) 780

Black Women in Sisterhood for Action, Inc., (U) 90

Blinded Veterans Association, (U) 355, (G) 980

Blinded Veterans Association Auxiliary, (U) 546

Bloomingdale's, (U) 212, (G) 867

Bobby Sox Softball, (U) 94

Boehringer Ingelheim Pharmaceuticals, Inc., (G) 1069

Boeing Company, (U) 647, (G) 1157, (P) 1467

Booktrust, (P) 1398

Boomer Esiason Foundation, (U) 221

Booz Allen Hamilton, (G) 782-783, 1087

Boston Scientific, (U) 96-97, (G) 785

Brandeis University. Hadassah-Brandeis Institute, (U) 269, (G) 908, (P) 1217, 1310-1311, 1454

British Academy, (P) 1422

Broadcast Music Inc., (U) 692, (G) 1185, (P) 1482

Brookhaven National Laboratory, (U) 100, (P) 1305, 1414

Brown University. John Carter Brown Library, (G) 1101, (P) 1423

Brown University. Pembroke Center for Teaching and Research on Women, (P) 1405

Brunswick Corporation, (U) 516

Bryn Mawr College. Alumnae Association, (P) 1362

Burroughs Wellcome Fund, (G) 932, (P) 1239, 1332

Business and Professional Women of Iowa Foundation, (U) 101

Business and Professional Women of Maryland, (U) 98, 140, (G) 812

Business and Professional Women of Pennsylvania, (U) 508

Business and Professional Women's Clubs of New York State, (G) 905

C

California Department of Veterans Affairs, (U) 103

California Groundwater Association, (U) 581

California Job's Daughters Foundation, (U) 104

California State University. Office of the Chancellor, (G) 787

Caterpillar, Inc., (U) 112, (G) 792

Catholic Daughters of the Americas, (U) 325

Center for Advanced Study in the Behavioral Sciences, (P) 1245, 1300

Center for Scholarship Administration, Inc., (U) 224, 341

CH2M Hill, (G) 926

Chevron Corporation, (U) 122

Chi Omega Fraternity, (G) 800, 1011

Choice Hotels International, (U) 687, (G) 1181

Christian Church (Disciples of Christ), (U) 196, (G) 743, 979, 1020

Citizens Bank New Hampshire, (U) 650

Colgate-Palmolive Company, (G) 842, (P) 1266

College Board, (U) 64

College Scholarships Foundation, (U) 128, (G) 806

Collegium Budapest, (P) 1300

Colorado Federation of Business and Professional Women, (U) 132

Columbia University College of Physicians and Surgeons, (P) 1314

Committee of Presidents of Statistical Societies, (P) 1295

Committee on Women in Agricultural Economics, (G) 1138, (P) 1449

Community Foundation of Louisville, (U) 620, 695

Community Foundation of Middle Tennessee, (U) 281, 357, (G) 778

Community Foundation of New Jersey, (U) 173

Community Foundation of Sarasota County, (G) 1111

U–Undergraduates   **G–Graduate Students**   **P–Professionals/Postdoctorates**

"Negro Spiritual" Scholarship Foundation, (U) 261

Netflix, Inc., (P) 1293

Network of Executive Women, (U) 470, (G) 1058

Network of Presbyterian Women in Leadership, (G) 994

New Jersey Bankers Association, (U) 472

New Jersey State Elks, (U) 473

New Jersey State Federation of Women's Clubs, (G) 1001

New Jersey Utilities Association, (U) 475

New Mexico Baptist Foundation, (U) 356, (G) 981

New Mexico Elks Association, (U) 476

New Mexico Engineering Foundation, (U) 127

New Mexico Higher Education Department, (G) 1059

New York Public Library. Dorothy and Lewis B. Cullman Center for Scholars and Writers, (P) 1393

New York State Association for Health, Physical Education, Recreation and Dance, (U) 175

New York Women in Communications, Inc., (U) 109, 142, 212, 276, 305, 344, 487, 494, 561, (G) 813, 867, 969, 1065, 1068, 1106

New York Women in Film & Television, (P) 1360, 1480

Newberry Library, (G) 889, (P) 1300

Ninety-Nines, Inc., (U) 478, (G) 729, 1060, (P) 1199, 1392, 1395

Ninety-Nines, Inc. Eastern New England Chapter, (U) 659

Ninety-Nines, Inc. Florida Goldcoast Chapter, (U) 237, (P) 1297

Norman's Orchids, (G) 747

North Carolina Alliance for Athletics, Health, Physical Education, Recreation and Dance, (U) 466

North Carolina Federation of Business and Professional Women's Club, Inc., (U) 207, 481, (G) 865, 1062

North Carolina Society of Hispanic Professionals, (U) 308

North Dakota Council on Abused Women's Services, (U) 483

North Dakota. Department of Veterans Affairs, (U) 482

Northrop Grumman Corporation, (U) 484

Northwest Baptist Convention, (U) 548, (G) 1095

Northwest Women in Educational Administration, (U) 485

O

Oak Ridge Institute for Science and Education, (U) 257, (G) 903

Ohio Newspapers Foundation, (U) 488

Ohio State University. Byrd Polar Research Center, (P) 1238

Oklahoma Federation of Business Women, Inc., (U) 489, (G) 1066

Olin Corporation, (P) 1298

One Family, Inc., (U) 495

Optimist International, (U) 496

Orange Personal Communications Services Limited, (P) 1398

Order of the Amaranth. Grand Court of Pennsylvania, (U) 497

Order of the Eastern Star. Grand Chapter of Oregon, (U) 370, (G) 987

Order of the Eastern Star. Grand Chapter of Pennsylvania, (U) 498

Oregon Community Foundation, (U) 178

Oregon Farm Bureau, (U) 499

Oregon Student Assistance Commission, (U) 178, 236, 529

Organic Reactions, Inc., (G) 1069

Organic Syntheses, Inc., (G) 1069

Organization of American Historians, (P) 1257

Ortho-McNeil Pharmaceutical Corporation, (G) 911, 1082, (P) 1280, 1411, 1416

Orthopaedic Research and Education Foundation, (P) 1419, 1487

OutputLinks, (U) 502, (G) 1070

P

Patsy Takemoto Mink Education Foundation for Low-Income Women and Children, (U) 505, (G) 1072

Paul and Phyllis Fireman Charitable Foundation, (U) 495

Pennsylvania Federation of Business and Professional Women's Clubs, Inc., (U) 509

Pennsylvania Federation of Democratic Women, (U) 510

Pennsylvania Masonic Youth Foundation, (U) 5, 263, 497-498, 511-512, 660

P.E.O. Foundation. California State Chapter, (U) 106, 177, 181, 214, (G) 786, 836, 873, 1103

P.E.O. Sisterhood, (U) 514-515, (G) 1073, (P) 1406

Pepsi-Cola Company, (U) 516

Pfizer Inc., (G) 911, 1069, 1082, (P) 1280, 1411, 1416

Phi Beta Kappa Society, (G) 1008-1009, (P) 1374-1375

Philanthrofund Foundation, (U) 391, (G) 999

Pi Beta Phi, (U) 209, 240, 522, 585, (G) 1077-1078, (P) 1278, 1407

PilotMall.com Aviation Superstore, (U) 524, (P) 1408

PNC Private Bank, (G) 937

Presbyterian Church (USA), (U) 73

Presbyterians for Renewal, (G) 994

Pride Law Fund, (G) 1013

Princeton University. Institute for Advanced Study, (P) 1300

Print and Graphics Scholarship Foundation, (U) 48, 455

Professional Golfers' Association of America, (U) 532

Professional Solutions, LLC, (U) 65

Publishing Triangle, (P) 1233, 1343

Puget Sound Business Journal, (G) 1084

Putnam Investments, (U) 495

R

Radcliffe Institute for Advanced Study at Harvard University, (P) 1300

Ralph L. Smith Foundation, (P) 1399

Red River Valley Association Foundation, (U) 540, (G) 1089

Redi-Tag Corporation, (U) 541

Resources for the Future, (U) 547, (G) 965, 1093, 1159, (P) 1306, 1341

Rhode Island Commission on Women, (U) 549

Rhode Island Foundation, (U) 549, (G) 1004

Rhode Island Society of Certified Public Accountants, (U) 119, (G) 799

Rhode Island Women's Golf Association, (U) 550

Richard and Susan Smith Foundation, (U) 495

Richard Linn American Inn of Court, (G) 1005

Robert Wood Johnson Foundation, (P) 1315

Roche Pharmaceuticals, (G) 1069

Rockefeller Foundation, (P) 1206

Rockwell Automation, Inc., (U) 553

Rockwell Collins, Inc., (U) 554

Rolls-Royce Corporation, (U) 114

Rona Jaffe Foundation, (P) 1421

Rosetta Inpharmatics, (U) 574

Royal Neighbors of America, (U) 390, 471

Rural Mutual Insurance Company, (U) 558, 669

Ruth Jackson Orthopaedic Society, (G) 839, (P) 1419, 1426, 1487, 1489

S

Saint Paul Foundation, (U) 319

Sandia National Laboratories, (G) 1049

U–Undergraduates　　　　**G–Graduate Students**　　　　**P–Professionals/Postdoctorates**

University Interscholastic League, (U) 148, 371

University of California at Berkeley. Office for Faculty Equity, (P) 1247

University of California at Berkeley. Office of Equity and Inclusion, (P) 1456

University of Houston. African American Studies Program, (P) 1457

University of Leicester. Faculty of Law, (G) 1150, (P) 1462

University of Michigan. Center for the Education of Women, (P) 1246

University of Rochester. Rossell Hope Robbins Library, (G) 914

University Press of Mississippi, (P) 1284

UPS Foundation, (U) 630

U.S. Air Force. Office of Scientific Research, (G) 1044, (P) 1412

U.S. Army. Judge Advocate General's Corps, (G) 751

U.S. Army. Research Office, (G) 1044, (P) 1412

U.S. Army Women's Foundation, (U) 632

U.S. Centers for Disease Control and Prevention, (U) 533, (G) 1083, (P) 1314

U.S. Defense Intelligence Agency, (U) 149

U.S. Department of Agriculture. Agricultural Research Service, (P) 1412

U.S. Department of Agriculture. Cooperative State Research, Education, and Extension Service, (P) 1412

U.S. Department of Agriculture. Forest Service, (P) 1412

U.S. Department of Commerce. National Institute of Standards and Technology, (P) 1412

U.S. Department of Commerce. National Oceanic and Atmospheric Administration, (P) 1412

U.S. Department of Defense, (G) 1044

U.S. Department of Education. Office of Elementary and Secondary Education, (P) 1479

U.S. Department of Energy, (G) 1187, (P) 1486

U.S. Department of Energy. Office of Biological and Environmental Research, (U) 257, (G) 903

U.S. Department of Energy. Office of Defense Programs, (P) 1412

U.S. Department of Energy. Office of Fossil Energy, (U) 419, (G) 1021, (P) 1383

U.S. Department of Homeland Security, (P) 1258

U.S. Department of State, (U) 164, (G) 824, 826, 848, 876, (P) 1270-1271

U.S. Department of Transportation, (U) 600, (G) 1133, (P) 1412

U.S. Department of Transportation. Research and Innovative Technology Administration, (P) 1259

U.S. Department of Veterans Affairs, (U) 601, (G) 1134, (P) 1412

U.S. Environmental Protection Agency, (U) 210, (G) 1131

U.S. Library of Congress, (U) 372, (G) 988, (P) 1355

U.S. Library of Congress. John W. Kluge Center, (P) 1300

U.S. National Aeronautics and Space Administration, (U) 456-457, 462, (G) 909, 1043, 1050, (P) 1273, 1324, 1412

U.S. National Endowment for the Arts, (P) 1263

U.S. National Endowment for the Humanities, (P) 1206, 1331

U.S. National Institutes of Health, (P) 1412, 1445

U.S. National Institutes of Health. National Institute on Drug Abuse, (P) 1200

U.S. National Science and Technology Council, (P) 1412

U.S. National Security Agency, (G) 1049, 1187, (P) 1440, 1486

U.S. Navy. Naval Research Laboratory, (P) 1390

U.S. Navy. Office of Naval Research, (G) 897, 1044, 1187, (P) 1303, 1412, 1486

US Youth Soccer. Region III, (U) 40

USO World Headquarters, (U) 634

V

Vanguard Group, Inc., (U) 638

Verizon, (U) 639, (G) 1148

Vermont Elks Association, Inc., (U) 556

Vermont. Office of Veterans Affairs, (U) 640

Vermont Student Assistance Corporation, (U) 76, 586

Vermont Studio Center, (P) 1421

Veterans of Foreign Wars. Ladies Auxiliary, (U) 345

Villa I Tatti, (P) 1300

Virginia High School League, (U) 641

Virginia State Golf Association, (U) 643

Visionary Integration Professionals, (U) 642

W

Wal-Mart Foundation, (U) 1

Washington Metropolitan Area Corporate Counsel Association, Inc., (G) 1172

Washington Science Teachers Association, (U) 507, (P) 1404

Washington State Business and Professional Women's Foundation, (U) 653-654, (P) 1468

Washington University. Division of Biology and Biomedical Sciences, (U) 655

Washington Women in Need, (U) 656

Wellesley College, (G) 995, 1012

Western Art Association, (U) 264

Western Association of Women Historians, (G) 1164, (P) 1307

Whataburger Inc., (U) 148, 371

Whirly-Girls International, (P) 1317, 1470

Willa Cather Pioneer Memorial and Educational Foundation, (U) 480

William and Flora Hewlett Foundation, (P) 1206

Williams College. Dean of the Faculty, (G) 894, (P) 1302

Wilmington Women in Business, (U) 239

Wings Over America Scholarship Foundation, (U) 662

Wisconsin Department of Veterans Affairs, (U) 663, (G) 1169

Wisconsin Library Association, (P) 1309

Wisconsin Medical Society, (G) 1100

Wisconsin Office of State Employment Relations, (U) 609, (G) 1139

Wisconsin Public Service Corporation, (U) 668

Wisconsin Towns Association, (U) 558, 669

Wisconsin Women in Government, Inc., (U) 670

Woman's Missionary Union, (U) 330, (G) 790

Woman's Missionary Union of Virginia, (G) 884

Woman's National Farm and Garden Association, Inc., (G) 1110, (P) 1430

Women Chefs & Restaurateurs, (U) 672, (G) 1173

Women in Aviation, International, (U) 27-28, 116, 143, 154-157, 229, 244, 524, 646-647, 675, 682, (G) 814, 1157, (P) 1212, 1256, 1260, 1326, 1364, 1400, 1408, 1438, 1442, 1461, 1467, 1473, 1475

Women in Aviation, International. Washington State Chapter, (U) 321

Women in Defense, (U) 285, (G) 929, (P) 1323

Women in Defense. Michigan Chapter, (U) 286, (G) 930

Women in Federal Law Enforcement, (U) 676-677, (G) 1176-1177

Women in Film/Dallas, (U) 678

Women in Film/Los Angeles, (P) 1293

Women in Technology of Tennessee, (U) 628

Women Lawyers' Association of Greater St. Louis, (G) 989

Women Lawyers Association of Michigan Foundation, (G) 1171

U–Undergraduates **G–Graduate Students** **P–Professionals/Postdoctorates**

Residency Index

Some programs listed in this book are set aside for women who are residents of a particular state, region, or other geographic location. Others are open to applicants wherever they may live. The Residency Index will help you pinpoint programs available in your area as well as programs that have no residency restrictions at all (these are listed under the term "United States"). To use this index, look up the geographic areas that apply to you (always check the listings under "United States"), jot down the entry numbers listed for the recipient level that applies to you (Undergraduates, Graduate Students, or Professionals/Postdoctorates), and use those numbers to find the program descriptions in the directory. To help you in your search, we've provided some "see" and "see also" references in the index entries. Remember: the numbers cited here refer to program entry numbers, not to page numbers in the book.

A

Alabama: **Undergraduates,** 12-13, 40, 73, 213, 261, 320, 593, 599, 696; **Graduate Students,** 718, 771, 954, 972, 983. *See also* United States

Alaska: **Undergraduates,** 14, 51, 102, 266, 652, 702; **Graduate Students,** 749, 1063, 1160. *See also* United States

Alexandria, Virginia: **Undergraduates,** 49. *See also* Virginia

Arizona: **Undergraduates,** 53, 102, 337, 518, 685; **Graduate Students,** 966. *See also* United States; Western states

Arkansas: **Undergraduates,** 40, 54, 261, 696. *See also* United States

Arlington County, Virginia: **Undergraduates,** 49. *See also* Virginia

B

Benewah County, Idaho: **Graduate Students,** 1063. *See also* Idaho

Bonner County, Idaho: **Graduate Students,** 1063. *See also* Idaho

Boundary County, Idaho: **Graduate Students,** 1063. *See also* Idaho

Bowie County, Texas: **Undergraduates,** 206. *See also* Texas

C

California: **Undergraduates,** 46, 59, 102-106, 177, 181, 214, 262, 271, 331, 458, 581; **Graduate Students,** 786, 836, 873, 1045, 1103. *See also* United States; Western states

Calvert County, Maryland: **Undergraduates,** 49. *See also* Maryland

Charles County, Maryland: **Undergraduates,** 49; **Graduate Students,** 1162. *See also* Maryland

Charlotte, North Carolina: **Undergraduates,** 80. *See also* North Carolina

Chatham County, Georgia: **Undergraduates,** 341. *See also* Georgia

Clark County, Indiana: **Undergraduates,** 695. *See also* Indiana

Clearwater County, Idaho: **Graduate Students,** 1063. *See also* Idaho

Colorado: **Undergraduates,** 30, 102, 130-132, 192, 317; **Graduate Students,** 733, 845, 1151; **Professionals/Postdoctorates,** 1356. *See also* United States; Western states

Connecticut: **Undergraduates,** 109, 136, 142, 180, 185, 212, 242, 261, 276, 305, 344, 487, 494, 504, 517, 531, 561, 622, 659; **Graduate Students,** 813, 835, 867, 969, 1065, 1068, 1075, 1106, 1141. *See also* United States

Contra Costa County, California: **Graduate Students,** 888. *See also* California

Crawford County, Indiana: **Undergraduates,** 695. *See also* Indiana

D

Del Norte County, California: **Graduate Students,** 888. *See also* California

Delaware: **Undergraduates,** 4, 261, 572; **Graduate Students,** 871, 1116. *See also* United States

District of Columbia. *See* Washington, D.C.

F

Fairfax County, Virginia: **Undergraduates,** 49. *See also* Virginia

Fairfax, Virginia: **Undergraduates,** 49. *See also* Virginia

Falls Church, Virginia: **Undergraduates,** 49. *See also* Virginia

Fauquier County, Virginia: **Undergraduates,** 49. *See also* Virginia

Florida: **Undergraduates,** 40, 73, 125, 213, 231-233, 237, 261, 358, 401, 463, 564, 595, 696; **Graduate Students,** 803, 885, 1051; **Professionals/Postdoctorates,** 1297. *See also* United States

Florida, western: **Undergraduates,** 320; **Graduate Students,** 954. *See also* Florida

Floyd County, Indiana: **Undergraduates,** 695. *See also* Indiana

Frederick County, Maryland: **Undergraduates,** 49. *See also* Maryland

Tenability Index

Some programs listed in this book can be used only in specific cities, counties, states, or regions. Others may be used anywhere in the United States. The Tenability Index will help you locate funding that is restricted to a specific area as well as funding that has no tenability restrictions (these are listed under the term "United States"). To use this index, look up the geographic areas where you'd like to go (always check the listings under "United States"), jot down the entry numbers listed for the recipient group that represents you (Undergraduates, Graduate Students, Professionals/Postdoctorates), and use those numbers to find the program descriptions in the directory. To help you in your search, we've provided some "see" and "see also" references in the index entries. Remember: the numbers cited here refer to program entry numbers, not to page numbers in the book.

Subject Index

There are hundreds of specific subject fields covered in this directory. Use the Subject Index to identify these topics, as well as the recipient level supported (Undergraduates, Graduate Students, or Professionals/Postdoctorates) by the available funding programs. To help you pinpoint your search, we've included many "see" and "see also" references. Since a large number of programs are not restricted by subject, be sure to check the references listed under the "General programs" heading in the subject index (in addition to the specific terms that directly relate to your interest areas); hundreds of funding opportunities are listed there that can be used to support activities in any subject area (although the programs may be restricted in other ways). Remember: the numbers cited in this index refer to program entry numbers, not to page numbers in the book.

Law, general: **Undergraduates,** 171, 181, 282, 285, 299, 609; **Graduate Students,** 719, 740, 751, 754, 768, 795, 809, 829, 836, 838, 846, 862, 880, 886, 892, 898, 922, 925, 927-929, 972, 989, 1004, 1108, 1111-1112, 1139-1140, 1150, 1166, 1171-1172; **Professionals/Postdoctorates,** 1205-1206, 1210, 1248, 1290, 1300, 1323, 1393, 1462, 1481. *See also* Criminal justice; General programs; Paralegal studies; Social sciences; names of legal specialties

Law librarianship. *See* Libraries and librarianship, law

Lawyers. *See* Law, general

Leadership: **Graduate Students,** 834; **Professionals/Postdoctorates,** 1246, 1356. *See also* General programs; Management

Legal assistants. *See* Paralegal studies

Legal studies and services. *See* Law, general

Lesbianism. *See* Homosexuality

Librarians. *See* Library and information services, general

Libraries and librarianship, law: **Professionals/Postdoctorates,** 1397. *See also* General programs

Libraries and librarianship, technical services: **Professionals/Postdoctorates,** 1397. *See also* General programs; Library and information services, general

Libraries and librarianship, bibliographic services. *See* Bibliographies and bibliographic services

Library and information services, general: **Undergraduates,** 20, 81, 290, 372, 609; **Graduate Students,** 772, 988, 1139; **Professionals/Postdoctorates,** 1309, 1355, 1367. *See also* Archives; General programs; Information science; Social sciences; names of specific types of librarianship

Life insurance. *See* Actuarial sciences

Life sciences. *See* Biological sciences

Linguistics. *See* Language and linguistics

Literature: **Undergraduates,** 385, 480, 551; **Graduate Students,** 740, 858, 1012; **Professionals/Postdoctorates,** 1205-1206, 1210, 1248, 1284, 1300, 1393. *See also* General programs; Humanities; names of specific types of literature

Literature, American: **Undergraduates,** 372; **Graduate Students,** 988; **Professionals/Postdoctorates,** 1355. *See also* American studies; General programs; Literature

Literature, English: **Graduate Students,** 914; **Professionals/Postdoctorates,** 1422. *See also* General programs; Literature

Literature, French: **Graduate Students,** 1008; **Professionals/Postdoctorates,** 1374. *See also* General programs; Literature

Literature, German: **Professionals/Postdoctorates,** 1381. *See also* General programs; Literature

Literature, Greek: **Graduate Students,** 1009; **Professionals/Postdoctorates,** 1375. *See also* Classical studies; General programs; Literature

Lithuanian language. *See* Language, Lithuanian

Litigation: **Graduate Students,** 1023. *See also* General programs; Law, general

Logistics: **Undergraduates,** 44, 133, 265, 277, 287, 313, 378, 426, 527-528, 536, 578, 580, 629, 697; **Graduate Students,** 744, 804, 807, 912-913, 917, 931, 942, 1028, 1080-1081, 1085, 1123, 1161, 1186, 1188; **Professionals/Postdoctorates,** 1328-1330. *See also* General programs; Transportation

M

Macedonian language. *See* Language, Macedonian

Magazines. *See* Journalism; Literature

Management: **Undergraduates,** 155, 179, 229, 244, 258, 502, 647; **Graduate Students,** 752, 935, 942, 1070, 1112, 1157, 1182; **Professionals/Postdoctorates,** 1260, 1328-1330, 1364, 1431, 1467. *See also* General programs; Social sciences

Manufacturing engineering. *See* Engineering, manufacturing

Maps and mapmaking. *See* Cartography

Marine sciences: **Undergraduates,** 172, 688; **Graduate Students,** 830, 897, 1183; **Professionals/Postdoctorates,** 1303. *See also* General programs; Sciences; names of specific marine sciences

Marketing: **Undergraduates,** 65, 109, 142, 179, 212, 258, 397, 487, 494, 502, 575, 609; **Graduate Students,** 813, 867, 935, 1065, 1068, 1070, 1118, 1139; **Professionals/Postdoctorates,** 1218. *See also* Advertising; General programs; Public relations; Sales

Marriage. *See* Family relations

Mass communications. *See* Communications

Materials engineering. *See* Engineering, materials

Materials sciences: **Undergraduates,** 408; **Graduate Students,** 828, 909, 935, 1015, 1044, 1049, 1131. *See also* General programs; Physical sciences

Mathematics: **Undergraduates,** 16, 60, 63-64, 100, 140, 202, 223, 285-286, 382, 419, 456-457, 462, 467, 574, 609, 615, 680; **Graduate Students,** 714, 755, 812, 828, 863, 872, 877, 897, 909, 929-930, 935, 992, 1021, 1044, 1049-1050, 1059, 1087, 1117, 1125, 1139, 1149, 1168, 1187; **Professionals/Postdoctorates,** 1198, 1221, 1227, 1261, 1275, 1283, 1285-1286, 1303, 1323, 1359, 1378-1379, 1383, 1412, 1417, 1425, 1427, 1437, 1440, 1460, 1486. *See also* Computer sciences; General programs; Physical sciences; Statistics

Measurement. *See* Testing

Mechanical engineering. *See* Engineering, mechanical

Media. *See* Broadcasting; Communications

Media specialists. *See* Library and information services, general

Medical journalism. *See* Science reporting

Medical sciences: **Undergraduates,** 63, 100, 140, 177, 308, 331, 411, 562, 622; **Graduate Students,** 738, 745, 802, 812, 838, 840, 844, 850, 886, 911, 932, 948, 958, 985, 995, 1006, 1031, 1100, 1103, 1107, 1141, 1154; **Professionals/Postdoctorates,** 1250, 1314, 1327, 1332, 1370, 1380, 1385, 1414. *See also* General programs; Health and health care; Sciences; names of medical specialties; names of specific diseases

Medical technology: **Undergraduates,** 140, 428; **Graduate Students,** 812. *See also* General programs; Medical sciences; Technology

Medieval studies: **Graduate Students,** 914. *See also* General programs; Literature

Mental health: **Graduate Students,** 1152; **Professionals/Postdoctorates,** 1214, 1267. *See also* General programs; Health and health care; Psychiatry

Mental health nurses and nursing. *See* Nurses and nursing, psychiatry and mental health

Merchandising. *See* Sales

Metallurgy: **Undergraduates,** 408, 691; **Graduate Students,** 789, 1015; **Professionals/Postdoctorates,** 1242. *See also* General programs; Sciences

Meteorology: **Undergraduates,** 36, 58, 321, 353; **Graduate Students,** 739, 897, 909, 940; **Professionals/Postdoctorates,** 1303. *See also* Atmospheric sciences; General programs

Preservation: **Undergraduates,** 372; **Graduate Students,** 988; **Professionals/Postdoctorates,** 1355. *See also* General programs; names of specific types of preservation

Presidents, U.S. *See* History, American

Press. *See* Journalism

Print journalism. *See* Journalism

Printing industry: **Undergraduates,** 48, 455. *See also* General programs

Prints. *See* Art; Graphic arts

Psychiatric nurses and nursing. *See* Nurses and nursing, psychiatry and mental health

Psychiatry: **Professionals/Postdoctorates,** 1197, 1200, 1223. *See also* Behavioral sciences; Counseling; General programs; Medical sciences; Psychology

Psychology: **Undergraduates,** 171, 609, 655; **Graduate Students,** 714, 729, 740, 746, 748, 763, 766, 829, 860, 863, 869, 872, 883, 918, 964, 1082, 1088, 1125, 1127, 1139, 1149, 1152, 1165; **Professionals/Postdoctorates,** 1194, 1196, 1199, 1205-1206, 1210, 1214, 1245, 1248-1249, 1254, 1264, 1267, 1275, 1283, 1294, 1300, 1312, 1314, 1318, 1342, 1393, 1403, 1417, 1420, 1437, 1439, 1451-1453, 1460, 1469. *See also* Behavioral sciences; Counseling; General programs; Psychiatry; Social sciences

Public administration: **Undergraduates,** 133, 142, 164, 299, 369, 400, 411, 547, 609, 676-677, 711; **Graduate Students,** 746, 807-808, 813, 824, 880, 986, 1093, 1139, 1176-1177; **Professionals/Postdoctorates,** 1253, 1290, 1306, 1315, 1353, 1471. *See also* General programs; Management; Political science and politics; Social sciences

Public affairs. *See* Public administration

Public health: **Undergraduates,** 308; **Graduate Students,** 842, 1131; **Professionals/Postdoctorates,** 1266, 1315. *See also* General programs; Health and health care

Public interest law: **Graduate Students,** 989, 1153; **Professionals/Postdoctorates,** 1477. *See also* General programs; Law, general

Public policy. *See* Public administration

Public relations: **Undergraduates,** 61, 65, 109, 142, 212, 258, 305, 332, 344, 487, 490, 494, 575; **Graduate Students,** 753, 813, 867, 959, 969, 1065, 1068, 1118. *See also* General programs; Marketing

Public sector. *See* Public administration

Public service: **Undergraduates,** 282, 340, 615, 670, 694; **Graduate Students,** 838, 922. *See also* General programs; Public administration; Social services

Public speaking. *See* Oratory

Public utilities. *See* Utilities

Publicity. *See* Public relations

Publishers and publishing: **Undergraduates,** 561; **Graduate Students,** 1106; **Professionals/Postdoctorates,** 1235, 1367. *See also* General programs

R

Radio: **Undergraduates,** 304, 372, 575; **Graduate Students,** 946, 988, 1118; **Professionals/Postdoctorates,** 1355. *See also* Communications; General programs

Radiology: **Graduate Students,** 932. *See also* General programs; Medical sciences

Rape: **Undergraduates,** 242. *See also* General programs; Violence; Women's studies and programs

Real estate: **Undergraduates,** 50, 609; **Graduate Students,** 1139. *See also* General programs

Regional planning. *See* City and regional planning

Religion and religious activities: **Undergraduates,** 30-31, 75, 150, 273, 320, 548, 616; **Graduate Students,** 733-734, 740, 743, 752, 759, 769-770, 777-778, 790, 797, 802, 816, 875, 880-881, 899-900, 921, 941, 949, 954, 967, 979, 991, 994, 1020, 1046, 1094-1095, 1109, 1146-1147, 1162; **Professionals/Postdoctorates,** 1205-1206, 1210, 1248, 1250, 1290, 1292, 1300, 1304, 1320, 1393, 1474, 1484. *See also* General programs; Humanities; Philosophy

Religious education. *See* Education, religious

Restaurants. *See* Food service industry

Retailing. *See* Sales

Risk management: **Graduate Students,** 1112, 1142. *See also* Actuarial sciences; Business administration; Finance; General programs

Robotics: **Graduate Students,** 909. *See also* General programs; Technology

Romanian language. *See* Language, Romanian

S

Safety studies: **Graduate Students,** 1142. *See also* Engineering, general; General programs

Sales: **Undergraduates,** 194, 276, 470, 502, 691; **Graduate Students,** 849, 1058, 1070. *See also* General programs; Marketing

School counselors. *See* Counselors and counseling, school

Schools. *See* Education

Science education. *See* Education, science and mathematics

Science reporting: **Undergraduates,** 100. *See also* Broadcasting; General programs; Journalism; Sciences

Science, history. *See* History, science

Sciences: **Undergraduates,** 60, 118, 123, 127, 223, 292, 382, 411, 456-457, 467, 615, 628, 680; **Graduate Students,** 796, 877, 938, 992, 1154, 1168; **Professionals/Postdoctorates,** 1261, 1285-1287, 1305, 1390, 1412, 1417. *See also* General programs; names of specific sciences

Sculpture: **Undergraduates,** 280; **Professionals/Postdoctorates,** 1225, 1282, 1434. *See also* Fine arts; General programs

Secondary education. *See* Education, secondary

Secret service. *See* Intelligence service

Security, national: **Undergraduates,** 285-286; **Graduate Students,** 880, 929-930, 1087; **Professionals/Postdoctorates,** 1258, 1290, 1323. *See also* General programs; Military affairs

Serbo-Croatian language. *See* Language, Serbo-Croatian

Sex discrimination. *See* Discrimination, sex

Sexual abuse. *See* Rape

Sight impairments. *See* Visual impairments

Singing. *See* Voice

Slovak language. *See* Language, Slovak

Slovene language. *See* Language, Slovene

Social sciences: **Undergraduates,** 210, 547, 676-677; **Graduate Students,** 740, 763, 826-827, 876, 1002, 1093, 1099, 1131, 1159, 1176-1177; **Professionals/Postdoctorates,** 1205-1206, 1210, 1248, 1262, 1270, 1300, 1306, 1315, 1331, 1370, 1372, 1393, 1405, 1443, 1457. *See also* General programs; names of specific social sciences

Social services: **Undergraduates,** 609; **Graduate Students,** 805, 838, 861, 1139. *See also* General programs; Public service; Social work

Calendar Index

Since most funding programs have specific deadline dates, some may have already closed by the time you begin to look for money. You can use the Calendar Index to identify which programs are still open. To do that, go to the recipient category (Undergraduates, Graduate Students, or Professionals/Postdoctorates) that interests you, think about when you'll be able to complete your application forms, go to the appropriate months, jot down the entry numbers listed there, and use those numbers to find the program descriptions in the directory. Keep in mind that the numbers cited here refer to program entry numbers, not to page numbers in the book.